Papers in
Biochemical Genetics

Consulting Editors

Papers in Biochemical Genetics

Edited by
GEOFFREY L. ZUBAY
Columbia University

Holt, Rinehart and Winston, Inc.
New York • Chicago • San Francisco • Atlanta • Dallas • Montreal • Toronto • London

Copyright © 1968 by Holt, Rinehart and Winston, Inc.
All rights reserved
Library of Congress Catalog Card Number: 68–26827

2723153

Printed in the United States of America
1 2 3 4 5 6 7 8 9

Preface

This volume is divided into eight sections concerned with DNA, RNA and protein synthesis and the regulation of synthesis. Each section begins with an introduction giving a brief resume of progress in that area and an indication as to where the chosen papers fit into the scheme of things. This is followed by a bibliography that is intended, firstly, to document some of the statements made in the introduction, and secondly, as a guide to further reading. The bibliography is arranged according to subject, and within each subject is arranged according to year. In many cases where the title of the paper indicates that the paper represents one of a series, the most recent rather than the most significant reference is given since it is a relatively simple matter to trace back to earlier papers. The last part of each section contains the selected readings. Each selected reading has been reproduced in its entirety without modification. Every effort has been made to give as broad coverage of the subject as is possible within the scope of 49 readings. Papers have been chosen that present highly significant findings with clarity and sound reasoning. No attempt has been made to pay homage to the most significant papers historically. In spite of these standards in selecting readings from a field with so many excellent papers, it has been difficult not to be somewhat personal and arbitrary. Most of the papers deal with bacteria or bacteriophage partly because of space limitations and partly because this is the material that has given us the most rigorous information about the subject at hand. The most important advances in the future will be made by applying the principles learned from these studies to the particular problems of higher forms.

This is not an elementary book and whether used in conjunction with a formal course of instruction or otherwise, it should be read after or accompanied by an elementary text such as Loewy and Siekevitz's *Cell Structure and Function*, Levine's *Genetics* or Watson's *Molecular Biology of the Gene*.

G.L.Z.

New York
February 1968

Acknowledgments

I wish to express my gratitude to the following group of persons who have helped in choosing the selections and writing the introductory sections: J. Bonner, J. D. Ebert, D. L. Engelhardt, J. C. Gerhart, M. Levine, A. G. Loewy, J. Marmur, B. J. McCarthy, R. L. Sinsheimer, N. D. Zinder and D. Zipser. I am also grateful to Mrs. Iris Bernard for manuscript preparation.

G.L.Z.

A Note to the Instructor

As a teacher of biochemical genetics to a group of beginning graduate students and advanced undergraduates, I feel that the greatest service I can perform is to direct the student to important papers in this field. This practice serves several functions: (1) it introduces the student to the literature that he must begin to read regularly as a graduate student, (2) it allows him to evaluate directly the conclusions that are so often stated glibly in textbooks, and (3) it introduces him to the techniques which have been crucial to the discovery process. Although the student cannot learn a technique through reading alone, he can develop a feeling for those techniques that he will have to learn in order to pursue his particular interests.

I intend to use most of the readings in this volume in a one semester course allowing one week each for Sections I, II, III, IV and VII and two weeks each for Sections V, VI and VIII. My accompanying lectures enlarge on what is said in the introductory sections with emphasis placed on the most recent findings. About two thirds of the way through the course I request a ten-page typewritten essay that is designed to review intensively and critically one aspect of the subject, such as the mechanism of replication of ϕX174 DNA or the mechanism of initiation of protein synthesis. This essay is expected to be carefully documented with references to literature that the student has read. In addition to giving a careful review, I encourage the student to initiate criticism of the work and to make suggestions for future experiments. If the over-all quality of the essays is high I dispense with the final comprehensive examination. This announcement has a surprisingly beneficial effect on the quality of the essays. Occasionally a student will be called in individually for an oral examination that deals with his essay or his general knowledge of biochemical genetics. If you think there is a better methodology for training students to think like researchers, I would be glad to hear from you.

G.L.Z.

Contents

PREFACE   v

ACKNOWLEDGMENTS   vi

A NOTE TO THE INSTRUCTOR   vii

I. IDENTIFICATION OF THE GENIC MATERIAL

Introduction   3

Bibliography   5

Biological Experiments

1. M. S. Fox and M. K. Allen (1964). On the Mechanism of Deoxyribonucleate Integration in Pneumococcal Transformation. Proc. Natl. Acad.
   Sci. U.S. **52**, 412–419   8

2. A. Gierer and G. S. Schramm (1956). Infectivity of Ribonucleic Acid
   from Tobacco Mosaic Virus. Nature **177**, 702–703   16

3. G. D. Guthrie and R. L. Sinsheimer (1960). Infection of Protoplasts of
   Escherichia coli by Subviral Particles of Bacteriophage φX174. J. Mol.
   Biol. **2**, 297–305   18

Physical and Chemical Characterization

4. J. D. Watson and F. H. C. Crick (1953). The Structure of DNA. Cold
   Spring Harbor Symp. Quant. Biol. **18**, 123–131   28

5. R. L. Sinsheimer (1959). A Single-stranded Deoxyribonucleic Acid from
   Bacteriophage φX174. J. Mol. Biol. **1**, 43–53   37

II. DNA SYNTHESIS AND CHROMOSOME DUPLICATION

Introduction   51

Bibliography   54

6. C. L. Schildkraut, C. C. Richardson and A. Kornberg (1964). Enzymic
   Synthesis of Deoxyribonucleic Acid XVII. Some Unusual Physical Properties of the Product Primed by Native DNA Templates. J. Mol. Biol. **9**,
   24–45   58

7. M. Meselson and F. W. Stahl (1958). The Replication of DNA in
   Escherichia coli. Proc. Natl. Acad. Sci. U.S. **44**, 671–682   80

8. M. Abe and J. Tomizawa (1967). Replication of the *Escherichia coli* K12
   Chromosome. Proc. Natl. Acad. Sci. U.S. **58**, 1911–1918   92

III. GENE RECOMBINATION, REPAIR AND RELATED PHENOMENA

Introduction   103
Bibliography   105

Recombination

  9. M. Meselson (1964). On the Mechanism of Genetic Recombination
    Between DNA Molecules. J. Mol. Biol. 9, 734–745   110

Lysogeny and Induction

  10. J. Weil and E. R. Signer (1968). Recombination in Phage λ: II. Site-
    specific Recombination Promoted by the Integration System. Paper sub-
    mitted for publication to the Journal of Molecular Biology   124

Repair

  11. R. B. Setlow and W. L. Carrier (1964). The Disappearance of Thymine
    Dimers from DNA: An Error-Correcting Mechanism. Proc. Natl. Acad.
    Sci. U.S. 51, 226–231   134

  12. B. Weiss and C. C. Richardson (1967). Enzymatic Breakage and Joining
    of Deoxyribonucleic Acid. I. Repair of Single-strand Breaks in DNA by
    an Enzyme System from *Escherichia coli* Infected with T_4 Bacteriophage.
    Proc. Natl. Acad. Sci. U.S. 57, 1021–1028   140

IV. MOLECULAR BASIS OF MUTAGENESIS

Introduction   151
Bibliography   153

  13. S. Brenner, L. Barnett, F. H. C. Crick and A. Orgel (1961). Theory of
    Mutagenesis. J. Mol. Biol. 3, 121–124   155

  14. F. H. C. Crick, L. Barnett, S. Brenner and R. J. Watts-Tobin (1961).
    General Nature of the Genetic Code for Proteins. Nature 192, 1227–1232   159

  15. S. P. Champe and S. Benzer (1962). Reversal of Mutant Phenotypes by
    5-Fluorouracil: An Approach to Nucleotide Sequences in Messenger-
    RNA. Proc. Natl. Acad. Sci. U.S. 48, 532–546   165

V. RNA SYNTHESIS

Introduction   180
Bibliography   183

DNA Primed

  16. M. Chamberlin and P. Berg (1962). Deoxyribonucleic Acid-directed
    Synthesis of Ribonucleic Acid by an Enzyme from *Escherichia coli*. Proc.
    Natl. Acad. Sci. U.S. 48, 81–94   188

  17. U. Maitra and J. Hurwitz (1965). The Role of DNA in RNA Synthesis IX.
    Nucleoside Triphosphate Termini in RNA Polymerase Products. Proc.
    Natl. Acad. Sci. U.S. 54, 815–822   202

18. S. A. Yankofsky and S. Spiegelman (1963). Distinct Cistrons for the Two Ribosomal RNA Components. Proc. Natl. Acad. Sci. U.S. **49**, 538–544   210

19. E. K. F. Bautz, T. Kasai, E. Reilly and F. A. Bautz (1966). Gene-specific mRNA, II. Regulation of mRNA Synthesis in *E. coli* after Infection with T$_4$. Proc. Natl. Acad. Sci. U.S. **55**, 1081–1088   217

20. K. Taylor, Z. Hradecna and W. Szybalski (1967). Asymmetric Distribution of the Transcribing Regions on the Complementary Strands of Coliphage λ DNA. Proc. Natl. Acad. Sci. U.S. **57**, 1618–1625   224

RNA Primed

21. D. H. L. Bishop, N. R. Pace and S. Spiegelman (1967). The Mechanism of Replication: A Novel Polarity Reversal in the *In Vitro* Synthesis of Qβ-RNA and its Complement. Proc. Natl. Acad. Sci. U.S. **58**, 1790–1797   234

22. N. R. Pace and S. Spiegelman (1966). *In Vitro* Synthesis of an Infectious Mutant RNA with a Normal RNA Replicase. Science **153**, 64–67   242

23. H. F. Lodish and N. D. Zinder (1966). Semi-conservative Replication of Bacteriophage f2 RNA. J. Mol. Biol. **21**, 207–209   246

VI. PROTEIN SYNTHESIS

Introduction   251

Bibliography   254

24. M. B. Hoagland, M. L. Stephenson, J. F. Scott, L. I. Hecht and P. C. Zamecnik (1958). A Soluble Ribonucleic Acid Intermediate in Protein Synthesis. J. Biol. Chem. **231**, 241–257   260

25. M. Fuller and A. Hodgson (1967). Conformation of the Anticodon Loop in tRNA. Nature **215**, 817–821   277

26. H. M. Dintzis (1961). Assembly of the Peptide Chains of Hemoglobin. Proc. Natl. Acad. Sci. U.S. **47**, 247–261   282

27. J. R. Warner, P. M. Knopf and A. Rich (1963). A Multiple Ribosomal Structure in Protein Synthesis. Proc. Natl. Acad. Sci. U.S. **49**, 122–129   297

28. J. F. Speyer, P. Lengyel and C. Basilio (1962). Ribosomal Localization of Streptomycin Sensitivity. Proc. Natl. Acad. Sci. U.S. **48**, 684–686   305

29. D. Nathans, G. Notani, J. H. Schwartz and N. D. Zinder (1962). Biosynthesis of the Coat Protein of Coliphage f2 by *E. coli* Extracts. Proc. Natl. Acad. Sci. U.S. **48**, 1424–1431   308

30. H. G. Zachau, D. Dutting, H. Feldman, F. Melchers and W. Karan (1966). Serine Specific Transfer Ribonucleic Acids. XIV. Comparison of Nucleotide Sequences and Secondary Structure Models. Cold Spring Harbor Symp. Quant. Biol. **31**, 417–424   316

31. M. Nirenberg and J. H. Matthaei (1961). The Dependence of Cell-free Protein Synthesis in *E. coli* upon Naturally Occurring or Synthetic Polyribonucleotides. Proc. Natl. Acad. Sci. U.S. **47**, 1588–1602   324

32. M. Nirenberg and P. Leder (1964). RNA Codewords and Protein Synthesis: The Effect of Trinucleotides Upon the Binding of sRNA to Ribosomes. Science **145**, 1399–1407   339

33. M. Nirenberg, T. Caskey, R. Marshall, R. Brimacombe, D. Kellogg, B. Doctor, D. Hatfield, J. Levin, F. Rottman, S. Pestka, M. Wilcox and F. Anderson (1966). The RNA Code and Protein Synthesis. Cold Spring Harbor Symp. Quant. Biol. **31**, 11–24 348

34. F. H. C. Crick (1966). Codon-anticodon Pairing: The Wobble Hypothesis. J. Mol. Biol. **19**, 548–555 362

35. M. A. Smith, M. Salas, W. M. Stanley, Jr., A. J. Wahba and S. Ochoa (1966). Direction of Reading of the Genetic Message, II. Proc. Natl. Acad. Sci. U.S. **55**, 141–147 370

36. R. E. Webster, D. L. Engelhardt and N. D. Zinder (1966). *In Vitro* Protein Synthesis: Chain Initiation. Proc. Natl. Acad. Sci. U.S. **55**, 155–161 377

37. J. A. Last, W. M. Stanley, Jr., M. Salas, M. B. Hille, A. J. Wahba and S. Ochoa (1967). Translation of the Genetic Message IV. UAA as a Chain Termination Codon. Proc. Natl. Acad. Sci. U.S. **57**, 1062–1067 384

VII. PROTEINS CONSIDERED AS GENE PRODUCTS

Introduction 393

Bibliography 396

Colinearity of Gene and Polypeptide Chain

38. C. Yanofsky, B. C. Carlton, J. R. Guest, D. R. Helinski and U. Henning (1964). On the Colinearity of Gene Structure and Protein Structure. Proc. Natl. Acad. Sci. U.S. **51**, 266–272 400

Suppression

39. S. Brody and C. Yanofsky (1963). Suppressor Gene Alteration of Protein Primary Structure. Proc. Natl. Acad. Sci. U.S. **50**, 9–16 408

40. S. Brenner, A. O. W. Stretton and S. Kaplan (1965). Genetic Code: The 'Nonsense' Triplets for Chain Termination and Their Suppression. Nature **206**, 994–998 416

41. N. K. Gupta and H. G. Khorana (1966). Missense Suppression of the Tryptophan Synthetase A-protein Mutant A78. Proc. Natl. Acad. Sci. U.S. **56**, 772–779 421

42. J. Davies, W. Gilbert and L. Gorini (1964). Streptomycin, Suppression, and the Code. Proc. Natl. Acad. Sci. U.S. **51**, 883–889 429

Complementation

43. M. J. Schlesinger and C. Levinthal (1963). Hybrid Protein Formation of *E. coli* Alkaline Phosphatase Leading to *in vitro* Complementation. J. Mol. Biol. **7**, 1–12 438

44. A. Garen and S. Garen (1963). Complementation *in vivo* between Structural Mutants of Alkaline Phosphatase from *E. coli*. J. Mol. Biol. **7**, 13–22 451

VIII. REGULATION

Introduction 463

Bibliography 468

45. F. Jacob and J. Monod (1961). Genetic Regulatory Mechanisms in the Synthesis of Proteins. J. Mol. Biol. **3**, 318–356   474

46. F. Jacob and J. Monod (1965). Genetic Mapping of the Elements of the Lactose Region in *Escherichia coli*. Biochem. Biophys. Res. Comm. **18**, 693–701   513

47. J. R. Sadler and A. Novick (1965). The Properties of Repressor and the Kinetics of its Action. J. Mol. Biol. **12**, 305–327   522

48. M. Ptashne (1967). Specific Binding of the λ Phage Repressor to λ DNA. Nature **214**, 232–234   545

49. G. Zubay, M. Lederman, and J. DeVries (1967). DNA-directed Peptide Synthesis, III. Repression of β-Galactosidase Synthesis and Inhibition of Repressor by Inducer in a Cell-free System. Proc. Natl. Acad. Sci. U.S. **58**, 1669–1675   548

Papers in
Biochemical Genetics

I
Identification of the Genic Material

Introduction

Biological Experiments

The stage for the contemporary approach to biochemical genetics was set by the startling discovery of Avery and his colleagues[1] that hereditary information is not carried by protein but by nucleic acid. Avery and his colleagues isolated the DNA from one strain of pneumococcus bacteria, transferred it to a second strain of pneumococcus bacteria, and thereby transformed the second strain into the genotype of the DNA donor strain. It is generally accepted that the DNA must become an integral part of the host bacterial chromosome before it can be duplicated and express its genetic potential. Only one DNA strand of the donor DNA is integrated into the recipient chromosome.[6, 12] The detailed mechanism of this incorporation process is the subject of the paper by Fox and Allen in this collection. In order to understand the technique of CsCl density gradient centrifugation used in the Fox and Allen investigation the reader may wish to refer first to an explanation of this technique in the Meselson and Stahl paper of Section II. The most important conclusion to arise from transformation studies was the fact that DNA is a carrier of genetic information. Transformation has only been observed in a small number of microorganisms including *Hemophilus influenzae* and *Bacillus subtilis*.[6] *B. subtilis* has many advantages for research purposes because it is easy to grow and handle, and detailed mapping is possible through the availability of transducing viruses. Many interesting studies utilizing *B. subtilis* have been done.[7] Transformation of the pneumococcal type has never been demonstrated in higher forms although numerous attempts have been made to do so. The term "cellular transformation" has been used to describe a virus induced transition from normal to tumorous cells.

Demonstration that nucleic acid is the genetic substance of viruses came after the Avery work. In 1952, Hershey and Chase,[2] from differential labeling studies, argued that it was the DNA of the T bacteriophage and not the bacteriophage protein that carried the genetic substance. Although these conclusions were correct and the application of techniques was very interesting, their experiments were not as clearcut as later experiments. There is always some protein injected with the bacteriophage DNA. Eventually it became possible to strip off part of the bacterial cell wall and infect the resulting protoplasts with purified phage DNA. This was done first for the T phages which infect *E. coli*. A similar demonstration of Guthrie and Sinsheimer which used the DNA of bacteriophage ϕX174 has been included in this collection. The authors refer to much of the earlier work.

There are RNA viruses as well as DNA viruses and the first indications that RNA could also be the bearer of genetic information came from studies on Tobacco Mosaic Virus (TMV). Gierer and Schramm (in collection), using RNA isolated from TMV, rigorously demonstrated that the RNA carries all the information necessary for reproduction of the virus in the tobacco leaf. A somewhat different approach was used by Fraenkel-Conrat and Singer.[3] The RNA and protein parts of two different mutant variants of the mature virus were isolated and then recombined in all possible combinations with one another. The four different types of reconstituted virus were used for infection and it was found that the virus formed is of the parental RNA type.

Physical and Chemical Characterization

The Watson and Crick paper in this section presents a detailed description of DNA double helix structure and an account of the important physical and chemical evidence that led to the construction of their molecular model. The most significant of these were: (1) the base analyses of Chargaff which showed that most DNAs contained four bases of DNA, adenine (A), guanine (G), cytosine (C), and thymine (T), in amounts so that the ratios of A:T and G:C are equal to unity; and (2) the x-ray diffraction studies of the Wilkins and Franklin groups—all diffraction patterns of DNA could be interpreted in terms of a double helix structure.

The complementary duplex nature of the DNA structure and the requirement for a precise doubling of the chromosome in every cell division led Watson and Crick to propose a mechanism of DNA duplication that involved the separation of the parental polymeric chains, followed by the adsorption of monomers onto the single-stranded polymer surface and their polymerization. From the nature of the hydrogen bonding between polymer and adsorbed mononucleotides it seemed likely that the polymer could serve as a template for only the four most abundant nucleotides. These notions springing quite naturally from the DNA structure were to serve as most valuable working hypotheses to future investigations into the mode of synthesis and mutagenesis of DNA.

There are some DNAs that do not occur in the double helix form. The first of these to be discovered was the single–stranded DNA of the bacteriophage ϕX174. A paper by Sinsheimer discussing the physical–chemical properties of this DNA has been included in this collection. Since this DNA was introduced as an exception to the general rule, Sinsheimer has been particularly careful and thorough in giving a description of the properties of both single- and double-stranded DNAs. The life cycle of the ϕX174 virus will be discussed in the next section.

For a long time the molecular weights of DNA isolated from natural sources hovered around the values of $5–20 \times 10^6$. It was eventually appreciated that in addition to degradation which might result from nucleases, physical forces capable of shearing the double helix were generated by conventional blending or stirring procedures used in isolation.[14] Once this was appreciated it was found that the DNA in many viruses contained a single molecule of DNA. The ends of this molecule behave as though one polynucleotide chain extends beyond the other with a complementary sequence of bases at opposite ends.[46] This enables the DNA to assume a circular structure, which can under some circumstances become secured by covalent linkages. Circular DNA structures have also been found for some bacterial chromosomes and cytoplasmic DNAs from various sources.[17, 31-44, 46]

Just as most DNAs occur in the double helix form so do most RNAs occur in the single polynucleotide chain form. RNAs serve more functions than DNAs and it is more difficult to generalize about their properties. Like DNAs they contain mainly four bases similar to the bases contained in DNA except that uracil replaces thymine. Numerous bases have been found in minor concentrations.[102] There are RNA molecules which carry the genetic information found in viruses. These often serve as templates for protein synthesis as do the DNA transcribed genetic messengers. There are also the ribosomal RNAs and transfer RNAs which serve special functions in protein synthesis. The detailed structure of these will be taken up in Section VI. Some viral RNAs possess the double helix structure like DNA.[19] The detailed structure of other RNAs requires closer examination and in fact it may be necessary to determine their primary structure before we can understand their secondary structure.

A good deal of information about nucleic acid structure has come from the extensive work done on synthetic polynucleotides.[47] The discovery of the enzyme polynucleotide phosphorylase made possible the synthesis of simple homopolymers such as polyriboadenylic acid and polyribouridylic acid. These can form a 1:1 double helix structure similar to DNA or a 1:2 triple helix structure depending upon the conditions under which they are mixed.[13, 23] A variety of other double and triple helix structures have been observed.[47] As yet no biologically significant triple helix structure has been isolated.

The stability of the double helix structure is due largely to hydrogen-bonding between the bases although the stacking free energy between the bases also is believed to play a significant role.[48] The higher the GC content of the DNA the higher the melting point. This is due to the fact that the GC base pair in DNA makes three hydrogen bonds instead of two like the AT base pair. Reference to the Watson and Crick paper shows the potentially pairable ligands, an amino group on guanine and a keto group on cytosine. Watson and Crick do not mention the third hydrogen bond for the GC base pair.

Bibliography

BIOLOGICAL EXPERIMENTS

1. O. T. Avery, C. M. Macleod and M. McCarty, (1944). Studies on the Chemical Nature of the Substance Inducing Transformation of Pneumococcal Types. Induction of Transformation by a Deoxyribonucleic Acid Fraction Isolated from Pneumococcus Type III. J. Exptl. Med. **79**, 137.

2. A. D. Hershey and M. Chase, (1952). Independent Functions of Viral Protein and Nucleic Acid in Growth of Bacteriophage. J. Gen. Physiol. **36**, 39.

3. H. Fraenkel-Conrat and B. Singer, (1957). Virus Reconstitution II. Combination of Protein and Nucleic Acid from Different Strains. Biochem. Biophys. Acta. **24**, 540.

4. J. A. Peters, (1962). Classic Papers in Genetics, Prentice–Hall, Inc.

5. P. R. Reich, B. H. Black and S. M. Weissman, (1966). Nucleic Acid Homology Studies of SV 40 Virus-Transformed and Normal Hamster Cells. Proc. Natl. Acad. Sci. U.S. **56**, 78.

6. Symposium on Genetic Transformation in J. Gen. Physiol. **49**, No. 6, Part 2, July, 1966, pp 183–258.

7. For example, A. O'Sullivan and N. Sueoka, (1967). Sequential Replication of the *B. subtilis* Chromosome IV. Genetic Mapping by Density Transfer Experiment. J. Mol. Biol. **27**, 349.

8. S. H. Goodgal and E. H. Postel, (1967). On the Mechanism of Integration Following Transformation with Single-Stranded DNA of H. Influenzae. J. Mol. Biol. **28**, 261.

9. J. A. Kiger, E. T. Young and R. L. Sinsheimer, (1967). Infectivity of Single-Stranded Rings of Bacteriophage Lambda DNA. J. Mol. Biol. **28**, 157.

10. J. F. Watkins and R. Dulbecco, (1967). Production of SV 40 Virus in Heterokaryons of Transformed and Susceptible Cells. Proc. Natl. and Acad. Sci. U.S. **58**, 1396.

11. J. E. D. Siegel and M. Hayashi, (1967). Complementary Strand Infectivity in ΦX174 Replicative Form DNA. J. Mol. Biol. **27**, 443.

12. S. Lacks, B. Greenberg and K. Carlson, (1967). Fate of Donor DNA in Pneumococcal Transformation. J. Mol. Biol. **29**, 327.

PHYSICAL AND CHEMICAL CHARACTERIZATION

General

13. G. Felsenfeld, D. Davies and A. Rich, (1957). Formation of a 3 Stranded Polynucleotide Molecule. J Am. Chem. Soc. **79**, 2023.

14. P. F. Davidson, (1959). The Effect of Hydrodynamic Shear on the Deoxyribonucleic Acid from T_2 and T_4 Bacteriophages. Proc. Natl. Acad. Sci. U.S. **45**, 1560.

15. P. Doty, H. Boedtker, J. R. Fresco, R. Haselkorn and M. Litt, (1959). Secondary Structure in Ribonucleic Acids. Proc. Natl. Acad. Sci. U.S. **49**, 482.

16. A. Rich, D. R. Davies, F. H. C. Crick, and J. D. Watson, (1961). The Molecular Structure of Polyadenylic Acid. J. Mol. Biol. **3**, 71.

17. J. Cairns, (1963). The Chromosome of *Escherichia coli*. Cold Spring Harbor Symp. Quant. Biol. **28**, 43.

18. E. B. Freese and E. Freese, (1963). DNA Strand Separation. Biochem. **2**, 707.

19. P. J. Gomatos and I. Tamm, (1963). Animal and Plant Viruses with Double Helical RNA. Proc. Natl. Acad. Sci. U.S. **50**, 878.

20. J. Eigner and P. Doty, (1965). Native, Denatured and Renatured States of DNA. J. Mol. Biol. **12**, 549.

21. D. M. Crothers, N. R. Kallenback and B. H. Zimm, (1965). The Melting Transition of Low-Molecular Weight DNA: Theory and Experiment. J. Mol. Biol. **11**, 802.

22. E. N. Moudrianakis and M. Beer, (1965). Base Sequence Determination in Nucleic Acids with the Electron Microscope, III. Chemistry and Microscopy of Guanine Labeled DNA. Proc. Natl. Acad. Sci. U.S. **53**, 564.

23. R. D. Blake and J. R. Fresco, (1966). Polynucleotides VII. Spectrophotometric Study of the Kinetics of Formation of the Two Stranded Helical Complex Resulting from the Interaction of Polyriboadenylate and Polyribouridylate. J. Mol. Biol. **19**, 145.

24. D. T. Denhardt, (1966). A Membrane-Filter Technique for the Detection of Complementary DNA. Biochem. Biophys. Res. Comm. **23**, 641.

25. S. McGavin, H. R. Wilson and G. C. Barr, (1966). Intercalated Nucleic Acid Double

5

Helices: Stereochemical Possibility. J. Mol. Biol. **22**, 187.

26. M. J. Waring and R. J. Britten, (1966). Nucleotide Sequence Repetition. A Rapidly Reassociating Fraction of Mouse DNA. Science **154**, 791.

27. J. Eisinger and R. G. Shulman, (1967). Energy Transfer in Poly dAT. J. Mol. Biol. **28**, 445.

On Circularity

28. R. B. Inman, (1967). Denaturation Maps of the Left and Right Sides of the Lambda DNA Molecule Determined by E.M. J. Mol. Biol. **28**, 103.

29. W. Fuller, F. Hutchinson, M. Spencer and M. H. F. Wilkins, (1967). Molecular and Crystal Structure of Double-helical RNA I. An X-ray Diffraction Study of Fragmented Yeast RNA and a Preliminary Double-helical RNA Model, (and following three references). J. Mol. Biol. **27**, 507.

30. G. Milman, R. Langridge and M. J. Chamberlain, (1967). Structure of a DNA-RNA Hybrid. Proc. Natl. Acad. Sci. U.S. **57**, 1804.

31. C. A. Thomas and L. MacHattie, (1964). Circular T_2 DNA Molecules. Proc. Natl. Acad. Sci. U.S. **52**, 1297.

32. A. D. Hershey and E. Burgi, (1965). Complementary Structure of Interacting Sites at the Ends on Lambda DNA Molecules. Proc. Natl. Acad. Sci. U.S. **53**, 325.

33. J. C. Wang and N. Davidson, (1966). On the Probability of Ring Closure of Lambda DNA. J. Mol. Biol. **19**, 469.

34. A. Lipton and A. Weissbach, (1966). Formation of Circular DNA after Lysogenic Induction. Biochem. Biophys. Res. Comm. **23**, 436.

35. G. Streisinger, J. Emrich and M. M. Stahl, (1967). Chromosome Structure in Phage T_4 III. Terminal Redundancy and Length Determination. Proc. Natl. Acad. Sci. U.S. **57**, 292.

36. L. A. MacHattie, D. A. Ritchie, C. A. Thomas and C. C. Richardson, (1967). Terminal Repetition in Permuted T_2 Bacteriophage DNA Molecules. J. Mol. Biol. **23**, 355.

37. M. Gellert, (1967). Formation of Covalent Circles of Lambda DNA by *E. coli* Extracts. Proc. Natl. Acad. Sci. U.S. **57**, 148.

38. H. Ogawa and J. Tomizawa, (1967). Bacteriophage Lambda DNA with Different Structures Formed in Infected Cells. J. Mol. Biol. **23**, 265.

39. R. Wu and A. D. Kaiser, (1967). Mapping the 5′–Terminal Nucleotides of the DNA of Bacteriophage Lambda and Related Phages. Proc. Natl. Acad. Sci. U.S. **57**, 170.

40. L. V. Crawford and M. J. Waring, (1967). Supercoiling of Polyoma Virus DNA Measured by its Interaction with Ethidium Bromide. J. Mol. Biol. **25**, 23.

41. R. Radloff, W. Bauer and J. Vinograd, (1967). A Dye-Buoyant Density Method for the Detection and Isolation of Closed Circular Duplex DNA: The Closed Circular DNA in HeLa Cells. Proc. Natl. Acad. Sci. U.S. **57**, 1514.

42. T. F. Roth and D. R. Helinski, (1967). Evidence for Circular DNA Forms of a Bacterial Plasmid. Proc. Natl. Acad. Sci. **58**, 650.

43. E. A. C. Follett and L. V. Crawford, (1967). E.M. Study of the Denaturation of Human Papilloma Virus DNA. I. Loss and Reversal of Supercoiling Turns. II. Specific Location of Denatured Regions. J. Mol. Biol. **28**, 455.

44. F. T. Hickson, T. F. Roth and D. R. Helinski, (1967). Circular DNA Forms of a Bacterial Sex Factor. Proc. Natl. Acad. Sci. U.S. **58**, 1731.

Review Articles

45. J. Josse and J. Eigner, (1966). Physical Properties of Deoxyribonucleic Acid. Ann. Rev. Biochem. **35**, 789.

46. C. A. Thomas and L. A. MacHattie, (1967). The Anatomy of Viral DNA Molecules. Ann. Rev. Biochem. **36**, 485.

47. D. R. Davies, (1967). X-ray Diffraction Studies of Macromolecules. Ann. Rev. Biochem. **36**, 321.

48. G. Felsenfeld and H. T. Miles, (1967). The Physical and Chemical Properties of Nucleic Acids. Ann. Rev. Biochem. **36**, 407.

Biological Experiments

ON THE MECHANISM OF DEOXYRIBONUCLEATE INTEGRATION IN PNEUMOCOCCAL TRANSFORMATION*

BY MAURICE S. FOX AND MARCIA K. ALLEN†

DEPARTMENT OF BIOLOGY, MASSACHUSETTS INSTITUTE OF TECHNOLOGY

Communicated by S. E. Luria, June 22, 1964

In the transformation of *Diplococcus pneumonia*, fragments of the transforming deoxyribonucleate (DNA) are inserted into the genome of recipient transformable bacteria. This entire process requires little or no net DNA synthesis.[1,2]

Immediately following its fixation, the transforming DNA can be reisolated from the transformed bacterial population and can be demonstrated to be without biological activity. The newly introduced DNA recovers its activity with a half time of about 3 min and thereafter replicates in synchrony with the bulk DNA of the recipient bacteria.[1,3] Lacks[4] has examined the inactive transforming DNA extracted from transformed bacteria. Some of the material was degraded and the remainder was denatured. He concluded that the denatured DNA was single-stranded and proposed an integration mechanism on this basis.

We will present evidence demonstrating that the transforming DNA extracted, prior to its replication, from transformed bacteria is a hybrid, which is apparently formed with the DNA of the recipient bacteria and which extends over a region of about one or two million daltons. Furthermore, the newly introduced DNA appears to be covalently linked to the DNA of the recipient bacteria.

Experimental.—Transforming DNA carrying the density labels deuterium and nitrogen-15 was isolated from a streptomycin-resistant, p-nitrobenzoic acid-sensitive strain of pneumococcus,[5] RF_6S. The bacteria were allowed many generations of growth in a heavy-isotope-labeled medium containing P^{32} in the form of phosphate. The nutrients in the medium were in the form of sugar and amino acid extracts from algae that had been grown in a deuterium, nitrogen-15-substituted medium.[6] The algal extracts were generously provided by H. Crespi.

The bacteria were centrifuged, washed two times in 0.15 M NaCl, 0.01 M versene, pH 7.5, and then lysed with a mixture of sodium dodecyl sulphate and deoxycholate at a final concentration of 0.05% and 0.025%, respectively. The lysate was shaken with chloroform and isoamyl alcohol[2] and either (a) treated with boiled ribonuclease, alcohol precipitated, redissolved in $M/40$ phosphate buffered saline, pH 7.5, and filtered through an HA Millipore filter before using, or (b) DNA reisolated from a preparative equilibrium density gradient centrifugation in CsCl.

Equilibrium density gradient centrifugation was performed by adding DNA samples to a concentrated solution of CsCl (Trona) to give a final density of 1.70, a final volume of 1.5 ml, and a DNA concentration of less than 10 μg/ml. Samples were centrifuged at 36,000 rpm and 21°C for 42 hr. The centrifuge tubes were punctured with a needle, and 26–32 fractions of two drops each were collected. The drops were diluted with 5 vol of $M/40$ phosphate buffered saline, pH 7.5, and aliquots were scanned for radioactivity and assayed for biological activity. Both the donor marker, streptomycin resistance, and the recipient marker, p-nitrobenzoic acid resistance, were assayed on the test strain RF6 which is sensitive to both drugs. Under these conditions, native "heavy" DNA may be separated from native light DNA by 10 fractions as is shown in Figure 1. Denaturation in boiling water for 10 min, followed by rapid chilling, shifts the position of a given DNA preparation by 5 fractions. This shift is consistent with a density increase of 0.015 gm/cc. The heavy DNA, therefore, has a buoyant density in CsCl of about 0.03 gm/cc greater than that of native light DNA.

In order to examine the fate of the heavy transforming DNA, transformation was carried out in the following manner. About 300 ml of a frozen transformable culture[7] of strain R6 (resistant to p-nitrobenzoic acid and streptomycin-sensitive) were incubated at 30° for 15 min, centrifuged in the cold, and resuspended in 10 ml of casein hydrolyzate medium[8] supplemented with 10^{-3} M

CaCl₂. The labeled DNA was added to the culture at 30°C. After 8 min, DNase (Worthington, IX crystallized) was added to give a final concentration of 10 μg/ml and the culture was transferred to 37°C. After 1, 4, and 15 min of incubation, samples were chilled to 0°C, centrifuged in the cold, and resuspended in an equal volume of casein hydrolyzate medium containing 10 μg/ml DNase. The samples were further washed three times by centrifuging and resuspending in 2 ml of 0.15 *M* NaCl, with 0.01 *M* versene, and 0.02% albumin. This washing was sufficient to remove residual traces of transforming DNA that had not been fixed by the treated bacteria. After final resuspension, the culture was lysed with 0.05% sodium dodecyl sulfate and 0.025% deoxycholate. The suspensions cleared in about 1 min at 37°C and were shaken for 15 min at room temperature with an equal volume of chloroform and 1/20 vol of isoamyl alcohol. The aqueous layers were recovered and examined by density gradient centrifugations. Small variations in the above procedure are described in the text.

The procedures that have been described permit the ·recovery in the density gradient of between 80 and 90% of the radioactivity added to the cesium chloride solution, and this in turn accounts for at least 90% of the radioactivity that has been irreversibly fixed by the transformable bacterial population.

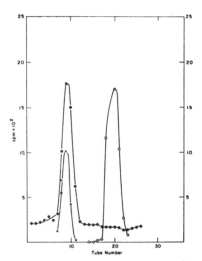

Fig. 1.—Distribution of pneumococcal transforming activities of light (O) and heavy (X) DNA after CsCl density gradient centrifugation. The heavy DNA is also labeled with P³² (solid dots). Transformants: X, heavy marker (in 10⁻³ ml); O, light marker (in 10⁻³ ml).

Results.—The density gradient patterns of DNA extracted from transformed bacteria that had been treated in the manner described above are illustrated in Figure 2. A small amount of cold heavy transforming DNA was added to the gradients as a position marker. At 1 min, only 21 per cent of the biological activity of newly introduced DNA has recovered from eclipse; by 4 min, about 60 per cent has recovered; and by 15 min, the newly introduced DNA has almost reached equilibrium. The distribution of radioactivity among the DNA fractions, heavy denatured, light nativelike, and soluble in 5 per cent trichloroacetic acid (TCA), is given in Table 1. It can be seen that there exists little or no material in the gradients

TABLE 1

DISTRIBUTION OF RADIOACTIVITY IN EXTRACTS OF TRANSFORMED BACTERIA

Incubation time following DNase addition (min)	% TCA-soluble	% Heavy denatured	% Resembling light native	% Recovery from eclipse
1	43	21	36	21
4	37	5	54	60
15	19	0	81	90

that physically resembles the original heavy transforming DNA. At a time when the input marker has recovered only 21 per cent of its biological activity, all of this activity and more than a third of the DNA radioactivity has been so altered as to band in a position very near that of the light recipient DNA. The remaining DNA radioactivity is distributed so that 20 per cent appears in a position to be expected of heavy denatured DNA and 40 per cent is in degraded TCA-soluble fragments. These latter components are lost on incubation, and their P³² becomes associated with light native DNA. Lacks[4] has similarly reported the denaturation and deg-

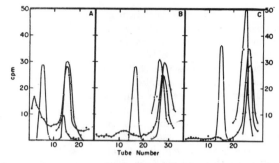

FIG. 2.—Density gradient distributions of extracts from transformed bacteria that had been allowed 8-min exposure to labeled DNA followed by (*A*) 1-min, (*B*) 4-min, and (*C*) 15-min incubation with 10 μg/ml DNase at 37°C. The distributions show the radioactivity (●) and biological activity (◑) of the donor DNA, the biological activity of the recipient DNA (○), and the biological activity of nonradioactive heavy DNA added as a position marker (X). Gradient (*A*) contains 30% more extract than the others. Transformants: ○, resident marker (in 4 × 10⁻⁴ ml); ◑, input marker (in 0.25 ml); X, heavy marker (in 4 × 10⁻² ml).

radation of newly fixed transforming DNA. The quantitative differences that exist between Lacks' results and those reported here are probably the consequence of a difference in methods of DNA isolation.

In order to increase the amount of material available for study, the remaining experiments were carried out on extracts from bacteria that had been allowed 15 min exposure at 30°C to the transforming DNA, followed by 3 min at 37° with 10 μg/ml of DNase. Under these conditions, most of the newly introduced DNA has recovered from eclipse, and there has been no detectable multiplication of the DNA element responsible for the transformation.[2] The density gradient pattern of such an extract is shown in Fig. 3*A*, and the distribution of radioactivities is given in Table 2. All of the biological activity and most of the radioactivity of

TABLE 2

DISTRIBUTION OF RADIOACTIVITY IN GRADIENT FRACTIONS

Treatment of extract	% TCA-soluble	% Heavy denatured	% Light denatured	% Resembling native
None	36	17	...	46
Heat-denatured	39	19	42	...
Alkali-denatured	30	25	45	...
Sonicated	38	11	...	51
Sonicated and heat-denatured	37	39	23	...
Sonicated and alkali-denatured	34	39	27	...

the newly introduced DNA is physically associated with sufficiently large elements of light native DNA so as to mask about 90 per cent of the density label. A similar association between the transforming DNA and the DNA of the recipient bacteria has been observed in *B. subtilis* by Szybalski[9] and Bodmer and Ganesan.[10] In addition, it can be seen that there is no biological or physical material resembling the native heavy DNA with which these bacteria had been transformed. The irreversible fixation of transforming DNA must, therefore, require a reaction more complex than the mere passage across the bacterial membrane.

Zone sedimentation in a sucrose gradient demonstrates that the macromolecular P³² in the transformed bacterial extracts sediments at the same rate and with the same distribution as does freshly isolated H³-labeled T7 DNA. Since T7 DNA has

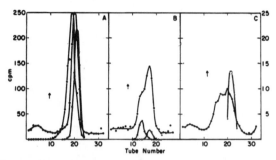

Fig. 3.—Density gradient distributions of extracts from transformed bacteria subjected to (*A*) no sonication, (*B*) 1-min sonication, and (*C*) 6-min sonication. The arrows indicate the gradient position to be expected for heavy DNA, and the biological activity (X) of added light DNA constitutes a position marker in gradient (*C*). The distributions show the radioactivity (●) and biological activity (◐) of the donor DNA, and the biological activity of the recipient DNA (○). Transformants: ○, resident marker (in 10^{-6} ml); ◐, input marker (in 5×10^{-3} ml); X, light marker (in 10^{-4}).

a molecular weight of 20 million,[11] the P^{32} must be associated with elements having approximately the same molecular weight. Sonication of the extract for 1 min and 6 min, in the manner described by Freifelder and Davison,[12] reduces the sedimentation coefficient from $30S$ to $13S$ and $11S$, respectively (on the basis of linear distance moved in the gradient). These sedimentation coefficients correspond, according to Doty *et al.*,[13] to molecular weights of about two and one million, respectively.

The distribution of material in density gradients of extracts that had been sonicated for 1 and 6 min are shown in Figure 3*B* and *C*. As a consequence of the sonication, the biological activity of the input DNA shifts away from that of the resident DNA toward a position of higher density and approaches a density that is halfway between that of heavy and light native DNA. Moreover, the P^{32}-containing material, with increasing sonication, becomes spread over a broader and broader density region which ultimately appears to extend from the position of light DNA to the position where one might expect to find "hybrid" DNA. Fractions taken from various positions in the broad band of the sonicated sample retain their positions with respect to light DNA when centrifuged again in a density gradient. It is thus demonstrated that the DNA molecules produced by sonication are heterogeneous with respect to density. In spite of the very substantial reduction in molecular weight to one or two million daltons, little, if any, radioactivity appears in the density position of native fully heavy DNA.

Sonication of an artificial mixture of P^{32}-labeled heavy DNA and a large excess of light DNA produces no P^{32} in the position of light native DNA, nor does the P^{32}-band pattern manifest any heterogeneity.

The structure of the complex between the heavy transforming DNA and the light DNA of the recipient bacteria is further elucidated by examining its fate upon heat and alkali denaturation. The heat denaturation was accomplished by placing the DNA extract in boiling water for 7 min and chilling rapidly. Alkali denaturation was brought about by adding enough alkaline phosphate to raise the pH to 12.3 (Beckman combination electrode) incubating at 45°C for 5 min, chilling, and neutralizing with HCl. The density gradient pattern of the DNA extracted from transformed bacteria is shown in Figure 4, which compares the untreated extract with the heat-denatured and the alkali-denatured samples. On denaturation a

11

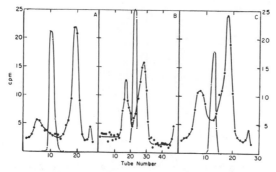

FIG. 4.—The extract from transformed bacteria showing the distribution of radioactivity (●) present in the donor DNA. The extract was (A) untreated, (B) heat-denatured, and (C) alkali-denatured. The biological activity of added heavy DNA (X) constitutes a position marker. Transformants: X, heavy marker (in 4×10^{-2} ml).

small additional amount of P^{32}-containing material moves to the position of heavy denatured DNA, but most of the P^{32} is still associated with large elements of light, now denatured, DNA.

The same DNA extract described in Figure 4 was sonicated for 4 min, and aliquots were heat- and alkali-denatured. The density gradients are shown in Figure 5. Following sonication and denaturation, a large portion of the macromolecular P^{32} behaves like heavy denatured DNA. Table 2 summarizes the distribution of radioactivity among the various fractions.

Sonication creates no fully heavy native DNA, only hybrid material which can, by denaturation, be demonstrated to be largely if not entirely an association of fully heavy and light subunits.

Discussion.—In extracts from transformed bacteria, the heavy transforming DNA that has been fixed is associated with elements of recipient DNA sufficiently large to obscure most of its characteristic buoyant density. Since most of these elements remain associated with the light DNA after either thermal or alkali denaturation, they would appear to be covalently linked to the light DNA of the recipient bacteria. After sonication, to reduce the molecular weight of the DNA in the extracts from twenty million to about one million, the elements with which the biological activity of the heavy DNA are associated increase in density, approaching the density to be expected of hybrid DNA.

Extracts also contain components of the heavy transforming DNA that have been denatured and that have been degraded. These components are rapidly converted into material that resembles light native DNA.

When the DNA of a sonicated extract is denatured by heat or exposure to high pH, the bulk of the P^{32} is then found associated with heavy denatured DNA. A substantial amount is also found in association with light denatured DNA. This light denatured band is probably best explained as the product of new synthesis of DNA using predominantly light precursors but reutilizing the acid soluble P^{32}-containing products of that portion of the transforming DNA that has been degraded. The heavy denatured band represents material which could not have been more than hybrid in the native configuration and which becomes fully heavy on denaturation. The fraction of the native material that was hybrid must therefore have been half heavy because it was heavy in one strand and light in the other.

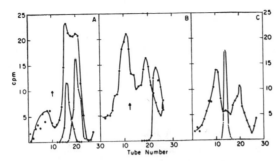

FIG. 5.—Density gradient distributions of an extract from transformed bacteria that had been sonicated for 4 min (*A*), then (*B*) heat-denatured or (*C*) alkali-denatured. The arrows indicate the position that native heavy DNA would be expected to assume. The distributions show the radioactivity (●) and biological activity (◐) of the donor DNA and the biological activity of the recipient DNA (○), as well as the biological activity of a light position marker (◑) in (*B*) and a heavy position marker (*X*) in (*C*). Transformants: ○, resident marker (in 10^{-3} ml); ●, input marker (in 1.25 ml); *X*, heavy marker (in 5×10^{-3} ml); ◑, light marker (in 5×10^{-5} ml).

It is with this hybrid that all of the donor-type biological activity of the reisolated DNA is associated. These findings demonstrate that the transforming DNA that has recovered from eclipse in transformed bacteria is in the form of a duplex that contains only a single strand of the physical material of the native donor transforming DNA. The single strand is present in elements whose molecular weight is of the order of one to two million daltons and is both chemically and genetically[1] coupled with the DNA of the recipient bacteria.

A number of hypotheses will be considered regarding the origin of the hybrid that has been described. One might assume that only a unique strand of the transforming DNA is used. If this unique strand were to form a hybrid with the complementary DNA of the recipient bacterium, then after one bacterial doubling there would have been no increase in the transforming activity of the newly introduced marker—a strand of DNA would have been synthesized that would not be active in transformation. This model can be excluded, since the transforming activity of the newly introduced DNA multiplies in synchrony with that of the recipient DNA.[2-4]

A second possibility is that either strand can be used in transformation and that the strand used forms a hybrid with a rapidly synthesized new complementary strand of itself. Evaluation of this hypothesis can be made by re-examining the results of experiments in which the sensitivity of transforming activity to the disintegration of incorporated P^{32} was measured in preparations of DNA heavily labeled with P^{32}.[2] The rate of loss of the biological activity of DNA that has been reisolated very soon after fixation by transformable bacteria is not distinguishable from that of the original DNA. This model can, therefore, also be excluded, since the newly synthesized strand would carry biological activity and would not contain lethal P^{32} atoms.

A third possibility is that a unique strand of the transforming DNA forms a hybrid with a complementary, rapidly synthesized new strand. This model can only be assessed by examining the sensitivity to P^{32} disintegrations of transforming DNA that has been reisolated after one replication in the transformed bacteria. At this time, the transforming activity should be equally distributed between stable

13

and fully sensitive elements. After infinite decay of the P^{32}, DNA isolated from such a population would be expected to retain at least half of its original transforming activity. Since it has been observed[2] that substantially more than half of the replicated products are in fact subject to inactivation by P^{32} disintegration, this possibility seems to be excluded.

Since it is clear that, as Lacks suggested,[4] only a single strand of the transforming DNA is being used intact, the P^{32} target must be a single strand. The survival, after infinite P^{32} decay, of less than half of the transforming activity, reisolated after one doubling, must be the consequence of a disintegration in one strand inactivating the complementary strand. The data that have been presented[2] are consistent with a cross-strand inactivation at a level of one in every five or six inactivating disintegrations. The absence of such a cross-strand effect to be expected for DNA reisolated soon after recovery from eclipse would reduce its sensitivity to P^{32} disintegrations by 17–20 per cent. Such a reduction was observed but was assumed to be the consequence of a small amount of DNA replication.

The remaining and most appealing model is that in which the hybrid is formed by either strand of the transforming DNA with a complementary region in the DNA of the recipient bacterial genome. This hybrid element would be half as active in transformation as an element which carries the marker on both strands. Observations on annealed mixtures of DNA are consistent with such an assumption.[14]

Further support is lent such a model by the observations of Guild and Robison[15] which suggest that for at least one transformable marker, there exist, in alkaline-denatured DNA, two density species, apparently complementary strands of about equal activity. The authors concluded that either strand could carry transforming activity and suggested a similar single-strand displacement mechanism. Furthermore, observations reported by Hotchkiss[16] demonstrate the existence of phenotypically transformed bacteria capable of yielding on replication both transformed and untransformed progeny, with respect to a single selective marker. This would indicate that the transformants must have been heterozygous with respect to the selective property. It would therefore appear that the hybrid that has been described is a hybrid between the newly introduced strand of DNA and its bacterial complement. This hybrid has been formed without a substantial amount of DNA synthesis and at a time when there has been little or no detectable replication of the DNA entity responsible for the transformation.[2]

It may be that fixation of elements of transforming DNA is initiated by one of its strands pairing with an open unpaired region of its bacterial complement. As this pairing proceeds, bacterial exonucleases would hydrolyze the unused strand of the transforming DNA as it is released. This would explain the absence of native heavy DNA in extracts of transformed bacteria as well as the presence of TCA-soluble fragments and what appears to be heavy denatured DNA. Upon completion of this pairing, the enzyme or enzymes responsible for repairing various DNA damages might excise that region of the recipient DNA whose complementary region is now occupied by a strand of the transforming DNA. This step might possibly be the step responsible for recovery from eclipse. Following this recovery, the establishment of chemical continuity between the recipient and the donor DNA could occur. This step might reasonably be considered identical with that in which genetic linkage is established.[1] Reactions such as those that have been described are not substantially different from those that have been observed as being responsible for the dark reactivation of bacteria that have been irradiated with ultraviolet light.[17, 18]

In order to explain recombination within the region of the incorporated element of transforming DNA, it would be necessary to assume that the pairing process might be interrupted, perhaps by a break in the strand of donor DNA that is being incorporated. This might result in a switch, in which the other strand of donor DNA begins to pair with its complement in the host genome (later to be excised), and then a switch back to incorporate the remainder of the element of transforming DNA.

Whatever the final description of the mechanism of recombination, it is clear that, at least in the case of DNA-mediated transformation of *D. pneumonia*, the genetic exchange occurs by the physical insertion of a single strand of transforming DNA into the genetic material of the recipient bacterium.

The authors wish to thank Dr. P. F. Davison for his advice and suggestions, and Mr. J. Shamoun for his technical assistance.

* This work was supported by grants from the National Science Foundation (GB-644), and the National Institutes of Health (AI-05388).

† National Institutes of Health postdoctoral fellow.

[1] Fox, M. S., *Nature*, **187**, 1004 (1960).

[2] Fox, M. S., these PROCEEDINGS, **48**, 1043 (1962).

[3] Fox, M. S., and R. D. Hotchkiss, *Nature*, **187**, 1002 (1960).

[4] Lacks, S., *J. Mol. Biol.*, **5**, 119 (1962).

[5] Hotchkiss, R. D., and A. H. Evans, in *Exchange of Genetic Material: Mechanisms and Consequences*, Cold Spring Harbor Symposia on Quantitative Biology, vol. 23 (1958), p. 85.

[6] Crespi, H. L., J. Marmur, and J. J. Katz, *J. Am. Chem. Soc.*, **84**, 3489 (1962).

[7] Fox, M. S., and R. D. Hotchkiss, *Nature*, **179**, 1322 (1957).

[8] Fox, M. S., *J. Gen. Physiol.*, **42**, 737 (1959).

[9] Szybalski, W., *Journal de Chimie Physique et de Physico-Chimie Biologique*, **58**, 1098 (1961).

[10] Bodmer, W. F., and A. T. Ganesan, in *Proceedings of the Eleventh International Congress of Genetics*, ed. S. J. Geerts (Oxford: Pergamon Press, 1963), p. 30.

[11] Davison, P. F., and D. Freifelder, *J. Mol. Biol.*, **5**, 643 (1962).

[12] Freifelder, D., and P. F. Davison, *Biophys. J.*, **2**, 235 (1962).

[13] Doty, P., B. McGill, and S. A. Rice, these PROCEEDINGS, **44**, 432 (1958).

[14] Suzuki, K., H. Yamagami, and N. Rebeyrotte, *J. Mol. Biol.*, **5**, 577 (1962).

[15] Guild, W. R., and M. Robison, these PROCEEDINGS, **50**, 106 (1963).

[16] Hotchkiss, R. D., in *Enzymes: Units of Biological Structure and Function*, ed. O. H. Gaebler (New York: Academic Press, 1956), p. 119.

[17] Setlow, R., and W. Carrier, these PROCEEDINGS, **51**, 226 (1964).

[18] Boyce, R. P., and P. Howard-Flanders, these PROCEEDINGS, **51**, 293 (1964).

Infectivity of Ribonucleic Acid from Tobacco Mosaic Virus

A. GIERER AND G. S. SCHRAMM

In their experiments with bacteriophages, Hershey and Chase[1] have shown that only the nucleic acid component plays a part in the intracellular multiplication. There are also indications that in simple viruses containing ribonucleic acid the nucleic acid plays a dominant part in the infection. Thus, experiments with tobacco mosaic virus have shown that the protein can be changed chemically without affecting the activity and the genetic properties[2]; recently, it was even found[3] that part of the protein can be removed from tobacco mosaic virus without destroying the activity.

We have now obtained evidence that after complete removal of the protein, the ribonucleic acid itself is still infectious.

The protein was extracted from tobacco mosaic virus with phenol by a procedure elaborated by Schuster, Schramm and Zillig (to be published). After a short treatment at low temperatures, a preparation of ribonucleic acid is obtained which has a high molecular weight during the first few hours but depolymerizes in the course of time. Its physical properties will be described elsewhere.

A solution of 10 per cent tobacco mosaic virus in $0.02\,M$ phosphate buffer of pH 7·3 is shaken for 8 min. at 5° C. with an equal amount of water-saturated phenol. The aqueous phase which contains the ribonucleic acid is separated by centrifugation, and the process of extraction with phenol is repeated at least twice for 2 min. The phenol is then extracted by ether from the aqueous phase. The whole procedure is carried out at 5° C. and takes about 50 min.; it is followed immediately by testing the infectivity.

For that purpose, five to ten plants of *Nicotiana glutinosa* with five leaves each were inoculated with a diluted solution of the ribonucleic acid, and an equal number of plants with a standard solution of tobacco mosaic virus. The number of local lesions produced by ribonucleic acid and tobacco mosaic virus are compared in Table 1. It is found that 10 μgm. of ribonucleic acid produces about the same number of lesions as does 0·2 μgm. tobacco mosaic virus. The infectivity of the ribonucleic acid preparation is thus about 2 per cent of that of the native virus.

The following experiments, the results of which are collected in Table 2, have been carried out to show that the infection is due to the nucleic acid rather than to contamination of the ribonucleic acid with native virus.

(a) In the ribonucleic acid solution protein was not detectable by chemical methods (Schuster, Schramm and Zillig, unpublished work); thus the

amount must be less than 0·4 per cent of the ribonucleic acid content. By serological methods (complement fixation) it was shown that the ribonucleic acid contains less than 0·02 per cent of native tobacco mosaic virus protein.

(b) Treatment of both the ribonucleic acid and tobacco mosaic virus with normal rabbit serum (concentration 3×10^{-3}, applied for 10 min. at 4° C.) somewhat reduces the infectivity. There is no significant further reduction if the ribonucleic acid is treated with the same amount of tobacco mosaic virus antiserum, whereas with antiserum the infectivity of the virus itself is almost completely destroyed.

(c) Incubation of the stock solutions of ribonucleic acid (0·3 per cent) and tobacco mosaic virus (0·06 per cent) with 2 μgm. per ml. of ribonuclease at 4° C. for 10 min. reduces the activity of the ribonucleic acid to 0, whereas that of the virus remains almost unaffected.

(d) The sedimentation constant of the ribonucleic acid is 12–18 S, compared with 180 S for tobacco mosaic virus. We have centrifuged the stock solution of ribonucleic acid for 30 min. at 50,000 rev. per min. and found the supernatant liquid to be only a little less active than the original solution. If the solution of the virus is treated in the same manner, the activity of the supernatant liquid is very low.

(e) The ribonucleic acid is known to be unstable; and, as would be expected, its infectivity is much reduced after 48 hr. at 20° C., whereas that of the virus is much less affected.

These experiments show that protein, if present at all, is only there in very small amounts and does not resemble closely the native protein of tobacco mosaic virus. We are thus led to conclude that the infectivity is due to the nucleic acid itself.

Table 1. COMPARISON OF THE INFECTIVITY OF RIBONUCLEIC ACID AND TOBACCO MOSAIC VIRUS IN $0.1\,M$ PHOSPHATE BUFFER

pH	Ribonucleic acid μgm./ml.	lesions	Tobacco mosaic virus μgm./ml.	lesions
6·1	10	153	0·09	95
			0·8	445
7·3	10	815	0·27	1,048
7·3	1	524	0·05	795
7·5	10	998	0·27	685

Table 2. COMPARISON OF RIBONUCLEIC ACID (10 μgm./ml.) AND TOBACCO MOSAIC VIRUS (0·27 μgm./ml.) IN $0.1\,M$ PHOSPHATE BUFFER OF pH 7·3
(Infectivity expressed as lesions per 30 leaves)

	Ribonucleic acid	Tobacco mosaic virus
Normal	488	629
With normal serum	180	117
With antiserum	145	0
With ribonuclease	0	473
After ultracentrifugation	367	31
After 48 hr. at 20° C.	2	130

The infectivity of the ribonucleic acid preparation is about 0·1 per cent of that of the same amount of ribonucleic acid contained in native tobacco mosaic virus. Whether this relatively low value is due to a large inactive fraction of the ribonucleic acid preparation, or to low efficiency of the mechanism of infection, has still to be determined.

Studies on the combination of the ribonucleic acid with proteins are being carried out and may elucidate the connexion between our findings and the reactivation experiments of Fraenkel-Conrat and Williams[4], of Lippincott and Commoner[5], and of Hart[6].

We are much indebted to Prof. H. Friedrich-Freksa for helpful discussions, to Mr. R. Engler and Dr. H. Schuster for their co-operation, and to Miss A. Kleih for assistance.

A detailed account of this work will be published in the *Zeitschrift für Naturforschung*.

A. GIERER
G. SCHRAMM

Max-Planck-Institut für Virusforschung, Tübingen.
Feb. 10.

[1] Hershey, A. D., and Chase, M., *J. Gen. Physiol.*, **36**, 39 (1952).

[2] Schramm, G., and Müller, H., *Hoppe Seylers Z. physiol. Chem.*, **266**, 43 (1940); **274**, 267 (1942). Miller, G. L., and Stanley, W. M., *J. Biol. Chem.*, **141**, 905 (1941); **146**, 331 (1942). Harris, J. I., and Knight, C. A., *J. Biol. Chem.*, **214**, 215 (1955).

[3] Schramm, G., Schumacher, G., and Zillig, W., *Nature*, **175**, 549 (1955).

[4] Fraenkel-Conrat, H., and Williams, R. C., *Proc. U.S. Nat. Acad. Sci.*, **41**, 690 (1955).

[5] Lippincott, J. A., and Commoner, B., *Biochim. Biophys. Acta*, **19**, 198 (1956).

[6] Hart, R. G., *Nature*, **177**, 130 (1956).

J. Mol. Biol. (1960) **2**, 297-305

Infection of Protoplasts of *Escherichia coli* by Subviral Particles of Bacteriophage φX174†

GEORGE D. GUTHRIE AND ROBERT L. SINSHEIMER

Division of Biology, California Institute of Technology, Pasadena, California, U.S.A.

(*Received 11 July 1960*)

Infection of protoplasts of various strains of *Escherichia coli* may be obtained with purified DNA preparations from bacteriophage φX174 made by two distinctly different methods. Infection of such protoplasts can also be obtained with nucleoprotein particles made from φX174 by heat treatment. None of the particles, infective to protoplasts, are infective to whole cells and all are infective to protoplasts of strains of bacteria usually resistant to whole φX174 virus.

The protoplast-infective agents are in all cases destroyed by enzymatic treatment with DNase. The infective DNA is not inactivated by treatment with enzymatic amounts of trypsin but is by treatment with stoichiometric amounts, suggesting the formation of an inactive DNA-trypsin complex.

Studies of the properties of protoplast infection indicate certain general characteristics which distinguish it from the more familiar virus infection of whole bacterial cells.

1. Introduction

The use of protoplasts for the study of microbiological phenomena is becoming increasingly widespread. Investigations conducted more or less simultaneously by Spizizen (1957) and Fraser, Mahler, Shug & Thomas (1957) demonstrated that protoplasts could be infected by subviral particles of the bacteriophage T2. Fraser has discussed the general characteristics of such infections.

Bacteriophage φX174 has been characterized by Sinsheimer (1959*a*) as a minute particle containing a single molecule of DNA. This DNA molecule has been characterized physically and chemically (Sinsheimer, 1959*b*) as a small single-stranded polynucleotide of some 5,500 nucleotides. For these reasons, attempts have been made to obtain, from φX174, subviral particles with the ability to infect protoplasts. Such infective particles have been obtained by three different methods. These particles are of two types. One type is known from its behavior during sedimentation and from its density to have associated with it a large part of the original viral protein. The other type is the free nucleic acid of the virus. Evidence for the fact that this latter particle is the free DNA rests to a large extent on the physical-chemical characterization of the molecule as reported by Sinsheimer.

2. Materials and Methods

Stock solutions

All stocks including nutrient media are made up using either deionized water or double distilled water.

Tris buffers: Sigma 121 grade (Sigma Chemical Co., St. Louis, Mo.) is used in stock solutions of tris (2-amino-2-hydroxymethylpropane-1:3-diol) buffer.

† This research has been supported by U.S. Public Health Service grants C-3441 and 2G86. One of us (GDG) has been supported by a U.S. Public Health Predoctoral Fellowship (No. 10, 078) during most of this work.

Lysozyme: Worthington Biochemical Co. crystalline egg white lysozyme is made up weekly to a concentration of 2 mg/ml. in water, and stored in the cold.

EDTA: a 4% solution of EDTA (ethylenediaminetetra-acetic acid, Eastman Organic Chemicals) dissolved in water.

Modified 3XD broth: this is the casamino acid-glycerol broth of Fraser & Jerrel (1953) but contains only 0·9 g KH_2PO_4 and 2·1 g Na_2HPO_4 per liter.

Nutrient broth: the nutrient broth in which protoplasts are incubated is a modification of that used by Lederberg & St. Clair (1958) for the growth of protoplasts and L-forms of *E. coli*. It contains 10 g Casamino Acids (Difco), 10 g Nutrient Broth (Difco—a mixture of beef extract and peptones, 3 to 5), 1 g glucose, 100 g sucrose, per liter of water. After autoclaving, 10 ml. of a sterile 10% solution of $MgSO_4$ (anhydrous) are added.

Assay Procedure

The agar layer method (Adams, 1950) is used. Top agar for plating infected protoplasts is the nutrient broth (above) plus 1% agar. After the top agar (2·5 ml.) is pipetted into the plating tubes, 0·15 ml. BSA (Armour and Co. 30% sterile solution bovine serum albumin) is added per tube plus 0·2 ml. plating bacteria. The top agar for the assay of mature virus contains 1 g Tryptone, 0·5 g NaCl, and 0·8 g agar per 100 ml. water.

Bottom agar, for both protoplasts and virus, is 10 g Tryptone, 2·5 g NaCl, 2·5 g KCl, 10 g agar, 6 ml. 1 N-NaOH per liter of water. After autoclaving 1 ml. sterile 1 M-$CaCl_2$ is added.

Plating bacteria: *E. coli* C are grown, with aeration, to log phase at 37°C in "adsorption medium" (10 g Tryptone, 5 g KCl, 5×10^{-4} M-$CaCl_2$ per liter of water). 0·2 ml. plating bacteria are used per plate and plaques can be counted after 3 to 4 hr incubation at 37°C.

Protoplasts: during the development of this work the following strains of *E. coli* have been used to make protoplasts: C(BTCC no. 122), C/φX (isolated in this laboratory from C), B (Luria), and K12 nonlysogenic (obtained from Dr. Jean Weigle). Protoplasts of all of these strains can be infected by subviral particles with about the same efficiency but vary somewhat in ease of handling. All of the strains, after conversion to protoplasts by our method, exhibit, to some degree, the ability to reform cell walls and divide. As a consequence, the term protoplast is applied with some reservation. The particles are, however, spherical in shape, and "shock" when diluted 1 : 20 into water. With the exception of *E. coli* C, these strains are completely resistant to infection with whole virus φX174 when plated by our usual procedure. Also, incubation of either K12 cells or K12 protoplasts with whole virus under the same conditions as those used for infection with DNA produces no evidence of infection of even a small percentage of the cells or protoplasts.

To obtain protoplasts, cells of the desired strain† are inoculated, from either a slant or a saturated culture, into modified 3XD broth and allowed to grow at 37°C with aeration to 5×10^8/ml. (as determined in the Petroff-Hausser counting chamber). The cells are subcultured with a dilution of 1 : 25 into prewarmed medium and allowed to grow again to a concentration of 5×10^8/ml. (The concentration limits here are approximately 2 to 6×10^8/ml.)

Twenty ml. cells are then centrifuged at room temperature, 1,000 *g* for 10 min. The pellet is taken up in 0·35 ml. 0·5 M-sucrose; 0·1 ml. 0·25 M-Sigma 121 buffer pH 8·1 and 0·01 ml. lysozyme stock are added, then 0·02 ml. 4% EDTA. (Note that the cells are neither washed nor chilled.) Formation of protoplasts is complete (99·9%) within 5 to 10 min at room temperature. After 10 min the protoplasts are diluted fivefold into nutrient broth containing 2% BSA. A further fourfold dilution is made after 3 to 5 min into nutrient broth to reduce the concentration of BSA. This is the "protoplast stock."

Subviral Particles

In making each of the subviral particles a purified preparation of φX174 (Sinsheimer 1959a) is used.‡

---

†*E. coli* B (Luria) cannot be converted to protoplasts as easily as the other strains. The method of Fraser *et al.* (1957) has been used successfully for this strain. These protoplasts are more stable and will survive centrifugation at 1,000 *g* for 10 min at room temperature, without loss of activity.

‡A fourth method for obtaining subviral particles, treatment with 8 M-urea (Fraser *et al.*, 1957) has also been used. This method produces a mixture of protein containing particles and free DNA but in general the particles do not appear to be as infective as the others described.

I. Heated particle† *(HTϕX):* purified ϕX (at a concentration of 10^{15}/ml.) is diluted 1/100 into 0·1 M-tris buffer pH 7·5. It is then heated at 70°C for 5 min and cooled. Samples treated in this manner show a loss of infectivity (as assayed by normal plating procedure) of between 10^6 and 10^8/ml. From electron micrographs of this particle (Hall, Maclean & Tessman, 1959) it appears that, on heating, the virus breaks open and that the DNA, possibly with some protein, is extruded from the protein coat. HTϕX has a density in rubidium chloride of 1·42 g/cm³ (0·02 g/cm³ greater than the whole virus). Its sedimentation coefficient in 0·1 M-tris pH 8·0 is 47 s, less than that of either the whole virus (114 s) or the protein "coat" (70 s), a result which would be expected for a particle of the type seen in the micrographs. Upon treatment with DNase the sedimentation coefficient of the residual protein particle rises to 70 s. Also present in the HTϕX preparation is a small amount of material which is probably free DNA. This material may be separated from the HTϕX particle by banding in a cesium chloride density gradient (*vide infra*); both the DNA and HTϕX particle are biologically active when tested with protoplasts.

II. Phenol-prepared DNA: the preparation of this particle (the free DNA) is described and the molecule is characterized as the free DNA by Sinsheimer (1959b).

III. Calcium particle (CaϕX-DNA): a third method for obtaining a biologically active subviral particle is the following: purified ϕX is diluted tenfold (from a stock of 10^{14} to 10^{15} virus/ml.) into cold 4 M-CaCl₂ (analytical reagent grade recrystallized once from 95% ethanol and dissolved in deionized water), allowed to stand at room temperature for 30 min and stored in the cold for another 90 min. A heavy precipitate forms which contains almost all of the virus. This is centrifuged in the cold for 30 min (12,000 g in the Servall SS 1 centrifuge). The supernatant‡ is discarded. The pellet is resuspended in 0·1 M-tris buffer pH 7·5 to 8·0, centrifuged and the supernatant retained. This supernatant contains from 30 to 50% of the original viral DNA. Repeated extractions of the pellet, which presumably contains the rest of the DNA, are largely unsuccessful.

The ultraviolet absorption spectrum of this calcium-prepared DNA is the same as the spectrum of the DNA from the phenol treatment with a minimum at 230 mμ and a maximum at 257 mμ. Its sedimentation coefficient is that of phenol-prepared DNA (23 s). In the cesium chloride density gradient it bands at a density of 1·72 g/cm³ as does phenol-prepared DNA. On the basis of these criteria the CaϕX-DNA is believed to be the same molecule as that prepared by the phenol method. Data obtained using either of these particles are reported as data resulting from the infection of protoplasts by free ϕX-DNA.

General Method for Infecting Protoplasts with Subviral Particles of ϕX174

Cells are grown and converted to protoplasts as described above. The infecting particle, which is stored in 0·1 M-KCl, 0·001 M-tris buffer, pH 7·5 (under these conditions infectivity is retained for weeks if the sample is kept in the cold), is diluted at least tenfold into 0·01 M-tris pH 8·0 to 8·3. To a volume of infecting particles is added an equal volume of "protoplast stock." The mixture is incubated at 37°C for 10 to 15 min, after which it is diluted fivefold into nutrient broth. After another 90 min incubation the sample is titered for mature ϕX phage. If infective centers are to be assayed the sample is diluted and plated after the 10 min adsorption period. Dilutions for infective centers are made through nutrient broth plus 2% BSA and plating is performed as described above.

Experiments have shown that, while 2% BSA is necessary for the initial stabilization of the protoplasts, the BSA concentration during incubation of the infected protoplasts in liquid medium must be below 0·2% for maximum final phage yield. During incubation of the protoplasts on agar plates, however, BSA at a concentration of from 1 to 2% is used.

3. Experiments and Results

Banding of the infective particles in the cesium chloride density gradient: each of the three particles has been banded by cesium chloride density gradient centrifugation (Meselson, Stahl & Vinograd, 1957). After fractionation by drop collection from the

† This method for obtaining a subviral particle was suggested to us by Dr. Irwin Tessman.

‡ This first supernatant has ultraviolet absorption with a maximum at 270 mμ and apparently contains a small amount of viral protein.

sample tube the fractions were assayed for biological infectivity using protoplasts and were also assayed for ultraviolet absorption in the Beckman DK-2 Spectrophotometer. In each case the biological activity was found in the fractions corresponding to those with the u.v. absorption spectrum of the particle. The amount of infectivity corresponds reasonably directly to the particle concentration as calculated from the u.v. absorption. Examples of such experiments are shown in Figs. 1 and 2. One of these experiments (CaϕX-DNA, Fig. 2) was done in a manner to permit compensation for the nonlinearity of assay (*vide infra*); the other was not. *Particles banded in this manner and assayed by the usual plating procedure for viable phage produce no plaques.*

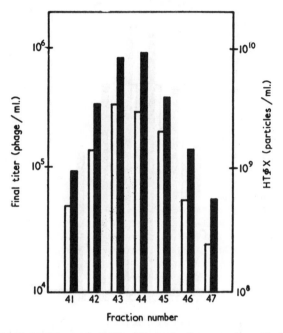

Fig. 1. Infectivity and particle concentration of samples from a cesium chloride density gradient band of HTϕX particles. Mean density of the band is 1·42 g/cm³. Biological activity is represented by open bars; particle concentration, as calculated from u.v. absorption, by solid bars.

Growth curves: the multiplication of phage in infected protoplasts can be followed in a manner similar to that used for virus infected whole cells. Figs 3 and 4 show the results of such experiments using *E. coli* C protoplasts and *E. coli* K 12 protoplasts, respectively.

Each growth curve consists of two assays. One is made in a manner which measures total infective centres (infected protoplasts† plus free phage). This assay indicates the kinetics of "adsorption" and infection as well as the "latent period." The other curve is made by plating with an initial 1/20 dilution through water to "shock" any infected protoplasts in order to assay only mature phage particles. At later times of incubation, the latter assay is found to indicate 3 to 5 times more virus than the former. This is not a plating artifact since "shocked" samples plated in the same manner as infective centers (on BSA plates) give the same titer as those plated by the usual method. The result is interpreted to mean that protoplasts do not lyse in

---

†We do not know what fraction of the infected protoplasts survive and form infective centers on the agar plates. Characteristics of such growth on agar are discussed by Lederberg & St. Clair (1958).

the manner ordinarily observed with whole infected cells (due possibly to the presence of sucrose in the nutrient medium), and that a portion of the virus produced by the protoplasts is not released from them unless they are shocked into water.

Since the adsorption of DNA by protoplasts occurs in the presence of nutrient, events are measured from the time of mixing. The "zero time" infective centers simply represent those infections occurring between the time of mixing the DNA and protoplasts and the time the first sample is plated, i.e. within about the first minute. The mature phage curve (curve B of Figs. 3 and 4) is extrapolated back from the time of the first appearance of mature phage.

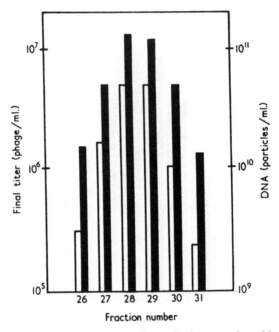

FIG. 2. Infectivity and particle concentration of samples from a cesium chloride density gradient band of CaφX-DNA. Mean density of the band is 1·72 g/cm³. Biological activity is shown by open bars; particle concentration, calculated from the u.v. absorption, by solid bars.

There is an obvious difference between the two growth curves at later times of incubation. The curve from the K12 experiment resembles more closely the shape of the growth curve of virus in whole cells, while the *E. coli* C curve continues to rise. *E. coli* C is a normal host for φX while K12 is not; also, protoplasts made by our method seem to show some capability of resynthesizing cell wall. These facts, coupled with the observation that the infected tube of C protoplasts remains clear while the control (uninfected protoplasts) is found to contain a high concentration of whole cells after incubation, lead to the conclusion that residual C cells or protoplasts which have regrown a portion of their cell wall are infected by the phage initially produced by the infected protoplasts, resulting in the continued production of phage. For this reason it is preferable in these experiments to use protoplasts of an organism which is resistant to mature φX174.

Dilution experiments: if successive dilutions of DNA are used to infect a constant number of protoplasts, activity curves of the general shape of those shown in Fig. 5 result. At high concentrations of DNA there is an apparent saturation of protoplasts susceptible to infection. At lower concentrations of infecting particle a linear relationship (plotted on log-log coordinates) is observed between phage yield and infecting particle concentration, while at still lower concentrations a higher efficiency of infection per DNA particle is observed. If the "saturation level" in the assay for infective centers (curve A, Fig. 5) is taken as an indication of the number of protoplasts capable of being infected, rather than an indication of some sort of interference

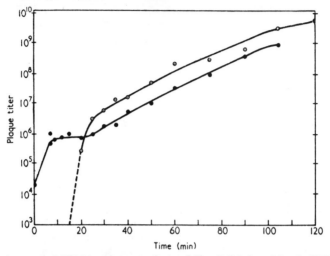

FIG. 3. Growth curve of ϕX174 using protoplasts of *E. coli* C infected by CaϕX-DNA. Curve A (●──●) indicates infective centers (infected protoplasts† plus free phage), curve B (○──○) mature phage.

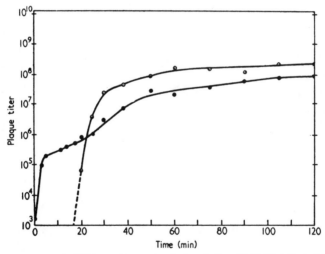

FIG. 4. Growth curve of ϕX174 using protoplasts of *E. coli* K 12 infected by CaϕX-DNA Curve A (●──●) indicates infective centers (infected protoplasts† plus free phage), curve B (○──○) mature phage.

phenomenon between DNA molecules which limits infection, the second break in the curve occurs at a concentration of infecting particles such that the multiplicity of DNA per susceptible protoplast is between 1 and 3. These data suggest that about 0·1% of the protoplasts can be infected by DNA, while a small fraction of these are more easily infected, and give rise to a greater efficiency at low DNA concentration.

† We do not know what fraction of the infected protoplasts survive and form infective centers on the agar plates. Characteristics of such growth on agar are discussed by Lederberg & St. Clair (1958).

At the lowest concentration represented in Fig. 5 the number of infective centers obtained is equivalent to 3% of the DNA particles (the number of DNA particles is calculated from the u.v. absorption). The final phage yield at this concentration contains 5·5 times as much ϕX-DNA in mature phage particles as was initially

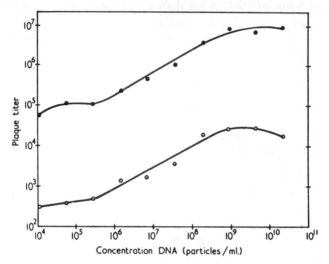

FIG. 5. Dilution curve (nonlinearity of assay). Curve A ($\odot$——$\odot$) indicates infective centers (plated after 10 min adsorption), curve B ($\bullet$——$\bullet$) represents mature phage produced after 2 hr incubation.

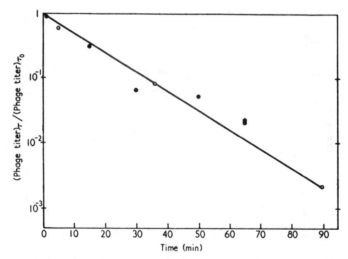

FIG. 6. DNase inactivation of CaϕX-DNA. The curve represents the normalized decline in final phage titer as a result of DNase inactivation of the infective particle. The actual inactivation is somewhat greater since the nonlinearity of assay tends to make lower concentrations of infective particles more efficient. Temperature 25 °C, reaction mixture contained 0·005 M-MgSO$_4$, 0·1 M-tris pH 7·5, approx. 10^{13} CaϕX-DNA particles/ml. and 10^{11} DNase molecules/ml.

present in the infection mixture as free DNA, clearly indicating that new DNA is being made (rather than input DNA simply being "coated" with viral protein).

Reactions of DNase and trypsin with subviral particles: studies have been made of the actions of DNase and trypsin on CaϕX-DNA and HTϕX particles. Fig. 6 demonstrates that the action of DNase on CaϕX-DNA follows the kinetics of an enzymatic inactivation of the particle. (These are the results of two different experiments and were not corrected for the nonlinearity of assay.) At a concentration of 1 enzyme molecule per DNA molecule the reaction is so rapid that it is impossible to measure the kinetics of inactivation. The same is true for the action of DNase on the HTɸX particle.

With trypsin, an inactivation of ɸX-DNA is observed which does not appear to be enzymatic. At molar concentrations of trypsin molecules comparable to or less than the molar concentration of the infecting particle, i.e. at "enzymatic" concentrations, there is no loss of infectivity, even with incubations up to 2 hours. However, at higher concentrations (approximately 10 or more enzyme molecules per infecting particle) there is a drastic loss of activity in the sample which is complete within 10 min. This is apparently the result of a stoichiometric binding of the basic protein, trypsin, to the DNA molecule. Additional evidence that ɸX-DNA is subject to non-enzymatic attachment to molecules such as trypsin may be obtained from "ring tests" similar to those used to test for antigen-antibody reactions. If a solution of ɸX-DNA is layered over a solution of trypsin a precipitate forms at the interface. On standing for 12 hr the "ring" remains, indicating that the binding between the molecules is strong.

Similar ring reactions are also observed with ɸX-DNA and lysozyme, with ɸX-DNA and anti-ɸX rabbit serum and with ɸX-DNA and normal (non-immune) rabbit serum. It thus appears that the highly charged polynucleotide probably combines readily with most basic proteins forming a "nucleoprotein" which appears to be biologically inactive.†

4. Discussion

From the results of the experiments it is clear that protoplasts of *E. coli* can be infected with the DNA of ɸX174. This DNA can be infective after it is separated from the protein coat or when, as with the HTɸX particle, it still has attached to it at least part of the viral protein. Using free ɸX-DNA, which has been purified by banding in the cesium chloride density gradient, the kinetics of infection of protoplasts by DNA can be studied in a manner similar to that used for the study of whole cells infected by virus.

The dilution experiments, however, suggest that "infection" is similar to the interaction of plant virus and their host plant cells. In particular, such dilution curves have been found for tobacco mosaic virus (TMV) infection (Kleczkowski (1950) reports dilution curves for TMV; Mundry & Gierer (1958) report data for TMV and TMV-RNA). The extent to which the kinetics of ɸX-DNA infection of protoplasts compare with those of TMV infection of sensitive leaves is not known. The results do seem to indicate that with this DNA, as with TMV and TMV-RNA, there is no specific attachment mechanism by which efficient infection can take place.

The stability of ɸX-DNA as compared to infectious TMV-RNA, the relative accuracy with which results can be reproduced with protoplasts, and the extensive background of information available on the growth of virus in bacteria suggest that this protoplast system has advantages for the investigation of viral replication initiated by free nucleic acid.

†BSA, at the proper concentration, also forms a precipitate with lysozyme. It is possible that BSA, in addition to stabilizing the protoplasts, serves to "protect" DNA in the adsorption mixture by binding lysozme and other basic molecules which might be present in the adsorption mixture due to the rupture of a few protoplasts.

The evident ability of these protoplasts to take up a single-stranded DNA suggests that bacterial transformation or infection with the DNA of other viruses might be achieved if the DNA employed were first converted to the single-stranded form (Doty, Marmur, Eigner & Schildkraut, 1960).

It is a pleasure to acknowledge the capable technical assistance of Miss Faith Poole. Several talks with Dr. Dean Fraser, Indiana University, about the preparation and use of protoplasts were of considerable value in developing the techniques for this research. Dr. Wolfgang Mundry's contributions in numerous discussions are gratefully acknowledged.

REFERENCES

Adams, M. H. (1950). *Methods in Medical Research* Vol. 2. Chicago: The Year Book Publishers.

Doty, P., Marmur, J., Eigner, J. & Schildkraut, C. (1960). *Proc. Nat. Acad. Sci., Wash.* **46**, 461.

Fraser, D. & Jerrel, E. A. (1953). *J. Biol. Chem.* **205**, 291.

Fraser, D., Mahler, H., Shug, A. & Thomas, C., Jr. (1957). *Proc. Nat. Acad. Sci., Wash.* **43**, 939.

Hall, C. E., Maclean, E. C. & Tessman, I. (1959). *J. Appl. Phys.* **30**, 2024.

Kleczkowski, A. (1950). *J. Gen. Microbiol.* **4**, 53.

Lederberg, J. & St. Clair, J. (1958). *J. Bact.* **75**, 143.

Meselson, M., Stahl, F. & Vinograd, J. (1957). *Proc. Nat. Acad. Sci., Wash.* **43**, 581.

Mundry, K. W. & Gierer, A. (1958). *Z. Vererbungslehre*, **89**, 614.

Sinsheimer, R. L. (1959a). *J. Mol. Biol.* **1**, 37.

Sinsheimer, R. L. (1959b). *J. Mol. Biol.* **1**, 43.

Spizizen, J. (1957). *Proc. Nat. Acad. Sci., Wash.* **43**, 694.

Physical
and
Chemical
Characterization

Reprinted from Cold Spring Harbor Symposia on Quantitative Biology Volume XVIII, 1953

THE STRUCTURE OF DNA

J. D. WATSON[1] AND F. H. C. CRICK

Cavendish Laboratory, Cambridge, England

(Contribution to the Discussion of Provirus.)

It would be superfluous at a Symposium on Viruses to introduce a paper on the structure of DNA with a discussion on its importance to the problem of virus reproduction. Instead we shall not only assume that DNA is important, but in addition that it is the carrier of the genetic specificity of the virus (for argument, see Hershey, this volume) and thus must possess in some sense the capacity for exact self-duplication. In this paper we shall describe a structure for DNA which suggests a mechanism for its self-duplication and allows us to propose, for the first time, a detailed hypothesis on the atomic level for the self-reproduction of genetic material.

We first discuss the chemical and physical-chemical data which show that DNA is a long fibrous molecule. Next we explain why crystallographic evidence suggests that the structural unit of DNA consists not of one but of two polynucleotide chains. We then discuss a stereochemical model which we believe satisfactorily accounts for both the chemical and crystallographic data. In conclusion we suggest some obvious genetical implications of the proposed structure. A preliminary account of some of these data has already appeared in Nature (Watson and Crick, 1953a, 1953b).

I. EVIDENCE FOR THE FIBROUS NATURE OF DNA

The basic chemical formula of DNA is now well established. As shown in Figure 1 it consists of a very long chain, the backbone of which is made up of alternate sugar and phosphate groups, joined together in regular 3' 5' phosphate di-ester linkages. To each sugar is attached a nitrogenous base, only four different kinds of which are commonly found in DNA. Two of these—adenine and guanine—are purines, and the other two—thymine and cytosine—are pyrimidines. A fifth base, 5-methyl cytosine, occurs in smaller amounts in certain organisms, and a sixth, 5-hydroxy-methyl-cytosine, is found instead of cytosine in the T even phages (Wyatt and Cohen, 1952).

It should be noted that the chain is unbranched, a consequence of the regular internucleotide linkage. On the other hand the sequence of the different nucleotides is, as far as can be ascertained, completely irregular. Thus, DNA has some features which are regular, and some which are irregular.

A similar conception of the DNA molecule as a long thin fiber is obtained from physico-chemical analysis involving sedimentation, diffusion, light scattering, and viscosity measurements. These techniques indicate that DNA is a very asymmetrical structure approximately 20 A wide and many thousands of angstroms long. Estimates of its molecular weight currently center between 5×10^6 and 10^7 (approximately 3×10^4 nucleotides). Surprisingly each of these measurements tend to suggest that the DNA is relatively rigid, a puzzling finding in view of the large number of single bonds (5 per nucleotide) in the phosphate-sugar back-

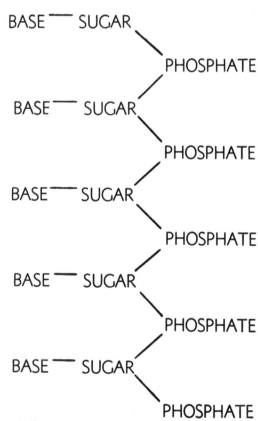

FIGURE 1. Chemical formula (diagrammatic) of a single chain of desoxyribonucleic acid.

[1] Aided by a Fellowship from the National Foundation for Infantile Paralysis.

bone. Recently these indirect inferences have been confirmed by electron microscopy. Employing high resolution techniques both Williams (1952) and Kahler *et al.* (1953) have observed, in preparations of DNA, very long thin fibers with a uniform width of approximately 15-20 A.

II. EVIDENCE FOR THE EXISTENCE OF TWO CHEMICAL CHAINS IN THE FIBER

This evidence comes mainly from X-ray studies. The material used is the sodium salt of DNA (usually from calf thymus) which has been extracted, purified, and drawn into fibers. These fibers are highly birefringent, show marked ultraviolet and infrared dichroism (Wilkins *et al.*, 1951; Fraser and Fraser, 1951), and give good X-ray fiber diagrams. From a preliminary study of these, Wilkins, Franklin and their co-workers at King's College, London (Wilkins *et al.*, 1953; Franklin and Gosling 1953a, b and c) have been able to draw certain general conclusions about the structure of DNA. Two important facts emerge from their work. They are:

(1) *Two distinct forms of DNA exist.* Firstly a crystalline form, Structure A, (Figure 2) which occurs at about 75 per cent relative humidity and contains approximately 30 per cent water. At higher humidities the fibers take up more water, increase in length by about 30 per cent and assume Structure B (Figure 3). This is a less ordered form than Structure A, and appears to be paracrystalline; that is, the individual molecules are all packed parallel to one another, but are not otherwise regularly arranged in space. In Table 1, we have tabulated some of the characteristic features which distinguish the two forms. The transition from A to B is reversible and therefore the two structures are likely to be related in ·a simple manner.

(2) *The crystallographic unit contains two polynucleotide chains.* The argument is crystallographic and so will only be given in outline. Structure B has a very strong 3.4 A reflexion on the meridian. As first pointed out by Astbury (1947), this can only mean that the nucleotides in it occur in groups spaced 3.4 A apart in the fiber direction. On going from Structure B to Structure A the fiber shortens by about 30 per cent. Thus in Structure A the groups must be about 2.5 per cent A apart axially. The measured density of Structure A, (Franklin

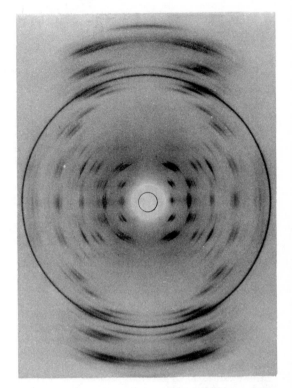

FIGURE 2. X-ray fiber diagram of Structure A of desoxyribonucleic acid. (H. M. F. Wilkins and H. R. Wilson, unpub.)

and Gosling, 1953c) together with the cell dimensions, shows that there must be *two* nucleotides in each such group. Thus it is very probable that the crystallographic unit consists of two distinct polynucleotide chains. Final proof of this can only come from a complete solution of the structure.

Structure A has a pseudo-hexagonal lattice, in which the lattice points are 22 A apart. This distance roughly corresponds with the diameter of fibers seen in the electron microscope, bearing in mind that the latter are quite dry. Thus it is probable that the crystallographic unit and the fiber are the one and the same.

III. DESCRIPTION OF THE PROPOSED STRUCTURE

Two conclusions might profitably be drawn from the above data. Firstly, the structure of DNA is

TABLE 1.
(From Franklin and Gosling, 1953a, b and c)

	Degree of orientation	Repeat distance along fiber axis	Location of first equatorial spacing	Water content	Number of nucleotides within unit cell
Structure A	Crystalline	28 A	18 A	30%	22-24
Structure B	Paracrystalline	34 A	22-24 A	>30%	20 (?)

structure is a well-defined one and all bond distances and angles, including van der Waal distances, are stereochemically acceptable.

The essential element of the structure is the manner in which the two chains are held together by hydrogen bonds between the bases. The bases are perpendicular to the fiber axis and joined together in pairs. The pairing arrangement is very specific, and only certain pairs of bases will fit into the structure. The basic reason for this is that we have assumed that the backbone of each polynucleotide chain is in the form of a regular helix. Thus, irrespective of which bases are present, the glucosidic bonds (which join sugar and base) are arranged in a regular manner in space. In particular, any two glucosidic bonds (one from each chain)

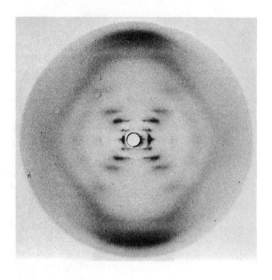

FIGURE 3. X-ray fiber diagram of Structure B of desoxyribonucleic acid. (R. E. Franklin and R. Gosling, 1953a.)

regular enough to form a three dimensional crystal. This is in spite of the fact that its component chains may have an irregular sequence of purine and pyrimidine nucleotides. Secondly, as the structure contains two chains, these chains must be regularly arranged in relation to each other.

To account for these findings, we have proposed (Watson and Crick, 1953a) a structure in which the two chains are coiled round a common axis and joined together by hydrogen bonds between the nucleotide bases (see Figure 4). Both chains follow right handed helices, but the sequences of the atoms in the phosphate-sugar backbones run in opposite directions and so are related by a dyad perpendicular to the helix axis. The phosphates and sugar groups are on the outside of the helix whilst the bases are on the inside. The distance of a phosphorus atom from the fiber axis is 10 A. We have built our model to correspond to Structure B, which the X-ray data show to have a repeat distance of 34 A in the fiber direction and a very strong reflexion of spacing 3.4 A on the meridian of the X-ray pattern. To fit these observations our structure has a nucleotide on each chain every 3.4 A in the fiber direction, and makes one complete turn after 10 such intervals, i.e., after 34 A. Our

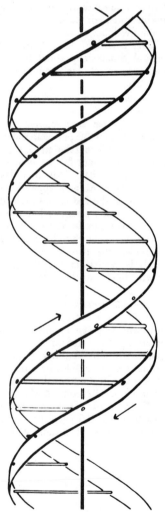

FIGURE 4. This figure is diagrammatic. The two ribbons symbolize the two phosphate-sugar chains and the horizontal rods. The paths of bases holding the chain together. The vertical line marks the fiber axis.

which are attached to a bonded pair of bases, must always occur at a fixed distance apart due to the regularity of the two backbones to which they are joined. The result is that one member of a pair of bases must always be a purine, and the other a pyrimidine, in order to bridge between the two chains. If a pair consisted of two purines, for example, there would not be room for it; if of two pyrimidines they would be too far apart to form hydrogen bonds.

In theory a base can exist in a number of tautomeric forms, differing in the exact positions at which its hydrogen atoms are attached. However, under physiological conditions one particular form of each base is much more probable than any of the others. If we make the assumption that the favored forms always occur, then the pairing requirements are even more restrictive. Adenine can only pair with thymine, and guanine only with cytosine (or 5-methyl-cytosine, or 5-hydroxy-methyl-cytosine). This pairing is shown in detail in Figures 5 and 6. If adenine tried to pair with cytosine it could not form hydrogen bonds, since there would be two hydrogens near one of the bonding positions, and none at the other, instead of one in each.

A given pair can be either way round. Adenine, for example, can occur on either chain, but when it does its partner on the other chain must always be thymine. This is possible because the two glucoside bonds of a pair (see Figures 5 and 6) are symmetrically related to each other, and thus occur in the same positions if the pair is turned over.

It should be emphasized that since each base can form hydrogen bonds at a number of points one can pair up *isolated* nucleotides in a large variety of ways. *Specific* pairing of bases can only be obtained by imposing some restriction, and in our

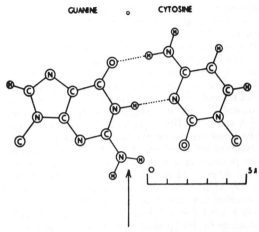

FIGURE 6. Pairing of guanine and cytosine. Hydrogen bonds are shown dotted. One carbon atom of each sugar is shown.

case it is in a direct consequence of the postulated regularity of the phosphate-sugar backbone.

It should further be emphasized that whatever pair of bases occurs at one particular point in the DNA structure, no restriction is imposed on the neighboring pairs, and any *sequence* of pairs can occur. This is because all the bases are flat, and since they are stacked roughly one above another like a pile of pennies, it makes no difference which pair is neighbor to which.

Though any sequence of bases can fit into our structure, the necessity for specific pairing demands a definite relationship between the sequences on the two chains. That is, if we knew the actual order of the bases on one chain, we could automatically write down the order on the other. *Our structure therefore consists of two chains, each of which is the complement of the other.*

IV. EVIDENCE IN FAVOR OF THE COMPLEMENTARY MODEL

The experimental evidence available to us now offers strong support to our model though we should emphasize that, as yet, it has not been proved correct. The evidence in its favor is of three types:

(1) The general appearance of the X-ray picture strongly suggests that the basic structure is helical (Wilkins et al., 1953; Franklin and Gosling, 1953a). If we postulate that a helix is present, we immediately are able to deduce from the X-ray pattern of Structure B (Figure 3), that its pitch is 34 A and its diameter approximately 20 A. Moreover, the pattern suggests a high concentration of atoms on the circumference of the helix, in accord with our model which places the phosphate sugar backbone on the outside. The photograph also indicates that the two polynucleotide chains are not

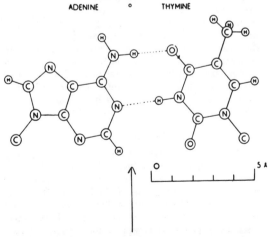

FIGURE 5. Pairing of adenine and thymine. Hydrogen bonds are shown dotted. One carbon atom of each sugar is shown.

spaced equally along the fiber axis, but are probably displaced from each other by about three-eignths of the fiber axis period, an inference again in qualitative agreement with our model.

The interpretation of the X-ray pattern of Structure A (the crystalline form) is less obvious. This form does not give a meridional reflexion at 3.4 A, but instead (Figure 2) gives a series of reflexions around 25° off the meridian at spacings between 3 A and 4 A. This suggests to us that in this form the bases are no longer perpendicular to the fiber axis, but are tilted about 25° from the perpendicular position in a way that allows the fiber to contract 30 per cent and reduces the longitudinal translation of each nucleotide to about 2.5 A. It should be noted that the X-ray pattern of Structure A is much more detailed than that of Structure B and so if correctly interpreted, can yield more precise information about DNA. Any proposed model for DNA must be capable of forming either Structure A or Structure B and so it remains imperative for our very tentative interpretation of Structure A to be confirmed.

(2) The anomolous titration curves of undegraded DNA with acids and bases strongly suggests that hydrogen bond formation is a characteristic aspect of DNA structure. When a solution of DNA is initially treated with acids or bases, no groups are titratable at first between pH 5 and pH 11.0, but outside these limits a rapid ionization occurs (Gulland and Jordan, 1947; Jordan, 1951). On back titration, however, either with acid from pH 12 or with alkali from pH 2½, a different titration curve is obtained indicating that the titratable groups are more accessible to acids and bases than is the untreated solution. Accompanying the initial release of groups at pH 11.5 and in the range pH 3.5 to pH 4.5 is a marked fall in the viscosity and the disappearance of strong flow birefringence. While this decrease was originally thought to be caused by a reversible depolymerization (Vilbrandt and Tennent, 1943), it has been shown by Gulland, Jordan and Taylor (1947) that this is unlikely as no increase was observed in the amount of secondary phosphoryl groups. Instead these authors suggested that some of the groups of the bases formed hydrogen bonds between different bases. They were unable to decide whether the hydrogen bonds linked bases in the same or in adjacent structural units. The fact that most of the ionizable groups are originally inaccessible to acids and bases is more easily explained if the hydrogen bonds are between bases within the same structural unit. This point would definitely be established if it were shown that the shape of the initial titration curve was the same at very low DNA concentrations, when the interaction between neighboring structural units is small.

(3) The analytical data on the relative proportion of the various bases show that the amount of adenine is close to that of thymine, and the amount of guanine close to the amount of cytosine + 5-methyl cytosine, although the ratio of adenine to guanine can vary from one source to another (Chargaff, 1951; Wyatt, 1952). In fact as the techniques for estimation of the bases improve, the ratios of adenine to thymine, and guanine to cytosine + 5-methyl cytosine appear to grow very close to unity. This is a most striking result, especially as the sequence of bases on a given chain is likely to be irregular, and suggests a structure involving paired bases. In fact, we believe the analytical data offer the most important evidence so far available in support of our model, since they specifically support the biologically interesting feature, the presence of complementary chains.

We thus believe that the present experimental evidence justifies the working hypothesis that the essential features of our model are correct and allows us to consider its genetic possibilities.

V. Genetical Implications of the Complementary Model

As a preliminary we should state that the DNA fibers from which the X-ray diffraction patterns were obtained are not artifacts arising in the method of preparation. In the first place, Wilkins and his co-workers (see Wilkins et al., 1953) have shown that X-ray patterns similar to those from the isolated fibers can be obtained from certain intact biological materials such as sperm head and bacteriophage particles. Secondly, our postulated model is so extremely specific that we find it impossible to believe that it could be formed during the isolation from living cells.

A genetic material must in some way fulfil two functions. It must duplicate itself, and it must exert a highly specific influence on the cell. Our model for DNA suggests a simple mechanism for the first process, but at the moment we cannot see how it carries out the second one. We believe, however, that its specificity is expressed by the precise sequence of the pairs of bases. The backbone of our model is highly regular, and the sequence is the only feature which can carry the genetical information. It should not be thought that because in our structure the bases are on the "inside," they would be unable to come into contact with other molecules. Owing to the open nature of our structure they are in fact fairly accessible.

A Mechanism for DNA Replication

The complementary nature of our structure suggests how it duplicates itself. It is difficult to imagine how like attracts like, and it has been suggested (see Pauling and Delbrück, 1940; Friedrich-Freksa, 1940; and Muller, 1947) that self duplication may involve the union of each part with an opposite or complementary part. In these discussions it has generally been suggested that protein and nucleic acid are complementary to each other and that self replication involves the alternate syntheses of these two components. We should like to propose instead that the specificity of DNA self replication is accomplished without recourse to specific protein synthesis and that each of our complementary DNA chains serves as a template or mould for the formation onto itself of a new companion chain.

For this to occur the hydrogen bonds linking the complementary chains must break and the two chains unwind and separate. It seems likely that the single chain (or the relevant part of it) might itself assume the helical form and serve as a mould onto which free nucleotides (strictly polynucleotide precursors) can attach themselves by forming hydrogen bonds. We propose that polymerization of the precursors to form a new chain only occurs if the resulting chain forms the proposed structure. This is plausible because steric reasons would not allow monomers "crystallized" onto the first chain to approach one another in such a way that they could be joined together in a new chain, unless they were those monomers which could fit into our structure. It is not obvious to us whether a special enzyme would be required to carry out the polymerization or whether the existing single helical chain could act effectively as an enzyme.

DIFFICULTIES IN THE REPLICATION SCHEME

While this scheme appears intriguing, it nevertheless raises a number of difficulties, none of which, however, do we regard as insuperable. The first difficulty is that our structure does not differentiate between cytosine and 5-methyl cytosine, and therefore during replication the specificity in sequence involving these bases would not be perpetuated. The amount of 5-methyl cytosine varies considerably from one species to another, though it is usually rather small or absent. The present experimental results (Wyatt, 1952) suggest that each species has a characteristic amount. They also show that the sum of the two cytosines is more nearly equal to the amount of guanine than is the amount of cytosine by itself. It may well be that the difference between the two cytosines is not functionally significant. This interpretation would be considerably strengthened if it proved possible to change the amount of 5-methyl cytosine in the DNA of an organism without altering its genetical make-up.

The occurrence of 5-hydroxy-methyl-cytosine in the T even phages (Wyatt and Cohen, 1952) presents no such difficulty, since it completely replaces cytosine, and its amount in the DNA is close to that of guanine.

The second main objection to our scheme is that it completely ignores the role of the basic protamines and histones, proteins known to be combined with DNA in most living organisms. This was done for two reasons. Firstly, we can formulate a scheme of DNA reproduction involving it alone and so

from the viewpoint of simplicity it seems better to believe (at least at present) that the genetic specificity is never passed through a protein intermediary. Secondly, we know almost nothing about the structural features of protamines and histones. Our only clue is the finding of Astbury (1947) and of Wilkins and Randall (1953) that the X-ray pattern of nucleoprotamine is very similar to that of DNA alone. This suggests that the protein component, or at least some of it, also assumes a helical form and in view of the very open nature of our model, we suspect that protein forms a third helical chain between the pair of polynucleotide chains (see Figure 4). As yet nothing is known about the function of the protein; perhaps it controls the coiling and uncoiling and perhaps it assists in holding the single polynucleotide chains in a helical configuration.

The third difficulty involves the necessity for the two complementary chains to unwind in order to serve as a template for a new chain. This is a very fundamental difficulty when the two chains are interlaced as in our model. The two main ways in which a pair of helices can be coiled together have been called plectonemic coiling and paranemic coiling. These terms have been used by cytologists to describe the coiling of chromosomes (Huskins, 1941; for a review see Manton, 1950). The type of coiling found in our model (see Figure 4) is called plectonemic. Paranemic coiling is found when two separate helices are brought to lie side by side and then pushed together so that their axes roughly coincide. Though one may start with two regular helices the process of pushing them together necessarily distorts them. It is impossible to have paranemic coiling with two regular simple helices going round the same axis. This point can only be clearly grasped by studying models.

There is of course no difficulty in "unwinding" a *single* chain of DNA coiled into a helix, since a polynucleotide chain has so many single bonds about which rotation is possible. The difficulty occurs when one has a pair of simple helices with a common axis. The difficulty is a topological one and cannot be surmounted by simple manipulation. Apart from breaking the chains there are only two sorts of ways to separate two chains coiled plectonemically. In the first, one takes hold of one end of one chain, and the other end of the other, and simply pulls in the axial direction. The two chains slip over each other, and finish up separate and end to end. It seems to us highly unlikely that this occurs in this case, and we shall not consider it further. In the second way the two chains must be directly untwisted. When this has been done they are separate and side by side. The number of turns necessary to untwist them completely is equal to the number of turns of one of the chains round the common axis. For our structure this comes to one turn every 34 A, and thus about 150 turns per million molecular weight of DNA, that is per 5000

A of our structure. The problem of uncoiling falls into two parts:

(1) How many turns must be made, and how is tangling avoided?

(2) What are the physical or chemical forces which produce it?

For the moment we shall be mainly discussing the first of these. It is not easy to decide what is the uninterrupted length of functionally active DNA. As a lower limit we may take the molecular weight of the DNA after isolation, say fifty thousand A in length and having about 1000 turns. This is only a lower limit as there is evidence suggesting a breakage of the DNA fiber during the process of extraction. The upper limit might be the total amount of DNA in a virus or in the case of a higher organism, the total amount of DNA in a chromosome. For T2 this upper limit is approximately 800,000 A which corresponds to 20,000 turns, while in the higher organisms this upper limit may sometimes be 1000 fold higher.

The difficulty might be more simple to resolve if successive parts of a chromosome coiled in opposite directions. The most obvious way would be to have both right and left handed DNA helices in sequence but this seems unlikely as we have only been able to build our model in the right handed sense. Another possibility might be that the long strands of right handed DNA are joined together by compensating strands of left handed polypeptide helices. The merits of this proposition are difficult to assess, but the fact that the phage DNA does not seem to be linked to protein makes it rather unattractive.

The untwisting process would be less complicated if replication started at the ends as soon as the chains began to separate. This mechanism would produce a new two-strand structure without requiring at any time a free single-strand stage. In this way the danger of tangling would be considerably decreased as the two-strand structure is much more rigid than a single strand and would resist attempts to coil around its neighbors. Once the replicating process is started the presence, at the growing end of the pair, of double-stranded structures might facilitate the breaking of hydrogen bonds in the original unduplicated section and allow replication to proceed in a zipper-like fashion.

It is also possible that one chain of a pair occasionally breaks under the strain of twisting. The polynucleotide chain remaining intact could then release the accumulated twist by rotation about single bonds and following this, the broken ends, being still in close proximity, might rejoin.

It is clear that, in spite of the tentative suggestions we have just made, the difficulty of untwisting is a formidable one, and it is therefore worthwhile re-examining why we postulate plectonemic coiling, and not paranemic coiling in which the two helical threads are not intertwined, but merely in close apposition to each other. Our answer is that with paranemic coiling, the specific pairing of bases would not allow the successive residues of each helix to be in equivalent orientation with regard to the helical axis. This is a possibility we strongly oppose as it implies that a large number of stereochemical alternatives for the sugar-phosphate backbone are possible, an inference at variance to our finding, with stereochemical models (Crick and Watson, 1953) that the position of the sugar-phosphate group is rather restrictive and cannot be subject to the large variability necessary for paranemic coiling. Moreover, such a model would not lead to specific pairing of the bases, since this only follows if the glucosidic links are arranged regularly in space. We therefore believe that if a helical structure is present, the relationship between the helices will be plectonemic.

We should ask, however, whether there might not be another complementary structure which maintains the necessary regularity but which is not helical. One such structure can, in fact, be imagined. It would consist of a ribbon-like arrangement in which again the two chains are joined together by specific pairs of bases, located 3.4 A above each other, but in which the sugar-phosphate backbone instead of forming a helix, runs in a straight line at an angle approximately 30° off the line formed by the pair of bases. While this ribbon-like structure would give many of the features of the X-ray diagram of Structure B, we are unable to define precisely how it should pack in a macroscopic fiber, and why in particular it should give a strong equatorial reflexion at 20-24 A. We are thus not enthusiastic about this model though we should emphasize that it has not yet been disproved.

Independent of the details of our model, there are two geometrical problems which *any* model for DNA must face. Both involve the necessity for some form of super folding process and can be illustrated with bacteriophage. Firstly, the total length of the DNA within T2 is about 8×10^5 A. As its DNA is thought (Siegal and Singer, 1953) to have the same very large M.W. as that from other sources, it must bend back and forth many times in order to fit into the phage head of diameter 800 A. Secondly, the DNA must replicate itself without getting tangled. Approximately 500 phage particles can be synthesized within a single bacterium of average dimensions $10^4 \times 10^4 \times 2 \times 10^4$ A. The total length of the newly produced DNA is some 4×10^8 A, all of which we believe was at some interval in contact with its parental template. Whatever the precise mechanism of replication we suspect the most reasonable way to avoid tangling is to have the DNA fold up into a compact bundle as it is formed.

A POSSIBLE MECHANISM FOR NATURAL MUTATION

In our duplication scheme, the specificity of replication is achieved by means of specific pairing between purine and pyrimidine bases; adenine with thymine, and guanine with one of the cytosines. This specificity results from our assumption that each of the bases possesses one tautomeric form which is very much more stable than any of the other possibilities. The fact that a compound is tautomeric, however, means that the hydrogen atoms can occasionally change their locations. It seems plausible to us that a spontaneous mutation, which as implied earlier we imagine to be a change in the sequence of bases, is due to a base occurring very occasionally in one of the less likely tautomeric forms, at the moment when the complementary chain is being formed. For example, while adenine will normally pair with thymine, if there is a tautomeric shift of one of its hydrogen atoms it can pair with cytosine (Figure 7). The next time pairing occurs, the adenine (having resumed its more usual tautomeric form) will pair with thymine, but the cytosine will pair with guanine, and so a change in the sequence of bases will have occurred. It would be of interest to know the precise difference in free energy between the various tautomeric forms under physiological conditions.

GENERAL CONCLUSION

The proof or disproof of our structure will have to come from further crystallographic analysis, a task we hope will be accomplished soon. It would be surprising to us, however, if the idea of complementary chains turns out to be wrong. This feature was initially postulated by us to account for the crystallographic regularity and it seems to us unlikely that its obvious connection with self replication is a matter of chance. On the other hand the plectonemic coiling is, superficially at least, biologically unattractive and so demands precise crystallographic proof. In any case the evidence for both the model and the suggested replication scheme will be strengthened if it can be shown unambiguously that the genetic specificity is carried by DNA alone, and, on the molecular side, how the structure could exert a specific influence on the cell.

REFERENCES

ASTBURY, W. T., 1947, X-Ray Studies of nucleic acids in tissues. Sym. Soc. Exp. Biol. 1:66-76.

CHARGAFF, E., 1951, Structure and function of nucleic acids as cell constituents. Fed. Proc. 10:654-659.

CRICK, F. H. C., and WATSON, J. D., 1953, Manuscript in preparation.

FRANKLIN, R. E., and GOSLING, R., 1953a, Molecular configuration in sodium thymonucleate. Nature, Lond. 171:740-741.

1953b, Fiber diagrams of sodium thymonucleate. I. The influence of water content. Acta Cryst., Camb. (in press).

1953c, The structure of sodium thymonucleate fibers. II. The cylindrically symmetrical Patterson Function. Acta Cryst., Camb. (in press).

FRASER, M. S., and FRASER, R. D. B., 1951, Evidence on the structure of desoxyribonucleic acid from measurements with polarized infra-red radiation. Nature, Lond. 167:760-761.

FRIEDRICH-FREKSA, H., 1940, Bei der Chromosomen Konjugation wirksame Krafte und ihre Bedeutung für die identische Verdoppling von Nucleoproteinen. Naturwissenshaften 28:376-379.

GULLAND, J. M., and JORDAN, D. O., 1946, The macromolecular behavior of nucleic acids. Sym. Soc. Exp. Biol. 1: 56-65.

GULLAND, J. M., JORDAN, D. O., and TAYLOR, H. F. W., 1947, Electrometric titration of the acidic and basic groups of the desoxypentose nucleic acid of calf thymus. J. Chem. Soc. 1131-1141.

HUSKINS, C. L., 1941, The coiling of chromonemata. Cold Spr. Harb. Symp. Quant. Biol. 9:13-18.

JORDAN, D. O., 1951, Physiochemical properties of the nucleic acids. Prog. Biophys. 2:51-89.

KAHLER, H., and LLOYD, B. J., 1953, The electron microscopy of sodium desoxyribonucleate. Biochim. Biophys. Acta 10:355-359.

MANTON, I., 1950, The spiral structure of chromosomes. Biol. Rev. 25:486-508.

MULLER, H. J., 1947, The Gene. Proc. Roy. Soc. Lond. Ser. B. 134:1-37.

PAULING, L., and DEDBRÜCK, M., 1940, The nature of the intermolecular forces operative in biological processes. Science 92:77-79.

SIEGAL, A., and SINGER, S. J., 1953, The preparation and properties of desoxypentosenucleic acid. Biochim. Biophys. Acta 10:311-319.

VILBRANDT, C. F., and TENNENT, H. G., 1943, The effect of

ADENINE   THYMINE

ADENINE   CYTOSINE

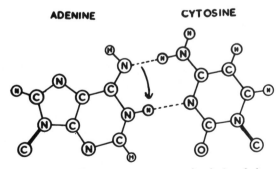

FIGURE. 7. Pairing arrangements of adenine before (above) and after (below) it has undergone a tautomeric shift.

pH changes upon some properties of sodium thymonucleate solutions. J. Amer. Chem. Soc. 63:1806-1809.

WATSON, J. D., and CRICK, F. H. C., 1953a, A structure for desoxyribose nucleic acids. Nature, Lond. 171:737-738. 1953b, Genetical implications of the structure of desoxyribose nucleic acid. Nature, Lond. (in press).

WILKINS, M. H. F., GOSLING, R. G., and SEEDS, W. E., 1951, Physical studies of nucleic acids—nucleic acid: an extensible molecule. Nature, Lond. 167:759-760.

WILKINS, M. H. F., and RANDALL, J. T., 1953, Crystallinity in sperm-heads: molecular structure of nucleoprotein in vivo. Biochim. Biophys. Acta 10:192 (1953).

WILKINS, M. H. F., STOKES, A. R., and WILSON, H. R., 1953, Molecular structure of desoxypentose nucleic acids. Nature, Lond. 171:738-740.

WILLIAMS, R. C., 1952, Electron microscopy of sodium desoxyribonucleate by use of a new freeze-drying method. Biochim. Biophys. Acta 9:237-239.

WYATT, G. R., 1952, Specificity in the composition of nucleic acids. In "The Chemistry and Physiology of the Nucleus," pp. 201-213, N. Y. Academic Press.

WYATT, G. R., and COHEN, S. S., 1952, A new pyrimidine base from bacteriophage nucleic acid. Nature, Lond. 170:1072.

J. Mol. Biol. (1959) **1**, 43-53.

A Single-Stranded Deoxyribonucleic Acid from Bacteriophage φX174†

ROBERT L. SINSHEIMER

Division of Biology, California Institute of Technology, Pasadena, California

(Received 16 January 1959)

The deoxyribonucleic acid (DNA) of bacteriophage φX174 can be extracted by phenolic denaturation of the virus protein. The DNA thus obtained has a molecular weight of $1 \cdot 7 \times 10^6$, indicating that there is one molecule per virus particle.

This φX DNA does not have a complementary nucleotide composition. The ultraviolet absorption of this DNA is strongly dependent upon temperature in the range 20° to 60°C, and upon NaCl concentration in the range 10^{-3} to 10^0 M. This DNA reacts with formaldehyde at 37°C and is precipitated by plumbous ions. This evidence is interpreted to mean that the purine and pyrimidine rings are not involved in a tightly hydrogen-bonded complementary structure.

Light scattering studies indicate that this DNA is highly flexible and that its configuration is strongly dependent upon the ionic strength of the solution. Upon treatment with pancreatic deoxyribonuclease, the weight-average molecular weight decreases in accordance with the function expected for a single-stranded molecule.

It is concluded that the DNA of bacteriophage φX174 is single-stranded.

In a previous paper (Sinsheimer, 1959) describing the properties of bacteriophage φX174, evidence was presented that the deoxyribonucleic acid (DNA) of this virus appeared to be unusual, in that the amino groups of the purine and pyrimidine rings were accessible to reaction with formaldehyde, and in that the atomic efficiency of inactivation of the virus by disintegration of ^{32}P atoms, incorporated into the viral DNA, was $1 \cdot 0$ (Tessman, 1959). In the present paper chemical and physical studies of the DNA extracted from this virus are presented. The evidence obtained indicates that each φX174 particle contains one molecule of a single-stranded DNA.

Materials and Methods

Bacteriophage φX174 was prepared and purified as previously described.

Preparation of φX DNA

To a cold suspension of φX174 containing 10 to 15 mg/ml. in borate buffer ‡ is added an equal volume of cold phenol § (Gierer & Schramm, 1956) previously equilibrated with borate buffer by shaking. The resultant emulsion is shaken for 5 min in the cold room and then spun at 1800 *g* for 5 min to separate the phases. The aqueous phase is removed, added to an equal volume of cold phenol, and the process repeated two more times. The final aqueous layer which contains the DNA is removed and allowed to stand.

---

† This research has been supported by grants from the U.S. Public Health Service, the American Cancer Society, and the California Division of the American Cancer Society.
‡ Borate buffer is a solution of sodium tetraborate, saturated at 4°C.
§ Mallinckrodt liquified phenol, AR " intended for chromatographic purposes," is used.

To improve the yield of DNA a volume of borate buffer, equal to one-half the initial volume of ϕX suspension, is added to the phenol phase from the first extraction, shaken and spun as above. The aqueous layer is removed and then used to extract in turn the DNA from the phenol layers of the second and third extractions. The final aqueous layer is pooled with the DNA solution obtained in the first series of extractions, and the combined solutions are shaken with an equal volume of cold ether. After shaking the emulsion is allowed to stand in a separatory funnel for 1 hr to allow the phases to separate. The clear aqueous layer is drawn off. The turbid ether layer is then extracted with a few ml. of borate, which, after separation of the phases, is added to the DNA solution. Two more ether extractions are employed to remove most of the residual phenol.

At this stage the DNA content of the extract accounts for 65 to 70 % of the DNA in the initial suspension of virus.

The DNA is now dialyzed against two changes of 1·3 M-potassium phosphate buffer, pH 7·5 (Kirby, 1957). There is no loss of ultraviolet absorbing material upon dialysis. To complete the removal of residual denatured protein, the DNA is extracted from the salt solution by shaking with one-half volume of either 2-methoxyethanol or N,N-dimethyl-formamide (Porter, 1955). After vigorous shaking the two phases are separated by centrifugation at 1800 *g* for 8 min. The upper organic layer contains all the DNA. A thin film of denatured material appears at the interface of the two phases.

The DNA solution is then dialyzed against three changes of 0·2 M-sodium chloride plus 0·001 M-phosphate buffer, pH 7·5. 20 to 30 % of the ϕX DNA dialyses from the organic phase through the membrane into the first two changes.†

Methods of purine and pyrimidine analysis

Degradation to purines and pyrimidines was carried out with either 12 N-HClO$_4$ at 100°C (Marshak & Vogel, 1951) or with glass distilled 6 N-HCl at 100°C (Hershey, Dixon & Chase, 1953). With either method, the purines and pyrimidines recovered accounted for over 90 % of the phosphorus of the DNA preparation. Phosphorus analyses were made by a modification of the method of Allen (1940). Purines and pyrimidines were separated by descending chromatography in the isopropanol-water-HCl solvent of Wyatt (1951) using S. and S. 597 paper. In two instances this separation was checked, with good agreement, by a paper electrophoretic separation of the same digest, using 20 volts/cm at pH 3·2, 0·1 M-tris formate buffer, and Whatman no. 3 paper (Nutter & Sinsheimer, 1959). In all cases the purines and pyrimidines were eluted from the ultraviolet absorbing spots in 0·1 N-HCl and the quantities determined by measurement of the ultraviolet absorption, after subtraction of the absorption of appropriate blanks. The extinction coefficients employed were: adenine, $A_M = 13,100$ at 260 mμ (Beaven, Holiday & Johnson, 1955); guanine, $A_M = 11,400$ at 248 mμ (ibid.); thymine, $A_M = 7,890$ at 264·5 mμ (Shugar & Fox, 1952); and cytosine, $A_M = 10,400$ at 275 mμ (ibid.).

Degradation to nucleotides was accomplished by successive use of pancreatic deoxyribonuclease (DNase) (Worthington Biochemical Company) and venom phosphodiesterase (Koerner & Sinsheimer, 1957). Ion exchange fractionation of the nucleotides with 98 % recovery of the ultraviolet absorption was carried out as previously described (Sinsheimer & Koerner, 1951). Extinction coefficients for the nucleotides have been previously presented (Sinsheimer, 1954).

All spectra were obtained on a Beckman DK2 spectrophotometer.

Light scattering

All light scattering measurements were made in a Brice-Phoenix light scattering photometer, model 1000 D, made by Phoenix Precision Instruments, Inc. ϕX DNA solutions were cleaned of dust by filtration through type AA Millipore filters.

---

† This DNA can be recovered by evaporation of the pooled dialysate and solution in 0·2 M-NaCl plus 6 M-urea plus 0·001 M-versene, pH 7·0, followed by dialysis versus 0·2 M-NaCl. This DNA which has passed through the membrane has the same physical properties and composition as the DNA which remains within. It was at first thought that the escape of the ϕX DNA was a consequence of attack upon the membrane by methoxyethanol but the same result was observed with N,N-dimethyformamide and subsequent studies have indicated that the membranes are not permanently changed. Apparently ϕX DNA, in a largely organic medium, assumes a configuration in which it can slowly pass through the cellophane membrane.

Results

Composition of φX DNA

The results of several analyses of the purine and pyrimidine composition of two preparations of φX DNA are presented in Table 1. The nucleotide analysis achieved by enzymatic degradation is considered to be the most reliable. It is clear that the molar equalities of adenine and thymine and of guanine and cytosine observed in nearly all other DNA (Chargaff, 1955) are not observed. This DNA thus cannot have the complementary structure formulated by Watson & Crick (1953a). The only regularity that can be observed is that thymine/adenine = guanine/cytosine, but the significance of this is not immediately evident.

It appears that the methods of acid hydrolysis which have proven reasonably satisfactory for conventional forms of DNA are not entirely satisfactory for this DNA. A tendency to loss of thymine in $HClO_4$ hydrolysis (Wyatt, 1952) is exaggerated, as in the loss of adenine (Hershey, Dixon & Chase, 1953) in HCl hydrolysis.

Hydrogen bonding in φX DNA

The extracted DNA reacts with formaldehyde (Fig. 1) as does the native virus. This reaction is given by RNA (Fraenkel-Conrat, 1954; Staehelin, 1958) and by heat denatured DNA, but not by native DNA (Hoard, 1957). It is an indication that the amino groups of the purine and pyrimidine rings are accessible and are not involved in a tightly hydrogen bonded structure.

TABLE 1

Purine and pyrimidine composition of φX DNA

Preparation	Mode of degradation	Molar ratios			
		Adenine	Thymine	Guanine	Cytosine
A	6 N-HCl Hydrolysis	1·00	1·31	1·06	0·82
B	6 N-HCl Hydrolysis	1·00	1·31	1·06	0·82
B	12 N-HClO₄ Hydrolysis	1·00	1·06	0·99	0·76
B	Enzymatic digestion to nucleotides	1·00	1·33	0·98	0·75

Upon thermal denaturation of native DNA there is a disruption of the hydrogen bonded structure with a concomitant increase of ultraviolet absorption. With native DNA this transition takes place within a narrow temperature zone in the region of 80° to 90°C (Thomas, 1954; Lawley, 1956; Shack, 1958). Over the temperature range of 20° to 70°C there is very little influence of temperature upon the absorption of native DNA.

In contrast, the ultraviolet absorption of φX DNA is a marked function of temperature over a very wide range (Fig. 2). A temperature dependence of ultraviolet absorption of this nature is also observed with thermally denatured DNA (Shack, 1958), although the variation observed does not appear to be as great over the temperature region 20° to 50°C (Fig. 2). This variation of absorption with temperature is presumably the result, in part, of rupture of random intramolecular hydrogen bonds and, in part, a consequence of thermal expansion of the molecule.

Similarly, the ultraviolet absorption of φX DNA is strongly dependent upon ionic strength at values of ionic strength in which the absorption of native DNA is unaffected (Thomas, 1954; Lawley, 1956; Shack, 1958) (Fig. 3). Again the increase of absorption at lower ionic strength is presumably the result of decreased intramolecular hydrogen bonding and molecular expansion (*vide infra*) brought about by an increase of net charge upon the DNA.

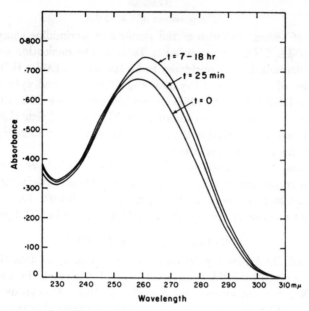

FIG. 1. Effect of formaldehyde (1·8 %) upon the ultraviolet absorption of φX DNA in 0·2 M-NaCl at 37°C. Concentration of DNA = 25·5 μg/ml.

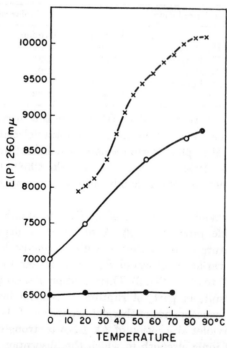

FIG. 2. Variation of the ultraviolet absorption of φX DNA at 260 mμ with temperature. E(P) = absorbance of a solution containing one mole of phosphorus per liter.

    x — x   DNA from φX in 0·2 M-NaCl + 10⁻³ M-phosphate buffer, pH 7·5.
    . — .   Native thymus DNA in 0·1 M-NaCl (from Shack, 1958).
    0 — 0   Heat denatured thymus DNA in 0·1 M-NaCl (from Shack, 1958).

It may be noted that $E(P)$, the absorbance per mole of phosphorus (Chargaff & Zamenhof, 1948), is 8700 for φX DNA in 0·2 M-NaCl at 37°C. This is considerably higher than has been observed with native or denatured DNA under comparable conditions. In accord with this observation, there is only an 11 % increase in the ultraviolet absorption of φX DNA upon degradation with pancreatic DNase in 0·2 M-sodium chloride at 37°C, as compared to the 30 to 35 % increase observed with native thymus DNA (Kunitz, 1950).

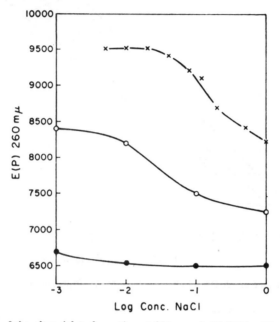

FIG. 3. Variation of the ultraviolet absorption at 260 mμ of φX DNA with salt concentration.
    x — x   DNA from φX, at 37°C.
    . — .   Native thymus DNA, at 22°C (from Shack, 1958).
    0 — 0   Heat denatured thymus DNA, at 22°C (from Shack, 1958).

Stevens & Duggan (1957) showed that thermally denatured thymus DNA is precipitated by Pb++ ion under conditions such that native DNA remained soluble. Similarly, φX DNA is completely precipitated from a solution in 0·1 M sodium chloride containing 165 μg per ml. by addition of Pb++ ions to 0·017 M.

Light scattering observations

The particle weight of φX DNA has been measured by light scattering † (Figs. 4 and 5). Several preparations have been used under various ionic conditions and the weights obtained have always been within the range of 1·6 to 1·8 × 10⁶. This is in good agreement with the weight of DNA per φX particle calculated from the particle weight, 6·2 × 10⁶, and the DNA content, 25·5 %.‡ Hence there is one molecule of DNA per φX particle.

    † In this calculation, the refractive increment of the DNA has been assumed to be 0·201 cm²/g at 4358 Å (Northrop, Nutter & Sinsheimer, 1953), although this value may not be quite correct for a DNA of this type.
    ‡ The DNA content of φX was calculated from colorimetric analysis by the diphenylamine and p-nitrophenylhydrazine methods. In ordinary DNA these methods are believed to measure purine deoxyribosides (Dische, 1955). If this is still true with φX DNA, the total DNA content of φX will be slightly greater than 25·5 %, because the purine deoxyribosides comprise less than 50 % of the total DNA.

41

In 0·02 M-NaCl at 37°C the ϕX DNA has a radius of gyration of 1140 Å. Upon addition of salt to 0·2 M, this decreases to 440 Å (Fig. 6), while in 0·02 M-NaCl plus 4×10^{-3} M-Mg^{++} the radius of gyration is 325 Å.† ϕX DNA is thus a highly flexible

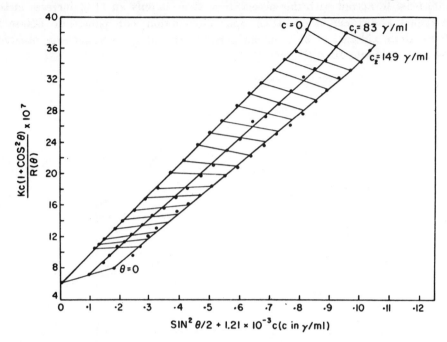

FIG. 4. Light scattering of ϕX DNA in 0·02 M-NaCl + 10^{-3} M-phosphate buffer, pH 7·5 at 37°C.

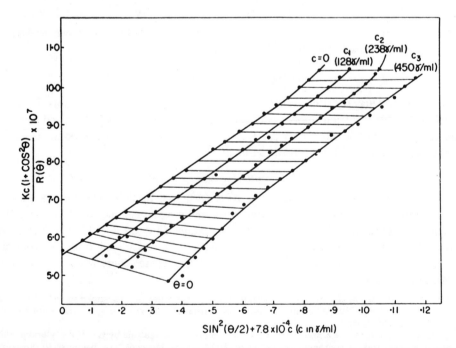

FIG. 5. Light scattering of ϕX DNA in 0·2 M-NaCl + 10^{-3} M-phosphate buffer, pH 7·5 at 37°C.

† At the same time, the ultraviolet absorption decreases by 14 % upon addition of Mg^{++}, and the sedimentation velocity increases (*vide infra*).

molecule. With native DNA, almost no change of radius of gyration is observed with change of ionic strength (Ehrlich & Doty, 1958). With alkali denatured DNA, a considerable variation is observed, nearly equal to that of ϕX DNA.

In 0·2 M-NaCl, the scattering envelope agrees well with that of a random coil (Doty & Steiner, 1950). For a random coil the radius of gyration should vary as $M^{0·5}$ (Tompa, 1956). For ϕX DNA in 0·2 M-sodium chloride, the ratio of $\sqrt{M}/\rho_g$ (M is the molecular weight in molecular weight units, ρ_g is the radius of gyration in Å) is 3·0. This may be

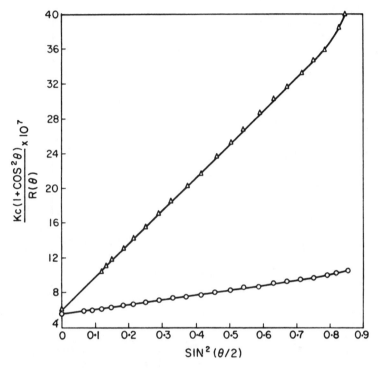

FIG. 6. Comparison of the scattering envelopes (extrapolated to zero concentration) of ϕX DNA in 0·02 M and 0·2 M-NaCl.

$$\triangle \text{———} \triangle \quad \text{in } 0·02 \text{ M-NaCl.}$$
$$0 \text{———} 0 \quad \text{in } 0·2 \text{ M-NaCl.}$$

compared with the ratio of 1·1 observed for native and sonicated thymus DNA (Reichmann, Rice, Thomas & Doty, 1954; Doty, McGill & Rice, 1958) and with a ratio of 2·5 to 2·6 observed with heat, acid, or alkali denatured thymus DNA in 0·2 M-sodium chloride (Rice & Doty, 1957; Thomas & Doty, 1956; Ehrlich & Doty, 1958). ϕX DNA is evidently more flexible than either native DNA or denatured DNA of thymus.

Kinetics of degradation by pancreatic deoxyribonuclease

As shown by Charlesby (1954) (also Tobolsky, 1957) the decline of the weight average molecular weight of a monodisperse single chain polymer upon random degration of the inter-monomeric links will be described by

$$\frac{M(p)}{M(O)} = \frac{2}{\gamma^2}[e^{-\gamma} + \gamma - 1]$$

where $M(p)$ is the weight average molecular weight when the probability of rupture of any link is p, $M(O)$ is the initial molecular weight and γ is proportional to p.

43

For a double chain structure, with cross linkage between the chains, the same equation applies except that γ is proportional to p^2, as shown by Thomas (1956).

Thomas and also Schumaker, Richards & Schachman (1956) have shown that the rate of splitting of bonds by pancreatic DNase is initially uniform with time ($p = kt$). Therefore, measurements were made of the decline with time (and thus with p) of the

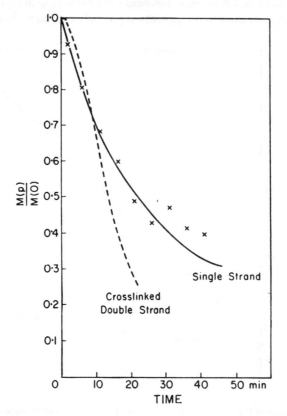

FIG. 7. Decline of weight-average molecular weight, as measured by light scattering, of ϕX DNA acted upon by pancreatic deoxyribonuclease. At $t = 0$, DNase in a final concentration of 3.7×10^{-7} μg/ml. was added to a solution containing 60 μg/ml. of ϕX DNA in 0.2 M-NaCl + 0.001 M-phosphate buffer, pH 7.5 + 0.02 M-magnesium acetate. The temperature was maintained at 34°C.

—— Function expected for a single-stranded molecule.

- - - - Function expected for a cross-linked double-stranded molecule.

xxxx Experimental observations.

The theoretical functions were fitted to intersect a smooth curve representing the experimental data at one point, at $\dfrac{M(p)}{M(O)} = 0.74$.

weight average molecular weight of ϕX DNA under attack by DNase. The form of the curve thus obtained (Fig. 7) agrees well with that expected for a single-stranded molecule and is clearly distinct from that expected for a two-stranded molecule with linked strands, such as native DNA.†

† On some occasions, with considerably lower concentrations of DNase, a slight curvature (concave downwards) has been observed in the initial stages of the digestion. This curvature, which was evident as an increase in slope to a value greater than the always finite initial slope, was not reproducible and has never been observed at the enzyme concentration employed in Fig. 7.

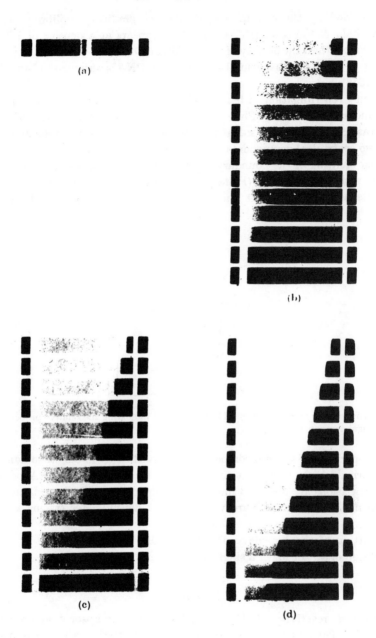

PLATE I (a). φX DNA and *E. coli* DNA banded in CsCl density gradient, after 20 hr at 44,770 rev/min. Density increasing to the right.

PLATE I (b). Ultracentrifuge sedimentation pattern of φX DNA (17 μg/ml.) in 0·2 M-NaCl at 20° C. Pictures taken every 4 min at 56,100 rev/min.

PLATE I (c). Ultracentrifuge sedimentation pattern of φX DNA (23 μg/ml.) in 0·04 M-NaCl at 20° C. Pictures taken every 4 min at 56,100 rev/min.

PLATE I (d). Ultracentrifuge sedimentation pattern at 20° C of φX DNA (32 μg/ml.) after 18 hr at 37° C in 1·8 % formaldehyde in 0·2 M-NaCl. Pictures taken every 4 min at 56,100 rev/min.

Ultracentrifuge studies

When banded by the cesium chloride density gradient equilibrium method of Meselson, Stahl & Vinograd (1957), φX DNA appears at a density of 1·72. This is distinctly higher than the density of native DNA (1·70) (Plate I (a)) and is very closely the density at which heat denatured salmon sperm DNA is observed to band (Meselson & Stahl, 1958).

In velocity centrifugation in 0·2 M-NaCl, φX DNA sediments as a single, rather sharp boundary, of $S = 23·8$ (Plate I (b)). At lower ionic strength, the sedimentation rate decreases, and below 0·08 M-NaCl the boundary splits in two indicating the presence of two centrifugal components (Plate I (c)).

A similar splitting of the boundary can be observed in 0·2 M-sodium chloride after treatment with formaldehyde (Plate I (d)). The sedimentation constants of the two components are 15·8 and 13·9 (measured in the presence of formaldehyde). The

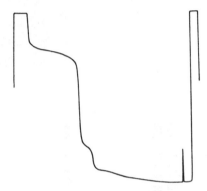

Fɪɢ. 8. Densitometer tracing of frame 11 of Plate I (d) indicating the relative proportions of the two centrifugal components.

relative proportions of the two components observed either in 0·04 M-sodium chloride or after formaldehyde treatment are the same for a given φX DNA preparation, although variations are observed in different preparations. The boundaries obtained after formaldehyde treatment are very sharp. A densitometer tracing is shown in Fig. 8.

The splitting of the boundary observed in dilute salt is completely reversible; upon addition of salt or Mg^{++} a single boundary is again observed.

Discussion

The chemical reactivity of φX DNA, its ultraviolet absorption properties, its density, and its flexibility as demonstrated by light scattering, all serve to distinguish the DNA of φX174 from conventional DNA. In several ways, such as the dependence of ultraviolet absorption upon temperature and ionic strength, and the dependence of the radius of gyration upon ionic strength, the properties of φX DNA appear to be an exaggeration of the properties of a denatured DNA, as contrasted to those of native DNA. The nucleotide composition rules out the possibility of a complementary structure, native or denatured. The simplest explanation of the properties observed is that the DNA of φX174 is a single-stranded structure. Such an explanation is also at least consistent with the high efficiency of inactivation of the φX virus by the decay of incorporated ^{32}P.

In order to test the possibility that some of the properties of φX DNA were artifacts produced by the method of extraction and purification, samples of native thymus and of native *E. coli* DNA were taken through the entire extraction and purification procedures. It was shown that these procedures have no effect upon the density of these DNA samples in the density gradient equilibrium method, or upon the increase in ultraviolet absorption observed when they were degraded with deoxyribonuclease. In addition the reactivity of φX DNA with formaldehyde before extraction from the virus may be cited.

The presence of two centrifugal components in the φX DNA preparation is not understood. They appear when the molecule is caused to take an extended form, either by destruction of intramolecular hydrogen bonds by formaldehyde or by lowering of the ionic strength. At one time it was thought that these might represent complementary strands of a DNA which had been separated biologically before incorporation into separate virus particles. However, it has been observed that the proportions of the two components varied from 62/38 to 79/21 in different preparations. Despite these variations, the preparations had identical nucleotide composition. This observation would appear to rule out the hypothesis of complementary chains.

The nucleotide composition of this DNA fulfils neither the adenine, thymine and cytosine, guanine equalities of ordinary DNA, nor the guanine plus uracil (thymine) equals adenine plus cytosine relation proposed for RNA by Elson & Chargaff (1954). In this respect, as in molecular size, this DNA is similar to the ribonucleic acid of the small plant viruses. It is, however, a DNA and differs notably from the RNA of TMV, for instance, with respect to stability and to several physical properties.

DNA fractions with compositions deviating from complementarity have been reported on other occasions (Lucy & Butler, 1954; Bendich, Pahl & Beiser, 1956). It might be very worth while to examine such fractions for the possible presence of single-stranded DNA components, by comparison of their properties with any of the distinctive properties of φX DNA. The existence of a single-stranded DNA would seem to imply the existence of a distinct mode of DNA replication (Watson & Crick, 1953b; Meselson & Stahl, 1958). It would be surprising if this were limited to a special class of bacterial viruses.

It is a pleasure to acknowledge the capable technical assistance of Miss Sharon Palmer.

REFERENCES

Allen, R. J. L. (1940). *Biochem. J.* **34**, 858.
Beaven, G. H., Holiday, E. R. & Johnson, E. A. (1955). Ch. 14 in *The Nucleic Acids*, Vol. I, ed. by E. Chargaff & J. N. Davidson. New York: Academic Press.
Bendich, A., Pahl, H. B. & Beiser, S. M. (1956). *Cold Spr. Harb. Symp. Quant. Biol.* **21**, 31.
Chargaff, E. (1955). Ch. 10 in *The Nucleic Acids*, Vol. I, ed. by E. Chargaff & J. N. Davidson. New York: Academic Press.
Chargaff, E. & Zamenhof, S. (1948). *J. Biol. Chem.* **173**, 327.
Charlesby, A. (1954). *Proc. Roy. Soc.* A **224**, 120.
Dische, Z. (1955). Ch. 9 in *The Nucleic Acids*, Vol. I, ed. by E. Chargaff & J. N. Davidson. New York: Academic Press.
Doty, P., McGill, B. B. & Rice, S. A. (1958). *Proc. Nat. Acad. Sci., Wash.* **44**, 432.
Doty, P. & Steiner, R. F. (1950). *J. Chem. Phys.* **18**, 1211.
Ehrlich, P. & Doty, P. (1958). *J. Amer. Chem. Soc.* **80**, 4251.
Elson, D. & Chargaff, E. (1954). *Nature*, **173**, 1037.
Fraenkel-Conrat, H. (1954). *Biochim. biophys. Acta*, **15**, 307.
Gierer, A. & Schramm, G. (1956). *Z. Naturf.* **11b**, 138.

Hershey, A. D., Dixon, J. & Chase, M. (1953). *J. Gen. Physiol.* **36**, 777.

Hoard, D. E. (1957). Ph.D. Thesis, University of California, Berkeley.

Kirby, K. S. (1957). *Biochem. J.* 495.

Koerner, J. F. & Sinsheimer, R. L. (1957). *J. Biol. Chem.* 1049.

Kunitz, M. (1950). *J. Gen. Physiol.* **33**, 349.

Lawley, P. D. (1956). *Biochim. biophys. Acta*, **21**, 481.

Lucy, J. A. & Butler, J. V. (1954). *Nature*, **174**, 32.

Marshak, A. & Vogel, H. J. (1951). *J. Biol. Chem.* **189**, 597.

Meselson, M. & Stahl, F. W. (1958). *Proc. Nat. Acad. Sci. Wash.* **44**, 671.

Meselson, M., Stahl, F. W. & Vinograd, J. (1957). *Proc. Nat. Acad. Sci., Wash.* **43**, 581.

Northrop, T. G., Nutter, R. L. & Sinsheimer, R. L. (1953). *J. Amer. Chem. Soc.* **75**, 5134.

Nutter, R. L. & Sinsheimer, R. L. (1959). *Virology*, in press.

Porter, R. R. (1955). pp. 98-112 in *Methods in Enzymology*, Vol. I, ed. by S. P. Colowick & N. O. Kaplan. New York: Academic Press.

Reichmann, M. E., Rice, S. A., Thomas, C. A. & Doty, P. (1954). *J. Amer. Chem. Soc.* **76**, 3047.

Rice, S. A. & Doty, P. (1957). *J. Amer. Chem. Soc.* **79**, 3937.

Schumaker, V. N., Richards, E. G. & Schachman, H. K. (1956). *J. Amer. Chem. Soc.* **78**, 4230.

Shack, J. (1958). *J. Biol. Chem.* **233**, 677.

Shugar, D. & Fox, J. J. (1952). *Biochim. biophys. Acta*, **9**, 199.

Sinsheimer, R. L. (1954). *J. Biol. Chem.* **208**, 445.

Sinsheimer, R. L. (1959). *J. Mol. Biol.* **1**, 37.

Sinsheimer, R. L. & Koerner, J. F. (1951). *Science*, **114**, 42.

Staehelin, M. (1958). *Biochim. biophys. Acta*, **29**, 410.

Stevens, V. L. & Duggan, E. L. (1957). *J. Amer. Chem. Soc.* **79**, 5703.

Tessman, I. (1958). Personal communication.

Thomas, Jr., C. A. (1956). *J. Amer. Chem. Soc.* **78**, 1861.

Thomas, Jr., C. A. & Doty, P. (1956). *J. Amer. Chem. Soc.* **78**, 1854.

Thomas, R. (1954). *Biochim. biophys. Acta*, **14**, 231.

Tobolosky, A. (1957). *J. Polym. Sci.* **26**, 247.

Tompa, H. (1956). Polymer Solutions. London: Butterworths Scientific Publications.

Watson, J. D. & Crick, F. H. C. (1953a). *Nature*, **171**, 737.

Watson, J. D. & Crick, F. H. C. (1953b). *Nature*, **171**, 964.

Wyatt, G. R. (1951). *Biochem. J.* **48**, 584.

Wyatt, G. R. (1952). *J. Gen Physiol.* **36**, 201.

II
DNA Synthesis and Chromosome Duplication

Introduction

In the detailed discussion by Watson and Crick in Section I of the DNA structure and many of its implications, considerable attention is focused on the mechanism of DNA synthesis. The complementary duplex nature of the DNA structure and the necessity for precise doubling of DNA prior to cell division led to the suggestion that DNA synthesis occurs by the unwinding of the double helix, adsorption of complementary mononucleotides to each polynucleotide strand, and polymerization. In this mode of semiconservative replication, newly duplicated DNA should consist of one old strand and one newly synthesized strand. Evidence that this is the case for *E. coli* DNA synthesized *in vivo* was provided by Meselson and Stahl in 1958 (in collection) using the technique of CsCl density gradient centrifugation. By slightly varying the procedures it was possible for others to show that the replication of DNA in higher forms is also semiconservative.[49]

Another consequence of the Watson and Crick postulated mechanism for DNA synthesis is that DNA should be a required catalyst for the synthesis of more DNA. The question of whether or not an enzyme is also required for the polymerization was left open. The idea of a template mechanism for the synthesis of nucleic acids seems to have become an important working hypothesis from this time on. Thus it seemed likely that all biologically significant nucleic acid polymerization processes would be found to involve nucleic acids as templates and that the newly synthesized nucleic acid would be a complementary copy of the template. It so happened that the first enzyme isolated which catalyzed the synthesis of nucleic acid was polynucleotide phosphorylase which catalyzes the synthesis of polyribonucleic acid from nucleotide diphosphates.[270] This enzyme has no template requirement and further research has made it seem most unlikely that this enzyme is involved in the biosynthesis of polymers. Nevertheless, it has been useful for the synthesis of a large variety of polyribonucleotides.

Kornberg and his colleagues were the first to discover an enzyme with a strict requirement for template. This enzyme is called DNA polymerase as it makes a deoxypolynucleotide product complementary to the DNA template present from the four commonly occurring nucleotide triphosphates. The paper from the Kornberg laboratory reproduced here (Schildkraut, Richardson and Kornberg) presents an investigation of some of the unusual physical properties of the DNA made using purified DNA polymerase in a cell-free system. Though many of the properties of DNA polymerase are those to be expected, there are still important differences between the *in vitro* and *in vivo* synthesized DNA.

Other results from Kornberg's laboratory indicate that DNA synthesis is a progressive process that starts by the stepwise addition of nucleotide triphosphates to the 3′-OH terminus of the growing chain. It is customary to imagine that the double helix molecule gradually unwinds to serve as template for the growing chains. This requirement for unwinding introduces two fundamental dilemmas that have yet to be resolved. (1) Due to the antiparallel nature of the double helix and the directional sense observed for DNA synthesis *in vitro*, progressive synthesis during unwinding could occur only on the one template strand with a 3′-OH terminus. The copying of the other DNA strand would have to wait until the double helix was unfolded. If progressive synthesis does occur from both chains it will have to be explained by some new observations. Several possibilities exist. The Kornberg enzyme may polymerize in both directions but not under the strict *in vitro* conditions usually used. Another enzyme yet to be discovered may exist that catalyzes polymerization from the 3′ to the 5′ end. In a recent study from Kornberg's laboratory,[62] an explanation has been offered which is consistent with the known properties of DNA polymerase. As the double helix unwinds, synthesis is progressive on the template strand with a 3′-OH terminus. On the other strand synthesis in the usual directional sense takes place in spurts after partial unfolding of the parent double helix, leaving interruptions in the newly synthesized chain that would have to be mended by another enzyme. (2) Unwinding of a DNA double helix requires that the ends undergo rotation about one another. This becomes more cumbersome the larger the DNA.[68] With circular chromosomes an entire chromosome must rotate every time ten bases are replicated; the absurdity of this scheme should compel us to examine other possibilities. Transiently formed single strand breaks in the double helix judiciously spaced along the DNA at some distance from the point of synthesis would enable the DNA to unwind by rotation about the single bonds in the remaining intact polynucleotide strand. This would provide us with an escape from the second dilemma. This suggestion has some similarities to the linker model proposed by Taylor to account for other aspects of chromosome replication in higher forms (to be discussed presently).

Another prediction of Watson and Crick is that the DNA template could account for the coding of only four bases; the presence of other bases such as methylated and glucosylated bases in the DNA must be accounted for in some way that does not require coding by the template. A large number of enzymes have been found which modify normal bases in polymeric DNA.[95, 96, 102] This brings the presence of unusual bases in accord with the existing template hypothesis but it does not explain why some bases are modified and others are not. Such explanations are important and may provide clues about DNA tertiary structure, initiation and termination points for RNA synthesis, points with high mutagenic activity or recombination frequency at different points along the chromosome.

The usual in vitro system uses high molecular weight DNA as template. E. coli DNA polymerase can use native double-stranded or denatured single-stranded DNA as template although single-stranded DNA is preferable. In contrast, Yoneda and Bollum[56] have shown that mammalian DNA polymerase can function only with single-stranded DNA. The significance to in vivo processes of this difference observed in the enzymes in cell-free systems is not clear. Indeed there is still no absolute certainty that the polymerases under investigation are the main enzymes used in vivo or merely repair enzymes.

With highly purified DNA polymerase the requirement for high molecular weight DNA template is not absolute. In the complete absence of DNA, the polymerase will synthesize alternating poly AT, poly G and poly C after a delay period.[51] It has also been found that small oligonucleotides can serve as template for much larger DNA products; the mechanism of the process has been discussed by Kornberg et al.[54] and Byrd, Ohtsuka, Moon and Khorana.[57] Just as the requirement for template can be shown not to be absolute so can a template effect be shown in the absence of enzyme. Schramm et al.[50] have described template catalysis of polynucleotides under non-enzymatic conditions. These observations are of possible significance to the study of evolution and beg the question as to which came first, the enzyme or the template.

DNA synthesis has also been studied at the level of the whole chromosome. Cairns[67] has obtained autoradiographic evidence that replication of the circular E. coli chromosome proceeds unidirectionally from a single point. Abe and Tomizawa (in collection) have genetically localized this initiation point and shown that the order of replication is fixed and independent of the sexual state of the cell. A male Hfr bacteria should have incorporated the sex factor, F, into the main body of the chromosome. Since the sex factor has a site of initiation for DNA synthesis, it is conceivable that some cases may exist where initiation occurs at the position of incorporation of the F factor rather than at the usual bacterial site determined by Abe and Tomizawa. In fact Nagata[69] had reported this to be the case some time ago but his work appears to have been dismissed. Lark and Lark[71] have obtained evidence that there are distinct protein requirements for initiation and propagation. Most of the foregoing evidence is consistent with the replicon model for DNA synthesis proposed by Jacob, Brenner and Cuzin in 1963.[70]

Taylor, Woods and Hughes,[65] and Taylor[66]

have shown that chromatids of *Vicia faba* root tips labeled with DNA precursors replicate semiconservatively. Together with the evidence of semiconservative replication of the DNA, this means that the chromatid, like the *E. coli* chromosome, behaves as one continuous double helix of DNA. Unlike *E. coli*, however, initiation seems to start at many different points along the chromatid. This has led Taylor to postulate special linkers along the chromosome which become broken before and are mended after DNA synthesis. Initiation at several points along the chromosome has been most clearly demonstrated by autoradiography in the polytene chromosomes of *D. melanogaster.*[77]

Most DNAs are of course double-stranded. The DNA of ϕX174 bacteriophage is single-stranded and the question of its mode of synthesis has occupied the Sinsheimer laboratory in particular for a number of years.[73, 78, 85] It appears that after infecting the bacteria the parental DNA with the help of bacterial enzymes undergoes conversion to a double-stranded so-called replicative form (RF) and that a special enzyme encoded by the bacteriophage DNA produces replicas of the parental DNA in conservative fashion using the RF as a template. It seems likely that the bacteriophage messengers are transcribed exclusively from the RF. Recently Goulian and Kornberg[64] have synthesized RF and demonstrated its infectivity; *E. coli* polymerase and polynucleotide-joining enzyme (the latter enzyme is discussed in Section III) were both required to make the RF. It is not clear to what extent this *in vitro* mode of synthesis parallels the *in vivo* mode of synthesis.

Bibliography

DNA SYNTHESIS

49. E. H. Simon, (1961). Transfer of DNA from Parent to Progeny in a Tissue Culture Line of Human Carcinoma of the Cervix (Strain HeLa). J. Mol. Biol. 3, 101.

50. G. Schramm, H. Grotsch and W. Pollman, (1962). Non-enzymatic Synthesis of Polymers. Angewandte Chemie 1, 1.

51. C. M. Radding and A. Kornberg, (1962). Enzymatic Synthesis of Deoxyribonucleic Acid XIII. Kinetics of Primed and De Novo Synthesis of Deoxynucleotide Polymers. J. Biol. Chem. 237, 2877.

52. R. M. Litman and W. Szybalski, (1963). Enzymatic Synthesis of Transforming DNA. Biochem. Biophys. Res. Comm. 10, 473.

53. E. B. Freese and E. Freese, (1963). Rate of DNA Strand Separation. Biochem. 2, 707.

54. A. Kornberg, L. L. Bertsch, J. F. Jackson and H. G. Khorana, (1964). Enzymatic Synthesis of Deoxyribonucleic Acid, XVI. Oligonucleotides as Templates and the Mechanism of their Replication. Proc. Natl. Acad. Sci. U.S. 51, 315.

55. C. C. Richardson, R. B. Inman and A. Kornberg, (1964). XVIII. The Repair of Partially Single–Stranded DNA Templates by DNA Polymerase. J. Mol. Biol. 9, 46.

56. M. Yoneda and F. J. Bollum, (1965). Deoxynucleotide-Polymerizing Enzymes of Calf Thymus Gland. J. Biol. Chem. 240, 3385.

57. C. Byrd, E. Ohtsuka, M. W. Moon and H. G. Khorana, (1965). Synthetic Deoxyribo-Oligonucleotides as Templates for the DNA Polymerase of E. coli. New DNA-Like Polymers Containing Repeating Nucleotide Sequences. Proc. Natl. Acad. Sci. U.S. 53, 79.

58. P. J. Gomatos, R. M. Krug and I. Tamm, (1965). Reovirus RNA-directed Synthesis of DNA. I. The Reaction Catalyzed by DNA Polymerase from E. coli. J. Mol. Biol. 13, 802.

59. R. B. Inman, C. L. Schildkraut and A. Kornberg, (1965). Enzymic Synthesis of DNA XX. Electron Microscopy of Products Primed by Native Templates. J. Mol. Biol. 11, 285.

60. P. J. Cassidy, (1966). The Synthesis of a DNA Polymer of Alternating Base Sequence from a DNA-RNA Hybrid Template. J. Biol. Chem. 241, 2173.

61. J. F. Speyer, J. D. Karam and A. B. Lenny, (1966). On the Role of DNA Polymerase in Base Selection. Cold Spring Harbor Symp. Quant. Biol. 31, 693.

62. S. Mitra, P. Reichard, R. B. Inman, L. L. Bertsch and A. Kornberg, (1967). Enzymic Synthesis of DNA XXII. Replication of a Circular Single-Stranded DNA Template by DNA Polymerase of E. coli. J. Mol. Biol. 24, 429.

63. E. B. Freese and E. Freese, (1967). On the Specificity of DNA Polymerase. Proc. Natl. Acad. Sci. U.S. 57, 650.

64. M. Goulian and A. Kornberg, (1967). Enzymatic Synthesis of DNA, XXIII. Synthesis of Circular Replicative Form of Phage ϕX174. Proc. Natl. Acad. Sci. U.S. 58, 1723.

CHROMOSOME SYNTHESIS

65. J. H. Taylor, P. S. Woods and W. L. Hughes, (1957). The Organization and Duplication of Chromosomes as Revealed by Autoradiographic Studies using Tritium-Labeled Thymidine. Proc. Natl. Acad. Sci. U.S. 43, 122.

66. J. H. Taylor, (1958). The Organization and Duplication of Genetic Material. Proc. 10th Intern. Congr. Genet. Montreal, 1, 63.

67. J. Cairns, (1963). Synthesis of E. coli Chromosome. Cold Spring Harbor Symp. Quant. Biol. 28, 43.

68. J. Cairns, (1963). The Bacterial Chromosome and its Manner of Replication as Seen by Autoradiography. J. Mol. Biol. 6, 208.

69. J. Nagata, (1963). The Molecular Synchrony and Sequential Replication of DNA in Escherichia coli. Proc. Natl. Acad. Sci. U.S. 49, 551.

70. F. Jacob, S. Brenner and F. Cuzin, (1963). On the Regulation of DNA Replication in Bacteria. Cold Spring Harbor Symp. Quant. Biol. 29, 329.

71. C. Lark and K. G. Lark, (1964). Evidence for Two Distinct Aspects of the Mechanism Regulating Chromosome Replication in E. coli. J. Mol. Biol. 10, 120.

72. P. C. Hanawalt and D. S. Ray, (1964). Isolation of the Growing Point in the Bacterial Chromosome. Proc. Natl. Acad. Sci. U.S. **52**, 125.

73. D. T. Denhardt and R. L. Sinsheimer, (1965). The Process of Infection with Bacteriophage ϕX174. IV. Replication of the Viral DNA in a Synchronized Infection. J. Mol. Biol. **12**, 647.

74. J. Cairns and C. I. Davern, (1966). Effect of ^{32}P Decay Upon DNA Synthesis by a Radiation Sensitive Strain of *E. coli*. J. Mol. Biol. **17**, 418.

75. C. I. Davern, (1966). Isolation of the DNA of the *E. coli* Chromosome in One Piece. Proc. Natl. Acad. Sci. U.S. **55**, 792.

76. P. F. Davison, (1966). Rate of Strand Separation in Alkali-treated DNA. J. Mol. Biol. **22**, 97.

77. W. Plaut, D. Nash and T. Fanning, (1966). Ordered Replication of DNA in Polytene Chromosomes of *D. melanogaster*. J. Mol. Biol. **16**, 85.

78. C. A. Hutchison and R. L. Sinsheimer, (1966). The Process of Infection with Bacteriophage ϕX174. Mutations in a ϕX174 Lysis Gene. J. Mol. Biol. **18**, 429.

79. A. O'Sullivan and N. Sueoka, (1967). Sequential Replication of the *B. subtilis* Chromosome IV. Genetic Mapping by Density Transfer Experiment. J. Mol. Biol. **27**, 349.

80. H. Yoshikawa, (1967). Initiation of DNA Replication in *B. subtilis*. Proc. Natl. Acad. Sci. U.S. **58**, 312.

81. D. J. Clark and O. Maaloe, (1967). DNA Replication and the Division Cycle in *E. coli*. J. Mol. Biol. **23**, 99.

82. H. Eberle and K. G. Lark, (1967). Chromosome Replication in *B. subtilis* Cultures Growing at Different Rates. Proc. Natl. Acad. Sci. U.S. **57**, 95.

83. L. A. Salzman and A. Weissbach, (1967). Formation of Intermediates in the Replication of Phage Lambda DNA. J. Mol. Biol. **28**, 53.

84. C. M. Berg and L. G. Caro, (1967). Chromosome Replication in *E. coli*. I. Lack of Influence of the Integrated F Factor. J. Mol. Biol. **29**, 419.

85. P. Rust and R. L. Sinsheimer, (1967). The Process of Infection with Bacteriophage ϕX174. XI. Infectivity of the Complementary Strand of the Replicative Form. J. Mol. Biol. **23**, 545.

CYTOPLASMIC DNA

86. E. Reich and D. J. L. Luck, (1966). Replication and Inheritance of Mitochondrial DNA. Proc. Natl. Acad. Sci. U.S. **55**, 1600.

87. H. E. Bond, W. G. Flamm, H. E. Burr and S. B. Bond, (1967). Mouse Satellite DNA. Further Studies on its Biological and Physical Characteristics and its Intracellular Localization. J. Mol. Biol. **27**, 289.

88. O. C. Richards, (1967). Hybridization of *Euglena gracilis* Chloroplast and Nuclear DNA. Proc. Natl. Acad. Sci. **57**, 156.

89. I. B. Dawid and D. R. Wolstenholme, (1967). Ultracentrifuge and E. M. Studies on the Structure of Mitochondrial DNA. J. Mol. Biol. **28**, 233.

90. B. Green, V. Heilporn, S. Limbosch, M. Boloukhere and J. Brachet, (1967). Cytoplasmic DNA's of *Acetabularia mediterranea*. Proc. Natl. Acad. Sci. U.S. **58**, 1351.

91. K. Chiang and N. Sueoka, (1967). Replication of Chloroplast DNA in *Chlamydomonas reinhardi*. During Vegetative Cell Cycle: Its Mode and Regulation. Proc. Natl. Acad. Sci. U.S. **57**, 1506.

EMBRYOLOGY

92. I. B. Dawid, (1965). DNA in Amphibian Eggs. J. Mol. Biol. **12**, 581.

93. G. A. Carden, S. Rosenkranz and H. S. Rosenkranz, (1965). DNA of Sperm, Eggs and Somatic Cells of the Sea Urchin, *Arbacia punctulata*. Nature **205**, 1338.

94. J. B. Gurdon, (1967). On the Origin and Persistence of a Cytoplasmic State Inducing Nuclear DNA Synthesis in Frogs' Eggs. Proc. Natl. Acad. Sci. U.S. **58**, 545.

METHYLATION AND GLUCOSYLATION

95. C. C. Richardson, (1966). Influence of Glucosylation of DNA on Hydrolysis by DNAses of *E. coli*. J. Biol. Chem. **241**, 2084.

96. M. Gefter, R. Hausmann, M. Gold and J. Hurwitz, (1966). Enzymatic Methylation of RNA and DNA X. Bacteriophage T_3-Induced S-Adenosylmethionine Cleavage. J. Biol. Chem. **241**, 1995.

MISCELLANEOUS

97. J. G. Gall, (1963). Kinetics of DNAse Action on Chromosomes. Nature **198**, 36.
98. J. A. Huberman and G. Attardi, (1966). Isolation of Metaphase Chromosomes from HeLa Cells. J. Cell. Biol. **31**, 95.
99. A. J. Mazaitis and K. F. Bautz, (1967). Partial Isolation of an rIIB Segment of T_4 DNA by Hybridization with Homologous RNA. Proc. Natl. Acad. Sci. U.S. **57**, 1633.

100. D. H. Lockwood, A. E. Voytovick, F. E. Stockdale and Y. J. Topper, (1967). Insulin-Dependent DNA Polymerase and DNA Synthesis in Mammary Epithelial Cells *in Vitro*. Proc. Natl. Acad. Sci. U.S. **58**, 658.

REVIEW ARTICLES

101. K. G. Lark, (1966). Bact. Reviews **30**, 3–32.
102. E. Borek and P. R. Srinivasan, (1966). The Methylation of Nucleic Acids. Ann. Rev. Biochem. **35**, 275.
103. I. R. Lehman, (1967). Deoxyribonucleases: Their Relationship to Deoxyribonucleic Acid Synthesis. Ann. Rev. Biochem. **36**, 645.

J. Mol. Biol. (1964) **9,** 24–45

Enzymic Synthesis of Deoxyribonucleic Acid
XVII. Some Unusual Physical Properties of the Product Primed by Native DNA Templates[†]

Carl L. Schildkraut[‡], Charles C. Richardson[§] and Arthur Kornberg

Department of Biochemistry, Stanford University School of Medicine
Palo Alto, California, U.S.A.

(Received 25 February 1964, and in revised form 3 April 1964)

Extensive replication of a helical DNA produces a complex of primer and product which can be dissociated by denaturing treatments. The physical characteristics of the enzymic product resemble those of a native DNA except in two ways: (1) an unusual capacity to resume a helical conformation after denaturing treatments ("non-denaturability"); and (2) appearance of a branched structure in the electron microscope. Exposure of the enzymic product to extensive protease, mild nuclease or prolonged heating treatment fails to alter its "non-denaturability". These and other studies suggest that in the replication of native DNA the new strands are not covalently linked to the primer and that a "multiple hairpin" or "pleated" structure may develop which recovers considerable helicity following denaturing treatments. By contrast, these and other studies (described by Richardson, Inman & Kornberg, 1964a) also indicate that in the repair of partially single-stranded DNA, the new strands are covalently linked to the primer and appear to have all the physical properties of naturally occurring DNA.

1. Introduction

Enzymically synthesized deoxyribonucleic acid has been characterized with respect to its chemical composition and nearest neighbor base frequencies. These studies, as well as other data (Wake & Baldwin, 1962; Richardson, Schildkraut & Kornberg, 1963b), have led to the conclusion that the priming DNA acts as a template to direct the sequential assembly of the monomeric units. Physical studies have further established (Schachman, Lehman, Bessman, Simms & Kornberg, 1958) that the product is a macromolecule with viscosity, sedimentation behavior and optical properties closely resembling those of the primer. However, the resolution at these levels has not eliminated the possibilities that regions of the template are missed in copying, that some regions are copied repeatedly or that the newly synthesized DNA serves as a template before the primer has been completely replicated. Our attempts to detect synthesis of transforming activity commensurate with chemical

---

[†] Paper XVI in this series is Kornberg, A., Bertsch, L., Jackson, J. F. & Khorana, H. G. (1964). *Proc. Nat. Acad. Sci., Wash.*, **51,** 315.

[‡] Postdoctoral Fellow of the National Science Foundation. Present address: Department of Cell Biology, Albert Einstein College of Medicine, New York, New York, U.S.A.

[§] Postdoctoral Fellow of the United States Public Health Service. Present address: Department of Biological Chemistry, Harvard Medical School, Boston, Massachusetts, U.S.A.

synthesis have not yet succeeded (Richardson *et al.*, 1963a), but such results do not imply directly that replication errors are responsible.

The present studies were undertaken in order to determine what a more detailed physical-chemical examination would reveal about the DNA synthesized by *Escherichia coli* polymerase. This report describes further similarities in properties between primer and product, and in addition an unusual feature of the product, namely, a greater facility towards renaturation following denaturation by heat or alkali. Current studies (Inman, Schildkraut & Kornberg, unpublished work; Richardson *et al.*, 1963b) describe another unusual feature of the product, namely, a highly branched structure observed in electron micrographs.

The collapse of secondary structure of DNA observed after heating and quickly cooling, or after alkali treatment and subsequent neutralization, has been called denaturation. The corresponding changes in physical properties following exposure to such denaturing treatments are not observed for DNA enzymically synthesized under conditions specified in this report. It is possible that irreversible structural changes do occur after heating and quickly cooling, or alkali treatment and subsequent neutralization, but escape detection. Another alternative is that denaturation takes place to some degree, but renaturation follows immediately upon the collapse of secondary structure. With these reservations in mind, the term "non-denaturable" will be used to denote the behavior of DNA when a denaturing treatment does not lead to a sustained collapse of its secondary structure. Whereas enzymic syntheses primed by native helical DNA produce a non-denaturable product, reactions primed by a partially single-stranded DNA produce, as a subsequent report will describe (Richardson, Inman & Kornberg, 1964a), fully denaturable molecules.

2. Materials and Methods

(a) *Nucleic acids and nucleotides*

Bacillus subtilis DNA (sample A) was prepared by the method of Marmur (1961). The molar extinction coefficient (at 260 mμ) with respect to phosphorus was 6700. The RNA content was less than 0·5% and protein less than 3% by weight. The buoyant density in CsCl of the native DNA was 1·703 g cm^{-3}, and that of heated, alkali-treated or formamide-treated samples was 1·720 g cm^{-3}. The DNA was stored at 4°C at a concentration of 2·4 μmoles per ml. in SSC† saturated with chloroform. Immediately before use it was dialyzed against 0·02 M-KCl at 4°C.

B. subtilis DNA (sample B) was prepared as sample A except that, after ribonuclease treatment, the residual RNA was removed by Norit rather than by precipitation with isopropanol. The extinction coefficient with respect to phosphorus was also 6700.

^{15}N^{2}H^{3}H-labeled *B. subtilis* DNA was prepared according to the procedure of Bodmer & Schildkraut (1964), who have described some of its physical and biological properties. DNA containing heavy isotopes or bromine will be referred to as heavy DNA, and the corresponding unsubstituted samples will be referred to as light DNA.

^{3}H-labeled DNA was prepared from T7 bacteriophage according to Richardson *et al.* (1964a), who have described its physical properties.

Transfer-RNA was prepared according to the method of Zubay (1962). ^{32}P-labeled deoxyribonucleoside triphosphates were prepared as described previously (Lehman, Bessman, Simms & Kornberg, 1958). Unlabeled deoxyribonucleoside triphosphates were purchased from the California Corporation for Biochemical Research.

Concentrations of DNA and RNA are expressed as equivalents of nucleotide phosphorus.

---

† Abbreviations: SSC, 0·15 M-NaCl containing 0·015 M-sodium citrate; 1/10 SSC, 0·015 M-NaCl containing 0·0015 M-sodium citrate; dAT, copolymer of deoxyadenylate and deoxythymidylate; dBUTP, deoxynucleoside triphosphate of 5-bromouracil.

(b) *Enzymes and other materials*

The most purified fraction (hydroxylapatite, fraction IX) of polymerase† was used in these studies. This fraction had a specific activity of 18,800 and was prepared as described elsewhere (Richardson, Schildkraut, Aposhian & Kornberg, 1964*b*). Exonuclease I (DEAE-cellulose fraction; Lehman, 1960), exonuclease II (polymerase fraction IX; Lehman & Richardson, 1964), endonuclease I (IRC-50 fraction; Lehman, Roussos & Pratt, 1962), and DNA phosphatase-exonuclease (phosphocellulose fraction; Richardson & Kornberg, 1964) were prepared and assayed as described previously. Pronase, research grade (lot no. 502117), was obtained from the California Corporation for Biochemical Research. Subtilisin (Nagarase, batch no. CGL-1272) was manufactured in Japan by Teikoku Chemical Industry Company, Ltd. Crystalline bovine chymotrypsin (lot no. 10705) was purchased from Armour & Company. Crystalline trypsin and pancreatic DNase were products of the Worthington Biochemical Corporation. CsCl, optical grade, was purchased from the Harshaw Chemical Company, Cleveland, Ohio.

(c) *Assay to measure acid-insoluble radioactive material*

The solution to be assayed was diluted to 0·3 ml. with cold water, and 0·5 ml. of cold 1 N-perchloric acid was added. After 5 min at 0°C, 2·5 ml. of cold water were added. A glass filter (Whatman GF/C glass paper, 2·4 cm diameter) was placed on the wire mesh net of a specially made stainless steel filter assembly and the mixture was filtered with the aid of suction. The paper was washed with three 3-ml. portions of cold water, transferred to a glass bottle and dried. The filter was covered with 10 ml. of a scintillator solution consisting of 4 g of 2,5-diphenyloxazole (PPO) and 50 mg of 1,4-bis-2-(4-methyl-5-phenyloxazolyl)-benzene (dimethyl POPOP) per liter of toluene and counted in a Packard Tri-Carb liquid-scintillation counter. ^{32}P and ^{3}H were counted simultaneously. When only ^{32}P was present, the paper was dried on a planchet and counted in a gas-flow counter.

(d) *Incubation of DNA with exonuclease I*

To the DNA solution was added (per 0·3 ml. final volume) 20 μmoles of glycine buffer, pH 9·2, 2 μmoles of $MgCl_2$, 0·5 μmole of 2-mercaptoethanol and exonuclease I (two units per mμmole of DNA). After incubation at 37°C for 30 min the mixture was assayed for acid-insoluble radioactive material as described above.

(e) *Synthesis of DNA*

The reaction mixture contained (per ml.): 67 μmoles of potassium phosphate buffer at pH 6·8, 6·7 μmoles of $MgCl_2$, and 1·0 μmole of 2-mercaptoethanol. DNA, the four deoxynucleoside triphosphates (dATP, dTTP, dGTP and dCTP), one of which contained a radioactive label, and polymerase were present at the concentrations given in Table 1. The presence or absence of DNA phosphatase-exonuclease is also noted in Table 1. To measure the extent of replication, portions were withdrawn from the reaction mixture and assayed for acid-insoluble radioactive material as described above.

(f) *Absorbancy–temperature measurements*

The DNA was present at a concentration of 45 to 60 mμmoles/ml. and contained in a 1-ml. quartz cuvette. Absorbancies at 260 mμ were measured while the solutions were held at the elevated temperatures, using the procedure described by Inman & Baldwin (1962).

(g) *Density-gradient centrifugation at neutral pH*

Samples of DNA (approximately 0·2 ml. containing 6 to 30 mμmoles of DNA) were added to 0·7 ml. of a stock solution of CsCl dissolved in 0·05 M-tris, pH 8·5, containing 0·001 M-EDTA, sodium salt. The density of the final solution, determined from the refractive

---

† Whenever the terms polymerase, exonuclease I, exonuclease II, DNA phosphatase-exonuclease, or endonuclease I are used in this paper, they refer to the enzymes isolated from *E. coli*.

TABLE 1

Conditions for the replication of DNA by polymerase

Location in paper	Experiment	Primer DNA		Polymerase	DNA phosphatase-exonuclease	Concentration of deoxynucleoside triphosphates	^{32}P-labeled triphosphate
			mμmoles/ml.	units/ml.	units/ml.	mμmoles/ml. of each	
Fig. 7	1	T7	60	260	0	30	dCTP
Fig. 6 and Table 2	2	T7	60	260	0	400‡	dCTP
Fig. 1	3	B. subtilis (^{15}N^{2}H^{3}H)	37	66	0·07†	50	dTTP
Figs 2 and 5	4	B. subtilis (^{15}N^{2}H^{3}H)	33	66	0·07†	50	dATP
Figs 3 and 4	5	T7	60	260	0	400§	dCTP
Fig. 5 and Table 3	6	B. subtilis (B)	37	66	0·07†	67	dATP
Fig. 6 and Table 4	7	B. subtilis (A)	60	260	16	400	dCTP
Table 5	8	B. subtilis (^{15}N^{2}H^{3}H), single-stranded	60	260	16	400	dGTP

† Reaction mixture was incubated for 20 min at 37°C with phosphatase; polymerase was then added.
‡ 200 (rather than 400) mμmoles/ml. each of [α-^{32}P]dCTP and ^{14}C-labeled dTTP were present.
§ 200 (rather than 400) mμmoles/ml. of [α-^{32}P]dCTP were present.

index, was between 1·71 and 1·75 g cm^{-3}. Approximately 0·75 ml. of the final CsCl solution was placed in a cell containing a plastic (Kel-F) centerpiece and centrifuged in a Spinco model E analytical ultracentrifuge at 44,770 rev./min at 25°C. After 20 hr of centrifugation, ultraviolet absorption photographs were taken on Kodak commercial film.

Densities were calculated as previously described (Schildkraut, Marmur & Doty, 1962) using 1·710 g cm^{-3} as the density of *E. coli* DNA. DNA from *Tetrahymena pyriformis* ($\rho = 1·684$ g cm^{-3}) was used as a standard for density determination.

(h) *Density-gradient centrifugation at alkaline pH*

To 0·89 g of CsCl was added 0·10 ml. of Na$_2$CO$_3$–NaOH buffer (0·5 M-Na$_2$CO$_3$ + 0·044 M-NaOH, pH 12·0). A portion of the DNA sample in 0·02 M-KCl was then added along with sufficient water to make the refractive index of the final solution approximately 1·4065. The total volume of solution added to the CsCl was 0·615 ml. This contained from 12 to 20 mμmoles of DNA. The pH of the final solution was 12·0 to 12·2. The pH was measured by means of a Leeds & Northrup miniature glass electrode. Immediately before the readings were taken, the electrodes were standardized with Beckman standard buffers of pH 9·18 and 12·45. Since these solutions contained very high salt concentrations, the pH values reported above do not necessarily represent the true pH of the solutions, but they are reproducible instrument readings. Approximately 0·7 ml. of the resulting solution was added to the centrifuge cell. dAT polymer was used as a density standard; the density of the dAT was calculated to be 1·737 g cm^{-3}. This density was obtained by assuming that light *B. subtilis* DNA isolated from natural sources undergoes an increase in density of 0·064 g cm^{-3} in alkaline CsCl (Vinograd, Morris, Davidson & Dove, 1963). Thus, the density of the light natural *B. subtilis* DNA in alkaline CsCl was taken to be 1·767 g cm^{-3}. From this, the density of 1·737 g cm^{-3} was obtained for dAT polymer. This density was then used for all the calculations in the alkaline density-gradient centrifugations in this paper.

(i) *Microdensitometer tracings*

Tracings were made from the ultraviolet photographs with a Joyce–Loebl double-beam recording microdensitometer. In the tracings shown in this paper, the ordinate is proportional to the concentration of DNA at any point in the gradient; the abscissa represents the buoyant density. The magnification in the direction of the abscissa is the same for each tracing in a given figure; the magnification in the direction of the ordinate varies from one tracing to another. For purposes of clarity, the density standard has been omitted from the tracings.

(j) *Sedimentation*

For boundary sedimentation, a DNA solution (40 mμmoles/ml.) was placed in a cell containing a 30-mm Kel-F centerpiece and centrifuged in a Spinco model E analytical ultracentrifuge at 29,500 rev./min at 25°C. Band-sedimentation velocity was carried out according to the method of Vinograd, Bruner, Kent & Weigle (1963). The bulk solution was 0·9 M-NaCl containing 0·1 M-NaOH.

(k) *Viscosity*

Relative viscosities were measured with a one-bulb capillary viscometer of the Ostwald type. All measurements were at 25°C; the flow time for water was 290 sec. The gradient was about 100 sec^{-1}. The DNA concentration was approximately 30 mμmoles/ml.

3. Results

Under conditions which support a threefold replication of DNA in six to eight hours, there is no evidence of endonucleolytic scissions in the primer. Boundary sedimentation at alkaline pH of a T7 primer DNA (see Materials and Methods) revealed no significant decrease in sedimentation coefficient, and viscosity measurements showed a reduction of only 10%. Degradation of the primer by the polymerase preparation entails the release of about 10% of the DNA as nucleotides, an amount attributed to the exonuclease II activity in the polymerase (Richardson *et al.*, 1964*b*).

(a) *Physical properties of the product*

(i) *A primer–product complex revealed by density gradient analysis*

B. *subtilis* DNA labeled with ^{15}N, ^{2}H and ^{3}H was used as primer; the deoxynucleoside triphosphate substrates (^{14}N^{1}H) contained ^{32}P as a marker. The ^{15}N and ^{2}H labels distinguish the heavy primer from the product DNA on the basis of their different buoyant densities in CsCl; the ^{3}H and ^{32}P markers permit a sensitive radiochemical assay of the primer and product atoms, respectively. At several intervals during the course of replication, samples were analyzed for buoyant density distribution in a CsCl gradient, with the results shown in Fig. 1. The heavy primer

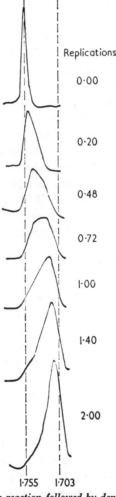

FIG. 1. *Course of the net synthesis reaction followed by density-gradient centrifugation.* ^{15}N^{2}H^{3}H-labeled B. *subtilis* DNA was incubated with polymerase under conditions given for experiment 3 (see Table 1). Synthesis proceeded linearly to 2·0 replications at 160 min. Samples were removed at intervals, dialysed at 4°C against 1/10 SSC and then centrifuged in CsCl as described in Materials and Methods. The number of replications is defined as the ratio of μmoles of enzymically synthesized DNA to μmoles of primer added.

(top of the figure) forms a band at a density of $1.755 \, \mathrm{g \, cm^{-3}}$; the position at which light *B. subtilis* DNA would be expected to form a band is given by the reference line at a density of $1.703 \, \mathrm{g \, cm^{-3}}$. As synthesis proceeded, the heavy DNA disappeared and a new broad band of lower density appeared; the mean densities of the broad bands observed in Fig. 1 are at positions expected from the extent of replication, assuming that the primer and product in this new complex contribute independently to the density. The complex did not dissociate to give two bands after phenol treatment by the method of Mandell & Hershey (1960).

When the primer was not pre-treated with the DNA phosphatase-exonuclease and this enzyme was not present in the reaction mixture, some of the primer DNA remained in the region of high density, as though it were not being replicated (Richardson *et al.*, 1963*a*).

To obtain additional evidence that the decrease in density observed above was a result of DNA synthesis, the following control experiments were performed. Heavy *B. subtilis* DNA was incubated for three hours with polymerase under the conditions of experiment 4 (Table 1) but in the absence of DNA phosphatase-exonuclease and dATP. The mixture was dialyzed and centrifuged in CsCl. There was no change in buoyant density and no qualitative change in band profile. Similarly, heavy *B. subtilis* DNA was incubated for three hours with DNA phosphatase-exonuclease under the conditions of experiment 4 but in the absence of polymerase and dATP. Again, there was no change in buoyant density and no qualitative change in band profile. It is also possible that structural changes which alter the buoyant density of DNA have occurred and that the apparent association of primer and product is fortuitous. However, a preparative density-gradient experiment (Richardson *et al.*, 1963*a*), in which the successive fractions of a fivefold replication sample were analyzed for ³H and ³²P, demonstrated the presence of ³H in the fractions containing ³²P. These results indicate that primer atoms are responsible for the higher density of the product and support the interpretation that primer and product are closely associated.

(ii) *Influence of heating or alkali treatment on the primer–product complex as determined by density-gradient analysis*

Heavy *B. subtilis* DNA was used as primer and the behavior of the density gradient of the primer–product mixture at two stages of replication is shown for reference in Fig. 2. Heating (and quick cooling) of a mixture of heavy primer and a standard sample of light *B. subtilis* DNA resulted in the usual buoyant density increments of $0.017 \, \mathrm{g \, cm^{-3}}$ over the values observed for untreated samples (Fig. 2). Similar heat treatment of the primer–product complex followed by density-gradient analysis revealed two distinct bands; these were of approximately equal size after 1·0 replication and in the approximate ratio of 1 : 2·5 after 2·5 replications. The position of one of the bands at $1.769 \, \mathrm{g \, cm^{-3}}$ coincided with, and can be taken to represent, that of the primer DNA. As for the other band, its area, density and distribution about this density relative to the primer DNA all suggest that it is a light product. However, its position at a density of $1.703 \, \mathrm{g \, cm^{-3}}$ corresponded to that of undenatured light *B. subtilis* DNA rather than that of single-stranded DNA. It may be presumed, therefore, that the primer component of the complex has been converted by the heating treatment to a single-stranded state whereas the product has remained helical. This presumption is borne out by the susceptibility to exonuclease I, an enzyme which has a high specificity towards single-stranded DNA.

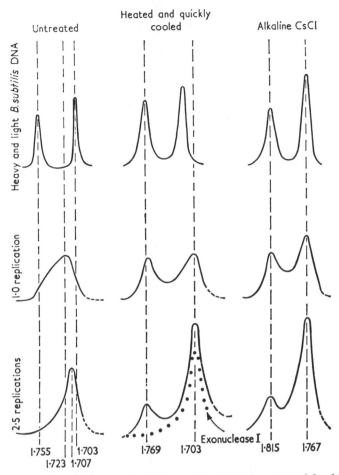

FIG. 2. *Separation of product and primer* B. subtilis *DNA demonstrated by density-gradient centrifugation.* ¹⁵N²H³H-labeled *B. subtilis* DNA was incubated with polymerase under conditions given in experiment 4 (see Table 1).

Untreated samples. These were removed at 1·0 replication (85 min) and 2·5 replications (240 min). The reaction was stopped by the addition of 1/5 vol. of 10 × SSC followed by dialysis at 4°C against 1/10 SSC. After dialysis, samples were centrifuged in CsCl as described in Materials and Methods.

Heated and quickly cooled samples (53 to 90 mμmoles/ml.) were held at 100°C for 5 min in 1/10 SSC and chilled in ice. The dotted tracing in this column represents the 2·5-fold replication sample treated with exonuclease I as described in Materials and Methods.

Alkaline CsCl samples were centrifuged in this medium as described in Materials and Methods. Shown in the top row, for comparison, are heavy and light naturally occuring DNA's.

After treatment of the heated primer–product mixture with this enzyme, the heavy band disappeared (Fig. 2) and, as judged by counts for acid-soluble ³H material, was completely degraded (more than 95%). On the other hand, the band profile and position of the light component were unaffected by the exonuclease I treatment (Fig. 2), nor was there any indication from ³²P counts that the radioactive material became soluble in acid (less than 5%). Less than 5% of the unheated primer–product mixture was susceptible to exonuclease I as determined from counts for acid-soluble ³H and ³²P material, respectively.

Density-gradient centrifugation at alkaline pH also resolved the primer–product

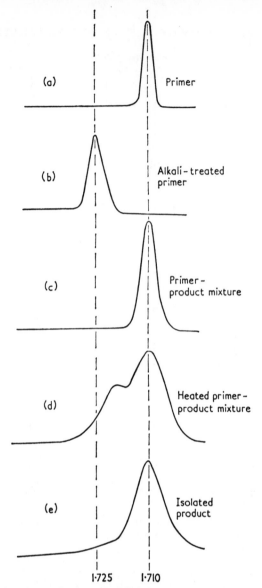

Fig. 3. *Separation of product and primer T7 DNA demonstrated by density-gradient centrifugation.*
(a) Native T7 primer DNA.

(b) T7 (8 mμmoles/ml.) incubated at 25°C in 0·03 M-KOH for 30 min and then brought to pH 7.

(c) ³H-labeled T7 DNA was incubated with polymerase under conditions given in experiment 5 (see Table 1). At 2·5 replications, 1/10 vol. 10 × SSC was added and the reaction mixture was heated at 70°C for 10 min to inactivate the polymerase. The *primer–product mixture* was then dialyzed at 4°C for 60 hr (7 1-liter changes) against 0·4 M-KCl containing 0·01 M-EDTA, sodium salt and 0·01 M-tris, pH 8·0, and then dialyzed against 0·02 M-KCl.

(d) The mixture of product (123 mμmoles/ml.) and primer DNA (47 mμmoles/ml.) was heated in 0·02 M-glycine buffer, pH 9·2, at 95°C for 5 min.

(e) The enzymic product was isolated from the primer by treatment with exonuclease I as described in Materials and Methods. The sodium salt of EDTA was added to 0·0067 M and the mixture heated for 5 min at 95°C. It was then dialyzed at 4°C against 0·2 M-KCl containing 0·01 M-EDTA, sodium salt, and 0·01 M-tris, pH 8·0, followed by dialysis against 0·02 M-KCl. The dialyzed product DNA was made 0·1 M in KCl and 0·1 M in potassium phosphate buffer, pH 7·4, shaken with an equal volume of phenol (saturated with the same buffer solution) and then centrifuged. The phenol layer was removed and the DNA-containing solution shaken again with an equal volume of phenol (saturated with the KCl–phosphate buffer). The phenol layers were extracted with the KCl–phosphate buffer. This extract was combined with the DNA solution and the phenol was removed by dialysis for 65 hr (7 1-liter changes) at 4°C against 0·02 M-KCl. The recovery of enzymically synthesized DNA was 77%.

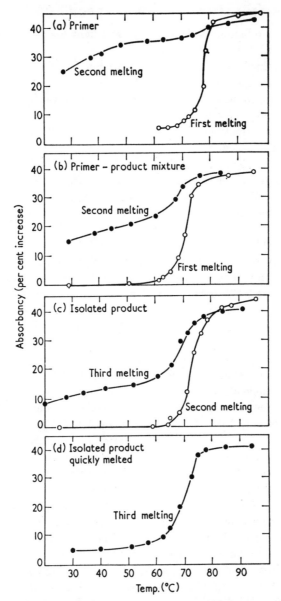

FIG. 4. *Reversible melting of the enzymic product.* Melting profiles of DNA samples described in more detail in the legend to Fig. 3. The initial absorbancy at 25°C was measured with the sample, in 0·02 M-KCl, placed in a 1-ml. quartz cuvette. This value was then used to express all subsequent absorbancies, corrected for the expansion of water, as the relative percentage increase, i.e.

$$\text{percentage increase} = 100 \left(\frac{\text{absorbancy at ambient temperature}}{\text{initial absorbancy at 25°C}} - 1 \right).$$

When the sample had been heated to 95°C, the cuvette was removed from its housing and placed in an ice-water bath at 0°C. The cuvette was then replaced in its housing and heated again. The percentage increase in absorbancy is relative to the absorbancy at 25°C measured before the initial heating of the sample in the cuvette. The quickly melted isolated product was heated in a cuvette at 95°C for 5 min, quickly cooled, and heated again in the same cuvette.

The primer DNA solution was diluted to a final salt concentration of 0·02 M-KCl. The contribution of salt from the stock solution of primer DNA may thus have raised the T_m. In other unpublished experiments, using DNA isolated from λdg phage and wheat germ (Zimmerman, S. B. & Kornberg, A.), the T_m values of primer DNA and the respective primer–product mixtures were less than 2°C apart.

complex, giving two bands. Both the heavy and light bands corresponded in density to single-stranded DNA.

The results obtained with *B. subtilis* DNA are not peculiar to this source of DNA, nor do they require the use of density labels. Similar studies with T7 DNA yielded comparable results, as shown in Fig. 3. Since the primer was light, its replication with light triphosphates produced no shift of density in the primer–product complex. However, after heat treatment, two bands were observed; the heavier material had the density of single-stranded T7 DNA and was completely susceptible to exonuclease I (98% rendered dialyzable); the lighter one had the density of native T7 DNA and resisted the action of exonuclease I (97% remained non-dialyzable and was insoluble in acid). As described below, the changes in absorbancy on heating the product further identified it as helical DNA.

(iii) *Effect of heating on absorbancy of primer–product complex and the isolated product*

The absorbancy of a T7 DNA primer–product mixture (30% primer and 70% product) as a function of temperature resembled that of the primer by itself (Fig. 4(a) and (b)). At or near 70°C, both samples underwent a sharp increase in absorbancy with a total change of about 40%. After quickly cooling the heated samples in the cuvettes, the primer–product mixture gave a lower absorbancy than did the primer; a second cycle of melting then revealed a distinct transition in the 70°C region only for the primer–product mixture. On the basis of the density-gradient studies, it seems likely that the second melting profile of the primer–product mixture consists of two independent components: a helical product which exhibits most of its 40% hyperchromic change and a single-stranded primer which shows a hyperchromic change of only 15%. To establish this point, the primer was removed from the mixture by exonuclease I treatment (after heating for five minutes at 95°C followed by quick cooling); released nucleotides were removed by dialysis and exonuclease I was removed by phenol treatment. The product, freed of primer, gave a melting profile similar to that of native T7 DNA primer or of the primer–product mixture (Fig. 4(c)). After quickly cooling the melted samples, the absorbancy came to within 8% of the original value. A third exposure to elevated temperatures showed a significant hysteresis and a lowered T_m (midpoint of transition). The second heating cycle required a three-hour period and probably resulted in significant degradation of the DNA. If instead of this prolonged exposure during the second heating cycle the DNA product was simply brought to 95°C for five minutes, quickly cooled and then subjected to a third melting, the profile and T_m were much closer to that of helical DNA (Fig. 4(d)).

Thus, after having been heated under conditions that would make primer DNA single stranded, the T7 product DNA exhibits a melting profile that resembles helical rather than single-stranded DNA. The same was true for products prepared using DNA from T6 phage, λ*dg* phage, or wheat germ as primers (Zimmerman & Kornberg, unpublished results).

(iv) *Influence of alkaline treatment of the primer–product complex as judged by viscometry*

The primer–product mixture prepared using T7 DNA as a primer had a reduced viscosity (η_{sp}/c) similar to that of the primer (Table 2). In the presence of alkali and at low salt concentration, the viscosity of the primer remained high, as did that of the primer–product mixture. This indicates that, like the primer DNA, the product

TABLE 2

Viscosity of the enzymic product

Treatment	Reduced viscosities		
	Primer alone	Primer–product mixture	Isolated product
		dl. gm^{-1}	
0·01 M-KCl	76	66 (55)	28
Alkali treated (0·01 M-KCl + 0·015 M-KOH)	59	66 (47)	39
Alkali treated and neutralized (low salt concentration)	24	14 (24)	21
Alkali treated and neutralized (high salt concentration)	<1	14 (12)	21

The values in parentheses are for a primer–product mixture heated at 70°C (see below) to denature polymerase. T7 DNA was used as a primer (experiment 2, Table 1) and synthesis allowed to proceed to 2·7 replications.

The *primer–product mixtures* were obtained as follows: the sodium salt of EDTA was added (final concentration of 0·01 M) and the mixture divided into two parts. To one portion was added 1/10 vol. of 10×SSC and heated for 5 min at 70°C to denature polymerase. Both portions were then dialyzed, first against 0·4 M-NaCl containing 0·01 M-EDTA, sodium salt and 0·01 M-tris of pH 7·4 and then against 0·05 M-KCl containing 0·01 M-tris of pH 7·4.

The *isolated product* was obtained from a similar but not identical primer–product mixture as described in Fig. 3. Flow times were measured in the four solvents listed in Table 2 without removing the sample from the viscometer. Each sample (1 ml.) was placed in the viscometer in 0·01 M-KCl. Then 0·015 ml. of 1 M-KOH was added. The KOH was neutralized by the addition of 0·015 ml. of 0·5 M-sodium citrate, pH 3·3 (low salt condition). The high salt condition was obtained by the addition of 0·03 ml. of 2 M-KCl.

DNA is an extended chain in the presence of alkali and has a high molecular weight. After neutralization and in a solution of relatively low salt concentration, the primer–product mixture still had a viscosity similar to that of the primer alone. The low values obtained for the alkali-treated primer–product mixture in a solution of high salt concentration are based on times of flow which were only two to three seconds greater than that of the solvent and therefore would be relatively more affected by impurities in the solution.

Also given in Table 2 is the viscosity behavior of the isolated T7 product described in Fig. 3. The initial value was relatively low. In alkali, the viscosity increased slightly and then returned to its initial value on neutralization. Here again the low times of flow relative to that of the solvent do not permit accurate determinations. However, it appears significant that the isolated product DNA was viscous and that the reduced viscosity actually increased in the presence of alkali.

The sedimentation coefficient of the isolated T7 product, determined by band centrifugation as described in Materials and Methods, was 12 s.

(b) *Attempts to determine the basis for non-denaturability of the product*

The foregoing results indicate that enzymically synthesized DNA has a double-helical character resembling that of naturally occurring DNA. Since a hyperchromic change on heating has been observed for synthesized DNA, we infer that the double-helical structure and the stacking of the bases can be disrupted, although we do not know precisely to what extent this occurs. The synthetic DNA differs from naturally occurring DNA in its greater facility towards re-naturation following denaturation by heat or alkali treatments. Among the various alternatives that might explain this behavior, three have been considered: (1) the helical regions arise from interstrand interactions, and the strands separate but are unusual in their capacity to reunite (anneal); (2) the helical regions arise as in (1) from interstrand base pairing, but although the bases become unstacked and the double-helical structure is disrupted, the strands fail to separate; (3) the helical regions arise from intra-strand base pairing and take the form of hairpin turns ("pleats"); and at elevated temperatures or at alkaline pH, the hairpins open, but re-form on the removal of denaturing conditions. Experiments to select among these alternatives include an attempt to hybridize DNA products, attempts to modify the DNA product to render it susceptible to denaturation, and studies of conditions during replication that influence the denaturability of the product. In most of these studies, susceptibility to exonuclease I after heating and quick cooling was used as a rapid assay for denaturability.

(i) An attempt to hybridize two DNA products

To test the first alternative, a heavy DNA product containing bromouracil was synthesized, and mixed and heated with an unlabeled light DNA product. Density-gradient analysis of the rapidly cooled mixture failed to detect the production of bands of intermediate density representing hybrids of the light and heavy DNA components (Fig. 5). Instead, the patterns after heating revealed bands at the densities characteristic of undenatured DNA, unaltered by the heating procedure. If the heating had led to a separation of the strands of the two synthetic DNA's, then, barring interference by the bromouracil substituents, hybrids should have been produced. For DNA from natural sources, it has already been shown (Schildkraut, Wierzchowski, Marmur, Green & Doty, 1962) that hybrids can be formed between DNA strands containing bromouracil and unsubstituted DNA strands. Thus this result argues against the first alternative and suggests a closer study of the others.

(ii) Attempts to convert the DNA product to a denaturable form

(1) *Use of heating.* More extended and drastic heating treatments were imposed to determine whether the standard procedures might have been inadequate for complete unwinding of the strands. A sample held at 100°C (more than 25°C above the T_m) up to one hour was still 80% resistant to exonuclease I action (Table 3). Another sample (as in Table 3), kept in SSC at 90°C for one hour and then quickly cooled,

TABLE 3

Effect of heating on the denaturability of enzymically synthesized DNA

Time at 100°C (min)	Denaturability (%)
0	<5
10	10
30	26
60	21

The light product DNA described in Fig. 5 was heated at a concentration of 24 mμmoles/ml. in 1/10 SSC and quickly cooled. Susceptibility to exonuclease I was determined as described in Materials and Methods. Less than 5% of the samples heated for 10 or 30 min was rendered acid-soluble as a result of the heating treatment itself.

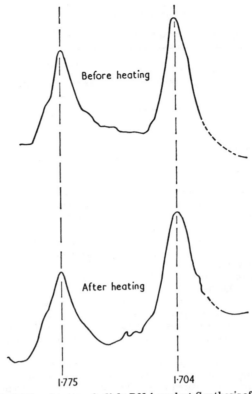

FIG. 5. *An attempt to hybridize a heavy and a light DNA product.* Synthesis of light DNA product was carried to the extent of 3·3 replications using $^{15}N^2H^3H$-labeled *B. subtilis* DNA as a primer (experiment 4, Table 1). After dialysis, the mixture of product plus primer was heated at 100°C for 5 min in 1/10 SSC, quickly cooled and treated with exonuclease I (see Materials and Methods) to remove the primer DNA. 95% of the material giving ^3H counts (primer DNA) were made acid-soluble and 100% of the material giving ^{32}P counts (product DNA) remained acid-insoluble. Synthesis of heavy DNA product involved the use of *B. subtilis* DNA (sample B) as a primer (experiment 6, Table 1) and d$\overline{BU}$TP to produce the heavy DNA containing 5-bromouracil. Instead of 67 mμmoles/ml. of dTTP, 25 mμmoles/ml. of dTTP + 42 mμmoles/ml. of d$\overline{BU}$TP were used. Primer DNA was removed as described above. Density-gradient centrifugation showed no detectable light primer DNA remaining after exonuclease I treatment. The samples of heavy and light enzymic products were mixed at a concentration of 18 mμmoles/ml. each in SSC (*before heating* pattern in figure) and then heated for 5 min at 100°C and quickly cooled (*after heating* pattern in figure).

revealed the same buoyant density as that of the native *B. subtilis* DNA which had been used to prime its synthesis.

(2) *Use of proteases.* DNA exposed to certain mutagenic agents also returns to a helical configuration after denaturing treatments, and this behavior has been attributed to cross-linkage between the strands (Marmur & Grossman, 1961; Geiduschek, 1961; Iyer & Szybalski, 1963). To test the possibility that the polymerase or other protein components in the *in vitro* system were cross-linking the strands, the enzymically synthesized DNA was subjected to treatment with several proteases. Hydrolysis of a hypothetical peptide linking substance should then permit the DNA strands to separate upon heating, and make the synthesized DNA susceptible to exonuclease I. As shown in Table 4, none of the protease treatments produced a significant increase in the denaturability of the DNA product. The amounts of proteases used in these incubations were 10^3 to 10^4 times greater than necessary to hydrolyze the quantity

TABLE 4

Effect of proteases on the denaturability of enzymically synthesized DNA

Protease	Denaturability	
	Incubation in absence of protease	Incubation in presence of protease
Pronase	27%	25%
Trypsin	25%	26%
Chymotrypsin	25%	38%
Subtilisin	9%	6%

[32]P-labeled DNA (enzymic product) was prepared with *B. subtilis* DNA as primer (see Table 1, experiment 7). After 2·5 replications, the product was dialyzed extensively against 0·2 M-KCl + 0·01 M-EDTA, sodium salt, pH 7, followed by 0·02 M-KCl. The material was incubated as described below, without removal of the primer DNA.

Pronase. The reaction mixture (0·3 ml.) contained 6 μmoles of tris buffer, pH 8·0, 4 mμmoles of enzymic product and 2·8 μg of pronase. After incubation for 30 min at 40°C the reaction mixture was placed in a boiling water-bath for 10 min. Susceptibility of the product to exonuclease I was determined after adjustment of pH to 9·2 with KOH and addition of the constituents given in Materials and Methods. The final volume was 0·35 ml. and contained the heated pronase.

Trypsin and chymotrypsin. The reaction mixture (0·3 ml.) containing 6 μmoles of tris buffer, pH 8·0, and 4 mμmoles of enzymic product was heated for 10 min at 100°C and then treated with 28 μg of trypsin or chymotrypsin. After incubation for 30 min at 37°C, the reaction mixture was placed in a boiling water-bath for 10 min. Susceptibility to exonuclease I was tested as described above for pronase.

Subtilisin. The reaction mixture (0·3 ml.) contained 15 μmoles of potassium phosphate buffer, pH 12·0, 4 mμmoles of enzymic product and 3·2 μg of subtilisin. After incubation for 30 min at 37°C, the reaction mixture was placed in a boiling water-bath for 10 min. Susceptibility to exonuclease I was tested (at a final pH adjusted to 9·2 with HCl) in the presence of the heated subtilisin as described above for pronase. Incubation with subtilisin at pH 11·7 gave the same results as at pH 12.

To demonstrate that the proteases (after heating) did not destroy exonuclease I (and thus vitiate the test), a control with ^{32}P-labeled *E. coli* DNA was always included. In every case, this DNA carried through the same procedures was more than 90% susceptible to exonuclease I.

of polymerase used to synthesize the DNA, assuming that it would be degraded as readily as heated casein; based on its action on native serum albumin, the amount of pronase used was 100 times greater than necessary. The use of subtilisin at pH 12 ensured that the DNA product was in its random coil configuration when exposed to this protease.

(3) *Use of endonucleases and other treatments.* The resistance to denaturation might be due to cross-linkage by non-protein factors, or perhaps to some twisting of strands that prevents their being disentangled. In either case, the reduction in molecular size by endonuclease treatment or shearing should have a profound effect on the denaturability of the enzymic product. Upon treatment with endonuclease I to the extent of 10% acid-solubilization of the DNA, there should have been at least a 90% decrease in molecular weight as inferred from viscosity changes (Lehman *et al.*, 1962); and yet (despite a heating treatment) the DNA is still about 70% resistant to exonuclease I (Fig. 6). While extensive digestion with endonuclease I does render the DNA ultimately susceptible to exonuclease I, this is a late rather than early consequence of endonuclease action. (Heating was a factor in making DNA treated with endonuclease I susceptible to exonuclease I. Treatment by endonuclease I (18% acid-solubilization) produced an acid-insoluble DNA which was only 12%

susceptible to exonuclease I. However, heating of this DNA increased its denaturability to 50%.)

The effects of treatment with pancreatic DNase were similar to those observed with endonuclease I (Fig. 6).

The primer–product mixture described earlier (Fig. 3) was subjected to 0·001 M-KOH at room temperature for 30 minutes, after which the solution was

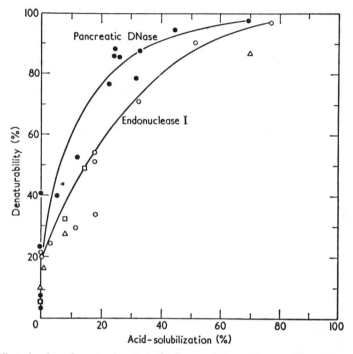

FIG. 6. *Effect of endonuclease treatment on the denaturability of the enzymic product.*

Endonuclease I treatment. The *B. subtilis*-primed enzymic product DNA, prepared and dialyzed as described in the legend to Table 4, was made 0·1 M in KCl and heated for 10 min at 70°C to inactivate any residual polymerase. The reaction mixture (0·45 ml.) contained 9 μmoles of tris buffer, pH 8·0, 3 μmoles of MgCl₂, 7 mμmoles of the enzymic product DNA and 0·01 to 0·4 unit of endonuclease I. Incubation was at 37°C for 30 min.

Pancreatic DNase treatment. The T7 enzymic product, heated at 70°C in SSC and dialyzed as described in the legend to Table 2, was incubated with pancreatic DNase as fcllows. The reaction mixture (0·45 ml.) contained 15 μmoles of pH 6·9 tris buffer, 1·5 μmoles of MgCl₂, 13 mμmoles of synthesized DNA, and 0·002 to 0·5 unit (endonuclease I unit) of pancreatic DNase. Incubation was at 37°C for 30 min.

Assay for nuclease susceptibility. Three different assays were used: (1) After the addition of the sodium salt of EDTA (3 μmoles for the samples treated with endonuclease I and 1·5 μmoles for the samples treated with pancreatic DNase), the reaction mixture was heated for 5 min at 100°C and two 0·22-ml. samples were removed. To each sample was added 2·0 μmoles of glycine buffer, pH 9·4, 2 μmoles of MgCl₂, 0·5 μmole of 2-mercaptoethanol and, in the case of the samples treated with endonuclease I, 0·34 μmole of transfer-RNA. To one sample, 5 to 10 units of exonuclease I were added. Both samples (0·3 ml. final volume) were incubated at 37°C for 30 min and assayed by the filter assay for acid-insoluble radioactive material (see Materials and Methods). The percentage denaturability was expressed relative to the acid-insoluble DNA present in the sample not containing exonuclease I. (□, ●), values determined in this manner. (2) As in (1), except that acid-insoluble radioactive material was determined by the centrifuge assay described by Lehman *et al.* (1958). (○), values determined in this manner. (3) The endonuclease I reaction mixture was chilled and dialyzed at 4°C against 0·02 M-KCl. The dialyzed mixture was heated for 10 min at 100°C, divided into two parts and treated with exonuclease I as in (1) above. The filter assay (see Materials and Methods) was used to determine acid-insoluble ³²P. (△), values determined in this manner.

neutralized. The primer was more than 90% susceptible to exonuclease I, but the product DNA was less than 5% susceptible.

Isolation of the enzymic product from the primer–product mixture described earlier (Fig. 3) entailed heating and exonuclease I treatment, phenol extractions and dialyses, with the result that the molecular weight of the product was in the vicinity of only two million. Despite these manipulations and the relatively small size of the product separated, the latter was not denaturable (less than 5% susceptible to exonuclease I).

Sonication of synthesized DNA primed by T6 phage DNA reduced the viscosity by a factor of 4, but showed no effect on denaturability as judged by absorbancy-temperature melting curves (Zimmerman & Kornberg, unpublished results).

(c) *Factors influencing the denaturability of the product during the course of replication*

(i) *Influence of extent of replication on denaturability*

The enzymically synthesized, non-denaturable products examined up to this point were obtained after extensive replication. How early in the replication process does this non-denaturable behavior become manifest? As shown in Fig. 7, for the

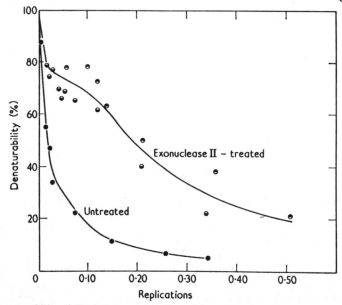

FIG. 7. *Denaturability of T7 DNA as a function of the extent of replication.*

Nuclease treatment. T7 DNA was treated with exonuclease II in a reaction mixture containing (per ml.) 67 μmoles of glycine buffer, pH 9·2, 6·7 μmoles of $MgCl_2$, 1 μmole of 2-mercaptoethanol, 70 mμmoles of ^{3}H-labeled T7 DNA and 21 units of exonuclease II. The mixture was incubated at 37°C. Samples were taken periodically and the extent of exonuclease II action was determined by measuring acid-soluble radioactive material as described (Lehman & Richardson, 1964). When 22% of the material giving ^{3}H counts had been made acid-soluble (after 2 hr of incubation), the solution was chilled and dialyzed overnight at 4°C against 1 liter of 0·067 M-potassium phosphate buffer, pH 6·8.

Replication. At various stages (experiment 1, Table 1) 0·1-ml. samples were withdrawn and diluted to 0·22 ml. with 0·0056 M-EDTA, sodium salt, pH 7. These solutions were heated for 5 min at 100°C, divided into two portions, and assayed (see Materials and Methods) for susceptibility to exonuclease I and for the extent of replication. The constituents present during replication were not removed before incubation with exonuclease I. The presence of phosphate buffer lowered the pH to approximately 8·8. (◑, ◐), values from separate experiments on different days.

standard ("untreated") reaction mixture, the DNA product is already 80% non-denaturable when its synthesis represents only a 10% increase (0·1 replication) over the amount of primer present. At the point of 0·2 replication the product is more than 90% non-denaturable. There are indications that the replication process is of at least two types, one producing a denaturable and the other a non-denaturable product. The first evidence came from using an initial pulse [^{32}P]dATP. At 0·02 replication, 70% of the synthesized DNA was denaturable. Then synthesis was continued to 0·22 replication (using [^{14}C]dTTP), and 52% of the DNA synthesized with the initial pulse of [^{32}P]dATP remained denaturable. In a control experiment, 18% of the DNA synthesized at the stage of 0·22 replication was denaturable. This suggests that certain portions of the DNA, especially those synthesized early in replication, are fully denaturable and remain that way; the other DNA, including most of the DNA synthesized in later stages of replication, would then be completely non-denaturable. We presume, on the basis of other studies (Richardson *et al.*, 1964*a*) and results to be stated below, that the replication process responsible for the production of denaturable DNA proceeds by a repair mechanism. Thus, the denaturability of the synthetic DNA depends on how much of the primer DNA can be replicated by the repair mechanism. As will be discussed below, the presence of nucleases under various conditions of replication will significantly affect the denaturability of the product.

(ii) *Influence of nucleases on the synthesis of denaturable DNA*

In recent replication experiments, the DNA phosphatase-exonuclease (exonuclease III) has been used frequently to remove from the primer any terminal 3'-phosphoryl residues which may be present; such residues inhibit synthesis and make strands containing such groups unavailable for replication (Richardson *et al.*, 1963*a*). However, the action of the DNA phosphatase-exonuclease for an extended period results in the removal of up to 40% of each strand (starting from the 3'-hydroxyl end) (Richardson & Kornberg, 1964). When such a partially single-stranded DNA is used as a primer for replication, the section of synthesized DNA which replaces the region removed by the exonuclease appears to be covalently linked to the primer and is fully denaturable (Richardson *et al.*, 1964*a*). The DNA synthesized subsequent to the completion of the repair process is not covalently linked to the primer and is non-denaturable. The action of exonuclease II (Lehman & Richardson, 1964) also leads to a partially single-stranded DNA which can subsequently be repaired by polymerase. After incubation with exonuclease II, the amount of denaturable product formed was greater than that obtained under standard conditions (Fig. 7). It is possible that exonucleolytic action on the primer persists throughout replication, and the repair of this damage accounts for the persistence of a small fraction of denaturable product DNA in the primer–product complex.

(iii) *Influence of formamide treatment of the primer on the synthesis of denaturable DNA*

Results with a heavy primer denatured by formamide treatment differed from the foregoing findings with helical primers in two ways: (1) the product was 44% rather than 5% denaturable; and (2) the primer became partially resistant to denaturation (70% as compared with nearly 100% denaturable) (Table 5). Density-gradient analyses of the primer–product complexes indicated that approximately 30% of the product was in a band of hybrid density and was not separable from the primer by

TABLE 5

Denaturability of DNA synthesized with a single-stranded primer

Replications	Denaturability	
	Primer	Product
0·0	95%	—
0·36	69%	44%
0·59	73%	44%
0·76	70%	44%
1·1	70%	44%
4·3	67%	27%

$^{15}N^2H^3H$-labeled *B. subtilis* DNA was made single-stranded by dialysis (0·75 μmole DNA/ml.) at 25°C against two changes of 99% formamide containing 0·005 M-KCl and then removal of formamide by dialysis at 4°C against 0·02 M-KCl. The DNA was incubated with polymerase as described in experiment 8 (Table 1). Portions were taken and dialyzed at 4°C against 0·2 M-KCl + 0·01 M-EDTA, sodium salt, followed by 0·02 M-KCl. Samples were tested for susceptibility to exonuclease I as described in Materials and Methods.

heating or alkali treatments. These results suggest that a substantial fraction of the synthesized DNA is covalently linked to the primer and behaves as in the repair of a partially single-stranded DNA (Richardson *et al.*, 1964a); conversely, there is the implication that a significant fraction of the primer (about 30%) has become non-denaturable through some complex and as yet poorly understood association with the product DNA.

4. Discussion

Chemical and physical evidence indicates that the structure of enzymically synthesized DNA has the basic features of the Watson–Crick model (Kornberg, 1961). Data on base composition indicate base pairing (adenine–thymine, guanine–cytosine), hypochromicity indicates base stacking, the sedimentation coefficient and viscosity indicate a high molecular weight and a relatively rigid structure, and electron micrographs show long fibers. Whereas these data indicate structural similarities between enzymically synthesized DNA and primer DNA, more recent results have revealed two differences when native DNA is the primer.

One difference observed was the presence of branches on the fibers of the synthetic DNA when it was examined in the electron microscope. The second distinction is the capacity of synthetic DNA to return to a helical conformation after denaturing treatment (non-denaturability). These two properties are found in DNA synthesized as in the present studies using a native primer; the synthetic DNA, it would appear, is found in new chains not covalently linked to the primer. When DNA is synthesized with a partially single-stranded primer (Richardson *et al.*, 1964a), the process is essentially one of repair; the product appears to be covalently bound to the primer, is denaturable and contains no observable branches. Replication beyond the point of repair yields a branched, non-denaturable product readily separable from the primer. Our speculations have associated branching, non-denaturability and new-chain synthesis, although convincing evidence for this is lacking.

The discussion which follows will attempt to rationalize the results which relate to the non-denaturability characteristic, while the electron micrographic findings will be considered in more detail in a later publication (Inman, Schildkraut & Kornberg, unpublished work).

Examples of non-denaturability in naturally occurring DNA are found in the circular helical forms of polyoma DNA (Dulbecco & Vogt, 1963; Weil & Vinograd, 1963) and replicative ϕX174 DNA (Kleinschmidt, Burton & Sinsheimer, 1963) and in DNA treated with chemical or physical agents to produce cross-linkages (Geiduschek, 1961; Marmur & Grossman, 1961; Iyer & Szybalski, 1963). Neither explanation seems applicable to the synthetic DNA. Were it circular, it would be expected to become linear and then single-stranded and denaturable as a result of the rigorous heating or mild endonuclease treatments applied. It would also be difficult to explain the early appearance of non-denaturable DNA when only a small fraction of the primer has been replicated. Evidence to support the presence of cross-linkage has been sought without success. Protease, phenol and sonication treatments fail to produce denaturable segments; the failure of heating and exposure to mild endonucleases has also been mentioned. Is there then some mysterious adhesive that characterizes exposure to polymerase, or is non-denaturability a consequence of its replicative action? When the primer DNA is incubated with polymerase in the absence of one of the four triphosphates, the primer remains denaturable. With all four triphosphates present and after extensive synthesis, the primer can be shown to be still denaturable. A further argument against cross-linkage being a necessary consequence of polymerase action is found in the denaturability of synthesized DNA when it becomes covalently linked to the primer in the repair of a partially single-stranded DNA (Richardson et al., 1964a).

Recent in vivo autoradiographic and genetic studies (Cairns, 1963; Nagata, 1963; Yoshikawa & Sueoka, 1963) indicate that DNA synthesis proceeds with the simultaneous replication of both strands of the chromosome, starting from one end. If these conclusions applied at the nucleotide level, then in vitro polymerizations would require two different mechanisms to replicate the two strands of opposite polarity. One of the mechanisms is that demonstrated for the purified E. coli DNA polymerase (Adler, Lehman, Bessman, Simms & Kornberg, 1958; Kornberg, 1961) and involves the interaction of the terminal 3'-hydroxyl group of a DNA chain with the 5'-nucleotidyl phosphorus of the deoxynucleoside triphosphate. The other mechanism (described as "B" in Kornberg, 1957) would entail the reaction of the 3'-hydroxyl group of the deoxynucleoside triphosphate with the 5'-nucleotidyl phosphorus of a triphosphate terminating a DNA chain. Whether the latter mechanism, if it exists, can be employed by the E. coli DNA polymerase in certain circumstances or is the function of another polymerase yet to be isolated, is a matter of speculation. The possibility that concerns us at this point is that, under the conditions of synthesis used in the present study, many chains grow from the end of the primer DNA and that some of these growing chains may end in 5'-triphosphate. This activated end might react with an incoming triphosphate, or occasionally with the 3'-hydroxyl end of an adjacent growing strand. In this way, two strands could be linked covalently, resulting in a branched structure. The resulting twisting of strands might then prevent their being completely disentangled during denaturing treatment. While this possibility has not been eliminated, another scheme, described below, seems more plausible at present.

In preference to these several alternatives, we are inclined to consider at this time a model for the synthetic DNA which is consistent with most of the observations, including the electron micrographs. This model pictures the synthetic DNA as a multiple-hairpin or pleated structure. The large degree of intra-strand helicity inherent in such a structure explains its ready restoration after denaturing treatments, and the retention of this non-denaturable feature even after scissions by heating and endonuclease. The branches seen in the electron microscope would be ascribed to the hairpin-like extensions from a main chain.

Is there any explanation for the development of this hypothetical pleated structure? One might speculate, as illustrated in Fig. 8, that replication of one strand from the

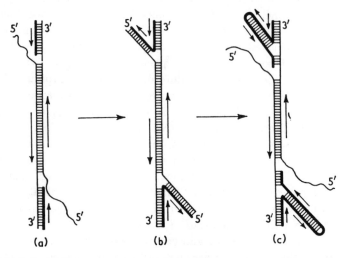

FIG. 8. *A hypothetical model to account for the non-denaturability of synthesized DNA.* The primer is indicated by thin lines, the product DNA by heavy lines. Hydrogen bonds between strands are shown as horizontal lines. According to this scheme, replication proceeds by pairing with the base at the 3'-hydroxyl end of the template strand; the directions of the arrows show the direction of synthesis and polarity of the strand.

end of the priming helix leaves the sister strand of the primer loose and unmatched (scheme (a)). This free strand may at some point successfully attract the preceding end of the growing strand and now serve instead as its template (scheme (b)). When the end of the sister strand is reached, the growing strand might loop about and replicate itself to form the hairpins shown at each end of the structure in scheme (c). A further conjecture is that this kind of aberration in secondary structure, if in fact it occurs in synthetic DNA, is avoided in nature by simultaneous replication of both strands as suggested in recent *in vivo* experiments (Cairns, 1963; Nagata, 1963; Yoshikawa & Sueoka, 1963) or by some other control of the loose sister strand.

This investigation was supported in part by grants from the National Institutes of Health, United States Public Health Service and the National Science Foundation.

REFERENCES

Adler, J., Lehman, I. R., Bessman, M., Simms, E. S. & Kornberg, A. (1958). *Proc. Nat. Acad. Sci., Wash.* **44**, 641.
Bodmer, W. & Schildkraut, C. L. (1964). *Analyt. Biochem.*, in the press.
Cairns, J. (1963). *J. Mol. Biol.* **6**, 208.
Dulbecco, R. & Vogt, M. (1963). *Proc. Nat. Acad. Sci., Wash.* **50**, 236.

Geiduschek, E. P. (1961). *Proc. Nat. Acad. Sci., Wash.* **47**, 950.

Inman, R. B. & Baldwin, R. L. (1962). *J. Mol. Biol.* **5**, 172.

Iyer, V. N. & Szybalski, W. (1963). *Proc. Nat. Acad. Sci., Wash.* **50**, 355.

Kleinschmidt, A. K., Burton, A. & Sinsheimer, R. L. (1963). *Science,* **142**, 961.

Kornberg, A. (1957). *Advanc. Enzymol.* **18**, 191.

Kornberg, A. (1961). In *Enzymatic Synthesis of DNA.* New York: John Wiley & Sons.

Lehman, I. R. (1960). *J. Biol. Chem.* **235**, 1479.

Lehman, I. R., Bessman, M. J., Simms, E. S. & Kornberg, A. (1958). *J. Biol. Chem.* **233**, 163.

Lehman, I. R. & Richardson, C. C. (1964). *J. Biol. Chem.* **239**, 233.

Lehman, I. R., Roussos, G. G. & Pratt, E. A. (1962). *J. Biol. Chem.* **237**, 819.

Mandell, J. D. & Hershey, A. D. (1960). *Analyt. Biochem.* **1**, 66.

Marmur, J. (1961). *J. Mol. Biol.* **3**, 208.

Marmur, J. & Grossman, L. (1961). *Proc. Nat. Acad. Sci., Wash.* **47**, 778.

Nagata, T. P. (1963). *Proc. Nat. Acad. Sci., Wash.* **49**, 551.

Richardson, C. C., Inman, R. B. & Kornberg, A. (1964a). *J. Mol. Biol.* **9**, 46.

Richardson, C. C. & Kornberg, A. (1964). *J. Biol. Chem.* **239**, 242.

Richardson, C. C., Schildkraut, C. L., Aposhian, H. V. & Kornberg, A. (1964b). *J. Biol. Chem.* **239**, 222.

Richardson, C. C., Schildkraut, C. L., Aposhian, H. V., Kornberg, A., Bodmer, W. & Lederberg, J. (1963a). In *Informational Macromolecules,* ed. by H. Vogel, V. Bryson & J. Lampen, p. 13. New York: Academic Press.

Richardson, C. C., Schildkraut, C. L. & Kornberg, A. (1963b). *Cold Spr. Harb. Symp. Quant. Biol.* **28**, 9.

Schachman, H. K., Lehman, I. R., Bessman, M. J., Simms, E. S. & Kornberg, A. (1958). *Fed. Proc.* **17**, 304.

Schildkraut, C. L., Marmur, J. & Doty, P. (1962). *J. Mol. Biol.* **4**, 430.

Schildkraut, C. L., Wierzchowski, K. L., Marmur, J., Green, D. M. & Doty, P (1962). *Virology,* **18**, 43.

Vinograd, J., Bruner, R., Kent, R. & Weigle, J. (1963). *Proc. Nat. Acad. Sci., Wash.* **49**, 902.

Vinograd, J., Morris, J., Davidson, N. & Dove, W. F. (1963). *Proc. Nat. Acad. Sci., Wash.* **49**, 12.

Wake, R. G. & Baldwin, R. L. (1962). *J. Mol. Biol.* **5**, 201.

Weil, R. & Vinograd, J. (1963). *Proc. Nat. Acad. Sci., Wash.* **50**, 730.

Yoshikawa, H. & Sueoka, N. (1963). *Proc. Nat. Acad. Sci., Wash.* **49**, 559.

Zubay, G. (1962). *J. Mol. Biol.* **4**, 347.

Reprinted from the Proceedings of the NATIONAL ACADEMY OF SCIENCES
Vol. 44, No. 7, pp. 671–682.   July, 1958.

THE REPLICATION OF DNA IN ESCHERICHIA COLI*

By Matthew Meselson and Franklin W. Stahl

GATES AND CRELLIN LABORATORIES OF CHEMISTRY,† AND NORMAN W. CHURCH LABORATORY OF
CHEMICAL BIOLOGY, CALIFORNIA INSTITUTE OF TECHNOLOGY, PASADENA, CALIFORNIA

Communicated by Max Delbrück, May 14, 1958

Introduction.—Studies of bacterial transformation and bacteriaphage infection[1-5] strongly indicate that deoxyribonucleic acid (DNA) can carry and transmit hereditary information and can direct its own replication. Hypotheses for the mechanism of DNA replication differ in the predictions they make concerning the distribution among progeny molecules of atoms derived from parental molecules.[6]

Radioisotopic labels have been employed in experiments bearing on the distribution of parental atoms among progeny molecules in several organisms.[6-9] We anticipated that a label which imparts to the DNA molecule an increased density might permit an analysis of this distribution by sedimentation techniques. To this end, a method was developed for the detection of small density differences among

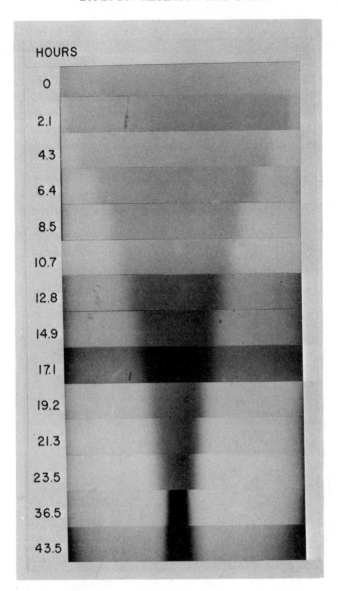

FIG. 1.—Ultraviolet absorption photographs showing successive stages in the banding of DNA from *E. coli.* An aliquot of bacterial lysate containing approximately 10^8 lysed cells was centrifuged at 31,410 rpm in a CsCl solution as described in the text. Distance from the axis of rotation increases toward the right. The number beside each photograph gives the time elapsed after reaching 31,410 rpm.

macromolecules.[10] By use of this method, we have observed the distribution of the heavy nitrogen isotope N^{15} among molecules of DNA following the transfer of a uniformly N^{15}-labeled, exponentially growing bacterial population to a growth medium containing the ordinary nitrogen isotope N^{14}.

Density-Gradient Centrifugation.—A small amount of DNA in a concentrated solution of cesium chloride is centrifuged until equilibrium is closely approached.

The opposing processes of sedimentation and diffusion have then produced a stable concentration gradient of the cesium chloride. The concentration and pressure gradients result in a continuous increase of density along the direction of centrifugal force. The macromolecules of DNA present in this density gradient are driven by the centrifugal field into the region where the solution density is equal to their own buoyant density.[11] This concentrating tendency is opposed by, diffusion, with the result that at equilibrium a single species of DNA is distributed over a band whose width is inversely related to the molecular weight of that species (Fig. 1).

If several different density species of DNA are present, each will form a band at the position where the density of the CsCl solution is equal to the buoyant density of that species. In this way DNA labeled with heavy nitrogen (N^{15}) may be

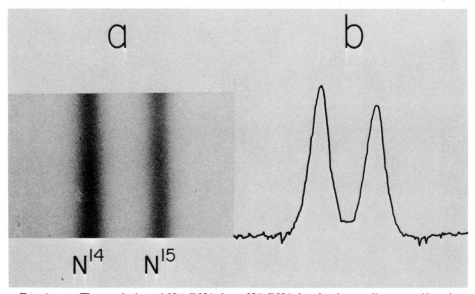

Fig. 2—*a:* The resolution of N^{14} DNA from N^{15} DNA by density-gradient centrifugation. A mixture of N^{14} and N^{15} bacterial lysates, each containing about 10^8 lysed cells, was centrifuged in CsCl solution as described in the text. The photograph was taken after 24 hours of centrifugation at 44,770 rpm. *b:* A microdensitometer tracing showing the DNA distribution in the region of the two bands of Fig. 2a. The separation between the peaks corresponds to a difference in buoyant density of 0.014 gm. cm.$^{-3}$

resolved from unlabeled DNA. Figure 2 shows the two bands formed as a result of centrifuging a mixture of approximately equal amounts of N^{14} and N^{15} *Escherichia coli* DNA.

In this paper reference will be made to the apparent molecular weight of DNA samples determined by means of density-gradient centrifugation. A discussion has been given[10] of the considerations upon which such determinations are based, as well as of several possible sources of error.[12]

Experimental.—*Escherichia coli* B was grown at 36° C. with aeration in a glucose salts medium containing ammonium chloride as the sole nitrogen source.[13] The growth of the bacterial population was followed by microscopic cell counts and by colony assays (Fig. 3).

Bacteria uniformly labeled with N^{15} were prepared by growing washed cells for

14 generations (to a titer of 2×10^8/ml) in medium containing 100 μg/ml of $N^{15}H_4Cl$ of 96.5 per cent isotopic purity. An abrupt change to N^{14} medium was then accomplished by adding to the growing culture a tenfold excess of $N^{14}H_4Cl$, along with ribosides of adenine and uracil in experiment 1 and ribosides of adenine, guanine, uracil, and cytosine in experiment 2, to give a concentration of 10 μg/ml of each riboside. During subsequent growth the bacterial titer was kept between

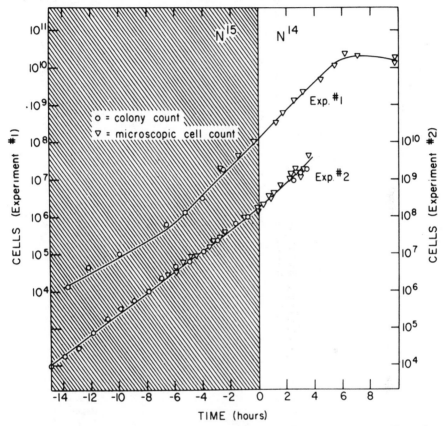

FIG. 3.—Growth of bacterial populations first in N^{15} and then in N^{14} medium. The values on the ordinates give the actual titers of the cultures up to the time of addition of N^{14}. Thereafter, during the period when samples were being withdrawn for density-gradient centrifugation, the actual titer was kept between 1 and 2×10^8 by additions of fresh medium. The values on the ordinates during this later period have been corrected for the withdrawals and additions. During the period of sampling for density-gradient centrifugation, the generation time was 0.81 hours in Experiment 1 and 0.85 hours in Experiment 2.

1 and 2×10^8/ml by appropriate additions of fresh N^{14} medium containing ribosides.

Samples containing about 4×10^9 bacteria were withdrawn from the culture just before the addition of N^{14} and afterward at intervals for several generations. Each sample was immediately chilled and centrifuged in the cold for 5 minutes at $1,800 \times g$. After resuspension in 0.40 ml. of a cold solution 0.01 M in NaCl and 0.01 M in ethylenediaminetetra-acetate (EDTA) at pH 6, the cells were lysed by the addition of 0.10 ml. of 15 per cent sodium dodecyl sulfate and stored in the cold.

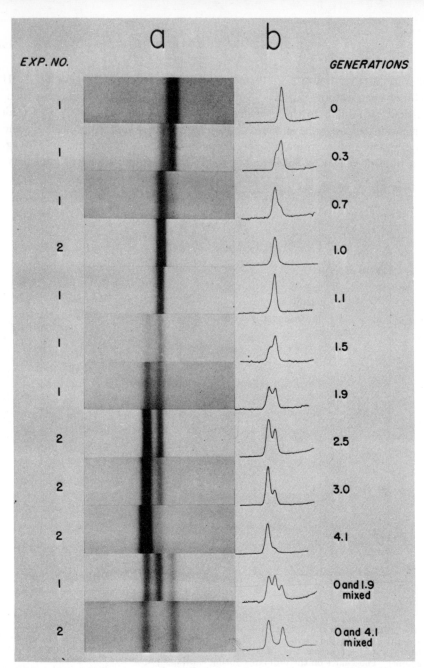

Fig. 4—*a:* Ultraviolet absorption photographs showing DNA bands resulting from density-gradient centrifugation of lysates of bacteria sampled at various times after the addition of an excess of N^{14} substrates to a growing N^{15}-labeled culture. Each photograph was taken after 20 hours of centrifugation at 44,770 rpm under the conditions described in the text. The density of the CsCl solution increases to the right. Regions of equal density occupy the same horizontal position on each photograph. The time of sampling is measured from the time of the addition of N^{14} in units of the generation time. The generation times for Experiments 1 and 2 were estimated from the measurements of bacterial growth presented in Fig. 3. *b:* Microdensitometer tracings of the DNA bands shown in the adjacent photographs. The microdensitometer pen displacement above the base line is directly proportional to the concentration of DNA. The degree of labeling of a species of DNA corresponds to the relative position of its band between the bands of fully labeled and unlabeled DNA shown in the lowermost frame, which serves as a density reference. A test of the conclusion that the DNA in the band of intermediate density is just half-labeled is provided by the frame showing the mixture of generations 0 and 1.9. When allowance is made for the relative amounts of DNA in the three peaks, the peak of intermediate density is found to be centered at 50 ± 2 per cent of the distance between the N^{14} and N^{15} peaks.

For density-gradient centrifugation, 0.010 ml. of the dodecyl sulfate lysate was added to 0.70 ml. of CsCl solution buffered at pH 8.5 with 0.01 M tris(hydroxy-methyl)aminomethane. The density of the resulting solution was 1.71 gm. cm.$^{-3}$ This was centrifuged at 140,000$\times$ g. (44,770 rpm) in a Spinco model E ultracentrifuge at 25° for 20 hours, at which time the DNA had essentially attained sedimentation equilibrium. Bands of DNA were then found in the region of density 1.71 gm. cm.$^{-3}$, well isolated from all other macromolecular components of the bacterial lysate. Ultraviolet absorption photographs taken during the course of each centrifugation were scanned with a recording microdensitometer (Fig. 4).

The buoyant density of a DNA molecule may be expected to vary directly with the fraction of N^{15} label it contains. The density gradient is constant in the region between fully labeled and unlabeled DNA bands. Therefore, the degree of labeling of a partially labeled species of DNA may be determined directly from the relative position of its band between the band of fully labeled DNA and the band of unlabeled DNA. The error in this procedure for the determination of the degree of labeling is estimated to be about 2 per cent.

Results.—Figure 4 shows the results of density-gradient centrifugation of lysates of bacteria sampled at various times after the addition of an excess of N^{14}-containing substrates to a growing N^{15}-labeled culture.

It may be seen in Figure 4 that, until one generation time has elapsed, half-labeled molecules accumulate, while fully labeled DNA is depleted. One generation time after the addition of N^{14}, these half-labeled or "hybrid" molecules alone are observed. Subsequently, only half-labeled DNA and completely unlabeled DNA are found. When two generation times have elapsed after the addition of N^{14}, half-labeled and unlabeled DNA are present in equal amounts.

Discussion.—These results permit the following conclusions to be drawn regarding DNA replication under the conditions of the present experiment.

1. *The nitrogen of a DNA molecule is divided equally between two subunits which remain intact through many generations.*

The observation that parental nitrogen is found only in half-labeled molecules at all times after the passage of one generation time demonstrates the existence in each DNA molecule of two subunits containing equal amounts of nitrogen. The finding that at the second generation half-labeled and unlabeled molecules are found in equal amounts shows that the number of surviving parental subunits is twice the number of parent molecules initially present. That is, the subunits are conserved.

2. *Following replication, each daughter molecule has received one parental subunit.*

The finding that all DNA molecules are half-labeled one generation time after the addition of N^{14} shows that each daughter molecule receives one parental subunit.[14] If the parental subunits had segregated in any other way among the daughter molecules, there would have been found at the first generation some fully labeled and some unlabeled DNA molecules, representing those daughters which received two or no parental subunits, respectively.

3. *The replicative act results in a molecular doubling.*

This statement is a corollary of conclusions 1 and 2 above, according to which each parent molecule passes on two subunits to progeny molecules and each progeny molecule receives just one parental subunit.   It follows that each single molecular reproductive act results in a doubling of the number of molecules entering into that act.

The above conclusions are represented schematically in Figure 5.

The Watson-Crick Model.—A molecular structure for DNA has been proposed by Watson and Crick.[15] It has undergone preliminary refinement[16] without alteration of its main features and is supported by physical and chemical studies.[17] The structure consists of two polynucleotide chains wound helically about a common axis.   The nitrogen base (adenine, guanine, thymine, or cytosine) at each level

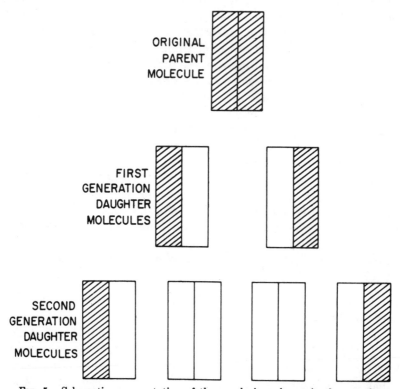

ORIGINAL
PARENT
MOLECULE

FIRST
GENERATION
DAUGHTER
MOLECULES

SECOND
GENERATION
DAUGHTER
MOLECULES

Fig. 5.—Schematic representation of the conclusions drawn in the text from the data presented in Fig. 4.   The nitrogen of each DNA molecule is divided equally between two subunits.   Following duplication, each daughter molecule receives one of these.   The subunits are conserved through successive duplications.

on one chain is hydrogen-bonded to the base at the same level on the other chain. Structural requirements allow the occurrence of only the hydrogen-bonded base pairs adenine-thymine and guanine-cytosine, resulting in a detailed complementariness between the two chains.   This suggested to Watson and Crick[18] a definite and structurally plausible hypothesis for the duplication of the DNA molecule. According to this idea, the two chains separate, exposing the hydrogen-bonding sites of the bases.   Then, in accord with the base-pairing restrictions, each chain serves as a template for the synthesis of its complement.   Accordingly, each daughter molecule contains one of the parental chains paired with a newly synthesized chain (Fig. 6).

The results of the present experiment are in exact accord with the expectations of the Watson-Crick model for DNA duplication. However, it must be emphasized that it has not been shown that the molecular subunits found in the present experiment are single polynucleotide chains or even that the DNA molecules studied here correspond to single DNA molecules possessing the structure proposed by Watson and Crick. However, some information has been obtained about the molecules and their subunits; it is summarized below.

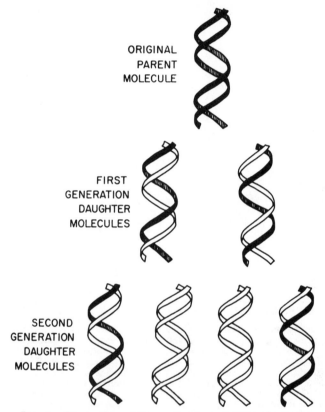

ORIGINAL
PARENT
MOLECULE

FIRST
GENERATION
DAUGHTER
MOLECULES

SECOND
GENERATION
DAUGHTER
MOLECULES

FIG. 6.—Illustration of the mechanism of DNA duplication proposed by Watson and Crick. Each daughter molecule contains one of the parental chains (*black*) paired with one new chain (*white*). Upon continued duplication, the two original parent chains remain intact, so that there will always be found two molecules each with one parental chain.

The DNA molecules derived from *E. coli* by detergent-induced lysis have a buoyant density in CsCl of 1.71 gm. cm.$^{-3}$, in the region of densities found for T2 and T4 bacteriophage DNA, and for purified calf-thymus and salmon-sperm DNA. A highly viscous and elastic solution of N^{14} DNA was prepared from a dodecyl sulfate lysate of *E. coli* by the method of Simmons[19] followed by deproteinization with chloroform. Further purification was accomplished by two cycles of preparative density-gradient centrifugation in CsCl solution. This purified bacterial DNA was found to have the same buoyant density and apparent molecular weight, 7×10^6 as the DNA of the whole bacterial lysates (Figs. 7, 8).

Heat Denaturation.—It has been found that DNA from *E. coli* differs importantly from purified salmon-sperm DNA in its behavior upon heat denaturation.

Exposure to elevated temperatures is known to bring about an abrupt collapse of the relatively rigid and extended native DNA molecule and to make available for acid-base titration a large fraction of the functional groups presumed to be blocked by hydrogen-bond formation in the native structure.[19, 20, 21, 22]   Rice and Doty[22] have reported that this collapse is not accompanied by a reduction in molecular weight as determined from light-scattering.   These findings are corroborated by density-gradient centrifugation of salmon-sperm DNA.[23]   When this material is

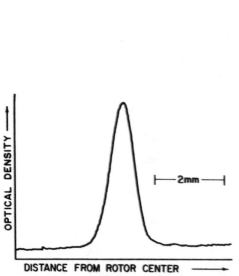

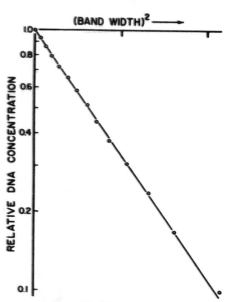

FIG. 7.—Microdensitometer tracing of an ultraviolet absorption photograph showing the optical density in the region of a band of N[14] *E. coli* DNA at equilibrium.   About 2 μg. of DNA purified as described in the text was centrifuged at 31,410 rpm at 25° in 7.75 molal CsCl at pH 8.4. The density gradient is essentially constant over the region of the band and is 0.057 gm./cm.[4]. The position of the maximum indicates a buoyant density of 1.71 gm. cm.$^{-3}$ In this tracing the optical density above the base line is directly proportional to the concentration of DNA in the rotating centrifuge cell.   The concentration of DNA at the maximum is about 50 μg./ml.

FIG. 8.—The square of the width of the band of Fig. 7 plotted against the logarithm of the relative concentration of DNA.   The divisions along the abscissa set off intervals of 1 mm.[2].   In the absence of density heterogeneity, the slope at any point of such a plot is directly proportional to the weight average molecular weight of the DNA located at the corresponding position in the band.   Linearity of this plot indicates monodispersity of the banded DNA.   The value of the slope corresponds to an apparent molecular weight for the Cs-DNA salt of 9.4 × 10[6], corresponding to a molecular weight of 7.1 × 10[6] for the sodium salt.

kept at 100° for 30 minutes either under the conditions employed by Rice and Doty or in the CsCl centrifuging medium, there results a density increase of 0.014 gm. cm.$^{-3}$ with no change in apparent molecular weight.   The same results are obtained if the salmon-sperm DNA is pre-treated at pH 6 with EDTA and sodium dodecyl sulfate.   Along with the density increase, heating brings about a sharp reduction in the time required for band formation in the CsCl gradient.   In the absence of an increase in molecular weight, the decrease in banding time must be ascribed[10] to an increase in the diffusion coefficient, indicating an extensive collapse of the native structure.

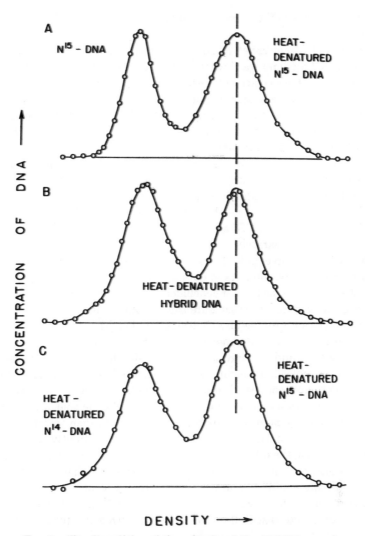

Fig. 9.—The dissociation of the subunits of *E. coli* DNA upon heat denaturation. Each smooth curve connects points obtained by micro-densitometry of an ultraviolet absorption photograph taken after 20 hours of centrifugation in CsCl solution at 44,770 rpm. The baseline density has been removed by subtraction. *A:* A mixture of heated and unheated N^{15} bacterial lysates. Heated lysate alone gives one band in the position indicated. Unheated lysate was added to this experiment for comparison. Heating has brought about a density increase of 0.016 gm. cm. $^{-3}$ and a reduction of about half in the apparent molecular weight of the DNA. *B:* Heated lysate of N^{15} bacteria grown for one generation in N^{14} growth medium. Before heat denaturation, the hybrid DNA contained in this lysate forms only one band, as may be seen in Fig. 4. *C:* A mixture of heated N^{14} and heated N^{15} bacterial lysates. The density difference is 0.015 gm. cm. $^{-3}$

The decrease in banding time and a density increase close to that found upon heating salmon-sperm DNA are observed (Fig. 9, *A*) when a bacterial lysate containing uniformly labeled N^{15} or N^{14} *E. coli* DNA is kept at 100° C. for 30 minutes in the CsCl centrifuging medium; but the apparent molecular weight of the heated bacterial DNA is reduced to approximately half that of the unheated material.

Half-labeled DNA contained in a detergent lysate of N^{15} *E. coli* cells grown for one generation in N^{14} medium was heated at 100° C. for 30 minutes in the CsCl centrifuging medium. This treatment results in the loss of the original half-labeled material and in the appearance in equal amounts of two new density species, each with approximately half the initial apparent molecular weight (Fig. 9, *B*). The density difference between the two species is 0.015 gm. cm. $^{-3}$, close to the increment produced by the N^{15} labeling of the unheated DNA.

This behavior suggests that heating the hybrid molecule brings about the dissociation of the N^{15}-containing subunit from the N^{14} subunit. This possibility was tested by a density-gradient examination of a mixture of heated N^{15} DNA and heated N^{14} DNA (Fig. 9, *C*). The close resemblance between the products of heating hybrid DNA (Fig. 9 *B*) and the mixture of products obtained from heating N^{14} and N^{15} DNA separately (Fig. 9, *C*) leads to the conclusion that the two molecular subunits have indeed dissociated upon heating. Since the apparent molecular weight of the subunits so obtained is found to be close to half that of the intact molecule, it may be further concluded that the subunits of the DNA molecule which are conserved at duplication are single, continuous structures. The scheme for DNA duplication proposed by Delbrück[24] is thereby ruled out.

To recapitulate, both salmon-sperm and *E. coli* DNA heated under similar conditions collapse and undergo a similar density increase, but the salmon DNA retains its initial molecular weight, while the bacterial DNA dissociates into the two subunits which are conserved during duplication. These findings allow two different interpretations. On the one hand, if we assume that salmon DNA contains subunits analogous to those found in *E. coli* DNA, then we must suppose that the subunits of salmon DNA are bound together more tightly than those of the bacterial DNA. On the other hand, if we assume that the molecules of salmon DNA do not contain these subunits, then we must concede that the bacterial DNA molecule is a more complex structure than is the molecule of salmon DNA. The latter interpretation challenges the sufficiency of the Watson-Crick DNA model to explain the observed distribution of parental nitrogen atoms among progeny molecules.

Conclusion.—The structure for DNA proposed by Watson and Crick brought forth a number of proposals as to how such a molecule might replicate. These proposals[6] make specific predictions concerning the distribution of parental atoms among progeny molecules. The results presented here give a detailed answer to the question of this distribution and simultaneously direct our attention to other problems whose solution must be the next step in progress toward a complete understanding of the molecular basis of DNA duplication. What are the molecular structures of the subunits of *E. coli* DNA which are passed on intact to each daughter molecule? What is the relationship of these subunits to each other in a DNA molecule? What is the mechanism of the synthesis and dissociation of the subunits in vivo?

Summary.—By means of density-gradient centrifugation, we have observed the distribution of N^{15} among molecules of bacterial DNA following the transfer of a uniformly N^{15}-substituted exponentially growing *E. coli* population to N^{14} medium.

We find that the nitrogen of a DNA molecule is divided equally between two physically continuous subunits; that, following duplication, each daughter molecule receives one of these; and that the subunits are conserved through many duplications.

* Aided by grants from the National Foundation for Infantile Paralysis and the National Institutes of Health.

† Contribution No. 2344.

[1] R. D. Hotchkiss, in *The Nucleic Acids,* ed. E. Chargaff and J. N. Davidson (New York: Academic Press, 1955), p. 435; and in *Enzymes: Units of Biological Structure and Function,* ed. O. H. Gaebler (New York: Academic Press, 1956), p. 119.

[2] S. H. Goodgal and R. M. Herriott, in *The Chemical Basis of Heredity,* ed. W. D. McElroy and B. Glass (Baltimore: Johns Hopkins Press, 1957), p. 336.

[3] S. Zamenhof, in *The Chemical Basis of Heredity,* ed. W. D. McElroy and B. Glass (Baltimore: Johns Hopkins Press, 1957), p. 351.

[4] A. D. Hershey and M. Chase, *J. Gen. Physiol.,* **36,** 39, 1952.

[5] A. D. Hershey, *Virology,* 1, 108, 1955; **4,** 237, 1957.

[6] M. Delbrück and G. S. Stent, in *The Chemical Basis of Heredity,* ed. W. D. McElroy and B. Glass (Baltimore: Johns Hopkins Press, 1957), p. 699.

[7] C. Levinthal, these PROCEEDINGS, **42,** 394, 1956.

[8] J. H. Taylor, P. S. Woods, and W. L. Huges, these PROCEEDINGS, **43,** 122, 1957.

[9] R. B. Painter, F. Forro, Jr., and W. L. Hughes, *Nature,* **181,** 328, 1958.

[10] M. S. Meselson, F. W. Stahl, and J. Vinograd, these PROCEEDINGS, **43,** 581, 1957.

[11] The buoyant density of a molecule is the density of the solution at the position in the centrifuge cell where the sum of the forces acting on the molecule is zero.

[12] Our attention has been called by Professor H. K. Schachman to a source of error in apparent molecular weights determined by density-gradient centrifugation which was not discussed by Meselson, Stahl, and Vinograd. In evaluating the dependence of the free energy of the DNA component upon the concentration of CsCl, the effect of solvation was neglected. It can be shown that solvation may introduce an error into the apparent molecular weight if either CsCl or water is bound preferentially. A method for estimating the error due to such selective solvation will be presented elsewhere.

[13] In addition to NH_4Cl, this medium consists of 0.049 M Na_2HPO_4, 0.022 M KH_2PO_4, 0.05 M NaCl, 0.01 M glucose, 10^{-3} M $MgSO_4$, and 3 $\times$ 10^{-6} M $FeCl_3$.

[14] This result also shows that the generation time is very nearly the same for all DNA molecules in the population. This raises the questions of whether in any one nucleus all DNA molecules are controlled by the same clock and, if so, whether this clock regulates nuclear and cellular division as well.

[15] F. H. C. Crick and J. D. Watson, *Proc. Roy. Soc. London,* A, **223,** 80, 1954.

[16] R. Langridge, W. E. Seeds, H. R. Wilson, C. W. Hooper, M. H. F. Wilkins, and L. D. Hamilton, *J. Biophys. and Biochem. Cytol.,* **3,** 767, 1957.

[17] For reviews see D. O. Jordan, in *The Nucleic Acids,* ed. E. Chargaff and J. D. Davidson (New York: Academic Press, 1955), 1, 447; and F. H. C. Crick, in *The Chemical Basis of Heredity,* ed. W. D. McElroy and B. Glass (Baltimore: Johns Hopkins Press, 1957), p. 532.

[18] J. D. Watson and F. H. C. Crick, *Nature,* **171,** 964, 1953.

[19] C. E. Hall and M. Litt, *J. Biophys. and Biochem. Cytol.,* **4,** 1, 1958.

[20] R. Thomas, *Biochim. et Biophys. Acta,* **14,** 231, 1954.

[21] P. D. Lawley, *Biochim. et Biophys. Acta,* **21,** 481, 1956.

[22] S. A. Rice and P. Doty, *J. Am. Chem. Soc.,* **79,** 3937, 1957.

[23] Kindly supplied by Dr. Michael Litt. The preparation of this DNA is described by Hall and Litt (*J. Biophys. and Biochem. Cytol.,* **4,** 1, 1958).

[24] M. Delbrück, these PROCEEDINGS, **40,** 783, 1955.

REPLICATION OF THE ESCHERICHIA COLI K12 CHROMOSOME[*]

By Mihoko Abe and Jun-ichi Tomizawa

DEPARTMENT OF CHEMISTRY, NATIONAL INSTITUTE OF HEALTH, TOKYO, JAPAN

Communicated by D. A. Glaser, August 28, 1967

Evidence now available indicates that the *Escherichia coli* chromosome is a single, circular DNA molecule whose replication proceeds in a semiconservative manner, at a single point, and unidirectionally.[1,2] However, it is still unclear whether in the *E. coli* chromosome, replication starts at a fixed point and proceeds in a fixed order. There exist already several genetic investigations and theories aimed at resolving these questions pertaining to the replication of the *E. coli* chromosome,[3–5] but since the conclusions drawn from these works are, in part, contradictory, further investigations are evidently needed.

It has been shown[6] that a transducing particle of phage P1 grown on *thy⁻* bacteria previously grown in a medium containing bromouracil (BU) carries DNA that is a fragment of the BU-labeled bacterial chromosome which already existed at the time of the infection.   Based on this observation, the following experiment seemed to offer an approach to the investigation of the dynamics of replication of the *E. coli* chromosome.   The growth of bacteria is synchronized by bringing their DNA replication cycles to completion, after which the cells are transferred to a medium containing bromouracil and allowed to grow for various lengths of time before infection with P1.   Phage growth and lysis take place in a medium without bromouracil.   If one centrifuges this P1 lysate in a CsCl density gradient and assays the transducing activities, one should be able to determine the order of the replication of the chromosome from the distribution of transducing particles carrying various loci.   In fact, we found an ordered replication of the *E. coli* chromosome with these experiments.   During the course of the investigation, however, we encountered an unexpected effect on chromosome replication caused by the addition of bromouracil to the medium.   Detailed investigations of the replication of the chromosome in the presence of bromouracil are reported below.

Materials and Methods.—*Bacterial and phage strains:*   A virulent mutant of phage P1kc[6] was used and is referred to as P1 in this paper.   Bacterial strains used were derivatives of *E. coli* K12: strains HfrC *thy⁻ met⁻*, HfrH *thy⁻*, and F⁻W3110 *thy⁻* are thymineless derivatives of Hfr Cavalli,[7] Hfr Hayes,[7] and W3110 (Lederberg), respectively, and used as donors.   AB440 *arg⁻ mtl⁻ xyl⁻ his⁻ gal⁻ lac⁻ pro⁻ thr⁻ leu⁻* (Adelberg), JE3423 *arg⁻ lys⁻* (Hirota), W4183 *argG⁻* (Udaka), and X36 *arg⁻ ara⁻ lac⁻ gal⁻ pyrF⁻ try⁻ his⁻ purC⁻ thy⁻ Str^r mal⁻ xyl⁻ mtl⁻* T1^r (Wolf) are recipients in transduction.   AB440 was also used as an indicator for P1 plaque assay.   *E. coli* 15T⁻ *arg⁻ met⁻ try⁻ thy⁻* (Lark) was used for comparison purposes in some experiments.

Media: The medium used for growth of bacteria was tris Casamino acids glucose medium (TCG)[8] or TG medium (Difco Casamino acids in TCG medium was replaced by 1.1 gm/liter of NH₄Cl) supplemented with 2 μg/ml of thymine or 5 μg/ml of 5-bromouracil (BU medium) and 10 μg/ml of required amino acids.   The doubling time of these bacteria in TCG and TG media supplemented with thymine was about 40 and 50 min, respectively.   L-broth, L-agar, soft agar, and minimal agar[6] were used for transduction experiments.   Dilution buffer contains 10^{-2} M tris buffer, pH 7.4, 5 gm/liter of NaCl and 10 mg/liter of bovine serum albumin.

Labeling and density gradient centrifugation of DNA: The labeling of total cellular DNA was accomplished by growing bacteria for several generations in a medium containing P³²O₄ (0.01 μc/μg P) or C¹⁴-thymine (0.01 μc/μg thymine).   A portion of the growing chromosome was labeled by a pulse of H³-thymine (0.5 μc/μg thymine) followed by a chase with 200 μg/ml of thymine for 1 min. The culture was filtered on a Millipore membrane filter, washed, and suspended in a medium with $P^{32}O_4$ or C^{14}-thymine and without H^3-thymine. Aliquots of the culture were taken at intervals into tubes containing crushed ice. DNA was extracted as described elsewhere,[9] except that the phenol extraction was done by hand shaking. The average size of the DNA thus gm/ extracted was about one fiftieth of a whole bacterial chromosome. The DNA was mixed with CsCl solution at a final density of 1.725 gm cm^{-3}, centrifuged in an SW39 rotor of a Spinco ultracentrifuge at 35,000 rpm for 48 hr at 15°C. After the run, 60–65 fractions were obtained by collecting drops after puncturing the bottom of the centrifuge tube. The radioactivities of the DNA fractions of each sample were measured in a scintillation spectrometer.

Synchronization of DNA replication: Amino acid starvation method: The method described by Lark[10] was generally followed. Phenethyl alcohol treatment:[11] To an exponentially growing culture of bacteria in TCG medium, phenethyl alcohol (Wako Pure Chemical Industry) was added to a final concentration of 0.3%. After incubation for 2 hr the culture was filtered and the cells were washed and suspended in a fresh medium. DNA synthesis then resumed after a lag of 15–20 min.

Preparation of P1 lysate and density gradient centrifugation of P1: An exponential culture of bacteria in TCG medium containing thymine was transferred to BU medium; samples were withdrawn after intervals of growth in BU medium and given KCN ($2 \times 10^{-3} M$), CaCl$_2$ ($2.5 \times 10^{-3} M$), and P1 at a multiplicity of infection of about three phages per cell. After 20 min the infected cells were collected by centrifugation and suspended in a medium containing thymine. The suspension was incubated for 90 min with shaking until lysis and sterilized with chloroform. The lysate was mixed to give 3.2 ml of CsCl solution of density 1.472 gm cm^{-3} which contains 0.5% Casamino acids and 0.01 M tris buffer, pH 7.5. The mixture was centrifuged in an SW39 rotor for 18 hr at 23,000 rpm at 15°C. After centrifugation about 60 fractions were obtained by drop collection. Each fraction was diluted in a suitable amount of dilution buffer and examined for infectivity and transducing activity.

Transduction: Recipient bacteria were grown in L-broth to a concentration of about 5×10^8 cells/ml, collected by centrifugation, and suspended in TG medium containing $2.5 \times 10^{-3} M$ CaCl$_2$ to give 5×10^8 cells/ml. The bacteria were infected with the phage in an equal portion of each fraction except those around the peak of infective particles, which were diluted to give a multiplicity of infection of less than 0.1, and incubated for 30 min at 37°C. The cells were spread on minimal agar plates containing appropriate supplements for selection of transductants and anti-P1 serum to K = 0.2/plate to reduce interference by phage produced on the plates. (We are indebted to Dr. Hisao Uchida for suggesting this procedure.) Colonies were counted after incubation at 37°C for 48 hr.

Results.— *Alteration of the replication point of the K12 chromosome by the addition of bromouracil:* An exponential culture of W3110 *thy$^-$* in TCG medium containing thymine and $P^{32}O_4$ was pulse-labeled with H^3-thymine for six minutes (about one eighth of a generation), and transferred to BU medium. Samples of the culture were taken at intervals during growth in the medium. DNA was extracted from the cells and analyzed for the distribution of radioactivity in a CsCl density gradient. If bromouracil is incorporated in continuation of the previous growing point of DNA, the pulse-labeled portion of the DNA should be found in association with BU-labeled DNA only after a majority of the total DNA has already replicated. This is the case in strain 15T$^-$, as was shown by Lark,[10] and can also be seen in Figure 1b. Evidently here the bulk of the total DNA was transferred to the hybrid density band before any similar transfer of the H^3-labeled region. In contrast, in strain W3110 *thy$^-$* replication of the pulse-labeled DNA occurred soon after the transfer of the culture to BU medium (Fig. 1a), and proceeded with almost the same rate as that of the total DNA (Fig. 2) until about 80 per cent of total H^3-DNA was replicated. The rate of H^3-DNA replication was then reduced. Fully heavy DNA appeared when about 70 per cent of DNA initially present had replicated.

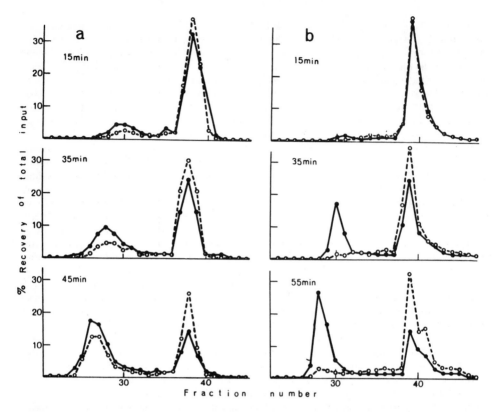

FIG. 1.—Distribution of radioactivity in CsCl density gradients of doubly labeled DNA. An exponential culture labeled continuously by P³² was pulse labeled by H³-thymine and transferred to BU medium containing P³²O₄. DNA was extracted at the times indicated, and centrifuged. (a) F⁻W3110 *thy⁻*, (b) 15T⁻; ● for P³²-total DNA, ○ for H³-pulse-labeled DNA.

Similar results were obtained with HfrC *thy⁻ met⁻* and HfrH *thy⁻*. The nearly proportional replication of the labeled region with the total DNA clearly indicates that in these K12 strains the replication sequence of the chromosome is altered by transferring cells to BU medium.

Initiation point induced by the addition of bromouracil: It has been shown that the replication of the chromosome of 15T⁻ is synchronized by amino acid starvation[10] or phenethyl alcohol treatment[11, 12] to completion of a cycle and starts at a fixed point after resumption of protein synthesis. In the following this point will be called the *origin* of the chromosome. It should be possible, by synchronizing the growth of the chromosome before the addition of bromouracil to locate the starting point of the replication induced by bromouracil. If the initiation point of the replication induced by the addition of bromouracil is the same as the chromosomal *origin*, DNA near the *origin* should replicate upon transferring the cells to BU medium when only a small part of the total DNA has replicated.

Cells of HfrC *thy⁻ met⁻* grown in TG medium containing methionine and C¹⁴-thymine were starved of methionine for two hours during which the total DNA increased about 50 per cent. The culture was transferred to a complete medium and H³-thymine was added to label the region adjacent to the *origin*. H³-thymine was

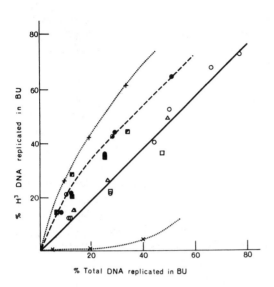

% H³ DNA replicated in BU

% Total DNA replicated in BU

Fig. 2.—Pattern of replication of pulse-labeled DNA. (*i*) DNA was pulse labeled by H³-thymine during exponential growth and then grown in BU medium (△ F⁻W3110 *thy*⁻, □ HfrC *thy*⁻, ○ HfrH *thy*⁻, × 15T⁻). (*ii*) DNA was pulse labeled after synchronization by amino acid starvation (■ HfrC *thy*⁻) or phenethyl alcohol treatment (▨ HfrC *thy*⁻, ◑ HfrII *thy*⁻), and grown in BU medium. In another experiment, the growth was randomized after synchronization and pulse labeling with H³-thymine. The culture was then transferred to BU medium (● HfrH *thy*⁻). (*iii*) DNA was labeled by H²-thymine after thymine starvation. The culture was randomized and transferred to BU medium (⊙ HfrH *thy*⁻). (*iv*) DNA of 15T⁻ was labeled by H³-thymine after the first amino acid starvation. Following randomization of growth and a second amino acid starvation, the culture was transferred to BU medium. (+ 15T⁻).

removed by filtration after 30 minutes (a lag and the initial replication period), and the cells were resuspended in a medium containing methionine and bromouracil. In other experiments, the cells were diluted tenfold in a medium with methionine and thymine and allowed to grow until the cell number had increased tenfold prior to the addition of bromouracil. By that time the synchronized growth was randomized. The DNA samples from the cells taken at intervals during the growth in BU medium were analyzed for the density distribution of the radio-activity. Experiments were also carried out in which cultures of HfrC *thy*⁻ *met*⁻ and HfrH*thy*⁻ were treated with phenethyl alcohol. The patterns of replication of H³-labeled DNA are shown in Figure 2. In every case a large fraction of H³-labeled DNA has moved to the hybrid density position early after the transfer of the cells to BU medium. This may mean that the initiation of the replication in BU medium occurred from the *origin* of the chromosome. Additional evidence which supports this interpretation was obtained from an experiment in which the *origin* was pulse labeled after thymine starvation for 30 minutes, and the replication of the pulse-labeled region was followed in BU medium. The result is presented in Figure 2. Again pulse-labeled DNA replicated early during the growth in BU medium.

In Figure 2, the result of an experiment performed with 15T⁻ is also shown. DNA of 15T⁻ cells was pulse-labeled after an amino acid starvation and their growth was randomized in a complete medium. After a second starvation bromouracil was added. If the amino acid starvation synchronizes the chromosomal replication perfectly, and if replication proceeds synchronously in BU medium, a strict preferential replication of H³-labeled region of 15T⁻ DNA should occur at a very early time. In accord with Lark's observation,[13] a large portion of H³-DNA replicated early in the growth in BU medium (Fig. 2). The observed rate of the initial replication of H³-DNA in 15T⁻ DNA was lower than expected, probably because neither one of the required conditions was exactly satisfied. This may also be true or more pronounced for the K12 strains. Furthermore, the synthesis of DNA may occur at the original growing point in some small proportion of K12 cells which would reduce the initial rate of replication of the pulse-labeled region. Under these circumstances, we consider that the similarity in the initial rate of replication of the H³-labeled region of 15T⁻ and K12 strains can be taken as a strong indication that the point at which chromosome replication is initiated by the addition of bromouracil is the chromosomal *origin* or the region very close to it.

Genetic localization of the initiation point induced by bromouracil and the order of replication of chromosomal markers: The alteration of the replication sequence by bromouracil and the probable identity of the chromosomal *origin* and the initiation point induced by bromouracil were revealed by density gradient analysis of DNA. With this in mind we attempted to locate genetically the initiation point and the order of the replication of the K12 chromosome by transduction analysis.

P1 phage lysates were periodically prepared from an exponential culture of HfrH *thy⁻* after a shift to BU medium, as described in *Materials and Methods*. The lysates were centrifuged in CsCl density gradients and the fractions were examined for the transducing activities of the markers shown in Figure 3. The patterns of distribution of transducing particles observed for each of these markers are presented in Figure 4. Experiments of the same type were carried out with HfrC *thy⁻ met⁻* and F⁻W3110 *thy⁻*, and typical results are summarized in Table 1 where the percentage of the transducing activity of each marker in the hybrid fraction (replicated) to the total activity is shown. The results clearly indicate that all markers do not have an equal probablity of replicating upon transfer to BU medium, but that there is a preferred region of early replication as was shown by the density gradient analyses of DNA discussed above. The results appear to suggest that the region at which the chromosomal replication commences is located between the *lysine* and *his-tidine* markers and proceeds in a clockwise fashion regardless of the sexual state of the cell.

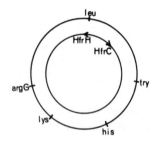

FIG. 3.—The genetic map of *E. coli* K12 chromosome, showing the location of markers used.

The results, however, show some inconsistency which is not in full accord with this interpretation. Several causes of the inconsistency in the order and the rate of the replication of the markers should be discussed. First, transducing particles of intermediate density between hybrid and light may be produced, especially at a very early period of growth after the transfer to BU medium. The markers replicated earlier would, therefore, overlap the light region more. As is clearly seen in the density-gradient analysis of the DNA (Fig. 1), DNA which was synthesized soon after the transfer was lighter than that synthesized later. Lags in the replacement of thymine by bromouracil causes underestimation of transducing activity of markers replicated early. Second, a variation may exist among cells in the duration of the lag before the starting of replication as well as in the rate of synthesis of DNA in BU medium. In accord with this assumption, twice-duplicated DNA was found in the fully heavy region, while some DNA (approximately 30%) was not yet replicated. This effect of bromouracil addition must decrease synchronous replication of the markers. An additional complication is the *leucine*

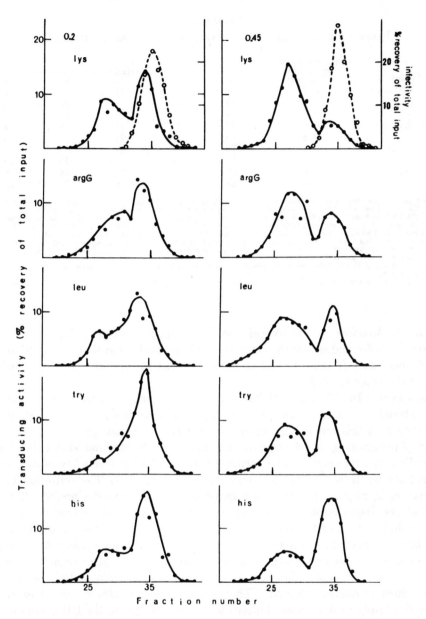

FIG. 4.—Density analyses of the transducing activities of P1 lysates from an exponential culture of HfrH *thy⁻* partially labeled by bromouracil. ● for transducing activity, ○ for infectivity. Numbers in the top frames show the fraction of DNA replicated in BU medium when the cells were infected with P1.

marker which was the first marker to appear in the fully heavy region. The *threonine* and *arabinose* markers were also found in fully heavy fractions when *leucine* was there, but other markers shown in the table were not. This was observed in the experiments with F⁻W3110 and HfrC *thy⁻ met⁻* indicating that it has no correlation with the sexual state of the cells. The fraction of the activity of *leucine* found in the fully heavy region was greater than the fraction of the

TABLE 1

PERCENTAGE OF TRANSDUCING ACTIVITY OF THE REPLICATED MARKERS
TO TOTAL ACTIVITY

| Strains | Fraction of DNA replicated in BU medium* | Markers | | | | |
		lys	argG	leu	try	his
F⁻W3110 thy⁻	0.2	17	31	17	18	17
	0.45	34	75	—	25	—
	0.8	91	74	54	—	38
HfrC thy⁻ met⁻	0.15	21	13	15	8	4
	0.4	—	28	21	—	8
	0.6	70	48	59	33	21
	0.8	88	76	62†	50	23
HfrH thy	0.2	35	36	25	14	8
	0.45	63	47	36	38	12

The calculations were done as follows: (1) The heavier half of the light particle region is overlapped with the hybrid particles. The activity of the light particle region was calculated from the lighter half of the light particle region, according to the observation that light transducing particles show the same distribution in CsCl density gradient as infective particles and have a density 0.002 heavier than the infective particles.⁶ (2) The activity of the hybrid region is the difference between the total activity and the light activity. Assuming that P1 can pick up both of the hybrid strands of a chromosome replicating in BU medium, the activity of the hybrid region was divided by 2, to obtain the fractional activity of the replicated marker in BU medium.

* The fraction of DNA replicated in BU medium was obtained from the density analysis of DNA totally labeled by P³²O₄.

† 35% of the *leucine* activity was found in the fully heavy region. None of the other markers was found in this region.

activity of *histidine* in the hybrid region. This may suggest that fully heavy markers were formed before the completion of one cycle of growth of chromosomes in BU medium. It must be noted, however, that at an early time the markers were in the proposed order.

Discussion.—In 15T⁻, as Lark has shown,[10] bromouracil can be incorporated into DNA strands to continue the previous replication sequence. In contrast, it has been shown in this report that bromouracil does change the pattern of the replication of the growing chromosome in strains of K12. Several models for the altered replication by bromouracil have been constructed and the feasibility of explaining our results by these models will now be considered: (1) The initiation of the replication at random point(s) on a chromosome. This model predicts that the label at the *origin* replicates proportionately to total DNA replication, and the density distribution of the transducing particles of every marker would be equal. (2) The reversal of direction after completion of a replication cycle. According to this model, fully heavy material should appear very early after transfer to a BU medium. (3) The replication proceeds from both the *origin* and the replication point which previously existed. This condition would also cause an early appearance of fully heavy material after the transfer of cells to the BU medium. (4) The replication is initiated at only one of the two *origins* of a partially replicated chromosome. With this mechanism, only half of the DNA pulse-labeled during random growth would be replicated. Our observations are not in accord with the predictions made by any of these models. Instead we propose that the replication is initiated prematurely at both of the *origins* of a replicating chromosome and that the replication at the growing point existing prior to the addition of bromouracil ceases. This model is different from the pattern of premature initiation induced by thymine starvation in 15T⁻ which was reported to occur both at the replication point previously existing and at one *origin* of two partial replicas of a replicating chromosome.[13] The possibility that the initiation occurs at one *origin* at first and then another *origin* starts to replicate after the completion of the half replica of a replicating chromosome is, although unlikely, not completely eliminated.

The replication sequence induced by bromouracil was genetically analyzed according to the above model. The results clearly showed an order of replication of the markers and revealed the presence of a genetically defined initiation point and orientation of the replication of a chromosome. The early appearance of the *leucine* marker in the fully heavy region cannot be explained at the present time. There may possibly be another effect of bromouracil which appears when the incubation in BU medium lasts a long time.

From these observations and considerations we tend to favor the conclusion that an initiation point and an order of replication of the chromosome were revealed by the present experiments. Namely, the initiation point is located somewhere between the *lysine* and *histidine* markers, and the replication proceeds clockwise, regardless of the sexual state of the cell.

The existence of a definite origin on the genetic map has been revealed in another laboratory.[14] The location and the direction of replication are in general agreement with the above conclusion.

Summary.—It was shown that in *E. coli* K12, the sequence of chromosome replication was altered by growing the cells in a medium containing bromouracil instead of thymine. In experiments with double labeling of DNA, the initiation point of the replication reoriented by bromouracil was shown to be the same as the point where the replication initiates after the amino acid starvation or phenethyl alcohol treatment.

By the density analysis of P1 transducing particles, the initiation point was located between the *lysine* and *histidine* markers, and the order of replication was shown to be clockwise, regardless of the sexual state of the cells.

The authors wish to thank Mrs. N. Okamoto for her technical assistance.

* This work was aided in part by research grant GM8384 from the National Institutes of Health, U.S. Public Health Service.

[1] Meselson, M., and F. W. Stahl, these PROCEEDINGS, **44**, 671 (1958).

[2] Cairns, J., *J. Mol. Biol.*, **6**, 208 (1963).

[3] Nagata, T., these PROCEEDINGS, **49**, 551 (1963).

[4] Jacob, F., S. Brenner, and F. Cuzin, *Cold Spring Harbor Symposia on Quantitative Biology*, vol. 28 (1963), p. 329.

[5] Berg, C. M., Ph.D. thesis, Columbia University (1966).

[6] Ikeda, H., and J. Tomizawa, *J. Mol. Biol.*, **14**, 85 (1965).

[7] Wollman, E. L., F. Jacob, and W. Hayes, *Cold Spring Harbor Symposia on Quantitative Biology*, vol. 21 (1956), p. 141.

[8] Kozinski, A. W., and W. Szybalski, *Virology*, **9**, 260 (1959).

[9] Anraku, N., and J. Tomizawa, *J. Mol. Biol.*, **11**, 501 (1965).

[10] Lark, K. G., T. Repko, and E. J. Hoffman, *Biochem. Biophys. Acta*, **76**, 9 (1963).

[11] Treick, R. W., and W. A. Konetzka, *J. Bacteriol.*, **88**, 1580 (1964).

[12] Lark, K. G., and C. Lark, *J. Mol. Biol.*, **20**, 9 (1966).

[13] Pritchard, R. H., and K. G. Lark, *J. Mol. Biol.*, **9**, 288 (1964).

[14] Wolf B., A. Newman, and D. A Glaser, submitted for publication.

Gene Recombination, Repair and Related Phenomena

Introduction

DNA polymerase probably makes the basic skeleton of the DNA. Special proteins in addition to the polymerase are most likely required for initiation and perhaps for termination. Special proteins are also involved in the modification of individual bases with methyl, glycosyl and other substituents.[95, 96, 102] We come now to a third group of enzymes which are involved in delicate surgical operations on the polymeric DNA. Such enzymes are required for repair of chromosome damage caused by radiation or chemical forces, lysogenization, recombination and related processes, and perhaps in the polymerization process itself to facilitate the unwinding problem (discussed in Section II). We are in the process of determining to what extent these related operations are carried out by the same or different enzymes. This area of investigation is undergoing tremendous progress at the present time; all we can do is to give a hint of the direction investigations are taking.

First let us consider the mechanism of recombination. The early history of crossing over and genetic recombination as it is observed in higher forms is discussed in Peters.[4] Crossing over in higher forms occurs during meiosis when related chromosomes pair, and the genetic exchange occurring between the paired chromosomes is usually a reciprocal process. Recombination in bacteriophage was discovered by Delbruck and Bailey in 1946.[104] Their observations were extremely important because phage recombination was to serve as the hyperfine tool for gene resolution bringing us to the point where we could truly study molecular aspects of heredity.[110, 114] In particular it made possible a scrutiny of the molecular events involved in recombination.

In 1951 Hershey and Rotman[105] concluded that recombination between vegetative phage does not usually involve reciprocal exchange of genetic substance between the two interacting parental chromosomes. These conclusions have been questioned by Meselson.[124] He found that recombination is usually reciprocal when the exchanging viral chromosomes are in the prophage state, with one prophage attached to the host bacterial chromosome and one prophage attached to an episome. Meselson[156] argues that Hershey and Rotman and others may not have noticed the reciprocal products because of inherent difficulties in detecting such reciprocal products when recombination is between vegetative phage. It is difficult to accept Meselson's argument without further evidence. However, even if Meselson is incorrect, recombination in microorganisms and higher forms may be quite a similar process at the molecular level. The study of one may elucidate the mechanisms of both.

Until 1961, two major theories for recombination based on the double-helix structure of DNA had been advanced: (1) The breakage recombination theory requires that breakage occur across both strands of the double helix and that mending take place between the broken parts. (2) The copy-choice theory states that recombination takes place during synthesis and involves a crossing over of the DNA polymerase between the two growing chromosomes. In 1961, by suitable labeling techniques Meselson and Weigle,[111] and Kellenberger, Zichichi and Weigle[112] were able to show that in bacteriophage the breakage recombination hypothesis was in large measure correct. The paper by Meselson (in collection) describes similar results which show in addition that some of the DNA is probably removed and resynthesized in the region where joining occurs between recombinant molecules. The steps in recombination envisaged by Meselson are, first, an unequal scission of parental DNA strands, second, joining of complementary strands from different parent molecules, and last, a mending process to complete the formation of an intact double helix. The steps would require the existence of several different kinds of enzymes. At the minimum one requires an endonuclease to make the initial internal chromosome breaks, a polymerase that adds nucleotides back in the region of joining where gaps exist, and a ligase to covalently link the repaired region to the rest of the intact polynucleotide strand. Enzymes

103

which fit this general description are already known (for examples of nucleases see references in Section II, for an example of a polymerase see the Schildkraut, Richardson and Kornberg paper in Section II, and for an example of a ligase see the Weiss and Richardson paper in this section). The extent to which known enzymes are involved in recombination and the related processes about to be discussed is unknown.

Lysogenization is the process whereby a virus chromosome becomes integrated as a linear portion of the host chromosome. The process has been most intensively studied for the lysogenization of λ and φ80 bacteriophage in *E. coli*. Campbell[106] has proposed that the linear λ chromosome, after entering the bacteria, becomes converted to a circular form that becomes integrated on a specific region of host chromosome, referred to as the attachment site, by a single reciprocal exchange. This single reciprocal exchange process is similar if not identical to the mechanism that has been invoked by Meselson to explain recombination, although different enzymes are probably involved. Induction of prophage replication is believed to involve a reversal of the steps involved in lysogenization. The paper by Weil and Signer in this section is a genetic study which demonstrates that there are at least two phage encoded enzymes involved in lysogenization that are unique to this process. It also shows that at least one of the enzymes required for bacterial DNA recombination is not used in lysogenization. In spite of this, bacterial extracts of normal *E. coli* contain an enzyme(s)

which catalyzes the circularization of λ phage,[134] a hypothesized step in lysogenization.

Reactions involved in episome integration, transduction and recombination via bacterial conjugation are not discussed here. However, it should be apparent that the surgical techniques involved in these processes have many similarities to the aforementioned processes.

The last topic to be considered in this section is the repair of chromosome damage. Whereas breakage and mending of DNA are involved in recombination and lysogenization, it is now apparent that there are enzyme systems that can repair a much wider variety of chromosome damage. Chemical abnormalities in the DNA structure that would otherwise lead to chromosome death are somehow detected, removed and replaced by normal DNA.

Although there are probably a number of ways of producing abnormalities, the problem of abnormality removal has been investigated most thoroughly by people studying photochemical damage. The paper by Setlow and Carrier in this section deals with the removal of ultraviolet-induced thymine dimers; it represents one of a series of studies on this subject from Setlow's laboratory. Howard-Flanders also has investigated this problem and has obtained evidence that some of the enzymes involved in ultraviolet repair are also used in bacterial recombination.[145]

As stated at the beginning of this section, tremendous progress is expected in the near future on the topics in Section III and the reader is advised to watch the journals for evidence of progress.

Bibliography

RECOMBINATION

104. M. Delbruck and W. T. Bailey, (1946). Cold Spring Harbor Symp. Quant. Biol. 11, 33.

105. A. D. Hershey and R. Rotman, (1951). Genetic Recombination Between Host-Range and Plaque-Type Mutants of Bacteriophage in Single Bacterial Cells. Genetics 34, 44.

106. A. Campbell, (1962). Episomes. Advan. Genetics, 11, 101.

107. A. D. Hershey and M. Chase, (1951). Genetic Recombination and Heterozygosis in Bacteriophage. Cold Spring Harbor Symp. Quant. Biol. 16, 471.

108. S. Benzer, (1955). Fine Structure of a Genetic Region in Bacteriophage. Proc. Natl. Acad. Sci. U.S. 41, 344.

109. J. H. Taylor, (1958). The Organization and Duplication of Genetic Material. Proc. 10th Intern. Congr. Genet. Montreal, 1, 63.

110. S. Benzer, (1959). On the Topology of the Genetic Fine Structure. Proc. Natl. Acad. Sci. U.S. 45, 1607.

111. M. Meselson and J. J. Weigle, (1961). Chromosome Breakage Accompanying Genetic Recombination in Bacteriophage. Proc. Natl. Acad. Sci. U.S. 19, 857.

112. G. Kellenberger, J. L. Zichichi and J. J Weigle, (1961). Exchange of DNA in the Recombination of Bacteriophage λ. Proc. Natl. Acad. Sci. U.S. 47, 869.

113. S. Benzer, (1961). On the Topography of the Genetic Fine Structure. Proc. Natl. Acad. Sci. U.S. 47, 403.

114. C. M. Radding and A. D. Kaiser, (1963). Gene Transfer by Broken Molecules of λ DNA: Activity of the Left Half-Molecule. J. Mol. Biol. 7, 225.

115. G. Mosig, (1963). Genetic Recombination in Bacteriophage T_4 During Replication of DNA Fragments. Cold Spring Harbor Symp. Quant. Biol. 28, 35.

116. M. Meselson, (1964). On the Mechanism of Genetic Recombination Between DNA Molecules. J. Mol. Biol. 9, 734.

117. A. Campbell, (1965). The Steric Effect in Lysogenization by Bacteriophage Lambda II. Chromosomal Attachment of the b_2 Mutant. Virology 27, 340.

118. H. L. K. Whitehouse and P. J. Hastings, (1965). The Analysis of Genetic Recombination on the Polaron Hybrid DNA Model. Genet. Res. Camb. 6, 27.

119. H. S. Jansz, C. Van Rotterdam and J. A. Cohen, (1966). Genetic Recombination of Bacteriophage ϕX174 in Spheroplasts. Biochem. Biophys. Acta 119, 276.

120. I. Tessman, (1966). Recombination of Phage S13 in a Recombination Deficient Mutant of E. coli K12. Biochem. Biophys. Res. Comm. 22, 169.

121. J. Tomizawa, N. Anraku and Y. Iwama, (1966). Molecular Mechanisms of Genetic Recombination in Bacteriophage VI. A Mutant Defective in the Joining of DNA Molecules. J. Mol. Biol. 21, 247.

122. F. Bonhoeffer, R. Hosselbarth and K. Lehmann, (1967). Dependence of the Conjugational DNA Transfer on DNA Synthesis. J. Mol. Biol. 29, 539.

123. D. T. Denhardt, D. H. Dressler and A. Hathaway, (1967). Abortive Replication of ϕX174 DNA in a Recombination-Deficient Mutant of E. coli. Proc. Natl. Acad. Sci. U.S. 57, 813.

124. M. Meselson, (1967). Reciprocal Prophage Recombination. J. Cell. Physiol. 70, 113 (supplement).

LYSOGENIZATION

125. A. Campbell, (1962). Episomes. Advan. Genetics 11, 101.

126. M. Ptashne, (1965). The Detachment and Maturation of Conserved Lambda Prophage DNA. J. Mol. Biol. 11, 90.

127. D. B. Cowie and A. D. Hershey, (1965). Multiple Sites of Interaction with Host-Cell DNA in the DNA of Phage λ. Proc. Natl. Acad. Sci. U.S. 53, 57.

128. M. H. Green, (1966). Inactivation of the Prophage Repression without Induction. J. Mol. Biol. 16, 134.

129. A. Lipton and A. Weissbach, (1966). The Formation of Circular DNA after Lysogenic

Induction. Biochem. Biophys. Res. Comm. **23**, 436.

130. A. H. Gelderman, T. L. Lincoln, D. B. Cowie and R. B. Roberts, (1966). A Further Correlation Between the Response of Lysogenic Bacteria and Tumor Cells to Chemical Agents. Proc. Natl. Acad. Sci. U.S. **55**, 289.

131. C. M. Radding, (1966). Regulation of λ Exonuclease I. Properties of λ Exonuclease Purified from Lysogens of λ_{T11} and wild Type. J. Mol. Biol. **18**, 235.

132. E. Signer and J. Beckwith, (1966). Transposition of the Lac region of *Escherichia coli*. III. Mechanism of Attachment of Bacteriophage to the Bacterial Chromosome. J. Mol. Biol. **22**, 33.

133. H. Ogawa and J. Tomizawa, (1967). Bacteriophage Lambda DNA with Different Structures found in Infected Cells. J. Mol. Biol. **23**, 265.

134. M. Gellert, (1967). Formation of Covalent Circles of Lambda DNA by *E. coli* Extracts. Proc. Natl. Acad. Sci. U.S. **57**, 148.

135. R. Gingery and H. Echols, (1967). Mutants of Bacteriophage λ Unable to Integrate into the Host Chromosome. Proc. Natl. Acad. Sci. U.S. **58**, 1507.

136. A. Weissbach and L. A. Salzman, (1967). Biosynthesis of Phage Lambda DNA: The Structure of the First Intermediate. Proc. Natl. Acad. Sci. U.S. **58**, 1096.

REPAIR

137. P. T. Emmerson and P. Howard-Flanders, (1965). Post-Irradiation Degradation of DNA Following Exposure of Ultraviolet-Sensitive and Resistant Bacteria to X-rays. Biochem. Biophys. Res. Comm. **18**, 24.

138. J. K. Setlow, M. E. Boling and F. J. Bollum, (1965). The Chemical Nature of Photoreactivable Lesions in DNA. Proc. Natl. Acad. Sci. U.S. **53**, 1430.

139. J. E. Donnellan and R. B. Setlow, (1965). Thymine Photoproducts but not Thymine Dimers Found in Ultraviolet Irradiated Bacterial Spores. Science **149**, 308.

140. M. E. Boling and J. K. Setlow, (1966). Resistance of Micrococcus Radiodurans to U.V. III. A Repair Mechanism. Biochem. Biophys. Acta **123**, 26.

141. S. Aoki, R. P. Boyce and P. Howard-Flanders, (1966). Sensitization of *E. coli* to Radiation by Bromouracil: Excessive Post-irradiation Breakdown of DNA without Concomitant Synthesis. Nature **209**, 686.

142. W. Carrier and R. Setlow, (1966). Excision of Pyrimidine Dimers from Irradiated DNA *in vitro*. Biochem. Biophys. Acta **129**, 318.

143. R. Setlow and W. Carrier, (1966). Pyrimidine Dimers in U.V.-irradiated DNAs. J. Mol. Biol. **17**, 237.

144. P. Howard-Flanders, R. P. Boyce and L. Theriot, (1966). Three Loci in *E. coli* K-12 that Control the Excision of Pyrimidine Dimers and Certain Other Mutagen Products from DNA. Genetics **53**, 1119.

145. P. Howard-Flanders and L. Theriot, (1966). Mutants of *E. coli* K-12 Defective in DNA Repair and in Genetic Recombination. Genetics **53**, 1137.

146. A. J. Clark, M. Chamberlin, R. P. Boyce and P. Howard-Flanders, (1966). Abnormal Metabolic Response to U.V. Light of a Recombination Deficient Mutant of *E. coli* K-12. J. Mol. Biol. **19**, 442.

147. M. Yarus and R. L. Sinsheimer, (1967). Ultraviolet Sensitivity of the Biological Activity of ΦX174 Virus, Single-Stranded DNA, and RF DNA. Biophys. J. **7**, 267.

148. T. Yamane, B. J. Wyluda and R. G. Shulman, (1967). Dihydrothymine from U.V.-Irradiated DNA. Proc. Natl. Acad. Sci. U.S. **58**, 439.

149. N. R. Cozzarelli, N. E. Melechen, T. M. Jovin and A. Kornberg, (1967). Polynucleotide Cellulose as a Substrate for a Polynucleotide Ligase Induced by Phage T_4. Biochem. Biophys. Res. Comm. **28**, 578.

150. E. K. Bautz, (1967). A Biological Assay for Polynucleotide Ligase: Recovery of Marker Activity in DNA-Transformation. Biochem. Biophys. Res. Comm. **28**, 641.

151. B. M. Olivera and I. R. Lehman, (1967). Diphosphopyridine Nucleotide: A Cofactor for the Polynucleotide-Joining Enzyme from *E. coli*. Proc. Natl. Acad. Sci. U.S. **57**, 1700.

152. P. C. Hanawalt, (1967). Normal Replication of DNA after Repair Replication in Bacteria. Nature **214**, 269.

153. A. Becker, G. Lyn, M. Gefter and J. Hurwitz, (1967). Enzymatic Repair of DNA, II.

Induction. Biochem. Biophys. Res. Comm. 23, 436.

130. A. H. Gelderman, T. L. Lincoln, D. B. Cowie and R. B. Roberts, (1966). A Further Correlation Between the Response of Lysogenic Bacteria and Tumor Cells to Chemical Agents. Proc. Natl. Acad. Sci. U.S. 55, 289.

131. C. M. Radding, (1966). Regulation of λ Exonuclease I. Properties of λ Exonuclease Purified from Lysogens of λ_{T11} and wild Type. J. Mol. Biol. 18, 235.

132. E. Signer and J. Beckwith, (1966). Transposition of the Lac region of Escherichia coli. III. Mechanism of Attachment of Bacteriophage to the Bacterial Chromosome. J. Mol. Biol. 22, 33.

133. H. Ogawa and J. Tomizawa, (1967). Bacteriophage Lambda DNA with Different Structures found in Infected Cells. J. Mol. Biol. 23, 265.

134. M. Gellert, (1967). Formation of Covalent Circles of Lambda DNA by E. coli Extracts. Proc. Natl. Acad. Sci. U.S. 57, 148.

135. R. Gingery and H. Echols, (1967). Mutants of Bacteriophage λ Unable to Integrate into the Host Chromosome. Proc. Natl. Acad. Sci. U.S. 58, 1507.

136. A. Weissbach and L. A. Salzman, (1967). Biosynthesis of Phage Lambda DNA: The Structure of the First Intermediate. Proc. Natl. Acad. Sci. U.S. 58, 1096.

REPAIR

137. P. T. Emmerson and P. Howard-Flanders, (1965). Post-Irradiation Degradation of DNA Following Exposure of Ultraviolet-Sensitive and Resistant Bacteria to X-rays. Biochem. Biophys. Res. Comm. 18, 24.

138. J. K. Setlow, M. E. Boling and F. J. Bollum, (1965). The Chemical Nature of Photoreactivable Lesions in DNA. Proc. Natl. Acad. Sci. U.S. 53, 1430.

139. J. E. Donnellan and R. B. Setlow, (1965). Thymine Photoproducts but not Thymine Dimers Found in Ultraviolet Irradiated Bacterial Spores. Science 149, 308.

140. M. E. Boling and J. K. Setlow, (1966). Resistance of Micrococcus Radiodurans to U.V. III. A Repair Mechanism. Biochem. Biophys. Acta 123, 26.

141. S. Aoki, R. P. Boyce and P. Howard-Flanders, (1966). Sensitization of E. coli to Radiation by Bromouracil: Excessive Post-irradiation Breakdown of DNA without Concomitant Synthesis. Nature 209, 686.

142. W. Carrier and R. Setlow, (1966). Excision of Pyrimidine Dimers from Irradiated DNA in vitro. Biochem. Biophys. Acta 129, 318.

143. R. Setlow and W. Carrier, (1966). Pyrimidine Dimers in U.V.-irradiated DNAs. J. Mol. Biol. 17, 237.

144. P. Howard-Flanders, R. P. Boyce and L. Theriot, (1966). Three Loci in E. coli K-12 that Control the Excision of Pyrimidine Dimers and Certain Other Mutagen Products from DNA. Genetics 53, 1119.

145. P. Howard-Flanders and L. Theriot, (1966). Mutants of E. coli K-12 Defective in DNA Repair and in Genetic Recombination. Genetics 53, 1137.

146. A. J. Clark, M. Chamberlain, R. P. Boyce and P. Howard-Flanders, (1966). Abnormal Metabolic Response to U.V. Light of a Recombination Deficient Mutant of E. coli K-12. J. Mol. Biol. 19, 442.

147. M. Yarus and R. L. Sinsheimer, (1967). Ultraviolet Sensitivity of the Biological Activity of ΦX174 Virus, Single-Stranded DNA, and RF DNA. Biophys. J. 7, 267.

148. T. Yamane, B. J. Wyluda and R. G. Shulman, (1967). Dihydrothymine from U.V.-Irradiated DNA. Proc. Natl. Acad. Sci. U.S. 58, 439.

149. N. R. Cozzarelli, N. E. Melechen, T. M. Jovin and A. Kornberg, (1967). Polynucleotide Cellulose as a Substrate for a Polynucleotide Ligase Induced by Phage T₄. Biochem. Biophys. Res. Comm. 28, 578.

150. E. K. Bautz, (1967). A Biological Assay for Polynucleotide Ligase: Recovery of Marker Activity in DNA-Transformation. Biochem. Biophys. Res. Comm. 28, 641.

151. B. M. Olivera and I. R. Lehman, (1967). Diphosphopyridine Nucleotide: A Cofactor for the Polynucleotide-Joining Enzyme from E. coli. Proc. Natl. Acad. Sci. U.S. 57, 1700.

152. P. C. Hanawalt, (1967). Normal Replication of DNA after Repair Replication in Bacteria. Nature 214, 269.

153. A. Becker, G. Lyn, M. Gefter and J. Hurwitz, (1967). Enzymatic Repair of DNA, II.

BIBLIOGRAPHY

Characterization of Phage-Induced Sealase. Proc. Natl. Acad. Sci. U.S. **58**, 1996.

154. J. W. Little, S. B. Zimmerman, C. K. Oshinsky and M. Gellert, (1967). Enzymatic Joining of DNA Strands, II. An Enzyme-Adenylate Intermediate in the DPN-Dependent-DNA Ligase Reaction. Proc. Natl. Acad. Sci. U.S. **58**, 2004.

155. G. C. Fareed and C. C. Richardson, (1967). Enzymatic Breakage and Joining of DNA, II. The Structural Gene for Polynucleotide Ligase in Bacteriophage T$_4$. Proc. Natl. Acad. Sci. U.S. **58**, 665.

REVIEW ARTICLES

156. M. Meselson, (1967). Symposium on Chromosome Mechanics at the Molecular Level. J. Cell. Physiol. **70**, no. 2 (supplement).

Recombination

J. Mol. Biol. (1964) **9**, 734-745

On the Mechanism of Genetic Recombination between DNA Molecules

Matthew Meselson

Biological Laboratories, Harvard University
Cambridge, Massachusetts, U.S.A.

(*Received 24 April 1964*)

A two-factor cross was performed between bacteriophages labeled with heavy isotopes. Recombinants were found with chromosomes formed entirely or almost entirely of parental DNA. This and other features of the distribution of parental DNA among recombinant phages and among their descendants show that genetic recombination occurs by breakage and joining of double-stranded DNA molecules. Also, there is some indication that a small amount of DNA is removed and resynthesized in the formation of recombinant molecules.

1. Introduction

Genetic recombination between bacteriophages was discovered by Delbrück & Bailey (1946) in the course of experiments designed to determine whether more than one infecting phage can multiply in a single bacterium. They examined phages produced by cells jointly infected with two types of phage differing from one another in two genetic characters and found not only the two parental phage types but also two types with combinations of the parental characters. For a time, it was suspected that the new types resulted from a novel process more akin to mutation than to recombination. However, Hershey & Rotman (1948) showed that the phenomenon was indeed genetic recombination, for its operation closely followed rules already worked out for recombination in higher organisms.

Although the details of the mechanism are not known, there is strong evidence in the case of bacteriophage λ that recombination results from the breakage and joining of DNA molecules. The initial evidence for breakage and joining came from measurements of the amount of labeled DNA in selected recombinants yielded by cells infected jointly with isotopically labeled and unlabeled phages (Meselson & Weigle, 1961; Kellenberger, Zichichi & Weigle, 1961). Recombinant phages were found to contain labeled DNA in discrete proportions, corresponding to the proportion of the λ genetic map lying beyond the selected site of recombination in the direction of the allele contributed by the labeled parent phage. Since the chromosome of λ is a single DNA molecule along which hereditary determinants are spaced at least approximately as they are along the λ genetic map (Kaiser, 1962 and personal communication), this simple result may be explained as the result of breakage and joining of chromosomes at the selected site of recombination. Alternatively, it could reflect the operation of a rather less plausible mechanism whereby a fragment of a parental chromosome is rebuilt by synthesis of its missing length on a template provided by the homologous portion of a chromosome of different parentage. The latter mechanism has been called breakage and copying.

Breakage and joining may be distinguished from breakage and copying by an examination of the amount of parental DNA in recombinant phages from a cross between parents *both* of which contain labeled DNA. Only the former of the two mechanisms can produce a recombinant containing label from both parents. Using host-induced modification as a label, Ihler & Meselson (1963) obtained evidence that both parents do contribute lengths of DNA which become joined together to form recombinant chromosomes.

The mechanism of recombination is specified more conclusively and in greater detail by the present results, a preliminary report of which has appeared elsewhere (Meselson, 1962). The occurrence of recombination by breakage and joining of λ chromosomes is confirmed, and the process is shown to be independent of chromosome replication in the sense that recombinants may be formed entirely, or almost entirely, of unreplicated chromosome fragments. However, there is some indication that a small amount of DNA is removed and resynthesized in the formation of recombinant chromosomes.

2. Materials and Methods

(a) *Bacteriophages*

Phage λ, the wild type of Kaiser (1957), and λhc were used as parents for all crosses. Phage λhc is a recombinant isolated from a cross of the λh of Kaiser (1962) by λc_{26}, a nitrous acid-induced c_1 mutant of λ.

All of these phages have buoyant density $1 \cdot 508$ g cm^{-3} in pure CsCl solution at 20°C. To insure homology of the two parental phages, the h allele was passed through five consecutive crosses alternately to λc_{26} and λ, selecting in the first case for λhc and in the second for λh. Although many thousands of plaques were examined, there was no indication of segregation of characters other than h and c.

Stocks of λ were prepared by the induction of lysogenic bacteria with ultraviolet light. Stocks of λhc were produced by lytic multiplication. Phages uniformly labeled with ^{13}C and ^{15}N were prepared and purified according to Meselson & Weigle (1961). The uniformity of labeling of each stock was verified by density-gradient centrifugation. The frequency of λh was found to be less than $0 \cdot 01\%$ in each stock.

(b) *Bacteria*

Escherichia coli K12 strain 3110 (E. M. Lederberg) was used for the preparation of all parental phage stocks. Strain C600·5, a mutant of *E. coli* K12 C600 (Appleyard, 1954), was used as host for all crosses. The host modification and restriction properties of this mutant are identical to those of *E. coli* strain C (Bertani & Weigle, 1953). Strain C 600·5 was used in preference to C, because λ is rapidly inactivated in lysates of our strain C. Strains C600, C600·5, and *E. coli* K12/λ (Kaiser, 1962) were used as indicators.

(c) *Methods*

Crosses and low-multiplicity growth cycles were performed on strain C600·5 following Ihler & Meselson (1963). In crosses, the multiplicity of infection was approximately three of each parental type. Recombinants λh were scored as turbid plaques on a mixed indicator containing equal concentrations of C600·5 and ultraviolet-irradiated K/λ. On this indicator λhc produces clear plaques whereas λ and λc give rise to barely discernable ghost plaques. Irradiation removes the barrier which otherwise would restrict phages produced on strain C600·5 from infecting K/λ. For the assay of unrestricted phages, a mixture of C600 and non-irradiated K/λ was used and is referred to as restricting indicator. The validity of both scoring procedures was established by appropriate reconstruction experiments. Only one parental type and one recombinant type, λhc and λh, were scored. Density-gradient centrifugation was performed according to Meselson & Weigle (1961).

3. Outline of the Experiments

When several λ phages simultaneously infect a cell, some of the chromosomes replicate semi-conservatively while others remain unreplicated (Meselson & Weigle, 1961). Accordingly, a cell infected with several isotopically labeled phages will contain chromosomes with both polynucleotide strands labeled, others with only one labeled strand, and still others with no label. If genetic recombination occurs by simple breakage and joining, then recombination at a given site followed by phage maturation could yield altogether nine discrete phage types with respect to the proportion of labeled DNA they contain. If the site of recombination is chosen at the center of the chromosome, the number of possible classes is reduced to five: fully labeled, three-quarter, one-half, one-quarter and unlabeled. The fully-labeled and three-quarter-labeled classes deserve special attention, because they are expected to result from breakage and joining but not from breakage and copying. An important result of the experiments described below is the discovery of these two classes among the recombinant phages from a suitably designed cross. However, this result does not prove that segments from different chromosomes have become permanently joined to one another. Instead, they could be only temporarily associated. That this is not the case is shown by the finding of half-labeled recombinant phages among the progeny yielded by cells singly infected with fully-labeled, three-quarter-labeled or half-labeled recombinant phages. This result shows that recombination results in an association between polynucleotide chains from different parent chromosomes which is not disrupted by the events of chromosome injection, replication or maturation.

The genetic markers h (host range) and c (clear plaque) were chosen for these experiments, because of their symmetrical location about the center of the linkage map of λ. That they also straddle the center of the λ chromosome is shown both by the present results and by the behavior of infectious molecules of λ DNA when they are broken in half by hydrodynamic shear (Kaiser, 1962). The frequency of recombination between h and c is approximately 7%, and the hc interval comprises about one third of the λ genetic map.

In order to improve the resolution of certain classes of labeled phages in the presence of a great excess of unlabeled phages, several gradients were assayed on restricting indicator as described under Materials and Methods. On this indicator, phages from strain C600·5 plate with very low efficiency unless they contain at least one strand composed of parental DNA (i.e., DNA synthesized on strain 3110). This is an example of the phenomena of host-induced modification and restriction elucidated by Arber & Dussoix (1962). It should be emphasized that we have relied on host-induced modification only as a means of suppressing the appearance of unlabeled phages, and not as a label for parental DNA.

4. Results

(a) *A cross with isotopically unlabeled phages*

Figure 1 shows the density distribution of phages from a cross of unlabeled λ with unlabeled λhc. It is seen that both λhc and λh form a single sharp band in the gradient. Bands of exactly the same shape and location were found from assays performed on restricting indicator bacteria. The complete absence of phages with atypically high density provides assurance that variations in the amount of isotopic label are the only cause of the density variations observed in the remainder of these experiments. The light tail seen on each band results from mixing caused by the method of collecting fractions.

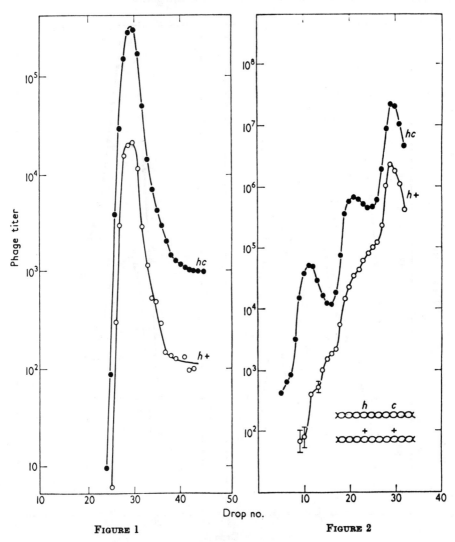

FIGURE 1   FIGURE 2

FIG. 1. Density distributions of λhc and λh from the cross λhc × λ.

FIG. 2. Density distributions of λhc and λh from the cross [^{13}C^{15}N]λhc × [^{13}C^{15}N]λ. Fractions 12 and 13 were pooled for the assay of λh. Error tags indicate 90% confidence limits. The three modes in the distribution of λhc are formed by phages with conserved, semi-conserved, and newly synthesized chromosomes, in order of decreasing density. The location of mutations h and c on the chromosome is indicated schematically at the lower right of the Figure.

(b) Crosses with isotopically labeled phages

The density distributions of λhc and λh from a cross of ^{13}C^{15}N-labeled λhc by ^{13}C^{15}N-labeled λ are shown in Fig. 2. The parental type λhc is seen to occur primarily in three discrete modes, corresponding to phages with conserved, semi-conserved and completely new chromosomes (Meselson & Weigle, 1961). The distribution of the recombinant type λh shows inflections at the positions expected for phages with fully-labeled, three-quarter-labeled, and one-half-labeled chromosomes; but lack of resolution prevents the positive identification of these categories.

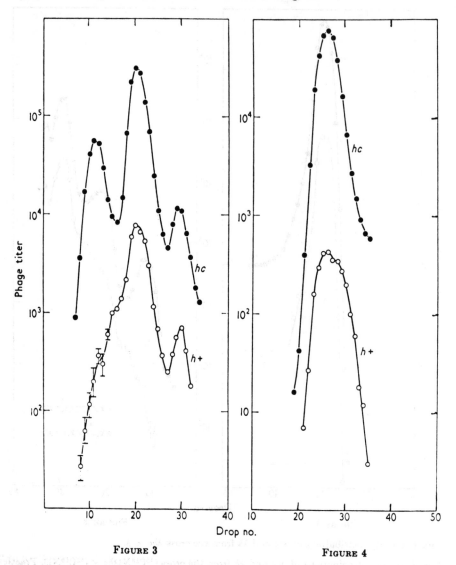

FIGURE 3

FIGURE 4

FIG. 3. Density distributions of λhc and λh in the gradient depicted in Fig. 2 found by assays on restricting indicator bacteria. Error tags indicate 90% confidence limits.

FIG. 4. Density distributions of λhc and λh from the fully-labeled region (fractions 10 to 13) of the gradient shown in Fig. 2.

An attempt was made to obtain increased resolution by assaying the distribution on restricting indicator bacteria, so as to suppress the appearance of phages lacking a completely labeled polynucleotide chain. Figure 3 shows that this procedure serves to reveal a discrete mode of half-labeled recombinants but that fully-labeled and three-quarter-labeled λh remain unresolved. The slight peaks at fraction 30 are formed by unlabeled phages plating at the low efficiency with which λ from strain C600·5 infects most K12 strains.

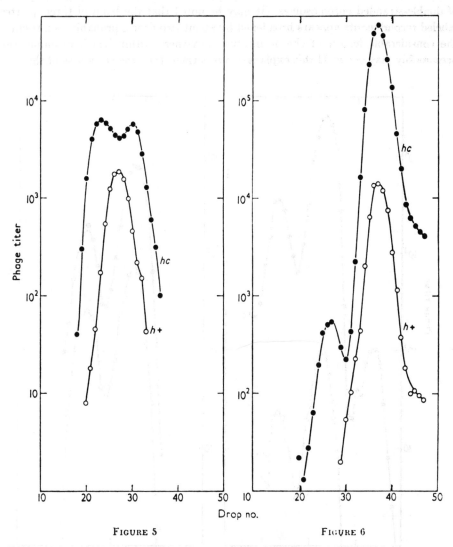

<FIGURE 5   FIGURE 6

FIG. 5. Density distributions of λhc and λh from the three-quarter-labeled region (fractions 14 to 17) of the gradient shown in Fig. 2. Conserved and semi-conserved λhc are seen to be barely resolved.

FIG. 6. Density distributions of λhc and λh from the one-half-labeled region (fractions 19 to 21) of the gradient shown in Fig. 2.

The difficulty caused by insufficient resolution was overcome by subjecting fractions from each region of interest in the original gradient to further density-gradient analysis. The distributions of phages in pooled fractions taken from the fully-, three-quarter-, and one-half-labeled regions of the original gradient are shown in Figs 4, 5 and 6 respectively. Discrete bands of recombinant phages are found in all three cases. The distributions of Fig. 5 are of special interest. The contrast between the distinct uni-modal band of three-quarter-labeled recombinants and the broad bimodal distribution of the accompanying non-recombinant phages shows most strikingly that the labeled recombinants are indeed a discrete density species formed by the breakage and joining of double-stranded chromosomes. (It may be noted that the band of three-quarter-labeled recombinants appears broadened by about two drops, probably as a result of the considerable length of the *hc* interval, anywhere within which recombination presumably may occur. If this explanation is correct, then the sharpness of the band

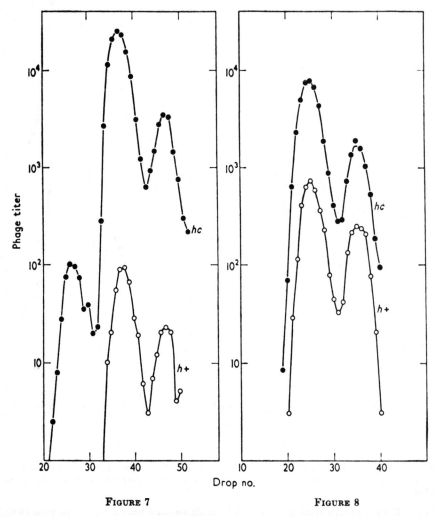

FIGURE 7   FIGURE 8

FIG. 7. Distributions of λ*hc* and λ*h* yielded by cells singly infected with fully-labeled phages from the gradient of Fig. 2. Assays were performed on restricting indicator bacteria. The most dense band of λ*hc* contains unadsorbed phages with fully-labeled chromosomes. The bands at fractions 37 and 47 contain phages with one-half-labeled and unlabeled chromosomes respectively.

FIG. 8. Distributions of λ*hc* and λ*h* yielded by cells singly infected with three-quarter-labeled phages from the gradient of Fig. 2. Assays were performed on restricting indicator bacteria. The bands at fractions 25 and 35 are formed by phages with half-labeled and unlabeled chromosomes respectively. One-quarter-labeled recombinant phages are not expected to plate on the restricting indicator and, accordingly, no indication of their presence is seen.

of half-labeled recombinants would suggest that most of them arose when the composition of the vegetative phage pool favored recombination between two conserved or two hybrid chromosomes more than recombination between a conserved and a completely new chromosome. In this regard, the relative amounts of the various labeled classes of parental and recombinant phages found in these experiments are compatible with the generally accepted view that recombination occurs throughout the latent period.)

Certain details of the distributions of Figs 4 to 6 should be noted. A light shoulder appears on the band of fully-labeled recombinants and possibly also on the band of three-quarter-labeled recombinants, whereas the half-labeled recombinants form a

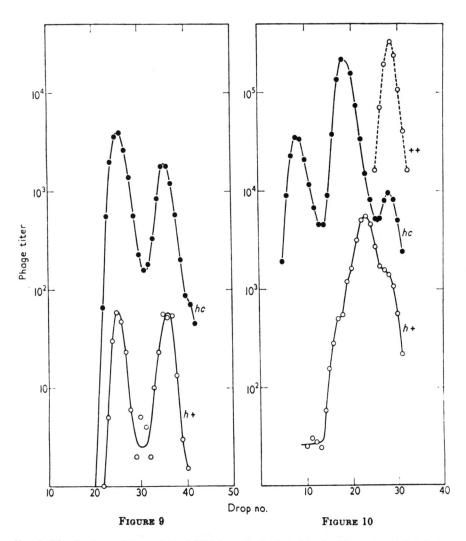

FIGURE 9 FIGURE 10

Fig. 9. Distributions of λhc and λh yielded by cells singly infected with one-half-labeled phages from the gradient of Fig. 2. Assays were performed on restricting indicator bacteria. The bands at fractions 26 and 36 are formed by phages with half-labeled and unlabeled chromosomes respectively.

Fig. 10. Distributions of λ, λhc and λh from the cross [$^{13}C^{15}N$]λhc × λ. Assays were performed on restricting indicator bacteria.

band as sharp as do non-recombinant phages. Upon repetition of the entire experiment, these features of the various distributions were found to recur.

(c) *One-step growth of the cross progeny*

Phages in reserve portions of the fully-, three-quarter-, and one-half-labeled fractions described above were allowed to multiply (one cycle) on strain C600·5. The total multiplicity of infection was 0·01 phage per bacterium. Each of the three lysates was analysed by density-gradient centrifugation with results shown in Figs 7, 8 and 9. Assays were performed on restricting indicator bacteria in order to suppress the appearance of unlabeled phages, which otherwise would obscure the discrete bands of half-labeled λhc and λh seen in each gradient. Comparison of Figs 7 to 9 with Figs 4 to 6 shows that, in each case, the recombinant phages give rise to half-labeled progeny with approximately the same efficiency as do the parent type phages.

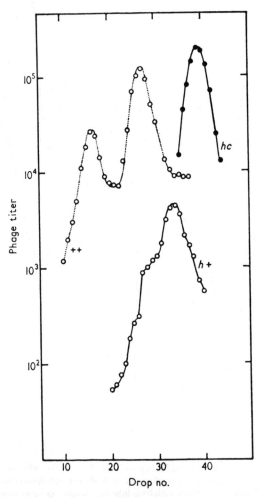

FIG. 11. Distributions of λ, λhc, and λh from the cross λhc × [^{13}C^{15}N]λ. Assays were performed on restricting indicator bacteria. The shoulder of λh at fractions 27 to 30 probably results from multiple recombination between hybrid and light chromosomes.

(d) *Crosses of labeled and unlabeled phages*

Two crosses were performed in which only one of the parental types was labeled with heavy isotopes. The results provide additional assurance that the fully-, three-quarter- and one-half-labeled recombinants examined above do in fact derive their label jointly from chromosomes of both parental types, as expected for recombination by simple breaking and joining. Figures 10 and 11 show the density distributions of progeny from the crosses $[^{13}C^{15}N]\lambda hc \times \lambda$ and $\lambda hc \times [^{13}C^{15}N]\lambda$ respectively. Assays were performed on restricting indicator bacteria in order to suppress the appearance of unlabeled phages. The prominent band of unrestricted λh found in both gradients occurs near the position expected for phages with one-quarter-labeled chromosomes. The exact location of the band corresponds to slightly less than one-quarter label when λ is the labeled parent, and slightly more when λhc is labeled. If the probability of recombination is relatively uniform in the region between h and c, then we may conclude that these markers are equidistant from a point about 55% of the way in from the "left" end of the chromosome.

Apart from the prominent band of one-quarter-labeled λh, there is an inflection in the distributions of Figs 10 and 11 suggesting the presence of half-labeled λh. No three-quarter- or fully-labeled recombinants are expected, nor is there any indication of their presence.

5. Discussion

Parental DNA is found in recombinant phages in discrete amounts which cannot be accounted for by breakage and copying, copy choice, or any process which would alter the genotype of a chromosome without substantial replacement of chromosomic material. Instead, the observed distribution of parental DNA among the progeny of crosses and among their descendants shows that genetic recombination in λ occurs by the breakage and joining of double-stranded phage chromosomes. However, a reservation must be placed on the interpretation of the evidence for the joining of chromosomes. The discovery of phages with half-labeled chromosomes among the descendants of labeled recombinants shows only that the two parental contributions to at least one strand of the recombinant chromosome are able to remain associated throughout the processes of injection, replication and phage maturation. Whether both strands retain their integrity in this fashion and whether the association results from the formation of a co-valent bond can not be decided.

It may be inquired whether breakage and joining are confined to a site or sites between h and c, while other mechanisms of recombination operate elsewhere on the λ chromosome. This possibility is rendered very unlikely by a number of observations, including the finding that chromosome breakage is associated with recombination in regions not overlapping the hc interval (Meselson & Weigle, 1961; Jordan & Meselson, unpublished experiments).

Considerable evidence for recombination by breakage and joining of DNA molecules has been obtained from experiments with T-even bacteriophages and with several bacteria. In the former case, it is well established that fragments of parental chromosomes appear in progeny phages (see Delbrück & Stent, 1957; Hershey & Burgi, 1956; Levinthal & Thomas, 1957; Roller, 1961; Kosinski, 1961; Kahn, 1964). Although other explanations can be devised, the implication is that recombination by breakage and joining is occurring in these cases. This interpretation is strengthened by the recent findings of Tomizawa & Anraku (1964), who have extracted from T4-infected cells structures containing DNA fragments from different parental chromosomes. In recombinants produced by bacterial conjugation, Siddiqi (1963) found an association between a paternal genetic character and radioisotope which had been used to label the female cells before mating. In bacterial transformation, structures which are either true recombinants or zygotes may be recovered very soon after the uptake of transforming DNA and under conditions which considerably inhibit DNA synthesis (Fox, 1960; Voll & Goodgal, 1961). It appears that these structures are inactivated at the same initial rate as in donor DNA if the latter is extensively labeled with ^{32}P (Fox, 1962). These various observations have been interpreted as evidence that double-stranded donor DNA is integrated directly into the recipient chromosome. This would be in accord with the finding of recombination by breakage and joining between unreplicated double-stranded λ DNA molecules. More recently, however, Lacks (1962), Bodmer & Ganesan (personal communication) and Fox (personal communication) have been led by studies of the fate of donor DNA after uptake by recipient cells to favor the possibility that only one strand of donor DNA is integrated during transformation. These apparently conflicting views might be reconciled with each other, and with our knowledge of the mechanism of recombination in λ, if joining were to take place through the agency of relatively extensive hybrid regions as described below.

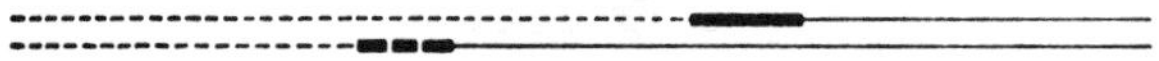

FIG. 12. Possible structure of an unreplicated recombinant DNA molecule. At least in mature phages, the possibility that the region of joining contains more than two DNA strands is made unlikely by the absence of heavy shoulders on all bands of recombinant phages and by the observation that λ heterozygotes are not more dense than other λ particles (Kellenberger, Zichichi & Epstein, 1962; Meselson, unpublished experiments).

Light solid and dashed lines represent polynucleotide strands contributed by two different parent molecules. Heavy lines represent either regions from which DNA has been removed and resynthesized along the opposing strand, or else regions in which missing DNA is not yet replaced. In the latter case, replacement is thought of as occurring during replication. The removal and repair of DNA may take place on only one strand rather than on both, as depicted in the Figure.

There is some suggestion in the present experiments that joining is accompanied by a small amount of DNA synthesis. A light shoulder appears with the band of fully-labeled recombinants; the band of three-quarter-labeled recombinants exhibits a slight and possibly significant light shoulder; whereas the one-half-labeled and un-labeled recombinants form bands as sharp in appearance as those of non-recombinant phages. These various features may be explained by assuming that up to five or ten per cent of the DNA of the λ chromosome is removed and resynthesized in the course of genetic recombination. The replacement of labeled DNA with unlabeled DNA would explain why a light shoulder appears with bands of fully-labeled recombinants, but not with unlabeled recombinants. The bands of three-quarter- and one-half-labeled re-combinants would possess light shoulders with intermediate displacements, which in the case of the latter may be so slight as to have escaped detection. An alternative explanation of the light shoulders is that they contain phages from which up to one or two per cent of the DNA has been removed without replacement. If most of the one-half-labeled and unlabeled recombinants replicate at least once before maturation, the missing DNA might usually be restored, or less likely, the deficient strands might be lost, explaining the absence of substantial light shoulders in these cases. Although neither explanation of the light shoulders can be substantiated without additional information, both entail the removal and probably the resynthesis of a small amount of DNA in recombinant chromosomes.

If we consider (1) the present demonstration that recombination occurs by breakage and joining of double-stranded DNA molecules, (2) the indication that some DNA is removed and resynthesized in the course of recombination, and (3) the extensive evidence that bacteriophage recombinants arise through the formation of partially heterozygous structures (see Luria, 1962), we are led to imagine that the unreplicated recombinant chromosome resembles the structure depicted in Fig. 12. The possibility that such structures are responsible for recombination in higher organisms as well as in bacteria and viruses has been discussed by Whitehouse (1963) and by the author (Meselson, 1963).

I am grateful to Mrs Miriam Wright for superb technical assistance in performing these experiments. This work was supported by grants from the U.S. National Science Foundation.

REFERENCES

Appleyard, R. K. (1954). *Genetics*, **39**, 440.
Arbor, W. & Dussoix, D. (1962). *J. Mol. Biol.* **5**, 18.
Bertani, G. & Weigle, J. (1953). *J. Bact.* **65**, 113.
Delbrück, M. & Bailey, W. T. (1946). *Cold Spr. Harb. Symp. Quant. Biol.* 11, 33.
Delbrück, M. & Stent, G. S. (1957). In *The Chemical Basis of Heredity*, ed. by W. D. McElroy & B. Glass, p. 699. Baltimore: Johns Hopkins Press.
Fox, M. S. (1960). *Nature*, **187**, 1004.
Fox, M. S. (1962). *Proc. Nat. Acad. Sci., Wash.* **48**, 1043.
Hershey, A. D. & Burgi, E. (1956). *Cold Spr. Harb. Symp. Quant. Biol.* **21**, 91.
Hershey, A. D. & Rotman, R. (1948). *Proc. Nat. Acad. Sci., Wash.* **34**, 89.
Ihler, G. & Meselson, M. (1963). *Virology*, **21**, 7.
Kahn, P. L. (1964). *J. Mol. Biol.* **8**, 392.
Kaiser, A. D. (1957). *Virology*, **3**, 42.
Kaiser, A. D. (1962). *J. Mol. Biol.* **4**, 275.
Kellenberger, G., Zichichi, M. L. & Epstein, H. T. (1962). *Virology*, **17**, 44.
Kellenberger, G., Zichichi, M. L. & Weigle, J. J. (1961). *Proc. Nat. Acad. Sci., Wash.* **47**, 869.
Kosinski, A. W. (1961). *Virology*, **13**, 124.
Lacks, S. (1962). *J. Mol. Biol.* **5**, 119.
Leventhal, C. & Thomas, C. A. Jr. (1957). *Biochim. biophys. Acta*, **23**, 453.
Luria, S. E. (1962). *Ann. Rev. Microbiol.* **16**, 205.
Meselson, M. (1962). *Pontificiae Acad. Sci. Scripta Varia*, **22**, 173.
Meselson, M. (1963). *Symposium of 16th International Congress of Zoology.* New York: Doubleday & Co.
Meselson, M. & Weigle, J. J. (1961). *Proc. Nat. Acad. Sci., Wash.* **47**, 857.
Roller, A. (1961). Ph.D. Thesis, California Institute of Technology.
Siddiqi, O. H. (1963). *Proc. Nat. Acad. Sci., Wash.* **49**, 589.
Tomizawa, J. & Anraku, N. (1964). *J. Mol. Biol.* **8**, 516.
Voll, M. J. & Goodgal, S. H. (1961). *Proc. Nat. Acad. Sci., Wash.* **47**, 505.
Whitehouse, H. L. K. (1963). *Nature*, **199**, 1034.

Lysogeny and Induction

PAPER SUBMITTED FOR PUBLICATION TO THE J. MOL. BIOL.

RECOMBINATION IN PHAGE λ: II. SITE-SPECIFIC
RECOMBINATION PROMOTED BY THE INTEGRATION SYSTEM

Jon Weil* and E. R. Signer

Biological Laboratories, Harvard University
Cambridge, Massachusetts
and
Department of Biology, Massachusetts Institute of Technology
Cambridge, Massachusetts

* Present address: Department of Molecular Biology,
Vanderbilt University, Nashville, Tennessee.

Summary

General vegetative recombination in phage λ can be promoted either
by a phage (Red) or by a bacterial (Rec) recombination system. This
paper shows that λ produces a third recombination system, Int, which
promotes vegetative recombination exclusively in the prophage attachment region. Its properties indicate that Int also promotes such
site-specific recombination in prophage integration.

The deletion mutant λb2 undergoes site-specific recombination
promoted by Int, even though it cannot integrate efficiently. The
allelic state of b2 influences the frequency of this recombination,
with $b2^+$ x $b2^-$) $b2^+$ x $b2^+$) $b2^-$ x $b2^-$. These findings suggest that
the prophage attachment region of λ is structurally complex.

1. Introduction

In the preceding paper, we showed that bacteriophage λ produces at
least part of a system that promotes general vegetative λ recombination (Signer & Weil, 1968; see also Echols & Gingery, 1968). In
this paper we show that λ produces in addition at least part of a
system that promotes site-specific recombination at the prophage attachment region and is involved in prophage integration.

There is now very good evidence supporting the Campbell (1962)
model of prophage integration (see Signer, 1968). According to this
model, the λ genome circularizes after infection and is then linearly
inserted into the bacterial chromosome by recombination. This recombination occurs in a specific region of both the phage and bacterial
chromosome ($att\emptyset$* and att^B, respectively). There is considerable
evidence that it is brought about by a special, phage-produced recombination system rather than by the mechanism of normal vegetative

---

*Abbreviations used: rec^-, recombination-deficient bacterial mutant;
red^-, recombination-deficient λ mutant; int^-, integration-deficient λ
mutant; $att\emptyset$ and att^B, phage and bacterial regions respectively of
prophage integration defined to include the site(s) of recombination
plus any regions involved in pairing or recognition; sus, suppressor
sensitive (amber) mutant. Italics are used for genetic loci (e.g.,
red^+ and red^- alleles at the red locus), and Roman type for functional
products (e.g., the Red system).

recombination (Signer & Beckwith, 1966; Campbell & Zissler, 1966; Fischer-Fantuzzi, 1967; Zissler, 1967a).

One way to study integration is to use λ mutants that block prophage integration and allow only abortive lysogeny. There are two such mutations, b2 and int. The b2 deletion is located near attø (Kellenberger, Zichichi & Weigle, 1961; Jordan, 1964), and it apparently affects a region of λ DNA that is structurally required for integration (Campbell, 1965). It was originally thought to have deleted attø. However, Fischer-Fantuzzi (1967) has shown that λb2 can be integrated by the special recombination system into a bacterial chromosome carrying the cryptic (partially deleted) prophage. From this she concluded that b2 deletes only part of attø and that attø is structurally complex.

The int mutations, on the other hand, affect function. They map outside the b2 deletion, are complemented by b2 in trans, and can be temperature-sensitive and amber. An obvious candidate for the int lesion is the site-specific recombination system that brings about integration (Zissler, 1967b personal communication; Gingery & Echols, 1967; Gottesman & Yarmolinsky, 1968).

This paper demonstrates that there is site-specific vegetative recombination at or near attø, that it depends on the product of the int gene, and that it can occur between phages that carry the b2 deletion. It can be studied when general vegetative recombination is eliminated by the use of recombination-deficient (red⁻) phage mutants in a recombination-deficient (rec⁻) bacterial host. From the similarities between this recombination system and the mechanism of prophage integration, we conclude that the Int system promotes site-specific recombination in prophage integration.

Similar conclusions are presented in the accompanying paper by Echols, Gingery & Moore (1968).

2. Materials and Methods

These are described by Signer & Weil (1968). In the construction of phage strains the method of Gottesman & Yarmolinsky (1968) was used to score for the b2 marker; all presumptive b2⁻ strains were shown to have the density of λb2 by CsCl density gradient centrifugation. A map of λ is shown in Figure 1.

Figure 1

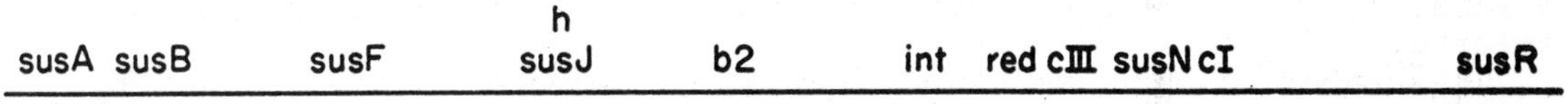

susA susB	susF	h susJ	b2	int red cIII susN cI	susR

Figure 1. Vegetative map of λ showing markers used in this study (see Signer & Weil, 1968).

3. Results
(a) Experimental System

To test for recombination specific to attø, we used a three-factor cross with the markers susJ, cI and susR (see Figure 2). The interval susJ-cI spans attø and reflects both specific and general recombination, while the interval cI-susR is affected only by general recombination and serves as a control. λsusJ6 was crossed with λcI857

Figure 2

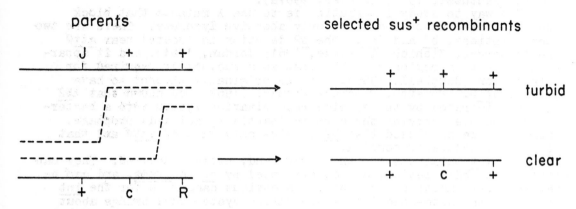

parents   **selected sus⁺ recombinants**

turbid

clear

Figure 2. Experimental system for comparing Int- and Red-promoted recombination; see text.

susR5; sus⁺ recombinants were selected and scored directly as cI⁻ (clear) or cI⁺ (turbid). As shown in Figure 2, a cI⁺sus⁺ recombinant represents odd-numbered exchanges in the interval susJ-cI, whereas a cI⁻sus⁺ recombinant represents odd-numbered exchanges between cI and susR. This method provides a very sensitive comparison of recombination in the two intervals. Although in repetitions of a given cross the frequency of sus⁺ recombinants varied within a factor of about 2, the ratio of exchanges in the two intervals remained quite constant.

The effect of a particular mutation (red⁻, int⁻ or both) was tested by introducing it into both parental strains. All crosses were done in a rec⁻ host to eliminate any contribution from the bacterial recombination system (Signer & Weil, 1968).

(b) Site-specific recombination promoted by Int

The crosses presented in Tables 1 and 2 show the effect of int⁻ and red⁻ mutations on recombination in the two test intervals. Recombination between cI and susR is reduced more than 100-fold by red3 (Table 1) and about 20-fold by red5 (Table 2). In both cases the reduction is about the same as for the interval susB-susJ (Signer & Weil, 1968). The int⁻ mutation does not affect recombination between cI and susR.

Recombination between susJ and cI is reduced to some extent by either the int⁻ or the red⁻ mutations. Both mutations together are required to reduce recombination in this interval to the low level seen in the other intervals with red⁻ alone.

These results indicate that the product of the int gene is involved in recombination at a specific site or sites between susJ6 and cI857, and that this recombination is largely independent of the recombination system defined by the red3 and red5 mutations. Consistent with this, λred3 and λred5 appear to integrate normally.

(c) Effect of b2 on Int-promoted recombination

When both parents carry red3, virtually all the recombination in the interval susJ-susR is promoted by the Int system. We have used this

126

TABLE 1

Effect of int6 and red3 on recombination

λsusJ⁻ x λcI⁻susR⁻

Genotype of both parents for		Recombination in interval	
int	red	susJ-cI	cI-susR
+	+	2.7	1.2
-	+	1.5	1.2
+	-	0.6	≤0.004
-	-	≤0.005	≤0.002

The crosses were performed in a rec⁻ host. In each cross both parents had the same genotype for int and red. Recombination is computed as twice the frequency of turbid sus⁺ (susJ-cI) or clear sus⁺ (cI-susR) recombinants x 2 x 100.

In this and succeeding tables, the notation "≤" indicates that a few plaques, corresponding to the recombination frequency shown, were found on the selection plates. These may be recombinants formed in the cross, or they may have arisen on the plates. "<" indicates that no recombinant plaques were found.

TABLE 2

Effect of int6 and red5 on recombination

λsusJ⁻ x λcI⁻susR⁻

Genotype of both parents for		Recombination	
int	red	susJ-cI	cI-susR
+	+	4.0	1.3
-	+	2.1	1.8
+	-	0.9	0.05
-	-	0.2	0.1

Crosses as in Table 1; all cI⁻susR⁻ phages were also h⁻.

TABLE 3

Effect of b2 on Int-promoted recombination

$$\lambda susJ^- \times \lambda cI^- susR^-$$

cross	Genotype of both parents for		Genotype of each parent for b2		a. Cross performed in rec⁻ host Recombination in interval		b. Cross performed in rec⁺ host Recombination in interval	
	int	red	susJ⁻ parent	cI⁻susR⁻ parent	susJ-cI	cI-susR	susJ-cI	cI-susR
1	+	−	$b2^+$	$b2^+$	1.4	≤0.003	2.6	0.6
2	+	−	$b2^-$	$b2^-$	0.4	≤0.01	1.3	0.9
3	+	−	$b2^+$	$b2^-$	8.8	≤0.01		
4	+	−	$b2^-$	$b2^+$	7.1	≤0.01	6.6	0.6
5	+	+	$b2^+$	$b2^+$	3.8	1.5		
6	−	−	$b2^+$	$b2^+$	<0.008	≤0.008		
7	+/−*	−	$b2^-$	$b2^+$	3.7	<0.01		

*This cross was $int^+b2^-susJ^- \times int^-b2^+cI^-susR^-$.

Crosses as in Table 1; alleles used were int6 and red3. All the crosses were done at the same time.

situation to test the effect of the b2 deletion on Int-promoted re-combination. The results are presented in Table 3a.

Crosses 1 through 4 test all possible combinations of $b2^+$ and $b2^-$. Crosses 5 and 6 are controls, and the interval cI-susR serves in each cross as a control for general recombination. Cross 7 is discussed in the next section. The main result is that Int-promoted recombination can occur between two phages each of which carries the b2 deletion. Therefore the deletion has not eliminated all sites of Int-promoted recombination.

The crosses also show that the frequency of Int-promoted re-combination depends on the b2 allele of each of the parents. These differences in frequency, which can be summarized as $b2^+$ x $b2^-$ > $b2^+$ x $b2^+$ > $b2^-$ x $b2^-$, have also been observed in each of the four sets of crosses we have done, and we believe they are significant.

These small differences might be due to a general effect of b2 on all recombination. We have ruled this out by doing the same crosses in a rec^+ host, where a low level of general recombination is superimposed on Int-promoted recombination (Signer & Weil, 1968; Echols & Gingery, 1968). The results are shown in Table 3b. Under these circumstances the magnitude of the differences in the interval susJ-cI is reduced, and the differences are not observed in the in-terval cI-susR. Therefore b2 affects specifically the frequency of Int-promoted recombination.

(d) Location of Int-promoted recombination

Since the Int system promotes recombination in the cross $b2^+$ x $b2^-$, we can use b2 as a genetic marker to delimit the region in which re-combination takes place. The expectations and results are shown in Table 4. Crosses 3 and 4 show that all the recombination takes place in the interval b2-cI. Further information comes from cross 7, in which both b2 and int are used as genetic markers. This cross shows that Int-promoted recombination occurs exclusively between b2 and int.*

4. Discussion

Our results demonstrate that λ produces a site-specific recombination system, defined by the int^- mutation, that promotes vegetative re-combination at or near the prophage attachment region, attø. Similar results have been obtained by Echols et al. (1968).

Thus there are three systems that can promote vegetative λ re-combination: the bacterial recombination system (Rec), the phage general recombination system (Red), and the phage integration system (Int). While it is clear that the rec, red and int genes can function independently of one another, we do not know to what extent the three systems share common enzymic steps. We have consistently found that the sum of the susJ-cI recombination frequencies in the int^+red^- and

---

* This cross also confirms that int^+ is the dominant allele (Zissler, 1967b; Gingery & Echols, 1967; Gottesman & Yarmolinsky, 1968). There is a 2-fold difference in frequency in Table 3 between cross 4 (int^+ x int^+) and cross 7 (int^+ x int^-), and even larger differences were seen in two repetitions of these crosses. This may mean that the int gene-product is rate-limiting under these conditions.

TABLE 4

Location of Int-promoted recombination in crosses $b2^+$ x $b2^-$

Number of the cross in Table 3a	Phenotype of sus$^+$ recombinants as a function of locus of recombination	Number of plaques tested which were Integrating	Non-integrating

3	J b2$^+$ + + — integrating
	  — non-integrating
	+ b2$^-$ c R
	J b2$^-$ + + — non-integrating
	  — integrating
		0	152

4	— non-integrating — integrating + b2$^+$ c R J b2$^-$int$^+$ + + — non-integrating	151	0

7	— non-integrating
	  — integrating
	  — non-integrating
	+ b2$^+$int$^-$ c R
		201	0

Phage progeny were plated on a non-permissive host at 38°. Bacteria from the center of turbid (cI$^+$) plaques were picked and tested for ability to integrate by the method of Gottesman & Yarmolinsky (1968).

130

the int⁻red⁺ crosses is slightly lower than the frequency in the int⁺red⁺ cross, and this might argue for some interaction of the two systems.

We have shown that Int-promoted recombination can occur outside the b2 deletion. Why, then, is λb2 normally unable to integrate efficiently? Fischer-Fantuzzi (1967), who found that λb2 can integrate efficiently if the host carries a cryptic prophage, suggested that attø includes both a region for pairing with att^B and a region reactive in Int-promoted recombination. If λb2 has lost only the pairing region it would not integrate well in a normal host, but it could integrate in a cryptic lysogen because its homology with the prophage remnant would allow pairing. This model adequately explains our results, since phages that mate vegetatively clearly have extensive homology. It is worth noting that the site specificity of the Int system means that there is no formal need for homology between attø and att^B. An enzyme that can recognize one site might just as easily recognize two non-homologous sites.

The b2⁺ x b2⁻ crosses show that a site or sites of Int-promoted recombination lie just to the right of the b2 deletion. This had been shown previously by Fischer-Fantuzzi (1967) in the cryptic prophage system. We should like to know if there are additional sites in the region deleted by b2. The effects of b2 on recombination frequency do not provide an answer because, surprisingly, b2⁺ x b2⁻ is the most reactive combination. We have preliminary results suggesting that these effects are structural rather than functional. It may then be that b2⁺ x b2⁻ is the closest structural approximation to the normal Int substrate, attø x att^B, possibly because it forms a loop of unpaired DNA. We are at present trying to unravel the apparent structural complexity of att and the sensitivity of Int to structural differences.*

The conclusion that Int is involved in site-specific recombination is rigorous only for vegetative crosses. However, the findings are completely congruent with all that is known about integration, including the properties of the b2 and int mutations. They demonstrate in a more direct way what had already been suggested by experiments on lysogeny, namely that prophage integration is brought about by a site-specific recombination system produced by the phage that includes the product of the int gene. Therefore, they may be taken as confirming Campbell's postulate of integration by recombination.

Acknowledgments

We wish to thank K. Manly, R. D'Ari, S. Heinemann, J. Zissler, M. Meselson, S. Luria, and D. Botstein for useful and stimulating discussion; G. Mosig and D. Kaiser for critical advice during preparation of the manuscript; Miss Judith Sparer and Miss Mary Bradford for excellent technical assistance; and R. Gingery, H. Echols, L. Moore, M. Gottesman, M. Yarmolinsky, K. Manly, and C. Radding for

---

* We wish to point out that the recombination promoted by Int in vegetative crosses presents obvious problems for quantitative λ mapping, including the estimation of the genetic size of the b2 deletion (Jordan, 1964).

making the results of their work available to us and allowing us to quote their results before publication. This work was supported by National Institutes of Health grant GM 14426 to E. Signer and National Science Foundation grant GB 5305 to M. Meselson and was carried out while J. W. was a National Institutes of Health postdoctoral fellow (grant 5F2-GM-28-775) in the laboratory of M. Meselson. E. R. S. is a Career Development Awardee of the National Institutes of Health.

REFERENCES

Campbell, A. (1962). Advanc. Genetics, 11, 101.
Campbell, A. (1965). Virology, 27, 329.
Campbell, A. & Zissler, J. (1966). Virology, 28, 659.
Echols, H. & Gingery, R. (1968) J. Mol. Biol. in the press.
Echols, H., Gingery, R. & Moore, L. (1968). J. Mol. Biol. in the press.
Fischer-Fantuzzi, L. (1967). Virology, 32, 18.
Gingery, R. & Echols, H. (1967). Proc. Nat. Acad. Sci., Wash. 58, 1507.
Gottesman, M. & Yarmolinsky, M. (1968). J. Mol. Biol. in the press.
Jordan, E. (1964). J. Mol. Biol. 10, 341.
Kellenberger, G., Zichichi, M. L. & Weigle, J. (1961). J. Mol. Biol. 3, 399.
Signer, E. R. (1968). Ann. Rev. Microbiol. in the press.
Signer, E. R. & Beckwith, J. R. (1966). J. Mol. Biol. 22, 33.
Signer, E. R. & Weil, J. (1968). J. Mol. Biol. in the press.
Zissler, J. (1967a). Ph.D. Thesis, University of Rochester.
Zissler, J. (1967b). Virology, 31, 189.

THE DISAPPEARANCE OF THYMINE DIMERS FROM DNA: AN ERROR-CORRECTING MECHANISM

BY R. B. SETLOW AND W. L. CARRIER

BIOLOGY DIVISION, OAK RIDGE NATIONAL LABORATORY*

Communicated by William Arnold, December 11, 1963

Recovery processes associated with ultraviolet irradiation (e.g., photoreactivation, heat reactivation, photoprotection, liquid-holding recovery, host-cell reactivation, and UV reactivation) probably act enzymatically.[1-5] These processes are not additive, but overlap one another,[5-9] indicating that even though they may act in different ways, they operate, at least in part, on identical UV lesions.

Ultraviolet irradiation of DNA results in the formation of intrastrand dimers between adjacent thymine residues.[10] The evidence indicates that such dimers account for a large fraction of the biological effects of UV on DNA.[10, 11] The dimers are split by 330–450 mu radiation in the presence of an extract from yeast,[12] and one may explain all the biological effects of photoreactivation on transforming DNA in terms of dimer-splitting.[13] Thymine dimers are stable to acid and to enzymic hydrolysis, and may be determined in small numbers when the DNA is labeled with tritium in thymidine. It is thus possible to follow the fate of radiation-induced lesions (thymine dimers produced by UV) in cells that are recovering from the effects of radiation, in the dark as well as in the light.

Thymine dimers block DNA synthesis *in vitro*[14] and *in vivo*.[15] Radiation-resistant cells (defined in terms of colony formation) can recover in the dark from such blocks and resume synthesis; sensitive cells cannot.[15] Cells that are to form colonies must synthesize DNA, and it is reasonable to assume that once DNA synthesis has resumed (and thymine dimers no longer block synthesis), the molecular events associated with the repair of damage to DNA have been completed. Thus, the time for DNA synthesis to resume in UV-irradiated cells can be considered a measure of the recovery time.

During and after the time that recovery takes place in the dark, dimers are conserved inside cells.[15]   Therefore, radiation-resistant cells do not recover in the dark by splitting thymine dimers.   The following data indicate that in resistant cells the dimers disappear from the acid-insoluble fraction of cells and appear in the acid-soluble fraction.   Thus, one step in the molecular repair process is the removal of thymine dimers from the polynucleotide chain.

Methods.—The following five strains of *Escherichia coli* were used: B_{s-1}, a radiation-sensitive strain that shows no host-cell reactivation;[16] B_{s-11}, a radiation-sensitive strain that shows host-cell reactivation;[17] and B, a strain of intermediate sensitivity, forming long filaments after UV, and showing host-cell reactivation. These three strains were obtained from Ruth Hill.   Strain B/r (ORNL), obtained from Howard Adler, is a radiation-resistant strain showing host-cell reactivation. Strain 15 T⁻ has the UV sensitivity of B.

Unless otherwise mentioned in figure legends, bacteria were labeled by growing them at 37°C for 4–5 generation times (35 min/generation) in M9 medium: NH_4Cl, 1 gm; NaCl, 5 gm; Na_2HPO_4, 6 gm; KH_2PO_4, 3 gm; $MgSO_4$, 0.1 gm; glucose, 4 gm; one liter of H_2O, also containing 2 μg/ml of thymidine-methyl-H^3 (6.7 c/ mmole), 100 μg/ml of adenosine, and 2.5 mg/ml of casamino acids.[18]   After several cycles of centrifugation and resuspension in nonradioactive medium, bacteria were resuspended at a concentration of about 5×10^7/ml in M9 or in M9 without glucose. After UV irradiation, the cells were kept at 37°C (in M9 without glucose) or grown in M9 plus casamino acids.   At various times approximately 1 ml of cell suspension was centrifuged.   Breakage of cells by sonication at this stage gave results similar to those obtained without sonication.   Trichloroacetic acid (TCA)-insoluble and -soluble fractions of cells were obtained as follows.   Cells were resuspended in 100 μl H_2O containing 75 μg calf thymus DNA (Worthington), and 100 μl of cold 10% TCA was added.   After 5 min the precipitates were spun down and the supernatants were removed.   The precipitates were resuspended and precipitated again with TCA.   The TCA supernatants were combined, extracted with ether to remove the TCA, and evaporated to dryness.   The TCA-insoluble material was washed with 95% ethyl alcohol and dried.   Samples were then resuspended in 150 μl of 98% formic acid and hydrolyzed in sealed tubes at 175°C.   Chromatographic and counting procedures were the same as used previously.[15]   Acid-insoluble samples had 30,000–100,000 (usually 60,000) counts/min.

Monochromatic UV was obtained from a large quartz-prism monochromator. The average intensity through the irradiated samples was approximately 5 ergs/ mm^2/sec.   Photoreactivating illumination, approximately 10,000 ergs/mm^2/min, between 310 and 400 mμ, was supplied by three black-light lamps placed 15 cm above samples in a 37°C incubator.

Results.—The radiation dose used in most of this work, 200 ergs/mm^2 at 265 mμ, stops DNA synthesis in strains B_{s-1} and B_{s-11},[15, 19] and inactivates colony-forming ability almost completely.[20]   It inhibits DNA synthesis for approximately 60 min in strains 15 T⁻, B, and B/r,[15, 19, 21] and yields 0.1%, 0.1%, and 10% colony formation, respectively, when cells are plated on M9 agar containing casamino acids.

Two types of experiments, indirect and direct, indicate that the ability of cells to resume DNA synthesis following UV irradiation is associated with a change in the state of the dimers.   The indirect experiment makes use of the fact that a

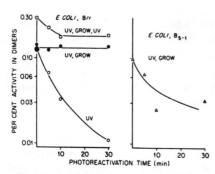

Fig. 1.—The effect of photoreactivating conditions on thymine dimers in bacterial cells. "UV" means a dose of 200 ergs/mm², 265 mμ followed by photoreactivation. "UV, grow" means that the cells were incubated at 37°C in M9 plus casamino acids for 1 hr before exposure to photoreactivating light, and "UV, grow, UV" means that cells were given a second dose of 200 ergs/mm² before photoreactivation.

photoreactivating enzyme preparation from yeast splits dimers in denatured DNA much more slowly than in native DNA and does not split dimers in small oligonucleotides.[22] Figure 1 shows that the dimers in B$_{s-1}$ are split by photoreactivating conditions at 1 hr of growth after UV irradiation. However, in resistant strain B/r only the dimers formed shortly before photoreactivation can be split. The dimers are not split if the cells grow between the initial ultraviolet irradiation and photoreactivating conditions.[23] The implication of these results is that in resistant bacteria the dimers, after a period of growth, are no longer in the native bacterial DNA, even though there has been negligible DNA synthesis during this time.

A direct indication that the dimers in B/r change state while DNA synthesis is blocked is given in Table 1, which shows that the dimers disappear from the acid-insoluble fraction and appear in the soluble fraction of cells growing after UV irradiation. The facts that (a) the fraction of dimers in the acid-soluble fraction increases with time, and (b) all the dimers appear in this fracton, show that we were observing the removal of dimer-containing oligonucleotides from the bacterial DNA, and not just a general DNA breakdown. Most of the thymine in the acid-soluble fraction comes from the nucleotide pool of the labeled cells.

Figure 2 shows the dimer content of the acid-insoluble fractions of several strains of *E. coli* as a function of time after irradiation. In such experiments both the total radioactive label and the number of dimers in cells are conserved.[24] In the sensitive strain the dimers remain in the acid-insoluble fraction, whereas in resistant strains they disappear from the insoluble and appear in the soluble fraction. The dimers in growing cells[25] are removed more rapidly from the acid-insoluble fraction than those in cells suspended in nonnutrient medium.

The dimers that appear in the acid-soluble fraction of resistant cells seem to be in oligonucleotides because before formic acid hydrolysis the radioactivity associ-

TABLE 1

THE DISTRIBUTION OF THYMINE DIMERS BETWEEN ACID-SOLUBLE AND -INSOLUBLE FRACTIONS OF *E. coli* B/r*

		Time after UV (min)		
Counts/min	Zero	30	60	90
Soluble $\left\{\begin{array}{l}\widehat{TT}\\ T\end{array}\right.$	0	69	94	80
	10,600	7,060	5,490	3,570
Insoluble $\left\{\begin{array}{l}\widehat{TT}\\ T\end{array}\right.$	72	26	4	7
	47,700	61,600	62,100	61,200
$\dfrac{\text{Total } \widehat{TT}}{\text{Total } T}$ (%)	0.124	0.138	0.145	0.134

* Bacteria irradiated with 200 ergs/mm², 265 mμ were incubated at 37° in M9 plus casamino acids. At various times approximately equal samples were removed, and radioactivity associated with thymine and thymine dimers in the TCA-soluble and -insoluble fractions was determined.

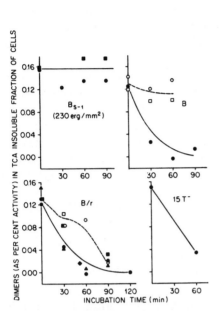

FIG. 2.—The fraction of thymine dimers in the TCA-insoluble fractions of several strains of *E. coli* at various times after irradiation with 200 ergs/mm², 265 mμ (230 ergs/mm² for strain B_{s-1}). Different symbols refer to separate experiments. Closed symbols and solid lines represent cells incubated in nutrient medium (M9 plus casamino acids), and open symbols and dashed lines cells in nonnutrient medium (M9 without glucose).

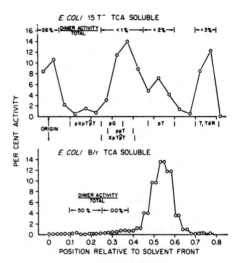

FIG. 3.—Chromatograms of the TCA-soluble fractions of cells incubated for 1 hr in M9 plus casamino acids after 200 ergs/mm², 265 mμ. Labeled cells were grown for approximately two division times in nonradioactive medium before irradiation, thus reducing the sizes of the labeled, acid-soluble pools to 4% for B/r and 2% for 15 T⁻. Acid-soluble material was applied to DEAE-cellulose paper, and the chromatograms were developed with 0.25 M NH₄HCO₃. They were cut into strips (1 cm for 15 T⁻, 0.5 cm for B/r), the radioactivity was eluted with 1 M NH₄HCO₃, and counted in a scintillation counter. The positions of known markers are indicated. The per cent activity in dimers for several of the regions of the chromatograms are shown.

ated with them migrates on DEAE paper at the same or slower rates than trinucleotides containing dimers[22, 26] (Fig. 3). The actual sizes of the pieces removed from DNA are not given by these data because long polynucleotides (a) are not acid-soluble, and (b) may be degraded by intracellular nucleases. An estimate of the number of nucleotides removed per dimer may be obtained from the increase in acid-soluble radioactivity in cells during the removal of dimers from DNA.[27] In the experiment on 15 T⁻ shown in Figures 2 and 3 we found that after 60 min growth there were in the acid-soluble fraction from 1 ml of cell suspension increases of 1200 counts/min in thymine and 160 counts/min in dimers. Thus, there were on the average 7.5 thymines or 30 bases hydrolyzed per dimer removed from DNA. The size of the polynucleotides remaining at the origin, shown in Figure 3, cannot be estimated from the value of TÎ/T because this fraction may be contaminated with a slight amount of acid-insoluble material. Presumably the charge on the oligonucleotides prevents them from escaping from cells, and thus accounts for the conservation of dimers in cells.

Discussion.—The disappearance of dimers from the acid-insoluble fraction in growing radiation-resistant cells is accomplished in approximately the time it takes DNA synthesis to resume. Although these data indicate nothing about the mechanism of dimer removal, nor what, if anything, takes their place in the DNA, it is reasonable to suppose that DNA synthesis resumes in resistant cells because thymine dimers are removed.[28]   Since DNA synthesis is necessary for continued cellular proliferation, the removal of dimers from DNA chains may be a necessary first step in the recovery of cells from UV irradiation.   However, since in growing B and B/r the dimers disappear from the acid-insoluble fraction at about the same rates, but the ability to form colonies is very different, removal of dimers cannot be the only step leading to recovery.[29]   Even in B/r the recovery process by dimer removal is not perfect, because photoreactivation conditions before growth lead to increased colony survival.   We may suppose that changes which influence the survival of cells take place before or after removal of dimers.   These changes may include a very slow random polymerization around the dimers,[14] further nuclease degradation of the DNA, and the insertion of bases into the vacancies left by the removal of dimer-containing oligonucleotides.[30]

The reactions that are responsible for the removal of dimers from DNA and those that restore DNA to the equivalent of its unirradiated state and the rates of these reactions are sufficient to explain many of the observed recovery phenomena of cells following UV irradiation.   In addition, the processes we have observed might be typical of all error-correcting mechanisms involving DNA chains of unnatural or non-Watson-Crick structure.

Summary.—Intrastrand thymine dimers formed by UV irradiation of DNA apparently account for a large fraction of the biological damage to DNA.   We have investigated the state of thymine dimers during the time in which resistant strains of *E. coli* recover from the UV-induced delays in DNA synthesis.   During this time the dimers disappear from the acid-insoluble fraction of the cells and appear in oligonucleotides in the acid-soluble fraction.   Dimers in the acid-soluble phase are not split by photoreactivating conditions.   In a sensitive strain the dimers remain in the insoluble phase and remain photoreactivable.   Thus, the onset of DNA synthesis is associated with thymine dimer removal, and one step in the recovery of cells from the effects of UV may be the removal of the dimers from DNA. This recovery mechanism could be applicable to other types of damage, or random errors in one strand of a double-stranded DNA.

We thank Paul Swenson for useful information and discussion.

* Operated by Union Carbide Corporation for the U.S. Atomic Energy Commission.

[1] Rupert, C. S., *J. Cellular Comp. Physiol.*, **58**, Suppl. 1, 57 (1961).

[2] Sauerbier, W., *Virology*, **15**, 465 (1961).

[3] Witkin, E. M., *J. Cellular Comp. Physiol.*, **58**, Suppl. 1, 135 (1961).

[4] Harm, W., in *Repair from Genetic Radiation Damage*, ed. by F. H. Sobels (New York: Macmillan, 1963), pp. 107–118.

[5] Harm, W., *Z. Vererbungslehre*, **94**, 67 (1963).

[6] Hill, R. F., and E. Simson, *J. Gen. Microbiol.*, **24**, 1 (1961).

[7] Metzger, K., *Photochem. Photobiol.*, **2**, 435 (1963).

[8] Jagger, J., W. C. Wise, and R. S. Stafford, *Photochem. Photobiol.*, in press.

[9] Castellani, A., J. Jagger, and R. B. Setlow, *Science*, in press.

[10] Wacker, A., *Progr. Nucl. Acid Res.*, **1**, 369 (1963).

[11] Setlow, R. B., and J. K. Setlow, these PROCEEDINGS, **48**, 1250 (1962).

[12] Wulff, D. L., and C. S. Rupert, *Biochem. Biophys. Res. Comm.*, **7**, 237 (1962).

[13] Setlow, J. K., and R. B. Setlow, *Nature*, **197**, 560 (1963).

[14] Bollum, F. J., and R. B. Setlow, *Biochim. et Biophys. Acta*, **68**, 599 (1963).

[15] Setlow, R. B., P. A. Swenson, and W. L. Carrier, *Science*, **142**, 1464 (1963).

[16] Ellison, S. A., R. R. Feiner, and R. F. Hill, *Virology*, **11**, 294 (1960).

[17] Hill, R. F., personal communication.

[18] Boyce, R. P., and R. B. Setlow, *Biochim. et Biophys. Acta*, **61**, 618 (1962).

[19] Setlow, R. B., and P. A. Swenson, unpublished results.

[20] The approximate mean lethal doses in ergs/mm² at 265 mμ for colony formation are: B_{s-1}, 0.5; B_{s-11}, 1.0; B, 25; B/r, 100.   The dose that acts as one effective block to DNA synthesis in strains B_{s-1} and B_{s-11} is 2 ergs/mm² (refs. 15, 19).

[21] Hanawalt, P., and R. Setlow, *Biochim. et Biophys. Acta*, **41**, 283 (1960).

[22] Setlow, R. B., W. L. Carrier, and F. J. Bollum, unpublished results.

[23] These results for dimer splitting are similar to those found for reactivation of colony formation.   Strains B and B/r are not photoreactivable if incubated for 1 hr in M9 plus casamino acids after UV, whereas B_{s-1} is photoreactivable under these conditions.

[24] In strain B_{s-11} (not as sensitive as B_{s-1} and showing host-cell reactivation) the dimers disappear from the acid-insoluble fraction at about one half the rate of those in B or B/r.   However, even for small UV doses, DNA synthesis does not resume, and at the doses used in this work many of the cells lyse (20% by 30 min and 40% by 60 min).   It is speculation that in this strain the dimers are "cut out" but that subsequent reactions are unable to "patch" the DNA to its original, native-type configuration, and hence the cells do not recover the ability to make DNA. In B_{s-1} there is a very slow appearance of dimers (20% in 60 min of growth) in the acid-soluble fraction; this may largely be the result of a generalized DNA breakdown in the absence of synthesis rather than a specific reaction that removes dimers from DNA.

[25] Both RNA and protein synthesis continue after UV.

[26] Bollum, F. J., and R. B. Setlow, *Fed. Proc.*, **21**, 374 (1962).

[27] This is a poor estimate because of uncertainty about the sizes of internal pools and the possible reincorporation of bases after degradation.

[28] Even a small number of blocks in DNA produce a large inhibitory effect on DNA synthesis. Therefore, detectable DNA synthesis does not begin during recovery until almost all the blocks have been removed.

[29] UV irradiation also induces a prolonged division delay in strain B, but not in B/r.   The 1/e dose for this delay is about 2 ergs/mm² [Deering, R. A., *J. Bacteriol.*, **76**, 123 (1958)].   This value is similar to that necessary to block DNA synthesis in the sensitive strains.

[30] We have been unable to determine if dimers removed from DNA are replaced by normal thymine residues in strain B/r.   The small amount of thymidine incorporation observed in irradiated cells placed in labeled medium 15–45 min after irradiation is approximately 10 times that necessary to replace all the dimers.   This incorporation may represent the regular synthesis that takes place as blocks to synthesis are removed, a slow synthesis around blocks, or replacement of oligonucleotides removed along with dimers.   The material incorporated after 200–400 ergs/mm², 265 mμ has the same relative TT frequency as normal DNA because irradiation of it with 30 × 10⁴ ergs/mm², 280 mμ produces the same fraction of activity in dimers (0.20–0.22) as found in normal DNA.   However, it is different from normal DNA in that it is degraded, in part, to acid-soluble material during irradiation *in vivo* with large UV exposures.   Moreover, in irradiated strain 15 T⁻ incorporated C¹⁴-bromouracil cannot be separated from the rest of the DNA by heating and quick cooling, as is possible for unirradiated 15 T⁻ [Pettijohn, D. E., and P. C. Hanawalt, *Biochim. et Biophys. Acta*, **72**, 127 (1963)].

ENZYMATIC BREAKAGE AND JOINING OF DEOXYRIBONUCLEIC ACID, I. REPAIR OF SINGLE-STRAND BREAKS IN DNA BY AN ENZYME SYSTEM FROM ESCHERICHIA COLI INFECTED WITH T4 BACTERIOPHAGE*

By Bernard Weiss† and Charles C. Richardson

DEPARTMENT OF BIOLOGICAL CHEMISTRY, HARVARD MEDICAL SCHOOL

Communicated by Eugene P. Kennedy, February 13, 1967

Enzymatic breakage and joining of preformed polynucleotide strands has been implicated in molecular recombination, the repair of ultraviolet-irradiated DNA, and the interconversion of linear and circular DNA molecules.[1] A possible intermediate, in each of these processes, is a duplex DNA molecule containing phosphodiester bond interruptions (single-strand breaks). This paper describes the purification and some properties of an enzyme system, polynucleotide ligase, which catalyzes the repair of single-strand breaks by the formation of phosphodiester bonds (Fig. 1). The enzyme system has been purified from *Escherichia coli* infected with T4 bacteriophage and found to require ATP for activity.

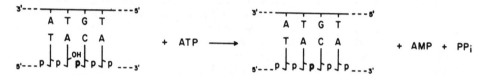

Fig. 1.—Polynucleotide ligase catalyzes the formation of a phosphodiester bond at the site of a single-strand break in a duplex DNA molecule, resulting in the covalent joining of two polynucleotides.

In order to isolate and to characterize the enzyme system, procedures have been developed (1) for the preparation and characterization of T7 DNA containing single-strand interruptions, (2) for distinguishing external 5'-phosphomonoesters from those located internally in a duplex molecule, and (3) for the removal of internal 5'-phosphomonoesters and their replacement with P³²-labeled groups. The latter procedure enables the synthesis of a unique substrate for the detection of enzymes which join polynucleotides.

Experimental Procedure.—Materials: Unlabeled and radioactively labeled nucleotides, salmon sperm DNA, and T7 phage DNA were obtained as previously described.[2] The purified enzymes were the same preparations previously described.[3] Spleen phosphodiesterase and pancreatic DNase (2000 units per standard vial) were products of the Worthington Biochemical Co. Concentrations of DNA are expressed as equivalents of nucleotide phosphorus.

Methods: (a) *Preparation of T7 DNA containing single-strand breaks (nicked DNA):* Pancreatic DNase is known to produce single-strand breaks in native DNA.[4, 5] The incubation mixture (12 ml) contained 1.3 mM T7 DNA, 67 mM Tris buffer (pH 8.0), 5 mM MgCl₂, and 0.17 unit of pancreatic DNase. The enzyme was diluted, immediately before use, into a solution containing 10 mM sodium acetate buffer (pH 5.5), 5 mM MgCl₂, 0.2 M NaCl, and bovine plasma albumin (0.5 mg per ml) to a concentration of 0.21 unit per ml. After incubation at 20° for 30 min, 0.4 ml of 0.5 M Na-EDTA (pH 8.0) was added, and the mixture was dialyzed against 0.01 M Tris buffer (pH 8.0)–0.02 M NaCl. This DNA, containing an average of eight single-strand breaks per strand (see section e), will be referred to as nicked DNA (Fig. 2b).

(b) *Preparation of T7 DNA containing internal P³²-phosphomonoesters:* Pancreatic DNase cleaves phosphodiester bonds so as to produce 5'-phosphoryl end groups.[6] These internal phos-

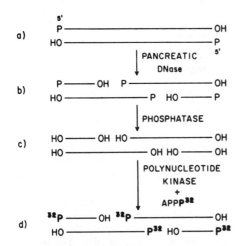

FIG. 2.—Scheme for the preparation of 5'-P³²-phosphoryl nicked DNA, substrate for polynucleotide ligase. The two strands of a duplex T7 DNA molecule are schematically represented by two parallel lines; the 5'-termini of each have been previously shown to bear phosphoryl groups.[2]

phomonoesters can be removed by incubation at elevated temperatures with alkaline phosphatase from *E. coli*. The incubation mixture (5.1 ml) contained 1.2 mM nicked DNA, 0.01 M Tris buffer (pH 8.0), 0.02 M NaCl, and 7 units of phosphatase. Incubation was at 65° for 30 min; additional enzyme (7 units) was added at 10 and 20 min. End-group analysis of the DNA revealed that 95% of the phosphomonoesters had been removed (Fig. 2c). These groups were replaced by P³²-phosphomonoesters by incubation with ATP³² in the polynucleotide kinase reaction.[7] The phosphatase incubation mixture was made 28 mM with Tris buffer (pH 8.0), 10 mM with MgCl₂, 17 mM with 2-mercaptoethanol, and 14 mM with potassium phosphate buffer (pH 7.5);[8] water was added to a final volume of 9 ml. After mixing, 0.17 μmoles of ATP³² (9 × 10⁹ cpm per μmole) and 500 units of polynucleotide kinase were added. Incubation was at 37° for 45 min with an additional 200 units of kinase added at 15 and 30 min.

The labeled nicked DNA was isolated by fractionation on a column of methylated albumin-Kieselguhr (20 ml of MAK in a column 3 cm in diameter).[9] A 6-ml portion of the phosphatase reaction mixture was diluted tenfold with 0.15 M NaCl–0.015 M sodium citrate and applied to the column. The adsorbent was washed with 100 ml of the above solution, followed by 200 ml of 0.05 M Tris buffer (pH 6.7)–0.4 M NaCl, and the DNA was eluted with 0.05 M Tris buffer (pH 6.7)–0.95 M NaCl. The eluate (25 ml) was dialyzed against 0.01 M Tris buffer (pH 7.9)–0.05 M NaCl.

The final preparation (3.7 μmoles of DNA in 30 ml) contained six 5'-P³²-phosphoryl end groups per original strand of T7 DNA (see below). Of these, 60% were located at the sites of single-strand interruptions. This DNA preparation will be referred to as 5'-P³²-phosphoryl nicked DNA (Fig. 2d), and details of its full characterization will be described separately.

(c) *Assay of polynucleotide ligase:* The standard assay measures the conversion of 5'-P³²-phosphomonoesters in nicked DNA into a form which remains acid-insoluble after incubation with phosphatase. Polynucleotide ligase was routinely diluted into a solution containing 0.05 M Tris buffer (pH 7.6), 0.01 M 2-mercaptoethanol, and bovine plasma albumin (0.5 mg per ml). The incubation mixture (0.3 ml) contained 0.02 mM 5'-P³²-phosphoryl nicked DNA, 0.066 mM ATP, 33 mM Tris buffer (pH 7.6), 6.6 mM MgCl₂, 6.6 mM 2-mercaptoethanol and 5 × 10⁻⁵ to 3 × 10⁻⁴ unit of enzyme. After incubation at 37° for 20 min, 0.2 ml of salmon sperm DNA (0.25 mg per ml), 0.5 ml of cold 0.6 M trichloroacetic acid, and 2.0 ml of cold water were added in succession. After centrifugation at 10,000 × g for 10 min, the supernatant fluid was discarded. Two ml of cold 0.01 M HCl were added to the tube, mixed, and recentrifuged, and the supernatant fluid was discarded. The precipitate was dissolved in 0.5 ml of 0.1 M NaOH and neutralized by adding 0.05 ml of 1.1 M HCl–0.2 M Tris. Alkaline phosphatase (10 μg) was added, and each reaction mixture was incubated for 15 min at 37°, followed by 15 min at 65°; then 0.5 ml of cold 0.6 M trichloroacetic acid and 2.0 ml of cold water were added. The precipitate was collected on glass filters, washed, and dried, and the radioactivity determined as previously described.[7]

The precipitate obtained from control incubations with ligase omitted contained 5% of the added radioactivity. The precipitate obtained from control incubations with both enzyme and phos-

TABLE 1

PURIFICATION OF POLYNUCLEOTIDE LIGASE

Fraction	Total activity (units)	Specific activity (units/mg)
I. Extract	1040	2.2
II. Streptomycin	450	1.0
III. Ammonium sulfate	450	3.9
IV. DEAE-cellulose	360	3.8
V. DEAE-cellulose	180	23
VI. Phosphocellulose	95	770

phatase omitted contained 95% of the added radioactivity.   One unit of the enzyme is defined as the amount catalyzing the conversion of 1 mμmole of P^{32}-phosphomonoesters into a phosphatase-resistant form in 20 min.   The activity was proportional to enzyme concentration in the range given above.

(d) *Large-scale preparation of DNA product of ligase reaction:*   For characterization of the DNA product of the reaction, 1.2 μmoles of 5'-P^{32}-phosphoryl nicked DNA was incubated in a reaction mixture (3 ml) containing 0.03 units of fraction VI and the same concentrations of the other components of the standard reaction mixture.   Incubation was for 60 min at 37°.   The reaction mixture was dialyzed extensively to remove ATP as previously described.[2]   Recovery of radioactivity and of DNA was 94%.

DNA containing only phosphatase-resistant P^{32} was prepared by incubating the product of the ligase reaction with phosphatase at 65°.   The phosphatase was removed by phenol extraction.[2]   After denaturation of the DNA product, 97% of the P^{32} was found to be resistant to phosphatase.

(e) *End-group analysis of DNA:*   The number of 5'-termini in a DNA preparation was determined, after denaturation and dephosphorylation of the DNA, by radioactive labeling of these end groups in the polynucleotide kinase reaction.[2, 3, 7]   The number of external 5'-termini in nicked DNA was measured by end-group labeling after treatment of the helical DNA with phosphatase at 37°.   Under appropriate conditions, at 37°, phosphatase will hydrolyze only external phosphomonoesters (less than 5% hydrolysis of internal phosphomonoesters).   The number of internal 5'-termini was determined by subtracting the number of external 5'-termini from the total number of 5'-termini, determined as described above.   The location of P^{32}-labeled phosphomonoesters in DNA preparations was determined in a similar manner.   A detailed description of the action of *E. coli* alkaline phosphatase on external and internal phosphomonoesters will be the subject of a separate paper.

(f) *Other methods:*   The following methods have been described previously: measurements of protein, deoxypentose, and phosphate; hydrolysis of DNA to either 5'- or 3'-mononucleotides;[2, 10] and electrophoretic separation of nucleotides and PP$_i$.[2]

(g) *Purification of polynucleotide ligase:*   All operations were performed at 4°, centrifugations were for 10 min at 10,000 $\times$ g, and all solutions contained 0.01 M 2-mercaptoethanol.   The results of a typical preparation are summarized in Table 1.

Preparation of extracts: T4r$^+$ phage-infected *E. coli* cells (5 gm) were grown, collected, and disrupted, and the cell debris was removed as previously described.[7]   The final supernatant fluid was diluted with buffer to an optical density at 260 mμ of 68 (fraction I).

Streptomycin: To 70 ml of extract were added, with stirring, 14 ml of 5% streptomycin sulfate over a 30-min period.   The suspension was centrifuged and the supernatant fluid was collected (fraction II).

Ammonium sulfate fractionation: To 77 ml of fraction II, 25.4 gm of ammonium sulfate were added, with stirring, over a 30-min period.   The precipitate was collected by centrifugation and dissolved in 10 ml of 0.01 M Tris buffer (pH 7.6)–0.1 M NaCl (fraction III).

DEAE-cellulose fractionation: A column of DEAE-cellulose (4 cm^2 $\times$ 12 cm) was washed with 1.5 liters of 0.01 M Tris buffer (pH 7.6).   Fraction III (135 mg of protein) was dialyzed against 2 liters of this buffer for 12 hr, and applied to the column.   The adsorbent was washed with 100 ml of the buffer, and the enzyme was eluted with 0.01 M Tris buffer (pH 7.6)–0.3 M NaCl.   Approximately 70% of the activity applied to the adsorbent was obtained in 50 ml of the eluate (fraction IV).

DEAE-cellulose chromatography: A column of DEAE-cellulose (4 cm^2 $\times$ 12 cm) was prepared and washed as before.   Fraction IV (100 mg of protein) was dialyzed for 12 hr against 2 liters of the washing buffer, applied to the column, and the adsorbent was washed with 100 ml of the same buffer. A linear gradient of elution (total volume of 900 ml) was applied with 0.01 M Tris buffer (pH 7.6) and 0.01 M Tris buffer (pH 7.6)–0.3 M NaCl as limiting concentrations. Of the activity applied, 80% was eluted between 6.6 and 8.7 resin bed volumes of effluent. The fractions containing enzyme of specific activity greater than 20 units per mg of protein were pooled (fraction V).

Phosphocellulose fractionation: A column of phosphocellulose (1 cm^2 $\times$ 11 cm) was prepared and washed with 1 liter of 0.01 M potassium phosphate buffer (pH 7.6)–0.1 M KCl. Sixty ml of fraction V were diluted to a volume of 110 ml with 0.01 M potassium phosphate buffer (pH 7.6) and then applied to the column. The adsorbent was washed with 25-ml portions of 0.01 M potassium phosphate buffer (pH 7.6) containing the following concentrations of KCl: 0.1 M, 0.25 M, of 0.5 M. Of the activity applied, 75% was obtained in 10 ml of the 0.5 M KCl eluate (fraction VI).

The phosphocellulose fraction was purified 350-fold over the extract and contained 10% of the activity initially present. Preparations of fraction VI have lost 50% of their activity during 2 weeks' storage in an ice bath.

Results.—*Appearance of polynucleotide ligase activity after infection with phage T4:* Polynucleotide ligase, measured by the standard assay, could be detected in extracts of *E. coli* about five minutes after infection with T4 phage. A maximal level of activity (2.2 units per mg of protein) was observed approximately 20 minutes after infection. Extracts of uninfected *E. coli* contained no detectable activity (less than 0.1 unit per mg of protein).

Properties of the purified enzyme: With fraction VI the activity in the standard assay was dependent upon the addition of ATP and Mg^{++} (Table 2). A sulfhydryl

TABLE 2

REQUIREMENTS FOR LIGASE ACTIVITY

Components	P^{32} resistant to phosphate ($\mu\mu$moles)
Complete system	0.20
Minus nicked DNA	<0.01
Minus ATP	<0.01
Minus Mg^{++}	<0.01
Minus 2-mercaptoethanol	0.12
Minus enzyme	<0.01

Conditions of the standard assay were employed with 2×10^{-4} unit of fraction VI in each tube. In testing the omission of 2-mercaptoethanol from the reaction mixture, the enzyme dilution was made in the absence of this compound.

compound was required for optimal activity. dATP, dTTP, GTP, or ADP could not replace ATP in the reaction mixture. The optimal pH range for the reaction is 7.5–8.0 in Tris buffer. During incubation in the standard assay, the purified enzyme (0.02 unit) released no acid-soluble radioactivity (less than 5%) from helical or denatured 5'-P^{32}-phosphoryl nicked DNA substrate, either in the presence or absence of ATP. There was no detectable hydrolysis of ATP^{32} (less than 1%) during a 30-minute incubation with 0.5 unit of fraction VI.

Reaction occurs at site of single-strand breaks: (1) *Requirement of single-strand breaks:* With the addition of excess ligase or with prolonged incubation, the amount of P^{32} resistant to phosphatase reached a limit. When an additional equal amount of DNA substrate was added to the reaction mixture, a further reaction occurred, equal in extent to that initially observed.

However, not all of the P^{32}-phosphomonoesters in the nicked DNA substrate were rendered resistant to phosphatase during prolonged incubation in the ligase reaction. As shown in Table 3, the limit of the reaction could be correlated closely with the number of internal P^{32}-phosphomonoesters present in a substrate.

TABLE 3
REQUIREMENT FOR SINGLE-STRAND BREAKS

DNA	P^{32} at single-strand breaks (%)	P^{32} made resistant to phosphatase (%)
Native DNA	<5	<5
Nicked DNA		
Externally labeled	<12	<5
Externally and internally labeled	50	50
Internally labeled	85	90
Denatured, nicked DNA	<5	<5

Each DNA preparation was tested in the standard assay. The percentage of total P^{32} made resistant to phosphatase represents the limit reached in a 30-min incubation with the addition of 0.02 unit of fraction VI at 0 and 15 min. The terms externally and internally labeled refer to the presence of external and internal 5'-P^{32}-phosphomonoesters, respectively. The DNA's were prepared and the amount of P^{32}-phosphomonoesters located at single-strand breaks in each was determined as described in *Methods*.

Samples of DNA's containing different ratios of internal to external phosphomonoesters were incubated in reaction mixtures containing an excess of enzyme. Native or nicked T7 DNA bearing only external P^{32}-phosphomonoesters did not serve as substrates. However, nicked DNA preparations in which 50 and 85 per cent of the P^{32}-phosphomonoesters were internally located were substrates; 50 and 90 per cent, respectively, of their total P^{32} became resistant to phosphatase. Denaturation of DNA preparations containing internal P^{32}-phosphomonoesters destroyed their ability to function as substrates.

(2) *Identification of P^{32}-phosphomonoesters after the ligase reaction:* Evidence that the reaction involved only internal phosphomonoesters was also obtained by determining the location of the unreacted phosphomonoesters in the DNA product (Table 4). All of the original external P^{32}-phosphomonoesters were still present as such; but 95 per cent of those phosphomonoesters initially present at single-strand breaks had become resistant to phosphatase.

Characterization of the DNA product: (1) *3', 5'-Phosphodiester bond formation at sites of joining.* A product of the ligase reaction, containing only phosphatase-resistant P^{32} (see *Methods*), was hydrolyzed with pancreatic DNase and snake venom phosphodiesterase. More than 95 per cent of the radioactivity was recovered as nucleoside 5'-monophosphates. When the sample was hydrolyzed with micrococcal and spleen nucleases, more than 95 per cent of the radioactivity was identified as nucleoside 3'-monophosphates. Confirmation of the presence of P^{32} in 3',5'-phosphodiester bonds was obtained by hydrolyzing the DNA with *E. coli* exonuclease I. All of the P^{32} (more than 90%) was recovered as 5'-mononucleotides. (Exonuclease I is unable to hydrolyze the phosphodiester bond of a dinucleotide and has been used previously to determine the location of P^{32} in a polynucleotide.)[7]

TABLE 4
IDENTIFICATION OF P^{32}-PHOSPHOMONOESTERS AFTER LIGASE REACTION

DNA	External P^{32}-monoesters	Internal P^{32}-monoesters (percentage of total P^{32})	Phosphatase-insensitive P^{32}
Nicked DNA substrate	33	67	<1
Product	35	3	62

The percentage of external and internal P^{32}-phosphomonoesters and of phosphatase-resistant P^{32} in the substrate and product were determined as described in *Methods*. The nicked DNA substrate, containing internal and external P^{32}-phosphomonoesters, and the product of the ligase reaction were prepared as described in *Methods*.

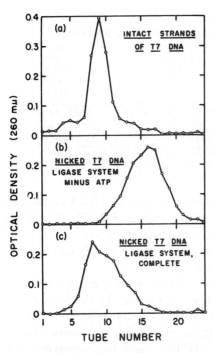

OPTICAL DENSITY (260 mμ)

(a) INTACT STRANDS OF T7 DNA

(b) NICKED T7 DNA LIGASE SYSTEM MINUS ATP

(c) NICKED T7 DNA LIGASE SYSTEM, COMPLETE

TUBE NUMBER

Fig. 3.—Analysis of the DNA product of the ligase reaction by preparative zone sedimentation in alkaline sucrose gradients. T7 DNA was sedimented prior to any enzymatic incubations (a), after treatment with pancreatic DNase (nicked DNA) followed by incubation in the ligase reaction from which ATP was omitted (b), and after treatment with pancreatic DNase followed by incubation in the complete ligase reaction (c). All DNA preparations were denatured prior to sedimentation.

Nicked T7 DNA (400 mμmoles) was prepared as described in *Methods* and incubated for 60 min in the ligase reaction (0.6 ml) with 0.15 unit of fraction VI. A control incubation contained no ATP. The reaction mixtures were chilled, and 0.025 ml of 0.5 M sodium EDTA (pH 8.0) was added. After dialysis for 18 hr at 4° against 0.01 M Tris buffer (pH 7.4)–0.05 M NaCl, the DNA was denatured and 300 mμmoles were analyzed by zone sedimentation in alkali as previously described.[2]

(2) *Demonstration, by sedimentation analysis, that polynucleotides are joined:* Zone sedimentation of DNA in alkali can provide information about the molecular weight of single polynucleotide strands.[11] Denatured T7 DNA, prior to any enzymatic treatment, sedimented as a single component (Fig. 3a). By contrast, denatured, nicked DNA sedimented at a greatly reduced rate; no intact single strands were found in the preparation. When the helical nicked DNA was incubated in the ligase reaction, at least 80 per cent of the fragmented DNA increased in sedimentation rate, and approximately 50 per cent acquired sedimentation properties indistinguishable from those of intact strands of T7 DNA (Fig. 3c). In a control experiment helical, nicked DNA was incubated in the ligase reaction in the *absence* of ATP and then analyzed in a similar manner (Fig. 3b). After incubation, this DNA had sedimentation properties identical to those of the untreated nicked DNA.

Zone sedimentation of these DNA preparations at neutral pH, without prior denaturation, revealed that they all had the same sedimentation properties. This finding indicated that no end-to-end joining of duplex molecules had occurred and confirmed the results described in Table 3.

(3) *Decrease in 5′-termini of DNA during ligase reaction:* End-group analysis of the nicked DNA and the DNA product of the polynucleotide ligase reaction provided an additional means for demonstrating the joining of polynucleotides. A preparation of nicked T7 DNA contained 1.7 external and 7.1 internal 5′-termini per original intact strand. After incubation in the ligase reaction (conditions of incubation and isolation of DNA as in Fig. 3), the DNA product still contained 1.7 external 5′-termini but only 1.6 internal 5′-termini per strand.

AMP and PP_i are products of the reaction: In order to identify the reaction products shown in Figure 1, T7 DNA was incubated with polynucleotide ligase in

TABLE 5

IDENTIFICATION OF AMP AND PP$_i$ AS PRODUCTS OF THE LIGASE REACTION

Time (min)	ATP (mμ moles)	AMP (mμ moles)	PP$_i$ (mμ moles)
0	10.4	<0.1	<0.1
30	7.2	3.4	3.4
Δ	−3.2	+3.4	+3.4

T7 DNA was incubated in a ligase reaction with pancreatic DNase. The reaction mixture (0.3 ml) contained 0.33 mM T7 DNA, 0.034 mM ATP (H^3-ATP and γ-P^{32}-ATP), 6.6 mM MgCl$_2$, 6.6 mM 2-mercaptoethanol, 33 mM Tris buffer (pH 7.6), 264 mM KCl, 10 μg of bovine plasma albumin, 0.18 units of pancreatic DNase, and 0.5 units of polynucleotide ligase (fraction VI). After 30 min of incubation at 37°, a 0.02-ml sample was removed and analyzed for AMP, ADP, ATP, and PP$_i$ by electrophoresis at pH 5 (see *Methods*). Recovery of radioactivity was greater than 95%. PP$_i$ was further identified by its failure to adsorb to Norit and to complex with molybdate[12] unless first treated with yeast pyrophosphatase. When DNA, pancreatic DNase, or the ligase was omitted, less than 1% of the ATP was consumed. No ADP (less than 1% of AMP formed) was detected in the reaction mixture, after 30 min of incubation.

the presence of pancreatic DNase. This permitted recycling of DNA in alternate hydrolysis and repair reactions, with a large net hydrolysis of ATP. The disappearance of ATP from the reaction mixture paralleled the appearance of equal amounts of AMP and PP$_i$ (Table 5). This reaction was completely dependent on the presence of DNA, DNase, and polynucleotide ligase.

Discussion.—T4 phage infection of *E. coli* induces an enzyme system which catalyzes the repair of single-strand breaks in a DNA duplex by the formation of phosphodiester bonds; ATP and Mg^{++} are required for the reaction. The observed cleavage of ATP to AMP and PP$_i$ suggests two possible mechanisms for the formation of these phosphodiester bonds. (1) PP$_i$ could be transferred from ATP to a 5'-phosphoryl terminus at a single-strand break, to form AMP and an activated 5'-terminus bearing a triphosphate. Condensation of the polynucleotides would release PP$_i$. (2) Alternatively, activation could result from the formation of a 5'-phosphoryl DNA adenylate intermediate (ADP-DNA), releasing PP$_i$. In this case the formation of phosphodiester bonds would eliminate AMP. Although the ligase system has been purified 350-fold, it is not known if more than one enzyme is involved in the over-all reaction. However, it appears that this enzyme system, by activating a polynucleotide, provides a mechanism for the formation of phosphodiester bonds which differs from those usually invoked for DNA synthesis.[13] (See *Note added in proof.*)

The function of this enzyme system *in vivo* is not known, but the molecular events which have been observed after T-even phage infection of *E. coli* suggest the following possible role. After infection, parental phage DNA undergoes extensive fragmentation and dispersion among other parental and progeny molecules.[14–16] These recombinant molecules contain single-strand interruptions which are eventually repaired, so that the recombined fragments are covalently joined. It is possible that polynucleotide ligase is involved in this last step. Although polynucleotide ligase activity has been identified only in cells infected with T4 phage, it is possible that it exists in greatly reduced amounts in uninfected cells. For example, Gellert[17] has recently described an activity in extracts of several *E. coli* strains which converts hydrogen-bonded circles of λ DNA to covalent circles.

Other *in vitro* studies on molecular recombination and DNA repair will be greatly facilitated by the availability of polynucleotide ligase. When used in conjunction with the techniques described in this paper, the ligase will enable the preparation of radioactively labeled DNA substrates for use in identifying other enzymatic steps involved in these processes.

Summary.—Polynucleotide ligase, purified 350-fold from *E. coli* infected with T4 bacteriophage, catalyzes the covalent joining of two segments of an interrupted strand in a DNA duplex. The reaction requires ATP and results in the formation of phosphodiester bonds, AMP, and PP_i. The enzymatic repair of single-strand breaks in T7 DNA has been demonstrated by sedimentation and end-group analysis.

Note added in proof: Purified preparations of polynucleotide ligase catalyze an ATP-PP_i^{32} exchange which is not dependent on DNA. If this exchange is a property of the ligase system, then activation of the DNA may involve an enzyme-adenylate intermediate.

We acknowledge the technical assistance of Mrs. Ann Thompson.

The abbreviations used in this paper are those described in *J. Biol. Chem.* Nicked DNA is used to describe bihelical DNA containing phosphodiester bond interruptions (single-strand breaks) in each of its two strands. 5'-P^{32}-phosphoryl nicked DNA is nicked DNA containing P^{32}-labeled phosphomonoesters located both internally and externally in the DNA duplex. External and internal phosphomonoesters are used to describe the location of these groups in a DNA duplex. ATP^{32} is ATP labeled with P^{32} in the γ-phosphate.

* This work was supported by U. S. Public Health Service grant AI-06045.

† Special fellow of the U. S. Public Health Service, award GM-29,562.

[1] See Meselson, M., in *Heritage from Mendel*, ed. R. A. Brink (Madison, Wis.: Univ. of Wis. Press, 1967), p. 81.

[2] Richardson, C. C., *J. Mol. Biol.*, **15**, 49 (1966).

[3] Weiss, B., and C. C. Richardson, *J. Mol. Biol.*, **23**, 405 (1967).

[4] Thomas, C. A., Jr., *J. Am. Chem. Soc.*, **78**, 1861 (1956).

[5] Schumaker, V. N., E. G. Richards, and H. K. Schachman, *J. Am. Chem. Soc.*, **78**, 4230 (1956).

[6] Sinsheimer, R. L., *J. Biol. Chem.*, **208**, 445 (1954).

[7] Richardson, C. C., these Proceedings, **54**, 158 (1965).

[8] The presence of phosphate in the reaction mixture effectively inhibits the action of *E. coli* alkaline phosphatase on the ATP and the phosphorylated DNA product.

[9] Sueoka, N., and T. Y. Cheng, *J. Mol. Biol.*, **4**, 161 (1962).

[10] Josse, J., A. D. Kaiser, and A. Kornberg, *J. Biol. Chem.*, **236**, 864 (1961).

[11] Studier, F. W., *J. Mol. Biol.*, **11**, 373 (1965).

[12] Martin, J. B., and D. M. Doty, *Analyt. Chem.*, **21**, 965 (1949).

[13] Mitra, S., and A. Kornberg, *J. Gen. Physiol.*, **49** (6), pt. 2, 59 (1966).

[14] Hershey, A. D., and E. Burgi, in *Genetic Mechanisms: Structure and Function*, Cold Spring Harbor Symposia on Quantitative Biology, vol. 21 (1956), p. 91.

[15] Shahn, E., and A. Kozinski, *Virology*, **30**, 455 (1966).

[16] Anraku, N., and J. Tomizawa, *J. Mol. Biol.*, **12**, 805 (1965).

[17] Gellert, M., these Proceedings, **57**, 148 (1967).

IV
Molecular Basis of Mutagenesis

Introduction

The understanding of mutation and its usefulness as a tool for biological investigation required the development of artificial methods of increasing the mutation rate by many orders of magnitude over the low spontaneous rate. Such methods involving the exposure of cells to x-rays were introduced in 1927 by H. J. Muller.[157] Other forms of radiation as well as a wide variety of chemical mutagens are now in use. Artificial transmutation has been most valuable in providing a wide variety of genetic variants for biologic study. Indeed the majority of the studies reported in this book have benefited directly or indirectly from this technique. This section will be limited to a discussion of chemicals that produce relatively specific point mutations since these have been the most useful to molecular biology. An excellent though somewhat dated review of this subject has been written by E. Freese.[167]

Watson and Crick suggested a mechanism for spontaneous mutation based upon their model for the DNA structure (see their paper in Section I). Their hypothesis was that a tautomeric shift in any of the four DNA bases would permit the alternative purine-pyrimidine pairing to occur between template and adsorbed mononucleotides during synthesis. Since the normally occurring tautomeric forms are strongly favored, the resulting mutation rate should be low. It is still not known if the tautomeric shift in base structure is a frequent cause of so-called spontaneous mutation, but the Watson-Crick suggestion was important because it introduced us to thinking about mutation in terms of nucleic acid structure. Subsequently Brenner, Barnett, Crick and Orgel (in collection) provided an explanation for the mutagenic character of two important classes of chemicals, the so-called base analogue class typified by 5-bromodeoxyuridine (BD) and the acridine class typified by proflavin (PF). Members of the base analogue class are believed to function by being incorporated into the DNA structure and producing a higher

than spontaneous frequency of mispairing. Members of the acridine class are believed to become sandwiched between existing bases or base pairs producing either deletions or additions of one or more bases to the DNA molecule during synthesis. This explanation accounts for the observation that mutants produced by a mutagen belonging to one of these groups are induced to revert by a mutagen of the same group but not the other group.

The subsequent studies presented in this section have supported the occurrence of these two different types of point mutation. In the Crick, Barnett, Brenner and Watts-Tobin paper (in collection) the suppressibility of acridine dye induced and spontaneously induced phase shift mutants was studied to obtain evidence on the general nature of the genetic code for proteins. The Crick *et al.* paper illustrates particularly well how one goes from an hypothesis to the planning and execution of a complex series of experiments. The most important contribution of this paper was the conclusion that the genetic code is highly degenerate; this was to be verified by later biochemical studies (Section VI). When this work was reported the absolute sign of any particular phase shift mutation was not known. That is, it was not known if any particular phase shift was the result of the addition or the loss of a base in the DNA. Recently Crick and Brenner[180] have found a method of predicting the sign of the phase shift and it turns out that the sign convention arbitrarily adopted in the Crick *et al.* paper was correct.

In the last paper of this section Champe and Benzer used two base analogues that become incorporated into DNA, 2-aminopurine and 5-bromodeoxyuridine, and one base analogue that becomes incorporated into RNA, 5-fluorouracil, in a preliminary attempt to decipher the sequence of nucleotides in a messenger RNA molecule. Although this may not be the best approach to studying messenger RNA sequences, this paper does illustrate the sophisticated uses to which base analogue mutagens can be put. We shall return to such uses in later sections.

It would be difficult to conclude this section without mentioning a very interesting

151

series of investigations on nitrous acid induced mutants of Tobacco Mosaic Virus.[168, 169] Nitrous acid acts directly on nucleic acid, converting the amino substituents of the bases to hydroxyl groups. Three of the four bases, adenine, guanine and cytosine, are converted by deamination to hypoxanthine, xanthine and uracil respectively. It is believed that hypoxanthine codes like adenine but that xanthine cannot code for any of the four bases. Brief treatment of TMV or TMV-RNA with HNO_2 followed by infection results in mutant viruses. The mutant viruses have been ex-amined for amino acid changes in the viral coat protein. The amino acid differences between wild type and mutant coat protein must have resulted from a deamination reaction on the virus RNA. By considering the large number of amino acid changes that are produced in this way it was possible to come to some conclusions about the relationship between amino acid codons. At one time it looked as though these investigations might crack the genetic code; however, the more direct biochemical approach of Nirenberg and Leder (Section VI) was to prevail.

Bibliography

157. H. J. Muller, (1927). Artificial Transmutation of the Gene. Science **66**, 84.

158. F. J. Ryan and L. K. Wainwright, (1954). Nuclear Segregation and the Growth of Clones of Spontaneous Mutants of Bacteria. J. Gen. Microbiol. **11**, 364.

159. H. Schuster, (1960). The Reaction of Nitrous Acid with Deoxyribonucleic Acid. Biochem. Biophys. Res. Comm. **2**, 320.

160. S. Benzer, (1961). On the Topography of the Genetic Fine Structure. Proc. Natl. Acad. Sci. U.S. **47**, 403.

161. L. S. Lerman, (1961). Structural Considerations in the Interaction of DNA and Acridines. J. Mol. Biol. **3**, 18.

162. A. Orgel and S. Brenner, (1961). Mutagenesis of Bacteriophage T₄ by Acridines. J. Mol. Biol. **3**, 762.

163. T. A. Trautner, M. N. Schwartz and A. Kornberg, (1962). Enzymatic Synthesis of Deoxyribonucleic Acid, X. Influence of Bromouracil Substitutions on Replication. Proc. Natl. Acad. Sci. U.S. **48**, 449.

164. S. P. Champe and S. Benzer, (1962). An Active Cistron Fragment. J. Mol. Biol. **4**, 228.

165. S. Benzer and S. P. Champe, (1962). A Change from Nonsense to Sense in the Genetic Code. Proc. Natl. Acad. Sci. U.S. **48**, 1114.

166. S. Benzer and S. Champe, (1962). Ambivalent rII Mutants of Phage T₄. Proc. Natl. Acad. Sci. U.S. **47**, 1025.

167. E. Freese, (1963). Molecular Mechanism of Mutations in Molecular Genetics Part I. Ed. by J. H. Taylor, Academic Press.

168. H. Schuster, (1963). The Ribonucleic Acids of Viruses, in the Nucleic Acids III. Academic Press.

169. A. Tsugita and H. Fraenkel-Conrat, (1963). Contributions from TMV Studies to the Problem of Genetic Information Transfers and Coding, in Molecular Genetics Part I. Ed. by J. H. Taylor, Academic Press, 477.

170. I. Tessman, R. K. Poddar and S. Kumar, (1964). Identification of the Altered Bases in Mutated Single-Stranded DNA. I. *In vitro* Mutagenesis by Hydroxylamine, Ethyl Methane Sulfonate and Nitrous Acid. J. Mol. Biol. **9**, 352.

171. B. D. Howard and I. Tessman, (1964). Identification of the Altered Bases in Mutated Single-Stranded DNA. II. *In vivo* Mutagenesis by 5-Bromodeoxyuridine and 2AP. III. Mutagenesis by U. V. Light. J. Mol. Biol. **9**, 364, 372.

172. D. M. Neville and D. R. Davies, (1966). Interaction of Acridine Dyes with DNA: An X-ray Diffraction and Optical Investigation. J. Mol. Biol. **17**, 57.

173. E. Terzaghi, Y. Okada, G. Streisinger, J. Emrich, M. Inouye and A. Tsugita, (1966). Change of a Sequence of Amino Acids in Phage T₄ Lysozyme by Acridine Induced Mutations. Proc. Natl. Acad. Sci. U.S. **56**, 500.

174. H. E. Kubitschek, (1966). Mutation Without Segregation in Bacteria with Reduced Dark Repair Ability. Proc. Natl. Acad. Sci. U.S. **55**, 269.

175. C. Yanofsky, E. C. Cox and V. Horn, (1966). The Unusual Mutagenic Specificity of an *E. coli* Mutator Gene. Proc. Natl. Acad. Sci. U.S. **55**, 274.

176. P. J. Zamenhof, (1966). A Genetic Locus Responsible for Generalized High Mutability in *E. coli*. Proc. Natl. Acad. Sci. U.S. **56**, 845.

177. S. Zamenhof, L. H. Heldenmuth and P. J. Zamenhof, (1966). Studies on Mechanisms for the Maintenance of Constant Mutability: Mutability and the Resistance to Mutagens. Proc. Natl. Acad. Sci. U.S. **55**, 50.

178. R. P. Boyce, (1966). Production of Additional Sites of DNA Breakdown in Bromouracil Containing *E. coli* Exposed to U. V. Light. Nature **209**, 688.

179. J. F. Speyer, J. D. Karam and A. B. Lenny, (1966). On the Role of DNA Polymerase in Base Selection. Cold Spring Harbor Symp. Quant. Biol. **31**, 693.

180. F. H. C. Crick and S. Brenner, (1967). The Absolute Sign of Certain Phase-Shift Mutants in Bacteriophage T₄. J. Mol. Biol. **26**, 361.

181. R. G. Martin, (1967). Frameshift Mutants in the Histidine Operon of S. typhimurium. J. Mol. Biol. **26**, 311.

182. D. Zipser and A. Newton, (1967). The Influence of Deletions on Polarity. J. Mol. Biol. **25**, 567.

183. M. Osborn, S. Person, S. Phillips and F. Funk, (1967). Mutagen Specificity in Bacteria using Nonsense Mutants of Bacteriophage T₄. J. Mol. Biol. **26**, 437.

184. P. D. Lawley and P. Brookes, (1967). Interstrand Cross-linking of DNA by Difunctional Alkylating Agents. J. Mol. Biol. **25**, 143.

185. A. M. Liquori, F. Ascoli, and M. Savino, (1967). Competitive Effect of Spermidine on the Solubilization of 3, 4-Benzpyrene in DNA Solutions. J. Mol. Biol. **24**, 123.

186. W. J. Brammer, H. Berger and C. Yanofsky, (1967). Altered Amino Acid Sequences Produced by Reversion of Frameshift Mutants of the Tryptophan Synthetase Gene of E. coli. Proc. Natl. Acad. Sci. U.S. **58**, 1499.

187. W. H. McClain and S. P. Champe, (1967). Detection of a Peptide Determined by the rIIB Cistron of Phage T₄. Proc. Natl. Acad. Sci. U.S. **58**, 1182.

188. R. J. Samaha, W. White and R. L. Herrmann, (1967). Effect of Acridine Orange Upon an Hfr Strain of E. coli K12 Displaying Unusual Transfer Kinetics. J. Mol. Biol. **28**, 513.

189. T. T. Puck and F. Kao, (1967). Genetics of Somatic Mammalian Cells. V. Treatment with 5-Bromodeoxyuridine and Visible Light for Isolation of Nutritionally Deficient Mutants. Proc. Natl. Acad. Sci. U.S. **58**, 1227.

190. M. Inouye, E. Akaboshi, A. Tsugita, G. Streisinger and Y. Okada, (1967). A Frameshift Mutation in the Deletion of Two Base Pairs in the Lysozyme Gene of Bacteriophage T₄. J. Mol. Biol. **30**, 39.

J. Mol. Biol. (1961) **3**, 121–124

The Theory of Mutagenesis

S. BRENNER, L. BARNETT, F. H. C. CRICK AND A. ORGEL

In this preliminary note we wish to express our doubts about the detailed theory of mutagenesis put forward by Freese (1959b), and to suggest an alternative.

Freese (1959b) has produced evidence that shows that for the r_{II} locus of phage T4 there are two mutually exclusive classes of mutation and we have confirmed and extended his work (Orgel & Brenner, in manuscript). The technique used is to start with a standard wild type and make a series of mutants from it with a particular mutagen. Each mutant is then tested with various mutagens to see which of them will back-mutate it to wild type.

It is found that the mutations fall into two classes. The first, which we shall call the base analogue class, is typically produced by 5-bromodeoxyuridine (BD) and the second, which we shall call the acridine class, is typically produced by proflavin (PF). In general a mutant made with BD can be reverted by BD, and a mutant made with PF can be reverted by PF. A few of the PF mutants do not appear to revert with either mutagen, but the strong result is that no mutant has been found which reverts identically with both classes of mutagens, and that (with a few possible exceptions) mutants produced by one class cannot be reverted by the other.

Freese also showed that 2-aminopurine falls into the base analogue class, and that most (85%) spontaneous mutants at the r_{II} locus were not of the base analogue type. We have confirmed this and shown that they are in fact revertible by acridines. We have also shown that a number of other acridines, and in particular 5-aminoacridine, act like proflavin (Orgel & Brenner, in manuscript).

Freese has produced an ingenious explanation of these results, which should be consulted in the original for fuller details. In brief he postulated that the base analogue class of mutagens act by altering an A—T base-pair on the DNA (A = adenine, T = thymine) into a G—C pair, or *vice versa* (G = guanine, C = cytosine, or, in the T even phages, hydroxymethylcytosine). The fact that BD, which replaces thymine, could act both ways (from A—T to G—C or from G—C to A—T) was accounted for (Freese, 1959a) by assuming that in the latter case there was an error in pairing of the BD (such that it accidentally paired with guanine) while *entering* the DNA, and in the former case after it was already in the DNA.

Such alterations only change a purine into another purine, or a pyrimidine into another pyrimidine. Freese (1959b) has called these "transitions." He suggested that other conceivable changes, which he called "transversions" (such as, for example, from A—T to C—G) which change a purine into a pyrimidine and *vice versa*, occurred during mutagenesis by proflavin. This would neatly account for the two mutually exclusive classes of mutagens, since it is easy to see that a transition cannot be reversed by a transversion, and *vice versa*.

We have been led to doubt this explanation for the following reasons.

Our suspicions were first aroused by the curious fact that a comparison between the *sites* of mutation for one set of mutants made with BD and another set made with PF (Brenner, Benzer & Barnett, 1958) showed there were no sites in the r_{II} gene, among the samples studied, common to both groups.

Now this result alone need not be incompatible with Freese's theory of mutagenesis, since we have no good explanation for "hot spots" and this confuses quantitative argument. However it led us to the following hypothesis:

that acridines act as mutagens because they cause the insertion or the deletion of a base-pair.

This idea springs rather naturally from the views of Lerman (1960) and Luzzati (in preparation) that acridines are bound to DNA by sliding *between* adjacent base-pairs, thus forcing them 6·8 Å apart, rather than 3·4 Å. If this occasionally happened between the bases on *one* chain of the DNA, but not the other, during replication, it might easily lead to the addition or subtraction of a base.

Such a possible mechanism leads to a prediction. We know practically nothing about coding (Crick, 1959) but on most theories (except overlapping codes which are discredited because of criticism by Brenner (1957)) the deletion or the addition of a base-pair is likely to cause not the substitution of just one amino acid for another, but a much more substantial alteration, such as a break in the polypeptide chain, a considerable alteration of the amino acid sequence, or the production of no protein at all.

Thus one would not be surprised to find on these ideas that mutants produced by acridines were not capable of producing a slightly modified protein, but usually produced either no protein at all or a grossly altered one.

Somewhat to our surprise we find we already have data from two separate genes supporting this hypothesis.

(1) The *o* locus of phage T4 (resistance to osmotic shock) is believed to control a protein of the finished phage, possibly the head protein, because it shows phenotypic mixing (Brenner, unpublished). Using various base analogues we have produced mutants of this gene, though these map at only a small number of sites. We have failed on several occasions to produce any *o* mutants with proflavin. On another occasion two mutants were produced; one never reverted to wild type, while the other corresponded in position and spontaneous reversion rate to a base analogue site. We suspect therefore that these two mutants were not really produced by proflavin, but were the rarer sort of spontaneous mutant (Brenner & Barnett, unpublished).

(2) We have also studied mutation at the *h* locus in T2L, which controls a protein of the finished phage concerned with attachment to the host (Streisinger & Franklin, 1956).

Of the six different spontaneous h^+ mutants tested, all were easily induced to revert to *h* with 5-bromouracil (BU)†. This is especially significant when it is recalled that 85% of the spontaneous r_{II} mutants could not be reverted with base analogues (Freese, 1959b).

We have also shown (Brenner & Barnett, unpublished) that it is difficult to produce h^+ mutants from *h* by proflavin, though relatively easy with BU. The production of *r* mutants was used as a control.

It can be seen from Table 1 that if the production of h^+ mutants by BU and proflavin were similar to the production of *r* mutants we would expect to have obtained $\frac{57 \times 26}{108} = 13h^+$ mutants with proflavin, whereas in fact we only found 1, and this may be spontaneous background.

† (Added in proof.) Five of these have now been tested and have been shown not to revert with proflavin.

Let us underline the difference between the *r* loci and the *o* and *h* loci. The former appear to produce proteins which are probably *not* part of the finished phage. For both the *o* and the *h* locus, however, the protein concerned forms part of the finished phage, which presumably would not be viable without it, so that a mutant can be picked up only if it forms an *altered* protein. A mutant which deleted the protein could not be studied.

TABLE 1

	r	*h⁺*
BU	108	57
Proflavin	26	1

It is clear that further work must be done before our generalization—that acridine mutants usually give no protein, rather than a slightly modified one—can be accepted. But if it turns out to be true it would support our hypothesis of the mutagenic action of the acridines, and this may have serious consequences for the naïve theory of mutagenesis, for the following reason.

It has always been a theoretical possibility that the reversions to wild type were not true reversions but were due to the action of "suppressors" (within the gene), possibly very closely linked suppressors. The most telling evidence against this was the existence of the two mutually exclusive classes of mutagens, together with Freese's explanation.

For clearly if the forward mutation could be made at one base-pair and the reverse one at a different base-pair, we should expect, on Freese's hypothesis, exceptions to the rule about the two classes of mutagens. Since these were not found it was concluded that even close suppressors were very rare.

Unfortunately our new hypothesis for the action of acridines destroys this argument. Under this new theory an alteration of a base-pair at one place *could* be reversed by an alteration at a different base-pair, and indeed from what we know (or guess) of the structure of proteins and the dependence of structure on amino acid sequence, we should be surprised if this did not occur.

It is all too easy to conceive, for example, that at a certain point on the polypeptide chain at which there is a glutamic residue in the wild type, and at which the mutation substituted a proline, a further mutation might alter the proline to aspartic acid and that this might appear to restore the wild phenotype, at least as far as could be judged by the rather crude biological tests available. If several base-pairs are needed to code for one amino acid the reverse mutation might occur at a base-pair close to but not identical with the one originally changed.

On our hypothesis this could happen, and yet one would still obtain the two classes of mutagens. The one, typified by base analogues, would produce the substitution of one base for another, and the other, typically produced by acridines, would lead to the addition or subtraction of a base-pair. Consequently the mutants produced by one class could not be easily reversed by the mutagens of the other class.

Thus our new hypothesis reopens in an acute form the question: which back-mutations to wild type are truly to the original wild type, and which only appear to be so? And on the answers to this question depend our interpretation of all experiments on back-mutation.

We suspect that this problem can most easily be approached by work on systems for which the amino acid sequence of the protein can be studied, such as the phage lysozyme of Dreyer, Anfinsen & Streisinger (personal communications) or the phosphatase from *E. coli* of Levinthal, Garen & Rothman (Garen, 1960). Meanwhile we are continuing our genetic studies to fill out and extend the preliminary results reported here.

Medical Research Council Unit
for Molecular Biology
Cavendish Laboratory

S. BRENNER
LESLIE BARNETT
F. H. C. CRICK

Pathology Laboratory
both of Cambridge University
England

ALICE ORGEL

Received 16 December 1960

REFERENCES

Brenner, S. (1957). *Proc. Nat. Acad. Sci., Wash.* **43**, 687.
Brenner, S., Benzer, S. & Barnett, L. (1958). *Nature*, **182**, 983.
Crick, F. H. C. (1959). In *Brookhaven Symposia in Biology*, **12**, 35.
Freese, E. (1959a). *J. Mol. Biol.* **1**, 87.
Freese, E. (1959b). *Proc. Nat. Acad. Sci., Wash.* **45**, 622.
Garen, A. (1960). 10th Symposium *Soc. Gen. Microbiol.*, London, 239.
Lerman, L. (1961). *J. Mol. Biol.* **3**, 18.
Streisinger, G. & Franklin, N. C. (1956). In *Cold Spr. Harb. Sym. Quant. Biol.* **21**, 103.

GENERAL NATURE OF THE GENETIC CODE FOR PROTEINS

By Dr. F. H. C. CRICK, F.R.S., LESLIE BARNETT, Dr. S. BRENNER
and Dr. R. J. WATTS-TOBIN

Medical Research Council Unit for Molecular Biology,
Cavendish Laboratory, Cambridge

THERE is now a mass of indirect evidence which suggests that the amino-acid sequence along the polypeptide chain of a protein is determined by the sequence of the bases along some particular part of the nucleic acid of the genetic material. Since there are twenty common amino-acids found throughout Nature, but only four common bases, it has often been surmised that the sequence of the four bases is in some way a code for the sequence of the amino-acids. In this article we report genetic experiments which, together with the work of others, suggest that the genetic code is of the following general type:

(a) A group of three bases (or, less likely, a multiple of three bases) codes one amino-acid.

(b) The code is not of the overlapping type (see Fig. 1).

(c) The sequence of the bases is read from a fixed starting point. This determines how the long sequences of bases are to be correctly read off as triplets. There are no special 'commas' to show how to select the right triplets. If the starting point is displaced by one base, then the reading into triplets is displaced, and thus becomes incorrect.

(d) The code is probably 'degenerate'; that is, in general, one particular amino-acid can be coded by one of several triplets of bases.

The Reading of the Code

The evidence that the genetic code is not overlapping (see Fig. 1) does not come from our work, but from that of Wittmann[1] and of Tsugita and Fraenkel-Conrat[2] on the mutants of tobacco mosaic virus produced by nitrous acid. In an overlapping triplet code, an alteration to one base will in general change three adjacent amino-acids in the polypeptide chain. Their work on the alterations produced in the protein of the virus show that usually only one amino-acid is changed as a result of treating the ribonucleic acid (RNA) of the virus with nitrous acid. In the rarer cases where two amino-acids are altered (owing presumably to two separate deaminations by the nitrous acid on one piece of RNA), the altered amino-acids are not in adjacent positions in the polypeptide chain.

Brenner[3] had previously shown that, if the code were universal (that is, the same throughout Nature), then all overlapping triplet codes were impossible. Moreover, all the abnormal human hæmoglobins studied in detail[4] show only single amino-acid changes. The newer experimental results essentially rule out all simple codes of the overlapping type.

If the code is not overlapping, then there must be some arrangement to show how to select the correct triplets (or quadruplets, or whatever it may be) along the continuous sequence of bases. One obvious suggestion is that, say, every fourth base is a 'comma'. Another idea is that certain triplets make 'senso', whereas others make 'nonsense', as in the comma-free codes of Crick, Griffith and Orgel[5]. Alternatively, the correct choice may be made by starting at a fixed point and working along the sequence of bases three (or four, or whatever) at a time. It is this possibility which we now favour.

Experimental Results

Our genetic experiments have been carried out on the B cistron of the r_{II} region of the bacteriophage $T4$, which attacks strains of *Escherichia coli*. This is the system so brilliantly exploited by Benzer[6,7]. The r_{II} region consists of two adjacent genes, or 'cistrons', called cistron A and cistron B. The wild-type phage will grow on both *E. coli* B (here called B) and on *E. coli* K12 (λ) (here called K), but a phage which has lost the function of either gene will not grow on K. Such a phage produces an r plaque on B. Many point mutations of the genes are known which behave in this way. Deletions of part of the region are also found. Other mutations, known as 'leaky', show partial function; that is, they will grow on K but their plaque-type on B is not truly wild. We report here our work on the mutant $P\ 13$ (now re-named $FC\ 0$) in the $B1$ segment of the B cistron. This mutant was originally produced by the action of proflavin[8].

We[9] have previously argued that acridines such as proflavin act as mutagens because they add or delete a base or bases. The most striking evidence in favour of this is that mutants produced by acridines are seldom 'leaky'; they are almost always completely lacking in the function of the gene. Since our note was published, experimental data from two sources have been added to our previous evidence: (1) we have examined a set of 126 r_{II} mutants made with acridine yellow; of these only 6 are leaky (typically about half the mutants made with base analogues are leaky); (2) Streisinger[10] has found that whereas mutants of the lysozyme of phage $T4$ produced by base-analogues are usually leaky, all lysozyme mutants produced by proflavin are negative, that is, the function is completely lacking.

If an acridine mutant is produced by, say, adding a base, it should revert to 'wild-type' by deleting a base. Our work on revertants of $FC\ 0$ shows that it usually

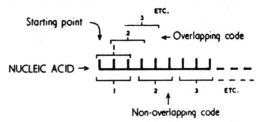

Fig. 1. To show the difference between an overlapping code and a non-overlapping code. The short vertical lines represent the bases of the nucleic acid. The case illustrated is for a triplet code

reverts not by reversing the original mutation but by producing a second mutation at a nearby point on the genetic map. That is, by a 'suppressor' in the same gene. In one case (or possibly two cases) it may have reverted back to true wild, but in at least 18 other cases the 'wild type' produced was really a double mutant with a 'wild' phenotype. Other workers[11] have found a similar phenomenon with r_{II} mutants, and Jinks[12] has made a detailed analysis of suppressors in the h_{III} gene.

The genetic map of these 18 suppressors of FC 0 is shown in Fig. 2, line a. It will be seen that they all fall in the $B1$ segment of the gene, though not all of them are very close to FC 0. They scatter over a region about, say, one-tenth the size of the B cistron. Not all are at different sites. We have found eight sites in all, but most of them fall into or near two close clusters of sites.

In all cases the suppressor was a non-leaky r. That is, it gave an r plaque on B and would not grow on K, This is the phenotype shown by a complete deletion of the gene, and shows that the function is lacking. The only possible exception was one case where the suppressor appeared to back-mutate so fast that we could not study it.

Each suppressor, as we have said, fails to grow on K. Reversion of each can therefore be studied by the same procedure used for FC 0. In a few cases these mutants apparently revert to the original wild-type, but usually they revert by forming a double mutant. Fig. 2, lines b–g, shows the mutants pro-duced as suppressors of these suppressors. Again all these new suppressors are non-leaky r mutants, and all map within the $B1$ segment for one site in the $B2$ segment.

Once again we have repeated the process on two of the new suppressors, with the same general results. as shown in Fig. 2, lines i and j.

All these mutants, except the original FC 0. occurred spontaneously. We have. however, pro-duced one set (as suppressors of FC 7) using acridine yellow as a mutagen. The spectrum of suppressors we get (see Fig. 2, line h) is crudely similar to the spontaneous spectrum, and all the mutants are non-leaky r's. We have also tested a (small) selection of all our mutants and shown that their reversion-rates are increased by acridine yellow.

Thus in all we have about eighty independent r mutants, all suppressors of FC 0, or suppressors of suppressors, or suppressors of suppressors of sup-pressors. They all fall within a limited region of the gene and they are all non-leaky r mutants.

The double mutants (which contain a mutation plus its suppressor) which plate on K have a variety of plaque types on B. Some are indistinguishable from wild, some can be distinguished from wild with difficulty, while others are easily distinguishable and produce plaques rather like r.

We have checked in a few cases that the pheno-menon is quite distinct from 'complementation'. since the two mutants which separately are pheno-typically r, and together are wild or pseudo-wild,

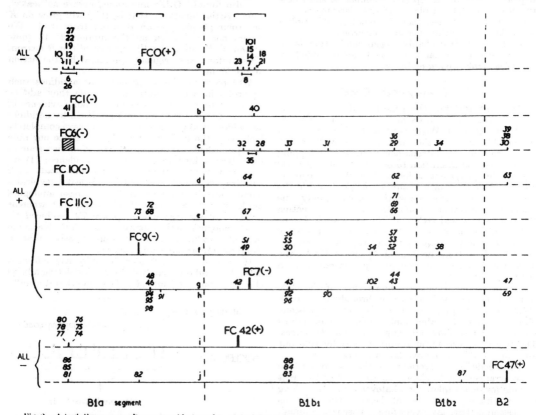

Fig. 2. A tentative map—only very roughly to scale—of the left-hand end of the B cistron, showing the position of the FC family of mutants. The order of sites within the regions covered by brackets (at the top of the figure) is not known. Mutants in italics have only been located approximately. Each line represents the suppressors picked up from one mutant, namely, that marked on the line in bold figures

must be put together in the same piece of genetic material. A simultaneous infection of K by the two mutants in separate viruses will not do.

The Explanation in Outline

Our explanation of all these facts is based on the theory set out at the beginning of this article. Although we have no direct evidence that the B cistron produces a polypeptide chain (probably through an RNA intermediate), in what follows we shall assume this to be so. To fix ideas, we imagine that the string of nucleotide bases is read, triplet by triplet, from a starting point on the left of the B cistron. We now suppose that, for example, the mutant FC 0 was produced by the insertion of an additional base in the wild-type sequence. Then this addition of a base at the FC 0 site will mean that the reading of all the triplets to the right of FC 0 will be shifted along one base, and will therefore be incorrect. Thus the amino-acid sequence of the protein which the B cistron is presumed to produce will be completely altered from that point onwards. This explains why the function of the gene is lacking. To simplify the explanation, we now postulate that a suppressor of FC 0 (for example, FC 1) is formed by deleting a base. Thus when the FC 1 mutation is present by itself, all triplets to the right of FC 1 will be read incorrectly and thus the function will be absent. However, when both mutations are present in the same piece of DNA, as in the pseudo-wild double mutant FC (0 + 1), then although the reading of triplets between FC 0 and FC 1 will be altered, the original reading will be restored to the rest of the gene. This could explain why such double mutants do not always have a true wild phenotype but are often pseudo-wild, since on our theory a small length of their amino-acid sequence is different from that of the wild-type.

For convenience we have designated our original mutant FC 0 by the symbol + (this choice is a pure convention at this stage) which we have so far considered as the addition of a single base. The suppressors of FC 0 have therefore been designated −. The suppressors of these suppressors have in the same way been labelled as +, and the suppressors of these last sets have again been labelled − (see Fig. 2).

Double Mutants

We can now ask: What is the character of any double mutant we like to form by putting together in the same gene any pair of mutants from our set of about eighty? Obviously, in some cases we already know the answer, since some combinations of a + with a − were formed in order to isolate the mutants. But, by definition, no pair consisting of one + with another + has been obtained in this way, and there are many combinations of + with − not so far tested.

Now our theory clearly predicts that all combinations of the type + with + (or − with −) should give an r phenotype and not plate on K. We have put together 14 such pairs of mutants in the cases listed in Table 1 and found this prediction confirmed.

Table 1. DOUBLE MUTANTS HAVING THE r PHENOTYPE

− With −	+ With +	
FC (1 + 21)	FC (0 + 58)	FC (40 + 57)
FC (23 + 21)	FC (0 + 38)	FC (40 + 58)
FC (1 + 23)	FC (0 + 40)	FC (40 + 55)
FC (1 + 9)	FC (0 + 55)	FC (40 + 54)
	FC (0 + 54)	FC (40 + 38)

At first sight one would expect that all combinations of the type (+ with −) would be wild or pseudo-wild, but the situation is a little more intricate than that, and must be considered more closely. This springs from the obvious fact that if the code is made of triplets, any long sequence of bases can be read correctly in one way, but incorrectly (by starting at the wrong point) in two different ways, depending whether the 'reading frame' is shifted one place to the right or one place to the left.

If we symbolize a shift, by one place, of the reading frame in one direction by → and in the opposite direction by ←, then we can establish the convention that our + is always at the head of the arrow, and our − at the tail. This is illustrated in Fig. 3.

We must now ask: Why do our suppressors not extend over the whole of the gene? The simplest postulate to make is that the shift of the reading frame produces some triplets the reading of which is 'unacceptable'; for example, they may be 'nonsense', or stand for 'end the chain', or be unacceptable in some other way due to the complications of protein structure. This means that a suppressor of, say, FC 0 must be within a region such that no 'unacceptable' triplet is produced by the shift in the reading frame between FC 0 and its suppressor. But, clearly, since for any sequence there are two possible misreadings, we might expect that the 'unacceptable' triplets produced by a → shift would occur in different places on the map from those produced by a ← shift.

Examination of the spectra of suppressors (in each case putting in the arrows → or ←) suggests that while the − shift is acceptable anywhere within our region (though not outside it) the shift ←, starting from points near FC 0, is acceptable over only a more limited stretch. This is shown in Fig. 4. Somewhere in the left part of our region, between FC 0 or FC 9 and the FC 1 group, there must be one or more unacceptable triplets when a ← shift is made; similarly for

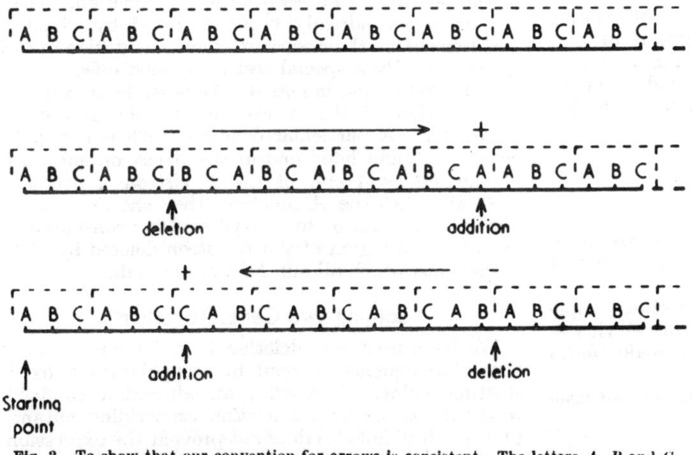

Fig. 3. To show that our convention for arrows is consistent. The letters A, B and C each represent a different base of the nucleic acid. For simplicity a repeating sequence of bases, ABC, is shown. (This would code for a polypeptide for which every amino-acid was the same.) A triplet code is assumed. The dotted lines represent the imaginary 'reading frame' implying that the sequence is read in sets of three starting on the left

the region to the right of the *FC* 21 cluster. Thus we predict that a combination of a + with a − will be wild or pseudo-wild if it involves a → shift, but that such pairs involving a ← shift will be phenotypically *r* if the arrow crosses one or more of the forbidden places, since then an unacceptable triplet will be produced.

Table 2. DOUBLE MUTANTS OF THE TYPE (+ WITH −)

−／+	FC 41	FC 0	FC 40	FC 42	FC 58*	FC 63	FC 38
FC 1	W	W	W		W		W
FC 86		W	W	W	W	W	
FC 9	r	W	W	W	W		W
FC 82	r		W	W	W	W	
FC 21	r	W			W		W
FC 88	r	r			W	W	
FC 87	r	r	r	r			W

W, wild or pseudo-wild phenotype; *W*, wild or pseudo-wild combination used to isolate the suppressor; *r*, *r* phenotype.
* Double mutants formed with *FC* 58 (or with *FC* 34) give sharp plaques on *K*.

We have tested this prediction in the 28 cases shown in Table 2. We expected 19 of these to be wild, or pseudo-wild, and 9 of them to have the *r* phenotype. In all cases our prediction was correct. We regard this as a striking confirmation of our theory. It may be of interest that the theory was constructed before these particular experimental results were obtained.

Rigorous Statement of the Theory

So far we have spoken as if the evidence supported a triplet code, but this was simply for illustration. Exactly the same results would be obtained if the code operated with groups of, say, 5 bases. Moreover, our symbols + and − must not be taken to mean literally the addition or subtraction of a single base.

It is easy to see that our symbolism is more exactly as follows:

+ represents +m, modulo n
− represents −m, modulo n

where n (a positive integer) is the coding ratio (that is, the number of bases which code one amino-acid) and m is any integral number of bases, positive or negative.

It can also be seen that our choice of reading direction is arbitrary, and that the same results (to a first approximation) would be obtained in whichever direction the genetic material was read, that is, whether the starting point is on the right or the left of the gene, as conventionally drawn.

Triple Mutants and the Coding Ratio

The somewhat abstract description given above is necessary for generality, but fortunately we have convincing evidence that the coding ratio is in fact 3 or a multiple of 3.

This we have obtained by constructing triple mutants of the form (+ with + with +) or (− with − with −). One must be careful not to make shifts

Table 3. TRIPLE MUTANTS HAVING A WILD OR PSEUDO-WILD PHENOTYPE

FC (0 + 40 + 38)
FC (0 + 40 + 58)
FC (0 + 40 + 57)
FC (0 + 40 + 54)
FC (0 + 40 + 55)
FC (1 + 21 + 23)

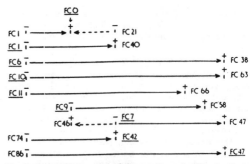

Fig. 4. A simplified version of the genetic map of Fig. 2. Each line corresponds to the suppressor from one mutant, here underlined. The arrows show the range over which suppressors have so far been found, the extreme mutants being named on the map. Arrows to the right are shown solid, arrows to the left dotted

across the 'unacceptable' regions for the ← shifts, but these we can avoid by a proper choice of mutants.

We have so far examined the six cases listed in Table 3 and in all cases the triples are wild or pseudo-wild.

The rather striking nature of this result can be seen by considering one of them, for example, the triple (*FC* 0 with *FC* 40 with *FC* 38). These three mutants are, by themselves, all of like type (+). We can say this not merely from the way in which they were obtained, but because each of them, when combined with our mutant *FC* 9 (−), gives the wild, or pseudo-wild phenotype. However, either singly or together in pairs they have an *r* phenotype, and will not grow on *K*. That is, the function of the gene is absent. Nevertheless, the combination of all three in the same gene partly restores the function and produces a pseudo-wild phage which grows on *K*.

This is exactly what one would expect, in favourable cases, if the coding ratio were 3 or a multiple of 3.

Our ability to find the coding ratio thus depends on the fact that, in at least one of our composite mutants which are 'wild', at least one amino-acid must have been added to or deleted from the polypeptide chain without disturbing the function of the gene-product too greatly.

This is a very fortunate situation. The fact that we can make these changes and can study so large a region probably comes about because this part of the protein is not essential for its function. That this is so has already been suggested by Champe and Benzer[13] in their work on complementation in the *r*$_{II}$ region. By a special test (combined infection on *K*, followed by plating on *B*) it is possible to examine the function of the *A* cistron and the *B* cistron separately. A particular deletion, 1589 (see Fig. 5) covers the right-hand end of the *A* cistron and part of the left-hand end of the *B* cistron. Although 1589 abolishes the *A* function, they showed that it allows the *B* function to be expressed to a considerable extent. The region of the *B* cistron deleted by 1589 is that into which all our *FC* mutants fall.

Joining two Genes Together

We have used this deletion to re-inforce our idea that the sequence is read in groups from a fixed starting point. Normally, an alteration confined to the *A* cistron (be it a deletion, an acridine mutant, or any other mutant) does not prevent the expression of the *B* cistron. Conversely, no alteration within the *B* cistron prevents the function of the *A* cistron. This implies that there may be a region between the two cistrons which separates them and allows their functions to be expressed individually.

We argued that the deletion 1589 will have lost this separating region and that therefore the two (partly damaged) cistrons should have been joined together. Experiments show this to be the case, for now an alteration to the left-hand end of the *A* cistron, if combined with deletion 1589, can prevent the *B* function from appearing. This is shown in Fig. 5. Either the mutant *P43* or *X142* (both of which revert strongly with acridines) will prevent the *B* function when the two cistrons are joined, although both of these mutants are in the *A* cistron. This is also true of *X142 S1*, a suppressor of *X142* (Fig. 5, case *b*). However, the double mutant (*X142* with *X142 S1*), of the type (+ with −), which by itself is pseudo-wild, still has the *B* function when combined with 1589 (Fig. 5, case *c*). We have also tested in this way the 10 deletions listed by Benzer[7], which fall wholely to the left of 1589. Of these, three (386, 168 and 221) prevent the *B* function (Fig. 5, case *f*), whereas the other seven show it (Fig. 5, case *e*). We surmise that each of these seven has lost a number of bases which is a multiple of 3. There are theoretical reasons for expecting that deletions may not be random in length, but will more often have lost a number of bases equal to an integral multiple of the coding ratio.

It would not surprise us if it were eventually shown that deletion 1589 produces a protein which consists of part of the protein from the *A* cistron and part of that from the *B* cistron, joined together in the same polypeptide chain, and having to some extent the function of the undamaged *B* protein.

Is the Coding Ratio 3 or 6 ?

It remains to show that the coding ratio is probably 3, rather than a multiple of 3. Previous rather rough extimates[10,14] of the coding ratio (which are admittedly very unreliable) might suggest that the coding ratio is not far from 6. This would imply, on our theory, that the alteration in *FC 0* was not to one base, but to two bases (or, more correctly, to an even number of bases).

We have some additional evidence which suggests that this is unlikely. First, in our set of 126 mutants produced by acridine yellow (referred to earlier) we have four independent mutants which fall at or

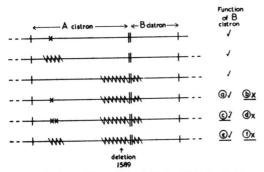

Fig. 5. Summary of the results with deletion 1589. The first two lines show that without 1589 a mutation or a deletion in the *A* cistron does not prevent the *B* cistron from functioning. Deletion 1589 (line 3) also allows the *B* cistron to function. The other cases, in some of which an alteration in the *A* cistron prevents the function of the *B* cistron (when 1589 is also present), are discussed in the text. They have been labelled (*a*), (*b*), etc., for convenience of reference, although cases (*a*) and (*d*) are not discussed in this paper. √ implies function; × implies no function

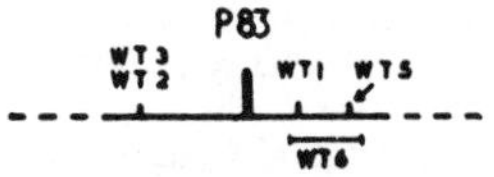

close to the *FC 9* site. By a suitable choice of partners, we have been able to show that two are + and two are −. Secondly, we have two mutants (*X146* and *X225*), produced by hydrazine[15], which fall on or near the site *FC 30*. These we have been able to show are both of type − .

Thus unless both acridines and hydrazine usually delete (or add) an even number of bases, this evidence supports a coding ratio of 3. However, as the action of these mutagens is not understood in detail, we cannot be certain that the coding ratio is not 6, although 3 seems more likely.

We have preliminary results which show that other acridine mutants often revert by means of close suppressors, but it is too sketchy to report here. A tentative map of some suppressors of *P 83*, a mutant at the other end of the *B* cistron, in segment *B 9a*, is shown in Fig. 6. They occur within a shorter region than the suppressors of *FC 0*, covering a distance of about one-twentieth of the *B* cistron. The double mutant *WT* (2 + 5) has the *r* phenotype, as expected.

Is the Code Degenerate?

If the code is a triplet code, there are 64 (4 × 4 × 4) possible triplets. Our results suggest that it is unlikely that only 20 of these represent the 20 amino-acids and that the remaining 44 are nonsense. If this were the case, the region over which suppressors of the *FC 0* family occur (perhaps a quarter of the *B* cistron) should be very much smaller than we observe, since a shift of frame should then, by chance, produce a nonsense reading at a much closer distance. This argument depends on the size of the protein which we have assumed the *B* cistron to produce. We do not know this, but the length of the cistron suggests that the protein may contain about 200 amino-acids. Thus the code is probably 'degenerate', that is, in general more than one triplet codes for each amino-acid. It is well known that if this were so, one could also account for the major dilemma of the coding problem, namely, that while the base composition of the DNA can be very different in different micro-organisms, the amino-acid composition of their proteins only changes by a moderate amount[16]. However, exactly how many triplets code amino-acids and how many have other functions we are unable to say.

Future Developments

Our theory leads to one very clear prediction. Suppose one could examine the amino-acid sequence of the 'pseudo-wild' protein produced by one of our double mutants of the (+ with −) type. Conventional theory suggests that since the gene is only altered in two places, only two amino-acids would be changed. Our theory, on the other hand, predicts that a string of amino-acids would be altered, covering the region of the polypeptide chain corresponding to the region on the gene between the two mutants. A good protein on which to test this hypothesis is

---

P83

Fig. 6. Genetic map of *P 83* and its suppressors, *WT* 1, etc. The region falls within segment *B9a* near the right-hand end of the *B* cistron. It is not yet known which way round the map is in relation to the other figures

the lysozyme of the phage, at present being studied chemically by Dreyer[17] and genetically by Streisinger[10].

At the recent Biochemical Congress at Moscow, the audience of Symposium I was startled by the announcement of Nirenberg that he and Matthaei[18] had produced polyphenylalanine (that is, a polypeptide all the residues of which are phenylalanine) by adding polyuridylic acid (that is, an RNA the bases of which are all uracil) to a cell-free system which can synthesize protein. This implies that a sequence of uracils codes for phenylalanine, and our work suggests that it is probably a triplet of uracils.

It is possible by various devices, either chemical or enzymatic, to synthesize polyribonucleotides with defined or partly defined sequences. If these, too, will produce specific polypeptides, the coding problem is wide open for experimental attack, and in fact many laboratories, including our own, are already working on the problem. If the coding ratio is indeed 3, as our results suggest, and if the code is the same throughout Nature, then the genetic code may well be solved within a year.

We thank Dr. Alice Orgel for certain mutants and for the use of data from her thesis, Dr. Leslie Orgel for many useful discussions, and Dr. Seymour Benzer for supplying us with certain deletions. We

are particularly grateful to Prof. C. F. A. Pantin for allowing us to use a room in the Zoological Museum, Cambridge, in which the bulk of this work was done.

[1] Wittman, H. G., Symp. 1, Fifth Intern. Cong. Biochem., 1961, for refs. (in the press).

[2] Tsugita, A., and Fraenkel-Conrat, H., *Proc. U.S. Nat. Acad. Sci.*, **46**, 636 (1960); *J. Mol. Biol.* (in the press).

[3] Brenner, S., *Proc. U.S. Nat. Acad. Sci.*, **43**, 687 (1957).

[4] For refs. see Watson, H. C., and Kendrew, J. C., *Nature*, **190**, 670 (1961).

[5] Crick, F. H. C., Griffith, J. S., and Orgel, L. E., *Proc. U.S. Nat. Acad. Sci.*, **43**, 416 (1957).

[6] Benzer, S., *Proc. U.S. Nat. Acad. Sci.*, **45**, 1607 (1959), for refs. to earlier papers.

[7] Benzer, S., *Proc. U.S. Nat. Acad. Sci.*, **47**, 403 (1961); see his Fig. 3.

[8] Brenner, S., Benzer, S., and Barnett, L., *Nature*, **182**, 983 (1958).

[9] Brenner, S., Barnett, L., Crick, F. H. C., and Orgel, A., *J. Mol. Biol.*, **3**, 121 (1961).

[10] Streisinger, G. (personal communication and in the press).

[11] Feynman, R. P.; Benzer, S.; Freese, E. (all personal communications).

[12] Jinks, J. L., *Heredity*, **16**, 153, 241 (1961).

[13] Champe, S., and Benzer, S. (personal communication and in preparation).

[14] Jacob, F., and Wollman, E. L., *Sexuality and the Genetics of Bacteria* (Academic Press, New York, 1961). Levinthal, C. (personal communication).

[15] Orgel, A., and Brenner, S. (in preparation).

[16] Sueoka, N. *Cold Spring Harb. Symp. Quant. Biol.* (in the press).

[17] Dreyer, W. J., Symp. 1, Fifth Intern. Cong. Biochem., 1961 (in the press).

[18] Nirenberg, M. W., and Matthaei, J. H., *Proc. U.S. Nat. Acad. Sci.*, **47**, 1588 (1961).

REVERSAL OF MUTANT PHENOTYPES BY 5-FLUOROURACIL: AN APPROACH TO NUCLEOTIDE SEQUENCES IN MESSENGER-RNA

BY SEWELL P. CHAMPE AND SEYMOUR BENZER

DEPARTMENT OF BIOLOGICAL SCIENCES, PURDUE UNIVERSITY

Communicated February 27, 1962

Genetic information in DNA is apparently expressed via transcription into RNA messengers[1-5, 10] which in turn act as the templates for protein synthesis. Thus, incorporation of base analogues into messenger-RNA could lead to errors in the reading of the message into an amino acid sequence. The effect would be an alteration of phenotype without a permanent change in the DNA genotype. A promising analogue for this purpose is 5-fluorouracil (5FU), which is readily incorporated into RNA, mostly in place of uracil.[6] Modification of proteins by 5FU has been reported by Naono and Gros[7] and by Bussard et al.[8] who found that the enzymes alkaline phosphatase and β-galactosidase synthesized in the presence of the analogue are abnormal.

A very sensitive method for the detection of induced errors in the translation of genetic information is to begin with a mutant that is defective in some function so that errors causing the appearance of a small amount of activity can be easily observed. This approach has been successful[9] using rII mutants of phage T4, which are ordinarily unable to grow on strain K of E. coli. Addition of 5FU after infection of the cell can partially reverse the phage mutant phenotype, leading to active development of the phage. The response is highly specific, occurring only with certain rII mutants and not others within the same cistron. Since, after phage infection, synthesis of ribosomal RNA and S-RNA is almost totally arrested,[10] it is plausible that the effect of 5FU on phage mutants is due to its incorporation into messenger-RNA.

Introduction of a fluorine atom at the 5-position in uracil would be expected to induce a positive charge elsewhere in the molecule, increasing the probability of loss of the proton from the 1-position. This would make it possible for 5FU to pair with guanine. Thus, 5FU might produce an effect by either (or both) of two mechanisms: by entering the messenger in place of U and behaving sometimes like C, or by going in (occasionally) like C and later pairing like U. In either case, assuming that the single-stranded messenger-RNA copies the DNA according to the Watson-Crick rules of base pairing, 5FU could reverse the effect of a mutation at a particular DNA site only if the corresponding base in the mes-

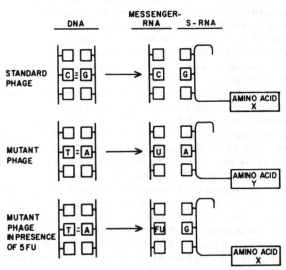

FIG. 1.—Proposed mechanism for the specific action of 5FU. The GC pair in the DNA of the standard (normal) phage is translated as C in the messenger-RNA, and a complementary S-RNA adaptor pairs with the latter, thus specifying amino acid X. For a mutant arising by a GC → AT transition, the base in the messenger-RNA becomes U, specifying an incorrect amino acid Y. In the presence of FU, however, U may be replaced by the analogue, which, when occasionally pairing like C, produces a normal message.

senger is a pyrimidine. An additional requirement, if the altered message is to correspond to the original nonmutant one, is that the mutant DNA must have been derived from the standard type by a "transition" mutation,[11] i.e.. a substitution in which the orientation of purine and pyrimidine between the two DNA chains remains unchanged.

Figure 1 illustrates the proposed mechanism for a mutant that has arisen by substitution, in the phage DNA, of an adenine-thymine (AT) pair for a guanine(hydroxylmethyl) cytosine (GC) pair. At the corresponding site in the messenger-RNA, the mutant has U instead of C, so that the message is incorrect. In the presence of 5FU, however, U may be replaced by the analogue, which, when functioning as C, produces a normal message.

Among mutants containing an AT base pair, the A can be in either strand of the DNA. If each strand of the DNA is transcribed into a functional messenger, all transition mutants containing AT as the mutant base pair should respond to 5FU. On the other hand, if only one strand of the DNA is transcribed into a useful messenger, about one half of the transition mutants containing AT as the mutant base pair should respond to 5FU.

In this paper, rII mutants of phage T4 are analyzed to characterize the mutations in their DNA (by induction of reverse mutations with DNA base analogues) and also for phenotypic response to 5FU. The results indicate that only one functional messenger is produced and suggest the assignment of bases to the various sites in the messenger-RNA.

Materials and Methods.—Bacterial strains: For crosses and for nonselective plating, *E. coli* B was used. *E. coli* BB, which does not discriminate between standard type (*r*+) phage and rII mutants, was used for growing all phage stocks and as the host for measuring induction of reverse mutations by base analogues. *E. coli* K (the specific variety used here being the KB strain) supports the growth of *r*+ but not rII mutants, and was used as selective host in detecting reversion from rII to *r*+. K was also used as the host in testing the 5FU effect on rII mutants. *E. coli* K10 and its phosphatase negative derivatives[12, 13] were obtained from Dr. Alan Garen.

rII mutants:[14] All were derived from phage T4B, with the exception of those designated by ED, which are spontaneous mutants derived from T4D. *Spontaneous mutant* numbers have either no prefix, or the prefixes SN or SD. Single-letter prefixes from A through J designate spontaneous mutants derived from revertants of spontaneous rII mutants. *Mutagen-induced mutants* are prefixed as follows: NA, NB, or NT induced by nitrous acid; EM by ethyl methane sulfonate; HB by hydroxylamine; N or M by 5-bromouracil or 5-bromodeoxyuridine; AP by 2-aminopurine; DAP by 2,6-diaminopurine; BC by 5-bromodeoxycytidine; P by proflavine; PT, PB by heat at low pH; UV by ultraviolet light. Many of the mutants were contributed by J. Drake, R. Edgar, E. Freese, M. Meselson, and I. Tessman.

Genetic mapping of rII mutants was done by techniques previously described.[14]

Media: Unless otherwise noted, the medium was broth (1% Difco bacto-tryptone plus 0.5% NaCl). For plates, 1.2% agar was added for the bottom layer and 0.7% for the top layer. In experiments involving 5-fluorouracil, a supplemented synthetic medium (M9S) was used containing, per liter of solution, 5.8 gm Na_2HPO_4, 3.0 gm KH_2PO_4, 0.5 gm NaCl, 1.0 gm NH_4Cl, 0.25 gm $MgSO_4 \cdot 7H_2O$, 2.7 mg $FeCl_3 \cdot 6H_2O$, 4.0 gm glucose, 20 mg L-tryptophan, and 2.5 gm Difco vitamin-free casamino acids. M9 is the same medium minus the casamino acids. M9 buffer is the same medium minus the carbon compounds. For experiments involving induction of alkaline phosphatase, Tris-glucose medium was used which contained, per liter, 12.1 gm Tris (Sigma Chemical Co.), 3.0 gm $MgSO_4 \cdot 7H_2O$, 1.0 gm $(NH_4)_2SO_4$, 0.5 gm sodium citrate, 50 mg methionine, and 1.0 gm glucose, pH adjusted to 7.4 with HCl. This medium was used either with 10 gm per liter KH_2PO_4 ("high phosphate") to repress phosphatase synthesis, or with 5 mg per liter ("low phosphate") to induce phosphatase synthesis.[15] *5-fluorouracil* was kindly donated by Dr. R. Duschinsky of the Hoffmann-LaRoche Company.

Reversion induction by base analogues: E. coli BB was grown in M9 to 10^8 cells/ml and the phage in question was added to give about 200 particles per ml. One ml of this mixture was then added to each of three tubes containing, respectively, 1 ml of (a) plain M9, (b) M9 plus 5-bromodeoxyuridine (0.1 mg/ml) and (c) M9 plus 2-aminopurine (1 mg/ml). The tubes were incubated at 37°C for 20 hr, then shaken with a few drops of chloroform to complete lysis. Each lysate was assayed on strain B for total plaque-forming particles and on strain K for revertants; the ratio of the titer on K to the titer on B is the *reversion index*. For all cases in which the reversion index appeared to be raised by a mutagen, the test was repeated at least once to assure that the effect was not due to a "jackpot"[16] (i.e., an abnormally large clone due to early appearance and subsequent replication of a revertant).

Reversion induction with hydroxylamine was tested by the procedure of Freese, Bautz, and Bautz-Freese.[17] One volume of phage stock was added to four volumes of a freshly made reaction mixture containing 1.25 M NH₂OH·HCl, 1.0 M NaCl, 0.001 M MgSO₄, 0.075 M Na₂HPO₄, the pH being adjusted to 7.5 with NaOH. Samples were taken before and after four hours of treatment at 37°C, diluting into a cold reaction-stopping mixture consisting of 0.5% bacto-tryptone, 6% NaCl, and 2% by volume of acetone. Under the conditions used, inactivation of the phage particles by hydroxylamine amounted to roughly 50 per cent. The results are given directly as the reversion index (i.e., ratio of titer on K to titer on B) before and after treatment. This was preferred to expressing them in terms of mutations per lethal hit, the latter quantity being difficult to measure when the killing is so small.

Verification of revertants: For any mutant that was induced to revert a number of plaques (from 4 to 30) was picked from the K plates and replated on strain B as a check on plaque type. In some cases, the plaques were r type on B, showing that the "revertants" were false, i.e., did not represent a return to the original standard type. Such false reversions may be due to suppressor mutations at some site other than the original mutation.[18, 19] Therefore, data are reported only for mutants most of whose induced revertants looked genuine on B. This is, of course, a necessary but still not sufficient criterion for genuineness of the revertants.

Assay of phosphatase activity:[20] p-nitrophenyl phosphate was dissolved at 5mg/ml in 1 M Tris buffer, pH 8.0, and extracted with ether until colorless. This removes traces of p-nitrophenol and increases the sensitivity of the assay at low levels of enzyme. The reagent was added to an equal volume of appropriately diluted bacterial culture (previously shaken with a few drops of chloroform) and incubated at 37°C. The rate of color development measured at 410 mμ is a measure of the phosphatase activity.

Results.—Effect of 5FU on rII mutants: Figure 2 shows the effect of 5FU on the activity of various *rII* mutants in *E. coli* strain K. The procedure was to infect K cells with the phage mutant, and dilute into media with or without 5FU. At various times thereafter, the infected cells were further diluted into broth and allowed to lyse. Reversal of the phenotype of an *rII* mutant is reflected in appearance of phage progeny, the yield per infected cell, as compared with that obtained for r^+ phage under the same conditions, being a measure of the degree of activity. While two of the mutants in Figure 2 produce a sizable fraction of the r^+ yield, the other three mutants show practically no response. This striking specificity, which applies to mutants of both cistrons, shows that the effect of 5FU cannot be a general removal of the block against *rII* mutants. Although 5FU is in general somewhat inhibitory, depressing the yield of the standard type phage by about twofold, the increase shown by responsive mutants is over and above this general inhibition.

Stimulation by 5FU was almost completely prevented by adding uracil at a concentration of 20 γ/ml. On the other hand, inclusion or omission of thymidine at the same concentration made no detectable difference. This indicates that the stimulating effect of 5FU is not due to its interference[21] with DNA synthesis.

It is essential to stress that the effect of 5FU is a physiological one and not due to mutagenesis. The progeny phage yielded by K in the presence of 5FU were no more active (in the absence of 5FU) than their parents.

167

Kinetics of the 5FU effect: To localize the time of action of 5FU in phage-infected cells, 3-minute pulse exposures to the analogue were given at various times before and after infection. The results (Fig. 3) show that pre-infection exposure causes little effect and that 5FU is most effective if present during the first 18 minutes at 26°. This is the first third of the eclipse period, a time during which there is active synthesis[1, 2] of messenger-RNA but before DNA synthesis has begun.[38]

That 5FU is rapidly incorporated into messenger-RNA has been shown by Gros *et al.*[22] Their studies were on uninfected cells, but, as indicated by the work of Nomura, Hall, and Spiegelman,[10] messenger-RNA may in fact be the only kind of RNA made after phage infection.

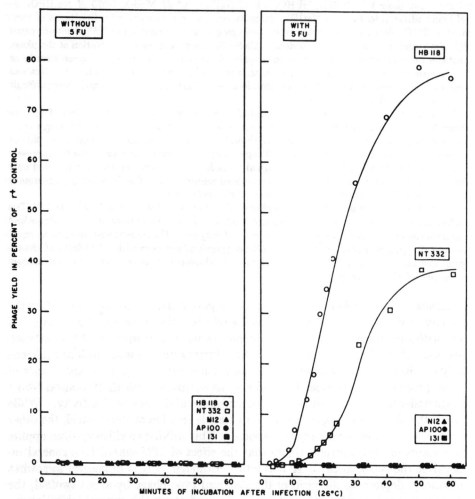

FIG. 2.—Effect of 5-fluorouracil on the activity of various *r*II mutants in *E. coli* K.

To K growing exponentially in M9S at 2.3 × 10⁸ cells/ml, 0.01 *M* NaCN was added followed by phage at 0.3 particle per bacterium. After 10 min adsorption at 37°C, anti-T4 serum was added to eliminate unadsorbed phage. Ten min later, phage development was initiated (time zero on the graph) by diluting 500-fold into M9S + 20 γ/ml thymidine at 26°C either without or with 10 γ/ml 5FU. At various times thereafter, samples were diluted 50-fold into broth supplemented with 20 γ/ml of uracil and 20 γ/ml of thymidine. After one hour at 37°C, the broth tubes were shaken with a few drops of chloroform to complete lysis and assayed for phage on *E. coli* B. As a control, *r*⁺ phage (not shown) was measured in precisely the same way. The *r*⁺ yield decreased somewhat with progressively later shifts from synthetic medium to broth medium so that the data for the mutants are expressed as per cent of the yield for *r*⁺.

As Garen[23] and Nomura[24] have shown, the metabolism of an *r*II-infected K cell is at first normal and even proceeds as far as the production of DNA replicas before the cell ceases to function.   Nevertheless, standard type recombinants arising during replication are unable to remove the block.[25]   This decision is presumably dictated by messenger-RNA made directly from the DNA of the infecting phage particles.

Generality of the 5FU effect: If the mechanism postulated for the action of 5FU on *r*II mutants is correct, the same phenomenon should be observable with mutants affected in other cistrons.   This has indeed been found for mutants of *E. coli* strain K10 that are defective in the enzyme alkaline phosphatase.   Twenty-five phosphatase-negative mutants,[12, 13] generously supplied by Dr. Alan Garen, were tested.   Each strain was grown in high phosphate medium (to repress formation of any enzyme) and then shifted to low phosphate medium, in which condition formation of the enzyme (if any) is induced.[15]   When induction was done in the presence of 5FU, two of the mutants formed active enzyme.   Figure 4 compares a responsive mutant (U8) with a nonresponsive mutant (U12).   Thus, the 5FU effect, although

highly site-specific within a given cistron, is of general applicability to other cistrons.

The increase in enzyme activity of U8 induced in the presence of 5FU, while some 30-fold over the control, was small (about 0.5%) relative to the phosphatase-positive strain under the same conditions. In the case of the *r*II mutants shown in Figure 2, the phage yield may, of course, be far out of proportion to the amount of r^+ activity.

Identification of DNA base pairs by mutagens: When DNA replicates in the presence of analogues of the normal DNA bases, mutations are readily induced,[26] apparently due to errors in pairing which lead to the permanent substitution of one base pair for another. As argued by Freese,[27] such errors in base pairing should lead to the substitution of a purine for a purine and a pyrimidine for a pyrimidine

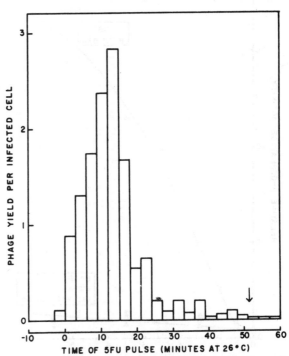

FIG. 3.—Effect of a three-minute pulse of 5-fluorouracil, applied at various times, on *r*HB118 infecting *E. coli* K. The procedure was as in Fig. 2 except that the infected cells were allowed to develop in M9S medium for various times before exposure to 5FU. The pulse was applied by diluting into an equal volume of the same medium plus 20 γ-ml 5FU. Three minutes later, the pulse was ended by dilution into uracil-containing broth and the experiment continued as in Fig. 2. Due to the short exposure to the analogue the phage yield per infected cell was much smaller than in Fig. 2. The arrow at 52 minutes indicates the end of the "eclipse" period, i.e., the time at which the number of mature phage particles reaches, on the average, one per cell for cells infected with r^+ in the absence of 5FU.

without changing their orientation with respect to the two DNA chains (transitions). Two base analogues that have been studied extensively are 2-aminopurine (2AP) and 5-bromodeoxyuridine (BDU). These induce mutations specifically at certain genetic sites,[28, 27, 14] and the mutants are, as a rule, also inducible by base analogues to revert to standard type.[11]

From the finding that mutants induced by BDU tend to be strongly revertible by 2AP, and vice versa, Freese[11] suggested that one of the mutagens favored the transition GC → AT while the other induced AT → GC. An indication of which is which came from experiments with hydroxylamine.[17, 29] Cytosine and its derivatives were shown to react more readily than the other bases that occur in DNA.

It is difficult, however, to extrapolate with assurance from the gross chemical effects of mutagens to the actual mutational events, which could be caused by a minority reaction. Schuster[30] and Brown and Schell[31] have shown that hydroxylamine indeed reacts to a slight extent with thymine in DNA. However, Schuster also showed that the rate of reaction of hydroxylamine with cytosine (in RNA) decreases with higher pH, whereas the reaction with uracil increases. The pH dependences of the reactions with thymine and hydroxymethylcytosine in phage DNA, although not yet determined, might be expected to be analogous to those of uracil and cytosine, respectively. To obtain further evidence as to which reaction is responsible for the mutagenic effect, we have examined the pH dependence of the mutagenic effect of hydroxylamine on the *r*II mutant *r*AP275. The observed mutation rates (induced revertants per survivor per unit time) at pH values of 6, 7.5, and 9 were in the ratio 28:12:1. The rates found by Schuster for the reaction with cytosine at similar pH values were in the ratio of 32:13:<4, whereas uracil reacted in the ratio <1:13:30. Six other

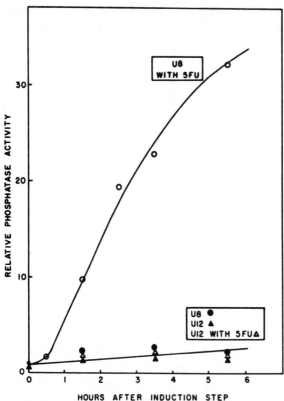

FIG. 4.—Reversal of a phosphatase-negative defect by 5-fluorouracil. Overnight cultures of the bacteria grown in repressing medium ("high phosphate" Tris-glucose) were diluted 20-fold into the same medium and aerated at 37°C for 3 hours. The cells were centrifuged, resuspended in chilled medium (less glucose and phosphate), centrifuged again, and resuspended in inducing medium ("low phosphate" Tris-glucose). The cultures were then divided into 2 parts, to one of which was added 20 γ/ml of 5FU, and both were aerated at 37°C (starting at time zero on the graph). Samples were taken at various times and assayed for alkaline phosphatase activity as described in *Methods*. The ordinate is in arbitrary units relative to the activity of mutant U8 at zero time.

mutants were tested and all showed the same pH dependence as r AP275.

This result reinforces the conclusion that hydroxylamine predominantly induces the transition GC → AT, and the correlation between hydroxylamine and BDU (Table 1, below) supports the conclusion that BDU acts in the same way. The action of 2AP, on the other hand, seems less specific than originally supposed. In the data of Freese et al.,[17] as well as those given below, 2AP-induced mutants are about equally divided with respect to their revertibility by hydroxylamine. 2AP apparently induces both transitions with comparable ease.

Therefore, the following rules may be used for identification of base pairs. Given a mutant (of any origin), if it is inducible to revert by 2AP, it can be classed as a transition mutant. If it reverts strongly in response to BDU and hydroxylamine as well, this suggests that the mutant base pair is GC; if it does not, the mutant base pair indicated is AT. These criteria identify the base pair at the corresponding site in the standard type phage as AT in the former case and GC in the latter case.

rII mutations have been located at some hundreds of distinct sites in the two rII cistrons. Most of the sites have many recurrences, some spontaneous, some induced with one mutagen or another.[14] One representative of each site in the rII region was chosen (usually the first mutant to indicate the site) and tested quantitatively for induction of reversions by 2AP and BDU. Where an increase over the spontaneous rate was observed, the revertants were examined for plaque type on strain B (see *Methods*).

Of the 339 mutants tested, 69 were unambiguously inducible to revert by 2AP (and/or BDU) to a form which was judged to be phenotypically r+ on strain B. (Some of these also showed false revertants in smaller numbers.) The mutants are listed in Table 1 (Groups I, II, and III) along with 40 mutants (Group IV) chosen at random from the larger group which showed no reversion induction. All 109 mutants were further tested for reversion by hydroxylamine.

Mutants of Groups I and II are those that are reverted strongly by 2AP but weakly, or not at all, by BDU. According to the rules based upon the mutagenic specificity of the analogues, these mutants must have arisen by GC → AT transitions. The base pairs deduced to be in the standard type DNA at the corresponding sites are listed in the table as GC.

Group III consists of mutants that respond not only to 2AP but also to BDU. It is seen that there is a good correlation between hydroxylamine and BDU induction, consistent with the idea that both of these agents act predominantly on GC base pairs. For mutants responding to *both* BDU and hydroxylamine, the base pair indicated in the standard type is AT. In the few cases where a mutant responds to BDU and not hydroxylamine, or vice versa, identification of the base pair cannot be made with assurance. The mutants of Group IV, not revertible by base analogues, could be transversions,[11] i.e., substitutions in which the orientation of purine and pyrimidine has been reversed, or tiny deletions or insertions.[32] For these mutants, no conclusion as to the original base pair can be reached.

Figure 5 shows the positions of the various mutations within the two cistrons of the rII region, as determined by genetic mapping. Mutations which showed no induced reversions by 2AP or BDU are represented as open circles. Those represented as solid circles are inducible to revert (either truly or falsely) by one or more of the mutagens. Where the base pair can be labeled unambiguously according to the data of Table 1, it is shown in the figure.

The remainder of the mutations indicated as responsive to mutagens showed either feeble induction or a large component of manifestly false revertants, and therefore no base pair designation can be given without further study. Of course, a revertant can be demonstrated to be false, but cannot be proved, by genetic analysis alone, to be identical with the original standard type, so that the possibility is not

TABLE 1
Response of rII Mutants to Mutagens and to 5FU

	Reverse Mutation Induction by Mutagens Reversion Index (K/B) in Units of 10^{-7}					Response to 5FU Progeny per cell		Summary				Indicated Bases r^+ / r^+	
r^+	Spont.	2AP	BDU	NH₂OH Control	NH₂OH Treated	Control 126.	5FU 79.	2AP	BDU	NH₂OH	5FU	Phage DNA	Messenger-RNA
						Group I							
rN55	1.4	1700	2.8	0.	0.5	0.00	0.9	+	0	0	+	GC	C
rHB118	0.5	2300	0.	0.5	0.	0.00	56.	+	0	0	+	GC	C
rC204	0.0	730	0.2	0.	0.	0.00	1.3	+	0	0	+	GC	C
rN11	1.3	2800	5.3	0.	0.	0.00	1.5	+	0	0	+	GC	C
rEM64	0.4	2500	1.3	0.9	0.5	0.00	33.	+	0	0	+	GC	C
rHB35	0.1	1400	0.2	2.2	2.0	0.00	9.6	+	0	0	+	GC	C
rHB129	0.2	1000	0.3	1.6	0.	0.00	24.	+	0	0	+	GC	C
rHB84	0.0	750	0.1	0.	0.	0.00	14.	+	0	0	+	GC	C
rN21	0.0	450	0.0	0.	0.	0.01	29.	+	0	0	+	GC	C
rEM84	0.2	1600	0.6	0.4	3.1	0.00	5.2	+	0	0	+	GC	C
rN24	3.0	4600	5.9	8.6	20.	0.02	8.2	+	0	0	+	GC	C
rHB74	0.3	3000	0.5	0.8	3.	0.00	0.6	+	0	0	+	GC	C
rNT332	0.2	1400	1.6	1.9	1.6	0.00	22.	+	0	0	+	GC	C
rB94	0.0	2800	0.3	2.	5.	0.00	7.4	+	0	0	+	GC	C
rSD160	0.5	1500	3.6	0.	3.	0.01	2.8	+	0	0	+	GC	C
rHB232	0.1	300	0.5	0.9	2.5	0.02	11.	+	0	0	+	GC	C
rAP53	0.6	890	0.5	0.3	2.5	0.04	48.	+	0	0	+	GC	C
						Group II							
rNA27	0.1	1600	0.5	1.	3.	0.00	0.05	+	0	0	0	GC	G
rN74	0.0	390	0.5	0.5	0.	0.04	0.2	+	0	0	0	GC	G
r1274	0.0	330	7.0	2.8	3.5	0.00	0.00	+	0	0	0	GC	G
r1249	0.1	1600	20.	1.8	1.7	0.00	0.01	+	0	0	0	GC	G
rNB4777	0.6	630	58.	2.4	4.8	0.00	0.05	+	0?	0	0	GC	G
rHB122	0.1	14000	4.6	0.7	0.5	0.00	0.08	+	0	0	0	GC	G
rBC11	0.0	15000	0.	1.	0.5	0.00	0.06	+	0	0	0	GC	G
rUV47	0.2	280	9.	0.9	0.8	0.00	0.05	+	0	0	0	GC	G
rAP211	0.0	200	0.5	0.	1.2	0.00	0.06	+	0	0	0	GC	G
rUV1	0.0	350	0.1	0.	0.	0.00	0.03	+	0	0	0	GC	G
r425	0.3	3300	1.4	0.	0.	0.00	0.00	+	0	0	0	GC	G
rEM20	0.0	3000	0.8	1.	0.5	0.00	0.01	+	0	0	0	GC	G
rUV122	0.5	1600	18.	2.2	3.7	0.16	0.06	+	0	0	0	GC	G
rHB32	0.1	4800	1.8	1.8	2.7	0.00	0.09	+	0	0	0	GC	G
r585	0.0	330	0.7	0.	5.	0.00	0.01	+	0	0	0	GC	G
r1310	0.0	1000	0.0	0.	0.5	0.00	0.00	+	0	0	0	GC	G
rHB80	0.0	3500	12.	0.4	0.8	0.00	0.07	+	0	0	0	GC	G
rAP126	0.0	2900	0.7	0.	0.8	0.00	0.06	+	0	0	0	GC	G
rUV375	0.6	6700	24.	0.9	1.7	0.00	0.04	+	0	0	0	GC	G
r360	0.0	530	0.6	0.	0.	0.00	0.03	+	0	0	0	GC	G
r375	0.3	2200	2.0	0.8	1.1	0.00	0.00	+	0	0	0	GC	G
rN17	0.0	1500	0.4	0.	0.	0.00	0.09	+	0	0	0	GC	G
rN90	0.4	8600	4.5	1.	2.	0.01	0.06	+	0	0	0	GC	G
rUV199	2.4	5900	7.1	0.7	0.3	0.00	0.2	+	0	0	0	GC	G
rN12	0.2	8500	1.3	0.6	1.5	0.02	0.05	+	0	0	0	GC	G
rN29	0.0	7600	0.	0.	4.	0.00	0.00	+	0	0	0	GC	G
rAP61	1.2	500	2.9	1.9	4.1	0.02	0.1	+	0	0	0	GC	G
r979	1.5	3200	24.	5.7	7.1	0.01	0.08	+	0	0	0	GC	G
rEM7	0.1	2000	0.6	0.2	0.0	0.00	0.04	+	0	0	0	GC	G
r1814	1.	8200	10.	0.9	72.	0.04	0.2	+	0	+	0	..	..
r287	2.1	2800	1.0	6.4	150.	0.00	0.00	+	0	+	0	..	..

The mutants are divided into groups according to their responses to mutagens and to 5FU. Within each group, they are listed according to their order in the recombination map (Fig. 5). In cases of positive response to 2AP or BDU, the reversion test was done two or more times and the value listed is the average reversion index, excluding extreme values occasionally observed due to "jackpots." A zero in the last decimal place indicates that the value in that place is less than one.

The control for hydroxylamine reversion is in some cases different from the spontaneous reversion index due to fluctuations of the r^+ background from one stock to another. Procedures for the mutagen tests are described in *Methods*. The measurements of response to 5FU were made as described in Figure 2, the dilution from the test medium being made about 45 minutes after the initiation of phage development.

TABLE 1 (Continued)
RESPONSE OF rII MUTANTS TO MUTAGENS AND TO 5FU

	Reverse Mutation Induction by Mutagens — Reversion Index (K/B) in Units of 10^{-7}					Response to 5FU — Progeny per cell		Summary				Indicated Bases r^+　r^+	
	Spont.	2AP	BDU	NH₃OH Control	NH₃OH Treated	Control	5FU	2AP	BDU	NH₃OH	5FU	Phage DNA	Messenger-RNA
GROUP III													
rAP129	4.1	6200	2100.	4.	680.	0.1	0.4	+	+	+	0	AT	..
rAP218	2.6	1200	250.	1.	730.	0.01	0.2	+	+	+?	0	AT	..
rH221	0.4	460	220.	0.	26.	0.00	0.04	+	+	+?	0	AT	..
rAP100	2.0	80	1800.	3.	2600.	0.00	0.01	+	+	+	0	AT	..
r607	0.9	340	7100.	1.9	1500.	0.03	0.02	+	+	+	0	AT	..
rEM114	30.	3200	1200.	100.	890.	0.5	0.8	+	+	+	0	AT	..
rNT88	0.5	230	500.	0.1	160.	0.00	0.04	+	+	+	0	AT	..
rDAP56	3.6	5500	2000.	16.	3100.	0.00	0.01	+	+	+	0	AT	..
r380	0.5	6600	2400.	0.	220.	0.4	1.8	+	+	+	+?	AT	..
rSN103	0.9	580	1800.	2.2	370.	0.01	0.07	+	+	+	0	AT	..
r263	7.8	3700	8900.	27.	3600.	0.6	3.3	+	+	+	+?	AT	..
rF72	0.7	120	680.	2.6	770.	0.00	0.01	+	+	+	0	AT	..
rJ33	1.5	2000	890.	4.	230.	0.00	0.04	+	+	+	0	AT	..
rBC35	2.1	46	760.	1.2	660.	0.00	0.01	+	+	+	0	AT	..
rAP275	1.9	580	4500.	4.1	1600.	0.00	0.04	+	+	+	0	AT	..
rUV363	0.7	26	3000.	3.5	600.	0.00	0.03	+	+	+	0	AT	..
rUV181	0.07	940	470.	0.8	1.4	0.00	0.06	+	+	0	0	..	..
rG178	0.07	970	86.	0.	0.5	0.00	0.02	+	+	0	0	..	..
r2074	4.7	25000	390.	19.	16.	0.00	0.01	+	+	0	0	..	..
r609	3.3	8800	450.	3.0	1.0	0.02	0.04	+	+	0	0	..	..
r1221	1.9	1900	170.	9.2	14.	0.2	5.6	+	+	0	+	..	..
GROUP IV													
r681	3.1	1.7	3.4	8.	16.	0.00	0.00	0	0	0	0	..	..
rUV11	0.1	0.1	0.4	0.	0.	0.00	0.02	0	0	0	0	..	..
r569	0.9	1.3	4.7	0.5	0.6	0.02	0.1	0	0	0	0	..	..
r1176	0.2	0.0	0.2	0.	0.	0.00	0.00	0	0	0	0	..	..
rUV68	1.2	1.1	3.0	2.6	1.4	0.00	0.01	0	0	0	0	..	..
rNT311	0.0	0.1	0.0	0.9	0.8	0.00	0.00	0	0	0	0	..	..
rBC81	0.0	0.0	0.1	0.0	0.0	0.00	0.01	0	0	0	0	..	..
r227	0.1	0.0	0.	0.	0.	0.00	0.00	0	0	0	0	..	..
r577	0.1	2.2	0.0	0.	0.	0.00	0.00	0	0	0	0	..	..
r1084	0.4	2.5	2.2	1.	0.	0.00	0.00	0	0	0	0	..	..
r205	0.0	0.0	0.1	0.5	0.5	0.00	0.01	0	0	0	0	..	..
rH201	3.5	0.8	3.5	0.8	2.9	0.00	0.00	0	0	0	0	..	..
r465	1.7	3.0	4.2	7.6	6.5	0.15	0.04	0	0	0	0	..	..
r1470	0.2	0.2	0.2	0.	0.	0.00	0.01	0	0	0	0	..	..
r447	0.4	0.3	0.2	0.8	1.4	0.00	0.01	0	0	0	0	..	..
rDAP66	1.0	2.0	1.3	0.7	1.	0.00	0.00	0	0	0	0	..	..
rH51	0.2	0.3	0.5	0.5	0.3	0.00	0.02	0	0	0	0	..	..
r2232	1.8	1.9	1.9	4.	2.	0.00	0.02	0	0	0	0	..	..
rP5	2.2	8.1	3.7	6.	5.	0.00	0.05	0	0	0	0	..	..
rF27	4.1	1.0	5.3	1.2	27.	0.00	0.00	0	0	+?	0	..	..
r285	0.6	0.3	0.4	0.6	3.3	0.00	0.00	0	0	0	0	..	..
rCl35	0.2	0.2	0.2	0.	0.	0.00	0.01	0	0	0	0	..	..
rSN181	2.4	0.7	2.2	10.	8.	0.01	0.02	0	0	0	0	..	..
rD2	3.9	4.7	4.0	3.5	43.	0.00	0.02	0	0	+?	0	..	..
r173	0.0	0.0	0.0	0.	0.	0.01	0.02	0	0	0	0	..	..
rUV118	0.3	0.2	0.4	0.7	0.	0.00	0.03	0	0	0	0	..	..
r240	0.1	0.0	0.1	3.6	3.7	0.00	0.01	0	0	0	0	..	..
r131	2.0	3.7	6.6	4.1	3.0	0.01	0.03	0	0	0	0	..	..
r244	8.0	6.1	22.	13.	14.	0.00	0.01	0	0	0	0	..	..
r326	0.3	0.6	1.2	0.	0.	0.00	0.01	0	0	0	0	..	..
rP4	0.3	0.0	0.	0.1	0.	0.00	0.00	0	0	0	0	..	..
rAP176	0.1	0.2	0.0	1.8	1.7	0.00	0.02	0	0	0	0	..	..
r117	16.	2.7	5.0	27.	37.	0.00	0.00	0	0	0	0	..	..
r1467	6.3	5.7	3.4	8.9	7.5	0.00	0.01	0	0	0	0	..	..
rB13	0.0	0.1	0.2	0.3	0.0	0.00	0.00	0	0	0	0	..	..
rJ241	0.1	0.1	0.7	0.	0.7	0.00	0.01	0	0	0	0	..	..
rEM113	0.0	0.1	0.1	0.	0.	0.00	0.01	0	0	0	0	..	..
rEM29	0.0	0.3	0.0	0.	0.	0.00	0.02	0	0	0	0	..	..
rUV124	0.0	0.0	0.0	0.5	0.0	0.00	0.01	0	0	0	0	..	..
rEM87	0.0	0.0	0.	0.5	0.6	0.00	0.01	0	0	0	0	..	..

ruled out that the apparent specificity is incorrect in certain cases. A more stringent test of genuineness is to cross the presumed revertant to standard type, in which case a suppressor mutation at another site may be revealed by the appearance of the unsuppressed mutant as a recombinant. A still more stringent test is to show that the revertant has the same forward mutability, at the same site, as

does the standard type.   While both of these criteria are satisfied by some revertants that have been studied, the tests have not yet been applied to the various
mutants of Table 1.   It is possible also that the 5FU effect could, in certain instances, act at a site distant from the one in question, producing the phenotypic
equivalent of a suppressor mutation.

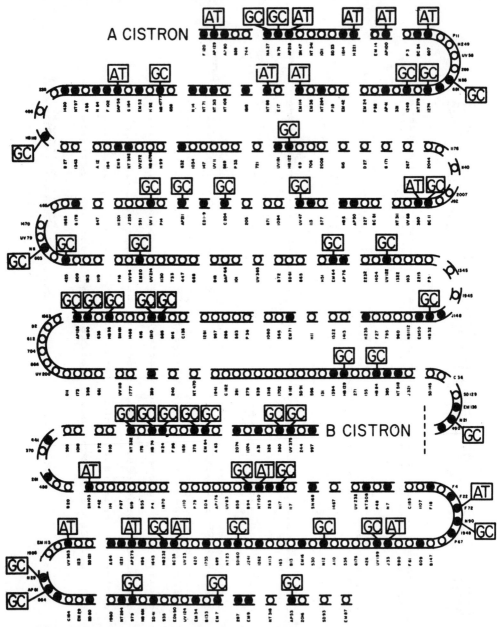

FIG. 5.—Genetic map of the *r*II region showing the base pairs in the standard type as deduced
from the data of Table 1.   Each circle represents a distinct mutational site.   Breaks in the map
indicate segments as defined by the ends of deletions.   While the order of the segments is known,
the arrangement of sites within any one segment has not been determined.
   ● Indicates mutants which are inducible to revert by one or more of the mutagens tested (2AP,
BDU, or hydroxylamine).   Where reversion was weak or false, no base pair is assigned.
   ○ Indicates mutants for which no induced reversion was detected with 2AP or BDU.

Specificity of response to 5FU: All of the mutants in Table 1 have been tested for reversal of phenotype by 5FU and the results are listed.

The first expectation from the proposed mechanism, namely, that only transition

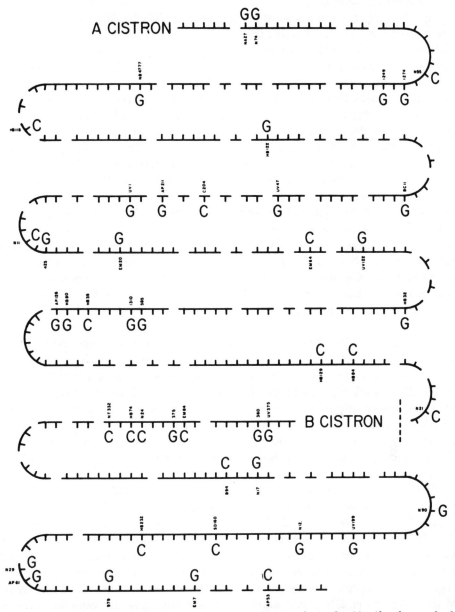

FIG. 6.—Map of the messenger-RNA for the *r*II region showing the nucleotides (for the standard type phage) suggested by the data of Table 1 (Groups I and II).

mutations (Groups I, II, and III) should respond to 5FU, is seen to be rigorously fulfilled.   Out of the 20 mutants judged to have a positive response to 5FU, 17 are among those induced to revert only by 2AP.   The other three (having rather high control values and weak response) are induced to revert also by BDU.   This distribution implies that 5FU acts predominantly by being incorporated into messenger-

175

RNA at sites corresponding to AT in the DNA. That is, it enters in place of U and acts partially like C. The weak but reproducible response observed with several BDU-reverting mutants is not surprising if 5FU can also (but more rarely) be incorporated in place of C.

Unfortunately there is not an absolutely sharp separation between 5FU responders and nonresponders. A slight though variable response to 5FU can be detected for almost every mutant. This small nonspecific effect can be seen for some of the Group IV nontransition mutants, and occurs even with deletion mutants, so it would seem to be due to a partial undoing of the general block against rII mutants. Even for mutants that definitely respond, the degree of response varies. This is perhaps ascribable to the influence of neighboring bases on the efficiency of incorporating the analogue or on its properties once it is in.

From Table 1 (Groups I and II) it is evident, nevertheless, that the mutants revertible solely by 2AP include some (17) that are responsive to 5FU and others (29) that are not. This is close to the expectation if only one DNA strand is copied as a useful messenger. Response to 5FU would thus specify the relative orientation of the DNA base pairs at the sites in question. Given a GC base pair in the standard type, which becomes, in the mutant, AT, the latter will respond to 5FU only if the A is in the "major" strand of the DNA, i.e., the one which is transcribed into messenger-RNA. Thus, a 5FU-responsive mutant would be one which has G at the corresponding site in the major strand of the DNA of the standard type. It follows that the base in the standard type messenger-RNA is C. Figure 6 summarizes the various nucleotides in normal rII messenger-RNA deduced according to this scheme.

Discussion.—Unlike the analogues BDU and 2AP, which cause heritable changes in the DNA, 5FU causes a temporary change in phenotype. It is effective on phage only if added in the period shortly after infection during a time when messenger-RNA is actively synthesized but soluble RNA and ribosomal RNA are not. Mutants that are not induced to revert by base analogues do not respond to 5FU. Of those mutants identified by chemical mutagenesis as having an AT pair at the mutant site, somewhat less than half respond more or less strongly to 5FU. Conversely, among mutants identified as containing GC pairs, response to 5FU is uncommon.

These observations are consistent with the scheme presented in Figure 1. The fact that roughly half of the AT mutants respond to 5FU would appear to suggest that only one strand of the DNA is transcribed as functional messenger-RNA. The 5FU effect makes it possible to define the orientation of the base pair in the two DNA strands and thus provides the key needed to reduce the genetic map to nucleotide sequences along one of the DNA strands. The messenger-RNA would then have the complementary sequence. 5FU permits the orientation of only one of the two kinds of DNA base pairs. It would obviously be desirable to find an analogue of cytosine or guanine, which would serve for the other.

The results suggest that only one *physiologically active* messenger is made from the two-stranded DNA, as also suggested by certain genetic experiments of Tessman.[33] However, it is known from the work of Chamberlin and Berg[34] that, *in vitro*, both strands of DNA *can* be copied as RNA by ribonucleotide polymerase. It may be, nevertheless, that for an intact chromosome, *in vitro*, there is a mechanism fixing the direction in which the messenger copies the DNA. Suggestive evidence for one-strand copying comes from the experiments of Bautz and Hall,[35] who have isolated T4 messenger-RNA and measured its base composition. Their results reveal a deviation from identity between the base compositions of T4 DNA and the messenger-RNA. This indicates that messenger-RNA copies only one DNA strand, and further that the bases are not equally distributed between the two strands. They found 21 per cent G and 15 per cent C in the purified T4 messenger-RNA. Although the number of G and C sites so far indicated for the *r*II messenger (Fig. 6) is not large enough to give a statistically reliable sampling and may also be a random sample of all possible G and C sites, it is interesting to note that they deviate from equality in the same direction, as observed by Bautz and Hall.

In the set of mutants studied so far, ones arising from changes at GC sites are about twice as numerous as those arising at AT sites. This might appear to be in contradiction with the known composition of T4 DNA, in which the relative abundance of the base pairs is just the reverse. However, this may very easily be due to the fact that most of the mutagens so far used in producing the mutants turn out to act preferentially on GC pairs. If this is so, it should prove possible to detect many more sites by exhaustive mapping of mutants induced by 2AP.

Regarding the behavior of 5FU in base pairing, Lengyel *et al.*[36] found polyfluorouridylic acid to be rather ineffective in stimulation of polyphenylalanine synthesis (as compared to polyuridylic acid, which is extremely effective).[37] This is evidence that the fluorine atom does cause an alteration in the behavior of U. By studying the properties of a mixed polymer made of U and 5FU, it should be feasible to determine directly whether 5FU indeed acts partially like C in coding for amino acids.

Summary.—5-Flourouracil partially reverses the defective phenotypes of certain *r*II mutants of phage T4 (as well as certain phosphatase-negative mutants of *E. coli*). From the kinetics of the effect and the specificity of action on various *r*II mutants, taken together with the responses of the mutants to specific mutagens, it is concluded that 5FU acts mainly by incorporation into messenger-RNA in place of uracil, there acting partially like cytosine. The results are consistent with the idea that only one strand of the DNA duplex is copied into useful messenger-RNA. This provides a means for determining the orientation of the nucleotide pairs with respect to the two DNA chains, as well as identification of the nucleotides at the corresponding sites in the *r*II messenger-RNA.

We wish to express our gratitude to Mmes. Daine Auzins, Judith Berry, and Barbara Williams for their tireless and able assistance with the experiments. This research has been supported by grants from the National Science Foundation and the National Institutes of Health.

[1] Volkin, E., and L. Astrachan, *Virology*, **2**, 149 (1956).

[2] Astrachan, L., and E. Volkin, *Biochim. et Biophys. Acta*, **29**, 536 (1958).

[3] Jacob, F., and J. Monod, *J. Mol. Biol.*, **3**, 318 (1961).

[4] Brenner, S., F. Jacob, and M. Meselson, *Nature*, **190**, 576 (1961).

[5] Gros, F., H. Hiatt, W. Gilbert, C. G. Kurland, R. W. Risebrough, and J. D. Watson, *Nature*, **190**, 581 (1961).

[6] Horowitz, J., and E. Chargaff, *Nature*, **184**, 1213 (1959).

[7] Naono, S., and F. Gros, *C.R. Acad. Sci. (Paris)*, **250**, 3889 (1960).

[8] Bussard, A., S. Naono, F. Gros, and J. Monod, *C.R. Acad. Sci. (Paris)*, **250**, 4049 (1960).

[9] Benzer, S., and S. P. Champe, these PROCEEDINGS, **47**, 1025 (1961).

[10] Nomura, M., B. D. Hall, and S. Spiegelman, *J. Mol. Biol.*, **2**, 306 (1960).

[11] Freese, E., *J. Mol. Biol.*, **1**, 87 (1959).

[12] Levinthal, C., in *Structure and Function of Genetic Elements*, Brookhaven Symposia in Biology, 12, 76 (1959).

[13] Garen, A., in *Microbial Genetics*, ed. W. Hayes and R. C. Clowes (Cambridge University Press, 1960).

[14] Benzer, S., these PROCEEDINGS, 47, 403 (1961).

[15] Torriani, A., *Biochim. et Biophys. Acta*, 38, 460 (1960).

[16] Luria, S. E., and M. Delbrück, *Genetics*, 28, 491 (1943).

[17] Freese, E., E. Bautz, and E. Bautz-Freese, these PROCEEDINGS, 47, 845 (1961).

[18] Crick, F. H. C., L. Barnett, S. Brenner, and R. J. Watts-Tobin, *Nature*, 192, 1227 (1961).

[19] Feynman, R., personal communication.

[20] Garen, A., and C. Levinthal, *Biochim. et Biophys. Acta*, 38, 470 (1960).

[21] Cohen, S. S., J. G. Flaks, H. D. Barner, M. R. Loeb, and J. Lichtenstein, these PROCEEDINGS, 44, 1004 (1958).

[22] Gros, F., W. Gilbert, H. H. Hiatt, G. Attardi, P. F. Spahr, and J. D. Watson, in *Cellular Regulatory Mechanisms*, Cold Spring Harbor Symposia on Quantitative Biology, vol. 26 (in press).

[23] Garen, A., *Virology*, 14, 151 (1961).

[24] Nomura, M., *Virology*, 14, 164 (1961).

[25] If K is infected with two rII mutants containing mutations far apart in the A cistron, r^+ recombinants should occur in many of the cells since DNA replicas are known to be formed. However, in such an experiment there is still no progeny yield such as would be expected if the recombinants could express their phenotype.

[26] Litman, R. M., and A. B. Pardee, *Nature*, 178, 529 (1956).

[27] Freese, E., these PROCEEDINGS, 45, 622 (1959).

[28] Benzer S., and E. Freese, these PROCEEDINGS, 44, 112 (1958).

[29] Freese, E., E. Bautz-Freese, and E. Bautz, *J. Mol. Biol.*, 3, 133 (1961).

[30] Schuster, H., *J. Mol. Biol.*, 3, 447 (1961).

[31] Brown, D. M., and P. Schell, *J. Mol. Biol.*, 3, 709 (1961).

[32] Brenner, S., L. Barnett, F. H. C. Crick, and A. Orgel, *J. Mol. Biol.*, 3, 121 (1961).

[33] Tessman, I., in *The Molecular Basis of Neoplasia*, 15th Annual Symposium on Fundamental Cancer Research, Houston, in press.

[34] Chamberlin, M., and P. Berg, these PROCEEDINGS, 48, 81 (1962).

[35] Bautz, E., and B. Hall, these PROCEEDINGS, 48, 400 (1962).

[36] Lengyel, P., J. F. Speyer, and S. Ochoa, these PROCEEDINGS, 47, 1936 (1961).

[37] Nirenberg, N. M., and J. H. Matthaei, these PROCEEDINGS, 47, 1558 (1961).

[38] Cohen, S. S., *J. Biol. Chem.*, 174, 218 (1948).

V
RNA Synthesis

Introduction

Since DNA and RNA both contain four major bases with similar hydrogen bonding potentialities, it seemed likely that if DNA could serve as a template for DNA synthesis it also could serve as a template for RNA synthesis. It also seemed likely that there might be biologically important cases where RNA would serve as a template for RNA synthesis. When Grunberg-Manago and Ochoa[270] reported the existence of polynucleotide phosphorylase, the first isolated enzyme to synthesize a polymeric nucleic acid, the scientific community waited with keen anticipation to see if this enzyme had a template requirement. The lack of a stringent requirement for template led others to continue the search for the biologically significant template requiring enzymes. A systematic search resulted in the discovery and isolation of a template requiring DNA polymerase (see Section II). The detection of RNA polymerases with a DNA template requirement was soon to follow. It seems likely that the latter enzymes are involved in the transcription of genetic information for use in the cell.

Initially Weiss[191] isolated a crude fraction from rat liver nuclei that synthesized RNA and was sensitive to DNAse. Added DNA did not stimulate synthesis further but this was believed to be due to the presence of sufficient DNA in the crude enzyme. Shortly thereafter purer enzymes with a requirement for added DNA were isolated from bacteria.

The purification and properties of the enzyme from *E. coli* are discussed by Chamberlain and Berg (in collection). Maitra and Hurwitz (in collection) provided evidence that DNA primed RNA is always synthesized in one directional sense beginning from the 5' end and that a purine usually occupies this position in the completed RNA molecule. It should be remembered that Kornberg had found DNA to be synthesized in the same directional sense.

RNA made *in vivo* or *in vitro* can be characterized as a DNA template directed product by its base composition and its ability to anneal specifically with a complementary site on the DNA primer. Annealing is carried out by mixing heat denatured DNA with an appreciable excess of RNA at an elevated temperature below the denaturation temperature of the DNA-RNA hybrid double helix. Over a period of many hours the RNA becomes attached to complementary sites on the DNA molecule. The resulting DNA-RNA double helix complex is recovered from solution in various ways as illustrated by several papers in this section (see Yankofsky and Spiegelman; Bautz, Kassi, Reilly and Bautz; and Taylor, Hradecna and Szybalski). In early *in vitro* polymerization studies it appears that RNA was transcribed about equally from both DNA strands.[193] A priori it seemed unlikely that both DNA strands would transcribe meaningful information and it became an enigma as to why both strands were transcribed *in vitro*. Two possibilities seemed foremost: (1) both DNA strands are transcribed *in vivo* but only one is utilized; (2) only one DNA strand is transcribed *in vivo; in vitro* conditions are not sufficiently selective. There has been a great deal of discussion about what was necessary to get selective transcription *in vitro*. The important point is that this now seems to have been accomplished in most laboratories. In a most elegant study on λ phage DNA, Taylor, Hradecna and Szybalski (in collection) have shown that not only is one DNA strand exclusively involved in transcription at any particular point on the DNA but that different regions transcribe at different times in the phage life cycle. Parallel *in vitro* and *in vivo* studies by Cohen, Maitra and Hurwitz[218] support the view that activation of different regions for transcription depends upon interaction of the DNA with one or more cytoplasmic factors.

The annealing technique has been modified by Bautz *et al.* (in collection) to make it especially suitable for the assay of single messenger RNA molecules. Annealing techniques also have been used to demonstrate that transfer RNA and ribosomal RNA are DNA derived products[194, 205] (see Yankofsky and Spiegelman, in collection). These latter studies are easier to execute than most messenger RNA studies because relatively large quantities of the purified RNAs are available.

The major types of cellular RNA appear to be synthesized on a DNA template. With the exception of the terminal residues on transfer RNA, there is no evidence that any biologically important cellular RNA is made without a DNA template. However, there are a large number of RNA viruses in which it appears that an RNA template must be used. Most known RNA viruses contain single-stranded ribopolynucleotides. There seems to be general agreement on the following replication scheme proposed by Weissmann et al.[229] for single-stranded RNA viruses. The viral RNA first serves as a messenger RNA catalyzing the synthesis of one or two polymerizing enzymes. The first enzyme (I) converts the so-called plus strand of the parent to a double-stranded form containing a plus strand and a newly synthesized Watson–Crick base paired minus strand; the second enzyme (II) produces plus strand RNA copies using the double-stranded form as template.

Lodish and Zinder (in collection), working with the single-stranded RNA containing bacteriophage f2, isolated a viral mutant that has a temperature sensitive enzyme I. Mild heat shocking during virus growth selectively destroys enzyme I. Under these conditions it can be demonstrated that the parental strand is rapidly displaced from the double helix replicative form, providing strong evidence that plus strand is replicated from the double helix RNA template semiconservatively. This is in marked contrast to the conservative replication scheme used by the RF form of the ϕX174 DNA virus. The Lodish and Zinder paper exemplifies the great value of temperature sensitive mutants to in vivo biochemical studies. Under ideal conditions one is able to selectively affect one enzyme function at any time during the life cycle of the organism or virus under study.

Despite the value of in vivo studies such as Lodish and Zinder's, most of what has been learned about the mechanism of viral RNA synthesis has come from in vitro studies in which partially purified polymerizing enzymes

isolated from virus infected cells have been used. Pace and Spiegelman (in collection) have perfected cell-free synthesis to the point where it is possible to replicate infectious viral RNA of the QB strain. It would be difficult to demonstrate more directly that the RNA product is a faithful copy of the viral RNA primer used. In subsequent studies Bishop, Pace and Spiegelman (in collection) have obtained further evidence on the mechanism of RNA synthesis. They suggest that whereas the synthesis of minus strand leading to the double helix replicative form proceeds in the customary 5' to 3' direction, the subsequent synthesis of parental plus strand copies proceeds with the opposite polarity. The use of β, α-p^{32}-labeled triphosphates to demonstrate the directional sense of synthesis is very similar to its use by Maitra and Hurwitz (in collection) to demonstrate the directional sense of DNA primed RNA synthesis. The proposal that plus strand copies are synthesized from 3' to the 5' end has yet to gain general acceptance. It is a curious though incontrovertible fact that in the highly purified polymerase preparations used in Spiegelman's laboratory that sufficient amounts of both enzymatic activities (referred to as I and II above) necessary for RNA replication are present.

Some RNA viruses normally contain double stranded RNA. When these infect cells it seems unlikely that the RNA first serves as message according to the Weissmann et al.[229] scheme since double-stranded nucleic acid cannot serve as messenger. An alternative mechanism would involve the direct utilization of the parental double-stranded form as a template for transcribing RNA messenger using the host RNA polymerase. In support of this scheme Krug, Gomatos and Tamm[230] have observed that double-stranded Reovirus RNA can serve as template for RNA synthesis using E. coli RNA polymerase.

Some aspects of the regulation of RNA synthesis are discussed in the Taylor, Hradecna and Szybalski paper in this section. Others will be taken up in Section VIII on regulation. Several aspects of RNA synthesis not discussed here are represented in the accompanying bibliography.

Bibliography

DNA-PRIMED RNA SYNTHESIS

191. S. B. Weiss, (1960). Enzymatic Incorporation of Ribonucleoside Triphosphates into the Interpolynucleotide Linkages of Ribonucleic Acid. Proc. Natl. Acad. Sci. U.S. 46, 1020.

192. E. P. Geiduschek, T. Nakamoto and S. B. Weiss, (1961). The Enzymatic Synthesis of RNA: Complementary Interaction with DNA. Proc. Natl. Acad. Sci. U.S. 47, 1405.

193. E. P. Geiduschek, J. W. Moohr and S. B. Weiss, (1962). The Secondary Structure of Complementary RNA. Proc. Natl. Acad. Sci. 48, 1078.

194. D. Giacomoni and S. Spiegelman, (1962). Origin and Biologic Individuality of the Genetic Dictionary. Science 138, 1328.

195. M. Chamberlain and P. Berg, (1963). Studies on DNA-Directed RNA Polymerase; Formation of DNA-RNA Complexes with Single-Stranded φX174 DNA as Template. Cold Spring Harbor Symp. Quant. Biol. 28, 67.

196. A. P. Nygaard and B. D. Hall, (1963). A Method for the Detection of RNA-DNA Complexes. Biochem. Biophys. Res. Comm. 12, 98.

197. A. P. Nygaard and B. D. Hall, (1964). Formation and Properties of RNA-DNA Complexes. J. Mol. Biol. 9, 125.

198. B. J. McCarthy and B. H. Hoyer, (1964). Identity of DNA and Diversity of Messenger RNA Molecules in Normal Mouse Tissues. Proc. Natl. Acad. Sci. 52, 915.

199. B. D. Hall, A. P. Nygaard and M. H. Green, (1964). Control of T$_2$-specific RNA Synthesis. J. Mol. Biol. 9, 143.

200. S. Nishimura, T. M. Jacob and H. G. Khorana, (1964). Synthetic Deoxyribopolynucleotides as Templates for RNA Acid Polymerase: The Formation and Characterization of a Ribopolynucleotide with a Repeating Trinucleotide Sequence. Proc. Natl. Acad. Sci. U.S. 52, 1494.

201. M. Chamberlain and P. Berg, (1964). Mechanism of RNA Polymerase Action: Characterization of the DNA-Dependent Synthesis of Poly A. J. Mol. Biol. 8, 708.

202. U. Maitra, A. Novogrodsky, D. Baltimore and J. Hurwitz, (1965). The Identification of Nucleoside Triphosphate Ends on RNA Formed in the RNA Polymerase Reaction. Biochem. Biophys. Res. Comm. 18, 801.

203. M. Oishi and N. Sueoka, (1965). Location of Genetic Loci of Ribosomal RNA on Bacillus subtilis Chromosome. Proc. Natl. Acad. Sci. 54, 483.

204. D. Dubnau, I. Smith and J. Marmur, (1965). Gene Conservation in Bacillus Species II. The Location of Genes Concerned with the Synthesis of Ribosomal Components and Soluble RNA. Proc. Natl. Acad. Sci. U.S. 54, 724.

205. F. M. Ritossa and S. Spiegelman, (1965). Localization of DNA Complementary to Ribosomal RNA in the Nucleolus Organizer Region of D. melanogaster. Proc. Natl. Acad. Sci. U.S. 53, 737.

206. D. Gillespie and S. Spiegelman, (1965). A Quantitative Assay for DNA-RNA Hybrids with DNA Immobilized on a Membrane. J. Mol. Biol. 12, 829.

207. W. S. Hayward and M. H. Green, (1965). Inhibition of E. coli and Bacteriophage Lambda Messenger RNA Synthesis by T$_4$. Proc. Natl. Acad. Sci. U.S. 54, 1675.

208. H. Latham and J. E. Darnell, (1965). Entrance of mRNA into HeLa Cell Cytoplasm in Puromycin-treated Cells. J. Mol. Biol. 14, 13.

209. E. H. McConkey and J. W. Hopkins, (1965). Subribosomal Particles and the Transport of Messenger RNA in HeLa Cells. J. Mol. Biol. 14, 257.

210. A. J. E. Colvill, L. C. Kánner, G. P. Tocchini-Valentine, M. T. Sarnat and E. P. Geiduschek, (1965). Assymetric RNA Synthesis in vitro: Heterologous DNA-Enzyme Systems; E. coli RNA-polymerase. Proc. Natl. Acad. Sci. U.S. 53, 1140.

211. P. Berg, R. D. Kornberg, H. Fancher and M. Dieckmann, (1965). Competition Between RNA Polymerase and DNA Poly-

merase for the DNA Template. Biochem. Biophys. Res. Comm. **18**, 932.

212. D. D. Anthony, E. Zaszatek and D. A. Goldthwait, (1966). Initiation by the DNA-Dependent RNA Polymerase. Proc. Natl. Acad. Sci. U.S. **56**, 1026.

213. E. P. Geiduschek, L. Snyder, A. J. E. Colvill and M. Sarnat, (1966). Selective Synthesis of T-even Bacteriophage Early Messenger *in vitro*. J. Mol. Biol. **19**, 541.

214. E. K. F. Bautz and E. Reilly, (1966). Gene-Specific Messenger RNA: Isolation by the Deletion Method. Science **151**, 328.

215. F. Gros, J. Gallant, R. Weisberg and M. Cashel, (1967). Decryptification of RNA Polymerase in Whole Cells of *E. coli*. J. Mol. Biol. **25**, 555.

216. R. G. Cutler and J. E. Evans, (1967). Relative Transcription Activity of Different Segments of the Genome throughout the Cell Division Cycle of *E. coli*. The Mapping of Ribosomal and Transfer RNA and the Determination of the Direction of Replication. J. Mol. Biol. **26**, 91.

217. N. W. Stead and O. W. Jones, (1967). Stability of RNA Polymerase–DNA Complexes. J. Mol. Biol. **26**, 131.

218. S. N. Cohen, U. Maitra and J. Hurwitz, (1967). Role of DNA in RNA Synthesis XI. Selective Transcription of λ DNA Segments *in vitro* by RNA Polymerase of *E. coli*. J. Mol. Biol. **26**, 19.

219. S. Naono and F. Gros, (1967). On the Mechanism of Transcription of the Lambda Genome during Induction of Lysogenic Bacteria. J. Mol. Biol. **25**, 517.

220. A. G. So, E. W. Davie, R. Epstein and A. Tissieres, (1967). Effects of Cations on DNA-Dependent RNA Polymerase. Proc. Natl. Acad. Sci. U.S. **58**, 1739.

221. K. Oda and W. K. Joklik, (1967). Hybridization and Sedimentation Studies on Early and Late Vaccinia Messenger RNA. J. Mol. Biol. **27**, 395.

222. S. N. Cohen and J. Hurwitz, (1967). Transcription of Complementary Strands of Phage λ DNA *in Vivo* and *in Vitro*. Proc. Natl. Acad. Sci. U.S. **57**, 1759.

223. B. P. Sonnenberg and G. Zubay, (1965). Nucleohistone as a Primer for RNA Synthesis. Proc. Natl. Acad. Sci. U.S. **54**, 415.

224. L. J. Greenberg and J. W. Uhr, (1967). DNA-RNA Hybridization Studies of Myeloma Tumors in Mice. Proc. Natl. Acad. Sci. U.S. **58**, 1878.

225. A. Landy, J. Abelson, H. M. Goodman and J. D. Smith, (1967). Specific Hybridization of Tyrosine Transfer RNAs with DNA from a Transducing Bacteriophage φ80 Carrying the Amber Suppressor Gene su$_{III}$. J. Mol. Biol. **29**, 457.

226. D. Pettijohn and T. Kamiya, (1967). Interaction of RNA Polymerase with Polyoma DNA. J. Mol. Biol. **29**, 275.

227. L. P. Gage and E. P. Geiduschek, (1967). Repression of Early Messenger Transcription in the Development of a Bacteriophage. J. Mol. Biol. **30**, 435.

RNA-PRIMED RNA POLYMERASE

228. R. H. Doi and S. Spiegelman, (1962). Homology Test Between the Nucleic Acid of an RNA Virus and the DNA in the Host Cell. Science **138**, 1270.

229. C. Weissmann, P. Borst, R. H. Burdon, M. A. Billeter and S. Ochoa, (1964). Enzymatic Synthesis of MS2 Phage RNA. Proc. Natl. Acad. Sci. U.S. **51**, 890.

230. R. M. Krug, P. J. Gomatos and I. Tamm, (1965). Enzymic Synthesis of RNA with Reovirus RNA as Template II. Nearest Neighbor Analysis of the Products of the Reaction Catalyzed by the *E. coli* RNA Polymerase. J. Mol. Biol. **12**, 872.

231. S. Spiegelman, I. Haruna, I. B. Holland, G. Beaudreau and D. Mills, (1965). The Synthesis of a Self-Propagating and Infectious Nucleic Acid with a Purified Enzyme. Proc. Natl. Acad. Sci. U.S. **54**, 919.

232. I. Haruna and S. Spiegelman, (1965). Recognition of Size and Sequences by an RNA Replicase. Proc. Natl. Acad. Sci. U.S. **54**, 1189.

233. F. Lodish and N. D. Zinder, (1966). Replication of the RNA of Bacteriophage f2. Science **152**, 372.

234. D. Baltimore, (1966). Purification and Properties of Poliovirus Double-Stranded RNA. J. Mol. Biol. **18**, 421.

235. G. N. Godson and R. L. Sinsheimer, (1967). The Replication of Bacteriophage MS2 VI.

Interaction Between Bacteriophage RNA and Cellular Components in MS2-infected *E. coli*. J. Mol. Biol. 23, 495.

236. A. K. Banerjee, L. Eoyang, K. Hori and J. T. August, (1967). Replication of RNA Viruses, IV. Initiation of RNA Synthesis by the QB RNA Polymerase. Proc. Natl. Acad. Sci. U.S. 57, 986.

237. M. Girard, D. Baltimore and J. E. Darnell, (1967). Poliovirus Replication Complex: Site for Synthesis of Poliovirus RNA. J. Mol. Biol. 24, 59.

238. K. Hori, L. Eoyang, A. K. Banerjee and J. T. August, (1967). Replication of RNA Viruses, V. Template Activity of Synthetic Ribopolymers in the QB RNA Polymerase Reaction. Proc. Natl. Acad. Sci. U.S. 57, 1790.

239. R. B. Kelly and R. L. Sinsheimer, (1967). Replication of MS2 VII. Nonconservative Replication of Double-Stranded RNA. J. Mol. Biol. 26, 169.

240. D. R. Mills, R. L. Peterson and S. Spiegelman, (1967). An Extracellular Darwinian Experiment with a Self-Duplicating Nucleic Acid Molecule. Proc. Natl. Acad. Sci. U.S. 58, 217.

241. R. Pollet, P. Knolle and C. Weissmann, (1967). Replication of Viral RNA XV. Purification and Properties of Q_B Minus Strands. Proc. Natl. Acad. Sci. U.S. 58, 766.

242. G. G. Maul and T. H. Hamilton, (1967). The Intranuclear Localization of Two DNA-dependent RNA Polymerase Activities. Proc. Natl. Acad. Sci. U.S. 57, 1371.

DNA: Mechanism and Specificity. J. Mol. Biol. 11, 445.

248. M. R. Lunt and R. L. Sinsheimer, (1966). Inhibition of RNA Bacteriophage Growth by Actinomycin D. J. Mol. Biol. 18, 541.

249. A. M. Haywood and J. M. Harris, (1966). Actinomycin Inhibition of MS2 Replication. J. Mol. Biol. 18, 448.

250. W. K. Roberts and J. F. E. Newman, (1966). Use of Low Concentrations of Actinomycin D in the Study of RNA Synthesis in Ehrlich Ascites Cells. J. Mol. Biol. 20, 63.

251. J. S. Paul, R. C. Reynolds and P. Montgomery, (1967). Inhibition of DNA-dependent RNA Polymerase by 4-Nitroquinoline-N-oxide in Isolated Nuclei. Nature 215, 749.

252. R. M. Friedman, (1967). Interferon Binding: The First Step in Establishment of Antiviral Activity. Science 156, 1760.

253. R. W. Hyman and N. Davidson, (1967). Binding of Actinomycin to Crab dAT; The Nature of the DNA Binding Site. Biochem. Biophys. Res. Comm. 26, 116.

254. A. Cerami, E. Reich, D. C. Ward and I. H. Goldberg, (1967). The Interaction of Actinomycin with DNA: Requirement for the 2-Amino Group of Purines. Proc. Natl. Acad. Sci. U.S. 57, 1036.

255. A. K. Field, G. P. Lampson, A. A. Tytell, M. M. Nemes and M. R. Hilleman, (1967). Inducers of Interferon and Host Resistance, IV. Double Stranded Replicative Form RNA (MS2-RF-RNA) from *E. coli*. Infected with MS2 Coliphage. Proc. Natl. Acad. Sci. U.S. 58, 2102.

INHIBITORS

243. A. Isaacs, (1963). Interferon. Adv. in Virus. Res. 10, 1.

244. B. Mach and E. L. Tatum, (1963). RNA Synthesis in Protoplasts of *E. coli*: Inhibition by Actinomycin. Science 139, 1051.

245. R. A. Flickinger, (1963). Actinomycin D Effects in Frog Embryos: Evidence for Sequential Studies of DNA-dependent RNA. Science 141, 1063.

246. J. W. Uhr, (1963). Actinomycin D: Its Effect on Antibody Formation *in vitro*. Science 142, 1476.

247. M. Gellert, C. E. Smith, D. Neville and G. Felsenfeld, (1965). Actinomycin Binding to

BASE MODIFICATION

256. P. W. Robbins and J. B. Hammond, (1962). Evidence for the Formation of Pseudouridine by the Rearrangement of a Uridine Derivative. J. Biol. Chem. 237, PC 1379.

257. M. Gefter, R. Hausmann, M. Gold and J. Hurwitz, (1966). The Enzymatic Methylation of RNA and DNA X. Bacteriophage T_3-induced S-Adenosylmethionine Cleavage. J. Biol. Chem. 241, 1995.

258. E. Borek and P. R. Srinivasan, (1966). The Methylation of Nucleic Acids. Ann. Rev. Biochem. 35, 275.

259. J. A. Boezi, R. L. Armstrong and M. De-Backer, (1967). Methylation of RNA in

Bacteriophage T₄ Infected *E. coli.* Biochem. Biophys. Res. Comm. 29, 281.

260. W. Hsu, J. W. Foft and S. B. Weiss, (1967). Effect of Bacteriophage Infection on the Sulfur-Labeling of sRNA. Proc. Natl. Acad. Sci. U.S. 58, 2028.

RNASES

261. P. F. Spahr and B. R. Hollingworth, (1961). Purification and Mechanism of Action of RNAse from *E. coli* Ribosomes. J. Biol. Chem. 236, 823.

262. M. F. Singer and G. Tolbert, (1965). Purification and Properties of a Potassium Activated Phosphodiesterase (RNAse II) from *E. coli.* Biochem. 4, 1319.

263. R. F. Gesteland, (1966). Isolation and Characterization of RNAse I Mutants of *E. coli.* J. Mol. Biol. 16, 67.

264. M. Fukai, Y. Anraku and D. Mizuno, (1966). The Role of Three Enzymes in Messenger RNA Degradation in Cell-free Systems from Normal or Phage-infected *E. coli.* Biochem. Biophys. Acta 119, 373.

265. H. D. Robertson, R. E. Webster and N. D. Zinder, (1967). A Nuclease Specific for Double-Stranded RNA. Virology 32, 718.

RIBOSOMES

266. M. H. Vaughan, J. R. Warner and J. E. Darnell, (1967). Ribosomal Precursor Particles in the HeLa Cell Nucleus. J. Mol. Biol. 25, 235.

267. C. P. Flessel, R. Ralph and A. Rich, (1967). Polyribosomes of Growing Bacteria. Science 158, 658.

268. G. Mangiarotti and D. Schlessinger, (1967). Polyribosomes Metabolism in *E. coli.* II. Formation and Lifetime of Messenger RNA Molecules, Ribosomal Subunit Couples and Polyribosomes. J. Mol. Biol. 29, 395.

269. R. Soeiro, M. H. Vaughan and J. E. Darnell, (1968). Effect of Puromycin on Intranuclear Steps in Ribosome Biosynthesis. J. Cell. Biol. 36, 91.

MISCELLANEOUS

270. M. Grunberg-Manago and S. Ochoa, (1955). Enzymatic Synthesis and Breakdown of Polynucleotides: Polynucleotide Phosphorylase. J. Am. Chem. Soc. 77, 3165.

271. J. B. Hall, J. W. Sedat, P. R. Adiga, I. Uemura and T. Winnick, (1965). Gramicidin S Messenger RNA I. Isolation and Characterization. II. Physical and Chemical Properties. J. Mol. Biol. 12, 162, 174.

272. S. J. S. Hardy and C. G. Kurland, (1966). The Polynucleotide Product of Poly A Polymerase from *E. coli.* Biochem. 5, 3668.

273. A. A. Infante and M. Nemer, (1967). Accumulation of Newly Synthesized RNA Templates in a Unique Class of Polyribosomes during Embryogenesis. Proc. Natl. Acad. Sci. U.S. 58, 681.

274. J. S. Krakow and M. Karstadt, (1967). Azotobacter vinelandii RNA Polymerase IV. Unprimed Synthesis of RIC Copolymer. Proc. Natl. Acad. Sci. U.S. 58, 2094.

275. J. Hindley, (1967). Fractionation of ^{32}P-labeled RNAs on Polyacrylamide Gels and their Characterization by Finger Printing. J. Mol. Biol. 30, 125.

DEOXYRIBONUCLEIC ACID-DIRECTED SYNTHESIS OF RIBONUCLEIC ACID BY AN ENZYME FROM ESCHERICHIA COLI*

By Michael Chamberlin† and Paul Berg

DEPARTMENT OF BIOCHEMISTRY, STANFORD UNIVERSITY SCHOOL OF MEDICINE

Communicated by Arthur Kornberg, November 17, 1961

Protein structure is under genetic control;[1-3] yet the precise mechanism by which DNA‡ influences the formation of specific amino acid sequences in proteins is unknown. Several years ago, it was discovered that infection of *Escherichia coli* with certain virulent bacteriophages induces the formation of an RNA fraction possessing both a high metabolic turnover rate and a base composition corresponding to the DNA of the infecting virus.[4-6] The existence of an analogous RNA component in noninfected cells has also been demonstrated; in this instance, however, the base composition of the RNA resembles that of the cellular DNA.[7, 8] These observations focused attention on the possible role of this type of RNA in protein synthesis, and some of the evidence consistent with this view has recently been summarized.[9]

Until recently there was no known enzymatic mechanism for a DNA-directed synthesis of RNA. Polynucleotide phosphorylase[10, 11] although it catalyzes the synthesis of polyribonucleotides, does not by itself provide a mechanism for the formation of RNA with a specific sequence of nucleotides. The one instance in which a unique sequence of nucleotides is produced involves the limited addition of nucleotides exclusively to the end of pre-existing polynucleotide chains.[12-14]

Our efforts were therefore directed toward examining alternate mechanisms for RNA synthesis, and in particular one in which DNA might dictate the nucleotide sequence of the RNA. In the present paper, we wish to report the isolation and some properties of an RNA polymerase from *E. coli* which, in the presence of DNA and the four naturally occurring ribonucleoside triphosphates, produces RNA with a base composition complementary to that of the DNA. Within the last year, several laboratories have reported similar findings with enzyme preparations from bacterial as well as from plant and animal sources.[15-24] In the following paper, the effect of enzymatically synthesized RNA on the rate and extent of amino acid incorporation into protein by *E. coli* ribosomes in the presence of a soluble protein fraction is described.

Experimental Procedure.—Materials: Unlabeled ribonucleoside di- and triphosphates were purchased from the Sigma Biochemical Corporation and the California Corporation for Biochemical Research. 8-C^{14}-labeled ATP was purchased from the Schwartz Biochemical Company; the other, uniformly labeled, C^{14} ribonucleoside triphosphates were prepared enzymatically from the corresponding monophosphate derivatives[25] isolated from the RNA of *Chromatium* grown on $C^{14}O_2$ as sole carbon source.[26] CTP labeled with P^{32} in the ester phosphate was obtained by enzymatic phosphorylation of CMP^{32} prepared according to Hurwitz.[27] The deoxyribonucleoside triphosphates were obtained by the procedure of Lehman *et al.*[25]

Calf thymus and salmon sperm DNA were isolated by the method of Kay *et al.*[28] DNA from *Aerobacter aerogenes*, *Mycobacterium phlei*, and bacteriophages T2, T5, T6 was prepared as described previously.[29] DNA from λ*dg* phage was prepared as reported elsewhere.[30] Unlabeled and P^{32} labeled DNA from *E. coli* were prepared as previously described.[31] d-AT and d-GC polymers were prepared according to Schachman *et al.*[32] and Radding *et al.*,[33] respectively. Transforming DNA from *Bacillus subtilis*[34] was a gift from E. W. Nester, and DNA from phage ØX

174 [49] was generously supplied by R. L. Sinsheimer. Double-stranded ØX 174 DNA was synthesized using *E. coli* DNA polymerase[25] with single-stranded ØX 174 DNA as primer.[35, 36] In this reaction, 2.7 times more DNA was synthesized than had been added as primer. RNA from tobacco mosaic virus was obtained from H. Fraenkel-Conrat, and ribosomal and amino acid–acceptor RNA were isolated from *E. coli* according to Ofengand *et al.*[26, 37] Nucleic acid concentrations are given as mμmoles of nucleotide phosphorus per ml.

Glass beads, "Superbrite 100," obtained from the Minnesota Mining and Manufacturing Company, were washed as previously described.[25] Streptomycin sulfate was a gift from Merck and Company, and protamine sulfate was purchased from Eli Lilly Company. DEAE-cellulose was purchased from Brown and Company. Crystalline pancreatic RNase and pancreatic DNase were products of the Worthington Biochemical Co.

Assays: The activities of *E. coli*-DNA polymerase,[25] -deoxyribonuclease[38] and -DNA diesterase,[31] were determined as previously described and ribonuclease activity was measured by the disappearance of amino acid–acceptor RNA activity.[26] Polynucleotide phosphorylase was measured by P_i^{32} exchange with ADP as reported by Littauer and Kornberg.[11] Protein was determined by the method of Lowry *et al.*[39]

The standard assay for RNA polymerase measures the conversion of either C^{14} or P^{32} from the labeled ribonucleoside triphosphates into an acid-insoluble form. Enzyme dilutions were made with a solution containing 0.01 M Tris buffer, pH 7.9, 0.01 M $MgCl_2$, 0.01 M β-mercaptoethanol, 5×10^{-5} M EDTA, and 1 mg per ml of crystalline bovine serum albumin. The reaction mixture (0.25 ml) contained: 10 μmoles of Tris buffer, pH 7.9, 0.25 μmole of $MnCl_2$, 1.0 μmole of $MgCl_2$, 100 mμmoles each of ATP, CTP, GTP, and UTP, 250 mμmoles of salmon sperm DNA, 3.0 μmoles of β-mercaptoethanol, and 10 to 80 units of enzyme. One of the nucleoside triphosphates was labeled with approximately 300 to 600 cpm per mμmole. After incubation at 37° for 10 min, the reaction mixture was chilled in ice, and 1.2 mg of serum albumin (0.03 ml) was added, followed by 3 ml of cold 3.5% perchloric acid (PCA). The precipitate was dispersed, centrifuged for 5 min at 15,000 × g, and washed twice with 3.0 ml portions of cold PCA. The residue was suspended in 0.5 ml of 2 N ammonium hydroxide, transferred to an aluminum planchet, and after drying, counted in a windowless gas-flow counter.

One unit of enzyme activity corresponds to an incorporation of 1 mμmole of CMP^{32} per hr under the conditions described above. The assay was proportional to the amount of enzyme added up to at least 80 units; thus 6.3, 12.5, and 25 μg of Fraction 4 enzyme incorporated 2.6, 5.1, and 10.0 mμmoles of CMP^{32}. The rate of the reaction remained constant for approximately 20 min, and then decreased after this time.

Since the radioactivity incorporated represents only one of the four nucleotides, the observed incorporation must be multiplied by a factor ranging from 3 to 5 for an estimate of the total amount of RNA synthesized. The exact factor depends on the composition of the DNA primer used.

Results.—Purification of RNA polymerase: (1) *Cells:* E. coli B was grown in continuous exponential phase culture[40] with a glucose–mineral salts medium.[41] Cells stored at −20° showed no loss of activity for over six months. The purification procedure and the results of a typical preparation are summarized in Table 1.

TABLE 1

PURIFICATION OF RNA POLYMERASE FROM *E. coli*

Fraction	Volume (ml)	Specific activity (units/mg)	Total activity (units)
1. Initial extract	260	40	370,000
2. Protamine eluate	37	1,600	205,000
3. Ammonium sulfate	5	2,500	200,000
4. Peak DEAE fraction	2	6,100	153,000

Unless noted otherwise, all operations were carried out at 4° and all centrifugations were at 30,000 × g for 15 min in an International HR-1 Centrifuge.

(2) *Extract:* Frozen cells (140 gm) were mixed in a Waring Blendor with 420 gm of glass beads and 150 ml of a solution (buffer A) containing 0.01 M Tris buffer, pH

7.9, 0.01 M MgCl$_2$, and 0.0001 M EDTA. After disruption of the cells at high speed for 15 min (maximum temperature 10°), a further 150 ml of buffer A was added and the glass beads were allowed to settle. The supernatant fluid was then decanted and the residue was washed with 75 ml of buffer A. The combined supernatant fluid and wash was centrifuged for 30 min and the resulting supernatant fluid collected (Fraction 1).

(3) *Streptomycin-protamine fractionation:* Fraction 1 was centrifuged in the Spinco Model L preparative ultracentrifuge for 4 hr at 30,000 rpm in the No. 30 rotor. The protein concentration in the supernatant fluid was adjusted to about 12 mg per ml with buffer A, and β-mercaptoethanol was added to a final concentration of 0.01 M. To 350 ml of the diluted supernatant solution was added 17.5 ml of a 10% (w/v) solution of Streptomycin sulfate with stirring. After 15 min, the solution was centrifuged, and to 350 ml of the supernatant fluid was added 14.0 ml of a 1% (w/v) solution of protamine sulfate. The precipitate, collected by centrifugation, was washed by suspension in 175 ml of buffer A containing 0.01 M β-mercaptoethanol. The washed precipitate was then suspended in 35 ml of buffer A containing 0.01 M mercaptoethanol and 0.10 M ammonium sulfate, centrifuged for 30 min, and the supernatant fluid was collected (Fraction 2).

(4) *Ammonium sulfate fractionation:* To 37 ml of Fraction 2 was added 15.8 ml of ammonium sulfate solution (saturated at 25° and adjusted to pH 7 with ammonium hydroxide). The mixture was stirred for 15 min, and the precipitate was removed by centrifugation. To the supernatant liquid was added an additional 16.2 ml of the saturated ammonium sulfate, and after 15 min the precipitate was collected by centrifugation for 30 min and dissolved in buffer B (0.002 M KPO$_4$, pH 8.4, 0.01 M MgCl$_2$, 0.01 M β-mercaptoethanol, and 0.0001 M EDTA) to a final volume of 5.0 ml (Fraction 3).

(5) *Adsorption and elution from DEAE-cellulose:* Fraction 3 was diluted to a protein concentration of about 3 mg per ml with buffer B and passed onto a DEAE-cellulose column (10 cm × 1 cm², washed with 150 ml of buffer B just prior to use) at a rate of about 0.5 ml per min. The column was washed with 10 ml of buffer B and then with enough of the same buffer containing 0.16 M KCl to reduce the absorbency of the effluent at 280 mμ to less than 0.05. The enzyme was eluted from the column with buffer B containing 0.23 M KCl. The activity appears within the first five ml of the latter eluant (Fraction 4).

(6) *Properties of the purified enzyme:* The specific activity of enzyme Fraction 4 was from 140 to 170 times greater than that of the initial extract. The purification as described here has been quite reproducible, with specific activities in the final fraction ranging from 5,500 to 6,100. The enzyme preparation (Fraction 4) has a ratio of absorbencies at 280 and 260 mμ of 1.5.

Fraction 4, stored at 0 to 2°, retains more than 90 per cent of its activity for up to two weeks and 40 to 60 per cent of the original activity after one month. Enzyme Fractions 1 through 3 are unstable, losing up to 30 per cent of their activity on overnight storage under a variety of conditions. Because of the marked instability of these earlier fractions, it is advisable to carry out the purification without stopping at intermediate stages.

(7) *Contaminating enzymatic activities:* Aliquots (100 μg) of Fraction 4 were assayed for contaminating enzymatic activities. This amount of enzyme cata-

lyzed an initial rate of incorporation of 2,000 mμmoles of nucleotide per hr. No detectable DNA polymerase was found (< 0.6 mμmole DNA per hr). DNase activity was barely detectable under conditions optimal for RNA polymerase. With either heated or unheated P^{32} DNA as substrate, no more than 0.13 mμmole of acid-soluble P^{32} was released during the course of a 30-min incubation. There was only slight RNase activity associated with Fraction 4. When 100 μg of the purified enzyme were incubated with 4 μmoles of purified acceptor RNA for 1 hr, there was no detectable inactivation of leucine-acceptor activity. Under similar conditions, 1 mg of enzyme produced a 30 per cent decrease in leucine-acceptor activity. With conditions optimal for RNA polymerase, sufficient polynucleotide phosphorylase activity was present to catalyze the exchange of 6.7 mμmoles of P_i^{32} into ADP per hour.

Requirements for the RNA polymerase reaction: With the purified enzyme, RNA synthesis was dependent on the addition of DNA, a divalent cation, and the four ribonucleoside triphosphates (Table 2). In a later section, we shall describe a

TABLE 2
REQUIREMENTS FOR RNA SYNTHESIS

Components	Incorporation of CMP^{32} (mμmoles)
Complete system	7.3
minus Mn^{++}	4.3
minus Mg^{++}	5.6
minus Mn^{++} and Mg^{++}	<0.03
minus DNA	<0.03
minus ATP, GTP, UTP	0.09
minus enzyme	<0.03

The standard system and assay procedure were used with 7.4 μg of Fraction 4 protein in each tube, except that $MgCl_2$ was omitted from the enzyme diluent.

TABLE 3
THE REQUIREMENT FOR RIBONUCLEOSIDE TRIPHOSPHATES IN RNA SYNTHESIS

Components	Incorporation of CMP^{32} (mμmoles)
Complete system	4.6
minus ATP	0.08
minus UTP	<0.03
minus GTP	<0.03
ATP, UTP, GTP replaced by dATP, dTTP, dGTP	0.05
ATP, UTP, GTP replaced by ADP, UDP, GDP	0.29

The standard system and assay procedure were used except that 250 mμmoles of calf thymus DNA were used as primer. 13 μg of Fraction 4 protein were used in each assay. 100 mμmoles of each nucleotide were added to each assay.

reaction in which ATP is converted to an acid-insoluble form in the absence of the other three triphosphates. Omission of β-mercaptoethanol from the reactiom mixture resulted in a 50 per cent loss in activity; however, dilution of the concentrated enzyme into solutions not containing a sulfhydryl compound resulted in as much as 90 per cent inactivation. The optimal pH for the reaction was between 7.8 to 8.2. At pH 6.1, 7.0, and 8.9 the activities were 13, 62, and 84 per cent, respectively, of the maximal value.

(1) *Nucleoside triphosphate specificity:* All of the ribonucleoside triphosphates are required for RNA synthesis (Table 3). The deoxyribonucleoside triphosphates do not function as substrates in the reaction, and the ribonucleoside diphosphates support synthesis only at a greatly reduced rate. The observed activity of the diphosphates may be due to the presence of small amounts of the nucleoside triphosphates in the diphosphate preparations or to the formation of the triphosphates through the action of nucleoside diphosphate kinase.

With CTP^{32} as the labeled substrate and salmon sperm DNA as primer, variation of the concentrations of all four ribonucleoside triphosphates as a group produced a variation in the rate of RNA synthesis. When the data were plotted according to Lineweaver and Burk,[42] a linear relationship was obtained from which

TABLE 4

THE EFFECT OF DIFFERENT NUCLEIC ACID
PREPARATIONS ON THE RATE OF RNA
SYNTHESIS BY RNA POLYMERASE

Source of primer	Incorporation of CMP[32]*
DNA	
Salmon sperm	100
Calf thymus	43
E. coli	34
ØX 174	38
B. subtilis	27
λdg phage	25
T2 phage	45
T6 phage	30
T5 phage	74
RNA	
E. coli amino acid-acceptor	<0.5
E. coli ribosomal	<0.5
TMV	<0.5

* The incorporation value for salmon sperm DNA
was 5.3 mμmoles and is set at 100 for comparison with
the other primers.
  Assay system and procedure as previously described, except that 100 mμmoles of each nucleic acid
were used in place of the usual primer. 7.4 μg of Fraction 4 protein were used in each assay.

TABLE 5

THE EFFECT OF DENATURATION ON THE
ABILITY OF DNA PREPARATIONS TO
PRIME FOR RNA SYNTHESIS

DNA	Incorporation of CMP[32] Native (mμmoles)	Heated
Calf thymus	2.7	2.3
Salmon sperm	6.1	2.5
T6 phage	1.9	0.8
E. coli	1.8	1.9

Assay procedure as described previously, except
that the usual primer was replaced by 200 mμmoles of
the DNA to be tested. 7.4 μg of Fraction 4 protein
were used in each assay. The DNA samples were
heated for 10 min at 95 to 99° in 0.05 M NaCl and
rapidly cooled in an ice bath. The absorbencies of
the heated DNA preparations were 30 to 40 per cent
higher than those of the unheated preparations at 260
mμ.

it was calculated that the rate of synthesis was half maximal when the concen-
tration of each of the triphosphates was 1.3×10^{-4} M. A similar value (1.4×10^{-4} M) was obtained using C^{14} ATP as a label and calf thymus DNA as
primer.

(2) *The nature of the primer:* All DNA samples tested were active in promoting ribonucleotide incorporation, although the efficiency varied significantly
(Table 4). Amino acid–acceptor RNA, ribosomal RNA from *E. coli*, and TMV
RNA did not substitute for DNA. With the synthetic copolymer d-AT as primer, only AMP and UMP were incorporated, and only GMP and CMP were incorporated in the presence of d-GC polymer (Table 7). It should be noted, however, that GTP was incorporated to a considerably greater extent in the latter
case. A qualitatively similar finding has been reported for the incorporation of
dGMP and dCMP by DNA polymerase with d-GC as primer.[33]

Increasing the amount of DNA in an assay mixture over the range 0 to 200
mμmoles resulted in an increase in nucleotide incorporation. Further increases in
the amount of DNA, up to 400 mμmoles, had no effect on the rate of RNA synthesis. A similar experiment using calf thymus DNA as primer gave a saturating
value of 250 mμmoles.

The effect of disrupting the DNA double helix by heating[43] is shown in Table 5.
It is seen that with several of the DNA preparations there is a significant decrease
in the rate of CMP[32] incorporation using the heated DNA while with others the
effect is insignificant. The ability of single-stranded DNA to function as a primer for RNA synthesis is further emphasized by the activity of the single-stranded
DNA from ØX 174 phage.

(3) *Metal ion requirements:* Optimal concentrations for Mn[++] and Mg[++]
when added separately to the reaction mixture were 2×10^{-3} M and 8×10^{-3} M, respectively (Figure 1). Addition of Mg[++] increased the rate at sub-
optimal levels of Mn[++]; thus, the addition of 10^{-3} M Mn[++] and 4×10^{-3} M

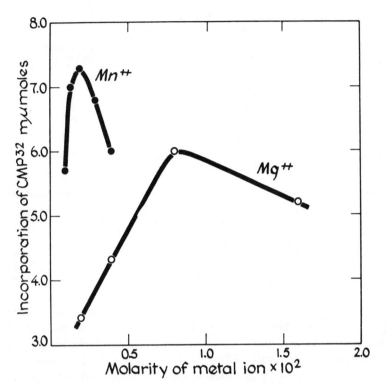

Fig. 1.—The Influence of Metal Ion Concentration on the Rate of CMP^{32} Incorporation. Standard assay conditions were used, except that the metal ion concentration was varied as shown. 7.4 μg of Fraction 4 enzyme were added to each assay.

  ○——○ Mg^{++} alone added to the assay mixture
  ●——● Mn^{++} alone added to the assay mixture

Mg^{++} to the same reaction mixture gave a rate of incorporation equal to that found with the optimal concentration of Mn^{++} alone ($2 \times 10^{-3} M$).

Characterization of the enzymatically synthesized RNA: (1) *Net synthesis of the RNA product:* With two times the level of the four ribonucleoside triphosphates and five to ten times the amount of enzyme used in the routine assay, the amount of RNA formed during an extended incubation exceeded the amount of DNA added to the reaction. We will designate this as "net synthesis." With most of the DNA preparations used, the amount of RNA formed was three to five times greater than the amount of DNA added, while with d-AT copolymer, up to 15 times as much of the corresponding AU polynucleotide was produced (Table 6). The rate of synthesis decreased after the first 20 min although further synthesis occurred up to two hr. Preliminary experiments indicate that this was not due to enzyme inactivation nor to destruction of the priming DNA, but other possibilities have not yet been investigated in detail.

(2) *Enzymatic and alkaline degradation of the product:* Exposure of the isolated "net synthesis" product to alkali converted > 98 per cent of the label to acid-soluble products which were electrophoretically identical with the 2'-(3') nucleoside monophosphates. Treatment with pancreatic DNase or *E. coli* DNA diesterase[31] produced no significant liberation of labeled acid-soluble products.

TABLE 6

NET SYNTHESIS OF RNA

Source of DNA primer	Labeled nucleotide incorporated	Calculated amount of RNA formed* (mμmoles)	Ratio of RNA isolated to DNA added	Method of isolation
	CMP^{32}			
Calf thymus	81	200	2.0	A
φX 174 phage	90	510	5.1	A
T2 phage	78	360	3.6	A
T2 phage	72	410	4.1	B
	C^{14}-AMP			
T2 phage	150	460	4.6	C
T5 phage	152	500	5.0	C
d-AT copolymer	155	310	15.0	C

* The amount of RNA in the isolated product was calculated from the amount of label incorporated and the base ratio of the primer DNA.

Synthesis: Each tube contained in a final volume of 0.5 ml: 20 μmoles of Tris buffer, pH 7.85; 8 μmoles of MgCl₂; 400 mμmoles each of ATP, CTP, UTP, GTP; 6 μmoles of β-mercaptoethanol; 100 mμmoles of DNA; and 100 μg of Fraction 4 protein. When d-AT was used as primer, only 20 mμmoles of primer were added and CTP and GTP were omitted from the mixture. The incubation time was 3 hr at 37°.

Product isolation: A. The incubation mixture was heated for 10 min at 60° in 0.4 *M* NaCl, then dialyzed 36 hr against 0.2 *M* NaCl–0.01 *M* Tris, pH 7.85. B. The reaction mixture was extracted two times with phenol and the phenol fractions were washed two times with 0.4 *M* NaCl. The aqueous layers were pooled and dialyzed as in A. C. The product was precipitated from the incubation mixture with a solution containing 60 per cent ethanol and 0.5 *M* NaCl at 0°, washed once with the same solution, and dissolved in 1 ml of 0.2 *M* NaCl., then dialyzed as in A.

Treatment of 10 to 20 mμmoles of enzymatically prepared CMP^{32}-labeled RNA with 0.1 μg of pancreatic RNase for 1 hr liberated 75 to 94 per cent of the P^{32} label as acid-soluble products. The amount of acid-insoluble P^{32} remaining after RNase treatment varied with different DNA primers and different methods of product isolation. Using 10 times the amount of RNase did not appreciably alter the results. The significance of this RNase resistant fraction is presently unknown.

(3) *Nucleotide composition:* The nucleotide composition of the product was examined by two different methods. In the first method, four separate assays, each containing a different labeled nucleoside triphosphate, were performed with each DNA preparation, and the molar ratio in which the labeled nucleotides were incorporated was measured (Method A). The second method utilized electrophoretic separation[44] of the mononucleotides resulting from the alkaline degradation of a "net synthesis" product in which all of the nucleoside triphosphates were labeled with C^{14} (Method B). The distribution of the label among isolated nucleotides was therefore a measure of the composition of the newly synthesized RNA. The results (Table 7) indicate that the gross composition of the product at all stages of synthesis was complementary to that of the primer within the accuracy of the method. For double-stranded DNA, this complementary relationship becomes one of identity, since in the priming DNA adenine equals thymine and guanine equals cytosine. However, in the case of single-stranded φX 174 DNA (Table 8), the composition is indeed complementary to that of the DNA, and in this instance the amounts of AMP and UMP incorporation and of GMP and CMP incorporation are not equal. Furthermore, when double-stranded φX 174 DNA is used, the nucleotide composition of the resulting RNA is again identical to that of the DNA primer.

(4) *Sedimentation velocity of the isolated product:* The sedimentation velocity of the isolated RNA product was determined in the Spinco Model E analytical ultracentrifuge using ultraviolet optics. Values obtained (S₂₀) in 0.2 *M* NaCl–

TABLE 7

NUCLEOTIDE COMPOSITION OF THE RNA PRODUCT

DNA primer	Method of analysis	Nucleotide Composition AMP	UMP	GMP	CMP	Primer* $\frac{A + T}{G + C}$	Product $\frac{A + U}{G + C}$	Product $\frac{A + G}{U + C}$
		(mμmoles)						
d-GC polymer	A	<0.03	<0.03	1.90	0.23	—	—	—
d-AT copolymer	B	21.7	20.0	—	—	—	—	—
d-AT copolymer	A	20.8	22.2	<0.03	<0.03	—	—	—
T2 phage	B	7.7	7.4	4.3	4.3	1.76	1.76	1.03
T5 phage	B	4.8	5.0	3.6	3.4	1.56	1.40	1.00
E. coli	A	1.8	1.9	1.9	2.0	1.01	0.95	0.95
M. phlei	A	3.7	4.0	7.9	8.5	0.48	0.47	0.93
A. aerogenes	A	1.8	1.7	2.3	2.2	0.80	0.78	1.05

* The values given for the ratio A + T/G + C in the priming DNA are those found by Josse et al.[10] except in the case of phage T5 DNA.[12]

Method A: For each DNA sample, four separate incubations were used, each containing a different C[14]-labeled nucleotide. The amounts of DNA used in the various tests were as follows: 20 mμmoles of M. phlei, 50 mμmoles of A. aerogenes, 180 mμmoles of E. coli, 20 mμmoles of d-AT, 20 mμmoles of d-GC. 12.5 μg of Fraction 4 enzyme were used in each incubation; all other conditions were those given for a standard assay.

Method B: The synthesis of the C24-labeled RNA was carried out under the following conditions. The reaction mixture (0.5 ml) contained: 20 μmoles of Tris buffer, pH 7.85, 0.5 μmole of MnCl₂, 2 μmoles of MgCl₂, 6 μmoles of β-mercaptoethanol, 100 mμmoles each of C[14]-ATP, C[14]-UTP, C[14]-GTP, C[14]-CTP, 100 mμmoles of DNA, and 180 μg of Fraction 4 enzyme. Where d-AT primer was used, 20 mμmoles of primer were added and no CTP or GTP were added. After 180 min at 37°, the product was precipitated and washed with cold 3 per cent PCA and incubated in 0.3 M KOH for 18 hr at 37°. An aliquot to which carrier nucleotides had been added was subjected to paper electrophoresis at pH 3.5 in 0.05 M citrate buffer. The individual nucleotides which were visualized with a UV lamp were eluted in 0.01 M HCl and counted. Recovery of the C[14]-label in the eluted fractions was >95 percent. 180 mμmoles, 140 mμmoles, and 200 mμmoles of polyribonucleotide were produced in the reactions primed with T2 DNA, T5 DNA, and d-AT, respectively.

TABLE 8

COMPARATIVE BEHAVIOR OF SINGLE- AND DOUBLE-STRANDED ØX 174 DNA AS PRIMER FOR RNA SYNTHESIS

State of DNA used as primer		Nucleotide Composition of RNA AMP	UMP	GMP	CMP
			(per cent)		
Single-stranded	Predicted*	32.8	24.6	18.5	24.1
" "	Found by method A	32.0	24.1	19.5	24.3
" "	Found by method B	35.0	24.6	19.3	21.1
Double-stranded	Predicted*	28.7	28.7	21.3	21.3
" "	Found by method B	28.9	29.1	20.9	20.9

Method A: Conditions as given in Table 7. 32 mμmoles of single-stranded ØX 174 DNA were used in each incubation with 8 μg of Fraction 4 enzyme.

Method B: Conditions as given in Table 7. With single-stranded DNA as primer, 25 mμmoles of priming DNA were added, 71 mμmoles of RNA were produced in a 60 min incubation with 80 μg of Fraction 4 enzyme. For the double-stranded DNA, 26 mμmoles of priming DNA were added; 32 mμmoles of RNA were produced in a 60 min incubation with 40 μg of Fraction 4 enzyme.

* The predicted values were calculated on the assumption that the single-stranded ØX 174 DNA would yield RNA with a composition complementary to the composition reported by Sinsheimer.[49] Upon replication of ØX 174 DNA with DNA-polymerase it was assumed that the product (presumably double-stranded DNA) had a base composition which is the average of the composition of the original and of the newly synthesized strands.

That this is a reasonable assumption is shown by unpublished studies of M. Swartz, T. Trautner, and A. Kornberg. When ØX 174 DNA was used to prime limited (<30 per cent) or extensive (600 per cent) DNA synthesis, the composition of the newly formed DNA was:

	dAMP	TMP	dGMP	dCMP
Limited synthesis	31.0	24.1	20.1	24.5
Extensive synthesis	29.4	26.9	22.3	21.3

0.01 M Tris, pH 7.9, ranged from 6 to 7.5 for 2- to 15-fold "net synthesis" products prepared by phenol extraction or by salt-ethanol precipitation.

DNA-dependent formation of polyadenylic acid: As pointed out earlier, RNA synthesis, as measured by the incorporation of either labeled CTP, UTP, or GTP did not occur in the absence of the other three nucleoside triphosphates or, in fact, in the absence of any one of the nucleoside triphosphates. It was therefore surprising to find that purified fractions of RNA polymerase catalyze the conversion of C^{14}-ATP to an acid-insoluble form in the absence of the other three ribonucleoside triphosphates. The ratio of the activities

$$\frac{\text{AMP incorporated in the absence of UTP, CTP, GTP}}{\text{AMP incorporated in the presence of UTP, CTP, GTP}}$$

increased from 0.5 to 10 as purification of the enzyme progressed.

(1) *Requirements for polyadenylic acid formation:* Polyadenylic acid formation from ATP occurred only in the presence of DNA, a divalent cation, and the purified enzyme (Table 9). Note that addition of unlabeled ADP produces only a

TABLE 9

REQUIREMENTS FOR POLYADENYLIC ACID FORMATION

System	Incorporation of AMP ($m\mu$moles)
Complete (with ATP as the only nucleoside triphosphate)	9.9
minus DNA	<0.03
minus Mn^{++}	2.5
minus Mg^{++}	8.7
plus RNase	6.9
plus DNase	0.3
plus ADP	7.6

The reaction mixture contained, in a final volume of 0.25 ml: 10 μmoles of Tris buffer, pH 7.85; 0.5 μmole of $MnCl_2$; 2 μmoles of $MgCl_2$; 3 μmoles of β-mercaptoethanol; 100 $m\mu$moles of C^{14}-ATP; 280 $m\mu$moles of calf thymus DNA; and 3 μg of Fraction 4 RNA polymerase. Where indicated, 25 μg of pancreatic RNase, 25 μg of pancreatic DNase, and 100 $m\mu$moles of ADP were added. The incubation time was 10 min at 37°.

TABLE 10

INCORPORATION OF SINGLE NUCLEOTIDES BY RNA POLYMERASE

Nucleotide added	Nucleotide incorporation ($m\mu$moles)
C^{14}-ATP	23
C^{14}-UTP	0.90
C^{14}-GTP	0.09
CTP^{32}	0.07

The conditions were the same as those described in Table 9, except that ATP was replaced where indicated by an equal amount of each of the other nucleoside triphosphates. 6 μg of Fraction 4 enzyme were added.

small dilution of the incorporation of label from C^{14}-ATP. The rate of incorporation was directly proportional to the amount of enzyme added; 1.8, 3.6, and 7.2 μg of Fraction 4 enzyme catalyzed the incorporation of 4.0, 8.2, and 17.5 $m\mu$moles of C^{14}-AMP in a standard 10 min assay. The rate of incorporation remained constant up to over 75 per cent utilization of the added ATP.

There was no incorporation of CMP or GMP when the corresponding nucleoside triphosphates were added singly to the reaction, although UMP incorporation occurred to a small, but significant, extent (Table 10).

(2) *The DNA requirement for polyadenylic acid formation:* The ability of various nucleic acid preparations to support polyadenylic acid synthesis is shown in Table 11. Note that neither RNA nor polyadenylic acid itself replaced the DNA requirement. To test whether DNA might be necessary only to initiate polyadenylic acid synthesis, an experiment was performed in which the priming DNA was destroyed after some polyadenylic acid formation had already occurred. It can be seen that destruction of the DNA by DNase blocked further synthesis of the polyadenylic acid (Table 12). This implies that the DNA is required not only for the initiation of polyadenylic acid synthesis, but also for the continued formation of the polynucleotide.

(3) *The effect of the other ribonucleoside triphosphates on polyadenylic acid formation:* The addition of the other ribonucleoside triphosphates resulted in an inhibition of the rate of C^{14} AMP incorporation (Table 13). It can be seen, for

TABLE 11

PRIMING EFFICIENCY OF VARIOUS NUCLEIC ACID PREPARATIONS FOR POLYADENYLIC ACID FORMATION

Primer	AMP incorporation (mμmoles)
Calf thymus DNA	10
Salmon sperm DNA	7.7
T2 phage DNA	4.9
d-AT copolymer	<0.03
Amino acid-acceptor RNA	0.35
Polyadenylic acid	0.07

The conditions of the incubation were as described in Table 9, except that the following amounts of nucleic acid were added: 300 mμmoles of salmon sperm DNA; 100 mμmoles of T2 phage DNA; 12 mμmoles of d-AT; 110 mμmoles of amino acid–acceptor RNA and 5 mμmoles of polyadenylic acid. 3 μg of Fraction 4 enzyme were added.

TABLE 12

THE EFFECT OF DEOXYRIBONUCLEASE ADDITION DURING POLYADENYLIC ACID SYNTHESIS

Tube	Treatment	AMP incorporation (mμmoles)
1	5-min incubation	7.1
2	10-min incubation	16.2
3	10-min incubation	6.9

The reaction mixtures were as described in Table 9, except that 6 μg of Fraction 4 was used. Tube 1 was incubated for 5 min, heated for 3 min at 100°, and then assayed as usual. Tube 2 was incubated for 10 min before assaying. Tube 3 was incubated for 5 min and heated as in the case of tube 1; 25 μg of pancreatic DNase were then added and the mixture incubated for an additional 5 min. At this time, 6 μg of fresh RNA polymerase were added and a third 5-min incubation was allowed.

TABLE 13

EFFECT OF THE OTHER RIBONUCLEOSIDE TRIPHOSPHATES ON POLYADENYLIC ACID FORMATION

Component	AMP incorporation (mμmoles)
Complete system	26
plus CTP	6.0
plus UTP	5.2
plus GTP	2.0
plus CTP, UTP	1.3
plus CTP, GTP	0.6
plus UTP, GTP	0.5
plus UTP, GTP, CTP	2.2

Complete system as in Table 9, except that 6 μg of Fraction 4 protein were added. Where indicated, 100 mμmoles of each nucleoside triphosphate were added.

example, that in the presence of any two of the other triphosphates the amount of polyadenylic acid formed is less than 5 per cent that of the control in which only ATP was added. As has been previously shown, in the presence of all four triphosphates, AMP is incorporated into a product having a base composition determined by the DNA primer, and hence under these conditions polyadenylic acid synthesis does not appear to occur.

(4) *Characterization of the polyadenylic acid product:* Preliminary characterization of the product is consistent with its identity as a polyadenylic acid. The addition of pancreatic RNase to the assay system lowered the rate of incorporation only slightly (about 30%). Treatment with 0.5 M KOH for 18 hr at 37° converted the product to an acid-soluble form. Of the C^{14} in the hydrolysate, 97 per cent was associated with 2'-(3') AMP on paper chromatography[44] and paper electrophoresis,[45] less than 1.5 per cent with adenosine, and less than 1.5 per cent was found in a region corresponding to adenosine 3'-5' diphosphate. This implies that the minimum chain length of the polyadenylate is in the order of 60 to 70 nucleotide residues.

Discussion.—There is a striking similarity between the reactions catalyzed by the RNA polymerase described here and *E. coli* DNA polymerase.[25] Both use only the nucleoside triphosphates as nucleotidyl donors, and both display absolute requirements for a divalent cation and a DNA primer for polynucleotide synthesis.§ In both cases, some ambiguity exists as to the relative efficiency of single as compared to double-stranded DNA for priming of polynucleotide synthesis. In each reaction, both forms of DNA are active as primers, but a meaningful comparison between the two with regard to the mechanism of priming must await a more detailed physical and chemical characterization of the different DNA preparations, and further purification of the enzymes involved.

The product formed by RNA polymerase, as in the analogous case of DNA polymerase[29] has a base composition which, within experimental error, is complementary to that of the priming DNA. This finding, which is in agreement with the results obtained by others[16, 17, 21], supports the view that the nucleotide sequences in the DNA direct the order of nucleotides in the enzymatically synthesized RNA. A more critical test of this hypothesis involves a comparison of the nucleotide sequence of the priming DNA and the newly synthesized RNA. In this regard, Furth *et al.*[19] have shown that the repeating sequence of dAMP and dTMP in d-AT copolymer is faithfully replicated by the RNA polymerase in the form of an alternating AMP and UMP sequence. More recently Weiss and Nakamoto[46] have shown that RNA synthesized with an RNA polymerase from *M. lysodeikticus* contains the same frequencies of dinucleotide pairs as occur in the DNA primer. Additional experiments[47] which demonstrate the formation of a DNA-RNA complex after heating and slow-cooling[48] suggest that the homology of nucleotide sequences may occur over relatively long regions.

Does RNA polymerase copy the sequence of only one or both strands of DNA? This question is relevant not only to an understanding of the enzymatic copying mechanism, but also to any speculations as to the mechanism of information transfer from DNA to RNA. The fact that with double-stranded DNA primers the base composition of the newly made RNA is essentially identical to the over-all composition of both strands of the DNA already suggests that each strand can function equally well. An alternative hypothesis is to suppose that only one strand can be copied, and that the "primer" strand has, in the case of every DNA studied, a base composition identical to the average composition of both strands. Using the double-stranded form of ØX 174 DNA[35, 36] in which it is known that the base compositions of the two strands differ,[49] it is possible to test this question directly. The results show that both strands of the duplex serve to direct the composition of the RNA product.

This result still leaves open the question of whether both strands are copied in one replication cycle or whether only one strand is copied at a time and the choice between strands is random. When considering the relevance of this finding to information transfer, one must bear in mind that the existence of artificially produced ends in an isolated DNA preparation may allow RNA formation to proceed from both ends of the double strand. This, however, may not occur with the DNA as it exists in the genome; that is, *in vivo* some structural feature in the chromosomal DNA may cause RNA synthesis to proceed in a unidirectional manner and therefore copy the sequence of only one of the two strands.

The formation of DNA-RNA complexes has been described by several groups of workers,[48, 50, 51] although only limited information is available concerning their chemical structure and their metabolic and chemical stability. The fact that in the enzymatic reaction net synthesis of RNA occurs argues against the formation of a stable, stoichiometric complex of RNA and DNA. A further argument against the formation of such a complex is the finding that most of the DNA remaining at the end of the reaction appears to be identical to the DNA added, and no component containing both DNA and newly synthesized RNA was detectable on CsCl gradient centrifugation.[47] Whether some transient complex is formed as an intermediate is somewhat more difficult to assess.

The formation of polyadenylic acid in a DNA-dependent reaction is significant in view of the fact that none of the other ribonucleoside triphosphates, taken singly or even in groups of three, are utilized to any appreciable extent for polynucleotide synthesis. An exception to this is, of course, the situation where the DNA dictates the incorporation of only one or two nucleotides (e.g., with poly dT,[18] d-AT,[19] or d-GC).

Three possibilities which could account for polyadenylic acid synthesis are that it results from (a) a special feature of RNA polymerase itself, (b) a separate polyadenylic acid polymerase, or (c) polynucleotide phosphorylase. The last possibility is least likely because of the absolute requirement for DNA in the initiation and continuation of synthesis, the failure of ADP to give a significant dilution of the incorporation from ATP, the low amounts of polynucleotide phosphorylase activity found in the enzyme preparation as measured by P_i^{32} exchange, the inability of Mg^{++} alone to support maximal rates of synthesis, the lack of polymerization of the other nucleoside triphosphates, and the marked inhibition of polyadenylic acid synthesis by any one or all four of the triphosphates The question of whether polyadenylic acid synthesis is catalyzed by RNA polymerase or by another enzyme cannot be resolved at the present time.

With regard to the mechanism of the DNA-dependent polyadenylic acid formation, two aspects deserve specific comment. The first concerns the mechanism of the inhibition of polyadenylic acid synthesis by any one or all of the other triphosphates. It should be recalled that polyadenylic acid synthesis does not occur in the presence of all four ribonucleoside triphosphates ($< 3\%$), since under these conditions the base composition of the newly synthesized RNA is very close to that predicted by the composition of the DNA primers. The second notable feature of the reaction is its complete dependence on DNA, and the failure of d-AT to prime polyadenylic acid synthesis. One way to account for these findings is to assume that a sequence of thymidylate residues in the DNA, which does not occur in d-AT, can prime the formation of a corresponding run of AMP residues and, by subsequent "slippage" of one chain along the other, lead to a DNA-dependent elongation of the polyadenylic acid chain. The introduction of any other nucleotide into the growing chain might block or inhibit the sliding process and thereby terminate the growing polyadenylic acid chain.

Summary.—An RNA polymerase has been isolated from *E. coli* which in the presence of the four ribonucleoside triphosphates, a divalent metal ion, and DNA synthesizes RNA with a base composition complementary to that of the priming DNA. Both strands of DNA can prime new RNA synthesis. Thus, while single-stranded ØX 174 DNA yields RNA with a base composition complementary to that of the single-stranded form, double-stranded ØX 174 DNA (synthesized with DNA polymerase) primes the synthesis of RNA with a base composition virtually the same as that in both strands of the DNA. A novel feature of the RNA polymerase preparations is their ability to catalyze a DNA-dependent formation of polyadenylic acid in the presence of ATP alone. Neither UTP, GTP, nor CTP yields corresponding homopolymers; the DNA-dependent formation of polyadenylic acid is virtually completely inhibited by the presence of the other nucleoside triphosphates.

* This work was supported by Public Health Service Research Grant No. RG6814 and Public Health Service Training Grant No. 2G196.

† Pre-doctoral Fellow.

‡ The abbreviations used in this paper are: RNA and DNA for ribo- and deoxyribonucleic acid, respectively; poly dT for polydeoxythymidylate; d-AT for the deoxyadenylate-thymidylate copolymer; d-GC for the deoxyguanylate-deoxycytidylate polymer; AMP, ADP and ATP for adenosine-5'-mono-, di-, and triphosphates, respectively. A similar notation is used for the cytidine (C), guanosine (G), and uridine (U) derivatives and their deoxy analogues (dA, dC, dG, dT). P_i is used for inorganic orthophosphate, TMV for tobacco mosaic virus, and DNase and RNase for deoxyribo- and ribonuclease activities, respectively.

§ Under certain conditions DNA polymerase preparations will, in the absence of DNA, produce d-AT or d-GC depending upon the nature of the substrates present.[32],[33]

[1] Ingram, V. M. and J. A. Hunt, *Nature* 178, 792 (1956).

[2] Yanofsky, C. and P. St. Lawrence, *Ann. Rev. Microbiol.*, 14, 311 (1960).

[3] Fincham, J. R. S., *Ann. Rev. Biochem.*, 28, 343 (1959).

[4] Volkin, E. and L. Astrachan, *Virology*, 2, 149 (1956).

[5] Volkin, E., these PROCEEDINGS, 46, 1336 (1960).

[6] Nomura, M., B. D. Hall and S. Spiegelman, *J. Mol. Biol.*, 2, 306 (1960).

[7] Yčas, M. and W. S. Vincent, these PROCEEDINGS, 46, 804 (1960).

[8] Gros, F., W. Gilbert, H. Hiatt, P. F. Spahr, and J. D. Watson, Cold Spring Harbor Symposia on Quantitative Biology, vol. 21, in press.

[9] Jacob, F., and J. Monod, *J. Mol. Biol.*, 3, 318 (1961).

[10] Ochoa, S. and L. Heppel, in *The Chemical Basis of Heredity*, ed. W. D. McElroy and B. Glass (Baltimore: The Johns Hopkins Press, 1957), p. 615.

[11] Littauer, U. Z. and A. Kornberg, *J. Biol. Chem.*, 226, 1077 (1957).

[12] Hecht, L. I., M. L. Stephenson, and P. C. Zamecnik, these PROCEEDINGS, 45, 505 (1959).

[13] Canallakis, E. S. and E. Herbert, these PROCEEDINGS, 46, 170 (1960).

[14] Preiss, J., M. Dieckmann, and P. Berg, *J. Biol. Chem.*, 236, 1749 (1961).

[15] Weiss, S. B., these PROCEEDINGS, 46, 1020 (1960).

[16] Weiss, S. B. and T. Nakamoto, *J. Biol. Chem.*, PC 18 (1961).

[17] Hurwitz, J., Bresler, A. and R. Diringer, *Biochem. Biophys. Res. Comm.*, 3, 15 (1960).

[18] Furth, J. J., J. Hurwitz, and M. Goldmann, *Biochem. Biophys. Res. Comm.*, 4, 362 (1961).

[19] *Ibid.*, 4, 431 (1961).

[20] Stevens, A., *Biochem. Biophys. Res. Comm.*, 3, 92 (1960).

[21] Stevens, A., *J. Biol. Chem.*, 236, PC 43 (1961).

[22] Ochoa, S., D. P. Burma, H. Kröger, and J. D. Weill, these PROCEEDINGS, 47, 670 (1961).

[23] Burma, D. P., H. Kröger, S. Ochoa, R. C. Warner, and J. D. Weill, these PROCEEDINGS, 47, 749 (1961).

[24] Huang, R. C., N. Maheshwari, and J. Bonner, *Biochem. Biophys. Res. Comm.*, 3, 689 (1960).

[25] Lehman, I. R., M. J. Bessman, E. S. Simms, and A. Kornberg, *J. Biol. Chem.*, 233, 163 (1958).

[26] Ofengand, E. J., Ph.D. Thesis, Washington University, St. Louis, Missouri (1959).

[27] Hurwitz, J., *J. Biol. Chem.*, 234, 2351 (1959).

[28] Kay, E. R. M., N. S. Simmons, and A. L. Dounce, *J. Am. Chem. Soc.*, 74, 1724 (1952).

[29] Josse, J., A. D. Kaiser, and A. Kornberg, *J. Biol. Chem.*, 236, 864 (1961).

[30] Kaiser, A. D., and D. S. Hogness, *J. Mol. Biol.*, 2, 392 (1960).

[31] Lehman, I. R., *J. Biol. Chem.*, 235, 1479 (1960).

[32] Schachman, H. K., J. Adler, C. M. Radding, I. R. Lehman, and A. Kornberg, *J. Biol. Chem.*, 235, 3243 (1960).

[33] Radding, C. M., J. Josse, and A. Kornberg, unpublished results.

[34] Nester, E. W., and J. Lederberg, these PROCEEDINGS, 47, 56 (1961).

[35] Lehman, I. R., *Ann. N. Y. Acad. Sci.*, 81–3, 745 (1959).

[36] Lehman, I. R., R. L. Sinsheimer, and A. Kornberg, unpublished results.

[37] Ofengand, E. J., M. Dieckmann, and P. Berg, *J. Biol. Chem.*, 236, 1741 (1961).

[38] Lehman, I. R., G. G. Roussos, and A. Pratt, *J. Biol. Chem.*, in press.

[39] Lowry, O., J. J. Rosebrough, A. L. Farr, and R. J. Randall, *J. Biol. Chem.*, **193**, 265 (1951).

[40] Monod, J., *Ann. Inst. Pasteur*, **79**, 390 (1950).

[41] Wiesmeyer, H., and M. Cohn, *Biochim. Biophys. Acta*, **39**, 417 (1960).

[42] Lineweaver, H., and D. Burk, *J. Am. Chem. Soc.*, **56**, 658 (1934).

[43] Doty, P., these PROCEEDINGS, **42**, 791 (1956).

[44] Markham, R. and J. P. Smith, *Biochem. J.*, **52**, 552 (1952).

[45] Magasanik, B., E. Vischer, R. Doniger, D. Élson, and E. Chargaff, *J. Biol. Chem.*, **186**, 37 (1950).

[46] Weiss, S. B., and T. Nakamoto, these PROCEEDINGS, **47**, 1400 (1961).

[47] Geiduschek, E. P., T. Nakamoto, and S. B. Weiss, these PROCEEDINGS, **47**, 1405 (1961).

[48] Hall, B. D., and S. Spiegelman, these PROCEEDINGS, **47**, 137 (1961).

[49] Sinsheimer, R. L., *J. Mol. Biol.*, **1**, 43 (1959).

[50] Rich, A., these PROCEEDINGS, **46**, 1044 (1960).

[51] Schildkraut, C. L., J. Marmur, J. R. Fresco, and P. Doty, *J. Biol. Chem.*, **236**, PC 2 (1961).

[52] Wyatt, G. R., and S. S. Cohen, *Biochem. J.*, **55**, 774 (1953).

THE ROLE OF DNA IN RNA SYNTHESIS, IX. NUCLEOSIDE TRIPHOSPHATE TERMINI IN RNA POLYMERASE PRODUCTS*

BY UMADAS MAITRA† AND JERARD HURWITZ

DEPARTMENT OF MOLECULAR BIOLOGY, ALBERT EINSTEIN COLLEGE OF MEDICINE, BRONX, NEW YORK

Communicated by A. D. Hershey, July 22, 1965

It has been shown previously that in RNA polymerase reactions primed with a variety of DNA preparations there is incorporation of P^{32} from $\beta\gamma$-labeled ATP into an acid-insoluble product and that triphosphate groups are present at the ends of the RNA chains formed during the reaction.[1]   Two schemes for initiation of the chains can thus be envisaged.   In one scheme, the initial nucleotide incorporated into RNA would retain its triphosphate end, while the growing end of the molecule would be a nucleoside.   In the second scheme, the situation is reversed: The nucleoside end would be the initiation point, and the triphosphate, the growing site of the molecule.   It is clear that these two schemes of initiation of RNA synthesis differ specifically in that the first would result in the initial nucleotide retaining the β and γ phosphate groups, whereas in the second scheme the last entering nucleotide would contain the β and γ phosphate group.

In the present communication, evidence will be presented that (1) initiation and subsequent elongation of RNA chains formed by RNA polymerase under the direction of a DNA template occur by a mechanism in which the first nucleotide incorporated into the RNA chain retains its triphosphate moiety, and (2) adenosine and guanosine triphosphate ends are preferentially formed.

Materials and Methods.—γ-P^{32}-GTP and UTP were prepared by photophosphorylation of the corresponding nucleoside diphosphates with $^{32}P_i$ and spinach chloroplasts by a modification of the procedure of Avron.[2] γ-P^{32}-CTP was prepared by the action of nucleoside diphosphokinase[3] on $\beta\gamma$-P^{32}-ATP and CDP in the presence of an excess of myokinase. $\beta\gamma$-P^{32}-ATP was prepared as described by Penefsky and Racker[4] in the presence of excess myokinase.   These P^{32}-labeled compounds were purified by chromatography on Dowex-1-Cl$^-$ and were free of P^{32} in the α-phosphate position.   The methods of preparation of other materials, including the DNA-dependent RNA polymerase of *Escherichia coli*, have been previously described.[1, 5]   Calf thymus DNA was obtained from General Biochemicals.

Enzyme assay: The presence of a triphosphate terminus in the RNA formed in an RNA polymerase reaction was measured by the incorporation of γ-P^{32} ribonucleoside triphosphate into an acid-insoluble product, and RNA synthesis was measured by the incorporation of α-P^{32} or C^{14}-labeled ribonucleoside triphosphate.   Reaction mixtures (0.50 ml) contained Tris buffer, pH 8.0, 25 μmoles; 2-mercaptoethanol, 4 μmoles; $MnCl_2$, 0.5 μmole; $MgCl_2$, 2.5 μmoles; DNA, 25 mμmoles; ATP, UTP, GTP, and CTP, 10 mμmoles each, one labeled with P^{32} in the γ-phosphate group (containing $1-2 \times 10^9$ cpm/μmole) for measurement of triphosphate termini or with C^{14}-ATP or GTP (containing $2-5 \times 10^6$ cpm/μmole) for measurement of the total amount of RNA formed in the reaction.   In either case, the reaction was initiated by the addition of enzyme.[6]   After incubation at 37° for the desired time, the reaction mixture was chilled in ice, and 0.1 ml of a bovine plasma albumin solution (5 mg/ml) was added, followed by 0.3 ml of 7% $HClO_4$.   The resulting precipitate was centrifuged for 5 min at $15,000 \times g$, and the pellet dissolved in 0.2 ml of ice-cold 0.2 N NaOH.   This was followed by the addition of 0.1 ml of nonradioactive triphosphate (25 μmoles/ml) corresponding to the γ-P^{32}-labeled triphosphate used in the reaction mixture and 5 ml of cold 5% TCA solution containing 0.01 M sodium pyrophosphate.   After the reaction mixture had stood in ice for 5 min, the acid-insoluble material was collected by centrifugation, and the washing procedure was repeated two more times. The final pellet was dissolved in 1.5 ml of 0.2 N NH$_4$OH, transferred to an aluminum planchet, and after drying, counted in a windowless gas-flow counter. The high specific radioactivities of the γ-P^{32}-labeled substrates necessitated the washing procedure to obtain consistently low blanks. When the total amount of RNA synthesized from C^{14}-nucleoside triphosphate (specific radioactivity 10^6–10^7 cpm/μmole) was measured, the washing procedure was not necessary, and the acid-insoluble RNA product was isolated by filtration on membrane filters as described previously.[1]

Results.—Incorporation of γ-P^{32}-labeled nucleoside triphosphates into RNA polymerase products: RNA polymerase, primed with dAT copolymer, catalyzes the incorporation of βγ-P^{32}-labeled ATP into an acid-insoluble polyribonucleotide product.[1] The incorporation of P^{32} is dependent on the presence of UTP, dAT copolymer, and RNA polymerase. The omission of any of these components, or the addition of RNase or DNase, results in a marked decrease in P^{32}-ATP incorporation. In contrast, similar experiments carried out with γ-P^{32}-UTP do not result in significant incorporation of P^{32}, as shown in Table 1. The low level of incorporation observed is not dependent on the simultaneous presence of ATP.[7]

TABLE 1

REQUIREMENTS FOR THE INCORPORATION OF βγ-P^{32}-LABELED ATP AND γ-P^{32}-UTP IN dAT-PRIMED POLY·rAU SYNTHESIS

Additions	βγ-P^{32}-ATP incorporated (μμmoles)	γ-P^{32}-UTP incorporated (μμmoles)
1. Complete system	4.40	0.40
2. Omit UTP	0.37	—
3. Omit ATP	—	0.40
4. Omit enzyme	0.13	0.11
5. Omit dAT copolymer	0.29	0.28
6. Complete + DNase (1 μg)	0.30	0.24
7. Complete + RNase (1 μg)	0.30	0.24
8. Complete with C^{14}-ATP in place of βγ-P^{32}-ATP	7200 (poly rAU)	

The conditions of the experiment were as described under *Enzyme Assay*, except that GTP and CTP were omitted and 10 mμmoles of dAT copolymer replaced DNA. βγ-P^{32}-ATP incorporation and γ-P^{32}-UTP incorporation were measured in separate mixtures. In the complete system, the total amount of nucleotide incorporated was calculated from the amount of C^{14}-AMP incorporated into the poly rAU product. Mixtures were incubated for 40 min and contained 3 units of RNA polymerase.

The finding that poly rAU chains contain ATP ends and very few UTP ends prompted an examination of the relative incorporation of P^{32} from each of the four γ-P^{32}-labeled nucleoside triphosphates with different DNA templates of varying base composition. The results, presented in Table 2, show that RNA chains are

TABLE 2

INCORPORATION OF γ-P^{32}-NUCLEOSIDE TRIPHOSPHATES WITH DIFFERENT DNA PREPARATIONS

DNA primer	RNA synthesis (μμmoles)	γ-P^{32}-Nucleotide Incorporated (μμmoles)			
		ATP	GTP	UTP	CTP
T2	4800	2.40	1.2	0.12	0.10
T5	4000	1.80	1.4	0.41	0.23
SP3	5480	1.25	1.0	0.39	0.12
Cl. perfringens	2800	1.60	2.1	0.28	0.25
E. coli	2660	0.43	1.4	0.13	0.10
M. lysodeikticus	2560	0.36	2.5	0.10	0.12
Calf thymus	3560	0.77	1.3	0.33	0.18
dAT copolymer	rAU = 7200	4.40	—	0.20	—
dGC homopolymer	rG = 1350	—	4.8	—	0.30
	rC = 120				

The conditions of the assay were as described under *Methods*. In each reaction mixture, only one of the four nucleoside triphosphates was labeled with P^{32} in the γ-phosphate group; the other three were nonradioactive. Incubation was for 40 min at 37° with 2 units of enzyme. Where indicated, 7.5 mμmoles of dGdC homopolymer and 10 mμmoles of dAT copolymer were added. Controls without enzyme and without DNA were included. In these controls incorporation was 0.2–0.3 μμmole of nucleotide, and the higher value was subtracted from the results listed above.

formed predominantly with ATP and GTP ends, whereas few chains are initiated with UTP and CTP. The relative number of triphosphate ends beginning with adenosine or guanosine varied with the DNA used to direct the reaction (Table 2). With various bacterial DNA's and calf thymus DNA, GTP ends predominated, although significant ATP incorporation also was observed. With DNA preparations from phages T2, T5, and SP3 (which have an A + T/G + C ratio > 1), ATP ends occurred slightly more often than GTP ends. Denaturation of DNA had marked effects on both RNA synthesis and the incorporation of P^{32} from γ-P^{32}-labeled nucleoside triphosphates (Table 3). These effects can be summarized as

TABLE 3

Effect of Denaturation of DNA on the Incorporation of γ-P^{32}-Labeled
Nucleoside Triphosphates

DNA primer	RNA synthesis ($\mu\mu$moles)	γ-P^{32}-Nucleotide Incorporated ($\mu\mu$moles)			
		ATP	GTP	UTP	CTP
T2	4800	2.3	1.2	0.13	0.10
T2 heat-denatured	1000	3.6	5.1	0.88	0.40
T2 alkali-denatured	1050	3.5	4.7	0.91	0.45
Calf thymus	5700	1.0	1.8	0.33	0.20
Calf thymus heat-denatured	2000	3.8	10.1	0.82	0.66
E. coli	2000	0.6	1.5	0.13	0.10
E. coli heat-denatured	1300	2.4	8.1	0.56	0.44

The condition of the assay was as described under *Methods*, with 20 mμmoles of each of the various DNA preparations, 2 units of enzyme, and 40 min of incubation at 37°. RNA synthesis was followed by incorporation of both C^{14}-AMP and C^{14}-GMP, and total RNA synthesis was calculated by multiplying the sum of these values by two.

follows: (1) RNA synthesis was markedly inhibited, (2) the incorporation of all four γ-P^{32} nucleoside triphosphates increased severalfold, and (3) there was an increase in the ratio of GTP to ATP termini as well as a significant though small number of RNA chains containing UTP and CTP ends.

Identification of guanosine triphosphate ends of RNA formed in the RNA polymerase reaction: As with $\beta\gamma$-P^{32}-labeled ATP,[1] the incorporation of γ-P^{32}-GTP into an acid-insoluble material had the same requirements found for RNA synthesis.

For identification of the site of GTP incorporation, an RNA product containing γ-P^{32}-GTP was prepared using denatured thymus DNA as template. Subjecting the P^{32}-labeled RNA product to the action of alkaline phosphatase or to acid hydrolysis (1 N HCl for 10 min at 100°) rendered the P^{32} acid-soluble and Norit nonadsorbable. The P^{32} present in the RNA product was not converted to P_i by the action of prostatic phosphomonoesterase.[8] The P^{32} product was insensitive to pancreatic DNase, since it remained acid-insoluble, whereas pancreatic RNase and alkaline hydrolysis released all the P^{32} into an acid-soluble but Norit-adsorbable form. These results indicate that the P^{32} incorporated from γ-P^{32}-GTP was in a terminal portion of the RNA structure, presumably $\overset{*}{p}ppGpXpYpZ$----, and not in an internucleotide link.

The expected products of alkaline hydrolysis of polynucleotides with the structure $\overset{*}{p}ppGpXpYpZ$---- are 2'(3')-nucleoside monophosphates and nucleoside tetraphosphates. Radioactivity from γ-P^{32}-GTP should be found only in guanosine tetraphosphate ($\overset{*}{p}ppGp$). The prediction was tested as follows: An alkaline hydrolysate (0.3 N KOH at 37° for 18 hr) of the labeled product was neutralized with Dowex-50 (H$^+$), and an aliquot of the solution containing 30,000 cpm was mixed with 2 μmoles each of GMP, GDP, GTP, ATP, and guanosine-5'-tetraphosphate.[9] The mixture was added to a column (1 × 12 cm) of Dowex-1-Cl$^-$ (100–

200 mesh, 2% cross-linked), and the nucleotides were eluted as follows: (a) 150 ml of 0.01 M HCl + 0.05 M LiCl (GMP); (b) 150 ml of 0.01 M HCl + 0.1 M LiCl (GDP followed by ATP); (c) 150 ml of 0.01 M HCl + 0.2 M LiCl (GTP); (d) 150 ml of 0.05 M HCl + 0.2 M LiCl, which eluted guanosine 5'-tetraphosphate. The elution profile and identification of each of the nucleotides were determined by measuring the optical densities of the effluents at 260 and 280 mμ. More than 90 per cent of the P^{32} added to the column was eluted as a sharp symmetrical peak in the last solvent with guanosine 5'-tetraphosphate, whereas 8 per cent of the added radioactivity was eluted in the GTP region. No P^{32} was detected in the other regions of the chromatogram. These results are consistent with the presence of pppGp. To characterize further the P^{32}-labeled product in the alkaline hydrolysate, another aliquot of the alkaline hydrolysate (containing 30,000 cpm) was incubated with 3.5 units[10] of prostatic phosphomonoesterase at pH 5.0 at 37° for 30 min. The mixture was then chromatographed on Dowex-1-Cl$^-$ under the conditions described above. Approximately 75 per cent of the added radioactivity now chromatographed with GTP and the remainder with guanosine 5'-tetraphosphate. These results are consistent with the structure pppGpXpYpZ----, i.e., γ-P^{32}-GTP is incorporated as such at the end of RNA chains.

Kinetics of nucleoside triphosphate incorporation: The rates of RNA synthesis and $\beta\gamma$-P^{32}-ATP incorporation were compared (Table 4). Whereas T2 DNA-directed

TABLE 4

KINETICS OF RNA SYNTHESIS VERSUS $\beta\gamma$-P^{32}-ATP INCORPORATION

Time of incubation (min)	RNA synthesis ($\mu\mu$moles)	$\beta\gamma$-P^{32}-ATP incorporated ($\mu\mu$moles)	Ratio
1	300	1.2	250
2	600	1.6	375
5	1500	2.4	630
10	2700	2.8	960
20	4500	3.2	1410
40	6100	3.7	1695
60	8400	3.7	2270

The assay was performed as described under *Methods*, except that 5 μmoles of MgCl$_2$ replaced MnCl$_2$, 2 units of RNA polymerase and 20 mμmoles of each of the nucleoside triphosphate were added, and the incubation was carried out at 25°. This procedure permitted slow growth of the RNA chains with T2 DNA as primer.

RNA synthesis continued during the entire experiment, 65 per cent of the total amount of $\beta\gamma$-P^{32}-ATP was incorporated by 5 min. The ratio of $\beta\gamma$-P^{32}-ATP ends to total nucleotide incorporation decreased progressively with time from a ratio of 1 ATP terminus per 250 RNA nucleotides during the first minute to 1 ATP terminus per 2270 nucleotides after 60 min.

A comparison of the kinetics of P^{32} incorporation from γ-P^{32}-GTP with native and with heat-denatured T2 DNA as template is summarized in Table 5. With native T2 DNA as template the incorporation of P^{32} was virtually complete in 20 min, although RNA synthesis continued throughout the incubation period. The ratio of GTP ends to RNA formed decreased progressively with time from a ratio of 1 GTP terminus per 1300 nucleotides in the first 5 min to 1 GTP terminus per 5100 nucleotides after 90 min. Under the same conditions, experiments with $\beta\gamma$-P^{32}-ATP indicated the presence of 1 ATP terminus per 600 nucleotides during the first 5 min of incubation and 1 ATP terminus per 3100 nucleotides after 90 min. In contrast, with denatured DNA as template, the incorporation of γ-P^{32}-GTP was severalfold faster and continued during the entire period of RNA synthesis. Similar results were obtained with $\beta\gamma$-P^{32}-ATP. In this case, with denatured DNA as template, the ratio of ATP ends to RNA formed was lower than that found with GTP (1/160 after 5 min of incubation and 1/540 after 60 min), since with denatured DNA more γ-P^{32}-GTP than $\beta\gamma$-P^{32}-ATP was incorporated. However, with either of these two triphosphates, the ratio of triphosphate ends formed to RNA synthesized was considerably smaller than that obtained with the corresponding native DNA as template. The ratios obtained in these experiments can be used as a measure of the length of the RNA product formed. Wood and Berg[11] found that RNA products formed with denatured DNA as template were smaller than those obtained with native DNA. The results summarized in Table 5 are in agreement with their findings.

TABLE 5

KINETICS OF RNA SYNTHESIS AND γ-P^{32}-GTP INCORPORATION WITH NATIVE AND DENATURED T2 DNA AS TEMPLATES

Experiment no.	Time of incubation (min)	RNA synthesized ($\mu\mu$moles)	γ-P^{32}-GTP incorporated ($\mu\mu$moles)	Ratio
I	5	1500	1.1	1360
	10	2700	1.4	1800
	20	5000	1.7	2900
	40	6200	1.9	3200
	60	8300	1.9	4150
	90	10400	1.9	5200
II	5	150	3.2	47
	10	300	4.8	62
	20	600	6.6	90
	40	1140	7.7	143
	60	1500	8.1	180
	90	2100	10.1	210

The conditions of the experiment were as described under *Methods*, except that 20 mμmoles each of γ-P^{32}-GTP, UTP, CTP, and ATP were added. Twenty-four mμmoles of native T2 DNA (approximate size = 35S) were added in experiment I, and an equimolar amount of heat-denatured T2 DNA was added in experiment II. Incubation was at 37°.

Direction of growth of RNA chains: In order to determine whether incorporation of the triphosphate terminus in RNA occurs according to the scheme in which the first nucleotide incorporated retains the triphosphate end, or by a mechanism in which the triphosphate moiety is at the growing point of the RNA molecule, the following experiment was performed. γ-P^{32}-GTP was incorporated into RNA for 5 min, and then a large excess of cold GTP was added to reduce the specific activity of the labeled nucleotide. The fate of P^{32} already incorporated at the ends of the RNA chains was then followed during subsequent RNA synthesis. If the initial nucleotide incorporated was present as the triphosphate end, subsequent synthesis should have no effect on the P^{32} already incorporated. In contrast, if the last entering nucleotide existed as the triphosphate terminus, subsequent synthesis should release the previously incorporated P^{32}. The fate of γ-P^{32}-GTP ends under the conditions described above is summarized in Figure 1. As shown, the addition of unlabeled GTP halted γ-P^{32} uptake immediately, and continuing RNA synthesis did not diminish the amount of P^{32} already incorporated.

Proof that the labeled chains actually increased in length after the addition of unlabeled substrates was obtained by the following experiment. RNA synthesis was carried out in the presence of γ-P^{32}-GTP and $\beta\gamma$-P^{32}-ATP. After the reaction

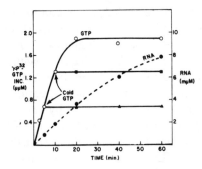

Fig. 1.—Effect of dilution on γ-P^{32}-GTP incorporation. Reaction mixtures were as described under *Methods*, with the exception that 20 mμmoles of each of the four nucleoside triphosphates were added, γ-P^{32}-GTP (1.1 × 10^9 cpm/μmole) was used, and incubation was carried out at 37°. In two separate reaction mixtures, one after 5 min and the other after 10 min, a 30-fold excess of unlabeled GTP was added. RNA synthesis was measured in separate reaction mixtures in which C^{14}-GTP was used as the only radioactive substrate, with all other additions as above. ▲, Incorporation of γ-P^{32}-GTP in the reaction mixture diluted with unlabeled GTP after 5 min; ■, incorporation in the reaction mixture diluted after 10 min.

had been allowed to proceed for 4 min, a large excess of unlabeled GTP and ATP was added. One sample was removed at this time, and a second after an additional 8 min of incubation. The sedimentation of the labeled RNA is illustrated in Figure 2, which shows that the sedimentation rate increased from about 6S to about 20S after the addition of unlabeled substrates. An increase in size of RNA products with time was also noted by Bremer and Konrad.[12]

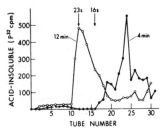

Fig. 2.—Zone sedimentation analysis of RNA. Two 0.5-ml reaction mixtures containing Tris buffer, pH 8.0, 25 μmoles; 2-mercaptoethanol, 4 μmoles; MgCl$_2$, 5 μmoles; ADP, 5 mμmoles; T5 DNA, 25 mμmoles; UTP and CTP, 25 mμmoles each; $\beta\gamma$-P^{32}-ATP and γ-P^{32}-GTP, specific activity 1 × 10^9 cpm/μmole, 25 mμmoles each; and 3 units of enzyme were incubated for 4 min at 25°. After that time, 1.5 μmoles each of nonradioactive ATP and GTP were added to each tube. One reaction was stopped immediately by the addition of sodium dodecyl sulfate and EDTA (0.5% and 0.01 M final concentration, respectively). The other tube was treated in the same manner after 12 min at 25°. Both samples were diluted to 1 ml with 0.5% sodium dodecyl sulfate, layered on 30 ml of a 15–30% sucrose solution gradient containing 0.05 M Tris buffer, pH 8.0, 0.1 M NaCl, and 0.2% sodium dodecyl sulfate, and centrifuged for 15 hr at 25,000 rpm in an SW 25.1 Spinco rotor at approximately 25°. Ribosomal RNA was used as an optical density marker. Fractions (1 ml) were collected through a hole punched in the bottom of the tube. The fractions were scanned through a Gilford recording spectrophotometer to locate the position of 23S and 16S ribosomal markers and assayed for P^{32}.

These results show that nucleoside triphosphates are incorporated at the point of initiation and not at the growing end of RNA chains, and, therefore, that chain growth occurs by the addition of nucleotides to the 3'-hydroxyl end.

Discussion.—The above results clearly show that RNA chains are initiated with ribonucleoside triphosphates, principally or exclusively ATP and GTP. Upon denaturation of DNA by heat or alkali, the incorporation of nucleoside triphosphates into terminal positions increases. Thus, RNA polymerase finds more and different initiation sites for RNA synthesis on denatured DNA than on double-stranded DNA. This conclusion is also supported by the observation that single-stranded and denatured DNA saturate RNA polymerase more effectively than native DNA.[13, 14]

The finding that the pyrimidine sites of DNA, especially when native, are preferentially utilized as initiation points for RNA synthesis was totally unexpected. In fact, the pyrimidine nucleoside triphosphate ends found in small numbers in the RNA may reflect the presence of small amounts of denatured DNA in all the primers used. The reason for this specificity is unknown, but it probably results from the manner in which the enzyme interacts with DNA.   It is probably not due to the selective binding of ATP and GTP versus UTP and CTP to the enzyme, since there is no difference in affinity constant of these nucleotides for RNA polymerase.[5]   The selective copying of the pyrimidine-rich strand of the DNA of *Bacillus subtilis* phages SP8 and 2C and *Bacillus megatherium* phage α *in vivo*[15, 16] and *in vitro*[17, 18] may be related to the preferential initiation of RNA chains with purine nucleotides. The selection of one DNA strand over another may thus be governed by runs of pyrimidine bases in native DNA.   The loss of asymmetric copying of DNA in RNA synthesis upon denaturation of the DNA[17] may be related to our finding that denaturation uncovers new sites in the DNA at which RNA chains can be started.

In vivo, RNA synthesis (i.e., gene expression) must begin at particular sites on DNA.   Since DNA of *E. coli* (and others) is uninterrupted,[19] there must be a high degree of specificity for initiation of RNA chains within the DNA duplex.   The results presented above suggest that these sites in DNA may be pyrimidine bases. In accord with this idea is the finding that sRNA molecules contain considerable amounts of guanine and adenine at the 5'-phosphate end.[20, 21]   How RNA polymerase can specifically recognize initiation points on DNA, and what factor controls the accessibility of the enzyme to such sites for RNA synthesis, are problems intimately involved in the mechanism of gene control.

Summary.—In the DNA-dependent RNA polymerase reaction, the RNA chains formed contain ribonucleoside triphosphates at their starting points and grow by the subsequent addition of ribonucleotides to the 3'-hydroxyl group of the ribonucleoside end.   Purine nucleoside triphosphates are preferentially found at the triphosphate end.   When denatured DNA is used as a template, there are an increase in the number and a change in the kind of starting points.

* This research was supported by grants from the National Institutes of Health, the National Science Foundation, and the New York City Public Health Research Council. Paper VIII of this series was concerned with the inhibition of RNA polymerase by histones (Skalka, A., A. Fowler, and J. Hurwitz, *J. Biol. Chem.*, in press). Communication no. 40 of the Joan and Lester Avnet Institute for Molecular Biology.

† Postdoctoral fellow of the Jane Coffin Childs Memorial Fund for Medical Research.

[1] Maitra, U., A. Novogrodsky, D. Baltimore, and J. Hurwitz, *Biochem. Biophys. Res. Commun.*, **18**, 801 (1965).

[2] Avron, M., *Anal. Biochem.*, **2**, 535 (1961).

[3] Berg, P., and W. K. Joklik, *J. Biol. Chem.*, **210**, 657 (1954).

[4] Penefsky, H., and E. Racker, *J. Biol. Chem.*, **235**, 3330 (1960).

[5] Furth, J. J., J. Hurwitz, and M. Anders, *J. Biol. Chem.*, **237**, 2611 (1962).

[6] In all reaction mixtures containing $\beta\gamma$-P³²-ATP, 2 mμmoles of ADP per 10 mμmoles of ATP were included to suppress the action of any possible contaminating polyphosphate forming enzyme [Kornberg, A., S. R. Kornberg, and E. S. Simms, *Biochim. Biophys. Acta*, **20**, 235 (1956)].

[7] In other experiments the incorporation of γ-P³²-UTP was <0.2 μμmoles. Evidence that this low incorporation was not due to the presence of an inhibitor in the P³²-UTP preparation was obtained by the finding that γ-P³²-UTP supported both C¹⁴-ATP and $\beta\gamma$-P³²-ATP incorporation with dAT copolymer as primer. The other γ-P³²-nucleoside triphosphates also supported RNA synthesis, and the omission of a single triphosphate resulted in a marked decrease in both RNA synthesis and chain initiation.

[8] Ostrowski, W., and A. Tsugita, *Arch. Biochem. Biophys.*, **94**, 68 (1961).

[9] Gardner, J. A. A., and M. B. Hoagland, *J. Biol. Chem.*, **240**, 1244 (1965). We are indebted to Dr. M. Hoagland for a gift of guanosine 5'-tetraphosphate.

[10] One unit of enzyme will cleave 1 μmole of 0-nitrophenylphosphate per minute at 37°.

[11] Wood, W. B., and P. Berg, *J. Mol. Biol.*, **9**, 452 (1964).

[12] Bremer, H., and M. W. Konrad, these Proceedings, **51,** 801 (1964).

[13] Hurwitz, J., J. J. Furth, M. Anders, and A. Evans, *J. Biol. Chem.,* **237,** 3752 (1962).

[14] Berg, P., R. D. Kornberg, H. Fancher, and M. Dieckmann, *Biochem. Biophys. Res. Commun.,* **18,** 932 (1965).

[15] Marmur, J., and C. M. Greenspan, *Science,* **142,** 387 (1963).

[16] Tocchini-Valentini, G. P., M. Stodolsky, M. Sarnat, A. Aurisicchio, F. Graziosi, S. B. Weiss, and E. P. Geiduschek, these Proceedings, **50,** 935 (1963).

[17] Colvill, A. J. E., L. C. Kanner, G. P. Tocchini-Valentini, M. T. Sarnat, and E. P. Geiduschek, these Proceedings, **53,** 1140 (1965).

[18] Fowler, A. V., J. Marmur, and J. Hurwitz, unpublished observations.

[19] Cairns, J., *J. Mol. Biol.,* **6,** 208 (1963).

[20] Ralph, R. K., R. J. Young, and H. G. Khorana, *J. Am. Chem. Soc.,* **85,** 2002 (1963).

[21] Bell, D., R. V. Tomlinson, and G. M. Tener, *Biochem. Biophys. Res. Commun.,* **10,** 304 (1963).

Reprinted from the PROCEEDINGS OF THE NATIONAL ACADEMY OF SCIENCES
Vol. 49, No. 4, pp. 538–544. April, 1963.

DISTINCT CISTRONS FOR THE TWO RIBOSOMAL RNA COMPONENTS*

BY S. A. YANKOFSKY† AND S. SPIEGELMAN

DEPARTMENT OF MICROBIOLOGY, UNIVERSITY OF ILLINOIS, URBANA

Communicated by T. M. Sonneborn, February 25, 1963

Previous investigations[1, 2] have established that *E. coli* DNA contains sequences complementary to homologous ribosomal RNA. The proof depended on demonstrating the formation of specific RNAase resistant complexes between labeled ribosomal RNA and heat-denatured DNA. It was further shown, by the use of two identifying isotopic labels, that nonribosomal RNA from the same organism does not compete for the DNA sites complementary to ribosomal RNA.

All of these experiments were carried out with the 23S ribosomal RNA and they left unanswered the relation of these findings to the 16S RNA component. The similarity in base composition[3, 4] and the fact that the molecular weights[5] of the 23S and 16S are almost in the relation of 2:1 suggest the possibility of a common origin, the 23S being perhaps a dimer of the 16S RNA. Definitive evidence on whether they do, in fact, derive from the same sequence can be readily obtained with the hybridizing technique of Hall and Spiegelman[6] as modified in the ribosomal RNA investigations[1, 2] cited.

The following sorts of information are pertinent to a resolution. (a) *Saturation plateaus:* If the 16S and 23S are derived from the same sequence, the RNA/DNA ratio found in the hybrid at saturation should be the same for each RNA. (b) *Additivity:* At the saturation RNA/DNA ratio of either, the addition of the other should lead to no further complex formation if they are derived from the same sequences. If the sequences of origin are different, additional hybrids should be observed. (c) *Competitive interaction:* By the use of two identifying isotopic labels the presence or absence of competition during hybridization can be established. Absence of competitive interaction would indicate distinct sequences and its existence would argue for identity.

The present paper describes experiments which provide the data necessary for a decision. To alleviate somewhat the current monotony of molecular biology and to extend our understanding of these matters beyond *E. coli*, the experiments to be described were performed with *B. megaterium*. The results indicate that the sequences of the 23S and 16S RNA components are dissimilar. They must therefore possess different genetic origins.

210

Materials and Methods.—(a) *Bacterial strain:* Strain 219, a pyrimidine-requiring derivative of KM isolated by the technique of Mangalo and Wachsman[7, 8] was kindly provided by Dr. J. T. Wachsman.

(b) *Media:* A basal medium[7] supplemented with 10 to 30 μg/ml uridine was generally used. For P^{32} incorporation experiments, the phosphate concentration was reduced from 0.024 M to 0.0012 M and 0.05 M Tris (pH 7.3) added for buffering.

(c) *Preparation of cells:* Cells suspended in basal medium supplemented with 20–30 μg/ml in uridine were shaken overnight at 37°C, harvested, and resuspended at an O.D.$_{660}$ of 0.200 in fresh medium containing 14 μg/ml uridine. When they attained an O.D.$_{660}$ of 0.400, the cultures were harvested, washed, and resuspended in basal medium to an O.D.$_{660}$ of about 1.000 for use as inocula in incorporation experiments.

(d) *Steady state isotope incorporation:* (1) H^3-*uridine:* Log phase cells, prepared as described, were suspended in basal medium to an O.D.$_{660}$ of 0.035 and shaken at 37°C for 15 min. Then 10.3 μg/ml of H^3-uridine (New England Nuclear Corp., 3.0 mc/mM) was added and the culture shaken at 37°C until growth stopped at an O.D.$_{660}$ of 0.240. The culture was harvested, washed, and resuspended in twice the original volume of basal medium containing 90 μg/ml of unlabeled uridine. The cells were incubated with aeration at 37°C for 0.8 generations to eliminate H^3 counts from the unstable RNA fraction, then harvested. (2) P^{32}-*orthophosphate:* Pyrophosphate-free, neutralized P^{32}-orthophosphate was added (630 μc/ml) to log phase cells at an O.D.$_{660}$ of 0.07 in basal medium, containing 0.0012 M phosphate, and incorporation continued until an O.D.$_{660}$ of 0.400 was reached. The culture was then "chased" for one generation in a medium adjusted to 0.024 M in nonradioactive phosphate.

(e) *Conversion to spheroplasts:* Log-phase cells were suspended to an O.D.$_{660}$ of about 1.2 in a medium consisting of 0.04 M Tris, pH 7.3 − 0.002 M MgSO$_4$ − 0.3 M sucrose, and equilibrated to 37°C. Armour's lysozyme (200 μg/ml) was added and conversion to spheroplasts followed with a phase-contrast microscope. Conversion was virtually complete within 15 min. The spheroplasts were harvested, then washed once in the above medium.

(f) *Lysis and bulk RNA extraction:* Washed spheroplast pellets were lysed by resuspension in 0.01 M Tris, pH 7.3 − 0.005 M MgCl$_2$ (TM) buffer containing lysozyme (200 μg/ml) and 25 μg/ml of DNAase (Worthington Biochemical). The lysate was then subjected to three freeze-thaw cycles and total cellular RNA was isolated and purified, all as detailed by Hayashi and Spiegelman.[9]

(g) *Purification of ribosomal RNA subclasses:* The two ribosomal RNA components were separated from each other by repeated chromatography on methylated-albumin-kieselguhr (MAK) columns prepared according to Mandell and Hershey.[10] All buffers used during chromatography contained 0.025 M NaH$_2$PO$_4$ − 0.025 M Na$_2$HPO$_4$ − pH 6.9. RNA preparations were loaded at 50 μg/ml or less, and elution accomplished with linear NaCl gradients ranging from 0.6 M to 1.25 M NaCl. The total eluting volume was from 320 to 380 ml, and 5 to 7 ml fractions were collected. The resulting purified RNA fractions were pooled and concentrated to about 50 μg/ml as follows: the ionic strength of the solvent was first changed to 0.01 M Tris, pH 7.3 − 0.002 M MgCl$_2$ − 0.02 M NaCl by dialyzing against at least 100 volumes of this buffer for about 15 hr with two buffer changes. The preparations were next reduced to the appropriate volume in a flash-evaporator at reduced pressure. The sample flask was held at 28°C and the collecting flask at 0°C. Concentrated RNA preparations were finally dialyzed against TMS buffer (0.01 M Tris, pH 7.3 − 0.001 M MgCl$_2$ − 0.3 M NaCl).

(h) *Sucrose gradient analysis:* The size distribution of RNA preparations was routinely determined by centrifugation through linear sucrose density gradients.[9, 11]

(i) *DNA isolation:* DNA was extracted and purified from spheroplasts and heat-denatured as previously described for *E. coli.*[1] Heat-denatured preparations will be designated by 1XDNA.

(j) *DNA sedimentation velocity analysis:* Sedimentation coefficients were determined in the Spinco E analytical ultracentrifuge using UV optics. Runs were performed at 25 μg/ml according to the procedure of Marmur.[12] Observed sedimentation coefficients were corrected to 20°C. No other corrections were applied. Molecular weights were estimated from the measured S$_{20}$ using the empirical relationship of Doty, McGill, and Rice.[13]

(k) *DNA-RNA hybridization:* All experiments described were performed with a heat-denatured DNA derived from a native preparation that had an S$_{20}$ of 21.8 and an estimated molecular weight of 7.3×10^6. DNA from *B. megaterium* undergoes renaturation rather readily; hence, the slow cool from higher temperatures employed in the earlier studies[1, 6] was avoided. Hybridizations were always performed by incubation at 41°–43°C.

Mixtures of 1XDNA at 50 μg/ml and labeled RNA at various concentrations in 0.7 ml of TMS buffer were incubated at 41°–43°C for 12 to 16 hr. Saturated CsCl was added to a final volume of about 3 ml and a density of 1.72. Centrifugation was carried out for 70 hr at 33,000 rpm in an SW 39 rotor of the Model L Spinco ultracentrifuge at a rotor temperature of 25°C. Fractions were collected from the bottom of the tube. Procedures for examining the DNA density region for RNAase resistant radioactivity on millipore membranes in a liquid scintillation spectrometer have been detailed by Yankofsky and Spiegelman.[1]

Results.—Purification of ribosomal RNA subclasses: Separation of labeled 16S and 23S RNA components was achieved by repeated chromatography on MAK columns. The purification was monitored by centrifugation in sucrose linear density gradients with unlabeled bulk RNA of *E. coli* added as size markers. The degree of cross contamination is readily determined by comparison of the radioactivity and O.D.$_{260}$ profiles.

An example of bulk *B. megaterium* RNA separation on a MAK column is shown in Figure 1. The profile is similar to those obtained in this laboratory with *E. coli* RNA preparations[14] except that the 16S region appears to be partially resolved into two components.

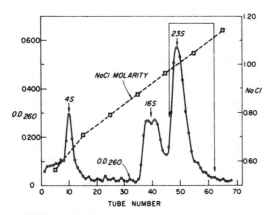

FIG. 1.—*Chromatographic separation of bulk RNA.* *B. megaterium* RNA was uniformly labeled with H³-uridine as in *Methods*. The column was equilibrated at 0.66 *M* NaCl; the RNA loaded at 50 μg/ml in 0.66 *M* NaCl and eluted with a 360 ml linear gradient running from 0.66 *M* to 1.25 *M* NaCl. 5 ml fractions collected.

The 23S RNA region, indicated by the arrows in Figure 1, was chromatographed repeatedly, and the profile on the fourth column is shown in Figure 2A. Here, the arrows denote the region pooled and concentrated for experimental use, and Figure 2B shows its size distribution in a sucrose gradient. As can be seen, the purified labeled component is virtually confined to the 23S region of the carrier bulk RNA added.

The 16S component of Figure 1 was similarly treated, and Figure 3A shows a representative profile on MAK. Again, the arrows indicate the region pooled, concentrated, and analyzed for size. Figure 3B shows the size distribution of this region compared to that of *E. coli* marker RNA. Although of interest, the abnormality seen in the 16S profile both in Figure 1 and Figure 3A is not directly pertinent to the present investigation and its discussion will be deferred for a subsequent publication. Comparison of 3A and 3B indicates that the asymmetry observed is not due to significant contamination with 23S RNA. All preparations employed in the

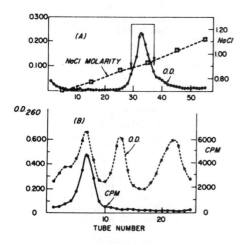

FIG. 2A.—*MAK column: Chromatographic profile after the fourth chromatography of the 23S region shown by the arrows in Figure 1.* The column was equilibrated at 0.68 M NaCl; 600 μg RNA loaded at 50 μg/ml in 0.68 M NaCl and eluted with a 320 ml linear gradient from 0.72 to 1.22 M NaCl.

FIG. 2B.—*Sucrose density gradient centrifugation.* An aliquot (0.5 μg RNA, 60,000 cpm) of the pooled tubes indicated by the arrows in (*A*) was used. 0.6 mg *E. coli* bulk RNA added as O.D. marker. 1.2 ml fractions collected and 0.3 ml samples from each tube plated for radioactive counts. The O.D. profile identified the known components in the added carrier material. The first major peak on the left is the 23S, the second the 16S, and the last corresponds to the 4S component.

present study were examined before use in sucrose gradients for cross contamination or evidence of breakdown. Samples showing evidence of either were discarded.

We now consider the details of the three types of experiments which can illuminate the origins of the 16S and 23S RNA components.

(1) *Saturation plateaus:* The proportion of RNAase resistant hybrid formed by incubating a fixed amount of 1XDNA with increasing amounts of each ribosomal RNA component are shown in Figure 4. The 23S RNA reaches a plateau when approximately 0.18% of the DNA is occupied, while about 0.14% of the DNA is capable of complexing with 16S RNA. In six repetitions, mean values of 0.179 ± 0.0072 and 0.136 ± 0.014 were obtained for the respective saturation values of 23S and 16S RNA. The fact that the saturation plateaus for the two are different supports the conclusion that the two types of RNA have different origins.

(2) *Additivity:* It will be noted from Figure 4 that for 50 μg DNA, saturation for the 23S RNA is achieved at 3 μg/ml, and 2 μg/ml saturates for the 16S component. We now inquire whether the addition of both at saturating levels to the same reaction mixture increases the amount of complex observed, and, if so, to what extent. The results of such an experiment are presented in Table 1. Addition of the values obtained when saturating amounts of each RNA subclass is complexed alone (mixture 1 + mixture 2) indicates that 0.303 per cent of the DNA would be hybridized. The amount of complex formed when both are incubated together (mixture 3) is within 4 per cent of this value. These results are difficult to reconcile

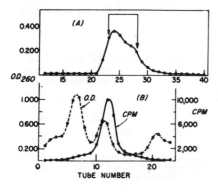

FIG. 3A.—*MAK column: Chromatographic profile of B. megaterium 16S RNA (steady state P[32] label) after third chromatography.* Column equilibrated at 0.6 M NaCl; 760 μg RNA loaded at 50 μg/ml in 0.6 M NaCl and eluted with a 340 ml linear gradient from 0.6 M to 1.2 M NaCl.

FIG. 3B.—*Sucrose density gradient centrifugation: Analysis of an aliquot (0.5 μg of RNA, 80,000 cpm) from the pooled tubes shown under the arrows in (A).* 0.6 mg *E. coli* bulk RNA added as O.D. marker. All other details as in Figure 2B.

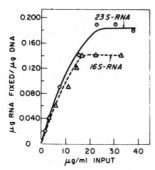

FIG. 4.—*Saturation plateaus: Saturation curves of B. megaterium 16S and 23S RNA hybridized with 50 μg/ml B. megaterium heat-denatured DNA. Each point represents RNAase resistant counts found in the DNA region after CsCl equilibrium density gradient centrifugation. Annealing and analytical procedures as described under Methods.*

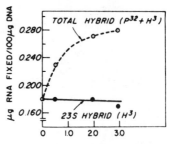

FIG. 5.—*Competitive interaction: Tests for competitive interactions between mixtures of 23S-H³-RNA and 16S-P³²-RNA from B. megaterium complexed with homologous heat-denatured DNA. All mixtures contain 50 μg/ml DNA, 3 μg/ml purified 23S-H³-RNA (see Fig. 2) and the indicated concentrations of purified 16S-P³²-RNA (see Fig. 3). Annealing and analytical procedures as described under Methods.*

with a common origin and are clearly consistent with the existence of distinct complementary regions.   We come now to the final available experimental test.

(3) *Competitive interaction:*   Increasing amounts of P³²-labeled 16S RNA were incubated in three tubes, each containing 50 μg of 1XDNA and H³-labeled 23S RNA at its saturation level (3.0 μg).   Because of the identifying isotopic labels, it was possible to determine independently the per cent hybrid formed by each of the two ribosomal RNA size classes in the three mixtures.   From the data shown in Figure 5 it is evident that the addition of the P³²-16S RNA results in no significant displacement of H³-23S RNA.   Furthermore, as more 16S RNA is added, the total hybrid approaches a level of saturation near that expected for the sum of the two subclasses incubated alone.   There is no evidence of competition between the two ribosomal RNA subclasses for common DNA sites.

Discussion.—In previous studies[1, 2] we have shown that specific complexes are formed between homologous ribosomal RNA and DNA in bacterial species having intermediate (52%) and high (64%) contents of guanosine-cytosine (GC) in their DNA.   The present study establishes a similar sequence complementarity in *B. megaterium* which has a low (38%) GC content.   The fact that ribosomal RNA

TABLE 1

TEST FOR ADDITIVITY DURING HYBRIDIZATION AT SATURATION LEVELS OF 16S AND 23S RNA

Mixture	Contents	RNAase resistant hybrid μg RNA fixed/100 μg DNA
1	50 μg/ml 1XDNA + 3.06 μg/ml 23S RNA	0.186
2	50 μg/ml 1XDNA + 2.21 μg/ml 16S RNA	0.117
		Sum = 0.303
3	50 μg/ml 1XDNA + 3.06 μg/ml 23S RNA + 2.21 μg/ml 16S RNA	0.291

The addition mixture (3) contained the same DNA and RNA preparations as the control mixtures (1 and 2). All three mixtures were annealed under identical conditions, centrifuged together, and the raw hybrids tested for RNAase resistance with the same enzyme preparation. Details of annealing and analytical procedures are given in *Methods*.

complementarity to DNA obtains in organisms of diverse DNA composition, lends credence to its generality.

These findings raise rather forcibly an interesting problem. The base composition of ribosomal RNA shows virtually no correlation with that of homologous DNA.[15, 16] Evidently the ribosomal RNA cistrons have been kept within narrow limits while the rest of the genome has undergone the widest variation in base composition permissible within a triplet coding mechanism. The specification of the selective mechanism which can produce this remarkable outcome poses an interesting problem for experimental resolution.

Sequence complementarity has previously been shown for the unstable messenger RNA,[9] transfer RNA,[17, 18] and 23S RNA.[1, 2] The present study demonstrates that it also holds for 16S RNA. Thus, the synthesis of all known cellular RNA components can be explained in terms of a DNA mediated reaction.

The present study had as its primary purpose to provide evidence which could decide whether the 16S and 23S ribosomal components are derived from the same or different complementary DNA sequences. The experiments reported indicate a difference in saturation plateaus, additivity of hybrid formation at saturation levels of each type, and absence of competitive interaction during hybrid formation. These findings are difficult to reconcile with a common sequence. They provide consistent evidence for distinct cistronic origins.

The further analysis into the nature of ribosomal RNA will require an examination for heterogeneity within each class. We have already pointed out[1, 2] that the level (0.2%) at which DNA is saturated by hybridizing with homologous 23S RNA would suggest that *E. coli* contains about 10 complementary cistrons for this component. The data presented here would suggest that 0.18% of *B. megaterium* DNA is complementary to its 23S ribosomal RNA and 0.14% to its 16S component. On the basis of the DNA content per "nuclear body"[19] one would estimate that the DNA contains approximately 35 stretches complementary to 23S RNA and 45 complementary to the 16S component. The significance of this apparent redundancy may be related to the rather large number of strands required for a full ribosomal complement which constitutes 85 per cent of the total cellular RNA. However, the existence of multiple copies in the genome provides a possibility for variation. It is of no little interest to determine whether this potentiality was exploited. It is evident that the use of column fractionation and competition experiments with identifying labels should provide data pertinent to this problem.

Summary.—The experiments reported were designed to decide whether the 16S and 23S ribosomal RNA components are derived from the same or different complementary sequences in the DNA. Specific hybrid formation. coupled with isotopic labeling was employed as the analytical device. The data establish that (*a*) the maximal amount of RNA which can hybridize per unit of DNA is different for the two; (*b*) at saturation concentrations of each, the amount of hybrid formed is additive when 16S and 23S RNA are both present; (*c*) no evidence of competitive interaction between the two for the same sites can be detected. All these findings are difficult to reconcile with a common origin. We conclude that 16S and 23S ribosomal RNA are derived from DNA sequences unique to each.

* This investigation was aided by grants-in-aid from the U.S. Public Health Service and the National Science Foundation.

† Predoctoral fellow trainee in Molecular Genetics (USPH 2G-319).

[1] Yankofsky, S. A., and S. Spiegelman, these Proceedings, **48,** 1069 (1962).

[2] Yankofsky, S. A., and S. Spiegelman, these Proceedings, **48,** 1466 (1962).

[3] Spahr, P. F., and A. Tissières, *J. Mol. Biol.*, **1,** 237 (1959).

[4] Yankofsky, S. A., and S. Spiegelman, unpublished observations (1962).

[5] Kurland, C. G., *J. Mol. Biol.*, **2,** 83 (1960).

[6] Hall, B. D., and S. Spiegelman, these Proceedings, **47,** 137 (1961).

[7] Mangalo, R., and J. T. Wachsman, *J. Bacteriol.*, **83,** 27 (1962).

[8] Mangalo, R., and J. T. Wachsman, *J Bacteriol.*, **83,** 35 (1962).

[9] Hayashi, M., and S. Spiegelman, these Proceedings, **47,** 1564 (1961).

[10] Mandell, J. D., and A. D. Hershey, *Analyt. Biochem.*, **1,** 66 (1960).

[11] Britten, R. J., and R. B. Roberts, *Science*, **131,** 32 (1960).

[12] Marmur, J., *J. Mol. Biol.*, **3,** 208 (1961).

[13] Doty, P., B. McGill, and S. A. Rice, these Proceedings, **44,** 432 (1958).

[14] Kano-Sueoka, T., and S. Spiegelman, these Proceedings, **48,** 1942 (1962).

[15] Spiegelman, S., in *Cellular Regulatory Mechanisms*, Cold Spring Harbor Symposia on Quantitative Biology, **26,** 75 (1961).

[16] Woese, C. R., *Nature*, **189,** 918 (1961).

[17] Giacomoni, D., and S. Spiegelman, *Science*, **138,** 1328 (1962).

[18] Goodman, H. M., and A. Rich, these Proceedings, **48,** 2101 (1962).

[19] Spiegelman, S., A. I. Aronson, and P. C. Fitz-James, *J. Bacteriol.*, **75,** 102 (1958).

GENE-SPECIFIC MRNA, II. REGULATION OF MRNA SYNTHESIS IN E. COLI AFTER INFECTION WITH BACTERIOPHAGE T4*

By E. K. F. Bautz, T. Kasai, E. Reilly, and F. A. Bautz

INSTITUTE OF MICROBIOLOGY, RUTGERS, THE STATE UNIVERSITY, NEW BRUNSWICK, NEW JERSEY

Communicated by Rollin D. Hotchkiss, March 18, 1966

Following infection of *E. coli* cells with a bacteriophage of the T-even series, enzymes needed for phage DNA synthesis are produced during the first few minutes. The structural components of the phage and enzymes concerned with their assembly do not appear until several minutes have elapsed and then continue to be synthesized up to the time of lysis of the host cell.[1] This temporal sequence of biochemical events, all specified by the phage genome, provides a unique opportunity to test some of the current concepts of how RNA and protein synthesis might be regulated. The regulation of protein synthesis is assumed to occur either at the level of transcription[2] or at the level of translation.[3, 4] These two alternatives should result in distinctly different patterns of RNA synthesis during phage development. If regulation occurs at the level of transcription, the sequential appearance of early and late proteins should be paralleled by a sequential production of early and late messages, i.e., the mRNA species present at early times after infection should be different from those found later. If regulation is entirely at the level of translation, transcription of all genes should occur indiscriminately at all times.

Early RNA has been found to differ from late RNA in its chromatographic behavior on methylated albumin columns.[5] Studies on the competition between RNA isolated early and late after infection to form complexes with limiting quantities of denatured phage DNA have led Hall *et al.*[6] to conclude that the genes concerned with early functions are transcribed both early and late, while the late function genes are transcribed at late times only. In contrast to these reports, observations on the phenotypic reversion of point mutations in late function genes by 5-fluorouracil have yielded evidence in favor of a moderate amount of transcription of late function genes at very early times.[7]

The most direct approach to the analysis of the transcription of a particular gene requires the isolation and the identification of a message specified by a known genetic region. The availability of deletion mutants of phage T4 covering the early function *r*II genes or the late function endolysin gene has permitted us to obtain mRNA fractions specific for these genetic regions. In this paper we report data on the appearance of *r*II and lysozyme messengers at different times after infection of *E. coli* B cells with bacteriophage T4.

Materials and Methods.—Stocks of T4 standard type (w) phage and of *r*II mutants (Benzer) used were grown in 1.3-liter quantities on host *E. coli* BB as described.[8] Lysozyme negative mutants *e*G19 and *e*G59 (Streisinger) were grown by infection of the same host cells (at a cell titer of 6 × 10⁸) with a multiplicity of 3. After aeration for 3 hr, chloroform and lysozyme (10 μg/ml) were added to induce lysis. The phage stocks were purified by differential centrifugation, and DNA was isolated as described.[8]

Preparation of DNA-nitrocellulose columns: A slurry of nitrocellulose, grade RS (Hercules Powder Co.), in 2 × SSC (2× standard saline citrate = 0.3 M NaCl + 0.03 M Na citrate) was ground in a mortar, the material which could be forced through a 45-mesh screen was collected, decanted to remove fines, and washed in a column with approximately 8 bed vol of 2 × SSC. Heat-denatured DNA[9] in 2 × SSC was added in the cold to a slurry of this material with rapid stirring. Two-layer columns were prepared by pouring a slurry of w-DNA (4 mg) on nitrocellulose into a jacketed column of 1.5 cm diameter heated to 60°C by a circulating water bath. After this material had settled, a blank column of plain nitrocellulose of 2 cm height was layered on top, and the nitrocellulose containing the deletion DNA (12 mg) was layered over the blank column. For each DNA column nitrocellulose was used at a column height of 1.5 cm per mg of DNA. The layers were visibly divided by thin layers of glass wool.

Isolation of deletion-specific RNA: *E. coli* B cells grown to OD_{660} = 0.5 in minimal medium with aeration were infected with T4w phage at a multiplicity of 3; at times indicated, 0.2 mc of uracil-H^3 (specific activity: 7 c/mM) were added per 100 ml of culture, aeration was continued for 2 min more and incorporation was stopped by rapid chilling. The cells were harvested and the RNA was extracted as described.[8] The pulse-labeled RNA, in 2 × SSC, was applied to the top of the nitrocellulose layer containing the deletion DNA and allowed to incubate for 90 min; then the column was connected to a flow pump which was activated by a time relay every 30 min to deliver a 1-ml portion of 2 × SSC to the top of the column. This resulted in equilibration of the RNA sample with the entire column for a period of 16 hr at 60°C. The column was then washed at 60°C with 100 ml of 2 × SSC, and the layers containing deletion and wild-type DNA were extruded with compressed air and collected separately. They were repacked individually into jacketed columns equilibrated at 60°C, washed once more with 2 × SSC, and the hybridized RNA was eluted with 0.01 × SSC at the same temperature. Fractions were collected and samples of 20 or 50 μl were placed on filters in scintillation vials, dried, and counted. The peak fractions obtained from the wild-type DNA columns were pooled, assayed for deletion-specific RNA, and, in the case of lysozyme mRNA, purified further by a second passage through a deletion-w-DNA column.

The preparation of DNA-nitrocellulose filter and the conditions of hybridization were those of Gillespie and Spiegelman,[10] except that the DNA was denatured by heat, the final volume of incubation was 2 ml in 2 × SSC, and treatment of the filters with RNase was omitted. Each filter was charged with 100 μg of DNA.

The radioactivity adsorbed to blank filters (no DNA) was found to be reduced, if the RNA eluted from the DNA columns was treated with DNase prior to incubation with the filters.[9] The same reduction of counts is obtained when the fractions are heated for 2 min at 95°C, cooled rapidly, made up to 2 × SSC, and filtered with suction through a Millipore filter. This treatment, like the addition of DNase, removes traces of DNA eluted together with the hybrid RNA fraction. The latter procedure is more convenient and allows a somewhat better recovery of RNA; it has been used throughout.

Calculation of the percentage of gene-specific RNA: It was assumed for all calculations that all T4 mRNA molecules hybridize with homologous DNA with equal efficiency. The fraction of the total hybridized RNA recovered from the two-layer DNA column which is found in the eluent of the w-DNA layer was calculated. This value was then multiplied by the percentage of the RNA hybridizing exclusively with w-DNA when the RNA was tested with both deletion and w-DNA filters.

Results.—(a) *Synthesis of rII messengers:* The function of the *rII* region can be classified as an early one.[11, 12] It was therefore of interest to see whether the *rII* specific RNA was produced early and late, or early only. *E. coli* K12 (λ) or *E. coli* B cells were infected with T4w phage at a multiplicity of 3, and to portions of the infected cultures uracil-H^3 was added for the times indicated, and the cells were harvested. The results in Table 1 show that the RNA homologous to the DNA region deleted by mutant *r1272* appears to be made continuously for at least 20 min. For the selection of *rII* RNA the deletion mutant stock *r1272* was employed in these first experiments because it covers the entire *rII* region. Moreover, it extends some ten recombination units into the right-hand side of the *rIIB* cistron.[13] While the use of such a big deletion was initially advantageous for the identification of deletion-specific RNA, in the present study it introduces an uncertainty, since the *rII* genes might be transcribed early only, followed by transcription of the genes next to the B cistron at later times. In order to avoid this uncertainty, T4 mRNA, pulse-labeled for 2 min at different times after infection, was fractionated on a column containing DNA from the deletion mutant *r1231* in the upper layer. This

TABLE 1

Synthesis of rII RNA in *E. coli* at Different Times after Infection with T4w Phage

Deletion DNA used in upper column	Period of labeling (min after infection) with uracil H³	Total hybridizable RNA eluted from lower w-DNA layer, %	Purity of w-hybrid fraction of RNA hybridizing with w-DNA exclusively	Deletion-specific RNA: % of total hybridizable RNA
*r*1272	1–3	2.1	0.70	1.5
*r*1272	6–8	4.5	0.49	2.2
*r*1272	11–13 + 16–18	4.8	0.30	1.5
*r*1272	2–4	1.6	0.55	0.9*
*r*1272	8–10	2.0	0.60	1.2*
*r*1272	16–18	2.5	0.60	1.5*
*r*1231	1–3	1.1	0.40†	0.44
*r*1231	9–11	2.7	0.27†	0.73
*r*1231	17–19	5.0	0.15†	0.75

* These experiments were performed using *E. coli* K12 (λ) as host.
† With internal control (P³² RNA isolated from T4-infected cells).

deletion terminates on both sides within the *r*II region. Because of the smaller size of this deletion, a smaller percentage of deletion-specific RNA was to be expected. In order to match the lower purity by an increase in the sensitivity of the filter tests, P³²-labeled T4 mRNA was added as an internal control to the incubation mixture. The data (also shown in Table 1) again indicate a continuous synthesis of *r*II RNA.

(b) *Accumulation of some T4 mRNA species:* The percentage of RNA recovered from the lower (w) column, which will still hybridize with DNA of the deletion mutant (e.g., 1231), is markedly higher in RNA preparations from cells which were harvested at later times after infection. This observation suggested an accumulation of some or possibly of all the T4 mRNA species. The presence of more RNA copies could conceivably result in a partial saturation of the DNA sites available in the upper mutant column layer, which would allow more RNA molecules to enter and to complex with the DNA in the lower column layer. To test whether the RNA species, which accumulate at late times, are already made early, the following experiment was performed.

A preparation of P³² RNA, pulse-labeled from 1 to 4 min after infection with T4w, was divided into two identical portions, which were both fractionated through double-layer columns, each containing 12 mg T4w DNA in the upper, and 4 mg of the same DNA in the lower layer. To one portion of the P³² RNA, 2 mg of 4′ unlabeled RNA was added; to the other portion, the same quantity of 14′ cold RNA was added. As shown in Table 2, the cold late RNA seems to have competed more

TABLE 2

(a) Competitive inhibition of DNA-RNA hybrid formation of P³²-labeled early RNA by cold late RNA

Column no.	Cold RNA added	RNA Eluted from w-DNA-Column Layer (cpm)		Total hybrid recovered from lower column, %
		Upper (× 10³)	Lower (× 10³)	
1	Early	548	2.3	0.41
2	Late	533	3.5	0.65

(b) Filter test of P³² RNA eluted from lower wild columns (L1 and L2) in the presence of a large excess of either early or late cold RNA plus H³ RNA pulse-labeled 1–4 min after infection

Filter no.	RNA samples in incubation mixture*	Cpm on Filter†			H³/P³² 4′ cold / H³/P³² 14′ cold
		H³	P³²	H³/P³²	
1	L1-P³² + 4′H³ + 4′ cold	720	95	7.6	0.96
2	L1-P³² + 4′H³ + 14′ cold	795	101	7.9	
3	L2-P³² + 4′H³ + 4′ cold	678	105	6.4	0.72
4	L2-P³² + 4′H³ + 14′ cold	805	99	8.1	

* Mixture contained 430 cpm of L1-P³² RNA or 730 cpm of L2-P³² RNA, 3,000 cpm of 1–4′ H³ RNA, and 0.2 mg of cold RNA.
† Each filter was counted for 2 × 30 min.

effectively with the early P³² RNA, since 0.65 per cent of the total hybrid recovered was found in the lower layer of column 2 versus 0.41 per cent found in the corresponding layer of column 1. Aliquots of the P³² RNA recovered from the lower column layers were then incubated with H³ early RNA pulse-labeled from 1 to 4 min together with an excess of either early (4′) or late (14′) cold RNA. While the late cold RNA does not discriminate between the unfractionated early H³ RNA and the fractionated P³² RNA of column 1, it shows some preference to compete with the P³² RNA eluted from column 2.

If all mRNA species, that are synthesized early, had been accumulating coordinately up to minute 14, then identical H³/P³² ratios should have been obtained for the competition with both cold early and cold late RNA. The change in this ratio suggests that only part of the phage genome is transcribed early as well as late, or that not all genes are transcribed at the same rate, or that not all mRNA species are degraded at the same rate.

(c) *Synthesis of lysozyme messengers:* The endolysin gene (e) coding for phage lysozyme is a late function gene. The discovery of deletion mutants missing the entire e region has made it possible to select for lysozyme-specific RNA. Table 3

TABLE 3

Synthesis of Lysozyme RNA in *E. coli* B at Different Times after Infection with T4w Phage

Period of labeling (min after infection) with uracil-H³	Total Hybridizable RNA Eluted from Lower w-DNA Layer, % Column 1	Column 2	Purity of w hybrid: fraction of RNA hybridizing with w-DNA exclusively	Deletion-specific RNA: % of total hybridizable RNA
1–4	0.61		0.28*	0.17
1–3	1.6	10	0.74*	0.12
4–6	0.47	9.4	0.69	0.03
10–12	5.5	2.9	0.50	0.08
17–20	7.3	3.1	0.62	0.14
1–3†	0.85	28	0.89	0.21
3–6†	2.1	2.5	0.69	0.035

DNA of the deletion eG19 was used in all experiments.
* With internal control (P32 RNA isolated from T4-infected cells).
† Infected with a phage stock of the *early* amber mutant am 82.

presents a summary of individual experiments on the detection of RNA specific for the deletion eG19, which extends with both ends into cistrons adjacent to the e region. The purification of this RNA proved to be more difficult since (a) the e region is far smaller than the rII region (∼400 vs. ∼3,000 base pairs), and (b) the rate of transcription of this late function message never seems to surpass that of the early function rII genes. Thus, the yield of eG19-specific RNA was at best one tenth that of r-1272-specific RNA, necessitating in all experiments but one a further purification of the first e⁺ hybrid. The RNA eluted from the second e⁺ DNA column layer was then sufficiently deletion-specific to allow a reasonable estimate of its quantity.

In T4-infected *E. coli* cells traces of lysozyme activity begin to appear at around 6 min after infection. A maximal rate of enzyme production is not observed until some time after minute 10.[1] Thus, one might expect the considerable quantities of lysozyme messengers found after minute 10, regardless of whether the mechanism of turning on lysozyme production is at the level of transcription or translation. However, the appearance of substantial amounts of e-specific RNA as early as 3 min after infection, and its temporary decline, would not necessarily be anticipated. Since the deletion mutant eG19 also extends into the neighboring cistron which is close to the cluster of early genes, the possibility had to be considered that the deletion of eG19 did extend into a cistron of early function, and that the deletion-specific RNA found early contained no lysozyme messengers at all. Consequently, we have tried to obtain RNA specific for the deletion of mutant eG59 which maps entirely within the e cistron. However, we were unable to obtain RNA specific for this region by the deletion method when we applied H³ RNA which had been pulse-labeled either early or late. But in this deletion only about 60 base pairs are missing; thus, the failure to select for RNA molecules specific for this small region is expected, since any mRNA fragment of only twice this size will possess sequences of enough homology to be retained by the eG59 column. On the other hand, by the time samples of the selected RNA are incubated with wild-type and mutant DNA filters for the purity tests, the RNA is heavily fragmented due to the thermal hydrolysis incurred during the long periods of incubation (at least 2×16 hr) at 60°C in the DNA columns. Therefore, RNA fragments, highly purified for the longer eG19 deletion, might be small enough to become partially excluded by eG59 DNA compared to w DNA in a filter test. The result of such a test (Table 4) suggests that of an RNA fraction obtained from cells labeled from 1 to 4 min after infection, which was found to be 80 per cent specific for the deletion of eG19, about 10–15 per cent is unable to complex with DNA of the mutant eG59. Since the total map distance of the e region is several times that of the region deleted in mutant eG59, this result suggests that most of the RNA homologous to the DNA region deleted in mutant eG19 is specified by the lysozyme gene.

TABLE 4

PURITY TEST FOR H³ RNA (PULSE-LABELED 1–4′ AFTER INFECTION) ENRICHED FOR SEQUENCES HOMOLOGOUS TO DELETION OF MUTANT eG19 BY TWO PASSAGES THROUGH eG19/w-DNA COLUMNS

DNA in filter	Cpm Retained on Filter		H^3/P^{32}
	H³ (input: 600 cpm)	P³² (input: 1500 cpm)	
w	319	784	0.41
eG59	303	859	0.35

This RNA preparation was 80% specific for the deletion of eG19. Each filter was counted for 2×30 min.

Early production of lysozyme messengers is also found when the nonpermissive host *E. coli* B is infected with an early *amber* mutant (*am* 82). As in cultures infected with wild-type phage, the synthesis of lysozyme RNA appears to drop off drastically after 3 or 4 min (Table 3). Thus, it seems that a gene not translated into functional proteins still produces an initial burst of RNA copies, followed by a period of reduced transcription, until translation of the messengers commences.

Discussion.—The finding of *r*II RNA both early and late after infection [*Results*, (a)] corroborates the results of Hall *et al.*[6] which indicated that early function genes are transcribed at late times as well. We could also confirm the conclusions by Kano-Sueoka and Spiegelman[5] that there is a shift in the chromatographic behavior of mRNA species with time. This shift, however, could have been also due to different stages of aggregation between phage mRNA and *E. coli* ribosomal RNA.[14] Our own results [*Results*, (b)] suggest that the same mRNA species may be produced both early and late, but that their relative proportions vary with time.

The finding of substantial amounts of lysozyme messengers immediately after infection [*Results*, (c)] conflicts with the conclusions of Hall *et al.*[6] who found no evidence for the existence of late messages at 6.5 min after infection. On the other hand, Edlin[7] has claimed the existence of at least some traces of late RNA shortly after infection.   However, the rather small response to 5-fluorouracil observed very early led him to conclude that synthesis of late function messages proceeds very slowly at early times, gradually increasing later.   This conclusion was reached with the assumption that late messages are quite stable and are therefore slowly but steadily accumulating during the latent period.   However, Edlin's results could be reconciled with ours if late messengers were unstable as long as they are not successfully translated.   Results suggesting the preferential breakdown of lysozyme messengers at early times have in fact been obtained.[15]   As a result of any instability of late function messages and the greatly reduced rate of their synthesis between minutes 3 and 6, their absolute number would be expected to reach a minimum at the time when the translation of late functions commences.   This is likely around minute $6^1/_2$ after infection, the time chosen by Hall *et al.* to collect their "early" RNA fraction, which yielded no appreciable quantities of late RNA.

If one calculates the number of lysozyme messengers present 3 min after infection per (infecting) phage genome, the most probable number is one.   For this calculation the number of base pairs missing in mutant *e*G19 is assumed to be between 600 and 1000, and the amount of total hybridizable T4 mRNA, synthesized in a 2-min period, is estimated at 2–3 per cent of the total host RNA.   Thus, upon entry of the phage DNA, the entire genome may be transcribed *once*, regardless of whether the information is needed right away or only later.   Genes whose messengers are being translated could then continue to be transcribed while each of the nontranslatable mRNA species represses the synthesis of further copies by some sort of feedback control.

It has been suggested on the basis of *in vitro* data[16–18] that ribosomes may play a role in the release of nascent mRNA from the DNA, thereby freeing the template for further mRNA production.   Our studies indicate that a similar regulatory mechanism is operative *in vivo;* furthermore, they provide direct evidence that for lysozyme in phage-infected cells, the primary site of regulation of protein synthesis is at the level of translation, rather than transcription.   The production of the first mRNA copy apparently is unaffected by repression; production of all subsequent copies then depends on the translation of the first copy.   Alternatively, one could assume that in order to repress the transcription of late function genes, a repressor protein may first have to be synthesized.   Such a mechanism would allow the synthesis of some enzymatically active lysozyme immediately after infection.   However, no lysozyme activity can be detected during the first half of the *eclipse* period.

Attardi *et al.*[19] have shown that the *lac* operon is not detectably transcribed in the presence of inducer in operator-negative (0°) mutants.   While this finding supports the original version of the operon hypothesis,[1] it can be just as well reconciled with our interpretations, if one accepts the idea that the failure of a particular mRNA species to associate with the first ribosome results in an effective shutdown of the production of further copies.   Thus, it seems that a nonsense (*ochre*) mutation within the operator region, by preventing the start of translation, concomitantly prevents further transcription.   However, once translation is initiated, production of more mRNA copies can apparently take place, regardless of whether the message is translated in its entirety, since we have found that the synthesis of that portion of a message distal to a nonsense triplet in the *r*IIA cistron is normal.[20]

If one assumes a feedback-regulation of mRNA synthesis, it becomes reasonable that early messengers continue to be produced long after the synthesis of early enzymes has come to a halt. The ever-increasing production of new phage genomes (starting around 7 min after infection) constantly makes available new templates for the synthesis of early function messengers, which may all be transcribed once. Therefore, the feedback mechanism may still be operative, but masked by the great number of templates available. In the phage system, the feedback mechanism of RNA synthesis is thus only truly successful in preventing excessive synthesis of unnecessary mRNA species before the onset of DNA synthesis. Subsequently, this mechanism, although formally still functional, *de facto* breaks down, and the phage apparently does not have an additional device to cope with the wasteful production of useless mRNA species.

Summary.—In *E. coli* B cells, infected with bacteriophage T4, transcription of the supposedly early function *r*II genes was found to occur throughout the latent period. The late function *e* gene, coding for the protein structure of phage lysozyme, was found to be transcribed immediately after infection, followed by a period of greatly reduced transcription. At later times the rate of transcription is found to increase again.

We have interpreted the unusual kinetics of the production of lysozyme messengers as the result of a feedback mechanism for the regulation of mRNA synthesis. We propose that upon entry of the phage genome, all genes are transcribed once, and that only those genes whose messengers are translated continue to be transcribed.

Thanks are due to S. Benzer and S. Champe for providing us with the *r*II deletion stocks, and to J. Emrich and G. Streisinger for the *e* deletion stocks and their generous advice concerning map positions and optimal growth conditions.

* Supported by grants from the National Science Foundation (GB 1882) and the U.S. Public Health Service (GM 10395), and by a U.S. Public Health Service Career Development Award (to E. B.). The first paper in this series is listed in ref. 9.

[1] Cohen, S. S., *Ann. Rev. Biochem.*, **32**, 83 (1963).
[2] Jacob, F., and J. Monod, *J. Mol. Biol.*, **3**, 318 (1961).
[3] Ames, B. N., and P. E. Hartman, in *Cold Spring Harbor Symposia on Quantitative Biology*, vol. 28 (1963), p. 343.
[4] Stent, G., *Science*, **144**, 816 (1964).
[5] Kano-Sueoka, T., and S. Spiegelman, these PROCEEDINGS, **48**, 1942 (1962).
[6] Hall, B. D., A. P. Nygaard, and M. H. Green, *J. Mol. Biol.*, **9**, 143 (1964).
[7] Edlin, G., *J. Mol. Biol.*, **12**, 363 (1965).
[8] Bautz, E. K. F., and B. D. Hall, these PROCEEDINGS, **48**, 400 (1962).
[9] Bautz, E. K. F., and E. Reilly, *Science*, **151**, 328 (1966).
[10] Gillespie, D., and S. Spiegelman, *J. Mol. Biol.*, **12**, 829 (1965).
[11] Krieg, D., *Virology*, **8**, 80 (1959).
[12] Garen, A., *Virology*, **14**, 151 (1961).
[13] Dove, W., personal communication (1965).
[14] Asano, K., *J. Mol. Biol.*, **14**, 71 (1965).
[15] Kasai, T., and E. K. F. Bautz, unpublished.
[16] Bremer, H., and M. W. Konrad, these PROCEEDINGS, **51**, 801 (1964).
[17] Byrne, R., J. G. Levin, H. A. Bladen, and M. W. Nirenberg, these PROCEEDINGS, **52**, 140 (1964).
[18] Shin, D. H., and K. Moldave, *Biochem. Biophys. Res. Commun.*, **22**, 232 (1966).
[19] Attardi, G., S. Naono, J. Rouvière, F. Jacob, and F. Gros, in *Cold Spring Harbor Symposia on Quantitative Biology*, vol. 28 (1963), p. 363.
[20] Bautz, E. K. F., *J. Mol. Biol.*, in press.

ASYMMETRIC DISTRIBUTION OF THE TRANSCRIBING REGIONS ON THE COMPLEMENTARY STRANDS OF COLIPHAGE λ DNA*

By Karol Taylor,† Zdenka Hradecna,‡ and Waclaw Szybalski

MCARDLE LABORATORY, UNIVERSITY OF WISCONSIN, MADISON

Communicated by J. F. Crow, April 10, 1967

It was demonstrated in this laboratory that poly G and other guanine-rich polynucleotides show differential affinity for the two complementary strands of various DNA's, indicating asymmetric distribution of poly G-binding sites.[1, 2] Furthermore, it was postulated that these sites, probably deoxycytidine(dC)-rich clusters, might act as the initiation points of the DNA-to-RNA transcription.[2, 3] For DNA which contains dC-rich clusters on *both* strands, as for instance coliphage λ DNA (Fig. 1),[3, 4] this hypothesis predicts that transcribing regions would be found on *both* strands. As will be shown, this prediction is confirmed for coliphage λ, which provides the first example of *in vivo* transcription from *both* DNA strands, as documented by DNA-RNA hybridization techniques.[3, 5] This result agrees with the conclusions based on genetic experiments with λ phage.[6, 7] In earlier studies employing other phages, only *one* DNA strand was found to hybridize with phage-specific mRNA.[8]

Fig. 1.—Genetic map of phage λ, including A to R *sus* markers,[9] "clear" markers c_I, c_{II}, and c_{III},[24] central b_2 region,[25, 26] markers x and y,[7] and marker a,[27] all superimposed over λ DNA.[6, 7] The base compositions (% G + C) of both arms of λ DNA and of the central b_2 region are indicated.[6, 25] 5'G and 5'A identify the 5' terminal nucleotides[23] and the polarity of the C and W strands.[4] Symbol C ("*DENSE*") indicates the DNA strand which is denser in the poly G-containing CsCl gradient (and "lighter" in the alkaline CsCl gradient[4, 6]) than strand W.[2-4] The arrows (mRNA) indicate the orientation, the region, and the strand of preference for the DNA-to-RNA transcription, as discussed in this paper. The distribution of cytosine-rich clusters is indicated by the symbols (-+-), and is based on the data of Hradecna and Szybalski.[4]

Materials and Methods.—Bacterial and phage strains: Escherichia coli K12 strains included C600, which is permissive for λ*sus* mutants, and W3110 and W3350, which are nonpermissive for *sus* mutants.[9] These were lysogenized or infected with appropriate λ mutants as listed in Table 1. Most of the λc_I, λ*dg*, and λ*sus* mutants and the lysogenic strains were obtained from Drs. W. F. Dove, H. Echols, A. Joyner, D. Pratt, M. Ptashne, and J. Adler. Strains T75[10] and T11 [= W3350-(λ/11)][7] were contributed by Dr. C. R. Fuerst. The subscript A–J indicates that genes A to J (entire left arm; Fig. 1) were deleted in λdg_{A-J} and replaced by a part of the galactose operon.[11] Biotin genes were substituted for deleted genes a-N or a-O in λdb_{a-N} (= λ/75) and λdb_{a-O}, respectively, the latter contributed by Dr. G. Kayajanian.

The cultivation of bacteria, infection or induction of phages, preparation of phage stocks, and purification of phages by high-low speed sedimentation and CsCl density gradient centrifugation followed the published procedures.[4, 6, 7, 9-13] The lysogenic cultures were induced by addition of 2 μg mitomycin C/ml.[12]

Pulse-labeling and isolation of bacterial and λ-specific RNA: The method employed followed closely the techniques described by Sly et al.[12]   A total of 0.5 mc of H[3]-uridine (8 c/mM) was added to 20 ml of the culture, which 2 min later was poured onto an equal volume of crushed ice prepared from minimal medium.   This was followed by rapid sedimentation of the bacteria at 4°C, lysis by 2% sodium dodecyl sulfate (SDS), and phenol extraction of the RNA at 60°C.   The upper aqueous phase was used for the "prehybridization" with λ DNA (see next section), after determination of the acid-precipitable radioactivity (total H[3]-labeled RNA: see Table 1).

DNA-RNA hybridization procedure: The hybridization procedure was based on the technique described by Gillespie and Spiegelman[14] with an additional "prehybridization" step.

(a) *Prehybridization:* Denatured λ DNA (50 μg), "baked" on a 25-mm B-6 filter (Schleicher & Schuell Co.),[14] was incubated (24 hr, 60°C) with 1 ml phenol-saturated 2×SSC containing homologous H[3]·RNA (total 100–500 μg RNA).   The filters were exhaustively washed with 2× SSC after this and each following step.   The nonspecifically bound RNA was digested with RNase (1 hr, 20°C, 4 ml of 2×SSC +20 μg RNase/ml).   The residual RNase was inactivated by incubation (40 min, 55°C) of the washed filters in 2 ml of 0.15 M iodoacetate at pH 5 (0.1 M Na-acetate buffer, 2×SSC).   The H[3]·RNA was eluted with 1.5 ml of 1/100×SSC (15 min, 95°C, 90% recovery of H[3] count), and treated with RNase-free (iodoacetate pretreated[16]) DNase (10 μg DNase [Worthington Co.]/ml of 0.05 M Tris, 0.004 M MgCl₂, pH 7.4, 20 min, 37°C), which was then inactivated by 10 min heating to 95°C, as recommended by Skalka (personal communication).

(b) *Hybridization:* Denatured DNA (25 μg) or the separated λ DNA strands (3–10 μg) "baked" on a 25-mm filter[14] were incubated (24 hr, 60°C, 1 ml phenol-saturated 2×SSC) with 1,000–10,000 cpm of λ mRNA eluted from the filter in the prehybridization-procedure. Following the RNase treatment (see prehybridization) and extensive washing with 2×SSC, the filters were dried (2 hr, 60°C) and transferred to toluene-2,5-diphenyloxazole (toluene-PPO) scintillation fluid for the H[3] count.   An excess of hybridization sites for binding up to 2,000 cpm of "prehybridized" mRNA is provided by 3 μg of separated DNA strands, since the $C:W$ ratios are unaffected by raising the DNA quantity to 10 or 25 μg per filter.   All hybridization values are corrected for H[3]·RNA counts bound by filters carrying denatured T4 coliphage DNA.

Preparative separation of the complementary DNA strands: To effect strand separation, the DNA is released, denatured, and reacted with poly IG, all three operations in a single step.[4]   When the phage suspension (50 μg DNA) is heated (2 min at 90°C) in 0.5 ml 10^{-3} M sodium versenate (EDTA) containing 100 μg poly IG and 0.1% Sarkosyl NL 97 (Geigy Chemical Corp., New York), and is chilled and centrifuged in a polyallomer tube (2.5 ml of CsCl solution, 1.72 gm/cm³, 70 hr, 15°C, 30,000 rpm SW39 rotor), the released and denatured DNA is distributed into two symmetrical bands separated by 12–14 mg/cm³.   Of the two complementary DNA strands, the one with the relatively higher content of poly IG-binding, dC-rich clusters[3, 4] (strand C) is found in the denser band, while the other (strand W) forms the less dense band (Fig. 1).   After collecting the separate fractions, each of the two pooled samples containing one kind of λ DNA strand was separately subjected to self-annealing (4 hr, 65°C, 5 M CsCl)[4] to convert any of the contaminating opposite strands to double helices, which would be inactive in the DNA-RNA hybridization procedure.   The functional purity of such "self-annealed" strands was over 99% as tested by preparing H[3]·mRNA specific for one strand only (cf. (a) *Prehybridization* in *Materials and Methods*) and comparing its affinities for the two strands.   The mRNA prehybridized and eluted from the C strands hybridized with strands C over 99 times more efficiently than with strands W (99.6:0.4 for $C:W$).   An analogous result was obtained for strand W-specific mRNA or for mRNA produced by the λt11 mutant (Table 1, line 11).   Proof for the integrity of the separated strands at over 85% level, their properties, orientation (Fig. 1), and the details of the strand separation procedure for λ DNA were published by Hradecna and Szybalski.[4]

Results and Discussion.—Temporal control of transcription: Shortly after infection with λc₇₂ phage, the amount of λ-specific mRNA rises rapidly, as previously shown by Sly et al.[12]   This "early" λ-mRNA hybridized preferentially with the W strand (Fig. 1) of λ DNA (5:95 for $C:W$, Table 1, line 3, and Fig. 2A).   At 30 or 40 minutes after infection, the preference for the transcription shifted to the C strand (85:15 for $C:W$, Table 1, lines 4 and 5; and Fig. 2A).   It appears, therefore, that the transcription from strand C rises sharply during the development of infectious phage, while the strand W-specific mRNA is synthesized at an almost constant rate (Table 1, line 3 versus 4, and 7 versus 18; Fig. 2A).

Chloramphenicol (CM) effects: Addition of CM before induction or infection with phage does not grossly affect the initial rate of λ-mRNA synthesis, but at all times such RNA retains the characteristics of early mRNA.[17] Temporally, we define the early λ-mRNA as that which could be produced in the absence of protein and DNA synthesis; it will be shown later that it is probably transcribed from the N-a and x-O regions. This definition is probably more restrictive than that used earlier.[12, 13, 21, 22] It appears essential to use at least 100 μg CM/ml for preparing early λ-mRNA, since the transcription from strand C preferentially increases at lower CM concentrations (Table 1, lines 7, 8, and 19).

Localization of the "switch sites": Transcription of both the W and C strands

TABLE 1

PERCENTAGE OF λ-SPECIFIC H³-LABELED RNA SYNTHESIZED BY VARIOUS λ MUTANTS AND THE
PROPORTION OF THIS mRNA HYBRIDIZING WITH COMPLEMENTARY STRANDS C AND W

| | | | | | Hybridized with Separated Strands Per Cent of Total,§ H³-Labeled RNA (λmRNA) | | | |
Expt. no.	mRNA donor* (host; phage)	Induction,† infection CM(μg/ml)‡	H³-uridine pulse† (min)	$C + W$	C	W	Ratio (%) C	W
1	W3110	None	2	0.001	—	—	—	—
2	W3350	None	2	0.002	0.001	0.001	50	50
3	W3110; λc_{72}	Inf.	0–2	2.0	0.1	1.9	5	95
4	W3110; λc_{72}	Inf.	28–30	8.4	7.1	1.3	85	15
5	W3350; λc_{72}	Inf.	38–40	8.1	6.9	1.2	85	15
6	W3350; λc_{72}	Inf.	38–40	8.0	7.8	0.2	97	3
				left arm				
7	W3350(λ⁺)	Ind. CM(100)	58–60	0.5	0.05	0.45	10	90
8	W3350(λ⁺)	Ind. CM(40)	58–60	0.7	0.16	0.54	23	77
9	W3350(λdg$_{A-J}$)	Ind. CM(100)	58–60	0.4	0.08	0.32	20	80
10	W3350(λdg$_{A-J}$)	Ind.	58–60	2.3	1.8	0.50	78	22
11	W3350(λt11)	Ind.	58–60	0.9	0.005	0.89	0.5	99.5
12	W3350(λt11)	Ind. CM(50)	58–60	0.6	0.018	0.58	3	97
13	W3350(λt11)	None	2	0.03	0.005	0.025	16	84
14	W3350(λind⁻)	None	2	0.04	0.003	0.037	8	92
15	W3350(λind⁻)	None	2	0.005	.0.003	0.002	56	44
				λi 434				
16	W3350(λind⁻)	None	2	0.004	0.002	0.002	47	53
				λi 21				
17	W3350(λ⁺)	None	2	0.05	0.01	0.04	18	82
18	W3350(λ⁺)	Ind.	58–60	3.4	2.9	0.48	86	14
19	W3350(λ⁺)	Ind. CM(50)	58–60	0.6	0.1	0.5	16	84
20	T75(λdb$_{a-N}$)	None	2	0.04	0.007	0.033	18	82
21	W3110b(λdb$_{a-O}$)	None	2	0.02	0.012	0.008	59	41
22	W3350(λN$_{53}$)	None	2	0.05	0.006	0.044	13	87
23	T75(λdb$_{a-N}$)	Ind.	58–60	0.04	0.027	0.013	68	32
24	T75(λdb$_{a-N}$)	Ind. CM(50)	58–60	0.06	0.017	0.043	28	72
25	W3110b(λdb$_{a-O}$)	Ind.	58–60	0.02	0.011	0.009	57	43
26	W3350(λN₇)**	Ind.	58–60	0.6	0.12	0.48	21	79
27	W3350(λN₇)**	Ind. CM(50)	58–60	0.4	0.09	0.31	22	78
28	W3350(λO₂₉)	Ind.	58–60	0.5	0.22	0.28	44	56
29	W3350(λO₂₉)	Ind. CM(50)	58–60	0.4	0.08	0.32	20	80
30	W3350(λP₈₀)	Ind.	58–60	0.6	0.34	0.26	57	43
31	W3350(λP₈₀)	Ind. CM(50)	58–60	0.6	0.11	0.49	19	81

* In expts. 1 and 2, bacteria free of λ phage were used. Infection is indicated by the semicolon, whereas the lysogenic state is indicated by parentheses.
† The bacteria were infected (Inf.) at multiplicity 5 (0°C, 10⁻² M Mg⁺⁺), and after 20 min for absorption (0°C) transferred to growth medium[12] (37°C) (= zero time). Induction (Ind.) was initiated by adding 2 μg mitomycin C/ml of growth medium.[12] The noninduced lysogens (None) were pulse-labeled for 2 min during the exponential growth phase at a cell concentration of 4 × 10⁸/ml.
‡ Chloramphenicol (CM) was present from 10 min before induction to the end of the H³-uridine pulse.
§ Percentage of total H³ RNA which was prehybridized (50 μg λcb₂ DNA or other DNA if so specified in the column), eluted from the filter, and hybridized again with 25 μg denatured λcb₂ DNA ($C + W$), or with 3 μg of self-annealed C and W strands of λcb₂ DNA per filter (see *Materials and Methods*). In expt. 6, H³·RNA was prehybridized with the "short left arm" of λc₁ DNA.
** Similar results were obtained with the λN₇N₅₃ double mutant.[20]

implies the presence of sites at which the λ-mRNA synthesis switches from one strand to another, either *converging* or *diverging* from such a *switch site*.   A major *switch site* should be on the right arm of the DNA, since both the early (+CM) and late mRNA's produced by *E. coli* lysogenic for λdg_{A-J}, in which the whole left arm is deleted[11] (Fig. 1), hybridize with both DNA strands (Table 1, lines 9 and 10).   It was previously shown that early mRNA hybridizes preferentially with the right arm of λ DNA.[18]

Employing prehybridization of H³-labeled RNA with λdg_{A-J} DNA (Fig. 1) at various times after λc_I infection, it was possible to follow the kinetics of tran-scription on the right arm only, for both the *C* and *W* strands (Fig. 2B).   The transcription on the right arm of strand *C* increases rapidly up to the 20th minute after infection and levels off around the 24th minute, whereas the transcription on the left arm of strand *C* commences at about the same time and rises sharply (Fig. 2B; *C(right)* and *C(left)*).   The kinetics of transcription for the right arm of strand *W* (Fig. 2B; *W(right)*) are similar to those for the whole strand *W* (Fig. 2A; *W*), although the small and possibly fortuitous differences between these

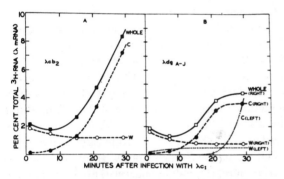

Fig. 2.—Percentage of H³-labeled RNA (2-min pulse) specific for λcb_2 (*A*; ■) and λdg_{A-J} (*B*; □), and for the *C* (●) and *W* (○) strands of these DNA's, at various times after infection of *Escherichia coli* W3110 with λc_{72} (see second footnote in Table 1, and *Materials and Methods;* pH of growth medium, 7.7).   RNA was prehybridized with 50 μg denatured DNA of λcb_2 (*A*) or λdg_{A-J} (*B*), treated with RNAse and iodoacetate (see *Materials and Methods*), eluted, and hybridized with 25 μg of denatured λcb_2 DNA (WHOLE, solid line) and with 3 μg of the separated *C* and *W* strands of λcb_2. The dashed-line values, which are fractions of the solid-line values proportional to the per cent of *C* or *W*, represent the amount of mRNA transcribed from the whole *C* or *W* strand (*A*) or from the right arms (Fig. 1) of the *C* or *W* strand (*B*).   The dotted line *C (left)* represents the difference between the *C* and *C (right)* values, and indicates the kinetics of transcription from the left arm (Fig. 1) of the *C* strand.   The dotted line *W (left)* represents the difference between the *W* and *W (right)* values.

values might be construed as indicative of some transcription from the left arm of strand *W* (Fig. 2B; *W(left)*).   However, it was found that mRNA prehybridized with the purified left arm of λc_{72} DNA and thus containing only the mRNA tran-scribed by the left arm, hybridized almost exclusively with the *C* strand (Table 1, line 6).   Thus, there is little reason to postulate any transcription from the left arm of strand *W*.

Where on the right arm of λ DNA is the "switch site" localized, and is it a *divergency* or *convergency* site?   The most direct answer is provided by an experi-ment with mutant λt11, in which a polar mutation in gene *x* inactivates the *x*-to-O functions[7] and at the same time blocks the transcription from strand *C* (0.5:99.5 for *C*:*W;* Table 1, line 11).   This correlation indicates that genes *x*-to-O are transcribed from strand *C*, i.e., from left to right.   If strand-*W*-specific mRNA is the product of region N to *a*, and thus is transcribed from right to left, a *diver-gency site* must be located between genes N and *x* (Fig. 1).   These interpretations

are based on the known polarities of strands C and W (Fig. 1) and on the 5'-to
-3' orientation of RNA synthesis in conjunction with work on heteroduplexes
in gene N.[6, 15] Since left-arm-specific mRNA seems to be transcribed from strand
C, i.e., in the left-to-right direction, a *convergency site* should be located somewhere
near or within region b_2 (Fig. 1). The products of the b_2 region are not included
in this study, since λcb_2 DNA with the b_2 region deleted (Fig. 1) was used either
for prehybridization or for the preparation of separated DNA strands. However,
similar studies on the transcribing function of the b_2 region are currently being
pursued in this laboratory.

Transcription from the prophage: To further localize the position of the major
switch, it is necessary to determine the orientation of the transcription from gene
c_1. The W3350(λind$^-$) lysogenic strain[19] was used for this purpose, since its spontaneous induction rate is very low, and thus its mRNA may consist mainly of the
gene c_1 product. Transcription rate from the noninduced λind$^-$ prophage (0.04%
of total $H^3 \cdot RNA$) is up to 40 times higher than the level obtained with λ-free
E. coli (Table 1, lines 1, 2, and 14). This mRNA hybridizes preferentially with the
W strand of λcb_2 (0.037%; 8:92 for $C:W$), and has hardly any affinity for strand
C (0.003%; Table 1, line 14) or for either DNA strand of λ hybrids with a heterologous c_1 region (0.002–0.003%; Table 1, lines 15 and 16). The levels of λ-specific
mRNA for several noninduced prophages were within relatively narrow limits
(0.03–0.05%; Table 1, lines 13, 17, 20, and 22; see also Sly *et al.*[12]); all these
mRNA's exhibited strong preference for strand W, with the exception of mRNA
produced by the λdb_{a-o} prophage, in which gene c_1 is deleted and which transcribes
poorly both before and after induction (Table 1, lines 21 and 25). These data
indicate that (1) in the noninduced state the bulk of λ-mRNA is the product of
gene c_1, and that (2) this is transcribed from strand W, i.e., from right to left, which
conclusion is similar to that based on the polar effects of the $sus34$ mutation located
at the right end of gene c_1.[20] Furthermore, these data suggest that the λ repressor
is a bifunctional protein (as represented by regions A and B[22]), which interacts
with two operator regions (deleted in $\lambda i434$), one adjoining the left end of the c_1
gene and controlling the N-a transcription from the W strand and the other located
next to the right terminal of gene c_1 and controlling the x-O transcription from the C
strand. According to this model, the lack of host inactivation upon transient thermal induction of the $c_1(B)$ prophage in the presence of CM (Lieb and Green[22])
can be explained by partial renaturation of the repressor with restoration of only
one (x-O repression) of its two functions; temporary expression of genes N-to-a
apparently has no lethal consequences.

Controls of early and late transcription: In the noninduced state, c_1 mRNA
seems to be the main transcription product (W strand). Immediately after infection or "early" (+CM) upon induction, the total transcription increases by
factors of 10–40, with strand W being predominantly transcribed, probably in the
N-a and still in the c_1 regions. Strand C is transcribed to a lesser extent (5:95
to 10:90 for $C:W$), most probably from the x-y-c_{II}-O operon, since the polar mutation in gene x abolishes this early transcription from strand C. The fact that CM
freezes this early stage of transcription indicates that (1) the N-a and x-O tran-
scriptions are not mutually dependent on their protein products, and (2) that there
is a need for some proteins to extend the transcription to other genes.

Which gene products are necessary for the shift to the later stages of transcription? At least two proteins, those missing in the N (as postulated by Thomas[21]) and x mutants, appear to be required; a low level of C-specific mRNA, characteristic of the early transcription pattern, persists upon induction of both the x and N mutants (Table 1, lines 11, 19, and 26). This pattern changes somewhat for the induced susO and P prophages.[12, 13] The "late" transcription from strand C for both the O and P mutants increases threefold when compared with the early transcription in the presence of CM (Table 1, lines 28–31); the analogous increase in C-specific transcription for the λ^+ is 30-fold and for the right arm of λ^+ or for λdg_{A-J} is approximately 20-fold (Table 1, lines 9, 10, 18, 19; Fig. 2B). These results indicate either a "leaky" character for the O and P mutations, or, more probably, a shift to the next stage of transcription from strand C.

Is it necessary to invoke any special control mechanisms for the early versus late transcription from strand W, which seems to be limited to the c_I and N-to-a regions? In the absence of DNA synthesis the differences between the early and late transcription from the W strand are small for the x, N, O, and P mutants (Table 1, lines 11, 12, 26–31). During the normal infection (Fig. 2) or induction process (Table 1, lines 18 and 19), the progressive decrease in synthesis of the strand W-specific mRNA also appears comparatively small. This small decrease, however, would become quite precipitous if the transcription rates were divided by the corresponding numbers of λ DNA copies in the vegetative pool. These results indicate that (1) only the *parental* W strands are transcribed and at a relatively steady rate, or that (2) strands W are transcribed in *all* λ DNA molecules at a rate which is controlled by the limiting amount of the "early" RNA polymerase. In the absence of DNA synthesis, the *parental* W strands are continuously transcribed, as shown for the susN, O, P and t11 mutants (Table 1, lines 11–12, 26–31).

Late during induction, the transcription from gene c_I seems to be repressed, as represented by the three- to fourfold decrease in the synthesis of W-specific λdb_{a-N} mRNA (Table 1, lines 20, 23, and 24); only gene c_I should be transcribed from strand W of λdb_{a-N}, since genes a–N are deleted.

Several recent papers discuss the control of induction and development of phage λ.[6, 7, 9, 10, 12, 13, 17, 18, 20–22, 25]

Conclusions and Summary.—Hybridization of the various λ-specific mRNA's with the separate strands of λ DNA provides a powerful new technique for determining the distribution of the transcribing regions. Several technical refinements were introduced, including (1) self-annealing of the separated DNA strands, which results in preparations of individual strands displaying a purity of over 99 per cent in hybridization tests, and (2) a highly selective two-step hybridization procedure, with prehybridization including RNase treatment followed by inactivation of RNase by iodoacetate. With the latter method it was possible to compare the levels of λ-specific mRNA in nonlysogenic *E. coli* (0.001–0.002%), in noninduced lysogens (0.03–0.06%), and early (0.5–2.0%) or late (6–12%) in induced nondefective lysogens or in infected cells, with the simplified ratio of these figures being represented as 1 (nonlysogenic):50 (noninduced):500 ("early" induced):5000 ("late" induced).

In the noninduced state the majority mRNA is transcribed from the W strand, most probably being the product of gene c_I. Upon induction or infection two regions adjoining the c_I gene start to be transcribed: the predominant product (90%) is copied from strand W in the same direction as gene c_I, through genes N-to-a, whereas the minority mRNA (10%) is copied in the opposite direction, i.e., from left-to-right, from strand C through the x-O operon. Both of these transcription and also translation products seem to be required to activate the further transcription of the λ genome, since the early transcription pattern could be frozen either by inhibition of protein synthesis (100 μg CM/ml) or by the nonsense or polar mutations in genes N or x. Within 10–20 minutes after infection the transcription changes to the "late" pattern, with over 85 per cent of the mRNA now being transcribed from the C strand, progressively more and more from its left arm. Thus, during the development of λ, the transcription of strand W decreases by only 10–30 per cent, whereas the transcription of strand C increases 30- to 70-fold. Transcription in the induced susO and P lysogens, unable to synthesize λ DNA, does not proceed far beyond the early stage, since upon removal of CM the transcription from strand C increases only threefold. The hybridization pattern obtained with the λdg$_{A-J}$ mutant, which transcribes both DNA strands although its left arm is entirely deleted, confirms that a *divergency switch* in the direction of mRNA synthesis is on the right arm of λ DNA. It is interesting to note that the segments of the individual DNA strands presently characterized as transcribing regions were independently shown to contain all the dC-rich clusters, which have been postulated by Szybalski *et al.*[3] to act as initiation points for the DNA-to-RNA transcription process. Thus, at the present level of resolution the asymmetry in the distribution of the poly IG-binding dC clusters, which permits the preparative separation of the complementary DNA strands, seems to be directly related to the asymmetric transcription pattern of mRNA and the changes in the orientation of this transcription.

The following abbreviations are employed: poly G, homopolymer of guanylic acid; poly IG, copolymer of guanylic and inosinic acids; CM, chloramphenicol; DNase, pancreatic deoxyribonuclease I; RNase, pancreatic ribonuclease; SSC, 0.15 M NaCl + 0.02 M trisodium citrate, pH = 7.4; 6×SSC, 2×SSC, 1/100×SSC, 6 or 2 times more concentrated SSC, or 100 times diluted SSC, respectively; mRNA, messenger RNA which operationally is that fraction of pulse-labeled RNA which specifically hybridizes with λ DNA (= λ mRNA); C and W strands, complementary strands of λ DNA which, when unbroken, exhibit a higher or lower affinity for poly IG and thus band at higher or lower density in the CsCl gradient, respectively (Fig. 1); SDS, sodium dodecyl sulfate; G, guanine; C, cytosine; A, adenine; T, thymine; sus, suppressor-sensitive mutation; dg, defective galactose transducing; db, defective biotin transducing.

We are greatly indebted to Dr. W. F. Dove, who guided us through many intricacies of λ genetics, and to Dr. H. Echols and his students and collaborators for their contributions of strains and technical advice. Drs. J. Adler, G. Kayajanian, E. Calef, A. D. Kaiser, M. Ptashne, and C. R. Fuerst also supplied us with strains. Their helpful advice and that of Drs. R. Thomas, D. K. Fraser, F. Gros, D. S. Hogness, C. M. Radding, S. N. Cohen, A. M. Skalka, A. D. Hershey, and L. H. Pereira da Silva, including correspondence and manuscripts, are also gratefully acknowledged. We are also very thankful to Drs. W. F. Dove, H. Echols, R. Thomas, M. Susman, and E. H. Szybalski for critical reading of the manuscript and editorial help.

* These studies were supported by a grant from the National Science Foundation (B-14976).
† On leave from the Institute of Marine Medicine, Gdańsk, Poland.
‡ On leave from the Biophysics Institute, Brno, Czechoslovakia.

[1] Opara-Kubinska, Z., H. Kubinski, and W. Szybalski, these Proceedings, **52**, 923 (1964).
[2] Kubinski, H., Z. Opara-Kubinska, and W. Szybalski, *J. Mol. Biol.*, **20**, 313 (1966).

[3] Szybalski, W., H. Kubinski, and P. Sheldrick, in *Cold Spring Harbor Symposia on Quantitative Biology*, vol. 31 (1966), p. 123.

[4] Hradecna, Z., and W. Szybalski, *Virology*, in press; Hradecna, Z., K. Taylor, and W. Szybalski, *Bacteriol. Proc.* (1967), p. 27.

[5] Taylor, K., Z. Hradecna, and W. Szybalski, *Federation Proc.*, **26**, 449 (1967); Szybalski, W., Z. Hradecna, and K. Taylor, *Abstracts*, 7th International Congress of Biochemistry, Tokyo, in press.

[6] Hogness, D. S., W. Doerfler, J. B. Egan, and L. W. Black, in *Cold Spring Harbor Symposia Quantitative Biology*, vol. 31 (1966), p. 129.

[7] Eisen, H. A., C. R. Fuerst, L. Siminovitch, R. Thomas, L. Lambert, L. Pereira da Silva, and F. Jacob, *Virology*, **30**, 224 (1966).

[8] Tocchini-Valentini, G. P., M. Stodolsky, A. Aurisicchio, M. Sarnat, F. Graziosi, S. B. Weiss, and E. P. Geiduschek, these PROCEEDINGS, **50**, 935 (1963); Marmur, J., and C. M. Greenspan, *Science*, **142**, 387 (1963); Hayashi, M., M. N. Hayashi, and S. Spiegelman, these PROCEEDINGS, **50**, 664 (1963).

[9] Campbell, A., *Virology*, **14**, 22 (1961); Kayajanian, G., and A. Campbell, *Virology*, **30**, 482 (1966).

[10] Fuerst, C. R., *Virology*, **30**, 581 (1966).

[11] Adler, J. and B. Templeton, *J. Mol. Biol.*, **7**, 710 (1963).

[12] Sly, W. S., H. Echols, and J. Adler, these PROCEEDINGS, **53**, 378 (1965); Joyner, A., L. N. Isaacs, H. Echols, and W. S. Sly, *J. Mol. Biol.*, **19**, 174 (1966); Echols, H., B. Butler, A. Joyner, M. Willard, and L. Pilarski, in *Edmonton Symposium on Molecular Biology of Viruses* (New York: Academic Press, 1967), p. 125.

[13] Dove, W. F., *J. Mol. Biol.*, **19**, 187 (1966).

[14] Gillespie, D., and S. Spiegelman, *J. Mol. Biol.*, **12**, 829 (1965).

[15] Experiments employing prehybridization with DNA from the λdb_{a-N} and λdb_{a-o} mutants are in progress. Preliminary results are consistent with the assignment of the W-specific transcription to the a-N region.

[16] Zimmerman, S. B., and G. Sandeen, *Anal. Biochem.*, **14**, 269 (1966).

[17] Naono, S., and F. Gros, *J. Mol. Biol.*, (in press); and in *Cold Spring Harbor Symposia on Quantitative Biology*, vol. 31 (1966), p. 363.

[18] Skalka, A., these PROCEEDINGS, **55**, 1190 (1966).

[19] Jacob, F., and A. Campbell, *Compt. Rend.*, **248**, 3219 (1959).

[20] Ptashne, M., these PROCEEDINGS, **57**, 306 (1967), and personal communication.

[21] Thomas, R., *J. Mol. Biol.*, **22**, 79 (1966).

[22] Green, M., *J. Mol. Biol.*, **16**, 134 (1966); and in *Edmonton Symposium on Molecular Biology of Viruses* (New York: Academic Press, in press); Lieb, M., *J. Mol. Biol.*, **16**, 149 (1966); Kourilsky, P., and D. Luzzati, *J. Mol. Biol.*, in press; Cohen, S. N., U. Maitra, and J. Hurwitz, *J. Mol. Biol.*, in press.

[23] Wu, R., and A. D. Kaiser, these PROCEEDINGS, **57**, 170 (1967).

[24] Kaiser, A. D., and F. Jacob, *Virology*, **4**, 509 (1957); Kaiser, A. D., *Virology*, **3**, 42 (1957); Isaacs, L. N., H. Echols, and W. S. Sly, *J. Mol. Biol.*, **13**, 963 (1965).

[25] Hershey, A. D., in *Carnegie Institution of Washington Year Book 65* (1966), p. 559.

[26] Kellenberger, G., M. L. Zichichi, and J. Weigle, *Nature*, **187**, 161 (1960).

[27] Gene *a* (called also *int*) controls the attachment and integration of the λ genome at a vacant bacterial site; Gingery, R. and H. Echols, personal commun.; Zissler, J., *Virology*, **31**, 189 (1967).

THE MECHANISM OF REPLICATION: A NOVEL POLARITY REVERSAL IN THE IN VITRO SYNTHESIS OF Qβ-RNA AND ITS COMPLEMENT*

BY D. H. L. BISHOP,† N. R. PACE,‡ AND S. SPIEGELMAN

DEPARTMENT OF MICROBIOLOGY, UNIVERSITY OF ILLINOIS, URBANA

Communicated August 24, 1967

The synthesis of biologically competent viral RNA has been demonstrated[1-3] with a purified Qβ-replicase[4] (an RNA-dependent RNA polymerase induced by the RNA bacteriophage Qβ). A kinetic analysis of the reaction was carried out using sucrose gradients[5] and electrophoretic separation in acrylamide gels.[6-8] Two classes of complexes containing both initiating templates and early product were shown[9, 10] to materialize prior to the formation of new infectious strands. The first complexes (HS) to appear correspond to the structures found in vivo by Francke and Hofschneider,[11] and one minute later a second class (FS) is synthesized resembling the complexes found by Franklin[12] in cells infected with R-17. The temporal order of their appearance with respect to each other and the final product is consistent with a mechanism of synthesis which involves the following sequence of events:

$$\text{Template Q}\beta\text{-RNA} \rightarrow \text{HS} \rightarrow \text{FS} \rightarrow \text{product Q}\beta\text{-RNA}.$$

We will detail elsewhere[13, 14] chemical and physical evidence supporting the conclusions that HS structures are *antiparallel duplexes* containing Qβ-RNA (plus strands) hydrogen-bonded to complete or partial complements (minus strands) and that FS complexes contain in addition newly synthesized plus strands at various stages of formation. The present paper assumes these structures and focuses attention on how they arise.

The particular issue being raised derives from the chemical polarity conferred on polynucleotide chains by the internucleotide linkage in which phosphorus is esterified to the 5'-carbon of the sugar on one side and to the 3'-carbon of the sugar on the other. Up to the present, the synthesis of all polynucleotides has been shown to occur from 5' to 3'. However, there are no theoretical reasons for excluding the possibility of 3' to 5' polymerizations and we shall here provide evidence that, in fact, they do occur in RNA replication. As will be seen, their existence can help resolve the "DNA-dilemma" of a single growing point for the two antiparallel chains.[15, 16]

To understand the rationale of the experiments to be described it is helpful to note that our reaction mixtures contain only 5'-ribosidetriphosphates. We must, therefore, assume that these substrates can participate in either a 5' to 3' or a 3' to 5' reaction, a possibility which raises, however, no real difficulty. In a 5' to 3' synthesis, the *pyrophosphate group of the monomer* can react with the *3'-OH of the terminating nucleotide* on the growing chain. The elimination of the β,γ-phosphorus atoms of the monomer provides the energy for the formation of the resulting internucleotide bond. Thus, the *first* residue added is the *5' terminus of* the complete strand and is the *only* one to retain its β,γ-phosphates.

Conversely, in a 3' to 5' synthesis the *3'-OH of the monomer* reacts with the *pyro-*

phosphate group *on the terminal* nucleotide of the growing chain.   Again the elimination of the β,γ-P atoms results in the diester bond.   However, the growing chain *retains* the β,γ-phosphates of the residue just added.   Note that in a 3' to 5' synthesis the *5' terminus* is the *last* residue added and again retains its β,γ-phosphates.

Figure 1 diagrams the different ways of forming HS and FS complexes made

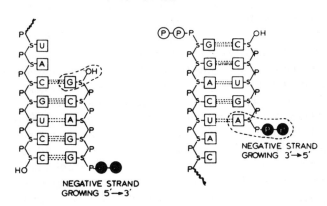

FIRST STAGE

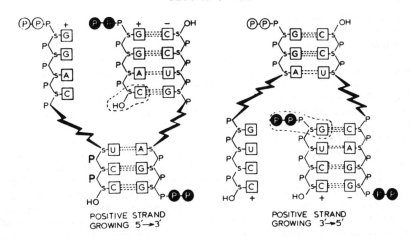

SECOND STAGE

Fig. 1.—Alternative methods for the synthesis of polymers complementary or identical to Qβ-RNA *First Stage:*   Formation of duplex HS-RNA; synthesis of the negative strands: The synthesis of a complementary negative strand in a 5' to 3' direction (*left-hand side*) or 3' to 5' direction (*right-hand side*) using Qβ-RNA as template is shown.   The 5' phosphates of the new polymer derived from the P^{32}, β,γ-labeled triphosphate are depicted as P in blackened circles in order to differentiate them from the unlabeled phosphates of the template or the α-phosphates of the triphosphates.   It is assumed that reactions are carried out with β,γ-P^{32} ribosidetriphosphates.   The last nucleotide to be added to the new polymer is enclosed in a broken line.
Second Stage: Formation of a multistranded FS-RNA; synthesis of the positive strands.   Subsequent 5' to 3' or 3' to 5' synthesis of positive strands on the negative strand template which has been synthesized in a 5' to 3' direction (*first stage, left hand side*) is shown.
The alternative methods of synthesis and predictions therefrom are discussed in the text.   Apart from the terminal bases the sequence of bases shown for the positive or negative strands is arbitrary.

possible by the availability of two chemical directions. It is apparent that each alternative makes rather precise predictions of what will be found in the isolated HS and FS structures. A decision can evidently be achieved by running individual syntheses with each of the ribosidetriphosphates labeled in the β,γ-P. The consequences for the HS complexes may be summarized as follows: (a) If the direction of synthesis of the negative is 5' to 3', then HS structures will contain only one particular nucleosidetriphosphate (the 5' terminus) carrying P^{32} in the β,γ positions; (b) if the 3' to 5' direction is followed, all four nucleosidetriphosphates will appear with β,γ-P^{32} in HS structures containing *incomplete* minus strands. The data to be described clearly demonstrate that β,γ-P^{32} GTP is the *only* residue detected in isolated HS structures. This finding shows that *G is the 5'-terminus of the negative strand and that the direction of its synthesis is 5' to 3'*.

With this known, one can make a similar set of predictions for the FS structures: (a) ·If the direction of new *positive strand* synthesis is 5' to 3', only the 5' termini of the FS will carry β,γ-P^{32}, i.e., at most, two out of the four possibilities will be found. These would correspond to the 5' termini of completed plus and minus strands. If the 5' termini of the two happen to be the same, which is in fact the case, then only one of the four possibilities will occur; (b) if the direction is 3' to 5', *all four* types of β,γ-P^{32}-labeled residues will be found in the FS complexes.

The results obtained establish that purified FS-complexes contain chains terminating with any one of the four possible nucleotides carrying a β,γ-P^{32} label. We conclude that the synthesis of Qβ-RNA involves an initial polymerization of the *negative* strand in a 5' to 3' direction, followed by a reversal of polarity to a 3' to 5' synthesis for the new *positives*.

Materials and Methods.—(A) *RNA, enzymes, substrates, and assays:* Purification of Qβ-replicase through the stages of cesium chloride and sucrose sedimentation,[3] assay for enzyme activity under standard conditions, and liquid scintillation counting of acid-precipitable product on membrane filters have been described previously.[17] Qβ-viral RNA employed as the initiating template was extracted from Qβ-virus and further purified by centrifugation through sucrose gradients.[18] H^3-labeled UTP (3.36×10^9 cp5m/μmole) and H^3-labeled CTP (1.48×10^9 cp5m/μmole), were purchased from Schwarz BioResearch. AMP-morpholydate was obtained from Calbiochem; the morpholydates of CMP, UMP, and GMP were purchased from Sigma. P^{32}-labeled pyrophosphate was obtained from Tracerlab (100–160 mc/mg phosphorus.)

(B) *Synthesis of β,γ-labeled riboside triphosphates:* Synthesis of P^{32}-β,γ-labeled ribosidetriphosphates from the corresponding nucleotide morpholydate and P^{32}-inorganic pyrophosphate was carried out by a variation of one of the procedures of Wehrli *et al.*,[19] 100–200 mc of P^{32}-labeled pyrophosphate, pyridine salt (1 ml) was mixed with 1 ml of pyridine and 0.03 ml of tributylamine. The mixture was evaporated to dryness and further dried five times by addition and subsequent evaporation of 3 ml anhydrous pyridine. The pyridine was then removed by benzene and 1 ml of dry dimethyl sulfoxide added. The solution was added to the anhydrous nucleotide morpholydate, prepared by mixing 100 mg of 5'-mononucleotide morpholydate with 3 ml of dried pyridine and evaporating the pyridine to dryness. This was repeated five times. Traces of pyridine were removed by addition of benzene, which was then evaporated. The mixture of pyrophosphate and mononucleotide morpholydate was left for 2 days at 30° in a sealed flask. The β,γ-labeled riboside triphosphate was initially isolated by chromatography on Dowex 1 Cl⁻ as described previously,[17] with the exception that the excess of mononucleotide morpholydate was removed by washing the column with 0.01 N HCl until the optical density of the eluant was less than 0.2. During the subsequent gradient elution three peaks were observed corresponding to the diphosphate, the triphosphate, and the tetraphosphate derivatives. The main fractions containing the triphosphate were pooled, neutralized with NaOH, and concentrated to 2 to 3 ml. The triphosphate was precipitated by addition of 0.05 ml of a saturated solution of $BaCl_2$ and

5 to 10 volumes of methanol. The precipitate was collected by centrifugation and resuspended in 1 ml of water. The sodium salt of the triphosphate was then obtained by Dowex 50 (H+) treatment and neutralization with NaOH. In order to further purify the triphosphate from residual traces of diphosphate, tetraphosphate, and pyrophosphate the solution was concentrated to 0.2 ml and subjected to paper electrophoresis in 0.1 M ammonium acetate, pH 3.8, at 5 kv and 50 ma for 90 min on Whatman 52 paper. The position of the triphosphate was identified by radioautography and its ultraviolet (UV) absorption. The triphosphate was eluted with water at 4°C, paper flock removed by centrifugation, and the triphosphate again purified by barium precipitation and finally converted to the sodium salt. Triphosphates prepared in this manner were free, as determined by paper electrophoresis, from nucleotide mono-, di-, and tetraphosphates as well as pyrophosphates, or P^{32}-orthophosphate. The specific activities of the β,γ-labeled triphosphates were 9×10^9 cpm/μmole for CTP and ATP, 1.1×10^{10} cpm/μmole for UTP, and 6×10^9 cpm/μmole for GTP.

(C) *Enzyme reactions, preparation of the sample for electrophoresis, and electrophoretic conditions:* Standard reaction mixtures were prepared containing 2 μmoles $MgCl_2$, 20 μmoles tris-HCl buffer pH 7.4, 0.7 μmole Mg ethylenediaminetetraacetate (EDTA), 80 μg enzyme preparation, 0.2 μmole of two unlabeled triphosphates, 0.2 μmole of a third H^3-labeled triphosphate, 0.1 μmole of P^{32}, β,γ-labeled triphosphate, and 2 μg unlabeled Qβ viral RNA per 0.25 ml volume. The H^3-labeled triphosphate was included to determine the net RNA synthesis and the lower concentration of β,γ-labeled triphosphate to conserve material. Unlabeled Qβ RNA was used as a template at 2 μg to minimize reincorporation of the product viral RNA. Reaction mixtures were incubated at 38° and terminated by addition of sodium dodecyl sulfate (0.2% final concentration). Contamination with radioactive substrates was reduced in some experiments by passage through Sephadex G-25 as described by Haruna and Spiegelman.[20] Fractions containing RNA were pooled and concentrated by placing in a dialysis bag and immersing in dry Sephadex G-100 until a volume of 0.2 ml was attained. Each RNA sample was mixed with sucrose crystals and loaded on a polyacrylamide gel for electrophoresis and subsequent counting of gel slices as detailed previously.[10]

Results.—Four reaction mixtures were set up containing one or another of the β,γ-P^{32}-ribosidetriphosphate and a second labeled with tritium, the remaining two being unlabeled. The tritium label was included as an internal monitor of the extent of synthesis. Aliquots were removed at 0, 4, 8, and 20 or 25 minutes, treated and analyzed on gels (*Methods*, section C) for the distribution of H^3 and P^{32} among the HS, FS, and Qβ-RNA products of the reaction.

Figure 2 shows representative examples of the profiles obtained with β,γ-P^{32}-ATP (Fig. 2A) and β,γ-P^{32}-GTP (Fig. 2B). A striking difference is immediately evident. The reaction containing labeled ATP shows evidence of β,γ-P^{32}-ATP termini *only in the FS region.* In contrast (Fig. 2B), all components (FS, HS, and Qβ) contain 5' termini consisting of β,γ-P^{32}-GTP. The earlier samples (4 and 8 min) yielded similar distribution patterns of the P^{32}. Again, only β,γ-P^{32}-GTP is found in the HS and Qβ-RNA regions of the gel, β,γ-P^{32}-ATP being confined to the FS structures.

The reaction mixtures containing either β,γ-P^{32}-UTP or β,γ-P^{32}-CTP yielded the same profiles as seen in Figure 2A, only the FS region showing evidence of labeling. Table 1 summarizes the results of all four reactions. In interpreting the data, it is important to recall that unlabeled initiating template was present in excess and hence that radioactivity identifies newly synthesized plus in the Qβ region, newly synthesized minus in the HS region, and both plus and minus in the FS structures.

The facts and their implications which emerge from Table 1 may be listed as follows: (1) The Qβ-RNA and Qβ-HS regions contain only β,γ-P^{32}-GTP.

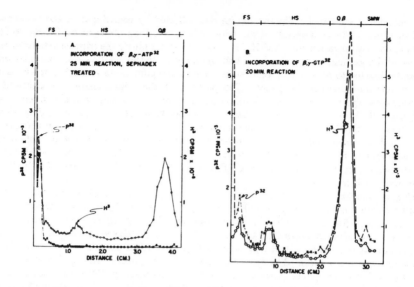

FIG. 2.—Incorporation of P^{32} β,γ-labeled GTP or ATP into the products of a Qβ-replicase reaction. Standard reaction mixtures containing H^3-labeled UTP and P^{32} β,γ-labeled ATP (*A*) or GTP (*B*) were incubated for 25 or 20 min, respectively, and either Sephadex-treated[20] (*A*) to remove triphosphates before electrophoresis (see *Methods*) or subjected to electrophoresis directly[10] (*B*). Subsequent to electrophoresis the gels were sliced, acid-washed, dissolved in H_2O_2, and counted in Kinards scintillation fluid as described previously.[10]

Consequently, the 5′-terminus of completed positive *and* negative strands is GTP. This immediately implies that cytosine constitutes the 3′-OH terminus of both plus and minus strands.   (2) The early appearance of β,γ-P^{32}-GTP in Qβ-HS and the absence of any of the other triphosphates establishes that new negative strands are synthesized in the 5′ to 3′ direction.   (3) Since the negative polymerizes from 5′ to 3′, the early (and late) appearance of *all four* β,γ-P^{32}-ribosidetriphosphates in the Qβ-FS structures *proves* that positive strands are synthesized in the 3′ to 5′ direction.

TABLE 1

INCORPORATION OF NUCLEOTIDES (IN $\mu\mu$MOLES) INTO THE PRODUCTS OF Qβ-REPLICASE REACTIONS

Gel Region	Reaction time (min)	Qβ-FS			Qβ-HS			Qβ		
(β,γ-P^{32}) XTP		H^3	P^{32}	P^{32} H^3	H^3	P^{32}	P^{32} H^3	H^3	P^{32}	P^{32} H^3
GTP	4	73	0.12	608	47	0.21	224	20	0.11*	182*
GTP	8	357	0.37	964	141	0.27	522	317	0.25	1,270
GTP	20	358	0.32	1,100	274	0.23	1,200	2,269	1.65	1,370
CTP	6	370	0.113	3,300	115	0.016	7,400	141	0.022	6,400
CTP	25	191	0.086	2,200	69	0.009	7,700	240	0.008	33,000
UTP	25	686	0.14	4,900	196	0.002	98,000	472	0	∞
ATP	25	325	0.17	1,900	100	0	∞	606	0	∞

Standard reaction mixtures containing one H^3-labeled triphosphate and another P^{32}-β,γ-labeled triphosphate were incubated at 38° as indicated. Except for reactions involving GTP, the reaction mixtures were Sephadex treated[20] prior to electrophoresis on 2.4% polyacrylamide gels.[7] The gels were sliced, acid-washed, dissolved in H_2O_2, and counted as described previously.[10] A control experiment lacking the H^3-labeled triphosphate, so that RNA synthesis was inhibited, but containing H^3-labeled Qβ RNA, was subjected to the same procedure. The sum of labels in the peak Qβ-FS, Qβ-HS, and Qβ regions—corrected for background P^{32} radioactivity by subtracting the equivalent values in the control experiment—was divided by the specific activity of the triphosphates (obtained under identical counting conditions) to obtain the $\mu\mu$mole incorporation of each triphosphate. The $\mu\mu$mole incorporation in the early reactions are for the whole Qβ-FS or Qβ-HS regions. Early reactions involving β,γ-UTP, like the β,γ-CTP, showed no appreciable incorporation in the Qβ-HS and Qβ regions.
  * The P^{32} peak in the Qβ region of the 4-min GTP reaction was slower than the H^3 peak, probably a reflection of immature duplexes possessing short segments of negative strands.

The ratio of H³ to P³² labels in the Qβ-RNA of the reaction containing β,γ-P³²-GTP yields the number of H³-nucleotides incorporated per terminal triphosphate, permitting an estimation of molecular weight.   The value of 1370 for the 20-minute GTP sample (Table 1) corresponds to a molecular weight of 1.5 × 10⁶.   This compares with 1.2–1.3 × 10⁶ as determined by relative electrophoretic mobility in polyacrylamide gels[7] and a minimal estimate of 0.9 × 10⁶ as found by light-scattering.[18]

The value of 1200 for the Qβ-HS structures in the 20-minute samples yields 1.3 × 10⁶ for the molecular weight of the negative strand and indicates the presence of a large proportion of completed duplexes.   This is in agreement with the RNase resistance and the gel profile after denaturation of Qβ-HS RNA isolated at these times from reaction mixtures.[14]

It should be noted that the corresponding H³ to P³² ratios of the early (4–8 min) HS and FS structures tend to be lower, in consonance with the expectation that they contain incomplete strands.

Discussion.— The performance of the experiments reported required the following: (1)   The availability of an enzyme preparation which was in fact making

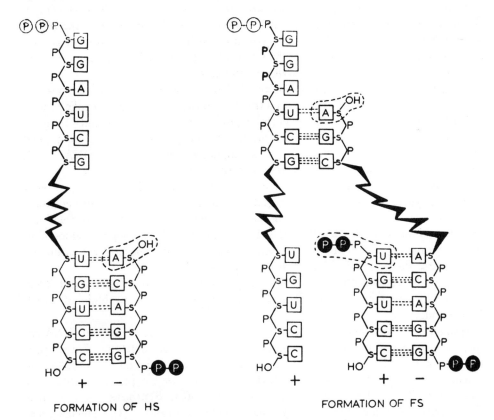

FORMATION OF HS   FORMATION OF FS

Fig. 3.—The mechanism of complementary and identical strands synthesis by QB-replicase. The postulated mechanism of 5′ to 3′ synthesis of the complementary strand of Qβ RNA and subsequent 3′ to 5′ synthesis of positive strands on the incomplete duplex is shown.   Reactions are assumed to be carried out with β,γ-P³² ribosidetriphosphates.   The symbols and conventions employed are the same as described in Fig. 1 and the text.

faithful copies; (2) a reliable method for the clean separation of the reaction products; (3) the synthesis of β,γ-P^{32}-labeled ribosidetriphosphate of very high levels of specific activity; (4) the inclusion of another isotopic label to monitor the extent of synthesis.

All requisites were realized and the outcome was satisfyingly clear-cut. The data revealed convincingly that the mechanism of the Qβ-replicase reaction (diagrammed in Fig. 3) involves polymerization of the negative in a 5' to 3' direction followed by a reversal of polarity which initiates synthesis of new positive strands from the 3' to the 5' terminus. It will be of no little interest to see whether the abbreviated variants of Qβ-RNA recently isolated[21] in a Darwinian selection experiment also use the same mechanism.

The indentification of GTP as the 5'-terminus of Qβ-RNA synthesized by Qβ-replicase is in agreement with the conclusions of Bannerjee *et al.*[22] Our results, in addition, establish that the negative strand also possesses GTP as the 5' end. The specification of cytosine as the 3' terminus of both strands follows immediately from the directions of the complementary copying. The fact that C is the first residue recognized may be related to the poly C-dependent poly G polymerase activity found[23, 24] in Qβ-replicase and shown[24] to be a property of one of the two components into which Qβ-replicase can be dissociated.

The reversal of polarity in the replicase reaction leads to the following predictions: (1) As indicated in the FS structure of Figure 3, the initiation of new positives should be possible *before negatives are completed:* (2) The base composition of early incomplete negative strands should complement that of the 3' end of Qβ-RNA. (3) Early FS should have short positive strands possessing a base composition similar to the 3' end of Qβ-RNA. *These predictions have been confirmed, and the experiments will be detailed elsewhere.*[13, 14]

As may be seen from Figure 3, the novel 3' to 5' polymerization of the positive strands has another interesting geometrical implication worthy of explicit note. The reversal of *chemical polarity* permits *positive and negative* strands to grow *simultaneously* in the *same sidereal* direction. This is precisely the feature implied by the single growth point for the two antiparallel complements of DNA. This apparent paradox may thus have the same explanation.

We have already noted in the introduction how one and the same monomer (a 5'-ribosidetriphosphate) can participate in polymerization of opposite chemical polarities. In the same sense, a single enzyme can also mediate both reactions. One need merely place the 3'-OH and 5'-PP recognition sites on opposite sides of an axis of symmetry; rotation of the enzyme molecule around this axis will automatically reverse the polarity of its catalytic function.

It seems likely that the facts and principles emerging from the study of RNA synthesis by Qβ-replicase will ultimately help illuminate the problem of DNA duplication.

Summary.—Experiments are described which analyzed the progress of RNA replication in reactions containing individual β,γ-P^{32} ribosidetriphosphates, permitting the identification of 5'-termini. The data obtained lead to the following conclusions: (1) The 5'-termini of Qβ-RNA and its complement consist of GTP. (2) The 3' terminus of both is cytosine. (3) Synthesis begins with a 5' to 3' polymerization of the negative complementary strand. (4) The chemical polarity is then reversed leading to a novel 3′ to 5′ polymerization of new plus strands.

The discovery of the 3′ to 5′ polymerization reported here explains how two antiparallel strands can grow simultaneously in the same sidereal direction. The data obtained provide a basis for a chemical understanding of the RNA replicating mechanism.

* This investigation was supported by U.S. Public Health Service research grant no. CA-01094 from the National Cancer Institute and grant no. GB-4876 from the National Science Foundation.

† D. H. L. Bishop holds a Wellcome Travel Scholarship.

‡ Postdoctoral fellow in Microbial and Molecular Genetics, U.S. Public Health training grant no. 5-T01-GM00-319.

[1] Spiegelman, S., I. Haruna, I. B. Holland, G. Beaudreau, and D. Mills, these PROCEEDINGS, **54**, 919 (1965).

[2] Pace, N. R., and S. Spiegelman, *Science*, **153**, 64 (1966).

[3] Pace, N. R., and S. Spiegelman, these PROCEEDINGS, **55**, 1608 (1966).

[4] Haruna, I., and S. Spiegelman, these PROCEEDINGS, **54**, 579 (1965).

[5] Mills, D. R., N. R. Pace, and S. Spiegelman, these PROCEEDINGS, **56**, 1778 (1966).

[6] Loening, U. E., *Biochem. J.*, **102**, 251 (1967).

[7] Bishop, D. H. L., J. R. Claybrook, and S. Spiegelman, *J. Mol. Biol.*, **26**, 373 (1967).

[8] Pace, N. R., D. H. L. Bishop, and S. Spiegelman, *J. Virol.*, **1**, 771 (1967).

[9] Bishop, D. H. L., J. R. Claybrook, N. R. Pace, and S. Spiegelman, these PROCEEDINGS, **57**, 1474 (1967).

[10] Pace, N. R., D. H. L. Bishop, and S. Spiegelman, these PROCEEDINGS, **58**, 711 (1967).

[11] Francke, B., and P. H. Hofschneider, *J. Mol. Biol.*, **16**, 544 (1966).

[12] Franklin, R. M., these PROCEEDINGS, **55**, 1504 (1966).

[13] Claybrook, J. R., D. H. L. Bishop, N. R. Pace, and S. Spiegelman, in preparation.

[14] Bishop, D. H. L., N. R. Pace, and S. Spiegelman, in preparation.

[15] Bonhoeffer, F., and A. Gierer, *J. Mol. Biol.*, **7**, 534 (1963).

[16] Cairns, J., *J. Mol. Biol.*, **6**, 208 (1963).

[17] Haruna, I., K. Nozu, Y. Ohtaka, and S. Spiegelman, these PROCEEDINGS, **50**, 905 (1963).

[18] Overby, L. R., G. H. Barlow, R. H. Doi, Monique Jacob, and S. Spiegelman, *J. Bacteriol.*, **92**, 739 (1966).

[19] Wehrli, W. E., D. L. M. Verheyden, and J. G. Moffatt, *J. Am. Chem. Soc.*, **87**, 2265 (1965).

[20] Haruna, I., and S. Spiegelman, these PROCEEDINGS, **55**, 1256 (1966).

[21] Mills, D. R., R. L. Peterson, and S. Spiegelman, these PROCEEDINGS, **58**, 217 (1967).

[22] Banerjee, A. K., L. Eoyang, K. Hori, and J. T. August, these PROCEEDINGS, **57**, 986 (1967).

[23] Hori, K., L. Eoyang, A. K. Banerjee, and J. T. August, these PROCEEDINGS, **57**, 1790 (1967).

[24] Eikhom, T. S., and S. Spiegelman, these PROCEEDINGS, **57**, 1833 (1967).

In Vitro Synthesis of an Infectious Mutant RNA with a Normal RNA Replicase

N. R. PACE AND S. SPIEGELMAN

Abstract. *When purified Qβ-RNA replicase is presented alternately with two genetically different Qβ-RNA molecules, the RNA synthesized is identical to the initiating template. The results establish that the RNA is the instructive agent in the replicative process and hence that it satisfies the operational definition of a self-duplicating entity. The data also eliminate alternative explanations which do not involve self-propagation of the input RNA. An opportunity is now provided for studying the genetics and evolution of a self-duplicating nucleic acid molecule under conditions permitting detailed control of environmental parameters and chemical components.*

Previous experiments with two serologically distinct (1, 2) RNA coliphages (MS-2 and Qβ) established (3, 4) that each induces in *Escherichia coli* a replicase (RNA replicating enzyme) which exhibits a unique requirement for intact (5) homologous RNA as a template. Further studies with purified Qβ replicase showed that the RNA synthesized is physically (6) and chemically (7) indistinguishable from the strands found in the Qβ virus.

The ability of the synthetic RNA to program the synthesis of complete virus particles was examined by protoplast infection in the course of a serial transfer (8). In these experiments, the products of a reaction initiated with Qβ-RNA was serially diluted to prime successive reactions until the original RNA was reduced to less than one strand per reaction mixture. The final tube contained new radioactive RNA which, when assayed in a bacterial protoplast system (9, 10), displayed the same ability to generate virus particles as the viral RNA used to start the reaction in the first tube. These experiments indicated that the synthesis of a self-propagating and infectious entity had been achieved in a simple system of known components.

The significance and potential usefulness of the finding encouraged further efforts at purifying the enzyme. A procedure for more extensive purification was developed (11) involving equilibrium banding in CsCl followed by zonal centrifugation in linear gradients of sucrose. Here, advantage was taken of expected disparities in size and density between the replicase protein and unwanted impurities. The resulting preparation was effectively free of residual virus particles, permitting direct assay for infectivity and thereby obviating the laborious purification of the RNA product required in the earlier (8) study. The concomitant removal of polynucleotide contaminants did not decrease, qualitatively or quantitatively, the ability of the replicase to respond to added Qβ-RNA by synthesizing infectious copies. This latter finding makes even more implausible arguments which would explain the increase in infectious units in terms of an "activation" of RNA preexistent in the enzyme by an unknown reaction which requires both added template and new RNA synthesis.

We now come to the central issue of the present communication which stems from the fact that two informed components are present in the reaction mixture, replicase and RNA template. None of the experiments thus far described proved that the RNA synthesized in this system is, in fact, a self-duplicating entity—that is, one which contains the requisite information and directs its own synthesis. What is required is a rigorous demonstration that the RNA, and not the replicase, is the instructive agent in the replicative process. A definitive decision would be provided by an experimental answer to the following question: if the replicase is provided alternatively with two distinguishable RNA molecules, is the product produced always identical with the initiating template?

A positive outcome would establish that the RNA is directing its own synthesis and simultaneously completely eliminate any remaining possibility of "activation" of preexisting RNA.

Our data establish that the RN[A] synthesized is a self-duplicating entit[y]. The discriminating selectivity of th[e] replicase for its own genome as templa[te] makes it impossible to employ heterologous RNA in the test experiments a[nd] recourse was, therefore, had to mutant[s]. For ease in isolation and simplicity [of] distinguishing between mutant and wil[d] type, temperature sensitive (ts) m[u]tants were chosen. Their diagnost[ic] phenotype is poor growth at 41°C compared with that at 34°C. The wi[ld] type grows equally well at both te[m]peratures.

Temperature-sensitive mutants of [Qβ] were isolated by a modification of t[he] method described by Davern (12[).] *Escherichia coli* K-38 (13) was grow[n] in a rotary shaker at 34°C in modifi[ed] 3XD medium (14) to an optical densi[ty] (660 mμ) of 0.15. Qβ bacteriopha[ge] was added to a multiplicity of 5, a[nd] the suspension was mixed and allow[ed] to stand for adsorption of virus at 34[°] for 5 minutes. Shaking was reinstitut[ed] for 10 minutes, whereupon 20 μg [of] fluorouracil was added per millilter [of] culture, and the incubation was co[n]tinued for 2 hours. The resulting lys[ate] was cleared by low-speed centrifugati[on] and plated for plaques arising at 34[°.] Isolated plaques were stabbed with [a] needle and suspended in 1 ml of wat[er.] A small loopful of the suspension w[as] transferred to each of two plates seed[ed] with *E. coli* K-38, and respective pla[tes] were incubated at 34° or 41°C. Plaq[ues] arising only at 34°C were picked [for] further testing, and those which [re]tained the ts phenotype were chos[en.] Mutant virus particles isolated in t[his] manner are quite stable to passage a[t]

Table 2. Efficiency of infection of pro[to]plasts by three RNA preparations. Infecti[ous] RNA assays were carried out on Qβ R[NA,] synthetic Qβ RNA and ts RNA. Duplic[ate] pairs were incubated at 34° and 41[°.] Efficiencies at 34° are defined as 100. [The] synthetic Qβ-RNA was the result of a [...]fold synthesis carried out by Qβ replic[ase] purified through CsCl and sucrose centrif[uga]tion; 0.1 μg of Qβ RNA was used to init[iate] the standard reaction.

	34°C	41°C
	Natural Qβ-RNA	
REOP	100	93
PFU	4.56×10^5/ml	4.24×10^6/[ml]
	Synthetic Qβ-RNA	
REOP	100	92
PFU	2.90×10^6/ml	2.66×10^6/[ml]
	Natural ts-Qβ-RNA	
REOP	100	1.5
PFU	1.86×10^6/ml	2.75×10^4/[ml]

Table 1. Relative efficiency of plating at 34° and 41°C. Dilutions were plated with *E. coli* K-38 as the indicator organism, and duplicate plating series were incubated at 34° and 41°C. The relative efficiency of plating (REOP) of 100 is defined relative to the plaque forming units (PFU) observed at 34°C.

	34°C	41°C
	Virus Qβ	
REOP	100	100
PFU	1.14×10^{13}/ml	1.16×10^{13}/ml
	Virus ts Qβ	
REOP	100	2.5×10^{-2}
PFU	4.4×10^7/ml	1.1×10^4/ml

ossess low efficiencies of plating at
1°C (Table 1). To provide a supply
f mutant RNA, large lysates were pre-
ared from plaque inocula of the ts-Qβ
nd RNA was isolated from the virus
s previously described (5).

The ts phenotype is easily recognized
y parallel platings of intact virus par-
icles at 34° and 41°C on receptor cells
Table 1). It remained, however, to be
een whether this difference would be
etained when the corresponding puri-
ed mutant RNA preparations were
ssayed for infectivity in the protoplast
ystem. This check is particularly neces-
ary since one of the steps requires a
0-minute incubation of the infected
rotoplasts at 35°C. During this inter-
al, "revertants" could be produced and
ontribute to the background of plaques
eveloping at 41°C. In addition, it was
ecessary to establish that the synthetic
roduct of the replicase, primed by a
ormal Qβ-RNA, behaves like the nat-
ral viral RNA in its behavior at 41°C
Table 2). It is evident that the syn-
netic wild type Qβ-RNA behaves ex-
ctly like its natural counterpart at the
vo temperatures. On the other hand,
ie ts-Qβ-RNA again shows the lower
ficiency at 41°C, although it will be
oted that the background at 41°C is
igher than in the intact cell assay
Table 1), as expected. The 65-fold
ifference at the two temperatures is,
owever, more than adequate for a
ear diagnosis.

It is evident that the system available
ill permit us to determine whether the
roduct produced by a normal replicase
rimed with ts-Qβ-RNA is mutant or
ild type. As in previous investigations,
iis is best done by a serial transfer
xperiment to avoid the ambiguity of
xamining reactions containing signifi-
int quantities of the initiating RNA.
ccordingly, seven standard reaction
iixtures (0.25 ml) were prepared, each
ontaining 60 μg of Qβ replicase iso-
ted from cells infected with normal
rus and purified through the CsCl
anding sucrose sedimentation steps (9).
o the first reaction mixture was added
2 μg of RNA, and synthesis was al-
wed to proceed at 35°C. After a
iitable interval, one-tenth of this re-
tion mixture was used to initiate a
cond reaction which, in turn, was
luted into a third reaction mixture,
d so on for seven transfers. A control
ries was carried out in a manner iden-
al to that just described, save that
RNA was added to the first tube.

Portions from each reaction mixture

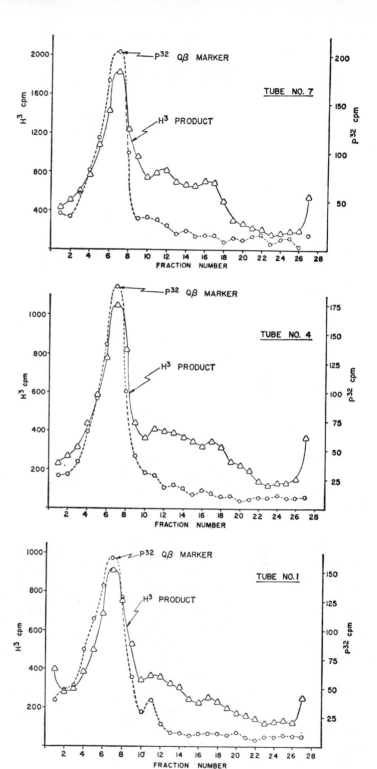

Fig. 1. Sedimentation analysis of products. A portion (0.04 ml) from reaction mixtures 1, 4, and 7 (see Table 3) were each mixed with 0.01 ml of P^{32}-Qβ-RNA, 0.01 ml 20 percent sodium dodecyl sulphate, and 0.20 ml TM (tris magnesium solution), and layered onto linear gradients of 2.5 to 15 percent sucrose in a solution of 0.01M tris, pH 7.4; 0.005M $MgCl_2$; and 0.1M NaCl. Gradients were centrifuged at 10°C for 14 hours in the Spinco SW-25 rotor. Fractions were collected and analyzed for radio-activity (count/min) as described previously (6).

243

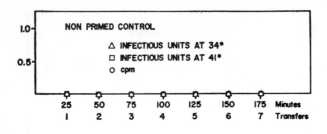

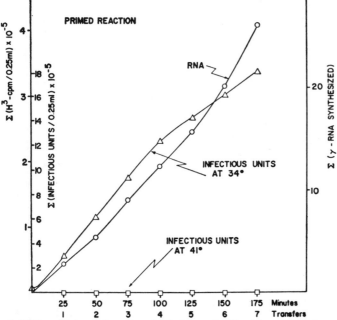

Fig. 2. RNA synthesis and formation of infectious units. The data are from the serial transfer experiment of Table 3.

were examined for radioactivity in material precipitable by trichloroacetic acid (TCA) and assayed for infectious RNA at 34° and 41°C. In addition, samples from reactions 1, 4, and 7 were examined for physical similarity to the input RNA by sedimentation through sucrose gradients. As shown in Fig. 1, the bulk of material synthesized is similar in sedimentation characteristics to ts-$Q\beta$-RNA derived from virus particles.

Table 3 is a record of such a serial transfer experiment. If we first focus attention of the RNA formation in the experimental series (columns 3 to 6), it is evident that ts-$Q\beta$-RNA serves as an excellent initiator for the normal replicase. Included also is the radioactivity (count/min) observed in the nonprimed control series (columns 7 and 8). No detectable synthesis occurs in the first three tubes although a few counts accumulate near the end which are, however, negligible from the point of view of the chemical amounts of RNA synthesized. Though quantitatively insignificant, this "long-term background" is persistently observed with some enzyme preparations.

Columns 9 and 10 of Table 3 give the actual number of plaques counted in the assay for infectious units at each transfer, the numbers representing the average of two duplicate plates. Comparisons of columns 9 and 10 reveal that the relative number of plaque formers at the two temperatures agree with those obtained with the original ts-$Q\beta$

Table 3. *Transfer Experiment with ts-Qβ-RNA*. Each 0.25 ml of standard reaction mixture (4) contained 60 μg of $Q\beta$ replicase purified through CsCl and sucrose centrifugation, and H³-CTP (cytidine triphosphate) at a specific activity such that 15,600 count/min signified 1 μg of synthesized RNA. The first reaction was initiated by addition of 0.2 μg of temperature sensitive infectious RNA. Each reaction was carried out at 35°C for 25 minutes, whereupon 0.02 ml was drawn for counting, and 0.025 ml was used to prime the next reaction. All samples were stored frozen at −70°C until infectivity assays were carried out. Dilutions for infectious RNA assays were made into solution of 0.01M tris, pH 7.4, and 0.005M MgCl$_2$, and used immediately. Columns 1 and 2 give the reaction number and total time elapsed during the experiment. Column 3 lists acid-precipitable radioactivity (count/min) found in each 0.25 ml reaction mixture and column 4 lists the corresponding sum. Similarly, columns 5 and 6 list the RNA formation during each reaction and their cumulative amounts. Columns 7 and 8 present radioactivity incorporated in the control transfer without added RNA. Columns 9 and 10 are the averages of plaques observed on duplicate plates in the assays for infectious RNA, on plates incubated at 34° and 41°C. In all cases, reaction products were diluted 1.6 × 10⁻³ during the course of the assay. Column 11 presents the actual number of infectious units appearing in each reaction tube and column 12 is the sum of infectious units appearing at 34°C.

		Formation of RNA						Formation of infectious units			
		With RNA				Without RNA		With RNA			
Transfer No.	Time (Min)	(count/min × 10⁻⁵) Radioactivity		Amt RNA		Radioactivity (count/min × 10⁻⁵)		PFU observed		Infectious units × 10⁻ at 34°C	
		Each	Sum	Each (μg)	Sum (μg)	Each	Sum	34°C	41°C	Each	Sum
1	2	3	4	5	6	7	8	9	10	11	12
1	25	0.446	0.446	2.86	2.86	0	0	487	9	3.04	3.04
2	50	.418	.864	2.68	5.54	0	0	486	10	3.04	6.08
3	75	.560	1.424	3.59	9.13	0	0	500	12	3.12	9.20
4	100	.508	1.932	3.26	12.39	0.002	0.002	464	4	2.90	12.10
5	125	.527	2.459	3.38	15.77	.012	.014	299	6	1.87	13.97
6	150	.685	3.149	4.39	20.16	.0007	.014	295	5	1.85	15.82
7	175	.927	4.071	5.94	26.10	.004	.018	289	2	1.81	17.63

RNA (Table 2) in the protoplast assay. The proportions of plaques seen at 41°C (Table 3, column 10) is not significantly different from the expected 1 to 2 percent of the numbers developing at 34°C. Thus the ts phenotype of the initiating ts-$Q\beta$ is faithfully inherited. Column 11 gives the number of ts-infectious units per reaction mixture calculated from the dilution used; column 12 lists the corresponding cumulative sums. No evidence of the synthesis of infectious RNA which could produce plaques at either 34° or 41° C appeared in the control nonprimed reaction. The corresponding negative columns are therefore omitted from Table 3.

The average infective efficiency of the RNA in the protoplast assay is 2×10^{-7}. The initial input in tube 1 was 0.2 μg corresponding to 1.2×10^{11} strands and 2.4×10^4 plaque forming units. Since each transfer involves a 1 to 10 dilution, it is clear that less than one of the 1.87×10^5 plaque formers observed in the 5th tube can be ascribed to the initiating ts-$Q\beta$-RNA. Finally, by tube 7 which contains 3.6 $\times 10^{12}$ new strands, the number of plaque formers (1.8×10^5) exceeds in absolute terms the number (1.2×10^4) of old strands present. It is clear that the serial dilution experiment has demonstrated the appearance of newly synthesized infectious RNA possessing the temperature-sensitive phenotype.

In the lower portion of Fig. 2 the outcome of the experiment shown in Table 3 is summarized by plotting against time the cumulative sums of the RNA synthesized (column 6) and plaque formers at 34°C (column 12). The fact that the plaque formers at 41°C are not statistically above the background of the assay of ts-$Q\beta$-RNA means that no detectable wild type $Q\beta$-RNA has been produced, a fact indicated by the open squares. For comparison the control reaction of Table 3, in which the initiating RNA was omitted, is similarly plotted on the same scale in the upper part of Fig. 2. No significant synthesis of either RNA or infectious units were observed.

It is apparent from the experiments described that one and the same normal replicase can produce distinguishably different but genetically related RNA molecules. The genetic type produced is completely determined by the RNA used to start the reaction and is always identical to it. The following two conclusions would appear to be inescapable from these findings; (i) the RNA is the instructive agent in the replicating process and therefore satisfies the operational definition of a self-duplicating entity; (ii) it is not some cryptic contaminant of the enzyme but rather the input RNA which multiplies.

The experiments described generate an opportunity for studying the genetics and evolution of a self-replicating nucleic acid molecule in a simple and chemically controllable medium. Of particular interest is the fact that such studies can be carried out under conditions in which the only demand made on the molecules is that they multiply; they can be liberated from all secondary requirements (for example, coding for coat protein, and so forth) which serve only the needs and purposes of the complete organism.

N. R. Pace
S. Spiegelman

Department of Microbiology,
University of Illinois, Urbana

References and Notes

1. I. Watanabe, *Nihon Rinsho* **22**, 243 (1964).
2. L. R. Overby, G. H. Barlow, R. H. Doi, M. Jacob, S. Spiegelman, *J. Bacteriol.* **91**, 442 (1966).
3. I. Haruna, K. Nozu, Y. Ohtaka, S. Spiegelman, *Proc. Nat. Acad. Sci. U.S.* **50**, 905 (1963).
4. I. Haruna and S. Spiegelman, *ibid.* **54**, 579 (1965).
5. ———, *ibid.*, p. 1189.
6. ———, *Science* **150**, 884 (1965).
7. ———, *Proc. Nat. Acad. Sci. U.S.*, in press (1966).
8. S. Spiegelman, I. Haruna, I. B. Holland, G. Beaudreau, D. Mills, *ibid.* **54**, 919 (1965).
9. G. D. Guthrie and R. L. Sinsheimer, *Biochem. Biophys. Acta* **72**, 290 (1963).
10. J. A. Strauss, Jr., *J. Mol. Biol.* **10**, 422 (1963).
11. N. Pace and S. Spiegelman, *Proc. Nat. Acad. Sci. U.S.* (in press).
12. C. I. Davern, *Australian J. Biol. Sci.* **17**, 726 (1964).
13. Supplied by N. Zinder, Rockefeller Institute.
14. D. Fraser and E. A. Jerrel, *J. Biol. Chem.* **205**, 291 (1953).
15. Supported by PHS research grant No. CA-01094 and research grant No. GB-2169 from NSF. N.R.P. is a predoctoral trainee in microbial and molecular genetics (grant no. USPH 5-T1-GM-319).

25 April 1966

J. Mol. Biol. (1966) **21**, 207–209

Semi-conservative Replication of Bacteriophage f2 RNA

H. F. Lodish and N. D. Zinder

The replication of the RNA genome of bacteriophage f2 (Zinder, 1965) proceeds in two steps (Lodish & Zinder, 1966a,b). In the first, parental RNA is template for synthesis of the complementary (minus) RNA strand. These two molecules are combined in a completely double-stranded structure (replicative form; Erikson & Franklin, 1966). In the second step, the minus strand of the duplex is template for synthesis of virus (plus) strands. Some of the newly synthesized plus strands become, by synthesis of complementary RNA molecules (first step), re-incorporated into a duplex structure, forming additional template for the second step. Our analysis of these processes has been facilitated by the use of f2 temperature-sensitive mutant, ts-6. At 43°C, ts-6 parental RNA is not incorporated into a double-stranded structure. When ts-6-infected cells growing at 34°C are transferred to 43°C, synthesis of minus strands (first step) is halted, but production of plus strands (second step) continues normally for some time (Lodish & Zinder, 1966a).

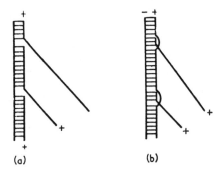

(a)   (b)

Fig. 1. Model for synthesis of virus plus strands. (a) Semi-conservative; (b) conservative. Both models are consistent with known facts about plus-strand production: Nascent plus strands are initially found in double-stranded form, presumably bound to the minus-strand template. As synthesis proceeds, they become free single strands. The RNA structure involved in plus-strand synthesis (replicative intermediate; Erikson & Franklin, 1966) is comprised of a double-stranded core to which is attached parts of one or more viral plus strands (Fenwick, Erikson & Franklin, 1964; Erikson, Fenwick & Franklin, 1965; Lodish & Zinder, 1966a; Billeter, Libonati, Vinuela & Weissmann, 1966).

The mechanism of plus-strand synthesis (second step) forms the subject of this note. Two models for this process have been proposed: a semi-conservative replication (Fig. 1(a)); and a conservative mechanism (Fig. 1(b)) (Weissmann, Borst, Burdon, Billeter & Ochoa, 1964; Erikson & Franklin, 1966). We can differentiate these models by following the fate of parental RNA after it has been incorporated into a duplex structure. The conservative model predicts that the parental RNA should remain in the double-stranded structure, when new plus strands are synthesized, while the semi-conservative mechanism postulates their displacement. The results obtained with wild-type f2 phage, namely, a slow and incomplete loss of parental label from the double-stranded form (Weissmann *et al.*, 1964) are not clear; possibly any displaced

RNA may be re-incorporated into a duplex structure. The predictions of the two models can be tested with mutant ts-6, because synthesis of plus strands occurs in the absence of minus-strand synthesis.

In the experiment recorded in Fig. 2, cells are infected with ^{32}P-labeled ts-6 and incubated for twelve minutes at 34°C, allowing maximum formation of ^{32}P-labeled double-stranded RNA. Within one minute after the cells are transferred to 43°C, more than 50% of the parental label is displaced from the double strand. No parental-labeled double-stranded RNA remains nine minutes after the temperature shift. Under conditions where minus- but not plus-strand synthesis is blocked, parental RNA molecules are displaced from a duplex structure and are no longer re-incorporated into double strands.

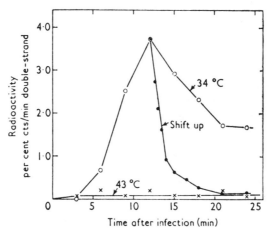

FIG. 2. Fate of ts-6 parental phage RNA. *Escherichia coli* strain K37 was grown in Tryptone broth to a density of 2×10^8/ml. 5 min before infection by ^{32}P-labeled ts-6 phage, the cells were placed at the indicated temperature. At 12 min after infection a portion of the 34°C culture was added to an equal volume of warmed broth at 43°C. RNA was isolated and the percentage ribonuclease-resistant activity determined (Lodish & Zinder, 1966a). At zero minute, 0·30% of the RNA was acid-precipitable after ribonuclease digestion, and this background has been subtracted. In a control experiment, the fate of ^{32}P-labeled wild-type f2 RNA after infection at both 34°C and 43°C was essentially identical to that of ts-6 RNA at 34°C.

The mechanism of plus-strand synthesis (second step) appears to be semi-conservative; as a new plus strand is made, it displaces the previously synthesized plus strand from a hydrogen-bonded (ribonuclease-resistant) interaction with the minus strand of the template (Fig. 1(a)).

Also consistent with our results is a modification of the semi-conservative model: some of the newly formed plus strands displace their counterparts from the duplex and some do not (cf. Chamberlin & Berg, 1964; Sinsheimer & Lawrence, 1964). It should be noted that the half-time of displacement of labeled parental RNA from a double strand (one minute, Fig. 2) is the same as that for newly made plus strands (Lodish & Zinder, 1966a; Billeter, Libonati, Vinuela & Weissmann, 1966). This means that, if the modified semi-conservative mechanism is correct, the probability of displacement of parental RNA from the duplex during the synthesis of each new plus strand must be approximately 50%. During infection by wild-type phage, or by ts-6 at 34°C (Fig. 2), parental RNA, after being displaced from a duplex, is again incorporated, by synthesis of a minus strand, into a double strand, and normally passes through several such cycles.

Given a semi-conservative mechanism for replication, it is apparent that the failure to find parental RNA in progeny phage particles (Davis & Sinsheimer, 1963; Doi & Spiegelman, 1963) needs explanation.

This work was supported by a grant from the National Science Foundation.

The Rockefeller University   HARVEY F. LODISH[†]
New York, New York, U.S.A.   NORTON D. ZINDER
Received 30 June 1966

REFERENCES

Billeter, M., Libonati, M., Vinuela, E. & Weissmann, C. (1966). *J. Biol. Chem.* in the press.
Chamberlin, M. & Berg, P. (1964). *J. Mol. Biol.* **8**, 297.
Davis, J. E. & Sinsheimer, R. L. (1963). *J. Mol. Biol.* **6**, 203.
Doi, R. H. & Spiegelman, S. (1963). *Proc. Nat. Acad. Sci., Wash.* **49**, 353.
Erikson, R. L., Fenwick, M. L. & Franklin, R. M. (1965). *J. Mol. Biol.* **13**, 399.
Erikson, R. L. & Franklin, R. M. (1966). *Bacteriol. Revs.* **30**, 267.
Fenwick, M. L., Erikson, R. L. & Franklin, R. M. (1964). *Science*, **146**, 527.
Lodish, H. F. & Zinder, N. D. (1966a). *Science*, **152**, 372.
Lodish, H. F. & Zinder, N. D. (1966b). *J. Mol. Biol.* **19**, 333.
Sinsheimer, R. L. & Lawrence, M. (1964). *J. Mol. Biol.* **8**, 289.
Weissmann, C., Borst, P., Burdon, R. H., Billeter, M. A. & Ochoa, S. (1964). *Proc. Nat. Acad. Sci., Wash.* **51**, 682.
Zinder, N. D. (1965). *Ann. Revs Microbiol.* **19**, 455.

† Present address: Medical Research Council Laboratory of Molecular Biology, Hills Road, Cambridge, England.

VI
Protein Synthesis

Introduction

An intricate biochemical machinery exists for the ordering and polymerization of amino acids into polypeptide chains. The requirements for protein synthesis include about 60 transfer RNA molecules, at least 20 activating enzymes which attach the amino acids to the tRNAs, special enzymes for initiation, propagation and termination of peptide synthesis, ribosomes containing three different structural RNAs and as many as 50 different structural proteins, messenger RNA, ATP, GTP and Mg^{+2}. A great deal of understanding of this process has been gained in the surprisingly short time of about ten years as the result of an enormous research effort. Much of the early work pinpointing the importance of ribonucleoprotein particles as the site of peptide synthesis and soluble ribonucleic as the agent that transports the amino acid to the ribosome, was done in Zamecnik's laboratory. This work is discussed in a paper by Hoagland et al. (in collection); the results are particularly convincing because wherever possible the cell-free studies are carried out in parallel with studies on intact cells. The development of a cell-free system for the study of protein synthesis was most important because only in the cell-free system is there the possibility that all the steps of protein synthesis can be studied and controlled. It remained for others to improve the synthetic efficiencies of such systems and to characterize the components in greater detail. Crick provided the theoretical framework for understanding the template process.[276] His adapter hypothesis states that amino acids are linked to specific adapter-RNA molecules; these become transferred to the ribosome where the adapter RNAs are joined by hydrogen bonds to complementary sites on an RNA template. Amino acids placed in the proper order are then linked together by peptide synthesis. Crick originally thought of the adapter as a trinucleotide containing only the anticodon for adsorption to the template; in fact, the transfer RNAs which serve this adapt-

er function are considerably larger, containing in addition to the anticodon region about 80 nucleotides in a single polynucleotide chain with a complex secondary and tertiary structure. There are one or more tRNAs for each of the 20 amino acids commonly found in proteins. From the primary sequence, folded model structures of tRNAs with a maximum number of Watson–Crick hydrogen-bonded base pairs have been built. For each tRNA it has been possible to build two model structures, one with a single loop and one with three loops (with approximately the same number of hydrogen bonds). These two possibilities are discussed in detail in the paper by Zachau et al. (in collection). Both of these structures contain an anticodon loop with the three anticodon bases exposed so that they can hydrogen bond to a complementary site on a single-stranded messenger RNA template. On the basis of the enzymatic degradation evidence the multilooped structure is favored by Zachau et al. However, there is evidence that one and the same tRNA may be found in two configurations[290] and it is possible that both configurations serve a special purpose at different stages in protein synthesis.

An exact three-dimensional configuration of the anticodon loop of tRNA and its manner of interaction with the messenger RNA template has been proposed by Fuller and Hodgson (in collection). In their model the anticodon region has the same configuration as three bases in the single strand of a double helix. Two bases on either side of the anticodon are left unpaired. It is shown that two adjacently oriented tRNAs can bind to a hexanucleotide segment of a single-stranded polynucleotide of messenger forming a double helix-like structure. The structure proposed by Fuller and Hodgson provides an explanation for the four unpaired bases invariably surrounding the anticodon loop. This correlates with the fact that the known sequences in this region would not permit these bases to form intramolecular Watson–Crick pairs. The flexibility in positioning the third base in the anticodon in the Fuller–Hodgson model suggests the possibility of ambiguous pairing of the third base in agreement with coding data

251

and Crick's Wobble Hypothesis (in collection). The Wobble Hypothesis was derived from the consideration of a large body of data on coding which indicates that one and the same tRNA can bind to different codons where the difference is in the third nucleotide of the anticodon.

Zamecnik's laboratory had established that peptide linkages are formed on cytoplasmic ribonucleoprotein particles. In the early work there was no way of distinguishing between template and ribosome. Nirenberg and Matthaei (in collection) demonstrated the separability of the ribosome and the messenger template; they showed that both natural and synthetic polyribonucleotides could be added to an *in vitro* system in such a way as to become adsorbed to the ribosome to direct peptide bond formation. In particular it was shown that polyridylic acid was a good messenger for polyphenylalanine; this result also represented a beginning to the solution of the coding problem. In the following three years, the laboratories of Ochoa and Nirenberg made some progress on the coding problem by determining the stimulatory effect of various synthetic heteropolynucleotide messengers on amino acid incorporation. This work established a correlation between the amino acids incorporated into peptide linkage and the base composition of the added messenger. The great weakness of the approach was that it was not possible to control the sequence of bases in the messenger. As a consequence only rough correlations were possible. The next major advance in decoding came again from Nirenberg's laboratory (Nirenberg and Leder, in collection), where it was discovered that particular trinucleotides when added to the ribosome stimulated the binding of particular aa-tRNAs to the ribosome. This was due to the affinity between codon and anticodon; and by studying the binding of aa-tRNAs stimulated by all 64 possible trinucleotides most codon assignments have been made. These results are described in a more recent paper from the Nirenberg laboratory (Nirenberg *et al.*, in collection).

Whereas the structure of tRNA and the solution to the coding problem have been amongst the most spectacular achievements in the study of protein synthesis, a number of other important findings relating to protein biosynthesis have been obtained since the pioneering efforts of the Zamecnik laboratory. Dintzis (in collection) in an *in vitro* study using a pulse labeling technique was able to show that protein synthesis begins with the N-terminal amino acid and proceeds uniformly to the C-terminal amino acid. Smith *et al.* (in collection) have shown that the translation of messenger RNA begins from the 5′-OH terminal nucleotide. It should be remembered that RNA synthesis also starts from this end. This means that protein synthesis could begin before messenger RNA synthesis finished. In bacteria, where there is no clearcut separation between nucleus and cytoplasm, the same theory has received experimental support.[356] Others have gone further and suggested that RNA and protein synthesis are strongly coupled so that one process cannot take place without the other. Evidence on coupling will be considered in Section VIII.

Messengers are often polycistronic and there must be signals to start and stop peptide synthesis in the middle of RNAs as well as at the ends. It appears that in *E. coli* the N-formylmethionyl-tRNA is always the first amino acid to be adsorbed to the messenger RNA template and that this triggers initiation. After synthesis the formyl group is invariably removed from the polypeptide chain *in vivo*. Sometimes methionine is removed (see Webster, Engelhardt and Zinder, in collection). Genetic and biochemical studies indicate that there are two or three different codons in messenger RNA which can trigger termination by some as yet unknown mechanism (see Last *et al.*, in collection).

The GTP requirement for peptide bond formation has baffled biochemists since its discovery in the Zamecnik laboratory. It now appears that GTP is required for both the initiation and propagation stages of translation even though the detailed mechanism of its action at the two stages is still unknown.[339, 342, 349, 376-378]

Ribosomes are large complex bodies consisting of RNA and protein. Extensive characterization of these molecules has been done but we are a long way from a complete understanding of their structure. *E. coli* ribosomes have been studied in the greatest detail; the 70S *E. coli* ribosome is a complex containing a 50S and a 30S subunit with molecular weights of 1.5×10^6 and 0.9×10^6 respectively. Each subunit contains about two-thirds by weight RNA and one-third by weight protein. The 50S subunit contains one 23S and one 5S RNA; the complete primary structure of the 5S RNA is known.[318] The 30S subunit contains a single 18S RNA. There are more than 20 different proteins on each of the subunits. The messenger RNA binding site is on the 30S subunit and two tRNA binding sites are located on the 50S subunit. It has been proposed that initiation of protein synthesis involves formation of a complex between the 30S ribosomal subunit, messenger RNA and the initiating N-formyl-methionyl tRNA followed by adsorption of a 50S subunit.[309, 310] A single messenger RNA often is being actively translated at more than one point along its length. This results in the appearance of polysomes (Warner, Knopf and Rich, in collection) which consist of a complex between one messenger RNA and two or more ribosomes engaged in protein synthesis.

Various drugs can bind to the ribosome and alter the reading of the messenger RNA. For example, the bacteriocidal action of streptomycin has been attributed to the misreading of messenger RNA produced by the binding of the drug to the 30S ribosomal subunit (Speyer, Lengyel and Basilio, in collection). Ribosomes from streptomycin-resistant bacteria have one of the 20 distinct proteins of the 30S ribosoma subunit altered.[296, 297] The gene site for streptomycin resistance is probably coincidental with the gene for this ribosomal protein. Drugs such as streptomycin or neomycin also permit single-stranded DNA to be translated.[331] It is likely that this effect is produced by interaction of the drug with DNA on the ribosome. It is not known if translation of single-stranded DNA is of any biological importance, but the possibility should not be overlooked, especially in the case of single-stranded DNA viruses.

Apart from the analysis of each step in the biochemistry of protein synthesis, it is important that the efficiency of *in vitro* systems be improved so that the synthesis of whole proteins can be studied. *De novo* synthesis of virus coat protein in a cell-free system stimulated by viral messenger has been rigorously demonstrated by Nathan *et al.* (in collection). Evidence for cell-free synthesis of other proteins also has been obtained.[394–403] In addition to protein synthesis resulting from the addition of messenger RNA, systems are being developed that start from the DNA going through the messenger pathway. Such systems are most important tools for the study of gene action and regulation, and they will be taken up in Section VIII.

Bibliography

tRNA

276. F. H. C. Crick, (1958). On Protein Synthesis. Symp. Soc. Exptl. Biol. **12**, 138.

277. F. Chapeville, F. Lipmann, G. von Ehrenstein, B. Weisblum, W. J. Ray and S. Benzer, (1962). On the Role of Soluble RNA in Coding for Amino Acids. Proc. Natl. Acad. Sci. U.S. **48**, 1086.

278. R. Marciello and G. Zubay, (1964). Quantitative Studies on the Rate of Reaction of Adapter RNA with Formaldehyde. Biochem. Biophys. Res. Comm. **14**, 272.

279. R. W. Holley, (1965). Structure of a Ribonucleic Acid. Science **147**, 1462.

280. B. Weisblum, F. Gonano, G. von Ehrenstein and S. Benzer, (1965). A Demonstration of Coding Degeneracy for Leucine in the Synthesis of Protein. Proc. Natl. Acad. Sci. U.S. **53**, 328.

281. T. P. Bennett, J. Goldstein and F. Lipmann, (1965). Coding and Charging Specificities of sRNAs Isolated by Counter–current Distribution. Proc. Natl. Acad. Sci. U.S. **53**, 385.

282. M. Matsuhashi, C. P. Dietrich and J. L. Strominger, (1965). Incorporation of Glycine into the Cell Wall Glycopeptide in Staphylococcus Aureus: Role of sRNA and Lipid Intermediates. Proc. Natl. Acad. Sci. U.S. **54**, 587.

283. M. Tomasz and W. Chambers, (1966). Chemistry of Pseudouridine VII. Selective Cleavage of Polynucleotides Containing Pseudouridylic Acid Residues by a Unique Photochemical Reaction. Biochem. **5**, 773.

284. M. Oishi, A. Oishi and N. Sueoka, (1966). Location of Genetic Loci of sRNA on the B. subtilis Chromosome. Proc. Natl. Acad. Sci. U.S. **55**, 1095.

285. M. Revel and U. Z. Littauer, (1966). The Coding Properties of Methyl-deficient Phenylalanine Transfer RNA from E. coli. J. Mol. Biol. **15**, 389.

286. B. Goehler, I. Kaneko and R. H. Doi, (1966). Regulation of a Serine Transfer RNA of B. subtilis. Biochem. Biophys. Res. Comm. **24**, 466.

287. Y. Kuriki and A. Kaji, (1967). Inability of sRNA Derived from Peptidyl sRNA to Accept Amino Acids. Biochem. Biophys. Res. Comm. **26**, 95.

288. R. M. Bock and F. C. Neidhardt, (1967). Genetic Mapping of Phenylalanyl-sRNA Synthetase in E. coli. Science **157**, 78.

289. M. Yarus and P. Berg, (1967). Recognition of tRNA by Aminoacyl tRNA Synthetases. J. Mol. Biol. **28**, 479.

290. T. Ishida and N. Sueoka, (1967). Rearrangement of the Secondary Structure of Tryptophan sRNA. Proc. Natl. Acad. Sci. U.S. **58**, 1080.

291. F. Cuzin, N. Kretchner, R. E. Greenberg, R. Hurwitz and F. Chapeville, (1967). Enzymatic Hydrolysis of N-Substituted Aminoacyl-tRNA. Proc. Natl. Acad. Sci. U.S. **58**, 2079.

RIBOSOMES

292. H. E. Huxley and G. Zubay, (1960). Electron Microscope Observations on the Structure of Microsomal Particles from E. coli. J. Mol. Biol. **2**, 10.

293. M. Cannon, R. Krug and W. Gilbert, (1963). Binding of S-RNA by E. coli Ribosomes. J. Mol. Biol. **7**, 360.

294. M. Takanami and T. Okamoto, (1963). Interaction of Ribosomes and Synthetic Polyribonucleotides. J. Mol. Biol. **7**, 323.

295. M. Takanami and G. Zubay, (1964). An Estimate of the Size of the Ribosomal Site for Messenger RNA Binding. Proc. Natl. Acad. Sci. U.S. **51**, 834.

296. E. C. Cox, J. R. White and J. G. Flaks, (1964). Streptomycin Action and the Ribosome. Proc. Natl. Acad. Sci. U.S. **51**, 703.

297. P. S. Leboy, E. C. Cox and J. G. Flaks, (1964). The Chromosomal Site Specifying a Ribosomal Protein in E. coli. Proc. Natl. Acad. Sci. U.S. **52**, 1367.

298. J. P. Waller, (1964). Fractionation of the Ribosomal Protein from E. coli. J. Mol. Biol. **10**, 319.

299. M. Oishi and N. Sueoka, (1965). Location of Genetic Loci of Ribosomal RNA on

Bacillus subtilis Chromosome. Proc. Natl. Acad. Sci. U.S. **54**, 483.

300. A. Goldberg, (1966). Mg^{++} Binding by *E. coli* Ribosomes. J. Mol. Biol. **15**, 663.

301. J. Wang and A. T. Matheson, (1966). Possible Role of Sulfhydryl Groups in the Dimerization of 70S Ribosomes from *E. coli.* Biochem. Biophys. Res. Comm. **23**, 740.

302. H. Kaji, I. Suzuka and A. Kaji, (1966). Binding of Specific Soluble RNA to Ribosomes. Binding of S-RNA to the Template 30S Subunit Complex. J. Biol. Chem. **241**, 1251.

303. T. Staehlin and M. Meselson, (1966). *In vitro* Recovery of Ribosomes and of Synthetic Activity from Synthetically Inactive Ribosomal Subunits. J. Mol. Biol. **16**, 245.

304. P. Traub, M. Nomura and L. Tu, (1966). Physical and Functional Heterogeneity of Ribosomal Proteins. J. Mol. Biol. **19**, 215.

305. K. Hosokawa, R. K. Fujimura and M. Nomura, (1966). Reconstitution of Functionally Active Ribosomes from Inactive Subparticles and Proteins. Proc. Natl. Acad. Sci. U.S. **55**, 198.

306. G. Blobel and V. R. Potter, (1967). Ribosomes in Rat Liver: An Estimate of the Percent of Free and Membrane-bound Ribosomes Interacting with Messenger RNA *in vivo*. J. Mol. Biol. **28**, 539.

307. H. J. Raskas and T. Staehlin, (1967). Messenger and sRNA Binding by Ribosomal Subunits and Reconstituted Ribosomes. J. Mol. Biol. **23**, 89.

308. A. Hirashima, K. Asano and A. Tsugita, (1967). A Cell-free Protein-Synthesizing System from *B. subtilis*. Biochem. Biophys. Acta **134**, 165.

309. D. Schlessinger, G. Mangiarotti and D. Apirion, (1967). Formation and Stabilization of 30S and 50S Ribosome Couples in *E. coli.* Proc. Natl. Acad. Sci. U.S. **58**, 1782.

310. G. Mangiarotti and D. Schlessinger, (1967). Polyribosome Metabolism in *E. coli* II. Formation and Lifetime of Messenger RNA Molecules, Ribosomal Subunit Couples and Polyribosomes. J. Mol. Biol. **29**, 395.

311. M. A. Vaughan, R. Soeiro, J. R. Warner and J. E. Darnell, (1967). Effects of Methionine Deprivation on Ribosome Synthesis in HeLa Cells. Proc. Natl. Acad. Sci. U.S. **58**, 1527.

312. M. Takanami, (1967). Nucleotide Sequences at the 5′-Termini of *E. coli* Ribosomal RNA. J. Mol. Biol. **29**, 323.

313. K. Igarashi and A. Kaji, (1967). On the Nature of Two Ribosomal Sites for Specific sRNA Binding. Proc. Natl. Acad. Sci. U.S. **58**, 1971.

314. H. Matthaei and M. Milberg, (1967). Mechanisms in Protein Synthesis V. Evidence for 2 Ribosomal Sites from Equilibria in Binding of Phenylalanyl-tRNA. Biochem. Biophys. Res. Comm. **29**, 593.

315. D. Nakada, (1967). Proteins of Ribosomes from "Relaxed Particles." J. Mol. Biol. **29**, 473.

316. J. R. Warner and R. Soeiro, (1967). Nascent Ribosomes from HeLa Cells. Proc. Natl. Acad. Sci. U.S. **58**, 1984.

317. W. K. Joklik and Y. Becker, (1965). Studies on the Genesis of Polyribosomes I. Origin and Significance of the Subribosomal Particles. J. Mol. Biol. **13**, 496, 511.

5S RNA

318. G. G. Brownlee, F. Sanger and B. G. Barrell, (1967). Nucleotide Sequence of 5S-ribosomal RNA from *E. coli*. Nature **215**, 735.

319. E. Knight and J. E. Darnell, (1967). Distribution of 5S RNA in HeLa Cells. J. Mol. Biol. **28**, 491.

320. H. Boedtker and D. G. Kelling, (1967). The Ordered Structure of 5S RNA. Biochem. Biophys. Res. Comm. **29**, 758.

MESSENGER AND FATE OF MESSENGER

321. S. Barondes and M. Nirenberg, (1962). Fate of a Synthetic Polynucleotide Directing Cell-free Protein Synthesis: Characteristics of Degradation Associated with Ribosomes. Science **138**, 810.

322. P. F. Spahr, (1964). Purification and Properties of RNAse II from *E. coli*. J. Biol. Chem. **239**, 3716.

323. M. Revel and H. H. Hiatt, (1964). The Stability of Liver Messenger RNA. Proc. Natl. Acad. Sci. U.S. **51**, 810.

324. H. Latham and J. E. Darnell, (1965). Entrance of mRNA into HeLa Cell Cytoplasm in Puromycin-treated Cells. J. Mol. Biol. **14**, 13.

325. S. Bloom, B. Goldberg and H. Green, (1965). Lifetime of Messenger RNA for Collagen and Cell Protein Synthesis in an Established Mammalian Cell Line. Biochem. Biophys. Res. Comm. **19**, 317.

326. R. K. Herman and A. B. Pardee, (1965). On the Stability of mRNA in a Polar Mutant. Biochem. Biophys. Acta **108**, 513.

327. H. Chantreene, (1965). On the Use of Actinomycin for Observing the Turnover of RNA. Biochem. Biophys. Acta **95**, 351.

328. K. F. Bautz, (1966). Effect of a Nonsense Triplet on the Stability of Messenger RNA. J. Mol. Biol. **17**, 298.

329. M. Fukai, Y. Anraku and D. Mizuno, (1966). The Roles of 3 Enzymes in Messenger RNA Degradation in Cell-free Systems from Normal or Phage-infected *E. coli*. Biochem. Biophys. Acta **119**, 373.

330. P. B. Moore, (1966). Polynucleotide Attachment to Ribsosomes. J. Mol. Biol. **18**, 8.

331. B. J. McCarthy and J. J. Holland, (1966). Cultured Mammalian Cell DNA as a Template for *in vitro* Protein Synthesis. Biochem. **5**, 1633.

332. J. Forchhammer and N. O. Kjeldgaard, (1967). Decay of Messenger RNA *in vivo* in a Mutant of *E. coli* 15. J. Mol. Biol. **24**, 459.

333. T. W. Borun, M. D. Scharff and E. Robbins, (1967). Rapidly Labeled, Polyribosome-Associated RNA Having the Properties of Histone Messenger. Proc. Natl. Acad. Sci. U.S. **58**, 1977.

INITIATION

334. J. P. Waller, (1963). The NH$_2$-Terminal Residues of the Protein from Cell-free Extracts of *E. coli*. J. Mol. Biol. **7**, 483.

335. J. M. Adams and M. R. Capecchi, (1966). N-formylmethionyl-sRNA as the Initiator of Protein Synthesis. Proc. Natl. Acad. Sci. U.S. **55**, 147.

336. J. M. Eisenstadt and P. Lengyel, (1966). Formylmethionyl-tRNA Dependence of Amino Acid Incorporation in Extracts of Trimethopterin-Treated *E. coli*. Science **154**, 524.

337. T. A. Sundarajan and R. E. Thach, (1966). Role of the Formylmethionine Codon AUG in Phasing Translation of Synthetic Messenger RNA. J. Mol. Biol. **18**, 68.

338. H. Weissbach and B. Redfield, (1967). Deformylation of N-formylmethionine by *E. coli* Extracts. Biochem. Biophys. Res. Comm. **27**, 7.

339. J. S. Anderson, M. S. Bretscher, B. F. C. Clark and K. A. Marcker, (1967). A GTP Requirement for Binding Initiator tRNA to Ribosomes. Nature **215**, 490.

340. A. Sarabhai and S. Brenner, (1967). A Mutant which Reinitiates the Polypeptide Chain after Chain Termination. J. Mol. Biol. **27**, 145.

341. J. H. Schwartz, R. Meyer, J. M. Eisenstadt and G. Brawerman, (1967). Involvement of N-formylmethionine in Initiation of Protein Synthesis in Cell-free Extracts of *Euglena gracilis*. J. Mol. Biol. **25**, 571.

342. P. Leder and M. N. Nau, (1967). Initiation of Protein Synthesis, III. Factor-GTP-Codon-Dependent Binding of F–Met–tRNA to Ribosomes. Proc. Natl. Acad. Sci. U.S. **58**, 774.

343. J. E. Allende and H. Weissbach, (1967). GTP Interaction with a Protein Synthesis Initiation Factor Preparation from *E. coli*. Biochem. Biophys. Res. Comm. **28**, 82.

344. H. P. Ghosh, D. Soll and H. G. Khorana, (1967). Studies on Polynucleotides LXVII. Initiation of Protein Synthesis *in vitro* as Studied by using Ribopolynucleotides with Repeating Nucleotide Sequences as Messenger. J. Mol. Biol. **25**, 275.

345. R. E. Monro and K. A. Marcker, (1967). Ribosome-catalysed Reaction of Puromycin with a Formylmethionine-containing Oligonucleotide. J. Mol. Biol. **25**, 347.

346. M. Salas, M. J. Miller, A. J. Wahba and S. Ochoa, (1967). Translation of the Genetic Message V. Effect of Mg^{++} and Formylation of Methionine in Protein Synthesis. Proc. Natl. Acad. Sci. U.S. **57**, 1865.

347. J. Lucas-Lenard and F. Lipmann, (1967). Initiation of Polyphenylalanine Synthesis

by N-Acetyl phenylalanyl-sRNA. Proc. Natl. Acad. Sci. U.S. **57**, 1050.

348. M. Nomura and C. V. Lowry, (1967). Phage f2 RNA-Directed Binding of Formyl-methionyl-tRNA to Ribosomes and the Role of 30S Ribosomal Subunits in the Initiation of Protein Synthesis. Proc. Natl. Acad. Sci. U.S. **58**, 946.

349. T. Ohta, S. Sarkar and R. E. Thach, (1967). The Role of Guanosine 5'-Triphosphate in the Initiation of Peptide Synthesis, III. Binding of Formylmethionyl-tRNA to Ribosomes. Proc. Natl. Acad. Sci. U.S. **58**, 1638.

350. M. Nomura, C. V. Lowry and C. Guthrie, (1967). Initiation of Protein Synthesis: Joining of the 50S Ribosomal Subunit to the Initiation Complex. Proc. Natl. Acad. Sci. U.S. **58**, 1487.

351. B. F. C. Clark, (1967). A Prerequisite Stage in the Initiation of Polypeptide Chains. J. Mol. Biol. **28**, 167.

PROPAGATION

352. J. R. Warner, A. Rich and C. Hall, (1962). Electron Microscope Studies of Ribosomal Clusters Synthesizing Hemoglobin. Science **138**, 1399.

353. W. Gilbert, (1963). Polypeptide Synthesis in *E. coli*. I. Ribosomes and the Active Complex. J. Mol. Biol. **6**, 374.

354. J. R. Warner and A. Rich, (1964). The Number of Growing Polypeptide Chains on Reticulocyte Polyribosomes. J. Mol. Biol. **10**, 202.

355. J. R. Warner and A. Rich, (1964). The Number of Soluble RNA Molecules on Reticulocyte Polyribosomes. Proc. Natl. Acad. Sci. U.S. **51**, 1134.

356. H. A. Bladen, R. Byrne, J. G. Levin and M. W. Nirenberg, (1965). An Electron Microscopic Study of a DNA-Ribosome Complex Formed *in vitro*. J. Mol. Biol. **11**, 78.

357. S. H. Wilson and M. B. Hoagland, (1965). Studies on the Physiology of Rat Liver Polyribosomes: Quantitative and Intracellular Distribution of Ribosomes. Proc. Natl. Acad. Sci. U.S. **54**, 600.

358. R. E. Thach, M. A. Cecere, T. A. Sundarajan and P. Doty, (1965). The Polarity of Messenger Translation in Protein Synthesis. Proc. Natl. Acad. Sci. U.S. **54**, 1167.

359. M. Salas, M. A. Smith, W. M. Stanley, A. J. Wahba and S. Ochoa, (1965). Direction of Reading of the Genetic Message. J. Biol. Chem. **240**, 3988.

360. L. Skogerson and K. Moldave, (1967). Binding of Aminoacyl Transferase II to Ribosomes. Biochem. Biophys. Res. Comm. **27**, 568.

361. J. Gordon and F. Lipmann, (1967). Role of Divalent Ions in Poly U-directed Phenylalanine Polymerization.

362. M. J. Voll, (1967). Translation and Polarity in the Histidine Operon III. The Isolation of Prototrophic Polar Mutations. J. Mol. Biol. **30**, 109.

363. G. R. Fink and R. G. Martin, (1967). Translation and Polarity in the Histidine Operon II. Polarity in the Histidine Operon. J. Mol. Biol. **30**, 97.

364. M. Capecchi, (1967). Polarity *in vitro*. J. Mol. Biol. **30**, 213.

TERMINATION

365. M. Takanami and Y. Yan, (1965). Release of Polypeptide Chains from Ribosomes in Cell-free Amino-Acid-Incorporating Systems by Specific Combinations in Synthetic Polyribonucleotides. Proc. Natl. Acad. Sci. U.S. **54**, 1450.

366. M. S. Bretscher, H. M. Goodman, J. R. Menninger and J. D. Smith, (1965). Polypeptide Chain Termination using Synthetic Polynucleotides. J. Mol. Biol. **14**, 634.

367. C. Ganoza and T. Nakamoto, (1966). Studies on the Mechanism of Polypeptide Chain Termination in Cell-free Extracts of *E. coli*. Proc. Natl. Acad. Sci. U.S. **55**, 162.

368. M. R. Capecchi, (1967). Polypeptide Chain Termination *in vitro*: Isolation of a Release Factor. Proc. Natl. Acad. Sci. U.S. **58**, 1144.

CODEWORDS

369. A. G. So, J. W. Bodley and E. W. Davie, (1964). The Influence of Environment on the Specificity of Polynucleotide-Dependent Amino Acid Incorporation into Polypeptide. Biochem. **3**, 1977.

370. C. G. Kurland, (1966). The Requirements for Specific sRNA Binding by Ribosomes. J. Mol. Biol. **18**, 90.

371. D. S. Jones, S. Nishimura and H. G. Khorana, (1966). Studies on Polynucleotides LVI. Further Synthesis, *in vitro*, of Copolypeptides Containing 2AAs in Alternating Sequence Dependent upon DNA-like Polymers Containing 2 Nucleotides in Alternating Sequence. J. Mol. Biol. **16**, 454.

372. D. Kellog, B. Doctor, J. E. Loebel and M. Nirenberg, (1966). RNA Codons and Protein Synthesis IX. Synonym Codon Recognition by Multiple Species of Valine, Alanine, and Methionine sRNA. Proc. Natl. Acad. Sci. U.S. **55**, 912.

373. J. W. Bodley and E. W. Davie, (1966). A Study of the Mechanism of Ambiguous Amino Acid Coding by Poly U: the Nature of the Products. J. Mol. Biol. **18**, 344.

374. T. H. Jukes, (1967). Indications of an Evolutionary Pathway in the Amino Acid Code. Biochem. Biophys. Res. Comm. **27**, 573.

375. A. Sarabhai and S. Brenner, (1967). Further Evidence that UGA does not code for Tryptophan. J. Mol. Biol. **26**, 141.

GTP EFFECT

376. Y. Nishizuka and F. Lipmann, (1966). Comparison of GTP Split and Polypeptide Synthesis with a Purified *E. coli* System. Proc. Natl. Acad. Sci. U.S. **55**, 212.

377. J. W. B. Hershey and R. E. Monro, (1966). A Competitive Inhibitor of the GTP Reaction in Protein Synthesis. J. Mol. Biol. **18**, 68.

378. J. M. Ravel, (1967). Demonstration of a GTP-Dependent Enzymatic Binding of Aminoacyl-RNA to *E. coli* Ribosomes. Proc. Natl. Acad. Sci. U.S. **57**, 1811.

INHIBITORS

379. D. Nathans, (1964). Puromycin Inhibition of Protein Synthesis: Incorporation of Puromycin into Peptide Chains. Proc. Natl. Acad. Sci. U.S. **51**, 585.

380. M. Takanami, (1964). The Effect of RNAse digests of Aminoacyl-sRNA on a Protein Synthesis System. Proc. Natl. Acad. Sci. U.S. **52**, 1271.

381. S. Pestka, R. Marshall and M. Nirenberg, (1965). RNA Codewords and Protein Synthesis, V. Effect of Streptomycin on the Formation of Ribosome-sRNA Complexes. Proc. Natl. Acad. Sci. U.S. **53**, 639.

382. J. L. Stern, H. D. Barner and S. S. Cohen, (1966). The Lethality of Streptomycin and the Stimulation of RNA Synthesis in the Absence of Protein Synthesis. J. Mol. Biol. **17**, 188.

383. P. Traub, K. Hosokawa and M. Nomura, (1966). Streptomycin Sensitivity and the Structural Components of the 30s Ribosomes of *E. coli*. J. Mol. Biol. **19**, 211.

384. J. Davies, D. S. Jones and H. G. Khorana, (1966). A Further Study of Misreading of Codons induced by Streptomycin and Neomycin using Ribopolynucleotides Containing 2 Nucleotides in Alternating Sequence as Templates. J. Mol. Biol. **18**, 48.

385. R. J. Collier, (1967). Effect of Diphtheria Toxin on Protein Synthesis: Inactivation of One of the Transfer Factors. J. Mol. Biol. **25**, 83.

386. S. H. Barondes and H. D. Cohen, (1967). Comparative Effects of Cycloheximide and Puromycin on Cerebral Protein Synthesis and Consolidation of Memory in Mice. Brain Res. **4**, 44.

387. I. H. Goldberg and K. Mitsugi, (1967). Sparsomycin Inhibition of Polypeptide Synthesis Promoted by Synthetic and Natural Polynucleotides. Biochem. **6**, 372.

388. W. Godchaux, S. D. Adamson and E. Herbert, (1967). Effects of Cycloheximide on Polyribosome Function in Reticulocytes. J. Mol. Biol. **27**, 57.

389. D. Cooper, D. V. Banthorpe and D. Wilkie, (1967). Modified Ribosomes Conferring Resistance to Cycloheximide in Mutants of Saccharomyces Cerevisiae. J. Mol. Biol. **26**, 347.

390. E. Cundliffe and K. McQuillen, (1967). Bacterial Protein Synthesis: The Effects of Antibiotics. J. Mol. Biol. **30**, 137.

391. R. W. Wolfgang and N. L. Lawrence, (1967). Binding of Streptomycin by Ribosomes of Sensitive, Resistant and Dependent B. megaterium. J. Mol. Biol. **29**, 531.

392. B. Peterkofsky and G. M. Tomkins, (1967). Effect of Inhibitors of Nucleic Acid Synthesis on Steroid-mediated Induction of Tyrosine Aminotransferase in Hepatoma Cell Cultures. J. Mol. Biol. **30**, 49.

393. R. Soeiro, M. H. Vaughan and J. E. Darnell, (1968). Effect of Puromycin on Intranuclear Steps in Ribosome Biosynthesis. J. Cell. Biol. **36**, 91.

TOTAL SYNTHESIS

394. H. Lamfrom and P. M. Knopf, (1964). Initiation of Hemoglobin Synthesis in Cell-free Systems. J. Mol. Biol. **9**, 558.

395. M. C. Ganoza, C. A. Williams and F. Lipmann, (1965). Synthesis of Serum Proteins by a Cell-free System from Rat Liver. Proc. Natl. Acad. Sci. U.S. **53**, 619.

396. C. A. Williams, M. C. Ganoza and F. Lipmann, (1965). Effect of Bacterial Infection on the Synthesis of Serum Proteins by a Mouse Liver Cell-free System. Proc. Natl. Acad. Sci. U.S. **53**, 622.

397. J. H. Schwartz, J. M. Eisenstadt, G. Brawerman and N. D. Zinder, (1965). Biosynthesis of the Coat Protein of Coliphage f2 by Extracts of *Euglena gracilis*. Proc. Natl. Acad. Sci. U.S. **53**, 195.

398. P. M. Knopf and H. M. Dintzis, (1965). Hemoglobin Synthesis in a Cell-free System. Biochem. **4**, 1427.

399. M. R. Capecchi, (1966). Cell-free Protein Synthesis Programmed with R17 RNA: Identification of 2 Phage Proteins. J. Mol. Biol. **21**, 173.

400. P. N. Campbell, E. Lowe and G. Serck-Hanssen, (1967). Protein Synthesis by Microsomal Particles from Regenerating Rat Liver. Biochem. J. **103**, 280.

401. B. Goldberg and H. Green, (1967). Collagen Synthesis on Polyribosomes of Cultured Mammalian Fibroblasts. J. Mol. Biol. **26**, 1.

402. K. Eggen, M. P. Oeschger and D. Nathans, (1967). Cell-free Protein Synthesis Directed by Coliphage MS2 RNA: Sequential Synthesis of Specific Phage Proteins. Biochem. Biophys. Res. Comm. **28**, 587.

403. R. F. Gesteland, W. Salser and A. Bolle, (1967). *In Vitro* Synthesis of T_4 Lysozyme by Suppression of Amber Mutations. Proc. Natl. Acad. Sci. U.S. **58**, 2036.

Reprinted from THE JOURNAL OF BIOLOGICAL CHEMISTRY
Vol. 231, No. 1, March, 1958
Made in United States of America

A SOLUBLE RIBONUCLEIC ACID INTERMEDIATE IN PROTEIN SYNTHESIS*†

BY MAHLON B. HOAGLAND,‡ MARY LOUISE STEPHENSON, JESSE F. SCOTT, LISELOTTE I. HECHT, AND PAUL C. ZAMECNIK

(*From the John Collins Warren Laboratories of the Huntington Memorial Hospital of Harvard University at the Massachusetts General Hospital, Boston, Massachusetts*)

(Received for publication, September 27, 1957)

The cell-free rat liver system in which C^{14}-amino acids are incorporated irreversibly into α-peptide linkage in protein has been used in our laboratories for a number of years as a measure of protein synthesis. The essential components of this system are the microsomal ribonucleoprotein particles, certain enzymes derived from the soluble protein fraction, adenosine triphosphate, guanosine di- or triphosphate, and a nucleoside triphosphate-generating system (1–3). The ribonucleoprotein particles of the microsomes appear to be the actual site of peptide condensation. The soluble enzymes and ATP[1] have been found to effect the initial carboxyl activation of the amino acids (4). The role of GTP is not yet understood, although the present paper sheds light on its probable locus of action.

Much evidence has accumulated in the past 8 years, beginning with the studies of Caspersson (5) and Brachet (6), implicating a role for cellular RNA in protein synthesis. The intermediate stages between amino acid activation and final incorporation into protein in the rat liver *in vitro* system offered us unexplored regions in which to seek more direct evidence for a chemical association of RNA and amino acids. A preliminary report of such an association has recently been presented by us (7). There it was shown that the RNA of a particular fraction of the cytoplasm hitherto uncharacterized became labeled with C^{14}-amino acids in the presence of ATP and the amino acid-activating enzymes, and that this labeled RNA subsequently was able to transfer the amino acid to microsomal protein

* This work was supported by grants from the United States Public Health Service, the American Cancer Society, and the United States Atomic Energy Commission.

† This is publication No. 916 of the Cancer Commission of Harvard University.

‡ Scholar in Cancer Research of the American Cancer Society. Present address, Cavendish Laboratory, Cambridge University.

[1] The abbreviations used in this paper are as follows: RNA, ribonucleic acid; pH 5 RNA, ribonucleic acid derived from the pH 5 enzyme fraction; AMP, adenosine 5'-phosphate; ATP, GTP, CTP, UTP, the triphosphates of adenosine, guanosine, cytosine, and uridine; PP, inorganic pyrophosphate; PPase, inorganic pyrophosphatase; PEP, phosphoenol pyruvate; Tris, tris(hydroxymethyl)aminomethane; and ECTEOLA, cellulose treated with epichlorohydrin and triethanolamine.

in the presence of GTP and a nucleoside triphosphate-generating system. This paper is a more definitive report on these studies.

Materials and Methods

Cellular fractions (microsomes and pH 5 enzymes) of rat liver and mouse Ehrlich ascites tumor were prepared by methods previously described (2, 3). Microsomes were generally sedimented at 105,000 $\times$ g for 90 to 120 minutes instead of the usual 60 minutes in order to insure more complete sedimentation of microsome-like particles. pH 5 enzymes were precipitated from the resulting supernatant fraction by adjusting the pH to 5.2.

Preparation of Labeled pH 5 Enzyme Fraction—The labeling of the pH 5 enzyme fraction was carried out by incubating 10 ml. of pH 5 enzyme preparation (containing 100 to 200 mg. of protein) dissolved in buffered medium (2) with 4.0 μmoles of C^{14}-L-leucine (containing 7.2 $\times$ 10^6 c.p.m.) and 200 μmoles of ATP in a final volume of 20 ml. for 10 minutes at 37°. The reaction mixture was then chilled to 0°, diluted 3-fold with cold water, and the enzyme precipitated by addition of 1.0 M acetic acid to bring the pH to 5.2. The precipitate was redissolved in 5 to 10 ml. of buffered medium, diluted again (to 60 ml.) with water, and the enzyme reprecipitated at pH 5.2 with M acetic acid. This final precipitate was washed with water and dissolved in 5.0 to 10.0 ml. of the cold buffered medium.

Isolation of pH 5 RNA—Isolation of pH 5 RNA was carried out by a minor modification of the method of Gierer and Schramm (8) and Kirby (9). The labeled pH 5 enzyme solution as prepared above was shaken in a mechanical shaker at room temperature for 1 hour with an equal volume of 90 per cent phenol, followed by centrifugation at 15,000 $\times$ g for 10 minutes. The top aqueous layer containing the RNA-leucine-C^{14} was removed with a syringe, more water was added, and, after thorough mixing, the centrifugation and withdrawal of the aqueous solution were repeated. Phenol was removed from the pooled aqueous solutions by three successive ether extractions. 0.1 volume of 20 per cent potassium acetate (pH 5) was then added, and the RNA was precipitated with 60 per cent ethanol at $-10°$, redissolved in water, and again precipitated from 60 per cent ethanol. The final precipitate was dissolved in a small volume of water and dialyzed against water for 4 hours in the cold. This method of extraction was used as a preparative procedure and yielded 50 to 70 per cent of the RNA initially present in the enzyme preparation, and was also used to prepare microsomal and unlabeled pH 5 RNA.

For analysis of pH 5 RNA-leucine-C^{14} in smaller incubations, NaCl was used to extract the RNA. To the incubation mixture (usually a volume of 2.0 ml.), 10 volumes of cold 0.4 N perchloric acid were added. The resulting acid-insoluble precipitate, containing RNA and protein, was washed four times with cold 0.2 N perchloric acid, once with 5:1 ethanol-0.2 N perchloric acid, once with ethanol in the cold, and once with 3:1 ethanol-ether at 50°. The RNA was then extracted with 10 per cent NaCl at 100° for 30 minutes. (During this extraction, the pH drops to around 2 to 3 and it is essential to permit this to occur; if the pH is held above 6, the isolated RNA contains little or no radioactivity.) The RNA was precipitated from the NaCl extract with 60 per cent ethanol at $-10°$, and was dissolved in water and again precipitated with ethanol. The final ethanol suspension was filtered by suction onto disks of No. 50 Whatman paper. The dried RNA was counted by using a Nuclear micromil window gas flow counter, was then eluted from the paper with 0.005 N alkali, and the concentration determined by measuring the absorption at 260 mμ in a Beckman spectrophotometer by using an extinction coefficient of 34.2 mg.$^{-1}$ cm.^{2} (10). This extraction procedure yielded 30 to 35 per cent of the RNA originally present in the incubation mixture. In experiments in which total counts are recorded, the specific activity of this NaCl-extracted RNA was multiplied by the total quantity of RNA initially added as determined by the method of Scott et al. (10). This was based on the assumption that the RNA extracted was a representative sample of the total.

For the determination of the specific activity of the protein, the methods described previously (1, 2) were employed.

The nucleoside triphosphate preparations, the triphosphate-generating system, and the C^{14}-amino acids used in these studies were the same as those used in other recent work reported from this laboratory (2). 1 μmole of Mg^{++} was added per micromole of nucleoside triphosphate in all cases.

Results

Labeling of RNA Cellular Fractions with Amino Acids—In the complete system required for incorporation of C^{14}-amino acids into protein (microsomes, pH 5 enzymes, ATP, GTP, nucleoside triphosphate-generating system, and C^{14}-amino acids), the RNA subsequently isolated was found to be labeled with C^{14}-amino acids. Incubation of the pH 5 enzyme fraction without microsomes under these conditions resulted in substantially more RNA labeling than in the complete system. Little labeling of RNA was observed when microsomes were incubated alone under the above conditions. Further analysis of the requirements for labeling of pH 5 RNA revealed that ATP alone was sufficient and that GTP and the generating system were not necessary. A survey of the extent of labeling of the RNA of various isolated liver cellular fractions with leucine is shown in Fig. 1, which shows that pH 5 RNA has the highest specific activity.

Fig. 2 shows the dependence of labeling of pH 5 RNA upon leucine concentration. Glycine-C^{14}, valine-C^{14}, or alanine-C^{14} gave about the same

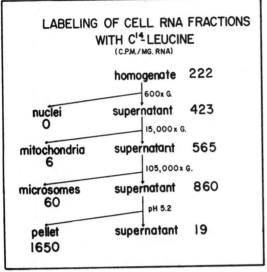

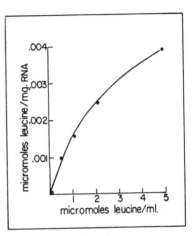

FIG. 1.   FIG. 2.

FIG. 1. Cellular fractions were prepared from rat liver and resuspended or dissolved in buffered medium (2). 0.75 ml. of each fraction was then incubated at 37° for 10 minutes with 10 μmoles of ATP, 0.1 μmole of L-leucine-C^{14} containing 180,000 c.p.m., 5 μmoies of PEP, and 0.04 mg. of pyruvate kinase in a final volume of 1.0 ml. 4 μmoles of potassium fumarate, 10 μmoles of potassium glutamate, and 10.0 μmoles of orthophosphate were added to the incubation mixtures containing the original homogenate, the 600 $\times$ g supernatant fraction, and the mitochondrial fraction, and these were shaken in an atmosphere of 95 per cent oxygen-5 per cent CO_2 during the incubation.

FIG. 2. Leucine concentration curve for labeling of pH 5 RNA. 1.2 ml. of rat liver pH 5 enzyme preparation (approximately 13 mg. of protein), in buffered medium were incubated for 10 minutes at 37° with 20 μmoles of ATP, L-leucine-C^{14} containing 3.6 $\times$ 10^5 c.p.m. at the concentrations indicated, in a final volume of 2.0 ml.

extent of labeling as leucine-C^{14} when each was present at a concentration of 0.007 M. When these amino acids were combined (0.007 M each), the labeling was approximately additive. The addition of a mixture containing fifteen C^{12}-amino acids (lacking leucine) did not affect the extent of labeling with leucine-C^{14}. Maximal labeling of 0.04 μmole of leucine per mg. of RNA was attained with the most active liver preparations by using 0.005 M leucine and 0.01 M ATP.

ATP was necessary for the labeling of the RNA with amino acids, and the extent of labeling depended upon the concentration of ATP (Fig. 3).

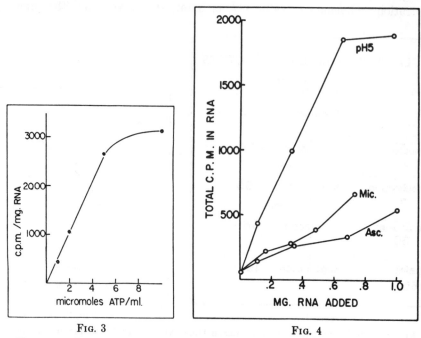

Fig. 3

Fig. 4

FIG. 3. ATP concentration curve for labeling of pH 5 RNA. 1.8 ml. of rat liver pH 5 enzyme preparation (20 mg. of protein) in buffered medium were incubated for 20 minutes at 37° with 0.2 μmole of L-leucine-C^{14} containing 3.6 × 10^5 c.p.m. and ATP at the concentrations indicated, in a final volume of 2.0 ml.

FIG. 4. Effect of addition of certain RNA preparations upon the labeling of pH 5 RNA with leucine-C^{14}. RNA was prepared from the pH 5 enzyme (pH 5) and microsome (Mic.) fractions of rat liver and from whole ascites cells (Asc.) by the phenol method. The quantities of RNA indicated, dissolved in 0.02 M Tris buffer, pH 7.6 (0.5 μmole of MgCl$_2$ added per mg. of RNA), were incubated at 37° for 10 minutes in 1.0 ml. volumes with pH 5 enzyme obtained from Ehrlich ascites cells (containing 0.12 mg. of RNA), and the following final concentrations of additions: 0.01 M ATP; 0.01 M PEP; 0.0038 M MgCl$_2$; 0.038 M Tris, pH 7.6; 0.018 M KCl; and 0.04 mg. of pyruvate kinase. The total radioactivity in RNA plotted was calculated as the product of the specific activity of the RNA isolated by extraction by the NaCl method and the total quantity of RNA present at the end of the incubation period. Addition of liver pH 5 RNA to the liver pH 5 enzyme fraction produces a similar enhancement of incorporation to that shown here with the tumor enzyme.

Maximal incorporation was reached at about 0.01 M. A similarly shaped ATP concentration curve had earlier been found for the amino acid activation reaction, as measured by hydroxamic acid formation (4). Also, as in the activation reaction, the requirement for ATP was specific since GTP, CTP, and UTP did not replace this nucleotide. GTP, which is necessary for the over-all incorporation of amino acids into protein, did not affect the rate of labeling of pH 5 RNA by the pH 5 enzyme fraction, in the presence or absence of a mixture containing fifteen C^{12}-amino acids (lacking leucine).

The amino acid labeling of RNA was sensitive to ribonuclease. 10 γ per ml. of Worthington crystalline ribonuclease gave 40 per cent inhibition, and 40 γ gave 90 per cent inhibition in the presence of 10 mg. of enzyme protein per ml. This inhibition was accompanied by a smaller loss of absorbance at 260 mμ in the acid-precipitable fraction. It is worth recalling at this point that the activation reaction, as measured by PP^{32}-ATP exchange and hydroxamic acid formation, is *not* affected by ribonuclease (4).

The extent of incorporation of leucine-C^{14} into pH 5 RNA was markedly stimulated by the addition of isolated pH 5 RNA as may be seen in Fig. 4. The enhancement of labeling was relatively specific for this particular RNA, rat liver microsomal RNA and mouse ascites whole cell RNA being of low activity. The small amount of stimulation by microsomal RNA shown in Fig. 4 may well be due to contamination of microsomes with the supernatant fraction, since the microsomes were centrifuged from the undiluted 15,000 $\times$ g supernatant fluid of a concentrated (30 per cent) homogenate.

The labeling reaction proceeded linearly with time for 3 minutes and was complete in 10 minutes. In those preparations in which precaution was taken to minimize contamination with microsomes (by preparing pH 5 enzymes from a 105,000 $\times$ g supernatant fraction obtained after a centrifugation for 90 to 120 minutes), there was no loss of leucine-C^{14} for a period of 20 minutes after maximal labeling had been reached. Slight microsomal contamination, however, resulted in a loss of leucine from RNA after maximal labeling had been reached.

After incubation of the pH 5 enzyme fraction with leucine-C^{14} and ATP, these latter compounds could be largely removed by reprecipitation of the pH 5 enzyme from dilute solution, as described. Upon subsequent incubation of this reprecipitated fraction, the leucine label was rapidly lost from the RNA unless ATP was added (Table I). The equivalent effect of a nucleoside triphosphate-generating system (PEP and pyruvate kinase), also shown in Table I, was probably mediated through the presence of very small amounts of adenylates which coprecipitate with the pH 5 enzyme. PP, on the other hand, increased the extent of loss of label from the RNA. These findings suggested that the labeling process might be *reversible*. This possibility was rendered more probable by the finding that, in the presence of added ATP, the addition of leucine-C^{12} produced a dilution of the leucine-C^{14} labeling, as shown in Experiment 2, Table I. This would be expected if the following reactions were occurring:

$$ATP + \text{leucine-}C^{14} + E \rightleftharpoons E(AMP \sim \text{leucine-}C^{14}) + PP \qquad (1)$$

$$E(AMP \sim \text{leucine-}C^{14}) + RNA \rightleftharpoons RNA \sim \text{leucine-}C^{14} + E + (AMP) \qquad (2)$$

The loss of label in the absence of added ATP would depend upon the presence of small amounts of indigenous PP. The failure of leucine-C^{12}

TABLE I

Effect of Various Additions upon Loss of Leucine-C^{14} from Labeled pH 5 Enzyme

Experiment No.	Addition	Amount	Per cent initial specific activity lost
		M	
1	None	0	75
	ATP	0.001	44
	"	0.005	35
	" + AMP	0.005 each	37
	PP	0.01	96
	PEP	0.01	24
2	None	0	79
	Leucine-C^{12}	0.01	84
	ATP	0.01	39
	" + leucine-C^{12}	0.01 each	68

L-Leucine-C^{14}-labeled pH 5 enzyme (0.4 ml.) was incubated at 37° for 7 minutes in a volume of 2.0 ml. with the concentrations of additions indicated. A concentration of $MgCl_2$ equal to that of PP was added with the latter. Pyruvate kinase (0.04 mg. per ml.) was added with the PEP. The initial specific activities of the RNA which were isolated from the pH 5 enzymes labeled during the preincubation were: Experiment 1, 770 c.p.m. per mg.; Experiment 2, 440 c.p.m. per mg.

to effect a dilution in the absence of added ATP would be anticipated since, due to the high ATPase activity of the preparation and the absence of a generating system, the ATP concentration would be effectively zero and the reaction would proceed rapidly to the left. It is of interest in this connection that Holley (11) has described an alanine-dependent, ribonuclease-sensitive incorporation of C^{14}-AMP into ATP catalyzed by the pH 5 enzyme preparation. This would suggest a reversal of an ATP-dependent reaction between alanine and RNA. However, other amino acids have not been found to stimulate such an exchange, suggesting that AMP is generally not a free product of reaction (2). The possibility must still be entertained, however, that ATP has some stabilizing effect upon the pH 5 RNA-amino acid bond not related to mass action.

A high concentration of NH_2OH such as 1.2 M, which was used to obtain amino acid hydroxamic acid formation with this preparation (4), also inhibits (90 per cent) the labeling of RNA with leucine.

Some Properties of pH 5 RNA-Leucine-C^{14}—The RNA of the enzyme pH 5 fraction of rat liver represents 2 per cent of the total RNA of the cell and only 20 per cent of the RNA of the 105,000 × g 2 hour supernatant fraction. It is present in a concentration of 3 mg. of RNA per 100 mg. of protein. In the mouse ascites tumor essentially all the RNA of the 105,000 × g supernatant fraction precipitates at pH 5.2 and amounts to 20 per cent of the total RNA of the cell.

The active component of the pH 5 enzyme fraction does not sediment at 105,000 × g in 3 hours. If one compares the activity and RNA content of the pH 5 enzyme prepared from a supernatant fraction obtained after 1 hour or 3 hour centrifugations at 105,000 × g, one finds that the latter preparation contains only 50 per cent as much RNA as the former. The amount of leucine incorporated into the RNA of both preparations is, however, the same, suggesting that the RNA sedimented during the additional centrifugation time is not active.

RNA-leucine-C^{14} gave a mean sedimentation constant of 1.85 $s_{20,w}$ at a concentration of 0.003 per cent in 0.15 M NaCl, 0.015 M citrate, pH 6.8.[2] Preliminary studies indicate that this value is lower when effort is made to remove magnesium ion first by dialysis against citrate buffer. The material does not appear homogeneous, however, and probably represents a range of molecular sizes. Preliminary results with paper electrophoresis suggest at least two major components.

A sample of pH 5 RNA-leucine-C^{14} extracted by the phenol method was fractionated on ECTEOLA (12). 1 mg. of RNA, dissolved in 0.01 M phosphate buffer at pH 7 and containing 4040 c.p.m. as leucine-C^{14}, was placed on a column 0.2 cm. in diameter containing 50 mg. of ECTEOLA-SF (0.16 meq. of N per gm.).[3] Elution was carried out with a gradient of NaCl in 0.01 M phosphate buffer at pH 7, which was established by feeding buffer containing 2.5 M NaCl into a 500 ml. mixing flask. 1.5 ml. fractions were collected at a flow rate of 1.8 ml. per hour. The NaCl gradient was continued until the molarity of the effluent was about 2. In accordance with the general procedure of Bradley and Rich (12), the gradient was discontinued, the column washed with water, and 10 ml. of 1 N NaOH were run through. Three fractions emerged: Fraction 1 failed to adhere to the exchanger and contained 14 per cent of the ultraviolet absorbance and 8 per cent of the radioactivity (*free* leucine, if present

---

[2] We wish to thank Dr. J. Fresco and Dr. P. Doty of Harvard University for performing these analyses.

[3] Kindly furnished by Dr. Alexander Rich.

would have been found in this fraction); Fraction 2 emerged at a mean molarity of 0.15 NaCl and contained 48 per cent of the absorbance and 2 per cent of the radioactivity; and Fraction 3 was eluted with NaOH and contained 36 per cent of the absorbance and 68 per cent of the radioactivity. The final recovery amounted to 98 per cent of the ultraviolet absorbance and 78 per cent of the radioactivity. The low recovery of the radioactivity is most likely due to self-absorption in the NaOH-eluted fractions when plated for counting. These results, compared with those published by Bradley and Rich, suggest that at least 68 per cent of the leucine is bound to 36 per cent of the RNA of high sedimentation coefficient relative to that of the bulk of the sample.

pH 5 RNA-leucine-C^{14} isolated from the pH 5 enzyme fraction by both the phenol and NaCl methods was readily bound by Dowex 1 and charcoal at neutral pH value. However, when the RNA-leucine-C^{14} was associated with pH 5 enzyme protein in the natural state, these agents did not take up the RNA. The isolated RNA-leucine-C^{14} was non-dialyzable and stable against water, 10 per cent NaCl, or 8 M urea. There was no detectable acid-precipitable protein in the RNA extracted by the phenol method (1 per cent contamination could have been detected (13)).

The leucine was completely released from the pH 5 RNA by 0.01 N KOH in 20 minutes at room temperature. At pH 4 to 6, it was relatively stable and the labeled material as prepared by the phenol method could be kept some weeks in the frozen state. The leucine appeared to be covalently linked to the RNA, as judged from the following indirect evidence. Treatment of the RNA-leucine-C^{14} with the ninhydrin reagent indicated the absence of free leucine, although leucine is slowly released from the RNA during the course of the ninhydrin procedure. Treatment with anhydrous hydroxylamine, followed by chromatography of the products on paper (75 per cent secondary butanol, 15 per cent formic acid, 10 per cent water), resulted in a spot corresponding to leucine hydroxamic acid which contained all the radioactivity originally bound to the RNA. (A control of this experiment, in which the RNA-leucine-C^{14} bond was first hydrolyzed in 0.01 N alkali, gave no radioactivity associated with the leucine hydroxamic acid spot.)

Labeling of RNA with Leucine-C^{14} in Intact Cell—If pH 5 RNA were on the pathway of protein synthesis, it would be reasonable to expect that in the intact cell it would become labeled with leucine-C^{14} earlier than microsome protein. Previous studies in this laboratory by Littlefield and Keller (3) had shown that treatment of mouse ascites tumor microsomes with 0.5 M sodium chloride facilitates the centrifugal separation of ribonucleoprotein particles rich in RNA (about 50 per cent RNA, 50 per cent protein). The protein moiety of these "sodium chloride-insoluble" particles was found to be the most highly labeled protein fraction after incorporation of leucine-C^{14} by intact cells. A preliminary experiment in the rat showed that, at the earliest time point which it was possible to obtain after injection of leucine-C^{14} (1 minute), both RNA of the pH 5 fraction and the protein of the ribonucleoprotein particles of the microsomes were already maximally labeled. By use of mouse ascites tumor cells, it was possible to slow down the reaction by reducing the temperature of incubation. After incubation of these cells with leucine-C^{14} at 25°, the cells were washed and lysed, and concentrated solutions were added to give a final concentration of 0.5 M NaCl, 0.005 M MgCl$_2$, and 0.01 M Tris buffer, pH 7.6 (3). "NaCl-insoluble" (NaCl particles) and "soluble" fractions of a 10 minute 15,000 $\times$ g supernatant fraction were separated by centrifugation at 78,000 $\times$ g for 2 hours. Both the protein and RNA were isolated. Since almost all of the RNA present in the soluble fraction of the ascites cells precipitates at pH 5, the RNA of this fraction may be considered pH 5 RNA. The proteins of the soluble fraction represent the proteins of the NaCl-soluble components of the microsomes and the soluble cell proteins. Littlefield and Keller (3) have shown that these two fractions become labeled at a slow rate and therefore they were not separated. The results of this experiment are shown in Fig. 5. Soluble and particle RNA became labeled maximally in 2 minutes and remained so as if a steady state had been reached, while the protein of the ribonucleoprotein particles continued to acquire new amino acid content throughout the incubation period. Incorporation into the other cell proteins started after an initial lag period and proceeded at the slowest rate. The rate of labeling of the pH 5 RNA is so rapid that it occurs to some extent at 0° and no satisfactory rate curve for this labeling process could be obtained, since the reaction is proceeding even during centrifugal separation of the fractions. Similar results were obtained when the cell fractions were prepared from a sucrose homogenate and the pH 5 RNA and the protein of the deoxycholate-soluble and -insoluble fractions of the microsomes were isolated. These data suggest that the pH 5 RNA-amino acid compound *could* be an intermediate in the incorporation of amino acids into the proteins of the ribonucleoprotein particles of the microsomes.

Transfer of Leucine-C^{14} from Labeled pH 5 Enzyme Fraction to Microsomal Protein—We have reported (7) that the leucine-C^{14}-labeled pH 5 enzyme fraction, freed from ATP and leucine-C^{14} by reprecipitation at pH 5.1 from dilute solution, will transfer the RNA-bound leucine-C^{14} to microsomal protein upon subsequent incubation with microsomes, a nucleoside triphosphate-generating system, and GTP (Table II). The other nucleoside triphosphates, including ATP, would not replace GTP in this reaction; ATP also failed to stimulate the transfer in the presence of GTP.

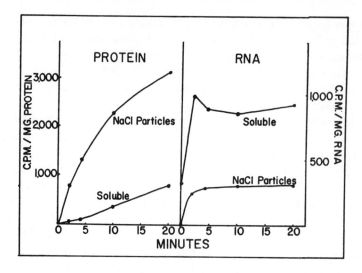

FIG. 5. Time-curve of incorporation of L-leucine-C^{14} into the RNA and protein of the ribonucleoprotein particles and the soluble fraction in intact ascites cells. Ascites tumor cells (approximately 10 gm. of packed cells) were incubated at 25° in 50 ml. of their own ascitic fluid fortified with glucose (0.04 M), Tris buffer, pH 7.6 (0.02 M), and containing 3 μmoles of L-leucine (3.5 × 10^6 c.p.m. per μmole). Aliquots were taken at the time points shown; NaCl-insoluble and -soluble fractions were prepared from the 15,000 × g supernatant fraction. The specific activities of the RNA and protein of these fractions are shown.

TABLE II

Transfer of Leucine-C^{14} from Labeled pH 5 Enzyme Fraction to Microsome Protein

	Total c.p.m. in	
	RNA	Protein
Before incubation: complete system.............................	478	22
After " : " "	182	433
Complete system minus GTP.................................	116	67
" " " generating system....................	62	101
" " " " " and minus GTP.....	29	23
" " " " " but with 5 × GTP..	176	91
Complete system CTP replacing GTP.........................	98	79
" " UTP " "	117	100
" " plus 0.005 M leucine-C^{12}.....................	178	371

The results shown are averaged values from two experiments. In each experiment 0.6 ml. of a microsome suspension containing about 15 mg. of protein and 0.4 ml. of a pH 5 enzyme fraction prelabeled with leucine-C^{14}, containing about 5 mg. of protein, were incubated for 15 minutes at 37° with the nucleoside triphosphates (0.0005 M), PEP (0.01 M), and pyruvate kinase (0.04 mg.) as indicated, in a final volume of 2.0 ml.

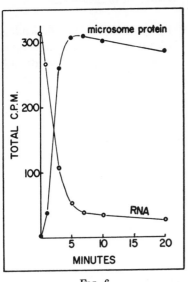

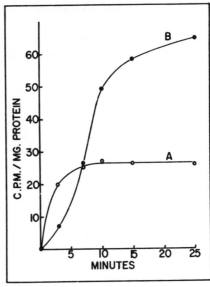

FIG. 6   FIG. 7

FIG. 6. Time-curve of transfer of leucine-C^{14} from prelabeled pH 5 enzyme fraction to microsome protein. 4.0 ml. of a leucine-C^{14}-labeled pH 5 enzyme preparation (containing 2.6 mg. of RNA), and 6.0 ml. of microsomes (21 mg. of RNA) were incubated at 37° with 20 μmoles of GTP, 200 μmoles of PEP, and 0.8 mg. of pyruvate kinase in a volume of 20.0 ml. 2.5 ml. aliquots were taken at the time points shown. These were chilled, diluted to 12.5 ml., and centrifuged at 105,000 × g for 60 minutes in the cold. The RNA and protein of the supernatant fluid and of the microsomes were separated. The total counts per minute in the pH 5 RNA (O) and in the microsomal protein (●) is plotted. Since there is about 50 per cent enzymatic loss of leucine-C^{14} from pH 5 RNA during the hour's centrifugation (determined directly by centrifuging an aliquot of labeled pH 5 enzyme of known specific activity under the same conditions), a correction for this loss was applied to the specific activity of RNA to give the final figures used.

FIG. 7. A comparison of the rates of the over-all incorporation reaction and the incorporation when starting with labeled pH 5 enzyme fraction. 40 ml. of an enzyme preparation at pH 5 were incubated for 10 minutes at 37° with 100 μmoles of ATP and 2 μmoles of leucine-C^{14} (3.6 × 10⁶ c.p.m.) in a volume of 10 ml. An equal aliquot of the same enzyme was incubated identically with ATP and leucine-C^{12}. Both enzymes were then precipitated twice at pH 5.1 from dilute solution. An aliquot of the labeled enzyme was taken for determination of RNA content and another for determination of specific activity of RNA-leucine-C^{14}. 1.8 ml. of leucine-labeled enzyme, dissolved in buffered medium and containing 1540 c.p.m. of bound leucine-C^{14}, were then incubated with 1.8 ml. of microsomes, 3 μmoles of GTP, 60 μmoles of PEP, and 0.24 mg. of pyruvate kinase in a volume of 6.0 ml. The same volume and amount of unlabeled enzyme were incubated with the same quantity of microsomes, GTP, PEP, and pyruvate kinase, plus 3 μmoles of ATP and 0.6 μmole of leucine-C^{14} containing 1.1 × 10⁶ c.p.m. The incubation mixtures were equilibrated at 30° for 1 minute before addition of microsomes and incubation was carried out at 30°. 1.0 ml. aliquots of each incubation were taken, each containing approximately 9 mg. of protein, at the times indicated and the protein of the samples was precipitated, washed, plated, and counted. Curve A, reaction with prelabeled pH 5 enzyme; Curve B, over-all reaction.

252

In the absence of GTP there was an equally rapid microsome-dependent loss of leucine-C^{14} from the intermediate, without concomitant appearance of amino acid in protein. (Rat liver microsomes contain considerable "ATPase" activity. Whether the loss of label is due to destruction of ATP still present in the system, thus permitting reversal of the reaction, or a manifestation of an uncoupling of the basic mechanism for trans-

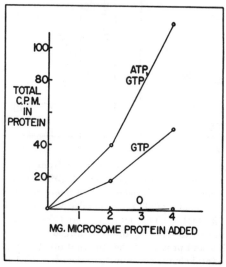

FIG. 8. Transfer of leucine-C^{14} from isolated pH 5 RNA-leucine-C^{14} to microsomal protein. 0.40 mg. of RNA, prepared by the phenol method, containing 600 c.p.m. of bound leucine-C^{14}, was incubated at 37° for 15 minutes in buffered medium (0.5 ml.) with the amount of microsomes indicated with added PEP (0.01 M), pyruvate kinase (0.04 mg.) in a volume of 1.0 ml. 0.5 μmole of ATP and GTP was added as indicated (0 = no addition of nucleotide). ATP alone gave the same activity as with no nucleotide additions. The microsomes used were sedimented from a 15,000 $\times$ g supernatant fraction which was diluted 3.5-fold before centrifugation at 105,000 $\times$ g.

ferring amino acid to microsomes is not known.) GTP had no effect on the considerably slower rate of loss of label from pH 5 enzyme in the absence of microsomes. The addition of a relatively high concentration of leucine-C^{12} did not appreciably dilute the radioactivity transferred to protein. Fig. 6 shows a time-curve for the transfer reaction and emphasizes the high efficiency of the transfer as well as its relatively rapid rate. Fig. 7 presents a comparison of the rates of the transfer of leucine-C^{14} to microsomal protein from free leucine-C^{14} and ATP (Curve B) and from the prelabeled intermediate in the absence of free leucine and ATP (Curve A). When starting with the labeled intermediate, the lag in the initial rate of the over-all reaction was absent, the efficiency of transfer was much greater, and the reaction attained completion at an earlier time.

Transfer of Leucine-C[14] *from Isolated Labeled pH 5 RNA to Microsomal Protein*—pH 5 RNA-leucine-C[14], extracted from labeled pH 5 enzyme by the phenol method, precipitated twice from ethanol and dialyzed against water, will, upon incubation with microsomes, transfer leucine-C[14] to microsomal protein. In seven experiments of this type, an average of 20 per cent of the leucine was transferred to protein (25 per cent maximum). In every case, pretreatment of the RNA-leucine-C[14] with 0.01 N KOH at room temperature for 10 to 20 minutes resulted in lack of transfer of the leucine. Again, leucine-C[12] did not inhibit the transfer. pH 5 RNA-leucine-C[14] extracted by the NaCl method was consistently found to be inactive.

GTP was again found to be necessary for this transfer, and there was no transfer in the absence of a nucleoside triphosphate-generating system. Furthermore, a partial requirement for ATP became apparent with this simplified system as shown in Fig. 8. The failure to elicit an ATP requirement for the transfer of amino acid from labeled pH 5 enzyme fraction to microsomes (previous section) was apparently due to the presence of ATP not washed free from the enzyme when reprecipitated at pH 5.

Microsomes alone appear not to react directly with pH 5 RNA-leucine but to require the mediation of enzymatic components of the pH 5 enzyme fraction. Microsomes prepared from dilute homogenates (to minimize contamination with pH 5 enzymes) were low in activity when incubated with pH 5 RNA-leucine-C[14], ATP, GTP, and the generating system but activity could be restored by addition of the pH 5 enzyme fraction.

DISCUSSION

The evidence presented supports the conclusion that there occur ATP-dependent enzymatic reactions between ribonucleic acid and amino acids. These reactions are catalyzed by an enzyme preparation which is known to activate the carboxyl groups of amino acids in the presence of ATP. The product formed, an RNA or ribonucleoprotein to which amino acids are apparently covalently linked, is capable of interacting with enzymatic components of the activating enzyme preparation and with microsomes to effect the transfer of the amino acid to peptide linkage in protein. It is therefore suggested that this particular RNA fraction functions as an intermediate carrier of amino acids in protein synthesis. A growing body of evidence from other laboratories also suggests the presence of an intermediate similar to the one herein described (14, 15, 11, 16).

Since the amino acid activation reaction is insensitive to ribonuclease and since an activating enzyme has been isolated relatively free from RNA (17), it is still necessary to invoke an initial enzymatic activation reaction as originally postulated (4), followed by a transfer of amino acid to linkage on RNA. Because of the impurity of the pH 5 enzyme system it cannot be stated that pH 5 RNA is naturally linked to amino acid-activating enzymes or that other enzymatic steps intervene between activation and linkage to RNA. The relative specificity of the reaction of the pH 5 enzyme fraction with pH 5 RNA shown in Fig. 4, does, however, emphasize the uniqueness of this particular RNA fraction in regard to ATP-dependent amino acid binding.

The present data suggest that the pH 5 RNA molecules, when associated with protein in the natural state, are considerably lower in average sedimentation coefficient than are the ribonucleoprotein particles of the microsomes. The latter are probably of the order of 80 S (18), while the former appear to be much lower. Furthermore, the results of other experiments from this laboratory, in which pH 5 RNA is enzymatically terminally labeled with the nucleoside monophosphate moieties of nucleoside triphosphates (19), suggest that the average molecular weight of the RNA is not likely to exceed 20,000 (based on maximal labeling, and assuming no branching). The sedimentation constant of 1.85 would be consistent with a molecular weight considerably lower than this.

Thus far we cannot assign a specific structure to the amino acid-RNA linkage. An attractive possibility is an acyl anhydride involving internucleotide phosphate groups or a terminal nucleotide residue. The acid stability and alkali lability of the linkage, qualitatively similar to the behavior of the synthetic amino acyl adenylates (20, 21), the formation of a hydroxamic acid, and the relative high energy of the linkage suggested by the possible reversibility of the reaction would support this type of anhydride linkage. The linkage would appear, however, to be more stable than a phosphate diester anhydride might be expected to be. We have also given thought to the possibility that internucleotide P—O bonds may be opened by reaction with an amino acyl adenylate, with resulting attachment of the amino acyl group to one of the opened ends of the nucleotide chain and adenylate to the other. Other possible linkages to be considered are carboxyl bonding to 2'-OH on ribose and bonding involving groups on the nucleotide bases themselves. It is, nevertheless, likely that, regardless of the type of bonding, amino acids are individually linked to pH 5 RNA and do not *condense* at this stage, for the amino acid may be recovered as the specific hydroxamic acid upon treatment with hydroxylamine.

The high efficiency of the GTP-dependent transfer of amino acid from intermediate to microsome protein is striking. There is no evidence that GTP is concerned either in the activation step or in the transfer of amino acid to pH 5 RNA. Its locus of action is thus narrowed down to the area of interaction between pH 5 RNA-amino acid and microsomes. The fact that enzymatic components of the pH 5 fraction are still required for the transfer from pH 5 RNA-leucine to microsomes could mean either that a new transfer enzyme is required. or that reassociation of intermediate with activating enzymes is necessary. If this latter is the case, the possibility that pH 5 RNA acts simply as a storage site for activated amino acids must be considered.

Other studies in this laboratory to be reported have shown that the same pH 5 enzyme fraction also catalyzes a rapid incorporation of the nucleotide monophosphate moieties of ATP, CTP, and UTP into pH 5 RNA. The appearance of these reactions in the same fraction which catalyzes the amino acid binding to RNA is intriguing, but thus far it has not been possible to obtain evidence for any clear direct link between the two reactions.

We have suggested elsewhere (22) a hypothetical reaction sequence for protein synthesis which accounts for the findings presented in this paper. Its central idea is that pH 5 RNA molecules, each charged with amino acids in characteristic sequence, polymerize in microsomes (in specific order determined by the complementary structure of microsomal RNA) to higher molecular weight units with resultant configurational changes which permit peptide condensation between contiguous amino acids. This working hypothesis will form the basis for further studies in these laboratories on the mechanism of protein synthesis.

SUMMARY

Evidence is presented that a soluble ribonucleic acid, residing in the same cellular fraction which activates amino acids, binds amino acids in the presence of adenosine triphosphate. Indirect evidence indicates that this reaction may be reversible. The amino acids so bound to ribonucleic acid are subsequently transferred to microsomal protein, and this transfer is dependent upon guanosine triphosphate.

The authors wish to thank Dr. Robert B. Loftfield for the radioactive amino acids used as well as for helpful criticism.

BIBLIOGRAPHY

1. Zamecnik, P. C., and Keller, E. B., *J. Biol. Chem.*, **209,** 337 (1954).
2. Keller, E. B., and Zamecnik, P. C., *J. Biol. Chem.*, **221,** 45 (1956).
3. Littlefield, J. W., and Keller, E. B., *J. Biol. Chem.*, **224,** 13 (1957).
4. Hoagland, M. B., Keller, E. B., and Zamecnik, P. C., *J. Biol. Chem.*, **218,** 345 (1956).
5. Caspersson, T. O., Cell growth and cell function, New York (1950).

6. Brachet, J., in Chargaff, E., and Davidson, J. E, The nucleic acids, New York, **2** (1955).
7. Hoagland, M. B., Zamecnik, P. C., and Stephenson, M. L., *Biochim. et biophys. acta,* **24,** 215 (1957).
8. Gierer, A., and Schramm, G., *Nature,* **177,** 702 (1956).
9. Kirby, K. S., *Biochem. J.,* **64,** 405 (1956).
10. Scott, J. F., Fraccastoro, A. P., and Taft, E. B., *J. Histochem. and Cytochem.,* **4,** 1 (1956).
11. Holley, R., *J. Am. Chem. Soc.,* **79,** 658 (1957).
12. Bradley, D. F., and Rich, A., *J. Am. Chem. Soc.,* **78,** 5898 (1956).
13. Nayyar, S. N., and Glick, D., *J. Histochem. and Cytochem.,* **2,** 282 (1954).
14. Hultin, T., *Exp. Cell Res.,* **11,** 222 (1956).
15. Hultin, T., von der Decken, A., and Beskow, G., *Exp. Cell Res.,* **12,** 675 (1957).
16. Koningsberger, V. V., van der Grinten, C. O., and Overbeek, J. T., *Ned. Akad. Wetnsch, Proc.,* series B, **60,** 144 (1957).
17. Davie, E. W., Koningsberger, V. V., and Lipmann, F., *Arch. Biochem. and Biophys.,* **65,** 21 (1956).
18. Petermann, M. L., and Hamilton, M. G., *J. Biol. Chem.,* **224,** 725 (1957).
19. Zamecnik, P. C., Stephenson, M. L., Scott, J. F., and Hoagland, M. B., *Federation Proc.,* **16,** 275 (1957).
20. DeMoss, J. A., Genuth, S. M., and Novelli, G. D., *Proc. Nat. Acad. Sc.,* **42,** 325 (1956).
21. Berg, P., *Federation Proc.,* **16,** 152 (1957).
22. Hoagland, M. B., Zamecnik, P. C., and Stephenson, M. L., Current activities in molecular biology, in press.

Conformation of the Anticodon Loop in tRNA

by

W. FULLER
A. HODGSON

Biophysics Department and
MRC Biophysics Research Unit,
King's College, University cf London

A molecular model for the anticodon arm is proposed which is
compatible with chemical, X-ray and genetic evidence. It provides
a stereochemical basis for Crick's "wobble" hypothesis.

NUCLEOTIDE sequences determined for a number of amino-
acid specific tRNA molecules[1-4] have led to the suggestion
that these molecules have a "clover leaf" structure (Fig. 1).
This was because, despite their different nucleotide
sequences, there are striking structural homologies when
the tRNA molecules are folded so that the number of
intramolecular Watson–Crick base-pairs is a maximum
(Fig. 1). Diagrams like Fig. 1, however, indicate little of
the three-dimensional appearance of such structures and
their implications. Therefore we have constructed three-
dimensional models, and here describe a molecular model-
building study of the anticodon arm.

Using chemical information about nucleotide sequence
and X-ray evidence on the conformation of base-paired
regions in the tRNA, the maintenance of reasonable
stereochemical constraints leads to a model for the
anticodon arm. This model accounts for the observed

degeneracy in the reading of the third position of the
codon and also makes a prediction about the site of the
distortion required to accommodate this degeneracy.

Model Building Technique

We used Corey, Pauling and Koltun[5] spacefilling models
and also skeletal models with a scale of 4 cm to 1 Å (ref. 6).
The former ensure that short van der Waals contacts are
avoided during preliminary investigations. Because,
however, the atomic centres in them are inaccessible, we
used skeletal models when preliminary study suggested
that a particular conformation merited detailed analysis.
Lengths and angles of covalent bonds and short van der
Waals contacts were calculated from atomic co-ordinates
measured on skeletal models and the co-ordinates were
adjusted until acceptable stereochemistry was obtained,

that is lengths of covalent bonds within 0·05 Å of accepted values, covalent angles within 6° and no non-covalently bonded contacts more than 0·4 Å short of the sum of the atomic van der Waals radii. We do not necessarily believe that our models describe the actual molecular conformations to an accuracy of a few hundredths of an angstrom, but the analysis shows that a model with the general characteristics we propose can be built with acceptable stereochemistry. Only if model building is treated as a rigid discipline with strict attention paid to detailed stereochemistry can the results of a study such as this be considered reliable and meaningful.

Conformation of the Anticodon Arm

X-ray diffraction suggests that the molecules of tRNA (ref. 7), in common with all RNA molecules so far studied by this method, contain helical regions with a conformation similar to that determined for two-stranded reovirus RNA (ref. 8). We have assumed that the Watson–Crick base-paired regions in the clover leaf structure have a conformation like the eleven-fold double-helical structure of reovirus RNA (rather than the less favoured ten-fold possibility). In the anticodon arm there is a loop of seven nucleotides at the end of the helical region. From considerations of biological function, the structural homologies in the different tRNA species might be expected to extend to the conformation of this loop.

The characteristic features of polynucleotide secondary structure are provided by interbase hydrogen bonding and base-stacking. The tRNA nucleotide sequences so far determined do not suggest an intramolecular base-pairing scheme which would give a similar structure for all the anticodon loops (Fig. 2). Therefore we searched for conformations of this loop which maximized single-

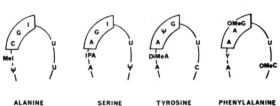

Fig. 2. The nucleotide sequences in yeast tRNA anticodon loops. The anticodon is shown boxed. The symbols ψ, MeI, C, G, I, U, A, IPA, DiMeA, Y, OMeG, OMeC stand for respectively: pseudouracil, 1-methyl-inosine, cytosine, guanine, inosine, uracil, adenine, isopentenyl-adenine, dimethyl-adenine, a so-far unidentified purine, O-methyl guanine, O-methyl cytosine. (The references from which the sequences were taken are in the caption to Fig. 1.)

stranded base-stacking. In doing this we also attempted to: (a) avoid negatively charged phosphate groups coming closer to each other than in accurately determined crystalline fibrous structures; (b) ensure that hydrogen bond donor groups on unpaired bases and ribose sugars were not buried in the structure, so they were unavailable for hydrogen bonding; (c) maintain single bond orientations in the polynucleotide chain (for example, the conformation at the glycosidic link) within the limits of values observed in model compounds and other polynucleotides.

When these stereochemical constraints are maintained, model-building studies suggest that the polynucleotide chain has surprisingly little conformational freedom. Furthermore, orientation of the single bonds in the only two polyribonucleotides whose structures have been determined in detail by X-ray analysis (two-stranded helical RNA (ref. 8), and two-stranded polyadenylic acid⁹) are rather similar. Therefore if stacking is to be maintained, the polynucleotide chain might be expected to have a conformation similar to that in one of the structures described for ribopolynucleotides. Stacking as much as possible of the anticodon loop on top of the double helical region of the anticodon arm might be expected to "nucleate" the structure of the single-stranded region so that its nucleotide conformation is similar to that in the double helical region, that is that of the eleven-fold model for reovirus RNA. (We refer to this conformation as standard.) There is some support from physical studies on solutions of polynucleotides and dinucleotides for postulating that the conformation of a single-stranded polynucleotide with base-stacking is similar to the conformation it would have as one of the strands in a two-stranded structure[10,11].

Figs. 3 and 4 illustrate the structure which stacks the greatest number of the nucleotides in the anticodon loop. Five nucleotides are stacked in the standard conformation so that they lie on the same helix as that chain in the anticodon arm double-helix nearer the tRNA 3' end. This structure represents a unique solution to the problem of maximizing base-stacking in the anticodon loop. Conformations with slightly different base tilt and rotation and translation of each nucleotide (for example if the standard nucleotide conformation was that of the ten-fold rather than eleven-fold RNA model) could of course give a similar degree of base-stacking. Stacking combinations of nucleotides other than those stacked in this structure however, result in less than five nucleotides being stacked. In particular five nucleotides cannot be arranged so that they lie on the same helix as that chain of the anticodon arm double-helix nearer the tRNA 5' end. This is shown in Fig. 4 where A and B are closer together than they would be for a structure with bases perpendicular to the helix axis. If, however, the five bases were stacked on the chain of the two-stranded helix nearer the tRNA 5' end, the base tilt would make the distance to be spanned by the two non-standard nucleotides greater than for a structure with bases perpendicular to the helix axis. In addition to this increased distance, the two nucleotides would have to span the RNA groove containing the 2-keto

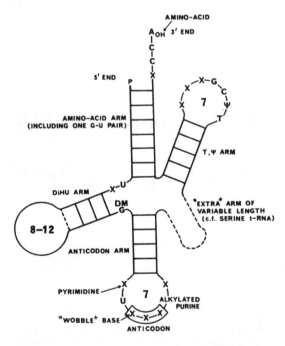

Fig. 1. Generalized clover-leaf structure for yeast tRNA based on sequences determined for tRNAs specific for alanine¹, serine², tyrosine³ and phenylalanine⁴. A base-pair is indicated by a line linking two parts of the RNA chain (a dashed line indicates a base-pair occurring in some tRNAs but not in others); X indicates a nucleotide which varies with the tRNA species; nucleotides which occur at an equivalent position in all sequences are denoted as follows—uracil (U), dimethylguanine (DMG), adenine (A), cytosine (C), thymine (T), pseudouracil (ψ). The number at the centre of each loop indicates the number of nucleotides in the loop.

oups rather than that containing the 6-keto groups
iich is spanned in the model illustrated in Figs. 3 and 4.
e RNA conformation is such that spanning the groove
ntaining the 2-keto groups requires a much longer poly-
cleotide chain.

In the structure illustrated in Figs. 3 and 4 the two
icleotides of the anticodon loop not in the standard
nformation have the planes of their bases approximately
rallel, with some overlap of their hydrophobic surfaces.
ere is, however, some flexibility in this region of the
ructure and this conformation should be regarded as
pical of a number of related possibilities. All the tRNA
icleotide sequences so far determined are compatible
th the poorer stacking of these two nucleotides as
mpared with that in the standard helix because these
ses are always pyrimidines (of which at least one is
acil). These bases are generally thought to stack least
ll. In all these sequences, the second of the five nucleo-
es in the single stranded helix (that is 7 in Fig. 4) has a
emically modified hydrogen bonding donor group on
e base. In addition to inhibiting base-pairing which
ght favour alternative structures to that in Figs. 3 and
this group may increase hydrophobic stabilization of
is stacked conformation.

The structure illustrated in Figs. 3 and 4 could describe
e conformation of the loop of 7 unpaired bases in the Tψ
op (Fig. 1). The occurrence of uracil and cytosine,
wever, at what would be positions 6 and 7 in the single-
anded helix (Fig. 4) make it a rather less attractive
lution than it is for the anticodon loop.

A loop at the end of an RNA double helix need be no
iger than three nucleotides[12]. The base-stacking in such
structure, however, is probably much less perfect than
at in the standard conformation and such a loop would
ly be expected to occur if it contained nucleotides with
or stacking interactions, for example the loop with UUU
d UCU at the end of the extra arm in the two serine
NAs (Fig. 1).

odon–Anticodon Interactions

From consideration of the likely anticodon in a number of
NAs and a knowledge of the different codons which will

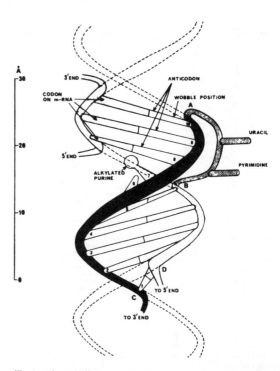

Fig. 4. Schematic diagram of the tRNA anticodon loop illustrating its
relationship to the codon and the helical character of the structure. The
letters A, B, C and D identify the same points on the structure as in
Fig. 3. The bases in nucleotides 1 to 10 are stacked on one another and
follow the regular helix which is shown black. The chain of the anticodon double helix between D and B is shaded like the codon to indicate
that they follow the same helix. This helix is complementary to the
black one. The two nucleotides not in the standard conformation are
represented by dark line shading. The representation of their conformation is very schematic because they lie behind nucleotides 8, 9 and 10 in
the black chain. The dotted lines indicate the generic helix from which
the structure can be imagined to be derived.

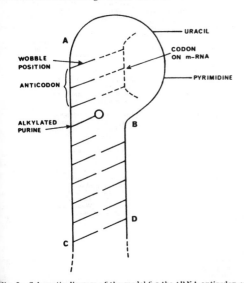

ig. 3. Schematic diagram of the model for the tRNA anticodon arm
llustrating its relationship to the codon. The helical regions are shown
s straight in this diagram. CD is the first base-pair in the double helical
egion of the anticodon arm and all the bases between A and C are
tacked on one another and follow a regular helix. The companion set
etween B and D and the set of three bases in the codon follow the com-
lementary helix. In space (see Fig. 4) A and B are quite close together
because five nucleotide pairs is about half a turn of the helix.

recognize a particular tRNA species, Crick[13] has proposed
a hypothesis for codon–anticodon recognition. This involves standard Watson–Crick base-pairing between the
bases in the codon and anticodon triplets while allowing
the possibility of "wobble" or limited alternative pairing
in the third position. When codon and anticodon are
paired in this way, the atomic sequence in one chain is the
reverse of that in the other and the two triplets can be arranged as the two strands in a regular RNA double helix.
In our model the anticodon triplet occupies positions 8, 9
and 10 of the anticodon helix (Figs. 3 and 4) and a messenger RNA (mRNA) codon can be base-paired to it without
steric hindrance between the rest of the anticodon arm and
adjacent mRNA codons. In fact simultaneous recognition
of two anticodon arms by adjacent codons is stereochemically possible (Fig. 5). There is not much flexibility in the
relative position and orientation of two anticodon arms
when they are interacting simultaneously with adjacent
mRNA codons. They can interact, however, with each
other in a way similar to neighbouring helices in crystalline fibres of reovirus RNA (ref. 8) (see caption to Fig. 5).
The possible biological significance of intermolecular hydrogen bonds between the sugar hydroxyl of one helix and
the phosphate oxygen of another has been noted[8]. One
such hydrogen bond is formed between the two anticodon
arms when arranged as in Fig. 5. Preliminary studies
suggest that it is possible to arrange the clover leaf arms of
the generalized tRNA molecule (Fig. 1) so that there is
no steric hindrance between two tRNA molecules whose
anticodon arms are interacting in this way.

It might be asked if mistakes in translation could occur
by codon "recognition" of bases at positions 7, 8 and 9

279

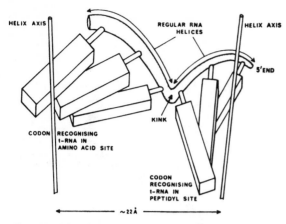

Fig. 5. Schematic diagram of successive codons in mRNA simultaneously recognizing anticodon arms. Each codon of the mRNA has the conformation illustrated in Figs. 3 and 4. The operation required to move the anticodon arm from the amino-acid site to the peptidyl site involves a rotation θ about and a translation t along the anticodon helix axis and a translation d perpendicular to the helix axis along a line joining the two helix axes illustrated in this figure. If the anticodon helices are linked by a hydrogen bond and have a stereochemical relationship like two reovirus RNA helices in the crystalline fibre then the symmetry operation can be defined precisely as follows (otherwise it is an approximate description). $\theta = 87.3°$ (that is 120-32.7), $t = -2.73$ Å, $d = 22$ Å. Values of θ and t which would move nucleotide 9 into the position occupied by nucleotide 10 (Fig. 4) are taken as positive.

(or even 6, 7 and 8) rather than 8, 9 and 10 of the anticodon helix. Studies with spacefilling models suggest that recognition of both 7, 8 and 9 and 6, 7 and 8 could not be excluded even if it is insisted that adjacent codons recognize anticodon arms simultaneously. Recognition of 6, 7 and 8 is the less plausible stereochemically. If the geometry of the tRNA–mRNA–ribosome interaction is inadequate to prevent mis-reading of this kind, it may be that it is prevented by the chemical modification which occurs at nucleotide 7 (Fig. 4) in all sequences determined so far[1-4].

Stereochemical Apects of the "Wobble" Hypothesis

We have considered possible distortions of our model for codon–anticodon interaction which would accommodate the alternative base-pairings described by Crick in his "wobble" hypothesis[13] (Table 1). The separation and relative orientation of the glycosidic links in these alternative base-pairs differ from that in the standard Watson–Crick pairs. The position of the wobble base-pair in our model is illustrated in Figs. 3 and 4. Accommodation of adenine-inosine in this position requires extension of the sugar–phosphate chain linking the second and third bases of the anticodon (at positions 9 and 10) or compression of the chain joining the second and third bases of the codon. The chain in the RNA helix is already rather compressed (about 5.6 Å between successive phosphates as compared to about 7 Å in a completely extended chain) and further compression results in steric hindrance between the 2′ hydroxyl (and the sugar carbon to which it is attached) and the base of the previous nucleotide. Therefore the principal distortion involved in accommodating adenine-inosine (and any other alternative pairs with an interglycosidic link separation larger than the standard pair) must occur at the anticodon.

In contrast accommodation of an alternative pair with an interglycosidic link separation smaller than the standard pair would require either extension of the sugar-phosphate chain between the second and third bases of the codon or compression of the chain between the second and third bases of the anticodon. Significant compression of the chain can be excluded, and so it appears that the principal distortion involved in accommodating pairs with

an interglycosidic link separation significantly shor[t] than standard must occur at the codon.

Site of Distortion in "Wobble" Pairing

Using skeletal models we have found that all the alt[er]native pairing required to account for the genetic evide[nce] on degeneracy in the third position of the codon–an[ti]codon interaction can be accommodated in our model [by] distortion of the anticodon alone (Table 1). Distortion [of] the codon conformation is not required. Further, our mo[del] building studies indicate that a uracil–uracil pairing c[an] be accommodated if distortion is allowed at the cod[on.] Therefore, because the genetic evidence excludes su[ch] pairing in this position, we can conclude that it does n[ot] occur because the codon conformation cannot be signi[fi]cantly distorted. It should be noted, however, that o[ur] criteria for an acceptable pairing relate to the geometry [of] the interbase hydrogen bonds and the stereochemistry [of] the sugar–phosphate chain. While these are clearly nece[s]sary requirements, other considerations may also [be] relevant to the occurrence of a particular alternative pa[ir] for example interbase dipole–dipole interactions. (It ma[y] be that non-occurrence of the uracil–uracil pair is t[he] result of such effects rather than of the codon being rigid[ly] held.)

The assignment of "wobble" distortion to the anticod[on] rather than the codon seems reasonable from gene[ral] considerations because one might expect each codon to [be] held on the 30S ribosome in a way which is independe[nt] of its position in the mRNA and therefore through bon[ds] involving groups near to or part of the sugar-phospha[te] chain of the codon currently being read. Such bonds wou[ld] be expected to limit the conformational flexibility of t[he] codon as compared with the anticodon (which is a relative[ly] small part of the tRNA molecule and not necessarily clo[se] to the ribosomal binding site on the tRNA) in a way whi[ch] is compatible with the above assignment of the distorti[on.]

Table 1. THE ACCOMMODATION OF ALTERNATIVE BASE-PAIRS AT T[HE] "WOBBLE" POSITION IN THE CODON-ANTICODON COMPLEX AS A FUNCT[ION] OF WHETHER THE DISTORTION IS ALLOWED IN THE CODON OR ANTICO[DON] CONFORMATION

Alternative codon-anticodon pairs (groups involved in interbase hydrogen bonding)	Genetic evidence for its occurrence (— denotes occurrence (X denotes non-occurrence)	Stereochemistry of the polynucleotide chain according to the site of distorti[on] (— denotes acceptable stereochemistr[y] (X denotes unacceptable stereochemist[ry])		
		Distortion at anticodon only	Distortion at codon only	Disto[r]tion [at] cod[on] an[d] ant[icodon]
Adenine-inosine (6-amino to 6-keto and N1 to N1)	—	(The torsion angle of the inosine glycosidic link is about 5° outside the acceptable range)	X	
Guanine-uracil (6-keto to N1 and N1 to 2-keto)	—	(There is a hydrogen-oxygen non-bonded contact of about 2.2 Å, i.e., about 0.3 Å less than the sum of the van der Waals radii of these atoms)	X	
Uracil-guanine (N1- to 6-keto and 2-keto to N1)	—	(There is a hydrogen-oxygen non-bonded contact of about 2.2 Å, i.e., about 0.3 Å less than the sum of the van der Waals radii of these atoms)	X	
Uracil-uracil (6-keto to N1 and N1 to 2-keto)	X	X	X	X
Uracil-uracil (N1 to 6-keto and 2-keto to N1)	X	X	—	—
Uracil-cytosine (6-keto to 6-amino and N1 to N1)	X	X	X	X

For none of the pairings denoted as "stereochemically acceptable" is [the] stereochemistry quite as satisfactory as that in the undistorted standa[rd] conformation. The departures from acceptable stereochemistry are no[t] large and are small enough for it to be concluded that the codon–anticodon comp[lex] could be distorted to accommodate these pairs. In contrast the ster[eo]chemistry of the pairs denoted "stereochemically unacceptable" is qu[ite] unacceptable with non-covalently bonded contacts 1 or 2 Å less than nor[mal] values and with torsion angles 40 to 50° outside the range of observed val[ues.]

sociated with "wobble" pairing to the anticodon. Further, the occurrence of the "wobble" base at the top of the single strand anticodon helix allows distortion in the part of the sugar-phosphate chain to which it is attached to be absorbed in the conformational flexibility of the two stacked pyrimidines next to it.

The model we propose for the anticodon arm of tRNA allows codon–anticodon interaction through Watson–Crick base-pairing. The codon and anticodon nucleotide triplets have the conformation of the two strands in a regular RNA double helix. The alternative or "wobble" pairings suggested for the third base of the anticodon can be accommodated in this model by distortion of the anticodon conformation. It is not necessary to postulate distortion of the anticodon conformation. The observation that uracil–uracil is not a wobble pairing suggests that codon information distortion does not take place. This model of the anticodon arm allows adjacent mRNA codons to simultaneously recognize anticodon arms.

In a study such as this it is important to identify clearly the principal assumptions on which the model building is based. Essentially the only assumption we make is that the number of stacked bases in the anticodon loop should be a maximum; this leads to a unique solution for the conformation of the loop. The model receives support from the base sequences which have been determined for the anticodon loop in a number of tRNAs (Fig. 2): the pyrimidines (mainly uracil) are in the irregular part of the loop, the wobble base is at that position in the stacked part of the structure which has the most conformational flexibility, and the modified purine is at a position which could prevent a wrong set of three nucleotides in the anticodon being recognized by the codon. There is no structural or genetic evidence in conflict with this model and, while the model building study does not prove it to be correct, its stereochemical neatness and the manner in which it accounts for what is known about the anticodon region of tRNA suggest that it is essentially correct.

One of us (A. H.) is the holder of a Medical Research Council award. We thank Professor Sir John Randall, Professor M. H. F. Wilkins, and Dr F. H. C. Crick for their interest, Miss A. Kernaghan for preparing the figures and Mr Z. Gabor for carrying out photographic work.

Received June 16; revised August 3, 1967.

[1] Holley, R. W., Apgar, J., Everett, G. A., Madison, J. T., Marquisee, M., Merrill, S. H., Penswick, J. R., and Zamir, A., Science, 147, 1462 (1965).
[2] Zachau, H., Dütting, D., and Feldman, M., Angew Chemie, 78, 393 (1966).
[3] Madison, J. T., Everett, G. A., and Kung, H., Science, 153, 531 (1966).
[4] RajBhandary, U. L., Chang, S. M., Stuart, A., Faulkner, R. D., Hoskinson, R. H., and Khorana, H. G., Proc. US Nat. Acad. Sci., 57, 751 (1967).
[5] Koltun, W. L., Biopolymers, 3, 665 (1965).
[6] Langridge, R., Marvin, D. A., Seeds, W. E., Wilson, H. R., Hooper, C. W., Wilkins, M. H. F., and Hamilton, L. D., J. Mol. Biol., 2, 38 (1960).
[7] Dover, S. D., Spencer, M., Wilkins, M. H. F., and Fuller, W. (in preparation).
[8] Arnott, S., Hutchinson, F., Spencer, M., Wilkins, M. H. F., Fuller, W., and Langridge, R., Nature, 211, 227 (1966).
[9] Rich, A., Davies, D. R., Crick, F. H. C., and Watson, J. D., J. Mol. Biol., 3, 71 (1961).
[10] McDonald, C. C., Phillips, W. D., and Lazar, J. (in the press).
[11] Buch, C. A., and Tinoco, jun., I., J. Mol. Biol., 23, 601 (1967).
[12] Spencer, M., Fuller, W., Wilkins, M. H. F., and Brown, G. L., Nature, 194, 1014 (1962).
[13] Crick, F. H. C., J. Mol. Biol., 19, 548 (1966).

ASSEMBLY OF THE PEPTIDE CHAINS OF HEMOGLOBIN*

By Howard M. Dintzis

DEPARTMENT OF BIOLOGY, MASSACHUSETTS INSTITUTE OF TECHNOLOGY

Communicated by John T. Edsall, January 16, 1961

The mechanism by which proteins are synthesized has been a matter of intense speculation in recent years.[1,2] Some published speculative models propose simultaneous bond formation between all neighboring activated amino acids on a preloaded template (a sort of stamping machine operation). Others suggest various forms of sequential addition of amino acids to a steadily growing polypeptide chain. In addition there have been hypothesized all degrees of exchange between amino acids already incorporated into growing peptide chains on the template and various classes of precursor "activated" amino acids in solution.[3]

A common concept of how peptide chains may grow is based on their linear chemical nature and assumes serial addition of amino acids, starting at one end of the chain and progressing steadily to the other end. A less orderly picture involves peptide sections growing randomly here and there on the template and finally coalescing into a single chain. Since we know very little about the geometric nature of the templates upon which protein synthesis occurs,[4] we cannot a priori rule out all manner of complex growth mechanisms. For example, if the substructure of the template is folded or coiled in a regular manner it is possible that short, evenly spaced bits of peptide chain are made first on those parts of the template most accessible to the external solution and that the intervening bits are added later at a slower rate. Also since nothing is known about the type of bonds holding the activated amino acids to the template just prior to peptide bond formation, we cannot assume that chain growth is necessarily unidirectional. It is possible that chain growth is initiated at both the amino end and the carboxyl end and progresses towards the middle, or conversely, begins in the middle and proceeds toward both ends.

It is apparent that there exists no shortage of hypothetical models of protein chain growth. The difficulty lies in finding an analytical technique capable of yielding enough information to eliminate conclusively most wrong models and, if possible, to narrow the choice to a single correct one.

Data concerning the actual mechanism of protein assembly should in'principle be obtainable by studying both the newly formed protein molecules and the ribosome templates on which they are supposedly formed. However, no method exists for fractionating from a cellular extract all ribosomes engaged in the production of a single type of protein molecule. If a type of cell could be found which is engaged solely in the synthesis of a single kind of protein molecule, then presumably all ribosomes in such a cell would contain incomplete bits of that kind of protein molecule and no others.

Fortunately, a close approximation to this highly desirable situation exists in the case of immature mammalian blood cells producing hemoglobin. These cells, reticulocytes, account for 80 to 90 per cent of the red cells present in the blood of rabbits made anemic by daily injection of phenylhydrazine. The cells may be isolated from the blood and placed in an incubation medium where they will continue producing hemoglobin for many hours.[5, 6] During such an incubation over 90 per cent of the soluble protein produced appears as hemoglobin. It is therefore reasonable to expect most of the growing peptide chains present in the ribosome fraction of such cells to represent incomplete hemoglobin molecules.

If we have available a technique for splitting the peptide chains of both completed and incompleted hemoglobin molecules at a definite number of specific sites, we should be in a position to test which one, if any, of the above hypothetical mechanisms of protein assembly is correct. This is so because each model of protein assembly leads to a definite prediction as to the time and space distribution of newly added amino acids in short sections of peptide chain, both in finished hemoglobin and in the ribosomal particles. Amino acids labeled with radioactive isotopes provide a means of detecting newly added amino acids. In living reticulocyte cells there exist a very large number of finished hemoglobin molecules (10–20% of the cell by weight) and in addition a large number of ribosomal particles, supposedly containing unfinished hemoglobin molecules in different stages of completion. If, at a given moment, we add a radioactively labeled amino acid to the incubation medium containing reticulocytes, then we expect polypeptide produced thereafter to be labeled with radioactive amino acid.

The data to be presented in this paper strongly support a model of protein synthesis involving growth by some kind of sequential addition of amino acids. In Figure 1 are shown some of the predicted consequences of this type of model. For the purposes of illustration we have chosen a model involving chain initiation at one end of the polypeptide followed by sequential addition of one amino acid after another until the other end is reached. We shall assume that some digestion technique can be used to split each polypeptide chain at a definite number of specific sites, yielding the set of peptides $a, b, c, \ldots g$, and that furthermore, the set can be separated and the amount of newly added amino acid present in each member $a, \ldots g$ determined quantitatively.

In the finished hemoglobin at short times, we would then expect a steep gradient of radioactive label through the peptides, with only a few peptides labeled at very short times. At longer times the gradient of radioactivity along the peptide chain should become shallower as more and more completely labeled molecules are produced. At all times, the peptide g, closest to the finish line, should have the most radioactive label, and the peptide a, closest to the starting line, should have the least radioactive label.

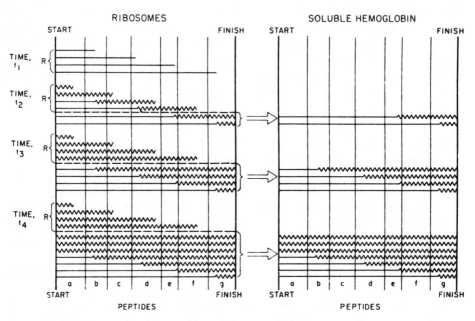

Fig. 1.—Model of sequential chain growth. The straight lines represent unlabeled polypeptide chain. The zigzag lines represent radioactively labeled polypeptide chain formed after the addition of radioactive amino acid at time t_1. The groups of peptides labelled R are those unfinished bits attached to the ribosomes at each time; the rest, having reached the finish line, are assumed to be present in the soluble hemoglobin. In the ribosome at time t_2, the top two completely zigzag lines represent peptide chains formed completely from amino acids during the time interval between t_1 and t_2. The middle two lines represent chains which have grown during the time interval but have not reached the finish line and are therefore still attached to the ribosomes. The bottom two chains represent those which have crossed the finish line, left the ribosomes, and are to be found mixed with other molecules of soluble hemoglobin.

On the other hand, in the ribosomes at very short times we would expect an almost uniform distribution of total label among the various peptides since each growing chain will have added only a small radioactive section (Fig. 1). After times long enough to flush out the nonradioactive bits of growing chain, there should be a gradient of total radioactivity from the initial peptide a, with the most, to the final peptide g, with the least. For this model this is so because there exist in a population of ribosomes at any moment, more sections of peptide a than b, more b than c, and so on. Thus, the expected gradient of label in the ribosomes is opposite to that in the finished hemoglobin, both in space direction and in time development.

General Experimental Considerations.—The technique used for forming and separating a reproducible set of peptides was a modification of the method involving a combination of paper electrophoresis and chromatography, at right angles, used by Ingram for human hemoglobin,[7] and termed "fingerprinting" by him. The enzyme trypsin, which splits polypeptides with high specificity wherever the amino acids lysine and arginine occur, furnishes the means of splitting at a definite number of sites. For various reasons, many details of Ingram's procedure for tryptic digestion, paper electrophoresis, and chromatography were modified in the present study.

The problem of obtaining quantitative data on the amount of radioactivity in each peptide was solved by the use of two different isotopic labels. Short incubations were done with H^3-leucine, and very long incubations with C^{14}-leucine. The very long incubations were assumed to give hemoglobin of uniform specific activity in each leucine position. The H^3- and C^{14}-labeled preparations were mixed and carried through the stages of digestion, electrophoresis and chromatography together. The ratio of H^3 to C^{14} was taken as a measure of the amount of label in each peptide obtained from the short time incubations. This method gave an internal standardization automatically correcting both for the differential losses and for the different number of leucine residues in the peptides.

In order to slow the rate of hemoglobin synthesis to the point where samples could be handled with convenience, incubations were tried at various temperatures below body temperature. It was found that the rate of incorporation of C^{14}-leucine into hemoglobin fell slowly with temperature until a point about 10° was reached, whereupon incorporation abruptly stopped. Incorporation of labeled amino acid was found to proceed smoothly at 15° at approximately $1/4$ of the rate at 37° (Table 1) and this temperature was routinely used for all short-time experiments.

TABLE 1

INCORPORATION OF C^{14} LEUCINE INTO RABBIT HEMOGLOBIN AT VARIOUS TEMPERATURES OF INCUBATION

Temperature of incubation	Experiment 1		Experiment 2	
	Cpm/mg	% of 37° value	Cpm/mg	% of 37° value
0	0	0.00	...	...
5	14	0.22	...	...
10	280	4.3	...	...
15	2,230	34	8,150	17
20	...	...	17,700	38
25	...	...	52,600	110
30	...	...	45,000	95
37	6,500	100	47,000	100

Hemoglobin was dialyzed for 5 days against water, precipitated with trichloroacetic acid, dissolved in dilute NaOH, reprecipitated with trichloroacetic acid, washed with acetone and ether, and then plated in thin layers containing approximately 20 mg. Counting was done using a Nuclear Chicago end window gas flow counter, the results corrected to zero thickness.

It has been previously shown that the structural protein of ribosomes is not appreciably labeled at short times of incubation.[8] It was therefore assumed that the labeled peptides resulting from a digest of ribosomes with ribonuclease and trypsin represent growing hemoglobin chains and not ribosomal structural proteins. On tryptic digestion the ribosome structural protein did yield a large number of ninhydrin staining peptides which were distinct from those of hemoglobin but, as expected, they did not contain radioactive label.

Incubation of cells: Rabbit reticulocytes prepared from phenylhydrazine-treated animals were washed and incubated according to the procedures of Borsook *et al.*[6] The cells were incubated at 37° for 15 min to allow them to renew metabolites, then at 15° for 5 min. To 1.8 ml cells in a total volume of 4 ml incubation mixture was added 0.24 mg 4, 5 H^3-DL-leucine (5 mc, New England Nuclear Corporation, 3.6 mc per μmole) and the incubation continued at 15°. At various intervals aliquots of approximately 1 ml were removed with a pipet and quickly placed in precooled vials surrounded by solid carbon dioxide.

Uniformly labeled C^{14} leucine hemoglobin was prepared in a similar manner from approximately 1 mg of L-leucine, uniform C^{14}, (50μc Nuclear Chicago), which was incubated with 10 ml of sterile whole blood at 37° for 5 or 24 hr. During 24-hr incubations a significant amount of cell lysis occurred, partly offsetting the approximately 50 per cent higher specific activity obtainable. Typical incubations with C^{14} L-leucine of specific activity 6–8 c/millimole gave hemoglobin of approximate activity 1×10^5 dpm/mg.

Preparation of hemoglobin and ribosomes for tryptic digestion: Samples containing approximately 0.45 ml cells were thawed and the broken cells diluted to a volume of 7 ml with cold solution containing 0.14 M KCl, 0.001 M MgCl$_2$ and 0.01 M Tris-Cl pH 7.3. Solution of this composition had been previously shown to stabilize rabbit reticulocyte ribosomes[3] and was used in all operations where ribosomes were present. The solutions were then centrifuged at 20,000 g for 10 min to remove cell walls and debris, and then at 130,000 g for 1$^1/_2$ hr to remove ribosomes.

Hemoglobin: The ribosome-free supernatant was dialyzed for 5–7 days in the cold against daily changes of 5×10^{-4} M KH$_2$PO$_4$, 5×10^{-4} M K$_2$HPO$_4$ saturated with toluene to prevent bacterial growth. The slight precipitate which formed was centrifuged off and the supernatant hemoglobin frozen until used

Short time labeled H^3-leucine hemoglobin (4–60 min at 15°) solution was mixed with long time labeled C^{14}-leucine hemoglobin (5–24 hr at 37°) solution in a ratio such that both the H^3 and C^{14} could be counted with good accuracy. This ratio was usually near 10 dpm H^3 per dpm C^{14}. The combined hemoglobin solution was then used to prepare globin by acid acetone precipitation.[4]

Ribosomes: The ribosome pellets were dissolved in 7 ml stabilizing buffer at 0°C, centrifuged for 5 min at 20,000 g to remove denatured protein and then reprecipitated by centrifuging at 130,000 g for 1$^1/_2$ hr. The ribosomes were redissolved and recentrifuged three times to remove

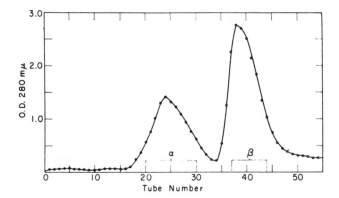

Fig. 2.—Separation of α- and β-chains of rabbit hemoglobin on carboxymethylcellulose column.

free leucine and hemoglobin. The final ribosome pellet was a very light yellowish color and completely transparent.

Separation of peptide chains of hemoglobin: The α- and β-chains of rabbit globin were separated on carboxymethyl cellulose using a linear concentration gradient of buffer between 0.2 M formic acid—0.02 M pyridine and 2 M formic acid—0.02 M pyridine (Fig. 2). Two samples of carboxymethyl cellulose were found to give good results: a preparation of 0.47 meq/g (Brown Co., Berlin, N. H.) and a preparation of 0.06 meq/g (Serva, Heidelberg, Germany). Several preparations of higher capacity from various companies did not give as good results. Solutions of separated chains were dried under vacuum in the presence of sulfuric acid and soda lime.

Tryptic digestion of hemoglobin samples: Autotitrator: Dried samples were dissolved in water to a concentration of 10–20 mg/ml. The pH was adjusted to 9.5 with 0.10 N NaOH from an initial value between 3 and 4. Dense precipitation occurred near neutral pH but the solution became clear again at pH 9.5. 0.01 ml of 1% trypsin (Worthington 2x crystallized, salt-free in 10^{-3} M HCl) was added for each ml of solution and the digestion was allowed to proceed at 37° until definite evidence of a plateau in base uptake was obtained (approximately 1$^1/_2$ hr).

Buffer: 10 mg of dried sample was dissolved in 0.5 ml water, 0.015 ml 0.5 M NH$_4$OH was added, followed by 0.01 ml 1% trypsin and 0.025 ml buffer made of 1 M NH$_4$OAc + NH$_4$OH to pH 9.75. Digestion proceeded for 4 hours at room temperature.

In all cases digestion was stopped by the addition of several drops of glacial acetic acid. The samples were then dried under high vacuum in the presence of sulfuric acid and soda lime and then dissolved at a concentration of 100 mg/ml in 0.4% acetic acid-0.1% pyridine, giving a preparation which was often clear, but sometimes had slight to medium turbidity.

Tryptic digestion of ribosome samples: The ribosome pellet from 0.45 ml cells, approximately 3 mg dry weight, was dissolved in 1 ml water. 10–20 mg uniformly labeled C^{14} leucine globin was dissolved in 1 ml water. The two solutions were mixed and adjusted to pH 8.5 in an auto-titrator at 37°. 0.02 ml 1% ribonuclease (Worthington crystalline) was added, followed, after 15 min, by 0.02 ml 1% trypsin. The digestion was followed in the autotitrator for 15 min, then the pH was raised to 9.5 and the digestion followed for approximately $1^1/_2$ hr until a plateau was reached. The samples were acidified and dried as in the case of hemoglobin digestion.

Paper electrophoresis: Electrophoresis was carried out on a water-cooled metal plate insulated with a thin sheet of polyethylene. Strips of Whatman No. 3MM paper 12 in. wide and 37 in. long were wet with buffer of pH 4.5 (2.5% pyridine, 2.5% acetic acid, 5% n-butanol, all concentrations v/v) and blotted. Eight-inch wicks made of 4 thicknesses of the same paper were overlapped at each end, and 0.02 ml of solution containing 2 mg of sample was applied at the origin. The paper was then covered with polyethylene sheeting pressed flat by weights applied over a sponge rubber pad. Electrophoresis was carried out at 2,000 volts and approximately 100 ma, for 16 hr, after which the paper was dried.

Chromatography: The dried papers were trimmed to a length of 33 in. and stapled into cylinders 12 in. high. Chromatography was then conducted at room temperature in glass jars 12 in. wide and 24 in. high, using a mixture of 42.5 vols n-butanol, 27.5 vols pyridine, 30 vols water. Occasionally it was necessary to increase the chromatographic resolution by sewing a 4-in. strip of paper to the top of the sample sheet before stapling into a circle.

Isolation and counting of peptides: The dried chromatograms were dipped in 0.25 per cent ninhydrin in acetone, dried, and heated at 90° for 5 min. The resulting blue paper spots were cut out, placed in 20 ml counting vials and 5 ml of water was added to each. The vials were then heated in an oven at 90° for 30 min to extract the peptides from the paper, after which time the paper was removed from the vial with a tweezer and the solution evaporated to dryness overnight in an oven at 90°. 0.20 ml of 0.01 HCl was added to each vial, followed by 20 ml of scintillator solution made up of three parts toluene, one part absolute ethanol, and containing 1% phenyl-biphenylyloxadiazole-1,3,4(PBD) and 0.05% p-bis [2-(5-phenyloxazolyl)]-benzene (POPOP). The resulting solutions were measured for C^{14} and H^3 activity simultaneously using a TriCarb scintillation counter equipped with split channel operation so that the lower voltage channel counted both C^{14} and H^3 while the upper voltage channel counted mainly C^{14} The recovery of radioactivity from eluted peptides of hemoglobin amounted to approximately 50 per cent of the amount applied at the origin spot for paper electrophoresis.

The TriCarb scintillation counter was run with 1040 volts on the photomultiplier tubes. The lower pulse height discriminator was set to register pulses between 10 and 50 volts, giving an efficiency of 6.5% for H^3 and 20% for C^{14} with a background of 40 cpm. The upper pulse height discriminator was set to register pulses of 100 volts or higher, giving an efficiency of 0.14% for H^3 and 37% for C^{14} with a background of 60 cpm. Mixtures of isotopes ranging from 2 dpm H^3/dpm C^{14} to 40 dpm H^3/dpm C^{14} were used.

Figure 3 shows a rather typical peptide separation. To improve photographic reproduction, the ninhydrin staining was done with twice the usual concentration of ninhydrin. The result shows more clearly than usual the presence of "ghost" spots, which are defined as weak spots sometimes present but usually absent or barely detectable. The spots which are always or almost always present have been numbered arbitrarily from left to right.

Peptide 31 is the leucine-containing peptide farthest from the origin as determined by radioactivity count on peptides made from uniformly labeled hemoglobin. There are approximately four ninhydrin staining spots farther from the origin than peptide 31, but since they were not labeled by leucine, they were routinely removed from the paper by electrophoresis, to increase the separation of the remaining peptides. The total number of peptides found with reasonable reproducibility is thus about 35, appreciably above the number 26 reported in human hemoglobin by Ingram.[7] It should be noted that a number of peptides, e.g., 2, 7, 16, 19, 23, stain quite weakly and may represent products of incomplete tryptic digestion, or partial digestion by other enzymes such as chymotrypsin which may be present as trace impurities in the trypsin.

The separation and identification of peptides was not uniformly good. In some runs spots were either missing or badly smeared into other spots. Consequently it was necessary to eliminate

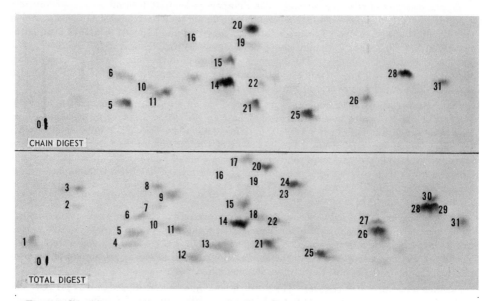

Fig. 3.—Peptide maps of tryptic digest of total rabbit globin (bottom) and column separated α-chain (top). The point of application of digest to the paper is marked by O. The positive electrode is to the left.

from elution and counting in each run those peptides which could not be identified with certainty or which badly overlapped with neighbors known to contain leucine.

A total of 18 peptides, 9 from the α-chain and 9 from the β-chain, were found reproducibly to contain leucine in significant quantity. The average relative yield of C^{14} in these peptides, obtained from digests of uniformly labeled single chains, is shown in Table 2. In addition, smaller

TABLE 2

RELATIVE YIELD OF C^{14} LEUCINE FROM TRYPTIC PEPTIDES

α-Chain Peptides		β-Chain Peptides	
Peptide number	Average relative yield	Peptide number	Average relative yield
10	0.4	1	1.2
11	0.7	3	0.8
14	4.5	9	2.6
16	0.3	12	0.5
20	1.0	13	1.0
21	0.4	17	1.2
22	0.2	18	0.5
25	0.6	24	1.0
31	0.6	27	0.6

amounts of label were found in peptides 2 (β), 6 (α), 19 (α), and 28 (β), but since their yields were quite small and variable, no attempt was made to do quantitative measurements on them (except for a few studies on peptide 28, reported below). This study, which is dependent on the use of radioactive leucine, is therefore based on slightly over half of the total number of recognizable peptides produced from hemoglobin by trypsin digestion. Extension to the remaining peptides awaits the availability of other amino acids, preferably lysine and arginine, of very high H^3 specific activity.

Results.—After 7 min of incubation at 15° in the presence of H³ leucine, a marked difference in the relative amount of tritium contained could be found in the peptides of both the α- and β-chains. The peptides could be arranged in a more or less definite order of increasing tritium content (Fig. 4), such that only the relative order of nearest neighbors was in doubt.

At different times of incubation the same relative order of the peptides was maintained (Fig. 5). The shape of the curves indicates extreme nonuniformity of labeling at 4 min of incubation, with a number of peptides containing no detectable H³ leucine. By 60 min of incubation the gradient of radioactivity has been largely, but not entirely, eliminated.

To check the significance of the varying amounts of H³ leucine found in different peptides two types of control experiments were made (Table 3). First, hemoglobins made by incubation for 5 hr at 37° with H³ leucine and with C¹⁴ leucine were mixed, digested and counted for H³ and C¹⁴. These samples gave a uniform ratio within experimental error; see Table 3, column (*a*). Next, samples from a 7-min incubation at 15° giving marked nonuniform labeling with H³ leucine (Table 3, column (*b*)) were checked to see if any systematic counting error was involved. To each sample

TABLE 3

CONTROLS ON COUNTING ACCURACY

Peptide number	(a) Long-time incubation	(b) Short-time incubation	(c) Increment ratio
α-Chain			
21	1.01	0.08	1.02
10	0.94	0.08	0.98
20	1.06	. . .	. . .
25	1.04	0.36	1.03
11	1.04	0.38	1.05
14	1.07	0.69	1.05
31	1.02	. . .	. . .
22	1.02	0.84	1.00
16	0.88	1.06	1.02
β-Chain			
13	. . .	0.05	0.98
24	0.93	0.10	1.02
1	1.01	0.16	1.03
17	0.94	0.23	1.02
3	0.94	0.34	0.88
9	0.99	0.54	1.02
18	0.97	0.59	0.89
12	1.05	0.70	1.00
27	0.86	. . .	. . .

(a) 5-hr incubation H³ leucine, 5-hr incubation C¹⁴ leucine, relative amount of tritium.
(b) 7-min incubation H³ leucine, 30-hr incubation C¹⁴ leucine, relative amount of tritium.
(c) Ratio of increases in H³ to C¹⁴ after adding H³ leucine and C¹⁴ leucine to each counting vial of (b).

vial a constant amount of H³ standard and C¹⁴ standard were added, and the radioactivity redetermined. The measured increments in H³ and C¹⁴ activity were constant within experimental error and the normalized ratio of increments $\Delta H^3 / \Delta C^{14}$ was also constant (Table 3, column (*c*)).

The results obtained by digesting ribosomes were less reproducible for a number of reasons. First, the α- and β-chains could not be separated, since by definition we were looking for incomplete chain fragments in the ribosomes, and thus did not dare lose fragments in an attempt at fractionation. Secondly, the over-all background of radioactivity between ninhydrin staining spots was much higher in the ribosomes. This is perhaps to be expected from the model in Figure 1, where there

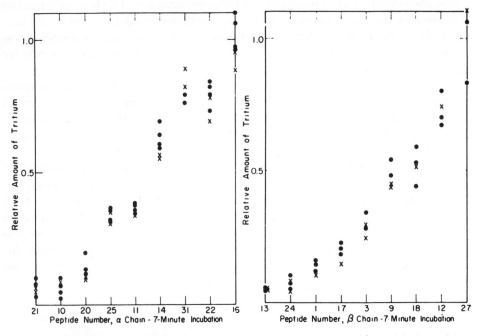

FIG. 4.—Distribution of H³-leucine among tryptic peptides of soluble rabbit hemoglobin. Peptides produced by tryptic digestion in an autotitrater are indicated by ●. Peptides produced from a separate incubation by tryptic digestion in buffer are indicated by X.

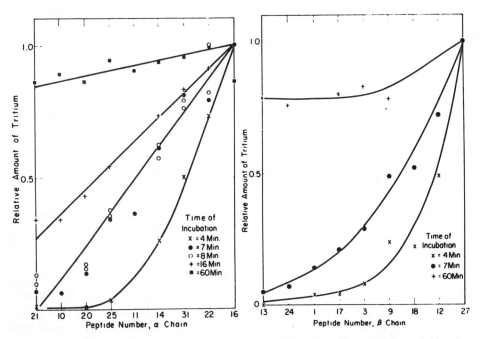

FIG. 5.—Distribution of H³-leucine among tryptic peptides of soluble rabbit hemoglobin after various times of incubation at 15°C. The points indicated for 7 minutes (●) are the result of averaging all points shown in Figure 4.

are shown end bits of growing chain which do not span vertical lines. Such bits would not correspond to tryptic peptides from hemoglobin and would not be expected to separate with the known peptides; hence they would contribute to the background of radioactivity.

Figure 6 shows the data obtained from ribosomes of cells which had been incubated for short periods (4 to 7 min) at 15°. It is hard to see any significant trend to the data, with the possible exception that the terminal peptides (16 and 27) seem lower than the rest. It thus appears that at these short times of incubation the hemoglobin peptides in ribosomes are labeled almost uniformly.

Figure 7 shows results from ribosomes of cells which had been incubated 60 min at 15°. In this case there is a clear trend visible in the peptides of the α-chain with a less definite result in the case of the β-chain. The gradient of radioactivity is opposite to that in Figure 4.

After 7 min of incubation with H^3 leucine at 15° the hemoglobin peptides isolated from soluble hemoglobin (Fig. 4) had an average specific activity of 1.2 × 10^5 dpm H^3 per mg. The average specific activity of the hemoglobin peptides prepared from the ribosomes isolated from the same cells may be calculated if one can make an estimate of the weight fraction of ribosomal particles which is present as growing hemoglobin chains. If we make the extreme assumption that the purified ribosomes are pure hemoglobin, then the specific activity of the average peptide in the ribosome (Fig. 6) is 7 × 10^6 dpm H^3 per mg, or 60 times that of the average peptide in soluble hemoglobin. If we take as more likely the previously reported[8] estimate that growing peptide chains amount to approximately 0.1 per cent of the ribosomal mass, then the ratio of peptide specific activity in ribosomes to that in soluble hemoglobin becomes 60,000. This latter assumption also leads to the conclusion that the specific activity of the H^3-leucine in the ribosomal hemoglobin peptides is approximately 1.5 times that of the H^3-leucine used for the incubation, a result obviously too high but within the combined errors of experiment and assumptions. These results indicate conclusively that the tryptic peptide fragments of hemoglobin isolated from ribosomal particles are precursors of finished hemoglobin molecules and do not represent contamination of the ribosomal particles by completed molecules from the soluble pool.

The results given in Figures 4, 5, 6, and 7 are in agreement with the model shown in Figure 1 in all particulars. The predicted gradient of radioactivity in the peptides of soluble hemoglobin, becoming less pronounced with time, and the inverse gradient in the peptides of the ribosomes, becoming more pronounced with time, are both found. The development of a gradient of radioactivity in the ribosomal hemoglobin peptides at long times is perhaps the most direct proof to date that ribosomes contain incomplete growing peptides. A gradient might be expected at short times in the ribosomes due to contamination from nonuniformly labeled molecules produced elsewhere, but it is hard to see how a gradient could develop with increasing time except by means of the mechanism shown in Figure 1.

It must be stressed that the data given thus far do not constitute proof of the correctness of the particular model in Figure 1, although they are in complete agreement with it. This is the case because all the data presented above are limited to time measurements. To test the model completely, the sequence of amino acid residues along the peptide chain must also be known. Specifically it must be

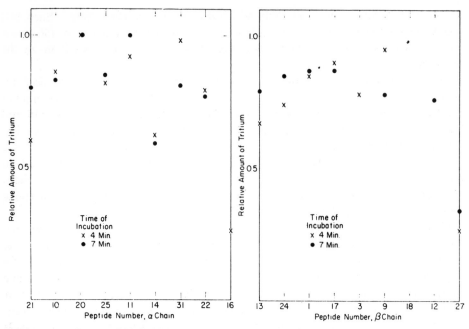

FIG. 6.—Distribution of H³-leucine among tryptic peptides of ribosomes after short incubations.

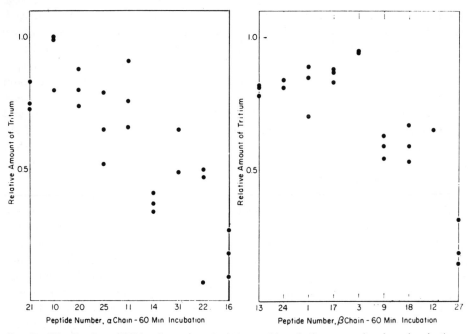

FIG. 7.—Distribution of H³-leucine among tryptic peptides of ribosomes after long incubations.

shown that peptides at the end of the time sequence, e.g., 21 and 31, are nearest to the end of the polypeptide chain, and furthermore that peptides which are neighbors in the time sequence of labeling with H³ leucine, e.g., 14 and 31, are also neighbors on the polypeptide chain.

An attempt has been made to identify the tryptic peptide nearest to the free carboxyl end of each hemoglobin chain. Guidotti has reported that by using a mixture of carboxypeptidases A and B he was able to remove sequentially approximately a dozen amino acids from the carboxyl end of the α- and β-chains of human globin.[10] In the case of human globin a leucine residue was one of those removed from each chain. It was therefore reasonable to assume that a similar operation on rabbit globin could remove a leucine residue from the peptide nearest to the carboxyl end.

Uniformly labeled C^{14} leucine globin was incubated according to the conditions of Guidotti with carboxypeptidase A (Worthington, DFP treated) and carboxypeptidase B (kindly donated by Dr. Martha Ludwig). After digestion it was heated at 100° for 15 min to denature the enzyme, and then mixed with undigested uniformly labeled H^3 leucine globin which had received the same treatment, except that no carboxypeptidase had been added to it. The mixture of C^{14} leucine globin and H^3 leucine globin was then digested with trypsin and the peptides were separated and counted as described above. If the carboxypeptidase had no effect on any recognizable leucine-containing peptide, then we would expect to obtain a constant ratio of H^3 to C^{14} in each resulting tryptic peptide e.g., see Table 3, column (a). If, however, C^{14}-leucine were removed from a peptide by the action of carboxypeptidase, we would expect a decrease in C^{14} leucine content in that peptide with a corresponding increase in the ratio of H^3 to C^{14}. The experiment was also done in reverse, with the H^3 leucine globin being digested with carboxypeptidase. As a final control both C^{14} leucine globin and H^3 leucine globin were carried through all operations except that no carboxypeptidase was added to either. The results are indicated in Table 4.

TABLE 4

RELATIVE TRITIUM CONTENT OF TRYPTIC PEPTIDES FOLLOWING CARBOXYPEPTIDASE ACTION

Peptide number, α-chain	(a) C^{14} Globin Digested with Carboxypeptidases			(b) H^3 Globin Digested with Carboxypeptidases		(c) No Digestion with Carboxypeptidases	
	—Digest 1—		Digest 2				
10	1.0	1.0	1.2	1.0	0.8	1.3	1.1
11	1.0	1.0	1.2	. . .	1.0	1.1	1.3
14	1.0	1.0	1.1	1.1	1.0	1.0	1.1
16	11.0	20.0	2.7	0.07	0.0	0.3	0.4
20	1.0	1.0	0.7	1.0	1.0	1.0	1.0
21	1.0	1.0	1.0	1.0	1.1	1.0	1.0
22	0.9	0.9	0.9	1.2	1.6	1.0	1.1
25	1.0	1.0	1.2	1.1	1.1	1.0	1.1
31	1.0	1.1	1.0	1.2	1.0	1.2	1.0
Peptide number, β-chain							
1	1.0	1.0	1.0	0.9	1.0	0.9	1.0
3	0.9	1.0	1.0	0.9	1.0	1.0	1.0
9	0.9	0.9	0.9	0.9	1.0	0.9	0.9
12	1.4	0.8	1.2	1.1	1.1	1.0	0.9
13	1.2	0.8	1.0	0.9	0.9	0.9	1.2
17	1.0	1.0	1.0	1.0	1.0	1.0	1.0
18	0.8	0.9	1.0	0.9	0.9	2.0	0.9
24	1.0	1.0	1.1	0.9	0.9	1.0	1.0
27	1.6	1.4	0.9	0.8	0.8	0.8	0.9
28	30.0	8.0	13.0	0.07	0.01	0.8	0.9

The only α-chain peptide which shows significant deviation from constant ratio in the expected direction is peptide 16. Unfortunately, the control experiment shows some ratio deviation in peptide 16 (column (c)) but not enough to upset the conclusion that peptide 16 is near the carboxyl end of the α-chain. The ratio variation of peptide 16 in the control experiment (Table 4, column (c)) may be due to the fact that the proteins were heated at 100° for 15 min to inactivate carboxypeptidase, whereas in previous experiments (Table 3, column (a)) this was not done.

In the β-chain none of the major yield peptides showed a significant ratio change, but peptide 28, which was previously sometimes present in minor yield, was present in good yield and clearly showed the behavior expected of a peptide near the carboxyl end of the β-chain. On re-examination of the data from 4- and 7-min H³-leucine incubations, four clear cases were found where peptide 28 had been present but in low yield. The average tritium content of peptide 28 in these four runs was found to be 1.06 ± 0.27 times the tritium content of peptide 27. Although the average yield of peptide 28 was only 0.18 ± 0.04 times the yield of peptide 27, it is tempting to conclude that peptide 28 is closely related to peptide 27 in the time sequence of labeling with H³ leucine.

It would thus appear that in both the α- and β-chains those leucine-containing peptides which are the first to be labeled with H³-leucine in the soluble hemoglobin are nearest to the free carboxyl end of the chain. According to the model shown in Figure 1, this implies that chain growth terminates at or near the free carboxyl end of the molecule.

Discussion.—The NH_2-terminal amino acid of both the α- and β-chains of rabbit hemoglobin is valine.[11] Attempts have been reported to find the rate of short time radioactive labeling of the NH_2-terminal valine relative to the average of all other valines in the hemoglobin molecule. Using whole rabbit reticulocytes, Loftfield[2] reported results indicating that the NH_2-terminal valine is labeled last. On the other hand, Bishop *et al.*,[12] using a cell-free system from rabbit reticulocytes, reported results indicating that the NH_2-terminal valine is labeled first. Reports on other protein-synthesizing systems are equally conflicting. Thus the work of Yoshida and Tobita[13] on bacterial amylase indicates that synthesis proceeds from the amino-terminal toward the carboxyl-terminal end. Complications are present in the interpretation of their work because of the very long times of incubation involved and the presence of various protein precursor pools. Shimura *et al.*[14] using the fibroin synthesizing gland of the silk worm obtained results indicating that the NH_2-terminal glycine is added last.

Muir *et al.*[15] reported finding uniform labeling in hemoglobin labeled *in vivo*. This is to be expected from the results reported in this paper. Thus Figure 5 shows that labeling is uniform within 20 per cent after 60 min of incubation at 15°, corresponding to 15 min of incubation at 37°. Kruh *et al.*[16] have reported nonuniform labeling in hemoglobin after very long *in vivo* experiments. This result is not consistent with the data reported in this paper and possibly represents phenomena different from the original synthesis.

A different approach was used by Loftfield and Eigner who reported kinetics of amino acid incorporation into ferritin[17] and hemoglobin[2] after short times of incubation. Their data indicate that for the first few minutes of labeling the specific activity of newly formed protein increases as the square of the time, becoming linear only after several minutes. From these data they concluded that a scheme essentially the same as that of Figure 1 is indicated. However, this result cannot distinguish between a random and a sequential process of attaching amino acids to the template.

It is perhaps worth noting that if the model shown in Figure 1 is finally proved to be correct, then the experimental technique described in this paper could be useful for structure determination. Thus, it should be possible to determine the spatial sequence of tryptic peptides in proteins of unknown structure by determining the time order of labeling.

It has previously been reported[8] that to account for the production of new hemoglobin in living rabbit reticulocytes, each ribosomal particle must, on the average, make one polypeptide chain of hemoglobin in 1.5 min. That result was obtained by dividing the total rate of hemoglobin synthesis by the total number of ribosomal particles. From Figure 5 it may be seen that the last peptide on each chain to be labeled receives its label at some time between 4 and 7 min of incubation at 15°. Since the rate of labeling was found to be approximately $1/4$ as great at 15° as at 37° (Table 1), this implies that the total time of assembly of each polypeptide chain at 37° is approximately 1.5 min. The agreement between the average rate of synthesis, 1.5 min, and the individual rate of chain synthesis, also 1.5 min, strongly implies that most of the ribosomal particles present in rabbit reticulocytes are, in fact, producing hemoglobin. Since there are approximately 150 amino acid residues in each chain, the average rate of growth is close to two amino acids added per second.

In all of the above discussion a number of possible complications have been ignored because of insufficient data to evaluate their effects. Thus we have ignored the effects of both delay time and dilution of specific activity suffered by labeled leucine during its passage into the cells and subsequent reactions prior to actual peptide bond formation. The fact that we have not needed to invoke these processes to explain the results suggests that the effects are small. Likewise we have ignored the possible existence of hemoglobin in transitory forms between completed polypeptide chains and final soluble hemoglobins. We might imagine, for example, that α-chains and β-chains are produced on separate ribosomal particles and that furthermore single α- and β-chains are insoluble and stay on the ribosomes, while α_2 and β_2 dimers are soluble. This leads to the notion of a small pool of completed chain attached to the ribosome, which would change slightly the results expected in Figure 1, and would lead to a less steep predicted slope in Figure 7.

The figures for this paper have been drawn with uniform spacing between adjacent peptides. This, of course, does not imply that the labelled amino acids are uniformly spaced along the actual polypeptide chain. When the actual sequence of the peptide chains is determined we shall be in a position to plot the relative amount of labeling in each amino acid against its position in the chain. Only when that is done will it be worthwhile to consider the detailed shape of the curves for evidence concerning uniformity of growth rate along the polypeptide chain.

In summary it may be concluded that the growth of the peptide chains of hemoglobin is not a random process but a steady sequential addition of amino acids to growing chains at the rate of approximately two amino acids per second. The number of initiation points per chain is, at most, very small and most likely only one.

The chain growth terminates near or at the free carboxyl end.   Taken together, these conclusions indicate that chain growth proceeds steadily from the free amino end toward the free carboxyl end in rabbit hemoglobin.

The author wishes to acknowledge the expert technical assistance of Miss Judith Karossa and Mrs. Ruth Langridge in the early and later parts, respectively, of this investigation.

* This work was supported by a grant from the National Institutes of Health.

[1] Steinberg, D., M. Vaughan, and G. B. Anfinsen, *Science*, **124**, 389 (1956).

[2] Loftfield, R., *Proc. 4th Intern. Congr. Biochem.*, **8**, 222 (1960).

[3] Borsook, H., *Proc. 3rd Intern. Congr. Biochem.*, 92 (1956).

[4] Dibble, W. E., and H. M. Dintzis, *Biochim. et. Biophys. Acta*, **37**, 152 (1960).

[5] Kruh, J., and H. Borsook, *J. Biol. Chem.*, **220**, 905 (1956).

[6] Borsook, H., E. H. Fischer, and G. Keighley, *J. Biol. Chem.*, **229**, 1059 (1957).

[7] Ingram, V. M., *Biochim. et Biophys. Acta*, **28**, 539 (1958).

[8] Dintzis, H., H. Borsook, and J. Vinograd, in *Microsomal Particles and Protein Synthesis*, ed. R. B. Roberts (New York: Pergamon Press, 1958), p. 95.

[9] Wilson, S., and D. B. Smith, *Can. J. Biochem. and Physiol.*, **37**, 405 (1959).

[10] Guidotti, G., *Biochim. et Biophys. Acta*. **42**, 177 (1960).

[11] Osawa, H., and K. Satake, *J. Biochem. (Tokyo)*, **42**, 905 (1956).

[12] Bishop, J., J. Leaky, and R. Schweet, these PROCEEDINGS, **46**, 1030 (1960).

[13] Yoshida, A., and T. Tobita, *Biochim. et Biophys. Acta*, **37**, 513 (1960).

[14] Shimura, K., H. Fukai, J. Sato, and R. Saeki, *J. Biochem. (Tokyo)*, **43**, 101 (1956).

[15] Muir, H., A. Neuberger, and J. Perrone, *Biochem. J.*. **52**, 87 (1952).

[16] Kruh, J., J. Dreyfus, and G. Schapira, *J. Biol. Chem.*, **235**, 1075 (1960).

[17] Loftfield, R. B., and E. A. Eigner, *J. Biol. Chem.*, **231**, 925 (1958).

Reprinted from the Proceedings of the NATIONAL ACADEMY OF SCIENCES
Vol. 49, No. 1, pp. 122–129. January, 1963.

A MULTIPLE RIBOSOMAL STRUCTURE IN PROTEIN SYNTHESIS

By Jonathan R. Warner,* Paul M. Knopf,† and Alexander Rich

DEPARTMENT OF BIOLOGY, MASSACHUSETTS INSTITUTE OF TECHNOLOGY

Communicated by John T. Edsall, November 3, 1962

It has been well established that the ribosomal particles are the site of protein synthesis, yet we have very little insight into the mechanism.[1] A great deal of attention has been directed toward the question of how the ribosomes contain the information necessary to effect the alignment of amino acids in a specific sequence. This problem has been resolved recently with the discovery of a rapidly metabolizing fraction of RNA, called messenger RNA, which has the ability to attach itself to the ribosomal particle and there to determine the sequence of amino acids.[2,3] This view has been considerably reinforced by *in vitro* experiments in which naturally occurring RNA, as well as synthetic polyribonucleotides, have been shown to provide the information necessary to determine the sequence of amino acids in a polypeptide chain.[4,5] Thus, the ribosome has a passive role in transmitting information; it can apparently polymerize a variety of proteins, depending upon the particular messenger RNA which is attached to it.

However, this state of affairs has puzzled many investigators for some time. The purely geometric aspects of the messenger RNA-ribosomal interaction leave several unresolved questions.   For example, the polypeptide chains in the hemoglobin molecule each contain roughly 150 amino acids and, using a triplet code,[6] this implies a messenger of 450 nucleotides or a molecule 1,500 Å long if there is one nucleotide every 3.4 Å.   How can this long polymer molecule transfer all of its sequence information to the ribosomal site at which the polypeptide chain is believed to grow?   This becomes an even greater puzzle if one considers that much longer messenger RNA molecules have been found.[5] Indeed, the length is so great that it would almost be physically impossible for one ribosome 230 Å in diameter to interact with the entire messenger chain.   However, Riseborough *et al.*[7] have shown that "heavy ribosomes" are seen in a sucrose gradient when labeled T2 messenger RNA is attached to *E. coli* ribosomes.   More recently, several investigators[8-10] have reported that polyuridylic acid induces the formation of a rapidly sedimenting ribosomal peak when it is added *in vitro* to a cell-free bacterial extract. We have therefore been prompted to look for the possible existence of a larger multiple ribosomal structure *in vivo* which might provide insight into the detailed mechanism of protein synthesis.

In these experiments, we have used reticulocyte ribosomes because it is possible to break open the reticulocyte cell wall gently with a minimum of mechanical manipulation.   This approach has been successful, and we have been able to demonstrate the existence of a multiple ribosomal structure held together by RNA.   In the reticulocyte, the predominant species contains five ribosomes. Furthermore, our experiments indicate that protein synthesis in the reticulocyte occurs only on this structure and not on a single ribosomal unit.

Materials and Methods.—Blood containing 80–90 per cent reticulocytes was collected by heart puncture from rabbits made anemic with phenylhydrazine as described by Borsook.[11] The cells were washed in a low magnesium saline (0.14 M NaCl, 0.005 M KCl, 0.0015 M MgCl$_2$) and then incubated at 37° in the presence of 0.2 mg/ml glucose, 0.12 mg/ml NaHCO$_3$, and 0.08 mg/ml Fe (NH$_4$)$_2$(SO$_4$)$_2$. After 15-min incubation, C^{14}-amino acids were added from an algal hydrolysate to a final concentration of 4 μc/ml. In one experiment, H^3 leucine was used. The reaction was stopped after 45 sec by the addition of cold saline. After centrifuging, the cells were gently lysed with two volumes of 0.0015 M MgCl$_2$ and then diluted with 3–5 volumes of standard buffer (0.01 M Tris, pH 7.4; 0.01 M KCl; and 0.0015 M MgCl$_2$). Cell walls and unbroken cells were removed by centrifugation at 10,000 × g for 15 min and the supernatant carefully decanted.

Linear sucrose gradients were made in Spinco SW 25 tubes using either 15 and 30 per cent w/w sucrose or 5 and 20 per cent w/w sucrose solutions containing the standard buffer. 1 ml of the lysate was layered on the sucrose gradient and centrifuged at 25,000 rpm (55,000 × g), for a 2-hr period at 5°C. At the end of the centrifugation, the bottom of the tube was punctured and the solution withdrawn by use of a finger pump and collected in 35–55 fractions. The optical density of the fractions was read at 260 mμ. After the addition of carrier serum albumin (0.1 mg/ml), the fractions were precipitated in trichloroacetic acid (5 per cent final concentration) and collected on Millipore filters. C^{14} radioactivity was counted in a Nuclear-Chicago low-background gas flow counter and tritium in a Packard Tricarb Scintillation Counter. C^{14} algal hydrolysate (1.6 mc/mg) and H$_3$ leucine (3.6 curies/millimole) were obtained from the New England Nuclear Corporation. Ribonuclease (RNAase, 3 × crystallized) and deoxyribonuclease (DNAase, 1 × crystallized) were obtained from Worthington Biochemical Company.

Results.—When the cell contents were isolated by gentle osmotic lysis, a characteristic sucrose density gradient pattern was produced, as in Figure 1(a). In addition to the large amount of hemoglobin that remained at the top of the tube, there are two optical density peaks, one sharp and the other heavier and broader. However, it is the heavy peak which contains all of the radioactivity that has sedimented appreciably from the meniscus. Occasional preparations which were handled less carefully produced sucrose gradients that showed some irregularities of the type illustrated in Figure 1(b). These will be discussed below. Similar results were

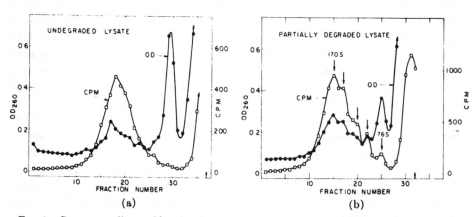

Fig. 1.—Sucrose gradients of lysed reticulocytes after a short incubation with C^{14} amino acids. 1 ml of lysate was layered on 25 ml of a 15–30 per cent sucrose gradient and then centrifuged (55,000 × g, 2 hr, 25° C). The short vertical arrow on the base line indicates the last fraction collected. The vertical arrows in the figure indicate peaks. (a) Undegraded lysate. (b) Partially degraded lysate.

obtained from experiments with a longer incubation period extending up to 20 min. Although there is some variation from one experiment to another, the light peak includes about 70 per cent of the area under the optical density curve, and yet it is totally inactive in the incorporation of amino acids. Since the light peak is so sharp, we conclude that the breadth of the heavy peak represents some heterogeneity, rather than spreading due to diffusion. The sedimentation constants of these peaks were determined in a Spinco Model E analytical ultracentrifuge with UV absorption optics. They were 76S for the small peak and 170S for the heavier peak. The light peak therefore corresponds to 78S ribosomes which have been isolated from reticulocytes by more vigorous methods.[1]

Ribosomes have been found attached to membranes[1] which sediment more rapidly than single ribosomes. Even though there is no endoplasmic reticulum in reticulocytes, experiments were carried out in which the lysate was incubated for 15 min with 0.5 per cent sodium deoxycholate, or 0.5 M NaCl. These have been shown to remove ribosomes from membranes,[1] but this treatment did not alter the 170S peak. In addition, no membranes were observed in the electron micrographs.

In order to make sure that we were examining the bulk of the nascent protein, the location of all radioactivity precipitable with trichloroacetic acid was determined (Table 1). After this short incubation time (45 sec), the ribosomes and soluble hemoglobin are about equally labeled and less than 7 per cent of the radioactivity sediments with the cell-wall fraction. Because there are often radioactive materials at the bottom of the tube after sucrose gradient centrifugation of the clarified lysate, a short centrifugation was carried out at low speed. However, no new peaks of optical density or radioactivity appeared, even though anything sedimenting as rapidly as 4,000S would have been seen. Thus, we can conclude that more than 85 per cent of the hemoglobin is being formed in the 170S peak, and this peak is therefore the site of protein synthesis *in vivo*.

From these initial experiments, we began to suspect that the 170S peak was a multiple ribosomal structure, perhaps held together by RNA. Since it is known that very small amounts of ribonuclease have a profound effect on protein synthesis *in vitro*,[12] it seemed likely that the enzyme might similarly affect the sites of synthesis *in vivo*. Therefore, an aliquot of clarified lysate was incubated at 4° for 1 hr with 0.25 μg/ml of ribonuclease and then layered on the gradient. A similar incubation and centrifugation was carried out with deoxyribonuclease at a concentration of 10 μg/ml. These results are shown in Figure 2. The deoxyribonuclease had no effect, while the ribonuclease almost completely destroyed the 170S peak, converting it to the more familiar single ribosomes. The nascent protein, however,

TABLE 1

Cell fraction	CPM	Per cent total count
Cell walls and unlysed cells	3,980	6.6
Ribosomes	28,200	47
Soluble fraction (hemoglobin)	28,000	46.4

0.75 ml of cells were incubated with C[14] algal hydrolysate for 45 sec, then chilled, washed, and lysed as described in *Methods*. Cell walls were centrifuged at 10,000 × g for 15 min and the supernatant carefully decanted. The cell-wall pellet was resuspended in 4.5 ml buffer and again centrifuged for 15 min at 10,000 × g, and the supernatant was added to the first supernatant. Ribosomes were collected from the supernatant by centrifuging at 35,000 rpm for 60 min in a Spinco SW 39 rotor and the supernatant (soluble fraction) decanted. Protein from each fraction was purified by a modification of the procedure of Siekevitz[20] and plated on Millipore filters, and the radioactivity was counted. All counts were corrected for self-absorption.

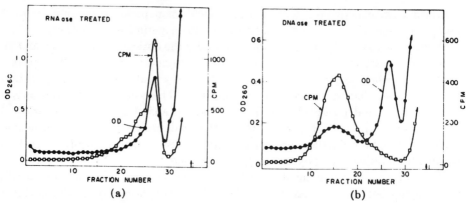

FIG. 2.—Sucrose gradients of reticulocyte lysate as in Figure 1 but incubated at 4°C for 1 hr with (a) 0.25 µg/ml RNAase—the 170S peak has disappeared and the radioactivity is now in the 76S peak, (b) 10 µg/ml DNAase—the 76S and 170S peaks are unchanged from Figure 1.

remained firmly attached to the single ribosomes. Higher concentrations of ribonuclease destroyed even the leading edge of the 78S peak. These experiments suggested that the heavy peak consisted of a multiple ribosome structure held together by RNA. We have called this a "polyribosome" or, a "polysome."

In general, ribosomes are very sensitive to the ionic environment and, in particular, to the concentration of Mg^{++} ions. In order to test the polysome structure for such sensitivity, a clarified lysate was dialyzed for 6 hr against three changes of a thousand-fold volume of 0.01 M Tris, pH 7.4, 0.01 M KCl, $5 \times 10^{-5} M$ MgCl$_2$. It was then layered on a 15–30 per cent sucrose gradient containing this low Mg^{++} buffer and centrifuged for 2 hr. This treatment had no effect on the centrifugal pattern and the results were the same as in Figure 1(a). However, when the lysate was made 0.01 M in ethylenediamine tetraacetate, both the polysome peak and the ribosome peak broke down to smaller units of 50S and 30S and most of the nascent protein was stripped off. Thus, in its reaction to changes in Mg^{++} concentration, the polysome resembles the "active" 70S ribosomes from *E. coli*.[4, 12]

In order to compare our results with earlier ribosome data, some experiments were done to test other techniques for preparing ribosomes. After either freeze-thawing or alumina grinding, the usual methods for preparing bacterial ribosomes, most of the optical density and nascent protein appeared in the 76S peak with no evidence of the polysomal structure. Therefore, the polysome is relatively fragile. Some indication of this fragility is suggested in Figure 1(b), where some fine structure begins to appear in the region between the 76S and the 170S peak. This is seen more clearly when the normal procedure is used for isolating reticulocyte ribosomes. To purify them, the ribosomes are usually centrifuged, the supernatant decanted, and the ribosomal pellet suspended free of hemoglobin. To study the effects of such treatment on the polysome structure, ribosomes from clarified lysate were pelleted and resuspended three times. The result is shown in Figure 3. Five peaks are clearly evident, both of radioactivity and of optical density. Once again, the heaviest peak has migrated about two and a half times as far as the lightest peak. Two considerations argue against this result being an artifact due to nonspecific aggregation during pellet formation. In the first place, the specific activity of the four heaviest peaks is nearly constant, while that of the lightest peak is much lower.

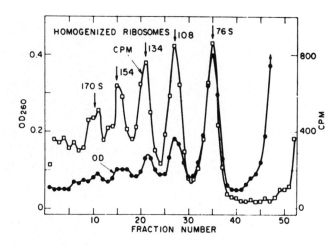

Fig. 3.—Sucrose gradient of lysed reticulocytes after incubation with H³ leucine. After lysis and low-speed centrifugation, the ribosomes were pelleted three times at 28,000 rpm and resuspended with a homogenizer, as described in *Methods*. A 5–20 per cent sucrose gradient was used. The numbers next to the arrows represent the sedimentation constants associated with each peak.

This is what would be expected if the polysomes were being degraded by steps to monomers. In addition, we have already seen indications of these intermediate peaks in preparations that were never centrifuged into a pellet (Figure 1 (b)). By calibrating the sucrose gradient with the 76S and 170S peaks, we could assign S values to the intermediate peaks (108S, 134S, 154S). It is of interest that three earlier papers have presented evidence for these additional peaks without realizing their origin.[13–15]

The regularity of the increments in sedimentation constant clearly suggested that we were observing a sequence of quantized steps in the disintegration of a multiple ribosomal structure, starting from the 170S peak and terminating in the 76S ribosome. The simplest hypothesis is that each new peak is created by the elimination of one ribosomal unit from the polysomal structure. By simple enumeration, we anticipated that the 170S peak should be a pentamer, and this was readily confirmed by studies in the electron microscope. Electron micrographs of shadowed preparations are shown in Figure 4(a–c). Figure 4(a) shows a typical field of 76S ribosomes, which have a diameter of approximately 230 A. Figure 4(b) shows a field taken from the trimer peak (134S), and it can be seen that most of the ribosomes are present as triads. Figure 4(c) shows a typical polysomal field from the 170S peak. Here, most of the clusters contain five ribosomal units, although occasional tetramers or hexamers are seen. A common configuration seen in the air-dried preparations is a tightly clumped group. In the air-dried preparation, the center-to-center distance between the ribosomal subunits is usually 300 to 350 Å, although frequently it is somewhat longer. In some cases, it is possible to see a thin fiber of diameter 10–20 Å connecting two adjacent ribosomes. Staining with uranyl acetate resulted in positive staining; occasionally, a thin thread of high electron density could be seen running between two ribosomal units in the polysome structure. The separation between the ribosomes was usually more clearly resolved in the preparations that were stained with uranyl acetate or phosphotungstic acid. A full description of these results will be published elsewhere.[16]

Discussion.—The evidence presented above clearly points to the polysomal structure as the site of protein synthesis. Earlier experiments in which the ribosomal monomers were isolated by more vigorous procedures, including the formation of

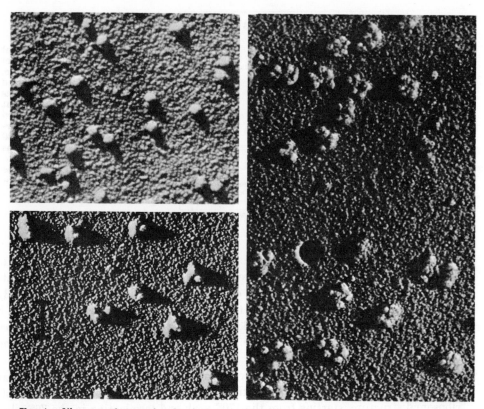

Fig. 4.—Electron micrographs of reticulocyte ribosomes.   The ribosomes were deposited on the grid as a droplet from the sucrose gradient, rinsed with buffer, and air-dried.   The Pt shadowing was at a 5:1 angle.   The vertical mark indicates 0.1μ.   (*a*) Upper left- droplet from the 76S peak.   (*b*) Lower left–droplet from the 134S peak showing triplets of ribosomes.   (*c*) Right— droplet from the 170S peak showing several ribosome pentamers.   (Photographs courtesy of C. E. Hall.)

hard pellets and their resuspension, resulted in degradation which suggested that the nascent protein was associated with the 76S particle.[13]   Directly this leads us to ask whether such polysomal structures exist in other cells as well.   We are inclined to believe that this is the case, even though complete evidence is not available as yet.   Palade observed long strings of ribosomes in thin slices made from a ribosomal pellet of guinea pig pancreas.[17]   In addition, Risebrough *et al.*[7] have studied the interaction of T₂ virus messenger RNA and *E. coli* ribosomes.   Their sucrose density gradient patterns show evidence for the existence of ribosomal dimers, trimers, and even small amounts of tetramers.   It is quite likely that the adoption of more gentle preparative procedures will reveal even larger units in bacteria.   Langridge and Holmes[18] have shown that ribosomes can apparently form linear aggregates in concentrated gels.   It remains to be seen if this is related in some way to polysome formation.

Four lines of evidence suggest that the ribosomal units are held together by RNA, possibly a single strand.   Mild treatment with ribonuclease results in dissociation to the ribosomal units; the mechanical fragility of the polysome suggests that the structural link is not large; the 10–20 Å threads seen in the electron micrographs are consistent with a single RNA strand; finally, these threads stain positively with uranyl acetate, which is known to react with nucleic acids. Somewhat less direct evidence suggests that the ribosomes are held together by messenger RNA. As mentioned above, the attachment of labeled T_2 messenger RNA to *E. coli* ribosomes leads to the formation of ribosomal aggregates with high S values.[7] Ribonuclease also breaks up that polysomal structure. In addition, the attachment of synthetic messenger RNA, polyuridylic acid, results in the formation of aggregates with large S values.[8-10] The simplest interpretation for all of these experiments is that the long thread of messenger RNA is attached to several ribosomes, five being the predominant number for hemoglobin synthesis. By comparing the center-to-center distance between ribosomes with their diameter, we note that there is a 50–100 Å spacing between ribosomes. Five ribosomal diameters plus these spacings have an overall length near the 1,500 Å which is the anticipated length for a messenger RNA strand coding for approximately 150 amino acids. However, further work will be needed to define the exact length of the hemoglobin polysome.

The width of the 170S peak suggests that it may include other species than the pentamer. A qualitative survey of electron micrographs confirms this, since tetramers as well as hexamers are seen. Air drying is known to produce an artificial clumping; accordingly, we cannot say much about the polysome configuration. We believe it to be a linear structure with considerable flexibility because the ribosomes are separated by short stretches of flexible RNA. However, we cannot exclude a circular arrangement.

Let us assume for the moment that a strip of messenger RNA has five ribosomal units attached to it. It has been shown by Dintzis[19] that the polypeptide chain grows sequentially from the amino to the carboxyl end. Since the ribosomes are slightly separated, it is most reasonable to assume that the growing polypeptide chain remains attached to an individual ribosome rather than skipping from one ribosome to the next. Since the ribosome must use the sequence information in the messenger RNA to govern the assembly of amino acids, it follows that the messenger RNA strand must move in some fashion relative to the ribosome. The possibility of such a ribosomal movement was first raised by Gilbert[8] in connection with his experiments on polyphenylalanine synthesis in an *E. coli* cell-free extract. A tentative view which we can adopt is that ribosomal particles begin protein synthesis by attaching to one end of a messenger RNA strand and then move along it as the polypeptide chain lengthens. If the messenger strip is very long, a correspondingly greater number of ribosomes will be attached at any one time. When the ribosomes reach the end of the strand, they release the polypeptide chain as well as the RNA. Thus, the released ribosome would contribute to the pool of inactive 76S monomers which we observe.

Of course, such a model raises questions. For example, what makes the ribosome flow over the messenger RNA strand? Is it possible that there is an energy-consuming mechanism, perhaps distantly related to that which occurs in muscle contraction? However, in addition to raising questions, such a model gives rise to some suggestions. For example, this represents a very efficient use of messenger, since several ribosomes are operating on it at the same time. It is possible that the hemoglobin messenger RNA may be stabilized by its five ribosomes. A new ribosome may attach just as another ribosome falls off at the other end with its completed chain. If these two events do not occur simultaneously, a certain number of tetramers or hexamers will form; this might account for the broad spread observed in the 170S peak. In addition, the mechanism described above raises the possibility that related groups of proteins are all manufactured at the same time. Thus, one genetic locus in the β-galactosidase system controls the production of a series of enzymes. If one long piece of messenger RNA was produced containing the information for all of these enzymes, ribosomes flowing over this strip might then produce the entire group of enzymes, one after another. Much of this is speculation at the present time, since it is based on the assumption that a messenger RNA strand passes through the five ribosomes. In any case, the demonstration that protein synthesis occurs in a polysomal structure will undoubtedly enhance our understanding of the function of the ribosome.

Summary.—It has been demonstrated that protein synthesis in the reticulocyte takes place in a multiple ribosomal structure containing five ribosomes. These ribosomes appear to be held together by an RNA strand, probably messenger RNA. The mechanism of protein synthesis is discussed in light of these observations.

We would like to thank C. E. Hall and Marsha Glynn for their assistance in obtaining electron micrographs. We acknowledge the capable technical assistance of Melissa Quinn. This research was supported by research grants from the National Institutes of Health and the National Science Foundation.

* Predoctoral Fellow of the National Science Foundation.

† Present address: MRC Laboratory of Molecular Biology, Cambridge, England.

[1] A review of ribosomal properties is published by Ts'o, P. O. P., *Ann. Rev. Plant Physiol.* **13**, 45 (1962).

[2] Gros, F., H. Hiatt, W. Gilbert, C. G. Kurland, R. W. Risebrough, and J. D. Watson, *Nature*, **190**, 581 (1961).

[3] Brenner, S., F. Jacob, and M. Meselson, *Nature*, **190**, 576 (1961).

[4] Nirenberg, M. W., and J. H. Matthaei, these PROCEEDINGS, **47**, 1588 (1961).

[5] Tsugita, A., H. Fraenkel-Conrat, M. W. Nirenberg, and J. H. Matthaei, these PROCEEDINGS, **47**, 846 (1962).

[6] Crick, F. H. C., L. Barnett, S. Brenner, and R. J. Watts-Tobin, *Nature*, **192**, 1227 (1961).

[7] Risebrough, R. W., A. Tissières, and J. D. Watson, these PROCEEDINGS, **48**, 430 (1962).

[8] Gilbert, W., personal communication.

[9] Spyrides, G., and F. Lipmann, these PROCEEDINGS, **48**, 1977 (1962).

[10] Barondes, S. H., and M. W. Nirenberg, *Science*, **138**, 813 (1962).

[11] Borsook, H. C., L. Deasy, A. J. Haagen-Smit, G. Keighley, and P. H. Lowy, *J. Biol. Chem.*, **196**, 669 (1952).

[12] Tissières, A., D. Schlessinger, and F. Gros, these PROCEEDINGS, **46**, 1450 (1960).

[13] Wallace, J. M., R. F. Squires, and P. O. P. Ts'o, *Biochim. et Biophys. Acta*, **47**, 130 (1960).

[14] Arnstein, H. R. V., *Biochem. J.*, **81**, 24 P.

[15] Lamfrom, H., and E. R. Glowacki, *J. Mol. Biol.*, **5**, 97 (1962).

[16] Warner, J. R., A. Rich, and C. E. Hall, *Science* (in press).

[17] Palade, G. E., in *Microsomal Particles and Protein Synthesis* (New York: Pergamon Press, 1958), p. 36.

[18] Langridge, R., and K. C. Holmes, *J. Mol. Biol.* (in press).

[19] Dintzis, H. M., these PROCEEDINGS, **47**, 247 (1961).

[20] Sickevitz, P., *J. Biol. Chem.* **195**, 549 (1952).

RIBOSOMAL LOCALIZATION OF STREPTOMYCIN SENSITIVITY*

By Joseph F. Speyer, Peter Lengyel, and Carlos Basilio†

DEPARTMENT OF BIOCHEMISTRY, NEW YORK UNIVERSITY SCHOOL OF MEDICINE

Communicated by Severo Ochoa, February 28, 1962

Erdös and Ullmann[1] reported that streptomycin inhibits the incorporation of labeled amino acids into protein in cell-free preparations of sensitive strains of *Mycobacterium friburgensis* but not in preparations of resistant strains. More recently Spotts and Stanier[2] advanced the hypothesis that streptomycin sensitivity, resistance, or dependence, is the result of modifications in the structure of the ribosomes that affect their affinity for messenger-RNA. They propose that the structure of the ribosomes of sensitive cells endows them with a high affinity for streptomycin and that combination with this antibiotic interferes with the attachment of messenger-RNA with corresponding inhibition of protein synthesis. The ribosomes of resistant cells are supposed to have no affinity for streptomycin; consequently the drug does not affect their function. It had been found by Hancock[3] that streptomycin sensitive, but not resistant, bacterial cells can bind small amounts of streptomycin irreversibly.

We wish to report on experiments showing that inhibition of protein synthesis by streptomycin in cell-free preparations of sensitive strains of *Escherichia coli* is due to interference of the drug with ribosomal function. Thus, streptomycin decreased the polyuridylic acid (poly U) dependent incorporation of C^{14}-labeled phenylalanine into acid-insoluble products[4] in a system containing (*a*) supernatant and ribosomes of sensitive, or (*b*) supernatant of resistant and ribosomes of sensitive *E. coli*. The drug had no effect with (*a*) supernatant and ribosomes of resistant, or (*b*) supernatant of sensitive and ribosomes of resistant cells. While these experiments point to the ribosomes as the site of streptomycin sensitivity, in agreement with the view of Spotts and Stanier, they throw no light on the actual mode of action of the drug.

Preparations and Methods.—These were as previously described[4] except that the preincubation of the ribosomes with supernatant, cold amino acids, and an adenosine triphosphate generating system, was left out, and for the omission of cold amino acids (only phenylalanine-C^{14} being present) from the incubation mixture. Addition of ribosomes and streptomycin preceded that of the remaining components of the system. Streptomycin inhibition was less pronounced if the drug was added last. *E. coli* transfer RNA was added in saturating amounts. The incubation was for 30 minutes at 37°. Poly U, sample 1 (sedimentation coefficient, 10. 3 S), was used. The amount of ribosomal protein, in a final volume of 0.25 ml, was approximately 0.78 mg in the case of streptomycin sensitive (*E. coli* W), and 0.61 mg in that of streptomycin resistant cells. A culture of the latter cells (*E. coli* K12 F⁻ 2341) was kindly provided by Dr. Alexander Tomasz, The Rockefeller Institute, New York. We are also indebted to Dr. David Perlman, The Squibb

Institute for Medical Research, New Brunswick, New Jersey, for gifts of streptomycin sulfate and streptidine carbonate.

Results.—As shown in Table 1, the poly U-dependent incorporation of phenylalanine by the system (supernatant and ribosomes) derived from sensitive cells was inhibited approximately 60% by 0.28×10^{-4} M streptomycin with no additional inhibition at 1.4×10^{-4} M. Prior incubation of the ribosomes with streptomycin, up to 30 minutes at 37°, did not augment the inhibitory effect of the drug. 0.62×10^{-4} M streptidine, the basic moiety of streptomycin, had no effect.

Table 2 shows the result of a typical experiment in which supernatants and ribo-

TABLE 1

EFFECT OF INCREASING CONCENTRATIONS OF STREPTOMYCIN ON PHENYLALANINE INCORPORATION IN *E. coli** SYSTEM WITH POLYURIDYLIC ACID

Streptomycin (mμmoles/ml)	Phenylalanine incorporation (mμmoles/mg ribosomal protein)	Inhibition (%)
0	31.3	0
0.28	32.4	0
1.4	28.3	9.6
5.6	20.2	34.4
28.0	13.1	58.2
140.0	14.0	55.2

* Streptomycin sensitive strain, *E. coli* W.

TABLE 2

EFFECT OF STREPTOMYCIN ON PHENYLALANINE INCORPORATION IN *E. coli* SYSTEM WITH POLYURIDYLIC ACID UNDER VARIOUS CONDITIONS

Supernatant		Ribosomes		Streptomycin (mμmoles/ml)	Phenylalanine incorporation*	Inhibition (%)
Sensitive strain	Resistant strain	Sensitive strain	Resistant strain			
+	−	+	−	0	31.3	...
+	−	+	−	28	13.1	58.2
−	+	−	+	0	24.4	...
−	+	−	+	28	24.8	0
−	+	+	−	0	26.0	...
−	+	+	−	28	7.3	71.8
+	−	−	+	0	22.6	...
+	−	−	+	28	21.4	5.3

* mμmoles/mg ribosomal protein.

somes derived from streptomycin sensitive and resistant cells were crossed. Streptomycin inhibited the incorporation of phenylalanine whenever ribosomes of the sensitive strain, whether with "sensitive" or "resistant" supernatant, were used. There was no inhibition with "resistant" ribosomes, whether with "resistant" or "sensitive" supernatant. Similar results were obtained in two other experiments of this kind. The same was true of an experiment, in the absence of poly U, with phenylalanine-C[14] and a mixture of the 19 remaining cold amino acids, although the incorporation of phenylalanine was much smaller in this case. This experiment was performed in order to see whether the results with poly U, i.e. with artificial messenger, could be duplicated with natural messenger for, under these conditions, amino acid incorporation is probably made possible by the presence of small amounts of messenger-RNA on the ribosomes. Streptomycin did not seem to act by releasing an inhibitor, e.g., ribonuclease, from "sensitive" ribosomes for, in experiments with mixtures of "sensitive" and "resistant" ribosomes, the degree of inhibition per mg of ribosomal protein decreased to the extent that the former were diluted by the latter.

Summary.—Streptomycin decreased the polyuridylic acid-dependent incorporation of C^{14}-labeled phenylalanine into acid-insoluble products in a cell-free system containing ribosomes of streptomycin sensitive *E. coli* and supernatant of either sensitive or resistant cells. There was no inhibition when the system contained ribosomes of streptomycin resistant *E. coli* and supernatant of either resistant or sensitive cells. The experiments show that streptomycin interferes with ribosomal function in sensitive bacteria and point to the ribosomes as the site of streptomycin sensitivity. They also show that the genetic locus determining streptomycin sensitivity is part of a ribosome-specific region of the bacterial chromosome.

We wish to acknowledge the participation of Jerry Atkins and Stanley Leibowitz in this work as "Research Project" students of the class of 1965.

* Aided by a grant from the National Institute of Arthritis and Metabolic Diseases (Grant A-1845) of the U. S. Public Health Service.

† International Postdoctoral Fellow of the National Institutes of Health, U. S. Public Health Service. Permanent address: Instituto de Química Fisiológica y Patológica, Universidad de Chile, Santiago, Chile.

[1] Erdös, T., and A. Ullmann, *Nature*, 183, 618 (1959).
[2] Spotts, C. R., and R. Y. Stanier, *Nature*, 192, 633 (1961).
[3] Hancock, R., *Biochem. J.*, 78, 7P (1961).
[4] Lengyel, P., J. F. Speyer, and S. Ochoa, these Proceedings, 47, 1936 (1961).

Reprinted from the Proceedings of the NATIONAL ACADEMY OF SCIENCES
Vol. 48, No. 8, pp. 1424–1431. August, 1962.

BIOSYNTHESIS OF THE COAT PROTEIN OF COLIPHAGE f2 BY E. COLI EXTRACTS*

BY D. NATHANS,† G. NOTANI, J. H. SCHWARTZ, AND N. D. ZINDER

THE ROCKEFELLER INSTITUTE

Communicated by Fritz Lipmann, June 15, 1962

Nirenberg and Matthaei[1] have discovered an assay system in which RNA serves as an activator of protein synthesis in *E. coli* extracts. RNA fractions from cells,[1] synthetic polyribonucleotides,[2, 3] and viral RNA[1, 4] can all stimulate amino acid incorporation into acid-insoluble products in *E. coli* extracts. Although in each case the product formed is presumed to be a protein or polypeptide whose structure is uniquely determined by the RNA, the products have not as yet been completely analyzed. A recent paper by Tsugita *et al.* presents evidence suggesting that the coat protein of TMV is synthesized by *E. coli* extracts.[5] With the availability of a bacteriophage attacking *E. coli* and containing RNA (coliphage f2),[6] it became possible to use the RNA isolated from this phage to stimulate amino acid incorporation into protein and to identify at least part of the product as the coat protein of the phage.

Materials and Methods.—Phage RNA and protein: Large amounts of the phage f2 were prepared by scaling up the procedure of Loeb and Zinder.[6] RNA was prepared by deproteinization of the phage suspension by shaking with phenol and precipitation of the RNA from the aqueous phase by the addition of two volumes of ethanol. The RNA was kept at $-20°$ in distilled water and used as needed. Its concentration was determined by measuring the optical density at 260 mμ and assuming a specific absorption of 24 per mg. Phage protein was prepared by extraction of purified f2 in 67 per cent acetic acid followed by dialysis and lyophilization. The following properties of the protein are pertinent to this paper. On the basis of chromatography on DEAE-cellulose, starch gel electrophoresis, and ultracentrifugation, the protein appears to be homogeneous. It has a probable molecular weight of 20,000 and contains 10 leucine, 5 lysine, 3 arginine, and no histidine residues per molecule.[7] Digestion of the oxidized protein by trypsin gives nine ninhydrin-reacting components which are resolved by two-dimensional electrophoresis; one of these has the mobility of free lysine. The details of the digestion procedure used in these experiments will be described below.

E. coli extracts: Preparation of the *E. coli* extracts was based on the procedure described by Nirenberg and Matthaei.[1] *E. coli* B was harvested in the log phase of growth. The washed, frozen cell paste was ground with $2^1/_2$ parts of Alumina (Alcoa A-303) and was extracted with $1^1/_2$ volumes of 0.01 M pH 7.4 Tris buffer that was 0.01 M in magnesium acetate. After the addition of 5 μg/ml of DNase, the extract was centrifuged at 15,000 $\times$ g for 10 min. To the resulting supernatant, β-mercaptoethanol was added to a final concentration of 0.005 M, and then it was centrifuged at 30,000 $\times$ g for 30 min. The 30,000 $\times$ g supernatant fraction (S-30) was incubated at 35° for 30 min with the components required for amino acid incorporation into protein: 0.003 M ATP, 0.0002 M GTP, 0.01 M phosphoenolpyruvate, 30 μg/ml pyruvate kinase, 0.01 M glutathione, 0.011 M magnesium acetate, 0.03 M KCl, 0.05 M Tris HCl pH 7.8, 4×10^{-5} M of each amino acid, 5 μg/ml DNase, 1 mg/ml sRNA, and a volume of S-30 equal to half the total incubation volume. After overnight dialysis against 0.01 M Tris HCl pH 7.8, 0.01 M magnesium acetate, 0.03 M KCl, and 0.005 M β-mercaptoethanol, the preincubated mixture was stored at $-20°$.

For the incorporation experiments to be described, the components present during preincubation (minus additional sRNA and DNase) were incubated at 35° with the appropriate C^{14}-amino acids using an amount of preincubated S-30 (containing 4.6 mg of ribosomal RNA/ml) equal to a quarter of the total volume. Amino acid incorporation into proteins was determined by counting the hot acid-precipitate (5 per cent trichloroacetic acid, 90° for 15 min) after washing with TCA and ethanol-ether.

Electrophoresis: High-voltage electrophoresis[8] of tryptic digests of protein (fingerprinting) was performed on Whatman 3 MM paper in a Servonuclear Company tank under Varsol (Standard Oil Co., N.J.). The first dimension was run for 1 hr in pH 4.7 buffer containing by volume 25 ml of acetic acid and 25 ml of pyridine/liter of water. The field strength was 50 volts/cm. At the completion of the run, the paper was dried and the strip containing the peptides cut out and sewn onto another piece of paper. The second dimension was run for 3–4 hr in pH 1.9 buffer containing 87 ml of acetic acid and 25 ml of 88 per cent formic acid/liter of water. The field strength was 20 volts/cm.

Radioactive amino acids: C^{14}-leucine, -arginine, and -lysine with specific activities of 144 mC/mmole and H^3-leucine with specific activity of 5 C/mmole were obtained from New England Nuclear Corporation, Boston, Mass. C^{14} counting was done with a windowless gas flow counter. H^3 and C^{14} in the same sample were determined by counting with and without a thin window and then making the appropriate corrections.

Results.—Characteristics of the amino acid incorporating system: The following

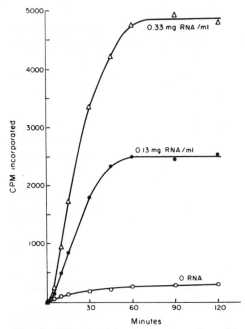

FIG. 1.—Kinetics of leucine incorporation with different concentrations of f2 RNA. The incubation mixtures were as described under *Methods* and contained C¹⁴-leucine (1.5 × 10⁷ cpm/μmole) and the concentration of RNA indicated. Each point represents the acid-insoluble counts in 0.20 ml.

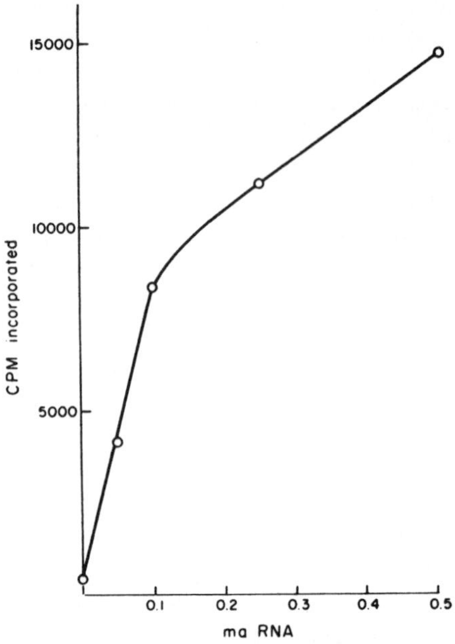

FIG. 2.—Effect of increasing concentration of f2 RNA on leucine incorporation. The components given in *Methods* were incubated with C¹⁴-leucine (1.5 × 10⁷ cpm/μmole) at 35° for 90 min. Total volume was 0.50 ml.

experiments show the extent of the stimulation of amino acid incorporation by *E. coli* extracts when exposed to f2 RNA. Figure 1 shows the kinetics of incorporation of leucine at different RNA concentrations. Both the rate of incorporation and the final amount of product vary directly with the RNA concentration. In Figure 2, the effect of increasing RNA concentration on the amount of leucine incorporated is shown. With the concentration of components used, there is a linear response up to 200 μg/ml and then a sharp break in the curve. Above this concentration, a smaller response per unit of RNA added is observed. Saturation is not achieved even at our highest RNA concentration, which stimulates some 40-fold. In the linear portion of the concentration curve, 0.53 mμ moles of leucine is incorporated per 100 μg of RNA. From this value, one can calculate that about 30 nucleotide residues are required for each molecule of amino acid incorporated. This estimation is based on the specific activity of the leucine, on the percentage composition of the leucine in the phage protein, and on the assumption that any other proteins synthesized have the same percentage of leucine as does the f2 protein.

To demonstrate that the reaction has the properties expected of a protein-synthesizing system, the antibiotics chloramphenicol and puromycin were added to the system. Both of these inhibitors of protein synthesis inhibited the incorporation of leucine (Table 1).

Identification of the product: Two kinds of experiments are to be described by which we characterize the product. The first involves chromatography of the

TABLE 1

Effect of Puromycin and Chloramphenicol on RNA-Dependent Protein Synthesis

Conditions	C^{14}-leucine (cpm incorporated)
Complete system	3650
+ puromycin (4×10^{-4} M)	44
+ chloramphenicol (3×10^{-4} M)	163
(Complete system minus f2 RNA	235)

The components given in *Methods* were incubated with C^{14}-leucine (1.5×10^{7} cpm/μmole) at 35° for 60 min. Total volume was 0.25 ml, containing 50 μg of f2 RNA.

product, the other analysis of tryptic digests of the partially purified product. Of the counts incorporated into the acid-insoluble fraction, 45–55 per cent remains bound to the ribosomes when the ribosomes are removed by centrifugation, and the remainder is found in the 105,000 × g supernatant. It is this latter fraction only that we are studying. Analyses were done only when there was about a 40-fold stimulation over the background incorporation by the extracts so that the unstimulated product may essentially be neglected.

In the first experiment, the product was prepared by incubating C^{14}-leucine with the components described in *Methods*. The ribosomes were removed by centrifugation at 105,000 × g for 2 hr; 3 mg of f2 protein were added to an aliquot of the supernatant and this material was chromotographed on DEAE-cellulose in 3 M urea (in the absence of urea, f2 protein cannot be eluted) with a gradient of 0.1 to 1.0 M potassium phosphate, pH 7.4. Of the 3,000 acid-precipitable counts applied, 60 per cent was recovered of which 45 per cent was in the f2 protein peak.

The next two experiments take advantage of the reproducibility of the fingerprints of f2 protein. In the first of these experiments, the product was prepared by incubating the components described in *Methods* with 0.5 ml of preincubated S-30, 0.8 mg of f2 RNA, and C^{14}-arginine and lysine in a total volume of 2 ml at 35° for 90 min. After removal of the ribosomes by centrifugation at 105,000 × g for 2 hr, the supernatant contained 640,000 cpm in the hot acid-precipitable fraction. To an aliquot containing 140,000 cpm was added 3 mg of f2 protein and a large excess of C^{12}-arginine and lysine. The f2 protein was precipitated with ammonium sulfate at 20 per cent saturation, and the precipitate was washed with ammonium sulfate and suspended in water. By this procedure, 98 per cent of the acid-insoluble counts was precipitated with the carrier f2 protein. Although only 2 per cent of the product was in the supernatant, 3 mg of carrier f2 protein was added to this fraction, and it was carried through the procedure described below as a control for the adsorption of free C^{14}-amino acids by the carrier protein.

The two fractions were prepared for trypsin digestion by first precipitating and extracting with 5 per cent TCA at 90° for 15 min, followed by two TCA washes at room temperature, and then washing with ethanol-ether and ether. The dried product was subjected to performic acid oxidation by a modification of Hirs's procedure.[9] The oxidized protein was then digested for 3 hr at 25° in 1 ml of 0.05 M ammonium bicarbonate pH 7.9 containing 4 per cent trypsin by weight of substrate. After lyophilization to dryness, the digest was dissolved in 20 μl of water, an aliquot containing 105,000 cpm was applied to paper, and the peptides were separated by two-dimensional electrophoresis.

The electropherograms were radioautographed for five days and stained with ninhydrin to identify the peptides. Figure 3 shows the electropherogram of the

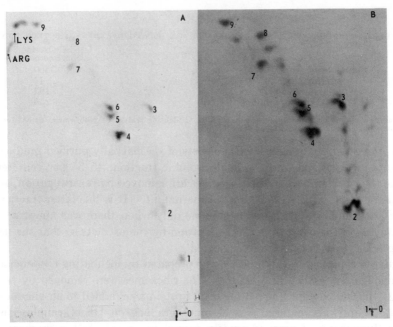

Fig. 3.—Electropherogram and radioautogram of the tryptic peptides from C^{14}-lysine- and arginine-labeled product and carrier f2 protein. *A* is the ninhydrin-stained paper, *B* is the radio-autogram. "Arg" and "lys" represent markers; *O* indicates the origin.

ammonium sulfate precipitate. As the product was labeled with C^{14}-lysine and arginine, and since trypsin cleaves specifically at the carbonyl groups of lysine and arginine, we would expect that all the peptides would be labeled with the exception of the carboxy-terminal peptide. The nine peptides of f2 are marked 1 through 9. It may be noted that all peptides specifically identified with f2 except peptide number 1 are labeled. The congruence of the ninhydrin spots with the radioactive spots is immediately apparent even though the film is not superimposed here on the electropherogram. On the other hand, the electropherogram of the ammonium sulfate supernatant had the same ninhydrin peptides but the radioautogram was blank. This result was to be expected since, as already mentioned, 98 per cent of the TCA-precipitable counts was found in the original ammonium sulfate precipitate. This negative result does show, however, that the correspondence of ninhydrin and radioactive spots is not due to adsorption of C^{14}-lysine and arginine.

A similar control experiment was carried out using egg white lysozyme (Worthington) as carrier in place of f2 protein. In this instance, it was necessary to make the solution 60 per cent saturated with ammonium sulfate in order to precipitate the lysozyme. In other respects, the experiment proceeded as described above except that 50,000 cpm of the lysine and arginine-labeled product were applied to the paper. Although we obtained a whole new spectrum of ninhydrin spots in the electropherogram, the spots that appeared on the radioautogram (Fig. 4) corresponded with those of f2 protein and not with the lysozyme.

Note added in proof: Using C^{14}-lysine and -arginine, we have repeated the experiments described above with RNA isolated from *E. coli* K12 W6, starved of methionine (courtesy of L. Mandel and E. Borek), and with RNA isolated from

312

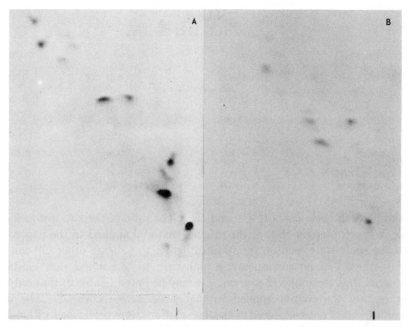

FIG. 4.—Electropherogram and radioautogram of the tryptic peptides from C¹⁴-lysine- and arginine-labeled product and carrier lysozyme. A is the ninhydrin-stained paper, B is the radioautogram.

TMV (obtained from D. Caspar). Fingerprints of each product with f2 protein added as carrier showed no correspondence of radioactivity with the ninhydrin spots. In addition, the product prepared with f2 RNA was fingerprinted with TMV protein. Again there were no overlapping spots. We conclude that the product formed in the presence of f2 RNA is peculiar to the nucleic acid of the bacteriophage.

The next experiment used a second isotopic label to identify those f2 peptides containing leucine. Carrier protein labeled with H^3-leucine was to be mixed with the product labeled with C^{14}-leucine. If the product was identical to the phage protein, those peptides with H^3, i.e., containing leucine, would also have C^{14}, and those peptides without H^3, i.e., containing no leucine, would not have C^{14}.

A small amount of H^3-leucine-containing phage was made by growing f2 on a leucine-requiring strain of the host bacteria in the presence of high-specific-activity H^3-leucine. This phage was added to a large amount of pure, unlabeled phage, and protein was prepared. Fingerprinting of this material followed by elution and tritium counting showed that only peptides 2 and 4 contain leucine. C^{14}-leucine-labeled product was prepared as described above except for the change in C^{14}-amino acid. In this instance, the 105,000 $\times$ g supernatant contained 810,000 acid-insoluble cpm. An aliquot with 100,000 cpm (C^{14}) was added to the mixed carrier protein containing 200,000 cpm (H^3), and this material was precipitated and digested as previously described. In this experiment, only the ammonium sulfate precipitate was analyzed since, again, nearly all of the TCA precipitable counts were in this fraction. The ninhydrin-stained peptides were eluted from the electropherogram with hot water and an aliquot counted to determine the C^{14} and H^3 content. In Table 2, we can see that only peptides 2 and 4 contain substantial

TABLE 2

RADIOACTIVITY OF f2 PEPTIDES

Peptide	C^{14} (cpm)	H^3 (cpm)	C^{14}/H^3
1	200	300	. . .
2	1,100	2,510	0.44
3	355	0	. . .
4	2,960	10,600	0.28
5	0	80	. . .
6	40	0	. . .
7	0	24	. . .
8	232	0	. . .
Origin	4,400	7,000	0.63
Total	9,290	20,500	. . .
cpm applied	47,000	104,000	0.45
% recovered	20	20	. . .

radioactivity and each has both C^{14} and H^3. The ratio of the two isotopes in each peptide is approximately that of the original material applied to the paper. Only a few faint spots were seen on the radioautogram to indicate other C^{14}-containing material; these had no corresponding ninhydrin spots nor did they contain H^3. The product thus resembles f2 protein. It may be noted (Table 2) that only about 20 per cent of the counts applied to the paper were recovered. The balance of the counts could not be located even when elutions were performed with 6 N HCl, nor were they found in the solvents used for the electrophoresis. Since both product and carrier are lost proportionately, these unexplained losses do not alter the conclusion that f2 protein is being made.

Discussion.—The experiments presented leave little room for doubt that the synthesis of f2 coat protein can be mediated by f2 RNA when it is added to *E. coli* extracts. Since the isotopic labels appear primarily in the f2 peptides, we conclude that the coat protein forms a major component of the product that is released from the ribosomes. Preliminary evidence based on the fact that f2 RNA also stimulates the incorporation of histidine, an amino acid which is lacking in the coat protein, indicates that other protein is also being made. In this instance, more than half of the radioactive protein remains bound to the ribosomes.

An important question raised by these results is whether viral RNA acts directly as a template or through some intermediate such as its complementary strand. Although the hypothesis that RNA acts directly is more appealing, the latter possibility cannot, as yet, be excluded.

With the demonstration that viral RNA directs the synthesis of the coat protein in cell extracts, problems relating to viral replication can now be studied in an experimental system more easily controlled than the infected cell.

* Supported by grants from the National Foundation, the National Science Foundation, and the National Cancer Institute, National Institutes of Health, U.S. Public Health Service.

† Post-doctoral fellow of the U.S. Public Health Service. Present address: Department of Microbiology, The Johns Hopkins University School of Medicine, Baltimore, Md.

[1] Nirenberg, M. W., and J. H. Matthaei, these PROCEEDINGS, **47**, 1588 (1961).

[2] Matthaei, J. H., O. W. Jones, R. G. Martin, and M. W. Nirenberg, these PROCEEDINGS, **48**, 666 (1962).

[3] Lengyel, P., J. F. Speyer, C. Basilio, and S. Ochoa, these PROCEEDINGS, **48**, 282 (1962).

[4] Ofengand, J., and R. Haselkorn, *Biochem. Biophys. Res. Comm.*, **6**, 469 (1962).

[5] Tsugita, A., H. Fraenkel-Conrat, M. W. Nirenberg, and J. H. Matthaei, these PROCEEDINGS, **48**, 846 (1962).

[6] Loeb, T., and N. D. Zinder, these PROCEEDINGS, **47, 282** (1961).

[7] Notani, G., and N. D. Zinder, unpublished observations.

[8] Ingram, V. M., *Nature*, **178,** 792 (1956); Katz, A. M., W. J. Dreyer, and C. B. Anfinsen, *J. Biol. Chem.*, **234,** 2897 (1959).

[9] Hirs, C. H. W., S. Moore, and W. H. Stein, *J. Biol. Chem.*, **219,** 623 (1956). Two ml of formic acid were mixed with 0.1 ml of 30 per cent hydrogen peroxide (superoxal) and allowed to stand for 2 hr at 0°. One-tenth ml of this mixture was added to the dried protein and was incubated for 1 hr at 0°. Oxidation was stopped by the addition of 1 ml of water and the protein was lyophilized.

Reprinted from Cold Spring Harbor Symposia on Qualitative Biology, Vol. XXXI, 1966.

Serine Specific Transfer Ribonucleic Acids. XIV. Comparison of Nucleotide Sequences and Secondary Structure Models[1]

H. G. Zachau, D. Dütting, H. Feldmann, F. Melchers, and W. Karau

Institut für Genetik der Universität Köln, Germany

Following the discussion of tRNA structure at the 1963 Cold Spring Harbor Symposium (Volume 28), the work on nucleotide sequences of tRNAs has progressed rapidly. Holley et al. (1965) reported the nucleotide sequence of an alanine tRNA from yeast, thus elucidating for the first time the primary structure of a nucleic acid. Recently the primary structures of two serine tRNAs (Zachau, Dütting, and Feldmann, 1966a) and of a tyrosine tRNA (Madison, Everett, and Kung, this volume) from yeast have been established.

The experimental account of the structural work on the serine tRNAs, which has been published elsewhere (Zachau et al., 1966b; Feldmann et al., 1966; Dütting et al., 1966; Zachau et al., 1966c), will not be reviewed here. Instead we shall discuss three topics, which are not covered by the other papers of this series.

Different Serine tRNAs

Serine tRNA I and II differ only in three nucleotides as can be seen from Fig. 1. One Cp and 2 Ap's of serine tRNA I correspond to one Up and 2 Gp's respectively in serine tRNA II. These differences were detected by analyzing the oligonucleotides from complete digests of the tRNAs: The respective oligonucleotides were found only in either serine tRNA I or II (Fig. 1). Furthermore, analogous oligonucleotide fragments were found in partial enzymatic digests, which were different only in one, two, or three of the positions (Fig. 2). Differences between serine tRNA I and II, which originate from a different arrangement of the oligonucleotides within the chains, could be excluded from the analyses of about 40 oligonucleotide fragments, which cover the whole tRNA molecules.

From the patterns of countercurrent distributions, which were discussed elsewhere (Zachau et al., 1966b), it can be seen that serine tRNAs I and II are the major serine tRNAs. The presence of additional minor serine tRNAs, which were removed in the fractionations, cannot be excluded.

[1] Dedicated to Max Delbrück, Pasadena ⇌ Köln, on the occasion of his 60th birthday.

It is not impossible that the two different serine tRNAs are derived from two different strains of yeast, which may be present in the brewer's yeast. On the other hand, serine tRNA I and II have been isolated as the major serine tRNAs from samples of brewer's yeast of quite different origin, which then would have to contain always a mixture of the same two strains. As a more likely alternative one should consider the possibility that each yeast cell produces both serine tRNA I and II. This uncertainty applies to any multiplicity that has been reported for tRNAs from brewer's or baker's yeast.

There have been reports of the existence of a number of tRNAs that are specific for the same amino acid and bind preferentially to different trinucleotides in the ribosome binding test (see for instance Söll et al., this volume). These tRNAs, therefore, probably differ in their anticodons, although this has not yet been directly proved by sequence analyses of the tRNAs concerned. It seems likely, however, that in these cases there is a certain correspondence between the degeneracy of the genetic code and the multiplicity of tRNAs. In serine tRNA I and II, on the other hand, the structural differences are outside of the probable anticodon, –I–G–A–. This, therefore, constitutes a new type of multiplicity of tRNAs.

–I–G–A– is considered to be the probable anticodon for the following reasons: (1) Serine tRNA I and II were both found to bind to U-rich and C-rich UC-copolymers, but not to AGU- and AGC-copolymers (Thiebe, 1965; Zachau et al. 1965). This makes unlikely for our tRNAs two of the six codons proposed for serine and leaves only U–C–U, U–C–C, U–C–A, and U–C–G to be considered. (2) An I in the anticodon would allow both serine tRNAs to recognize the first three (and possibly all four) of these codons by antiparallel interaction (Crick, 1966). (3) In alanine and valine tRNAs I-containing sequences have been found (Holley et al., 1965; Ingram and Sjöquist, 1963) which could serve as anticodons for the three (or four) codons proposed for each of these amino acids. (4) In secondary structure models of the serine tRNAs, –I–G–A– is located in an unpaired

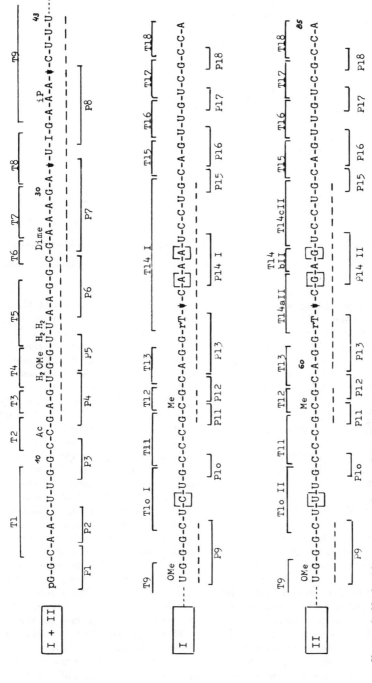

FIGURE 1. Nucleotide sequences of serine tRNA I and II. Upper line: Nucleotide sequence common to both serine tRNAs. Middle line: Continuation of the upper sequence for serine tRNA I. Lower line: Continuation of the upper sequence for serine tRNA II. Solid lines represent oligonucleotides from digestion with pancreatic (P1 – P18) and T1-RNase (T1 – T18). Broken lines signify overlapping sequences which could be constructed from these oligonucleotides with the aid of odd nucleotides. T5 contains 2UH₂ as the corresponding oligonucleotide of serine tRNA from bakers yeast (G. L. Cantoni, M. Molinari, and F. Neelon, pers. commun.; cf. Zachau et al. 1966b).

Abbreviations: AcC = N(6)-acetylcytidine; UH₂ = 4,5-dihydrouridine; OMeG = 2′-O-methylguanosine; DimeG = N(2)-dimethylguanosine; iPA = N(6)-(γ,γ-dimethylallyl)adenosine; OMeU = 2′-O-methyluridine; MeC = 5-methylcytidine.

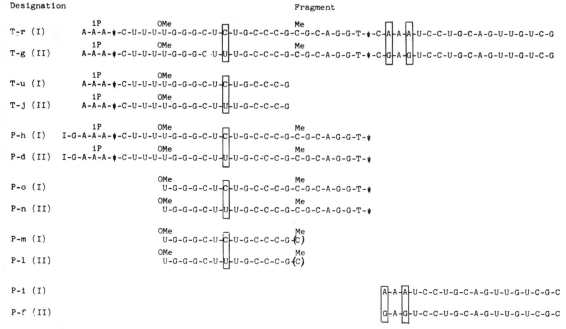

FIGURE 2. Analogous oligonucleotide fragments from serine tRNA I and II. The designation of fragments is the same as in Dütting et al., (1966); I and II indicate serine tRNA I and II, respectively. The pairs of equal chain length were found in partial digests of a mixture of serine tRNA I and II, and were separated into their constituents by chromatography on acidic DEAE-Sephadex columns.

region (see below) and is distinguished by the adjacent unusual nucleotide iPA (isopentenyladenosine), the structure of which has been elucidated recently (Biemann et al., 1966; Hall et al., 1966). Two other sequences, that theoretically could serve as anticodons, are rather unlikely to function in this way: –A–G–A– (position 29–31) probably occurs in a tightly paired region; –C–G–A– (position 65–67, only in serine tRNA II) is unlikely, since it occurs in an analogous position also in alanine tRNA.

None of these four points is proof that –I–G–A– is the anticodon of the serine tRNAs, but together they are highly suggestive.

SECONDARY STRUCTURE MODELS OF THE SERINE tRNAs

While the primary structure has been established unequivocally, the secondary structure can be discussed up to now only in terms of models. In constructing such models, we tried to maximize base pairing according to Watson and Crick, and did not consider other undoubtedly existing forces, which may help to stabilize particular forms of secondary structure. The models may have to be modified when these forces become better characterized and when the base-pairing properties of the unusual nucleotides are further investigated.

The nucleotide sequence of alanine tRNA has been folded into a clover leaf and into an extended model (Holley et al., 1965). In the case of serine tRNA we favor models of the clover-leaf type (Fig. 3) more than extended models (e.g. Fig. 4). Our preference is based on some results from partial enzymatic digestions.

Under conditions of incomplete enzymatic degradation (cf. legend to Fig. 3) certain internucleotide bonds in the serine tRNAs are split preferentially. This points to the presence in solution of distinct paired and unpaired regions if one remembers the general observation that single-stranded polynucleotides are much more susceptible to endonucleolytic attack than double-stranded ones. The arrows in Fig. 3 and 4 indicate such points of preferential enzymatic splitting. They are located predominantly in unpaired regions of both models, thus confirming the assumptions leading to their construction. In structures similar to the extended model, however, one would expect little splitting of the –G–MeC– bond and considerable splitting in the sequence between MeC and –rT–ψ–C–, which is in contrast to the observed fragmentation pattern. An extended model is somewhat unlikely also for other reasons: There may be some steric difficulties, particularly around the DimeG and the –rT–ψ–C–. In addition, in contrast to the clover-leaf model, one loses the fine pairing in the

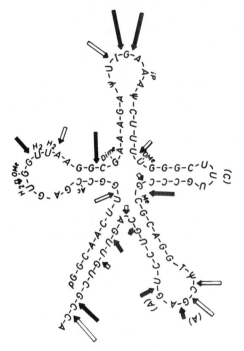

FIGURE 3. Clover-leaf model of serine tRNA I and II. Open and filled arrows point to the 5'- and 3'-ends of the major oligonucleotide fragments from partial enzymatic digests of serine tRNA I and II with pancreatic RNase (pH 7.5; 0°; 10 mM MgCl₂; 30 min) and Tl-RNase, respectively (pH 7.5; 0°; no MgCl₂; 30, 45, and 60 min). Not shown are those splits that yielded the "standard" oligonucleotides known from complete enzymatic degradation (Fig. 1).

The length of the arrows is proportional to the relative amounts of isolated fragments: In the calculations the amounts of fragments which start or terminate in the same position have been added, and the resulting numbers were normalized. The results from the three Tl-RNase digests were averaged. The calculated values are approximate since ε-values of the fragments can be only estimated, and possible losses during the purification of the fragments are not taken into account.

stem of the –rT–ψ–C– loop. We therefore discuss in the following only the clover leaf model.

A structure like the clover-leaf model (Fig. 3) may be stabilized by Mg⁺⁺, since there seem to be fewer splits in paired regions in the presence of Mg⁺⁺ (digestion with pancreatic RNase) than in its absence (digestion with Tl-RNase).

Most of the unusual nucleotides appear in loops and unpaired regions of the model (Fig. 3), even though in constructing it no special assumptions concerning their base-pairing properties have been made; (some of them may pair very well in complementary sequences).

In pairing the *5'- to the 3'-terminal region* one obtains six standard base pairs. The location of a G opposite to a U allows for an additional base pair of the type discussed recently by Crick (1966). The terminal –G–C–C–A is left unpaired. This is in agreement with the following results: In partial Tl-RNase digestions the resulting fragments seldom included the terminal –C–C–A; in exonucleolytic degradations by snake venom phosphodiesterase (PDE), also the fourth nucleotide from the end, the G, seems to be removed preferentially. In partial degradations with pancreatic RNase, on the other hand, the bond between the fourth and the fifth nucleotide from the end seems to be somewhat shielded (Mg⁺⁺) since the respective fragments (P–i and P–f in Fig. 2) contain a terminal –G–C.

The *UH₂ sequence* occurs in an unpaired region. It is uncertain, however, whether this region is located in a loop with a stem of paired nucleotides as shown in Fig. 3. Only two standard G:C pairs and one G:AcC pair are possible here. The paired region could get some stabilization from an additional G:A pair, which recently has been discussed as a terminal base pair in helical regions of RNA (Traub and Elson, 1966). Results from partial Tl-RNase digestions, on the other hand, indicate that this paired region is (at least in the absence of Mg⁺⁺) rather weak, since considerable splitting next to both G's of the –A–G–G–C– sequence has been found; (one split is shown in Fig. 3; the other one is not included, since it yields no large fragment, only the "normal" oligonucleotide UH₂–UH₂–A–A–G).

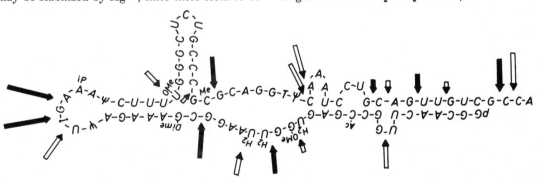

FIGURE 4. Extended model of serine tRNA I and II.

In contrast to the foregoing, the *anticodon loop* and its stem seem to be very distinct features of the secondary structure of the molecule. In partial enzymatic digestions no splits in the stem were observed, whereas the loop was found to be particularly susceptible to the enzymatic attack. No fragment containing an intact –I–G–A– has been detected in partial T1-RNase digests. One A:ψ pair has been included in the stem; an additional one is possible, which would narrow the loop.

The next paired region, which does not contain any odd nucleotide, has been termed, for lack of a better name, the *S-region* (S stands for serine, since this region seems to be a special feature of serine tRNA among the known tRNAs). The four G:C pairs in this region seem to stabilize its secondary structure strongly: In partial pancreatic and T1-RNase digestions no oligonucleotide fragment starting or terminating in this region has been found. Sequences from the S-region (P-1 to P-0 in Fig. 2) survived even a second partial digestion with pancreatic RNase (in the presence of Mg^{++}). This again does not exclude the possibility that another part of the starting material was split into mono- and small oligonucleotides (see legend to Fig. 3). In a second partial digestion with T1-RNase (in the absence of Mg^{++}) the –U–G–C– sequence of this region was split to a small extent, which was helpful in the elucidation of the nucleotide sequence. The S-region was found relatively resistant also toward snake venom PDE: degradation under limiting conditions seemed to stop in this region; fragments containing the S-region (T-u and T-j in Fig. 2) were resistant under these conditions, which were more severe than those normally used for sequential degradations.

The proposed secondary structure of the *–rT–ψ–C–region* is also supported by partial hydrolysis data (see Fig. 3). It is noteworthy that four oligonucleotide fragments have been found in pancreatic RNase digests, that end in –G–rT–ψ (P-d, P-h, P-n, and P-o in Fig. 2). The relative resistance of the rT–ψ– bond toward pancreatic RNase may be due to a specificity of the enzyme or to a special property of the dinucleotide rT–ψ. It also cannot be excluded that base pairing across the loop occurs, resulting in an rT:A– or a ψ:A–pair in serine tRNA II and possibly in both of these pairs in serine tRNA I.

Models of the clover-leaf type can be devised as readily for serine tRNA I as for serine tRNA II, since the differences in nucleotide sequence between the two tRNAs are located in loops, and therefore probably do not influence the secondary structure. The base pairing shown in the clover-leaf model

(14 G:C, 7 A:U, 1 A:ψ, 1 AcC:G) corresponds to 55% helical content. These figures could be increased by adding unorthodox base pairs and by making the loops narrower (see above: 1 G:U, 1 G:A, 1–2 A:ψ, 1 A:rT).

Nothing can be said from our data about the tertiary structure of the serine tRNAs. Theoretically, the –rT–ψ–C– region can fold over to allow an interaction of its unpaired nucleotides with complementary ones of the anticodon loop or the UH$_2$ loop (compare the folded model of alanine tRNA; Holley, 1966). Such folded structures certainly are more compact than open cloverleaf structures, and so they may be of functional significance. The term "quaternary structure" may not be meaningful in tRNAs, but it should be mentioned that an aggregation of serine tRNA has been observed (Zachau et al., 1966c).

COMPARISON OF SERINE tRNA WITH OTHER tRNAs

In this section, the similarities and differences in primary and secondary structure between serine tRNAs and the other tRNAs (Fig. 5 and 6) will be discussed. The similarities in the UH$_2$ region are obvious from Fig. 5. The distances between one of the UH$_2$'s, the common –G–C–DimeG– sequence, and the probable anticodon are identical in alanine, serine, and tyrosine tRNAs. The anticodon is flanked, in these tRNAs, by a Up at the 5′ side and an odd nucleotide (probably derived from Ap) at the 3′ side. In the –rT–ψ–C– region, the distance between the Cp or MeCp at the 5′ side and the rTp is identical. Serine tRNA I constitutes an exception among the tRNAs in possessing a –G–rT–ψ–C–A– sequence instead of the –G–rT–ψ–C–G– sequence found by Zamir et al., (1965) in high amounts in unfractionated yeast tRNA. This pentanucleotide sequence is flanked by an Ap or Ap derivative on its 3′ side. In each of the three tRNAs there are 2 nucleotides in between the rTp and the terminal adenosine.*

There is a particularly close similarity between serine and tyrosine tRNAs in the UH$_2$ and anticodon regions (Fig. 5).

* *Note added in proof 9/20/1966:*

A nucleotide sequence of a valine tRNA, which in some parts is still tentative, has been worked out by A. A. Bayev, T. V. Venkstern, A. D. Mirzabekov, A. I. Krutilina, V. D. Axelrod, L. Li, and V. A. Engelhardt (pers. commun.). Some of the regularities observed in other tRNAs are also present in this tRNA, for instance: (1) the probable anticodon sequence –I–A–C– is located also in the middle portion of the molecule and has a 5′-adjacent Up as the other tRNAs and a 3′-adjacent Ap (cf. the modified Ap in the other tRNAs); (2) the UH$_2$-region starts with a MeG as alanine tRNA and contains also the sequence –A–G–UH$_2$–C–G–G–UH$_2$–A–; (3) the –rT–ψ–C–G– sequence is in approximately the same part of the molecule as in the other tRNAs and also has a 3′-adjacent MeA.

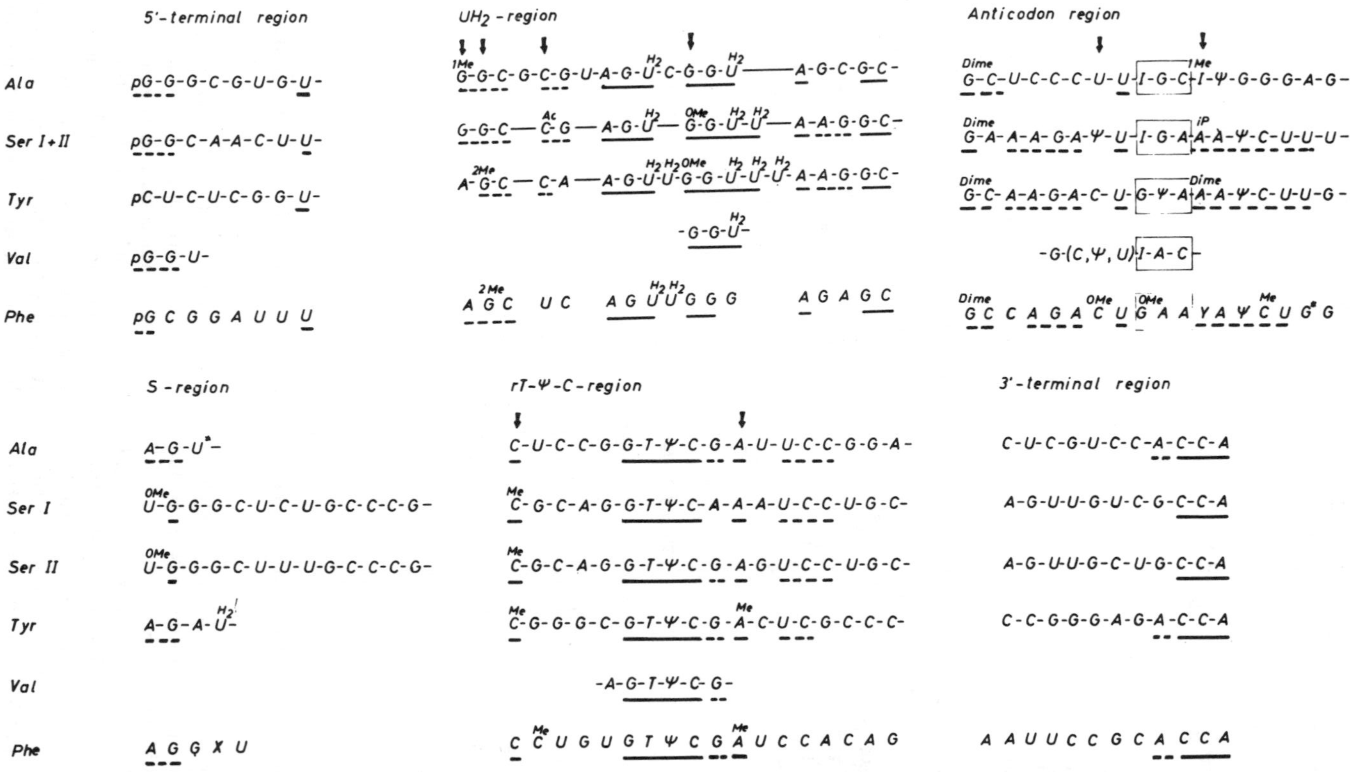

FIGURE 5. Homologies and analogies in primary structure between serine tRNA and other tRNAs. Underlining by solid and dotted lines indicate greater and lesser similarities. The nucleotide sequence of alanine and tyrosine tRNA are taken from Holley et al. (1965) and Madison et al. (this volume). The oligonucleotides of valine tRNA (Bayev et al., 1965; Ingram and Sjöquist, 1963) are arranged by us into analogous positions. The tentative sequence of phenylalanine tRNA is according to RajBhandary et al., in this volume. Vertical arrows point to positions where odd nucleotides and their "parent" nucleotides occur in analogous parts of the chains. *Note added in proof* (9/20/66): The 3'-terminal sequence of phenylalanyl tRNA is AAUUCGCACCA, instead of AAUUCCGCACCA, which means that the distance between rT and the terminal A is the same as in the other tRNAs (U. RajBhandary, pers. commun.).

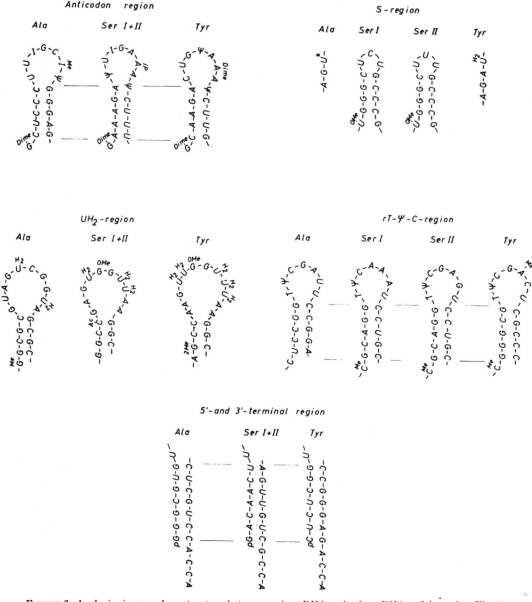

FIGURE 6. Analogies in secondary structure between serine tRNA and other tRNAs; cf. legend to Fig. 5.

The greater chain length of the serine tRNAs compared to alanine and tyrosine tRNAs is due to additional nucleotides in the S region.

Striking similarities between alanine, serine, and tyrosine tRNAs are apparent in secondary structure models of the clover-leaf type (Fig. 6). In the anticodon and –rT–ψ–C– regions, stems with 5 standard base pairs and loops with 7 nucleotides can be constructed. The stems of the –rT–ψ–C– and the UH$_2$ loops consist largely or exclusively of G:C pairs. In the 5'- and 3'- terminal region the paired parts have the same overall length and leave 4 nucleotides unpaired.

The odd nucleotides of the three tRNAs appear predominantly in loops and in analogous positions of the bends between the paired regions. It is interesting to note that in eight positions of the chains an odd nucleotide is found in one or two of the tRNAs, while the corresponding parent nucleotide is present in another tRNA (Fig.5).

enerally the odd nucleotides seem to be landmarks ı the secondary structure of tRNA.

The similarities in the nucleotide sequences and ıe clover leaf models of alanine, serine, and ɾrosine tRNAs point to the possibility that ıalogous regions may serve analogous functions ı the interaction with the aminoacyl tRNA syn-ıetases, the binding to ribosomes, and the mRNA ːcognition. A discriminating function such as the ıteraction with enzymes is probably not associated ith closely similar regions ($-rT-\psi-C-$ loops) but ith regions of greater dissimilarity (UH_2-, S–, ıd anticodon loops).

It is tempting to speculate that the similarities ɯong the tRNAs reflect not only similarities in ınction but also "evolutionary" relationships. he latter can be discussed in terms of point ıutations, insertions, deletions, and inversions f a hypothetical original tRNA cistron, some of ɦich are obvious from Fig. 5. Also, the above-ıentioned modification of nucleotides in certain ɒsitions, e.g. by methylation, which occurs in ɔme tRNAs but not in others, may be considered ı this connection. A fairly clear relation is found ɛtween serine tRNA I and II, where the dif-ɾrences may have originated from transitions in a ɛrine tRNA cistron of yeast DNA.

The rapidly progressing work on tRNA structures ill help in the understanding of relations between RNA structure and function, and perhaps even-ıally also of tRNA evolution.

REFERENCES

ᴀʏᴇᴠ, A. A., T. V. Venkstern, A. D. Mirsabekov, A. I. Krutilina, L. Li, and V. D. Axelrod. 1965. Oligonucleotide composition of enzymatic hydrolysates of yeast valine-specific transfer RNA. Biochim. Biophys. Acta *108:* 162–164.

ıᴇᴍᴀɴɴ, K., S. Tsunakawa, J. Sonnenbichler, H. Feldmann, D. Dütting, and H. G. Zachau. 1966. Struktur eines ungewöhnlichen Nucleotids aus serin-spezifischer Transfer-Ribonucleinsäure. Angew. Chemie *78:* 600. Internat. Ed. *5:* 590.

ʀɪᴄᴋ, F. H. C. 1966. Codon-anticodon pairing: The wobble hypothesis. J. Mol. Biol. *19:* 548–555.

ᴜ̈ᴛᴛɪɴɢ, D., H. Feldmann, and H. G. Zachau. 1966. Partial digestions with pancreatic and T1-ribonucleases of serine transfer ribonucleic acid. Hoppe Seyler's Z physiol. chem. *347:* 249.

ᴇʟᴅᴍᴀɴɴ, H., D. Dütting, and H. G. Zachau. 1966. Analyses of some oligonucleotide sequences and odd nucleotides from serine transfer ribonucleic acids. Hoppe Seyler's Z. physiol. chem. *347:* 236.

ᴀʟʟ, R. H., M. J. Robins, L. Stasiuk, and R. Thedford. 1966. Isolation of N(6)-(γ,γ-dimethylallyl) adenosine from soluble ribonucleic acid. J. Amer. Chem. Soc. *88:* 2614.

ᴏʟʟᴇʏ, R. W., J. Apgar, G. A. Everett, J. T. Madison, M. Marquisee, S. H. Merrill, J. R. Penswick, and

A. Zamir. 1965. Structure of a ribonucleic acid. Science *147:* 1462–1465.

Holley, R. W. 1966. The nucleotide sequence of a nucleic acid. Sci. Amer. *214:* No. 2: 30–39.

Ingram, V. M., and J. A. Sjöquist. 1963. Studies on the structure of purified alanine and valine transfer RNA from yeast. Cold Spring Harbor Symp. Quant. Biol. *28:* 133–138.

Thiebe, R. 1965. Beiträge zum Problem der Multiplizität von Transfer-Ribonucleinsäuren. PhD. Thesis, Universität Köln.

Traub, W., and D. Elson. 1966. RNA composition and base pairing. Science *153:* 178.

Zachau, H. G., D. Dütting, and H. Feldmann. 1966a. Nucleotidsequenzen zweier serinspezifischer Transfer-Ribonucleinsäuren. Angew. Chemie *78:* 392–393. Internat. Ed. 5: 422.

———, ———, ———. 1966b. The structures of two serine transfer ribonucleic acids. Hoppe Seyler's Z. physiol. chem. *347:* 212.

———, ———, ———. 1966c. On the primary structure of transfer ribonucleic acids. *In* Properties and function of genetic elements. (D. Shugar, ed.) Symp. Fed. European Biochem. Soc. Warsaw. Academic Press, New York and PWN, Warsaw, in press.

Zachau, H. G., D. Dütting, F. Melchers, H. Feldmann, and R. Thiebe. 1966. On serine specific transfer ribonucleic acids. p. 21. In Ribonucleic acid—structure and function. Symp. Fed. European Biochem. Soc., Vienna 1965. Pergamon Press, Oxford.

Zamir, A., R. W. Holley, and M. Marquissee. 1965. Evidence for the occurrence of a common penta nucleotide sequence in the structures of transfer ribonucleic acids. J. Biol. Chem. *240:* 1267–1273.

DISCUSSION

F. D. Cramer: Oxidation of adenylic residues in nucleic acids to form the 1-N-oxide derivation is specific for non-base-paired regions (H. Seidel and F. Cramer. 1965. Biochim. Biophys. Acta *108:*367). This allows the measurement of the number of base pairs in sRNA. A linear relationship between the helical regions is thus determined and the hyperchromicity is observed. Therefore the number of base pairs can be deduced from a measurement of the hyperchromicity once a standard ratio is established (H. Doepner, H. Seidel, and F. Cramer. 1966. Angew. Chemie, *78:* 601). Ser-tRNA exhibits a two-step melting curve, the first step up to 45° (6.1% hyperchromicity) corresponds to 2.5 base pairs, the second step from 45–100° (18.4% hyperchromicity) corresponds to 24.5 base pairs.

sRNA:	Brewer's yeast		*E. coli*	
	native	heated and cooled	native	heated and cooled
Hyperchromicity %	35	19	25	19
Base pairs determined by N-Oxidation	31.5	26	28	25.5

THE DEPENDENCE OF CELL- FREE PROTEIN SYNTHESIS IN E. COLI UPON NATURALLY OCCURRING OR SYNTHETIC POLYRIBONUCLEOTIDES

By Marshall W. Nirenberg and J. Heinrich Matthaei*

NATIONAL INSTITUTES OF HEALTH, BETHESDA, MARYLAND

Communicated by Joseph E. Smadel, August 3, 1961

A stable cell-free system has been obtained from *E. coli* which incorporates C^{14}-valine into protein at a rapid rate. It was shown that this apparent protein synthesis was energy-dependent, was stimulated by a mixture of. L-amino acids, and was markedly inhibited by RNAase, puromycin, and chloramphenicol.[1] The present communication describes a novel characteristic of the system, that is, a requirement for template RNA, needed for amino acid incorporation even in the presence of soluble RNA and ribosomes. It will also be shown that the amino acid incorporation stimulated by the addition of template RNA has many properties expected of *de novo* protein synthesis. Naturally occurring RNA as well as a synthetic polynucleotide were active in this system. The synthetic polynucleotide appears to contain the code for the synthesis of a "protein" containing only one amino acid. Part of these data have been presented in preliminary reports.[2, 3]

Methods and Materials.—The preparation of enzyme extracts was modified in certain respects from the procedure previously presented.[1] *E. coli* W3100 cells harvested in early log phase were washed and were disrupted by grinding with alumina (twice the weight of washed cells) at 5° for 5 min as described previously.[1] The alumina was extracted with an equivalent weight of buffer containing 0.01 M Tris(hydroxymethyl)aminomethane, pH 7.8, 0.01 M magnesium acetate, 0.06 M KCl, 0.006 M mercaptoethanol (standard buffer). Alumina and intact cells were removed by centrifugation at $20,000 \times g$ for 20 min. The supernatant fluid was decanted, and 3 μg DNAase per ml (Worthington Biochemical Co.) were added, rapidly reducing the viscosity of the suspension, which was then centrifuged again at $20,000 \times g$ for 20 min. The supernatant fluid was aspirated and was centrifuged at $30,000 \times g$ for 30 min to clear the extract of remaining debris. The liquid layer was aspirated (S-30) and was centrifuged at $105,000 \times g$ for 2 hr to sediment the ribosomes. The supernatant solution (S-100) was aspirated, and the solution just above the pellet was decanted and discarded. The ribosomes were washed by resuspension in the standard buffer and centrifugation again at $105,000 \times g$ for 2 hr. Supernatant fluid was discarded and the ribosomes were suspended in standard buffer (W-Rib). Fractions S-30, S-100, and W-Rib were dialyzed against 60 volumes of standard buffer overnight at 5° and were divided into aliquots for storage at −15°.

In some cases, fresh S-30 was incubated for 40 min at 35°. The reaction mixture components in μmoles per ml were as follows: 80 Tris, pH 7.8; 8 magnesium acetate; 50 KCl; 9 mercaptoethanol; 0.075 each of 20 amino acids;[1] 2.5 ATP, K salt; 2.5 PEP, K salt; 15 μg PEP kinase (Boehringen & Sons, Mannheim, Germany). After incubation, the reaction mixture was dialyzed at 5° for 10 hr against 60 volumes of standard buffer, changed once during the course of dialysis. The incubated S-30 fraction was stored in aliquots at −15° until needed (Incubated-S-30).

RNA fractions were prepared by phenol extraction using freshly distilled phenol. Ribosomal RNA was prepared from fresh, washed ribosomes obtained by the method given above. In later RNA preparations, a 0.2% solution of sodium dodecyl sulfate recrystallized by the method of Crestfield *et al.*[4] was added to the suspension of ribosomes before phenol treatment. The suspension was shaken at room temperature for 5 min. Higher yields of RNA appeared to be obtained when the sodium dodecyl sulfate step was used; however, good RNA preparations were also obtained when this step was omitted. An equal volume of H_2O-saturated phenol was added to ribosomes suspended in standard buffer after treatment with sodium dodecyl sulfate, and the suspension was shaken vigorously at room temperature for 8–10 min. The aqueous phase was aspirated from the phenol phase after centrifugation at $1,450 \times g$ for 15 min. The aqueous layer was extracted two more times in the same manner, using $^1/_2$ volume of H_2O-saturated phenol in each case. The final aqueous phase was chilled to 5° and NaCl was added to a final concentration of 0.1%. Two volumes of ethyl alcohol at −20° were added with stirring to precipitate the RNA. The suspension was centrifuged at $20,000 \times g$ for 15 min and the supernatant solution was decanted and discarded. The RNA pellet was dissolved in minimal concentrations of standard buffer (minus mercaptoethanol) by gentle homogenization in a glass Potter-Elvehjem homogenizer (usually the volume of buffer used was about $^1/_3$ the volume of the original ribosome suspension). The opalescent solution of RNA was dialyzed for 18 hr against 100 volumes of standard buffer (minus mercaptoethanol) at 5°. The dialyzing buffer was changed once. After dialysis, the RNA solution was centrifuged at $20,000 \times g$ for 15 min and the pellet was discarded. The RNA solution, which contained less than 1% protein, was divided into aliquots and was stored at −15° until needed.

Soluble RNA was prepared from $105,000 \times g$ supernatant solution by the phenol extraction method described above. Soluble RNA was also stored at −15°. Alkali-degraded RNA was prepared by incubating RNA samples with 0.3 M KOH at 35° for 18 hr. The solutions then were neutralized and dialyzed against standard buffer (minus mercaptoethanol). RNAase-digested samples of RNA were prepared by incubating RNA with 2 μg per ml of crystalline

RNAase (Worthington Biochemical Company) at 35° for 60 min. RNAase was destroyed by four phenol extractions performed as given above. After the last phenol extraction, the samples were dialyzed against standard buffer minus mercaptoethanol. RNA samples were treated with trypsin by incubation with 20 μg per ml of twice recrystallized trypsin (Worthington Biochemical Company) at 35° for 60 min. The solution was treated four times with phenol and was dialyzed in the same manner.

The radioactive amino acids used, their source, and their respective specific activities are as follows: U-C¹⁴-glycine, U-C¹⁴-L-isoleucine, U-C¹⁴-L-tyrosine, U-C¹⁴-L-leucine, U-C¹⁴-L-proline, L-histidine-2(ring)-C¹⁴, U-C¹⁴-L-phenylalanine, U-C¹⁴-L-threonine, L-methionine (methyl-C¹⁴), U-C¹⁴-L-arginine, and U-C¹⁴-L-lysine obtained from Nuclear-Chicago Corporation, 5.8, 6.2, 5.95, 6.25, 10.5, 3.96, 10.3, 3.9, 6.5, 5.8, 8.3 mC/mM, respectively; C¹⁴-L-aspartic acid, C¹⁴-L-glutamic acid, C¹⁴-L-alanine, obtained from Volk, 1.04, 1.18, 0.75 m C/mM, respectively; D-L-tryptophan-3 C¹⁴, obtained from New England Nuclear Corporation, 2.5 mC/mM; S³⁵-L-cystine obtained from the Abbott Laboratories, 2.4 mC/mM; U-C¹⁴-L-serine obtained from the Nuclear-Chicago Corporation, 0.2 mC/mM. Other materials and methods used in this study are described in the accompanying paper.[1] All assays were performed in duplicate.

Results.—Stimulation by ribosomal RNA: In the previous paper,[1] it was shown that DNAase markedly decreased amino acid incorporation in this system after 20 min. For the purpose of this investigation, 30,000 × *g* supernatant fluid fractions previously incubated with DNAase and other components of the reaction mixtures (Incubated-S-30 fractions) were used for many of the experiments.

Figure 1 shows that incorporation of C¹⁴-L-valine into protein by Incubated-S-30 fraction was stimulated by the addition of purified *E. coli* soluble RNA. Maximal stimulation was obtained with approximately 1 mg soluble RNA. In some experiments, increasing the concentration 5-fold did not further stimulate the system. Soluble RNA was added to all reaction mixtures unless otherwise specified.

Figure 2 demonstrates that *E. coli* ribosomal RNA preparations markedly stimu-

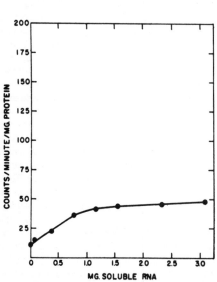

Fig 1.—Stimulation of amino acid incorporation into protein by *E. coli* soluble RNA. Composition of reaction mixtures is specified in Table 1. Samples were incubated at 35° for 20 min. Reaction mixtures contained 4.4 mg. of Incubated-S-30 protein.

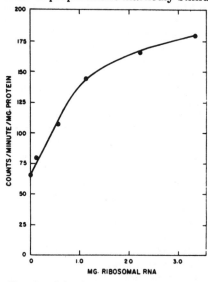

Fig. 2.—Stimulation of amino acid incorporation into protein by *E. coli* ribosomal RNA in the presence of soluble RNA. Composition of reaction mixtures is specified in Table 1. Samples were incubated at 35° for 20 min. Reaction mixtures contained 4.4 mg of Incubated-S-30 protein and 1.0 mg *E. coli* soluble RNA.

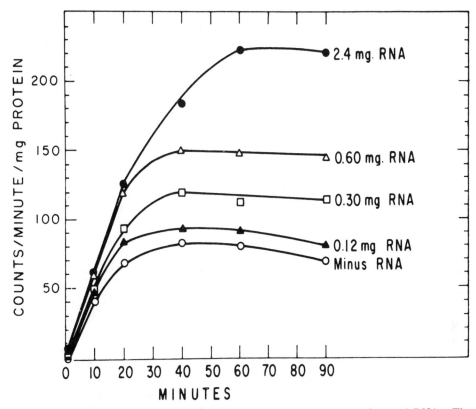

Fig. 3.—Dependence of C^{14}-L-valine incorporation into protein upon ribosomal RNA. The composition of the reaction mixtures and the incubation conditions are presented in Table 1. Reaction mixtures contained 0.98 mg of *E. coli* soluble RNA and 4.4 mg of Incubated-S-30-protein.

lated incorporation of C^{14}-valine into protein even though maximally stimulating concentrations of soluble RNA were present in the reaction mixtures. A linear relationship between the concentration of ribosomal RNA and C^{14}-valine incorporation into protein was obtained when low concentrations of ribosomal RNA were used. Increasing the soluble RNA concentration up to 3-fold did not replace the effect observed when ribosomal RNA was added.

The effect of ribosomal RNA in stimulating incorporation of C^{14}-valine into protein is presented in more detail in Figure 3. In the absence of ribosomal RNA, incorporation of C^{14}-valine into protein by the incubated-S-30 fraction was quite low when compared with S-30 (not incubated before storage at $-15°$) and stopped almost completely after 30 min. At low concentrations of ribosomal RNA, maximum amino acid incorporation into protein was proportional to the amount of ribosomal RNA added, suggesting stoichiometric rather than catalytic action of ribosomal RNA. Total incorporation of C^{14}-valine into protein was increased more than 3-fold by ribosomal RNA in this experiment even in the presence of maximally stimulating concentrations of soluble RNA. Ribosomal RNA may be added at any time during the course of the reaction, and, after further incubation, an increase in incorporation of C^{14}-valine into protein will result.

Characteristics of amino acid incorporation stimulated by ribosomal RNA: In Table 1 are presented the characteristics of C^{14}-L-valine incorporation into protein

TABLE 1

Characteristics of C^{14}-L-Valine Incorporation into Protein

Experiment no.	Addition				Counts/min/mg protein
1	− Ribosomal RNA				42
	+	"	"		204
	+	"	"	+ 0.15 μmole Chloramphenicol	58
	+	"	"	+ 0.20 μmole Puromycin	7
	+	"	"	deproteinized at zero time	8
2	− Ribosomal RNA				35
	+	"	"		101
	+	"	"	− ATP, PEP, PEP kinase	7
	+	"	"	+ 10 μg RNAase	6
	+	"	"	+ 10 μg DNAase	110
	+ Boiled Ribosomal RNA				127
	+ Ribosomal RNA, deproteinized at zero time				8
3	− Ribosomal RNA				34
	−	"	"	− 20 L amino acids	21
	+	"	"		99
	+	"	"	− 20-L-amino acids	52

The reaction mixtures contained the following in μmole/ml: 100 Tris(hydroxymethyl) aminomethane, pH 7.8; 10 magnesium acetate; 50 KCl; 6.0 mercaptoethanol; 1.0 ATP; 5.0 phosphoenolpyruvate, K salt; 20 μg phosphoenolpyruvate kinase, crystalline; 0.05 each of 20 L-amino acids minus valine; 0.03 each of GTP, CTP, and UTP; 0.015 C^{14}-L-valine (~70,000 counts); 3.1 mg. *E. coli* ribosomal RNA where indicated, and 1.0 mg *E. coli* soluble RNA; 3.2, 3.2, and 1.4 mg of incubated-S-30 protein were present in Experiments 1, 2, and 3, respectively. In addition 4.4 mg protein of W-Rib were added in Experiment 3. Total volume was 1.0 ml. Samples were incubated at 35° for 20 min, were deproteinized with 10 per cent trichloroacetic acid, and the precipitates were washed and counted by the method of Siekevitz.[22]

stimulated by the addition of ribosomal RNA. Amino acid incorporation was strongly inhibited by 0.15 μmoles of chloramphenicol and 0.20 μmoles/ml reaction mixture of puromycin. Furthermore, the incorporation was completely dependent upon the addition of ATP and an ATP-generating system and was totally inhibited by 10 μg/ml RNAase. Equivalent amounts of DNAase had no effect upon the incorporation stimulated by the addition of ribosomal RNA. Placing a ribosomal RNA preparation in a boiling water bath for 10 min did not destroy its C^{14}-valine incorporation activity; instead, a slight increase in activity was consistently observed. However, when these RNA preparations were placed in a boiling water bath, a copious, white precipitate resulted. Upon cooling the suspension in an ice bath, the precipitate immediately dissolved.

The data of Table 1 also demonstrate that the incorporation of amino acids into protein in the presence of ribosomal RNA was further stimulated by the addition of a mixture of 20 L-amino acids, suggesting cell-free protein synthesis.

C- and N-terminal analyses of the ribosomal RNA-dependent product of the reaction were performed with carboxypeptidase and 1-fluoro-2,4-dinitrobenzene respectively (Dr. Frank Tietze kindly performed these analyses). Four per cent of the radioactivity was released from the C-terminal end and 1% was associated with the N-terminal end. The remainder of the C^{14}-label was internal. Similar results were obtained when reactions were performed using S-30 enzyme fractions which had not been treated with DNAase. Protein precipitates isolated from reaction mixtures after incubation were completely hydrolyzed with HCl, and the C^{14}-label incorporated into protein was demonstrated to be valine by paper chromatography.

Many of the experiments presented in this paper were performed with enzyme fractions prepared with DNAase added to reduce their viscosity. Ribosomal

RNA also stimulated C^{14}-valine incorporation when enzyme extracts prepared in the absence of DNAase were used.

To be effective in stimulating amino acid incorporation into protein, the ribosomal RNA *required the presence of washed ribosomes.*   The data of Table 2 show

TABLE 2

THE INEFFECTIVENESS OF RIBOSOMAL RNA IN STIMULATING C^{14}-L-VALINE INCORPORATION INTO PROTEIN IN THE PRESENCE OF RIBOSOMES OR 105,000 × *g* SUPERNATANT SOLUTIONS ALONE

Additions	Counts/min
Complete	51
" + 2.1 mg Ribosomal RNA	202
" − Ribosomes	17
" − Ribosomes + 2.1 mg Ribosomal RNA	20
" − Supernatant solution	36
" − Supernatant solution + 2.1 mg Ribosomal RNA	45
" Deproteinized at zero time	25

The components of the reaction mixtures and the incubation conditions are presented in Table 1.   0.86 and 3.3 mg protein were present in the ribosome (W-Rib) and 105,000 × *g* supernatant (S-100) fractions, respectively.

that both ribosomes and 105,000 × *g* supernatant solution were necessary for ribosomal RNA-dependent amino acid incorporation.   No incorporation of amino acids into protein occurred when the 105,000 × *g* supernatant solution alone was added to ribosomal RNA preparations, demonstrating that ribosomal RNA preparations were not contaminated with intact ribosomes.   This conclusion also was substantiated by showing that the activities of ribosomal RNA preparations were not destroyed by boiling, although the activities of the ribosomes were destroyed by such treatment.

The effect of ribosomal RNA upon the incorporation of seven different amino acids is presented in Table 3.   The addition of ribosomal RNA increased the incorporation of every amino acid tested.

The effect shown by ribosomal RNA was not observed when other polyanions were used, such as polyadenylic acid, highly polymerized salmon sperm DNA, or a high-molecular-weight polymer of glucose carboxylic acid (Table 4).   Pretreatment of ribosomal RNA with trypsin did not affect its biological activity.   However, treatment of the ribosomal RNA with either RNAase or alkali resulted in a complete loss of stimulating activity.   The active principle, therefore, appears to be RNA.

The sedimentation characteristics of the ribosomal RNA preparations were examined in the Spinco Model E ultracentrifuge (Fig. 4*A*).   Particles having the characteristics of S-30, S-50, or S-70 ribosomes were not observed in these preparations.   The S_{20}^W of the first peak was 23, that of the second peak 16, and that of the third, small peak, 4.   Pretreatment with trypsin did not affect the S_{20}^W values of the peaks appreciably (Fig. 4*C*); however, treatment with RNAase completely destroyed the peaks (Fig. 4*B*), confirming the ancillary evidence which had suggested that the major component was high-molecular-weight RNA.

Preliminary attempts at fractionation of the ribosomal RNA were performed by means of density-gradient centrifugation employing a linear sucrose gradient. The results of one such experiment are presented in Figure 5.   Amino acid incorporation activity of the RNA did not follow absorbancy at 260 mμ; instead, the activity seemed to be concentrated around fraction No. 5, which was approximately one-third of the distance from the bottom of the tube.   These results again

TABLE 3

SPECIFICITY OF AMINO ACID INCORPORATION STIMULATED BY RIBOSOMAL RNA

C14-Amino Acid	Addition	Counts/min/mg protein
C14-L-Valine	Complete	25
"	" + Ribosomal RNA	137
C14-L-Threonine	"	31
"	" + Ribosomal RNA	121
C14-L-Methionine	"	121
"	" + Ribosomal RNA	177
C14-L-Arginine	"	49
"	" + Ribosomal RNA	224
C14-L-Phenylalanine	"	77
"	" + Ribosomal RNA	147
C14-L-Lysine	"	36
"	" + Ribosomal RNA	175
C14-L-Leucine	"	134
"	" + Ribosomal RNA	272
"	" Deproteinized at zero time	6

The composition of the reaction mixtures are presented in Table 1. The mixture of 20 L-amino acids included all amino acids except the C14-amino acid added to one reaction mixture. Reaction mixtures contained 4.4 mg Incubated-S-30 protein. Samples were incubated at 35° for 60 min. 2.1 mg ribosomal RNA were added where indicated.

TABLE 4

RIBOSOMAL RNA CONTROL EXPERIMENTS DESCRIBED IN TEXT

Experiment No.	Addition	Counts/min/mg protein
1	Complete	54
	" + 2.4 mg Ribosomal RNA	144
	" + 2.0 mg Polyadenylic acid	10
	" + 2.0 mg Salmon sperm DNA	41
	" + 2.0 mg Polyglucose carboxylic acid	49
	" + 2.4 mg Ribosomal RNA, deproteinized at zero time	7
2	Complete	39
	" + 2.0 mg Ribosomal RNA*	150
	" + 2.1 mg Ribosomal RNA preincubated with trypsin*	166
	" + 2.0 mg Ribosomal RNA preincubated with RNAase*,†	47
	" Deproteinized at zero time	8
3	Complete	20
	" + 1.2 mg Ribosomal RNA	82
	" + 1.2 mg Alkali degraded ribosomal RNA†	21
	" Deproteinized at zero time	7

The composition of the reaction mixtures and the incubation conditions are given in Table 1. 4.4, 3.2, and 4.4 mg Incubated-S-30 protein were present in Experiments 1, 2, and 3, respectively. 2.4, 0.98, and 0 mg *E. coli* soluble RNA were present in Experiments 1, 2, and 3, respectively.
* Ribosomal RNA preparations were deproteinized by phenol extraction after enzymatic digestion as specified under *Methods and Materials.*
† mg Ribosomal RNA refers to RNA concentration before digestion.

demonstrate that the activity was not associated with a soluble RNA fraction, present in maximum concentration in fraction No. 11, near the top of the tube. In addition, all amino acid incorporation analyses were performed in the presence of added soluble RNA, and the addition of more soluble RNA would not stimulate C14-L-valine incorporation into protein.

Effects of RNA obtained from different species: The data of Table 5 demonstrate that RNA from different sources stimulates C14-valine incorporation into protein. Yeast ribosomal RNA prepared by the method of Crestfield *et al.*[4] was considerably more effective in stimulating incorporation than equivalent amounts of *E. coli* ribosomal RNA. Yeast ribosomal RNA prepared by this method has little or no amino acid acceptor activity and has a molecular weight of about 29,000.[7] Tobacco mosaic virus RNA prepared by phenol extraction and having a molecular weight of

TABLE 5

Stimulation of Amino Acid Incorporation by RNA Fractions Prepared from Different Species

Additions	Counts/min/mg protein
None	42
+ 0.5 mg *E. coli* ribosomal RNA	75
+ 0.5 mg Yeast ribosomal RNA	430
+ 0.5 mg Tobacco mosaic virus RNA	872
+ 0.5 mg Ehrlich ascites tumor microsomal RNA	65

The components of the reaction mixtures and the incubation conditions are presented in Table 1. Reaction samples contained 1.9 mg Incubated-S-30 protein.

approximately 1,700,000[†] stimulated amino acid incorporation strongly. Marked stimulation due to tobacco mosaic virus RNA was observed also with *E. coli* enzyme extracts which had not been treated with DNAase. More complete details of this work will be presented in a later publication.

Stimulation of amino acid incorporation by synthetic polynucleotides: The data of Figure 6 show that the addition of 10 μg of polyuridylic acid[‡] per ml of reaction mixture resulted in a remarkable stimulation of C[14]-L-phenylalanine incorporation. Phenylalanine incorporation was almost completely dependent upon the addition of polyuridylic acid, and incorporation proceeded, after a slight lag period, at a linear rate for approximately 30 min.

The data of Table 6 demonstrate that no other polynucleotide tested could replace polyuridylic acid. The absolute specificity of polyuridylic acid was con-

TABLE 6

Polynucleotide Specificity for Phenylalanine Incorporation

Experiment no.	Additions	Counts/min/mg protein
1	None	44
	+ 10 μg Polyuridylic acid	39,800
	+ 10 μg Polyadenylic acid	50
	+ 10 μg Polycytidylic acid	38
	+ 10 μg Polyinosinic acid	57
	+ 10 μg Polyadenylic-uridylic acid (2/1 ratio)	53
	+ 10 μg Polyuridylic acid + 20 μg polyadenylic acid	60
	Deproteinized at zero time	17
2	None	75
	+ 10 μg UMP	81
	+ 10 μg UDP	77
	+ 10 μg UTP	72
	Deproteinized at zero time	6

Components of the reaction mixtures are presented in Table 1. Reaction mixtures contained 2.3 mg Incubated-S-30 protein. 0.02 μmoles U-C[14]-L-phenylalanine (~125,000 counts/minute) was added to each reaction mixture. Samples were incubated at 35° for 60 min.

firmed by demonstrating that randomly mixed polymers of adenylic and uridylic acid[‡] (Poly A-U, 2/1 ratio and 4/1 ratio) were inactive in this system. A solution of polyuridylic acid and polyadenylic acid (which forms triple-stranded helices) had no activity whatsoever, suggesting that single-strandedness is a necessary requisite for activity. Experiment 2 in Table 6 demonstrates that UMP, UDP, or UTP were unable to stimulate phenylalanine incorporation.

The data of Table 7 demonstrate that both ribosomes and 100,000 × *g* supernatant solution, as well as ATP and an ATP-generating system, were required for the polyuridylic acid–dependent incorporation of phenylalanine. Incorporation was inhibited by puromycin, chloramphenicol, and RNAase. The incorpora-

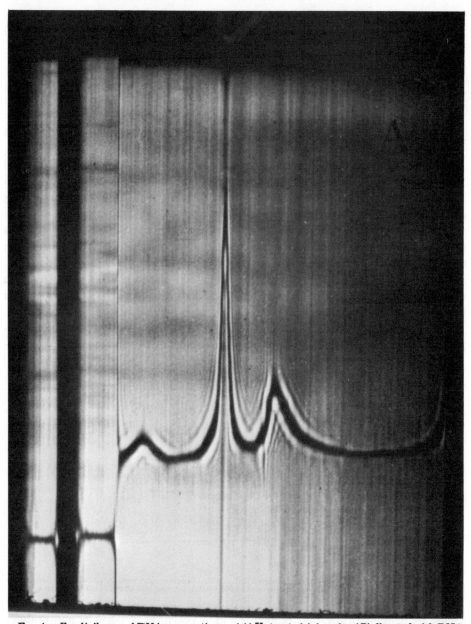

Fig. 4.—*E. coli* ribosomal RNA preparations. (*A*) Untreated (above). (*B*) digested with RNAaase; (*C*) digested with trypsin. Preparation and digestion of samples presented under *Methods and Materials*. 9.8 and 10.5 mg/ml RNA were present in *A* and *C*. 11.5 mg/ml RNA was present in *B*

(*Continued on facing page*)

tion was not inhibited by addition of DNAase. Omitting a mixture of 19 L-amino acids did not inhibit phenylalanine incorporation, suggesting that polyuridylic acid stimulated the incorporation of L-phenylalanine alone. This conclusion was substantiated by the data presented in Table 8. Polyuridylic acid had little effect in stimulating the incorporation of 17 other radioactive amino acids. Each labeled amino acid was tested individually, and these data, corroborating the results given in Table 8, will be presented in a subsequent publication.

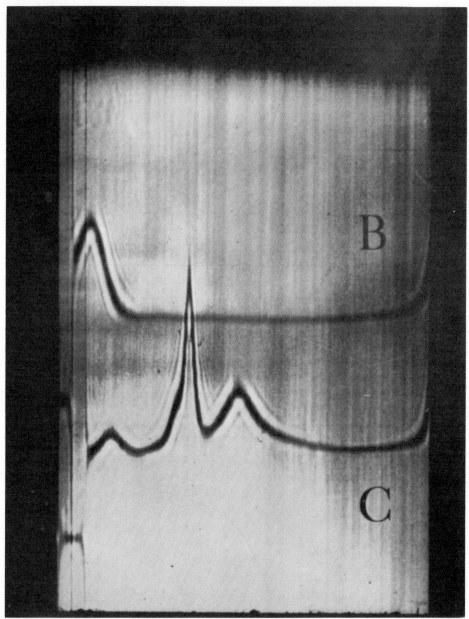

(*Fig. 4—continued*)
before digestion.   Photographs were taken in a model E Spinco ultracentrifuge equipped with schlieren optics.

The product of the reaction was partially characterized and the results are presented in Table 9.   The physical characteristics of the product of the reaction resembled those of authentic poly-L-phenylalanine, for, unlike many other polypeptides and proteins, both the product of the reaction and the polymer were resistant to hydrolysis by 6N HCl at 100° for 8 hr but were completely hydrolyzed by 12N HCl at 120–130° for 48 hr.

Poly-L-phenylalanine is insoluble in most solvents[25] but is soluble in 33 per cent

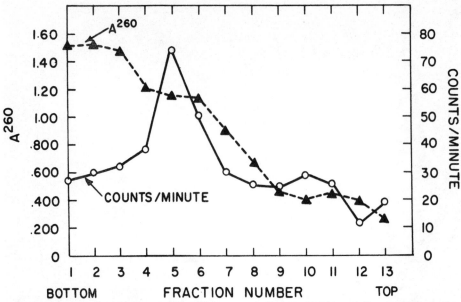

Fig. 5.—Sucrose density-gradient centrifugation of ribosomal RNA. A linear gradient of sucrose concentration ranging from 20 per cent at the bottom to 5 per cent at the top of the tube was prepared.[23] The sucrose solutions (4.4 ml total volume) contained 0.01 M Tris, pH 7.8, 0.01 M Mg acetate and 0.06 M KCl. 0.4 ml of ribosomal RNA (4.6 mg) was layered on top of each tube which was centrifuged at 38,000 × g for 4.5 hours at 3° in a swinging bucket rotor, Spinco type SW-39, using a Spinco Model L ultracentrifuge. 0.30 ml fractions were collected after piercing the bottom of the tube.[24]

0.025 ml aliquots diluted to 0.3 ml with H_2O were used for A^{260} measurements. 0.25 ml aliquots were used for amino acid incorporation assays. Reaction mixtures contained the components presented in Table 1. 0.7 mg of *E. coli* soluble RNA and 2.2 mg Incubated-S-30 protein were added. Control assays plus 0.25 ml 12.5 per cent sucrose in place of fractions gave 79 counts/min. This figure was subtracted from each value. Total volume was 0.7 ml. Samples were incubated at 35° for 20 min.

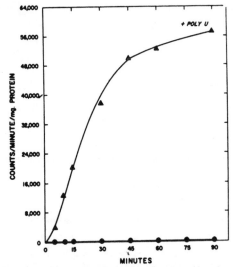

Fig. 6.—Stimulation of U-C[14]-L-phenylalanine incorporation by polyuridylic acid. ● without polyuridylic acid; ▲ 10 μg polyuridylic acid added. The components of the reaction mixtures and the incubation conditions are given in Table 1. 0.024 μmole U-C[14]-L-phenylalanine (∼500,000 counts/min) and 2.3 mg Incubated-S-30 protein were added/ml of reaction mixture.

TABLE 7

CHARACTERISTICS OF POLYURIDYLIC ACID–DEPENDENT PHENYLALANINE INCORPORATION

Additions	Counts/min/mg protein
Minus polyuridylic acid	70
None	29,500
Minus 100,000 $\times$ g supernatant solution	106
Minus ribosomes	52
Minus ATP, PEP, and PEP kinase	83
+ 0.02 μmoles puromycin	7,100
+ 0.31 μmoles chloramphenicol	12,550
+ 6 μg RNAase	120
+ 6 μg DNAase	27,600
Minus amino acid mixture	31,700
Deproteinized at zero time	30

The components of the reaction mixtures are presented in Table 1. 10 μg of polyuridylic acid were added to all samples except the specified one. 2.3 mg of Incubated-S-30 protein were added to each reaction mixture except those in which ribosomes alone and 100,000 $\times$ g supernatant solution alone were tested. 0.7 mg W-Rib protein and 1.3 mg S-100 protein were used respectively. 0.02 μmoles U-C^{14}-L-phenylalanine, Sp. Act. = 10.3 mC/mM ($\sim$125,000 counts/minute) were added to each reaction mixture. Samples were incubated at 35° for 60 min.

TABLE 8

SPECIFICITY OF AMINO ACID INCORPORATION STIMULATED BY POLYURIDYLIC ACID

Experiment no.	C^{14}-amino acids present	Additions	Counts/min/mg protein
1	Phenylalanine	Deproteinized at zero time	25
		None	68
		+ 10 μg polyuridylic acid	38,300
2	Glycine, alanine, serine, aspartic acid, glutamic acid	Deproteinized at zero time	17
		None	20
		+ 10 μg polyuridylic acid	33
3	Leucine, isoleucine, threonine, methionine, arginine, histidine, lysine, tyrosine, tryptophan, proline, valine	Deproteinized at zero time	73
		None	276
		+ 10 μg polyuridylic acid	899
4	S^{35}-cysteine	Deproteinized at zero time	6
		None	95
		+ 10 μg polyuridylic acid	113

Components of the reaction mixtures are presented in Table 1. The unlabeled amino acid mixture was omitted. 0.015 μM of each labeled amino acid was used. The specific activities of the labeled amino acids are present in the *Methods and Materials* section. 2.3 mg of protein of preincubated S-30 enzyme fraction were added to each reaction mixture. All samples were incubated at 35° for 30 min.

TABLE 9

COMPARISON OF CHARACTERISTICS OF PRODUCT OF REACTION AND POLY-L-PHENYLALANINE

Treatment	Product of reaction	Poly-L-phenylalanine
6 N HCl for 8 hours at 100°	Partially hydrolyzed	Partially hydrolyzed
12 N HCl for 48 hours at 120–130°	Completely hydrolyzed	Completely hydrolyzed
Extraction with 33% HBr in glacial acetic acid	Soluble	Soluble
Extraction* with the following solvents: H$_2$O, benzene, nitrobenzene, chloroform, N,N-dimethylformamide, ethanol, petroleum ether, concentrated phosphoric acid, glacial acetic acid, dioxane, phenol, acetone, ethyl acetate, pyridine, acetophenone, formic acid	Insoluble	Insoluble

* The product was said to be insoluble if <0.002 gm of product was soluble in 100 ml of solvent at 24°. Extractions were performed by adding 0.5 mg of authentic poly-L-phenylalanine and the C^{14}-product of a reaction mixture (1800 counts/min) to 5.0 ml of solvent. The suspensions were vigorously shaken for 30 min at 24° and were centrifuged. The precipitates were plated and their radioactivity was determined.

HBr in glacial acetic acid.§   The product of the reaction had the same apparent solubility as authentic poly-L-phenylalanine. The product of the reaction was purified by means of its unusual solubility behavior. Reaction mixtures were deproteinized after incubation, and precipitated proteins were washed in the usual manner according to the method of Siekevitz.[22] Dried protein pellets containing added carrier poly-L-phenylalanine were then extracted with 33 per cent HBr in glacial acetic acid, and the large amount of insoluble material was discarded. Polyphenylalanine was then precipitated from solution by the addition of H_2O and was washed several times with H_2O. Seventy per cent of the total amount of C^{14}-L-phenylalanine incorporated into protein due to the addition of polyuridylic acid could be recovered by this procedure. Complete hydrolysis of the purified reaction product with $12N$ HCl followed by paper electrophoresis** demonstrated that the reaction product contained C^{14}-phenylalanine. No other radioactive spots were found.

Discussion.—In this investigation, we have demonstrated that template RNA is a requirement for cell-free amino acid incorporation. Addition of soluble RNA could not replace template RNA in this system. In addition, the density-gradient centrifugation experiments showed that the active fractions in the ribosomal RNA preparations sedimented much faster than soluble RNA. It should be noted that ribosomal RNA is qualitatively different from soluble RNA, since bases such as pseudouracil, methylated guanines, etc., found in soluble RNA, are not present in ribosomal RNA.[5]

The bulk of the RNA in our ribosomal RNA fractions may be inactive as templates, for tobacco mosaic virus RNA was 20 times as active in stimulating amino acid incorporation as equivalent amounts of *E. coli* ribosomal RNA. In addition, preliminary fractionation of ribosomal RNA indicated that only a portion of the total RNA was active.

It should be emphasized that ribosomal RNA could not substitute for ribosomes, indicating that ribosomes were not assembled from the added RNA *in toto*. The function of ribosomal RNA remains an enigma, although at least part of the total RNA is thought to serve as templates for protein synthesis and has been termed "messenger" RNA.[12-14] Alternatively, a part of the RNA may be essential for the synthesis of active ribosomes from smaller ribosomal particles.[15-21]

Ribosomal RNA may be an aggregate of subunits which can dissociate after proper treatment.[6-8] Phenol extraction of *E. coli* ribosomes yields two types of RNA molecules with S_w^{20} of 23 and 16 (Fig. 4), equivalent to molecular weights of 1,000,000 and 560,000, respectively.[9, 10] These RNA species can be degraded by boiling to products having sedimentation coefficients of 13.1, 8.8, and 4.4, corresponding to molecular weights of 288,000, 144,000, and 29,000. Although the sedimentation distributions of the latter preparations suggest a high degree of homogeneity among the molecules of each class, these observations do not eliminate the possibility that the subunits are linked to one another *via* covalent bonds.[8] Preliminary evidence indicates that the subunits may be active in our system, since the supernatant solution obtained after boiling *E. coli* ribosomal RNA for 10 min and centrifugation at $105,000 \times g$ for 60 min was active. Examination of boiled ribosomal RNA with the Spinco Model E ultracentrifuge showed a dispersed peak with a sedimentation coefficient of 4–8. This may be the same material found in the sucrose density-gradient experiment (using non-boiled RNA preparations), where a small peak of activity somewhat heavier than soluble RNA was usually noted (Fig. 5).

In our system, at low concentrations of ribosomal RNA, amino acid incorporation into protein was proportional to the amount of ribosomal RNA added, suggesting a stoichiometric rather than a catalytic action of ribosomal RNA. In contrast, soluble RNA has been shown to act in a catalytic fashion.[11]

The results indicate that polyuridylic acid contains the information for the synthesis of a protein having many of the characteristics of poly-L-phenylalanine. This synthesis was very similar to the cell-free protein synthesis obtained when naturally-occurring template RNA was added, i.e., both ribosomes and 100,000 × *g* supernatant solutions were required, and the incorporation was inhibited by puromycin or chloramphenicol. One or more uridylic acid residues therefore appear to be the code for phenylalanine. Whether the code is of the singlet, triplet, etc., type has not yet been determined. Polyuridylic acid seemingly functions as a synthetic template or messenger RNA, and this stable, cell-free *E. coli* system may well synthesize any protein corresponding to meaningful information contained in added RNA.

Summary.—A stable, cell-free system has been obtained from *E. coli* in which the amount of incorporation of amino acids into protein was dependent upon the addition of heat-stable template RNA preparations. Soluble RNA could not replace template RNA fractions. In addition, the amino acid incorporation required both ribosomes and 105,000 × *g* supernatant solution. The correlation between the amount of incorporation and the amount of added RNA suggested stoichiometric rather than catalytic activity of the template RNA. The template RNA–dependent amino acid incorporation also required ATP and an ATP-generating system, was stimulated by a complete mixture of L-amino acids, and was markedly inhibited by puromycin, chloramphenicol, and RNAase. Addition of a synthetic polynucleotide, polyuridylic acid, specifically resulted in the incorporation of L-phenylalanine into a protein resembling poly-L-phenylalanine. Polyuridylic acid appears to function as a synthetic template or messenger RNA. The implications of these findings are briefly discussed.

Note added in proof. The ratio between uridylic acid units of the polymer required and molecules of L-phenylalanine incorporated, in recent experiments, has approached the value of 1:1. Direct evidence for the number of uridylic acid residues forming the code for phenylalanine as well as for the eventual stoichiometric action of the template is not yet established. As polyuridylic acid codes the incorporation of L-phenylalanine, polycytidylic acid‡ specifically mediates the incorporation of L-proline into a TCA-precipitable product. Complete data on these findings will be included in a subsequent publication.

* Supported by a NATO Postdoctoral Research Fellowship.

† Dr. Frankel-Conrat, personal communication.

‡ We thank Drs. Leon A. Heppel and Maxine F. Singer for samples of these polyribonucleotides, and Dr. George Rushizky for TMV-RNA.

§ We thank Dr. Michael Sela for this information.

** We thank Drs. William Dreyer and Elwood Bynum for performing the high-voltage electrophoretic analyses.

[1] Matthaei, J. H., and M. W. Nirenberg, these PROCEEDINGS, **47**, 1580 (1961).

[2] Matthaei, J. H., and M. W. Nirenberg, *Biochem. & Biophys. Res. Comm.*, **4**, 404 (1961).

[3] Matthaei, J. H., and M. W. Nirenberg, *Fed. Proc.*, **20**, 391 (1961).

[4] Crestfield, A. M., K. C. Smith, and F. W. Allen, *J. Biol. Chem.*, **216**, 185 (1955).

[5] Davis, F. F., A. F. Carlucci, and I. F. Roubein. *ibid.*, **234**, 1525 (1959).

[6] Hall, B. D., and P. Doty, *J. Mol. Biol.*, **1**, 111 (1959).

[7] Osawa, S., *Biochim. Biophys. Acta*, **43**, 110 (1960).

[8] Aronson, A. I., and B. J. McCarthy, *Biophys. J.*, **1**, 215 (1961).

[9] Kurland, C. G., *J. Mol. Biol.*, **2**, 83 (1960).

[10] Littauer, U. Z., H. Eisenberg, *Biochim. Biophys. Acta*, **32**, 320 (1959).

[11] Hoagland, M. B., and L. T. Comly, these Proceedings, **46**, 1554 (1960).

[12] Volkin, E., L. Astrachan, and J. L. Countryman, *Virology*, **6**, 545 (1958).

[13] Nomura, M., B. D. Hall, and S. Spiegelman, *J. Mol. Biol.*, **2**, 306 (1960).

[14] Hall, B. D., and S Spiegelman, these Proceedings, **47**, 137 (1961).

[15] Bolton, E. T., B. H. Hoyen, and D. B. Ritter, in *Microsomal Particles and Protein Synthesis*, ed. R. B. Roberts (New York: Pergamon Press, 1958), p. 18.

[16] Tissières, A., J. D. Watson, D. Schlessinger, and B. R. Hollingworth, *J. Mol. Biol.*, **1**, 221 (1959).

[17] Tissières, A., D. Schlessinger, and F. Gros, these Proceedings, **46**, 1450 (1960).

[18] McCarthy, B. J., and A. I. Aronson, *Biophys. J.*, **1**, 227 (1961).

[19] Hershey, A. D., *J. Gen. Physiol.*, **38**, 145 (1954).

[20] Siminovitch, L., and A. F. Graham, *Canad. J. Microbiol.*, **2**, 585 (1956).

[21] Davern, C. I., and M. Meselson, *J. Mol. Biol.*, **2**, 153 (1960).

[22] Siekevitz, P., *J. Biol. Chem.*, **195**, 549 (1952).

[23] Britten, R. J., and R. B. Roberts, *Science*, **131**, 32 (1960).

[24] Martin, R., and B. Ames, *J. Biol. Chem.*, **236**, 1372 (1961).

[25] Bamford, C. H., A. Elliott, and W. E. Hanby, *Synthetic Polypeptides* (New York: Academic Press, 1956), p. 322.

RNA Codewords and Protein Synthesis

The Effect of Trinucleotides upon the Binding of sRNA to Ribosomes

Marshall Nirenberg and Philip Leder

Although many properties of the RNA code and protein synthesis have been clarified with the use of synthetic polynucleotides containing randomly ordered bases, a more comprehensive understanding of certain aspects of the code clearly requires investigation with nucleic acid templates of demonstrated structure. Since oligonucleotides of known base sequence are readily prepared and characterized, we have tried, in many ways, to use defined oligonucleotide fractions for studies relating to the RNA code. In this article we describe a simple, direct method which should provide a general method for determining the genetic function of triplets of known sequence. The system is based upon interactions between ribosomes, aminoacyl sRNA (1), and mRNA which occur during the process of codeword recognition, prior to peptide-bond formation.

The binding of sRNA to ribosomes has been observed in many studies (2, 3); however, this interaction is not fully understood. An exchangeable binding of sRNA to ribosomes as reported by Cannon, Krug, and Gilbert (4). However, the addition of polyU induced, with specificity, Phe-sRNA binding to ribosomes, as demonstrated in the laboratories of Schweet (5–7) and Lipmann (8), by Kaji and Kaji (9, 10), and by Spyrides (11). Binding was reported to be dependent upon GTP (6, 7) and the first transfer enzyme (5–7), but not upon peptide-bond synthesis. However, the mechanism of binding and the possibility of a prior, nonenzymatic binding of amino-acyl sRNA induced by mRNA have not been clarified. The second

transfer enzyme was shown to be required for peptide bond formation (6, 7).

To determine the minimum chain length of mRNA required for codeword recognition and to test the ability of chemically defined oligonucleotides to induce C^{14}-aminoacyl-sRNA binding to ribosomes, we have devised a rapid method of detecting this interaction and have found that trinucleotides are active as templates.

Methods

Preparation, purification, and characterization of oligonucleotides. To obtain oligonucleotides with different terminal groups, polyA, polyU, and polyC (12) were digested as follows: (i) *Oligonucleotides with 5'-terminal phosphate*; 100 mg of polynucleotide were incubated at 37°C for 18 hours in a 28-ml reaction mixture containing 29mM tris, pH 7.2; 0.18mM $MgCl_2$; 0.23mM 2-mercaptoethanol; 8.0 mg crystalline bovine albumin and 0.5 mg pork liver nuclease (13). (ii) *Oligonucleotides with 3'(2')-terminal phosphate*; 100 mg of polynucleotide were incubated at 37°C for 24 hours in 20 ml of 7.0M NH_4OH. (iii) *Oligonucleotides without terminal phosphate*; Oligonucleotides with terminal phosphate were treated with *Escherichia coli* alkaline phosphatase (14) free of diesterase activity as described by Heppel *et al.* (15).

Oligonucleotide fractions were separated on Whatman 3 MM paper by chromatography with solvent A (H_2O:*n*-propanol:NH_3, 35:55:10, by volume) for 36 hours (fractions with terminal phosphate) or for 18 hours (fractions without terminal phosphate). This procedure fractionates oligonucleotides containing less than eight nucleo-

tide residues according to chain length. Oligonucleotides were eluted with H_2O and further purified on Whatman 3 MM paper by electrophoresis at pH 2.7 (0.05M ammonium formate, 80 v/cm for 15 to 30 minutes).

After elution the purity of each fraction was estimated by subjecting 2.5 A^{260} units of each to paper chromatography (Whatman 54 paper) both with solvent A and with solvent B (40 g ammonium sulfate dissolved in 100 ml 0.1M sodium phosphate, pH 7.0). In addition 3.0 A^{260} units of each oligonucleotide were subjected to chromatography on Whatman DE 81 (DEAE) paper with solvent C (0.1M ammonium formate), and 3.0 A^{260} units with solvent D (0.3M ammonium formate). The four chromatographic systems described separate homologous series of oligonucleotides according to chain length. Contaminating oligonucleotides present in amounts greater than 2 percent could be detected. Several preparations of each oligonucleotide were used during the course of this study. In almost all preparations, no contaminants were detected. The following preparations, specified in legends of figures or tables when used, contained contaminants in the proportions indicated: No. 591, $(Ap)_4$ [$(Ap)_3$, 11 percent]; No. 599, $(pA)_6$ [$(pA)_5$, 37 percent]; No. 610, $(pU)_3$ [$(pU)_3$, 10 percent]; No. 613 $(pU)_6$ [$(pU)_6$, 14 percent]; No. 617, $(Up)_4$ [$(Up)_3$, 12 percent].

Base composition and position of terminal phosphate were determined by digesting 2.0 A^{260} units of each oligonucleotide preparation with 3.5 × 10⁹ units of T_2 ribonuclease (16) in 0.1M NH_4HCO_3 at 37°C for 2.5 hours. The nucleotide and nucleoside products were separated by electrophoresis at pH 2.7 and identified by their mobilities and ultraviolet spectra at pH 2.0. Oligonucleotides with 5'-terminal phosphate yielded the appropriate 5'-3'(2')-nucleoside diphosphate, 3'(2')-nucleoside monophosphate, and nucleoside. From the ratio of these compounds the average chain length was calculated. Since oligonucleotides with 3'(2')-terminal phosphate yielded only the appropriate 3'(2')-nucleoside monophosphate (confirming its structure), terminal and total inorganic phosphate was determined (15, 17) in order to estimate the average chain length of each.

Oligo-d(pT) and oligo-d(pA) fractions were prepared and characterized by B. F. C. Clark as described previously (18). The UpUpUp with 3'-

The authors are affiliated with the Section of Biochemical Genetics of the National Heart Institute, National Institutes of Health, Bethesda, Maryland. These data were presented at the VIth International Congress of Biochemistry, 26 July–1 August 1964, New York City.

1399

Table 1. Characteristics of the system. Complete reactions contained the components described in the text, 15 mμmole uridylic acid residues in polyU, and 20.6 μμmole C14-Phe-sRNA (2050 count/min, 0.714 A^{260} units). Incubation was at 0°C for 60 minutes. Deacylated sRNA was added either at zero time or after 50 minutes of incubation, as indicated.

Modifications	C14-Phe-sRNA bound to ribosomes (μμ mole)
Complete	5.99
— PolyU	0.12
—Ribosomes	0
—Mg++	0.09
+sRNA (deacylated) at 50 min	
0.500 A^{260} units	5.69
2.500 A^{260} units	5.36
+sRNA (deacylated) at zero time	
0.500 A^{260} units	4.49
2.500 A^{260} units	2.08

terminal phosphate only was prepared and characterized by M. Bernfield [19].

Assay of ribosomal bound C14-aminoacyl-sRNA. Each 50-μl reaction mixture contained: 0.1M tris-acetate, pH 7.2; 0.02M magnesium acetate; 0.05M KCl; 2.0 A^{260} units of ribosomes (washed three times) and, as indicated for each experiment, oligo- or polynucleotide, and C14-aminoacyl sRNA. Tubes were kept at 0°C and C14-amino-acyl sRNA was added last to initiate binding (less binding was obtained if polynucleotide was added last). Incubation for 20 minutes at 24°C was often convenient for studies requiring max-

imum binding, and incubation for 3 minutes at 24°C or 30 minutes at 0°C for rate studies.

After incubation, tubes were placed in ice and each reaction was immediately diluted with 3 ml of buffer containing 0.10M tris-acetate, pH 7.2; 0.02M magnesium acetate; and 0.05M KCl, at 0° to 3°C. A cellulose nitrate filter (HA Millipore filter, 25 mm diameter, 0.45μ pore size) in a stainless steel holder was washed under gentle suction with 5 ml of buffer at 0° to 3°C. The diluted reaction mixture was immediately poured on the filter under suction and washed to remove unbound C14-aminoacyl sRNA with three, 3-ml portions of buffer at 0° to 3°C. Ribosomes and bound sRNA remained on the filter. Since reaction mixtures are not deproteinized, it is important to dilute and wash the ribosomes immediately after incubation, to use cold buffer, and to allow relatively little air to be pulled through the filter during the washing procedure. The filter was removed from the holder, glued with rubber cement to a disposable planchette, and dried. Radioactivity was determined in a thin-window, gas-flow counter [20] with a C14-counting efficiency of 23 percent. In some experiments, radioactivity was determined in a liquid scintillation counter with a C14-counting efficiency of 65 percent [21] and dried filters (not glued) were placed in vials containing 10 ml of

Table 2. Polynucleotide specificity. Reaction mixtures containing C14-Phe- and C14-Lys-sRNA were incubated for 60 minutes at 0°C; mixtures containing C14-Pro-sRNA were incubated for 20 minutes at 24°C. In addition to the components described in the text, reaction mixtures contained, in a final volume of 50 μl, the specified polynucleotide and C14-amino-acyl-sRNA (14.7 μμmole C14-Phe-sRNA, 2015 count/min, 0.960 A^{260} units; 16.5 μμmole C14-Lys-sRNA, 1845 count/min, 0.530 A^{260} units; 30 μμmole C14-Pro-sRNA, 2750 count/min, 1.570 A^{260} units).

Polynucleotide (mμmole base residues)	C14-Aminoacyl-sRNA bound to ribosomes (μμmole)		
	C14-Phe-sRNA	C14-Lys-sRNA	C14-Pro-sRNA
None	0.19	0.99	0.25
PolyU, 25	6.00	.67	.15
PolyA, 16	0.22	4.35	.17
PolyC, 19	.21	0.72	.80

toluene-PPO-POPOP phosphor solution [22].

Preparation of sRNA. Except where noted *E. coli* B sRNA [23], was used. Uniformly labeled C14-L-phenylalanine, C14-L-lysine, and C14-L-leucine with specific radioactivities of 250, 305, and 160 μc/μmole, respectively, were obtained commercially [24]. The *E. coli* W 3100 sRNA was prepared as described by Zubay [25] from cells grown to late log phase in 0.9 percent Difco nutrient broth, containing 1 percent glucose. The C14-amino acyl-sRNA was prepared by modifications of meth-

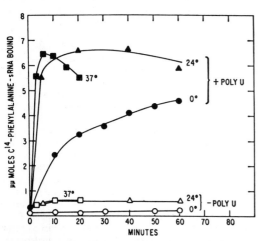

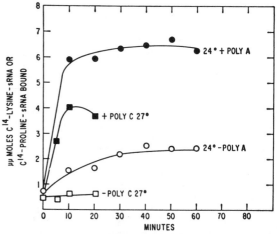

Fig. 1 (left). Effect of polyU upon the rate of C14-Phe-sRNA binding to ribosomes at 0°, 24°, and 37°C. Each point represents a 50 μl reaction mixture incubated for the time and at the temperature indicated. Reaction mixtures contain the components described under *Methods*; 9.65 μμmole of C14-Phe-sRNA (1180 count/min, 0.380 A^{260}); and polyU, 25 mμmole base residues, where specified.   Fig. 2 (right). The effect of polyA and polyC upon the rates of C14-Lys- and C14-Pro-sRNA binding to ribosomes, respectively. Each point represents a 50-μl reaction mixture as described under *Methods*. The reactions specified contained 27.5 μμmole C14-Lys-sRNA (3080 count/min, 0.880 A^{260} units) and polyA, 25 mμmole base residues, or 11.8 μμmole C14-Pro-sRNA (2660 count/min, 0.905 A^{260} units) and polyC, 25 mμmole base residues. The temperature and the time of incubation are shown in the figure.

ods described previously (26). Unless otherwise specified, sRNA was acylated with one C^{14}-amino acid plus 19 C^{12}-amino acids. The formation of C^{14}-aminoacyl sRNA was catalyzed by the supernatant solution obtained by centrifugation of E. coli (W-3100) extracts at 100,000g.

Elution and characterization of C^{14}-phenylalanine product bound to ribosomes. Reaction mixtures (0.5 ml) incubated at 24°C for 10 minutes with C^{14}-Phe-sRNA and polyU were washed on cellulose nitrate filters in the usual manner. The ribosomal bound C^{14}-product was eluted from filters by washing with 0.01M tris-acetate, pH 7.2; $10^{-5}M$ magnesium acetate; and 0.05M KCl at 0°C.

The C^{14}-product eluted from ribosomes was precipitated in 10 percent TCA at 3°C in the presence of 200 μg of bovine serum albumin. Specified samples were heated in 10 percent TCA at 90° to 95°C for 20 minutes and then were chilled. Precipitates were washed on filters with 5 percent TCA at 3°C. Aminoacyl sRNA was deacylated in 0.1M ammonium carbonate solution adjusted with NH_4OH to pH 10.2 to 10.5 by incubation at 37°C for 60 minutes.

Digestions with ribonuclease were performed by incubating 0.4-ml portions (each containing 1500 count/min precipitable by 10 percent TCA at 3°C) with and without 10 μg of purified pancreatic ribonuclease A (purified chromatographically) (27) at 37°C for 15 minutes.

Results and Discussion

Assay of ribosomal bound C^{14}-aminoacyl-sRNA. The assay is based upon the retention of ribosomes and C^{14}-aminoacyl sRNA bound to ribosomes by cellulose nitrate filters. After unbound C^{14}-aminoacyl sRNA is removed by washing with buffered salts solution, as already described, the radioactivity remaining on the filter is determined. Thirty reaction mixtures can be washed per hour easily. The sensitivity of the assay is limited primarily by the specific radioactivity of the aminoacyl-sRNA used. With sRNA which has accepted a C^{14}-amino acid of specific radioactivity 100 to 300 μc/μmole, the binding to ribosomes of 0.2 μμmoles of C^{14}-aminoacyl sRNA readily can be detected. A filter 25 mm in diameter with a pore size of 0.45 μ retains up to 1200 μg of E. coli ribosomes. The

use of larger filters or columns packed with cellulose nitrate may be useful for preparative procedures.

The retention of ribosomes by cellulose nitrate filters may be the result of absorption rather than of filtration, for filters with pores 100 times larger than E. coli 70S ribosomes can be used. The rapidity of this assay, compared to others which depend upon the centrifugation of ribosomes, has greatly simplified this study.

The data of Table 1 show that little C^{14}-Phe-sRNA was retained on filters after incubation with ribosomes in the absence of polyU. Incubation in the presence of both polyU and ribosomes resulted in marked retention of C^{14}-Phe-sRNA by the filter. Ribosomes, polyU, and Mg^{++} were required for retention of C^{14}-Phe-sRNA. Spyrides (28) and Conway (29) have reported that polyU-directed binding of Phe-sRNA to ribosomes is dependent upon K^+ or NH_4^+.

The addition of deacylated sRNA to reactions shortly before incubation was terminated, after C^{14}-Phe-sRNA binding had ceased, had little effect upon ribosomal bound C^{14}-Phe-sRNA. The bound C^{14}-Phe-sRNA fraction apparently is not readily exchangeable.

In contrast, the addition of deacylated sRNA at the start of incubation inhibited C^{14}-Phe-sRNA binding. In other experiments, the extent of inhibition was found to be affected by the ratio of deacylated to acylated sRNA. Deacylated sRNA added near the end of incubation often reduces background binding without polynucleotide and may afford a way of differentiating between exchangeable and nonexchangeable binding. It should be noted that the presence of a polynucleotide which is not recognized by a C^{14}-aminoacyl sRNA (for example, polyA and C^{14}-Phe-sRNA) also reduces background sRNA binding, perhaps by saturating ribosomal sites with specified nonexchangeable sRNA.

Characteristics of binding. The assay was validated further by demonstrating that the binding of sRNA to ribosomes was directed with specificity by different polynucleotides. As shown in Table 2, polyU, polyA and polyC specifically directed the binding to ribosomes of C^{14}-Phe-, C^{14}-Lys-, and C^{14}-Pro-sRNA, respectively. These data agree well with specificity data obtained with a sucrose-gradient centrifugation assay, reported by Nakamoto et al. (8) and Kaji and Kaji (9, 10) (also compare 5–7, 11) and with data on their specificity for

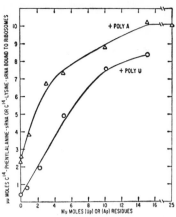

Fig. 3. Relation between polynucleotide concentration and C^{14}-aminoacyl-sRNA binding to ribosomes. Each point represents a 50-μl reaction mixture with the components described under *Methods*; △, polyA as specified and 27.5 μμmole C^{14}-Lys-sRNA (3080 count/min, 0.880 A^{260} units); ○, polyU as specified and 15 μμmole of C^{14}-Phe-sRNA (2050 count/min, 0.714 A^{260} units). Incubation was at 24°C for 20 minutes.

directing amino acid incorporation into protein (30, 31).

The rate of binding of Phe-sRNA to ribosomes at 0°, 24° and 37°C, in the presence and absence of polyU, is shown in Fig. 1. During incubation at each temperature polyU markedly stimulated C^{14}-Phe-sRNA binding; how-

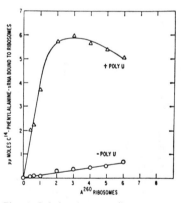

Fig. 4. Relation between ribosome concentration and C^{14}-Phe-sRNA binding. Each point represents a 50-μl reaction mixture containing the amount of ribosomes indicated; ○ No additions, (-poly U); △ + poly U, 25 mμmole base residues. In addition, reaction mixtures contain the components described under *Methods* and 9.65 μμmole of C^{14}-Phe-sRNA (1180 count/min, 0.380 A^{260}). Incubations were for 10 minutes at 24°C.

341

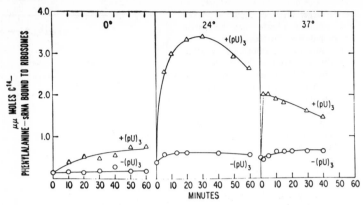

Fig. 5. Effect of pUpUpU upon the rate of C¹⁴-Phe-sRNA binding to ribosomes at 0°, 24°, and 37°C. ○, No addition; △, addition of 3.67 mμmole pUpUpU. Each point represents a 50-μl reaction mixture incubated for the time and at the temperature specified. Reaction mixtures contain the components described under *Methods*; 9.65 μμmole of C¹⁴-Phe-sRNA (1180 count/min, 0.380 A^{260}); and oligoU as specified.

the possible utility of this system for the purification of sRNA species (9).

In the absence of polyU, relatively little C¹⁴-Phe-sRNA associated with ribosomes. Such binding may be due to endogenous mRNA on ribosomes or in sRNA preparations. Alternatively, this binding may be nonspecific, possibly similar to that described by Cannon, Krug, and Gilbert (4).

The effect of polyA and polyC upon the rates of C¹⁴-Lys- and C¹⁴-Pro-sRNA binding to ribosomes is shown in Fig. 2. Maximum stimulation of C¹⁴-Lys-sRNA binding by polyA, and of C¹⁴-Pro-sRNA binding by polyC, occurred after 10 minutes of incubation at 24° and 27°C, respectively. In this experiment, C¹⁴-Lys-sRNA binding observed in the absence of polyA was higher than that found in experiments with other sRNA preparations.

The relation between polyU or polyA concentration and the amount of C¹⁴-Phe- or C¹⁴-Lys-sRNA bound to ribosomes is shown in Fig. 3. Binding of sRNA was proportional to polynucleotide concentration in both cases.

In experiments not presented here, the effect of *p*H upon sRNA binding was studied. PolyU directed C¹⁴-Phe-

ever, the rate of binding increased as the temperature of incubation was raised. Although polyU induced C¹⁴-Phe-sRNA binding at 0°C, maximum binding was not observed after 60 minutes of incubation. Maximum binding concentrations of C¹⁴-Phe-sRNA, 50 minutes of incubation at 24°C and

after 6 minutes at 37°C. In this experiment equal amounts of C¹⁴-Phe-sRNA were bound at 24° and 37°C. In other experiments, with limiting concentrations of C¹⁴-Phe-sRNA, 50 to 98 percent of the C¹⁴-Phe-sRNA was induced to bind to ribosomes by polyU. Kaji and Kaji have suggested

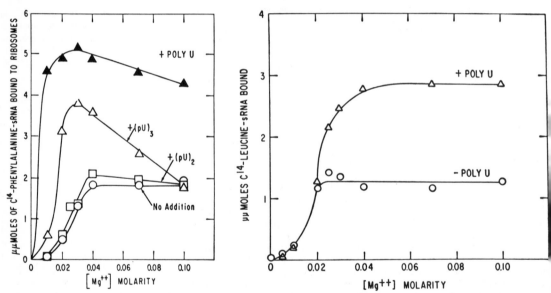

Fig. 6 (left). Effect of (Mg⁺⁺) concentration upon C¹⁴-Phe-sRNA binding to ribosomes. Each symbol represents a 50-μl reaction mixture containing: ○, polymer (no addition); □, pUpU, 10 mμmole base residues; △, pUpUpU, 10 mμmole base residues; ▲, polyU, 25 mμmole base residues; and the components described under *Methods;* the magnesium acetate concentrations of reaction mixtures and the washing buffer are shown in the figure; 3.5 A^{260} units of ribosomes; and 8.63 μμmole C¹⁴-Phe-sRNA (1025 count/min, 0.357 A^{260} units. Incubation was at 24°C for 20 minutes.   Fig. 7 (right). The polyU-leucine ambiguity. The effect of polyU upon C¹⁴-Leu-sRNA binding to ribosomes at different Mg⁺⁺ concentrations. Each 50-μl reaction contained the components described under *Methods*; the magnesium acetate concentration specified in the figure 23.7 μμmole C¹⁴-Leu-sRNA (1710 count/ min, 0.424 A^{260} units of *E. coli* W 3100 sRNA, charged only with C¹⁴-leucine); and polyU, 25 mμmole base residues where specified. Incubation was at 24°C for 20 minutes. Each reaction mixture was washed with a buffer containing Mg⁺⁺ at the concentration present during incubation.

Table 3. Oligonucleotide specificity. Reaction mixtures containing either C¹⁴-Phe-, C¹⁴-Lys-, or C¹⁴-Pro-sRNA, and oligonucleotide were incubated at 24°C for 20 minutes. Components of reaction mixtures are described in the legend accompanying Table 2. The numbers in parentheses are millimicromoles base residues.

Oligonucleotide (mμmoles base residues)	C¹⁴-Aminoacyl-sRNA bound to ribosomes (μμmole)		
	C¹⁴-Phe-sRNA	C¹⁴-Lys-sRNA	C¹⁴-Pro-sRNA
None	0.34	0.80	0.24
pUpUpU (10)	1.56	0.56	0.20
pApApA (7)	0.20	6.13	0.18
pCpCpC (8)	0.30	0.60	0.73

sRNA binding to ribosomes throughout the *p*H range tested, from 5.5 to 7.8. Binding was maximum in reactions buffered either with 0.1*M* tris, *p*H 7.2, or with 0.05*M* cacodylate, *p*H 6.5.

The addition of GTP, PEP, and PEP kinase to reactions, with or without polyU, did not stimulate C¹⁴-Phe-sRNA binding; however, further study is necessary to determine whether binding in this system is dependent upon enzymatic catalysis or GTP or both. Polyphenylalanine synthesis (that is, radioactivity in the fraction precipitable with hot TCA) was not detected in reaction mixtures incubated under optimum conditions for C¹⁴-Phe-sRNA binding in the presence of polyU. In additional experiments, C¹⁴-Phe-sRNA induced by polyU to bind to ribosomes was eluted with 10⁻⁵*M* Mg⁺⁺ as already described. Although 50 to 98 percent of the ribosomal-bound C¹⁴-product was eluted (in different experiments), few ribosomes were released from filters. The C¹⁴-product was insoluble in TCA at 3°C, but was converted quantitatively to a soluble product by (i) incubation at *p*H 10.2 for 60 minutes at 37°C, (ii) heating in TCA, or (iii), incubation with pancreatic ribonuclease. Further characterization of the bound C¹⁴-product is necessary; however, these preliminary results are in accord with the demonstration by Schweet and his co-workers that the binding of Phe-sRNA to ribosomes induced by polyU is not dependent upon peptide-bond formation (6, 7).

The relation between ribosome concentration and the amount of bound C¹⁴-Phe-sRNA is illustrated in Fig. 4. C¹⁴-Phe-sRNA binding was stimulated markedly by polyU and was proportional to the ribosome concentration, within the range 0 to 1.0 *A*²⁶⁰ units of ribosomes. The number of 70*S E. coli*

ribosomes and ribosomal-bound C¹⁴-Phe-sRNA molecules can be estimated from such data; however, various factors, such as the inhibitory effects of deacylated sRNA (see above) and mRNA terminal phosphate (described below) undoubtedly reduce the accuracy of such calculations. However, in the presence of polyU approximately 4.0 μμmole of C¹⁴-Phe-sRNA became bound to 23.2 μμmole of 70*S* ribosomes (*4*); therefore, the C¹⁴-Phe-sRNA ribosome ratio was 1 : 5.8. Arlinghaus *et al.* (*7*) and Warner and Rich (*32*) recently reported two binding sites for each ribosome for sRNA. One site is thought to hold the nascent polypeptide chain to the ribosome; the other, to bind the next aminoacyl-sRNA molecule specified by mRNA.

Effect of oligonucleotides on the binding of C¹⁴-aminoacyl sRNA to ribosomes. OligoU preparations of different chain length were prepared, and their effect upon C¹⁴-Phe-sRNA binding to ribosomes was determined. The effect of the trinucleotide, pUpUpU, upon C¹⁴-Phe-sRNA binding to ribosomes, at 0°, 24°, and 37°C, is shown in Fig. 5. The C¹⁴-Phe-sRNA binding was stimulated by pUpUpU at each temperature; however, binding was maximum in reactions incubated at 24°C for 20 to 30 minutes. These results demonstrate that a trinucleotide can direct C¹⁴-aminoacyl-sRNA binding to ribosomes and suggest a general method of great simplicity for determining the genetic function of other trinucleotide sequences.

The binding of C¹⁴-Phe-, C¹⁴-Lys-, and C¹⁴-Pro-sRNA was induced with apparent specificity by pUpUpU, pApApA, and pCpCpC, respectively (Table 3). In additional experiments, each trinucleotide had no discernible effect upon the binding to ribosomes of 15 aminoacyl-sRNA preparations, each charged with a different C¹⁴-amino acid (C¹⁴-asparagine and C¹⁴-glutamine-sRNA were not tested). Therefore, the specificity of each trinucleotide for inducing sRNA binding to ribosomes was high and clearly paralleled that of the corresponding polynucleotide.

The *T*ₘ of the interaction between pApApA and polyU is 17°C (*33*). Therefore, hydrogen-bonding between a triplet codeword in mRNA and a complementary "anticodeword" in sRNA would not by itself appear sufficient to account for the stability of the interaction between C¹⁴-Phe-sRNA, polyU, and ribosomes. An interaction between

Table 4. Template activity of oligodeoxynucleotides. The components of each 50 μl reaction mixture are presented in the text. In addition, each reaction mixture in Expt. 1 contained 9.65 μμmoles of C¹⁴-Phe-sRNA (1370 count/min, 0.380 *A*²⁶⁰ units); and in Expt. 2, 16.5 μμmoles C¹⁴-Lys-sRNA (1845 count/min, 0.530 *A*²⁶⁰ units) and the oligonucleotides specified. Mixtures were incubated at 24°C for 10 minutes.

Oligonucleotide (mμmole)	C¹⁴-Aminoacyl-sRNA bound to ribosomes (μμmole)
Experiment 1: C¹⁴-Phe-sRNA	
None	0.29
1.00 pUpUpU	1.29
3.33 pUpUpU	2.40
6.67 pUpUpU	2.90
3.33 oligo d(pT)₃	0.35
6.67 oligo d(pT)₃	0.39
10.00 oligo d(pT)₃	0.40
1.67 oligo d(pT)₁₂	0.31
2.50 oligo d(pT)₁₂	0.44
Experiment 2: C¹⁴-Lys-sRNA	
None	1.27
0.17 pApApA	3.48
1.37 pApApA	5.99
3.60 pApApA	7.40
0.65 oligo d(pA)₈	1.45
1.30 oligo d(pA)₈	1.68
2.00 oligo d(pA)₈	1.61

the -CpCpA end of sRNA and ribosomes is possible, for several laboratories (*3, 4, 34*) have reported that removal of the terminal adenosine of sRNA greatly reduces its ability to bind to ribosomes. The participation of an enzyme in the binding process also must be considered.

The data of Table 4 indicate that the 2′-hydroxyl of RNA codewords may be necessary for codeword recognition. Oligodeoxynucleotides such as oligo-d(pT)₃₋₁₂ and oligo-d(pA)₈ apparently were inactive as templates. In additional experiments not presented here, the effects of time and temperature of incubation (0°, 24°, 37°, and 43°C), template concentration, and chain length were studied. No template activity was found.

The template activities of pUpU, pUpUpU and polyU at different concentrations of Mg⁺⁺ are shown in Fig. 6. Both tri- and polyU induced maximal binding at approximately 0.03*M* Mg⁺⁺ (0.02 to 0.03*M* in other experiments). Although the dinucleotide, pUpU, stimulated binding slightly, it is not known whether the activity of pUpU indicates partial recognition of a triplet codeword as previously suggested (*35*). At 0.02*M* Mg⁺⁺, the concentration used throughout our study, little binding of C¹⁴-Phe-sRNA was found in the absence of polyU. However, at higher Mg⁺⁺ concentrations, Phe-sRNA binding in the absence of template RNA increased;

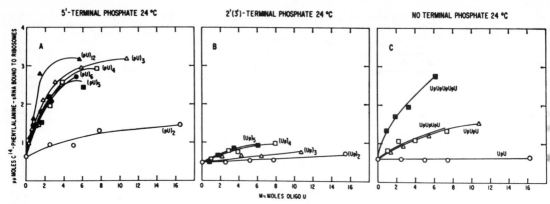

Fig. 8. *A*, *B*, and *C*, Relation between template activity and oligoU chain-length, concentration and end-group. The activities of oligoU with 5′-terminal phosphate are shown in Fig. 8*A*; with 2′(3′)-terminal phosphate in Fig. 8*B*; and without terminal phosphate in Fig. 8*C*. Symbols represent oligoU chain-lengths as follows: ○ 2; △ 3; □ 4; ■ 5; ● 6; ▲ 12. Each reaction mixture contained, in a volume of 50 μl, the components specified in the *Methods* section; oligoU preparations and concentrations specified; and 10.8 $\mu\mu$mole C¹⁴-Phe-sRNA (1880 count/min, 0.714 A^{260}). Oligonucleotide preparations (pU)₂, No. 610; (pU)₅, No. 613; (Up)₅, No. 617; with the contaminants specified under *Methods* were used in these experiments. Incubations were at 24°C for 30 minutes.

whereas binding induced by tri- and polyU, decreased. These data suggest that certain ribosomal binding sites become saturated with sRNA at Mg⁺⁺ concentrations greater than 0.03*M*, but are not saturated at lower concentrations.

Leucine-polyU ambiguity. Since polyU is known to direct some leucine incorporation into protein in cell-free systems (*36*), especially at high Mg⁺⁺ concentrations (*37*), the effect of polyU upon the binding of C¹⁴-Leu-sRNA was determined (Fig. 7). In the absence of polyU, background binding saturated at 0.02*M* Mg⁺⁺. The addition

of polyU clearly stimulated the binding of C¹⁴-Leu-sRNA. It is possible that the Mg⁺⁺-dependent leucine-polyU ambiguity occurs before peptide-bond synthesis.

As shown in Table 5, C¹⁴-Leu-sRNA binding was stimulated with specificity by polyU, but not by the trinucleotide, pUpUpU, polyA, or polyC at 0.07*M* Mg⁺⁺. In additional experiments, pUpUpU had no effect upon the binding of C¹⁴-Leu-sRNA at other Mg⁺⁺ concentrations. These data suggest that pUpUpU may be recognized by aminoacyl sRNA with greater specificity than polyU is recognized.

Effect of oligonucleotide chain length, concentration, and terminal phosphate. In Fig. 8 the template activity of oligoU preparations differing in chain length and position of terminal phosphate are compared at different oligoU concentrations. The activity of oligoU with 5′-terminal phosphate is shown in Fig. 8*A*; preparations with 2′(3′)-terminal phosphate in Fig 8*B*; and preparations without terminal phosphate, in Fig. 8*C*.

As shown in Fig. 8*A*, the dinucleotide with 5′-terminal phosphate, pUpU, had little template activity, whereas the trinucleotide, pUpUpU, markedly stimulated C¹⁴-Phe-sRNA binding. This ob-

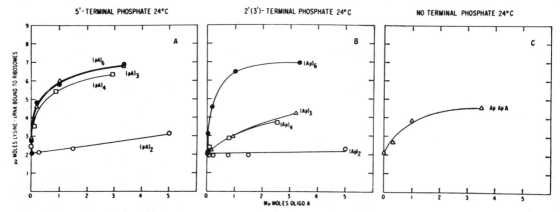

Fig. 9. *A*, *B*, and *C*, Relation between template activity and oligoA concentration, chain-length, and end group. The activity of oligoA with 5′-terminal phosphate is shown in Fig. 9*A*; preparation without terminal phosphate in Fig. 9*C*. The symbols indicate the chain-length of oligoA as follows: ○ 2; △ 3; □ 4; ● 6. Each 50 μl reaction mixture contained the components specified under methods; 15.9 $\mu\mu$mole of C¹⁴-Lys-sRNA (1780 count/min, 0.562 A^{260} units); and the oligoA preparation specified. Incubation was at 24°C for 20 minutes. Oligonucleotide preparations (pA)₆, No. 599 and (Ap)₄, No. 591, containing the contaminants specified under *Methods*, were used in this experiment.

servation provides direct experimental support for a triplet code for phenylalanine and is in full accord with earlier genetic and biochemical studies (*30, 38*).

In addition, the data demonstrate that the template activity of pUpUpU equals that of the corresponding tetra-, penta-, and hexanucleotides.

In striking contrast to these results, the trinucleotide, UpUpUp, with 2′(3′)-terminal phosphate, induced little or no binding of C¹⁴-Phe-sRNA to ribosomes (Fig. 8*B*). The template activity of the tetra- and pentauridylic acid fractions with 2′(3′)-terminal phosphate also were markedly reduced when compared to similar fractions with 5′-terminal phosphate.

As shown in Fig. 8*C*, UpUpU and UpUpUpU, without terminal phosphate, induced C¹⁴-Phe-sRNA binding, but less actively than pUpUpU. The template activity of the pentamer, UpUpUpUpU, was almost equal to that of pUpUpU.

Since the sensitivity of an oligonucleotide to digestion by a nuclease often is influenced by terminal phosphate, the relative stability of pUpUpU, UpUpUp, and UpUpU incubated with ribosomes at 37°C for 60 minutes was estimated by recovering mono- and oligonucleotides from reaction mixtures and separating them by paper chromatography. In each case, the expected trinucleotide was the only component found after incubation. Hydrolysis of oligoU was not observed.

The template activities of oligoA fractions with different end groups are shown in Fig. 9, *A*, *B*, and *C*. The results were similar to those obtained with oligoU; however, pApApA induced maximum C¹⁴-Lys-sRNA binding at one-fifth the oligonucleotide concentration required previously (compare with Fig. 8*A*). The hexamer with 3′-terminal phosphate induced as much C¹⁴-Lys-sRNA binding to ribosomes as the trimer with 5′-terminal phosphate, pApApA. When reaction mixtures were incubated at 0°C (Fig. 10) the difference between the template activities of ApApAp and pApApA was more marked than when incubations were at 24°C.

Since each oligonucleotide preparation with 2′(3′)-terminal phosphate is a mixture of molecules, some chains terminating with 2′-phosphate and others with 3′-phosphate, a trinucleotide, UpUpUp, with 3′-terminal phosphate only, was prepared and found to be in-

active as a template for C¹⁴-Phe-sRNA.

Attachment of ribosomes to mRNA. It is not known whether ribosomes attach to 5′-ends, 3′-ends, or internal positions of mRNA. The template activity of trinucleotides indicates that (i) ribosomes can attach to terminal codewords of mRNA, (ii) terminal codewords are capable of specifying the first and the last amino acids to be incorporated into protein, and (iii) the attachment of a ribosome to *only* the terminal triplet of mRNA may provide the minimum stability necessary for codeword recognition, and possibly for the initiation of protein synthesis.

The demonstration that terminal and internal codeword phosphates strongly influence the codeword recognition process indicates that phosphate may take part in the binding of codewords to ribosomes. Watson has suggested interaction between phosphate of mRNA and amino groups of ribosomes, because 30S ribosomes treated with formaldehyde were found by Moore and Asano to bind less polyU than did ribosomes not so treated (*39*).

Although terminal codeword phosphate is not required for the recognition of a codeword on a ribosome, the

observation that the template activity of trinucleotides with 5′-terminal phosphate equals that of tetra-, penta-, and hexanucleotides, even at limiting concentrations, suggests that 5′-terminal codewords may *attach to sites on ribosomes where codewords are recognized, in correct phase to be read.* A preferential, phased recognition of either terminal codeword by ribosomes would provide a simple mechanism for selecting the polarity of reading, the first word to be read, and the phase of reading. Since 5′-terminal codewords of mRNA most actively induce sRNA binding, such codewords would appear to serve these functions best. Although the polarity with which mRNA is read may be from the 5′- towards the 3′-terminal codeword, further work is necessary to clarify this point. The opposite polarity has been suggested (*45*).

We have reported (*40*) that trinucleotides can be used in this system to determine the base sequence of codewords and have shown that the sequence of the valine RNA codeword is GpUpU. Codewords are recognized with polarity in this system, for GpUpU induced C¹⁴-Val-sRNA binding to ribosomes, whereas UpUpG did not.

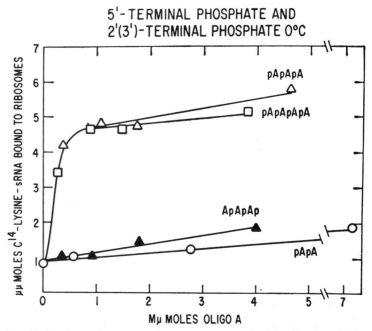

Fig. 10. Template activity of oligoA with 5′- or 2′(3′)-terminal phosphate in reaction mixtures incubated at 0°C for 60 minutes. OligoA concentrations, chain-lengths, and end-groups are shown in the figure. Each 50-μl reaction mixture contained the components specified under *Methods*; 11.8 μμmole C¹⁴-Lys-sRNA (2840 count/min, 0.767 A^{260} units); and the oligoA preparation specified.

Regulatory Codewords

Terminal codewords. We suggest that 5'-terminal, 3'-terminal and internal codewords of RNA and DNA constitute separate classes of codewords, for each differs in chemical structure as shown diagrammatically in Fig. 11. The 5'-terminal codeword contains a 5'-terminal hydroxyl, the internal codeword is attached to adjacent codewords on both sides by way of (3'-5')-phosphodiester bonds, and the 3'-terminal codeword contains 2'- and 3'-terminal hydroxyl groups. It should be noted that phosphate, linked to a terminal hydroxyl is a monoester, whereas, an internal phosphate is a diester. Therefore, the 5'-terminal, 3'-terminal, and internal codewords differ in chemical structure. To avoid confusion between the three codeword classes, the codeword with free or substituted 5'-hydroxyl will be designated the 5'-terminal codeword, and the codeword with a free or substituted 3'-hydroxyl, will be designated the 3'-terminal codeword. Internal codewords will not be designated by position. These differences raise the possibility that codewords may occur in three chemically distinct forms and that RNA and DNA may contain either one, two, or three forms of any triplet codeword, depending upon the position of the codeword in the molecule.

Sense-missense-nonsense codewords.

Genetic evidence suggests that certain mutations result in the conversion of readable into nonreadable codewords, that is, sense-nonsense interchanges (*41*). The addition of terminal phosphate to a 3'-terminal codeword similarly changes a readable into a nonreadable codeword and resembles a sense-nonsense interchange. Two additional mechanisms for converting readable into nonreadable words have been found in cell-free systems; that is, an increase in secondary structure (*37, 42*) and specific base methylations (*37*). It should be noted that each type of sense-nonsense interchange involves a modification of codewords rather than modification of a component required for codeword recognition.

It is possible that the synthesis of certain proteins may be regulated in vivo by sense-nonsense interchanges involving either modification of a codeword or, as proposed by Ames and Hartman (*43*), modification of sRNA, that is, codeword recognition. It seems probable that terminal codewords may have special functions in addition to directing amino acids into protein. For example, in mRNA they may specify (i) attachment and detachment of ribosomes, (ii) the first codeword to be read, (iii) the phase of reading, and (iv) the sensitivity of the message to degradation by exonucleases. Similarly, terminal DNA codewords may influence the rate with which DNA is copied

Table 5. Specificity of polyU-leucine-sRNA bound to ribosomes. Reaction mixtures contained 0.07*M* magnesium acetate; other components as described in the text; 3.1 $\mu\mu$moles of C[11]-Leu-sRNA (2280 count min, 0.565 A^{260} units of *E. coli* W 3100 sRNA acylated only with C[11]-Leucine); and oligo- or polynucleotides as specified. Incubations were at 24°C for 20 minutes. The magnesium acetate concentration of the solution used to wash ribosomes on filters after incubation was 0.07*M*.

Addition (base residues) (mμmole)	C[11]-Leu-sRNA bound to ribosomes ($\mu\mu$mole)
None	1.00
25 PolyU	2.02
15 pUpUpU	0.70
25 PolyA	.99
25 PolyC	.85

by DNA or RNA polymerase. Experimental observations support this possibility, for DNA without terminal phosphate has been found to serve as a template for DNA polymerase, whereas DNA with 3'-terminal phosphate has no template activity (*44*).

Terminal words with 3'-phosphate may be members of a larger class of DNA and mRNA nonsense words, with substituted 5'-, 3'-, or 2'-hydroxyl groups. Many enzymes have been described which catalyze the transfer of nucleotides, amino acids, methyl groups, carbohydrates, and other molecules, to or from mononucleotides or terminal ribose or deoxyribose of nucleic acids. Such enzymes may recognize terminal bases or conformations of nucleic acids and catalyze group transfer reactions with great specificity.

The data of Figs. 8 to 10, and the chemical and biological considerations described, suggest that *codeword modification* may serve a regulatory or operator function. Modification of codewords, at both terminal and internal positions, may regulate the reading of DNA or RNA by converting a readable word into one read incorrectly or not read. It should be noted that both 3'- and 5'-terminal codewords could serve, in different ways, as operator words.

The capacity of trinucleotides to direct the binding of sRNA to ribosomes and the ease with which the process can be assayed should provide a general method of great simplicity for studying the base sequence and genetic functions of each triplet codeword. In addition, this method should permit the detailed study of interactions between codewords, sRNA, and ribosomes during the codeword recognition process.

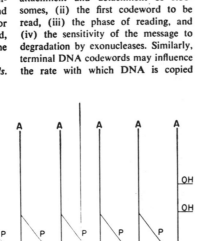

Fig. 11. The structures of three classes of codewords, 5'-terminal, internal, and 3'-terminal, are illustrated diagramatically. The figure represents oligoA of chain-length 9, ApApApApApApApA. Although the three triplet codewords have identical base-sequences, AAA, each differs in structure. The 5'-terminal codeword contains a 5'-terminal hydroxyl; the internal codeword is linked to adjacent codewords on either side by way of 3', 5'-phosphodiester bonds; and the 3'-terminal codeword contains 2', 3'-terminal hydroxyl groups (3'-hydroxyl only if deoxyribose). Phosphate, when present at 5'-, 3'-, or 2'-terminal hydroxyl positions, may be a phosphomonoester, and therefore may differ from an internal phosphate which is a phosphodiester.

Summary

A rapid, sensitive method is described for measuring C^{14}-aminoacyl-sRNA interactions with ribosomes which are specifically induced by the appropriate RNA codewords prior to peptide-bond formation. Properties of the codeword recognition process and the minimum oligonucleotide chain length required to induce such interactions are presented. The trinucleotides, pUpUpU, pApApA, and pCpCpC, but not dinucleotides, specifically direct the binding to ribosomes of phenylalanine-, lysine-, and proline-sRNA, respectively.

Since 5'-terminal, 3'-terminal, and internal codewords differ in chemical structure, three corresponding classes of codewords are proposed. The recognition of each class in this system is described. The template efficiency of trinucleotide codewords is modified greatly by terminal phosphate. Triplets with 5'-terminal phosphate are more active as templates than triplets without terminal phosphate. Triplets with 3'- or 3' (2')-terminal phosphate are markedly less active as templates. These findings are discussed in relation to the probable functions of terminal codewords. The modification of RNA and DNA codewords, converting sense into missense or nonsense codewords, is suggested as a possible regulatory mechanism in protein synthesis.

References and Notes

1. The following abbreviations and symbols are used: Phe-, phenylalanine; Leu-, leucine; Lys-, lysine; Pro-, proline; Val-, valine; polyU, polyuridylic acid; polyC, polycytidylic acid; polyA, polyadenylic acid; TCA, trichloracetic acid; d(pT), deoxythymidylic acid; d(pA), deoxyadenylic acid; sRNA, transfer RNA;

mRNA, messenger RNA; DEAE, diethylaminoethyl cellulose; PPO, 2,5-diphenyloxazole; POPOP, 1,4-bis-2'-(5'-phenyloxazolyl) benzene; PEP, phosphoenolpyruvate; T_m, melting temperature; A^{260}, at 260 mμ.

For mono- and oligonucleotides of specific structure, the p to the left of a terminal nucleoside initial indicates a 5'-terminal phosphate; the p to the right, a 2' (3')-terminal phosphate. Internal phosphates of oligonucleotides are (3'-5')-linkages.
2. A Von der Decken and T. Hultin, *Exptl. Cell. Res.* **15**, 254, (1958); L. Bosch, H. Bloemendal, M. Sluyser, *Biochim. Biophys. Acta* **34**, 272 (1959); M. B. Hoagland and L. T. Comly, *Proc. Natl. Acad. Sci. U.S.* **46**, 1554 (1960).
3. M. Takanami, *Biochim. Biophys. Acta* **55**, 132 (1962); L. Bosch, F. Huizinga, H. Bloemendal, *ibid.* **61**, 220 (1962).
4. M. Cannon, R. Krug, W. Gilbert, *J. Mol. Biol.* **7**, 360 (1963).
5. R. Arlinghaus, G. Favelukes, R. Schweet, *Biochem. Biophys. Res. Commun.* **11**, 92 (1963).
6. B. Hardesty, R. Arlinghaus, J. Schaeffer, R. Schweet, in *Cold Spring Harbor Symp. Quant. Biol.* **28**, 215 (1963).
7. R. Arlinghaus, J. Shaeffer, R. Schweet, *Proc. Natl. Acad. Sci. U.S.* **51**, 1291 (1964).
8. T. Nakamoto, T. Conway, J. Allende, G. Spyrides, F. Lipmann, in *Cold Spring Harbor Symp. Quant. Biol.* **28**, 227 (1963).
9. A. Kaji and H. Kaji, *Biochem. Biophys. Res. Commun.* **13**, 186 (1963).
10. ———, *Federation Proc.* **23**, 478 (1964).
11. G. J. Spyrides, Ph.D. dissertation, Rockefeller Institute (1963); *Federation. Proc.* **23**, 318 318 (1964).
12. Miles Chemical Company.
13. L. A. Heppel, personal communication.
14. Worthington Biochemical Corporation.
15. L. A. Heppel, D. Harkness, R. Hilmoe, *J. Biol. Chem.* **237**, 841 (1962).
16. G. W. Rushizky and H. A. Sober, *ibid.* **238**, 371 (1963).
17. P. S. Chen, Jr., T. Y. Toribara, H. Warner, *Anal. Chem.* **28**, 1756 (1956); B. N. Ames and D. T. Dubin, *J. Biol. Chem.* **235**, 769 (1960).
18. P. Leder, B. F. C. Clark, W. S. Sly, S. Pestka, M. W. Nirenberg, *Proc. Natl. Acad. Sci. U.S.* **50**, 1135 (1963).
19. M. Bernfield and M. W. Nirenberg, *Abstracts, 148th Meeting, American Chemical Society*, Chicago, Ill., August 1964.
20. Nuclear Chicago Corporation.
21. Packard Instrument Company.
22. J. R. Sherman and J. Adler, *J. Biol. Chem.* **238**, 873 (1963).
23. General Biochemicals Corporation.
24. New England Nuclear Corporation.
25. G. Zubay, *J. Mol. Biol.* **4**, 347 (1962).
26. M. W. Nirenberg, J. H. Matthaei, O. W. Jones, *Proc. Natl. Acad. Sci. U.S.* **48**, 104 (1962).
27. Sigma Chemical Company.

28. G. J. Spyrides, *Proc. Natl. Acad. Sci. U.S.* **51**, 1220 (1964).
29. T. W. Conway, *ibid.* **51**, 1216 (1964).
30. M. W. Nirenberg, O. W. Jones, P. Leder, B. F. C. Clark, W. S. Sly, S. Pestka, in *Cold Spring Harbor Symp. Quant. Biol. Vol.* **28**, 549 (1963).
31. J. S. Speyer, P. Lengyel, C. Basilio, A. J. Wahba, R. S. Gardner, S. Ochoa, *ibid.* **28**, 559 (1963).
32. J. R. Warner and A. Rich, *Proc. Natl. Acad. Sci. U.S.* **51**, 1134 (1964).
33. M. N. Lipsett, L. A. Heppel, D. F. Bradley, *J. Biol. Chem.* **236**, 857 (1961).
34. H. Bloemendal, F. Huizinga, M. de Vries, L. Bosch, *Biochim. Biophys. Acta* **61**, 209 (1962).
35. M. W. Nirenberg and O. W. Jones, in *Symposium on Informational Macromolecules*, H. Vogel, V. Bryson, J. Lempen, Eds. (Academic Press, New York, 1963); O. W. Jones and M. W. Nirenberg, *Proc. Natl. Acad. Sci. U.S.* **48**, 2115 (1962); R. S. Gardner, A. J. Wahba, C. Basilio, R. S. Miller, P. Lengyel, J. F. Speyer, *ibid..*, p. 2087.
36. J. H. Matthaei, O. W. Jones, R. G. Martin, M. W. Nirenberg, *Proc. Natl. Acad. Sci. U.S.* **48**, 666 (1962); M. S. Bretscher and M. Grunberg-Manago, *Nature* **195**, 283 (1962).
37. M. Grunberg-Manago and A. M. Michelson, *Biochim. Biophys. Acta* **80**, 431 (1964); W. Szer and S. Ochoa, *J. Mol. Biol.* **8**, 823 (1964).
38. F. H. C. Crick, L. Barnett, S. Brenner, R. J. Watts-Tobin, *Nature* **192**, 1227 (1961).
39. J. D. Watson, personal communication.
40. P. Leder and M. W. Nirenberg, *Proc. Natl. Acad. Sci. U.S.* **51** (1964), in press.
41. S. Benzer and S. P. Champe, *ibid.* **48**, 1114 (1962); A. Garen and O. Siddiqi, *ibid.*, p. 1121.
42. M. W. Nirenberg and J. H. Matthaei, *ibid.* **47**, 1588 (1961); O. W. Jones, R. G. Martin, S. H. Barondes, *Federation Proc. Symp.* **22**, 55 (1963); M. F. Singer, O. W. Jones, M. W. Nirenberg, *Proc. Natl. Acad. Sci. U.S.* **49**, 392 (1962); R. Haselkorn and V. A. Fried, *ibid.* **51**, 308 (1964).
43. B. M. Ames and P. E. Hartman, in *Cold Spring Harbor Symp. Quant. Biol.* **28**, 349 (1963).
44. C. C. Richardson, C. L. Schildkraut, H. V. Aposhian, A. Kornberg, W. Bodner, J. Lederberg, in *Informational Macromolecules*, H. Vogel, V. Bryson, J. Lampen, Eds. (Academic Press, New York, 1963), p. 13.
45. A. J. Wahla, C. Basilio, J. F. Speyer, P. Lengyel, R. S. Miller, S. Ochoa, *Proc. Natl. Acad. Sci. U.S.* **48**, 1683 (1962); presented by P. Doty, R. E. Thach, and T. A. Sundararajan at the VIth International Congress of Biochemistry (1964).
46. We thank Miss Norma Zabriskie and Mrs. Theresa Caryk for invaluable technical assistance; L. A. Heppel for his advice regarding preparation of oligonucleotides; and J. C. Keresztesy and D. Rogerson for providing *E. coli.*

Reprinted from Cold Spring Harbor Symposia on Qualitative Biology, Vol. XXXI, 1966.

The RNA Code and Protein Synthesis

M. Nirenberg, T. Caskey, R. Marshall, R. Brimacombe, D. Kellogg, B. Doctor†,
D. Hatfield, J. Levin, F. Rottman, S. Pestka, M. Wilcox, and F. Anderson

Laboratory of Biochemical Genetics, National Heart Institute, National Institutes of Health, Bethesda, Maryland and
† *Division of Biochemistry, Walter Reed Army Institute of Research, Walter Reed Army Medical Center, Washington, D.C.*

Many properties of the RNA code which were discussed at the 1963 Cold Spring Harbor meeting were based on information obtained with randomly ordered synthetic polynucleotides. Most questions concerning the code which were raised at that time related to its fine structure, that is, the order of the bases within RNA codons. After the 1963 meetings a relatively simple means of determining nucleotide sequences of RNA codons was devised which depends upon the ability of trinucleotides of known sequence to stimulate AA-sRNA binding to ribosomes (Nirenberg and Leder, 1964). In this paper, information obtained since 1963 relating to the following topics will be discussed:

(1) The fine structure of the RNA code

(2) Factors affecting the formation of codon-ribosome-AA-sRNA complexes

(3) Patterns of synonym codons for amino acids and purified sRNA fractions

(4) Mechanism of codon recognition

(5) Universality

(6) Unusual aspects of codon recognition as potential indicators of special codon functions

(7) Modification of codon recognition due to phage infection.

FINE STRUCTURE OF THE RNA CODE

FORMATION OF CODON-RIBOSOME-AA-sRNA COMPLEXES

The assay for base sequences of RNA codons depends, first upon the ability of trinucleotides to serve as templates for AA-sRNA binding to

ABBREVIATIONS

The following abbreviations are used: Ala-, alanine-; Arg-, arginine-; Asn-, asparagine-; Asp-, aspartic acid-; Cys-, cysteine-; Glu-, glutamic acid-; Gln-, glutamine-, Gly-, glycine, His-, histidine-, Ile-, isoleucine-, Leu-, leucine-, Lys-, lysine-, Met-, methionine-, Phe-, phenyl-alanine-, Pro-, proline-, Ser-, serine-, Thr-, threonine-, Trp-, tryptophan-, Tyr-, tyrosine-, and Val-, valine-sRNA; sRNA, transfer RNA; AA-sRNA, aminoacyl-sRNA; sRNA^{Phe}, deacylated phenylalanine-acceptor sRNA; Ala-sRNA^{Yeast}, acylated alanine- acceptor sRNA from yeast. U, uridine; C, cytidine; A, adenosine; G, guanosine; I, inosine; rT, ribothymidine; ψ, pseudo-uridine; DiHU, dihydro-uridine; MAK, methylated albumin kieselguhr; F-Met, N-formyl-methionine. For brevity, trinucleoside diphosphates are referred to as trinucleotides. Internal phosphates of trinucleotides are (3′,5′)-phosphodiester linkages.

TABLE 1. CHARACTERISTICS OF AA-sRNA BINDING TO RIBOSOMES

Modifications	C^{14}-Phe-sRNA bound to ribosomes ($\mu\mu$mole)
Complete	5.99
− Poly U	0.12
− Ribosomes	0.00
− Mg^{++}	0.09
+ deacylated sRNA at 50 min	
0.50 A^{260} units	5.69
2.50 A^{260} units	5.39
+ deacylated sRNA at zero time	
0.50 A^{260} units	4.49
2.50 A^{260} units	2.08

Complete reactions in a volume of 0.05 ml contained the following: 0.1 M Tris acetate (pH 7.2) (in other experiments described in this paper 0.05 M Tris acetate, pH 7.2 was used), 0.02 M magnesium acetate, 0.05 M potassium chloride (standard buffer); 2.0 A^{260} units of *E. coli* W3100 70 S ribosomes (washed by centrifugation 3 times); 15 mμmoles of uridylic acid residues of poly U; and 20.6 $\mu\mu$moles C^{14}-Phe-sRNA (0.71 A^{260} units). All components were added to tubes at 0°C. C^{14}-Phe-sRNA was added last to initiate binding reactions.

Incubation was at 0°C for 60 min (in all other experiments described in this paper, reactions were incubated at 24° for 15 min). Deacylated sRNA was added either at zero time or after 50 min of incubation, as indicated. After incubation, tubes were placed in ice and each reaction was immediately diluted with 3 ml of standard buffer at 0° to 3°C. A cellulose nitrate filter (HA type, Millipore Filter Corp., 25 mm diameter, 0.45 μ pore size) in a stainless steel holder was washed with gentle suction with 5 ml of the cold standard buffer. The diluted reaction mixture was immediately poured on the filter under suction and washed to remove unbound C^{14}-Phe-sRNA with three 3-ml and one 15-ml portions of standard buffer at 3°. Ribosomes and bound sRNA remained on the filter (Nirenberg and Leder, 1964). The filters were then dried, placed in vials containing 10 ml of a scintillation fluid (containing 4 gm 2,5-diphenyloxazole and 0.05 gm 1,4-bis-2-(5-phenyloxazolyl)-benzene per liter of toluene) and counted in a scintillation spectrometer.

ribosomes prior to peptide bond formation, and second, upon the observation that codon-ribosome-AA-sRNA complexes are retained by cellulose nitrate filters (Nirenberg and Leder, 1964). Results shown in Table 1 illustrate characteristics of codon-ribosome-sRNA complex formation. Ribosomes, Mg^{++}, and poly U are required for the binding of C^{14}-Phe-sRNA to ribosomes. The addition of deacylated sRNA to reactions at zero time greatly reduces the binding of C^{14}-Phe-sRNA (Table 1), since poly U specifically stimulates the binding of both deacylated sRNA^{Phe} and C^{14}-Phe-sRNA to ribosomes. Ribosomal bound

C[14]-Phe-sRNA is not readily exchangeable with unbound Phe-sRNA or deacylated sRNA[Phe] except at low Mg[++] concentrations (Levin and Nirenberg, in prep.). Later in this volume Dr. Dolph Hatfield discusses the characteristics of exchange of ribosomal bound with unbound AA-sRNA when trinucleotides are present.

Two enzymatic methods were devised for oligonucleotide synthesis, since most trinucleotide sequences had not been isolated or synthesized earlier. One procedure employed polynucleotide phosphorylase to catalyze the synthesis of oligonucleotides from dinucleoside monophosphate primers and nucleoside diphosphates (Leder, Singer, and Brimacombe, 1965; Thach and Doty, 1965); the other approach (Bernfield, 1966) was based upon the demonstration (Heppel, Whitfeld, and Markham, 1955) that pancreatic RNase catalyzes the synthesis of oligonucleotides from uridine- or cytidine-2',3'-cyclic phosphate and acceptor moieties. Elegant chemical procedures for oligonucleotide synthesis devised by Khorana and his associates (see Khorana et al., this volume) also are available.

TEMPLATE ACTIVITY OF OLIGONUCLEOTIDES WITH TERMINAL AND INTERNAL SUBSTITUTIONS

The trinucleotides, UpUpU and ApApA, but not the corresponding dinucleotides, stimulate markedly the binding of C[14]-Phe- and C[14]-Lys-sRNA, respectively. Such data directly demonstrate a triplet code and also show that codons contain three *sequential* bases. The template activity of triplets with 5'-terminal phosphate, pUpUpU, equals that of the corresponding tetra- and penta-nucleotides; whereas, oligo U preparations with 2',3'-terminal phosphate are much less active. Hexa-A preparations, with and without 3'-terminal phosphate, are considerably more active as templates than the corresponding pentamers; thus, one molecule of hexa-A may be recognized by two Lys-sRNA molecules bound to adjacent ribosomal sites (Rottman and Nirenberg, 1966).

An extensively purified doublet with 5'-terminal phosphate, pUpC, serves as a template for Ser-sRNA (but not for Leu- or Ile-sRNA), whereas a doublet without terminal phosphate, UpC, is inactive (see Figs. 1a and b). However, the template activity of pUpC is considerably lower than that of the triplet, UpCpU. The relation between Mg[++] concentration and template activity is shown in Fig. 1b. pUpC and UpCpU stimulate Ser-sRNA binding in reactions containing 0.02–0.08 M Mg[++]. These results demonstrate that a doublet with 5'-terminal phosphate can serve as a specific, although relatively weak, template for AA-sRNA. It is particularly intriguing to relate recognition of a doublet to the

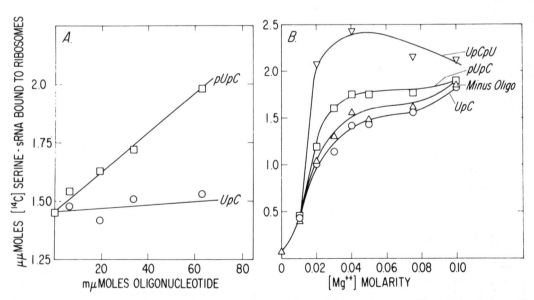

FIGURE 1a, b. The effects of UpC and pUpC on the binding of C[14]-Ser-sRNA to ribosomes. The relation between oligonucleotide concentration and C[14]-Ser-sRNA binding to ribosomes at 0.03 M Mg[++] is shown in Fig. 1a. It should be noted that the ordinate begins at 1.25 μμmoles of C[14]-Ser-sRNA. The relation between Mg[++] concentration and C[14]-Ser-sRNA binding to ribosomes is shown in Fig. 1b. As indicated, 50 mμmoles of UpC or pUpC, or 15 mμmoles of UpCpU, were added to each reaction. Each point in parts a and b represents a 50 μl reaction containing the components described in the legend to Table 1 except for the following: 14.3 μμmoles C[14]-Ser-sRNA (0.42 A[260] units); 1.1 A[260] units of ribosomes. Incubations were for 15 min at 24°C. (Data from Rottman and Nirenberg, 1966.)

TABLE 2. RELATIVE TEMPLATE ACTIVITY OF SUBSTITUTED
OLIGONUCLEOTIDES

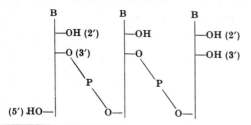

Oligonucleotide	Relative template activity
p-5'-UpUpU	510
UpUpU	100
CH₃O-pUpUpU	74
UpUpU-3'3-p	48
UpUpUp-OCH₃	18
UpUpU-2',3'-cyclic p	17
(2'-5')-UpUpU	0
Oligodeoxy T	0
p-5'-ApApA	181
ApApA	100
ApApA-3'-p	57
ApApA-2'-p	15
(2'-5')-ApApA	0
Oligodeoxy A	0

Relative template activities are approximations obtained by comparing the amount of AA-sRNA bound to ribosomes in the presence of limiting concentrations of oligonucleotides (0.50 or 0.12 mμmoles of oligonucleotides containing U or A, respectively) compared to either UpUpU, for C¹⁴-Phe-sRNA; or ApApA, for C¹⁴-Lys-sRNA (each assumed to be 100%). Data are from Rottman and Nirenberg (1966) except results with oligodeoxynucleotides which are from Nirenberg and Leder (1964).

possibility that only two out of three bases in a triplet may be recognized occasionally during protein synthesis, and also to the possibility that a triplet code evolved from a more primitive doublet code.

Further studies on template activities of oligonucleotides with terminal and internal modifications are summarized in Table 2. At limiting oligonucleotide concentrations, the relative template activities of oligo U preparations are as follows: p-5'-UpUpU > UpUpU > CH₃O-p-5'-UpUpU > UpUpU-3'-p > UpUpU-3'-p-OCH₃ > UpUpU-2',3'-cyclic phosphate. Trimers with (2'-5') phosphodiester linkages, (2'-5')-UpUpU and (2'-5')-ApApA, do not serve as templates for Phe- or Lys-, sRNA respectively. The relative template efficiencies of oligo A preparations are as follows: p-5'-ApApA > ApApA > ApApA-3'-p > ApApA-2'-p.

These studies led to the proposal that RNA and DNA contain three classes of codons, differing in structure; 5'-terminal, 3'-terminal, and internal codons (Nirenberg and Leder, 1964). Certainly

the first base of a 5'-terminal codon and the third base of a 3'-terminal codon may be recognized with less fidelity than an internal codon, for in the absence of a nucleotide neighbor a terminal base may have a greater freedom of movement on the ribosome. Substitution of 5'- or 3'-terminal hydroxyl groups may impose restrictions upon the orientation of terminal bases during codon recognition. 5'-Terminal and perhaps also 3'-terminal codons possibly serve, together with neighboring codons, as operator regions.

Since many enzymes have been described which catalyze the transfer of nucleotides, amino acids, phosphate, and other molecules to or from terminal ribose or deoxyribose of nucleic acids, modification of sugar hydroxyl groups was proposed as a possible mechanism for regulating the reading of RNA or DNA (Nirenberg and Leder, 1964).

NUCLEOTIDE SEQUENCES OF RNA CODONS

A summary of nucleotide sequences of RNA codons by *E. coli* AA-sRNA is shown in Table 3

TABLE 3. NUCLEOTIDE SEQUENCES OF RNA CODONS

1st Base	2nd Base				3rd Base
	U	C	A	G	
U	PHE*	SER*	TYR*	CYS*	U
	PHE*	SER*	TYR*	CYS	C
	leu*?	SER	TERM?	cys?	A
	leu*, f-met	SER*	TERM?	TRP*	G
C	leu*	pro*	HIS*	ARG*	U
	leu*	pro*	HIS*	ARG*	C
	leu	PRO*	GLN*	ARG*	A
	LEU	PRO	gln*	arg	G
A	ILE*	THR*	ASN*	SER	U
	ILE*	THR*	ASN*	SER*	C
	ile*	THR*	LYS*	arg*	A
	MET*, F-MET	THR	lys	arg	G
G	VAL*	ALA*	ASP*	GLY*	U
	VAL	ALA*	ASP*	GLY*	C
	VAL*	ALA*	GLU*	GLY*	A
	VAL	ALA	glu	GLY	G

Nucleotide sequences of RNA codons were determined by stimulating binding of *E. coli* AA-sRNA to *E. coli* ribosomes with trinucleotide templates. Amino acids shown in capitals represent trinucleotides with relatively high template activities compared to other trinucleotide codons corresponding to the same amino acid. Asterisks (*) represent base compositions of codons which were determined previously by directing protein synthesis in *E. coli* extracts with synthetic randomly-ordered polynucleotides (Speyer et al., 1963; Nirenberg et al., 1963). F-Met, represents N-formyl-Met-sRNA which may recognize initiator codons. TERM represents possible terminator codons. Question marks (?) indicate uncertain codon function. Data are from Nirenberg et al., 1965; Brimacombe et al., 1965; also see articles by Khorana et al., Söll et al., and Matthaei et al., in this volume.

TABLE 4. PATTERNS OF DEGENERATE CODONS FOR AMINO ACIDS

U C ●●A G	U C ●●A G	U C ●●A G	U C ●●(A)	U ●●C	A ●●G	●●G	U C A (G) ●●
U ●●C	G ●●(A?)						
SER	ARG LEU	GLY ALA VAL THR PRO	CYS ILE	ASP ASN HIS TYR PHE	GLU GLN LYS TERM?	MET TRP	F-MET

Solid circles represent the first and second bases of trinucleotides; U, C, A, and G indicate bases which may occupy the remaining position of degenerate codons. In the case of F-Met (N-formylmethionine), circles represent the second and third bases. Parentheses indicate codons with relatively low template activities.

and patterns of degeneracy in Table 4. Almost every trinucleotide was assayed for template specificity with 20 AA-sRNA preparations (unfractionated sRNA acylated with one labeled and 19 unlabeled amino acids). It is important to test trinucleotide template specificity with 20 AA-sRNA preparations, since relative responses of AA-sRNA are then quite apparent. In surveying trinucleotide specificity, unfractionated AA-sRNA should be used initially because altering ratios of sRNA species often influences the fidelity of codon recognition.

Almost all triplets correspond to amino acids; furthermore, patterns of codon degeneracy are logical. Six degenerate codons correspond to serine, five or six to arginine and also to leucine, and from one to four to each of the remaining amino acids. Alternate bases often occupy the third positions of triplets comprising degenerate codon sets. In all cases triplet pairs with 3′-terminal pyrimidines (XYU and XYC, where X and Y represent the first and second bases, respectively, in the triplet) correspond to the same amino acid; often XYA and XYG correspond to the same amino acid; sometimes XYG alone corresponds to an amino acid. For eight amino acids, U, C, A, or G may occupy the third position of synonym codons. Alternate bases also may occupy the first position of synonyms, as for N-formyl-methionine.

One consequence of logical degeneracy is that many single base replacements in DNA may be silent and thus not result in amino acid replacement in protein (cf. Sonneborn, 1965). Also, the code is arranged so that the effects of some errors may be minimized, since amino acids which are structurally or metabolically related often correspond to similiar RNA codons (for example, Asp-codons, GAU, and GAC, are similar to Glu-codons, GAA, and GAG). When various amino acids are grouped according to common biosynthetic precursors, close relationships among their synonym codons

sometimes are observed. For example, codons for amino acids derived from aspartic acid begin with A: Asp, GAU, GAC; Asn, AAU, AAC; Lys, AAA, AAG; Thr, ACU, ACC, ACA, ACG; Ile, AUU, AUC, AUA; Met, AUG. Likewise, aromatic amino acids have codons beginning with U; Phe, UUU, UUC; Tyr, UAU, UAC; Trp, UGG. Such relationships may reflect either the evolution of the code or direct interactions between amino acids and bases in codons (see Woese et al., this volume).

At the time of the 1963 meeting at Cold Spring Harbor, 53 base compositions of RNA codons had been estimated (14 tentatively) in studies with randomly-ordered synthetic polynucleotides and a cell-free protein synthesizing system derived from *E. coli* (Speyer et al., 1963; Nirenberg et al., 1963). Forty-six base composition assignments now are confirmed by base sequence studies with trinucleotides (shown in Table 3). Thus, codon base compositions and base sequence assignments, obtained by assaying protein synthesis and AA-sRNA binding, respectively, agree well with one another. In addition, codon base sequences are confirmed by most amino acid replacement data obtained in vivo (see Yanofsky et al.; Wittman et al., this volume).

PATTERNS OF SYNONYM CODONS RECOGNIZED BY PURIFIED sRNA FRACTIONS

Table 5 contains a summary of synonym codons recognized by purified sRNA fractions obtained either by countercurrent distribution or by MAK column chromatography. The following patterns of codon recognition involving alternate bases in the third positions of synonym codons were found; C = U; A = G; G; U = C = A; A = G = (U). For example, Val-sRNA$_3$ recognizes GUU and GUC, whereas the major peak of Val-sRNA (fractions 1 and 2) recognizes GUA, GUG and, to a lesser extent, GUU. The possibility that the latter Val-sRNA fraction contains two or more Val-sRNA components has not been excluded. Met-sRNA$_1$

351

TABLE 5. CODON PATTERNS RECOGNIZED BY PURIFIED sRNA FRACTIONS

Alternate acceptable bases in 3rd or 1st positions of triplet					
C U	A G	G	U C A	A G (U)	Possibly only 2 bases recognized
TYR$_{1,2}$ UA$^{C}_{U}$	LYS AA$^{A}_{G}$	LEU$_2$ CUG	ALA^{yeast} $\substack{U\\GCC\\A}$	ALA$_1$ $\substack{A\\GCG\\(U)}$	LEU$_3$ CU$^{(U)}_{(C)}$
VAL$_3$ GU$^{C}_{U}$		LEU$_5$ UUG	SER$^{yeast}_{2,3}$ $\substack{U\\UCC\\A}$	VAL$_{1,2}$ $\substack{A\\GUG\\(U)}$	LEU$_{4a,b}$ UU$^{(U)}_{(C)}$
		MET$_2$ AUG	F-MET$_1$ $\substack{U\\C\\UG\\A}$		LEU$_1$ (U)UG
		TRP$_2$ $\substack{U\\CGG\\(A)}$			

Patterns of degenerate codons recognized by purified AA-sRNA fractions. sRNA fractions are from *E. coli* B, unless otherwise specified. At the top of the table are shown the alternate bases which may occupy the third or first positions of degenerate codon sets. Purified sRNA fractions and corresponding codons are shown below. Parentheses indicate codons with relatively low template activity. sRNA fractions were obtained by counter-current distribution (Kellogg et al., 1966), unless otherwise specified. Yeast Ser-sRNA fractions 2 and 3 (Connelly and Doctor, 1966) are thought to be equivalent to yeast Ser-sRNA fractions 1 and 2, respectively, discussed by Zachau et al. in this volume. Yeast Ala-sRNA was the gift of R. W. Holley; results are from Leder and Nirenberg (unpubl.). Results obtained with Val-, Met-, and Ala-sRNA$^{E. coli}$ fractions are from Kellogg et al. (1966). For additional results with Tyr-sRNA fractions, see Doctor, Loebel and Kellogg, this volume. Leu-sRNA fractions (see Fig. 6 and Sueoka et al., this volume) and Lys-sRNA (Kellogg, Doctor, and Nirenberg, unpubl.) were obtained by MAK column chromatography. Three Leu-sRNA fractions also were obtained by counter-current distribution (Nirenberg and Leder, 1964). Reactions contained the usual components (see legend to Table 1) and 0.01 or 0.02 M Mg^{++}. Incubation was at 24° for 15 min.

responds to UUG, CUG, AUG and, to a lesser extent, GUG, and can be converted enzymatically to N-formyl-Met-sRNA, whereas, Met-sRNA$_2$ responds primarily to AUG and does not accept formyl moieties (see later discussion). Unfractionated Trp-sRNA responds only to UGG; however one fraction of Trp-sRNA, after extensive purification, responds to UGG, CGG and AGG. Possibly the latter responses depend upon the removal of sRNA for other amino acids (e.g., Arg-sRNA) which also may recognize CGG or AGG. Yeast Ala- and Ser-sRNA$_{2,3}$ fractions recognize synonyms containing U, C, or A in the third position. Leu-sRNA$_{1,3,4}$ bind to ribosomes in response to polynucleotide templates but not to trinucleotides. Possibly, only two of the three bases are recognized by these Leu-sRNA fractions.

MECHANISM OF CODON RECOGNITION

Crick (1966; also this volume) has suggested that certain bases in anticodons may form alternate hydrogen bonds, via a wobble mechanism, with corresponding bases in mRNA codons. This hypothesis and further experimental findings are discussed below.

Yeast Ala-sRNA of known base sequence and of high purity (>95%) was the generous gift of Dr. Robert Holley. In Figs. 2 and 3 are shown the responses of purified yeast and unfractionated *E. coli* C^{14}-Ala-sRNA, respectively, to synonym Ala-codons as a function of Mg^{++} concentration. Purified yeast C^{14}-Ala-sRNA responds well to GCU, GCC, and GCA, but only slightly to GCG. Similar results were obtained with unfractionated Ala-sRNA^{Yeast}. In contrast, unfractionated *E. coli* C^{14}-Ala-sRNA responds best to GCG and GCA, less well to GCU, and only slightly to GCC.

In Fig. 4a and b, the relation between concentration of yeast or *E. coli* C^{14}-Ala-sRNA and response to synonym Ala-codons is shown. At *limiting* concentrations of purified yeast C^{14}-Ala-sRNA, at least 59, 45, 45, and 3% of the available C^{14}-Ala-sRNA molecules bind to ribosomes in response to GCU, GCC, GCA, and GCG, respectively. The response of unfractionated *E. coli* C^{14}-Ala-sRNA to each codon was 18, 2, 38, and 64%, respectively. Similar results have been obtained by Keller and Ferger (1966) and Söll et al. (this volume). Since the purity of the yeast Ala-sRNA was greater than 95%, the extent of binding at limiting Ala-sRNA concentrations indicates that one molecule of Ala-sRNA recognizes 3, possibly 4, synonym codons. In addition, the data demonstrate marked differences between the relative responses of yeast and *E. coli* Ala-sRNA to synonym codons.

Correlating the base sequences of yeast Ala-sRNA with corresponding mRNA codons also provides insight into the structure of the Ala-sRNA

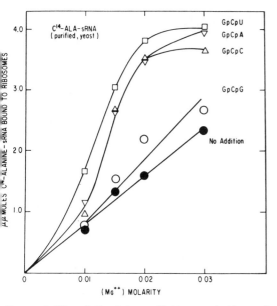

FIGURE 2. The relation between Mg++ concentration and binding to ribosomes of purified yeast C14-Ala-sRNA of known base sequence (Holley et al., 1965) in response to trinucleotides. Each point represents a 50 μl reaction containing the components described in the legend to Table 1 except for the following: 1.5 A260 units of *E. coli* ribosomes, 11.2 μμmoles of purified yeast C14-Ala-sRNA (0.038 A260 units); and 0.1 A260 units of trinucleotide as specified. Reactions were incubated at 24° for 15 min (Leder and Nirenberg, unpubl.).

anti-codon and the mechanism of codon recognition. Possible anticodon or enzyme recognition sequences in Ala-sRNA^{Yeast} are –IGC MeI– and DiHU–CGG–DiHU (Fig. 5; Holley et al., 1965). Each site potentially comprises a single-stranded loop region at the end of a hairpin-like double-stranded segment. If CGG were the anticodon, *parallel* hydrogen bonding with GCU, GCC, GCA codons would be expected. If IGC were the anticodon, *antiparallel* Watson-Crick hydrogen bonding between GC in the anticodon and GC in the first and second positions of codons, and alternate pairing of inosine in the anticodon with U, C, or A, but not G, in the third position of Ala-codons, would be expected. All of the available evidence is consistent with an IGC Ala-anticodon. Zachau has shown that Ser-sRNA$^{Yeast}_{1 and 2}$ contain, in appropriate positions, IGA sequences (Zachau, Dütting, and Feldmann, 1966), and we find that Ser-sRNA^{Yeast} fractions 2 and 3 (believed to correspond to fractions 1 and 2 of Zachau) recognize UCU, UCC, and UCA, but not UCG (see Table 5). A purified Val-sRNA^{Yeast} fraction contains the sequence IAC which corresponds to three Val-codons, GUU, GUC, and GUA (Ingram and Sjöqvist, 1963). In addition, the sequence, GψA, is found at the postulated anticodon site of Tyr-

sRNA^{Yeast} which corresponds to the Tyr-codons, UAU and UAC (Madison, Everett, and Kung, 1966).

Crick's wobble hypothesis and patterns of synonym codons found experimentally are in full agreement. In Table 6 are shown bases in anticodons which form alternate hydrogen bonds, via the wobble mechanism, with bases usually occupying the third positions of mRNA codons. U in the sRNA anticodon may pair alternately with A or G in mRNA codons; C may pair with G; A with U; G with C or U; and I with U, C, or A. In addition, we suggest that ribo T in the anticodon may hydrogen bond more strongly with A, and perhaps with G also, than U; and ψ in the anticodon may hydrogen bond alternately with A, G or, less well, U.

Dihydro U in an anticodon may be unable to hydrogen bond with a base in mRNA but may be repelled less by pyrimidines than by purines.

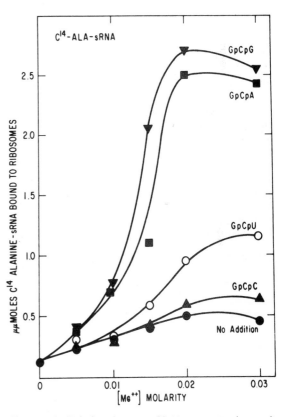

FIGURE 3. Relation between Mg++ concentration and binding of unfractionated *E. coli* C14-Ala-sRNA to ribosomes in response to trinucleotides. Each point represents a 50 μl reaction containing the components described in the legend to Table 1, 2.0 A260 units of ribosomes; 18.8 μμmoles of unfractionated *E. coli* C14-Ala-sRNA (0.54 A260 units); and 0.1 A260 unit of trinucleotide, as specified (Leder and Nirenberg, unpubl.).

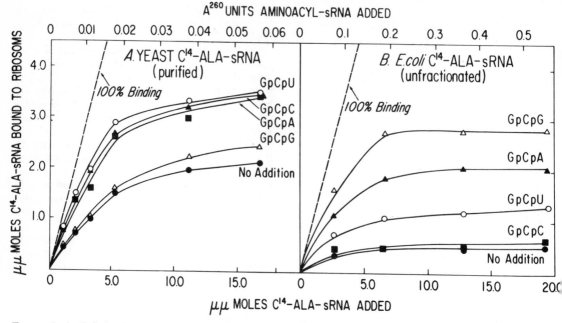

FIGURE 4a, b. Relation between the template activities of trinucleotides and the concentrations of purified yeast C14-Ala-sRNA (part a) and unfractionated *E. coli* C14-Ala-sRNA (part b). Each point represents a 50 μl reaction containing the components described in the legend of Table 1, and the following components: 0.02 M magnesium acetate; 0.1 A260 unit of trinucleotide as specified; 1.1 A260 units of *E. coli* ribosomes (part a) and 2.0 A260 units of *E. coli* ribosomes (part b); and C14-Ala-sRNA as indicated on the abscissa (Leder and Nirenberg, unpubl.).

Possibly, hydrogen bonds then form between the two remaining bases of the codon (bases 1 and 2, or 2 and 3) and the corresponding bases in the anticodon. Only two out of three bases in a codon would then be recognized. This possibility is supported by the studies of Rottman and Cerutti (1966) and Cerutti, Miles, and Frazier, (1966). Possibly, some synonym codon patterns may be due to the formation of two rather than three base pairs per triplet, particularly if both are

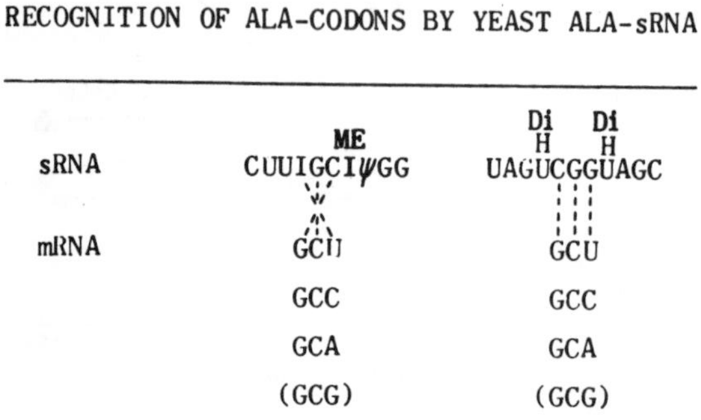

RECOGNITION OF ALA-CODONS BY YEAST ALA-sRNA

TABLE 6. ALTERNATE BASE PAIRING

sRNA Anticodon	mRNA Codon
U	A G
C	G
A	U
G	C U
I	U C A
rT	A G
ψ	A G (U)
DiHU	No base pairing

The base in an sRNA anticodon shown in the left-hand column forms antiparallel hydrogen bonds with the base(s) shown in the right-hand column, which usually occupy the third position of degenerate mRNA codons. Relationships for U, C, A, G, and I of anticodons are "wobble" hydrogen bonds suggested by Crick (1966; also this volume). See text for further details.

FIGURE 5. Base sequences from yeast Ala-sRNA shown in the upper portion of the figure represent possible anti-codons. Base sequences of synonym RNA Ala-codons are shown in the lower portion of the figure. The first and second bases of Ala-codons on the left would form antiparallel Watson-Crick hydrogen bonds with the anticodon, while those on the right would form parallel hydrogen bonds. See text for further details.

TABLE 7. NUCLEOTIDE SEQUENCES OF RNA CODONS RECOGNIZED BY AA-sRNA FROM BACTERIA AND AMPHIBIAN AND MAMMALIAN LIVER

		U	C	A	G	
U		PHE	SER	TYR	cys	U
		PHE	SER	TYR	cys	C
		leu?	SER	TERM?	[cys]	A
		leu, F-MET	[SER]	TERM?	trp	G
C		leu	PRO	HIS	ARG	U
		leu	PRO	HIS	ARG	C
		leu	PRO	gln	ARG	A
		leu	PRO	gln	[ARG]	G
A		ILE	THR	asn	[SER]	U
		ILE	THR	asn	[SER]	C
		[ILE]	THR	LYS	[ARG†]	A
		MET, F-MET?	THR	[LYS]	[ARG]	G
G		VAL	ALA	ASP	GLY	U
		VAL	ALA	ASP	GLY	C
		VAL	ALA	GLU	gly	A
		VAL	[ALA]	GLU	gly	G

Universality of the RNA code. Nucleotide sequences and relative template activities of RNA codons determined with trinucleotides and AA-sRNA from *E. coli*, *Xenopus laevis* and guinea pig liver. Rectangles represent trinucleotides which are active templates for AA-sRNA from one organism, but not from another. Assignments in capitals indicate that the trinucleotide was assayed with AA-sRNAs from *E. coli*, *Xenopus laevis* liver, and guinea pig liver. Assignments in lower case indicate that the trinucleotide was assayed only with *E. coli* AA-sRNA (with the exception of cys-codons which were assayed with both *E. coli* and guinea pig liver Cys-sRNA).

†Söll et al. (1965) reported that both AGA and AGG stimulate yeast Arg-sRNA binding to ribosomes. The trinucleotide, AGA, however, has little or no effect upon the binding of *E. coli*, *Xenopus laevis* or guinea pig Arg-sRNA to ribosomes.

Reactions contained components described in the legend to Table 1, 0.01 or 0.02 M Mg++, *E. coli* ribosomes, and 0.150 A²⁶⁰ units of trinucleotides (data from Marshall, Caskey, and Nirenberg, in prep.).

(C) · (G) pairs (also see earlier discussion concerning template activity of pUpC).

In summary, patterns for amino acids often represent the sum of two or more codon patterns recognized by different sRNA species. Specific sRNA patterns, in turn, often result from alternate pairing between bases in the codon and anticodon or, possibly, from the formation of only two base pairs if the remaining bases do not greatly repel one another.

UNIVERSALITY

The results of many studies indicate that the RNA code is largely universal. However, translation of the RNA code can be altered in vivo by extragenic suppressors and in vitro by altering components of reactions or conditions of incubation. Thus, cells sometimes differ in specificity of codon translation.

To investigate the fine structure of the code recognized by AA-sRNA from different organisms, nucleotide sequences and relative template activities of RNA codons recognized by bacterial, amphibian, and mammalian AA-sRNA (*E. coli*, *Xenopus laevis* and guinea pig liver, respectively) were determined (Marshall, Caskey, and Nirenberg, submitted for publication). Acylation of sRNA was catalyzed in all cases by aminoacyl-sRNA synthetases from corresponding organisms and tissues. *E. coli* ribosomes were used for binding studies. Therefore, the specificities of sRNA and AA-sRNA synthetases were investigated.

The results are shown in Table 7. Almost identical translations of nucleotide sequences to amino acids were found with bacterial, amphibian, and mammalian AA-sRNA. In addition, similar sets of synonym codons usually were recognized by AA-sRNA from each organism. However, *E. coli* AA-sRNA sometimes differed strikingly from *Xenopus* and guinea pig liver AA-sRNA in relative response to synonym codons. Differences in codon recognition are shown in Table 8. The following

TABLE 8. SPECIES DEPENDENT DIFFERENCES IN RESPONSE OF AA-sRNA TO TRINUCLEOTIDE CODONS

Codon		sRNA		
		Bacterial (*E. coli*)	Amphibian (*Xenopus laevis*)	Mammalian (Guinea pig liver)
ARG	AGG	±	++++	+++
	CGG	±	++++	++++
MET	UUG	++	±	±
ALA	GCG	++++	±	++
ILE	AUA	±	++	++
LYS	AAG	±	++++	++++
SER	UCG	++++	±	++
	AGU	±	+++	+++·
	AGC	±	+++	+++
CYS	UGA	±		+++

Possible differences: ACG, THR; AUC, ILE; CAC, HIS; GUC, VAL; and GCC, ALA.

No differences found: ASP, GLY, GLU, PHE, PRO, and TYR.

The following scale indicates the approximate response of AA-sRNA to a trinucleotide relative to the responses of the same AA-sRNA preparation to all other trinucleotides for that amino acid (except Gly-sRNA which was assayed only with GGU and GGC).

++++	70–100%
+++	50–70%
++	20–50%
±	0–20%

trinucleotides had little or no detectable template activity for unfractionated *E. coli* AA-sRNA but served as active templates with *Xenopus* and guinea pig AA-sRNA: AGG, CGG, arginine; AUA, isoleucine; AAG, lysine; AGU, AGC, serine; and UGA, cysteine. Those trinucleotides with high template activity for *E. coli* AA-sRNA but low activity for *Xenopus* or guinea pig liver AA-sRNA were: UUG, N-formyl-methionine; GCG, alanine; and UCG, serine. Possible differences also were observed with ACG, threonine; AUC, isoleucine; CAC, histidine; GCC, alanine; and GUC, valine. No species dependent differences were found with Asp-, Gly-, Glu-, Phe-, Pro-, and Tyr-codons.

Thus, some degenerate trinucleotides were active templates with sRNA from each species studied, whereas others were active with sRNA from one species but not from another.

UAA and UAG do not appreciably stimulate binding of unfractionated *E. coli* AA-sRNA (AA-sRNA for each amino acid tested); *Xenopus* Arg-, Phe-, Ser-, or Tyr-sRNA; or guinea pig Ala-, Arg-, Asp-, His-, Ile-, Met-, Pro-, Ser-, or Thr-sRNA.

Nucleotide sequences recognized by *Xenopus* skeletal muscle Arg-, Lys-, Met-, and Ser-sRNA were determined and compared with sequences recognized by corresponding *Xenopus* liver AA-sRNA preparations. No differences between liver and muscle AA-sRNA were detected, either in nucleotide sequences recognized or in relative responses to synonym codons.

Fossil records of bacteria 3.1 billion years old have been reported (Barghoorn and Schopf, 1966). The first vertebrates appeared approximately 510 million years ago, and amphibians and mammals, 355 and 181 million years ago, respectively. The presence of bacteria 3 billion years ago may indicate the presence of a functional genetic code at that time. Almost surely the code has functioned for more than 500 million years. The remarkable similarity in codon base sequences recognized by bacterial, amphibian, and mammalian AA-sRNA suggest that most, if not all, forms of life on this planet use almost the same genetic language, and that the language has been used, possibly with few major changes, for at least 500 million years.

UNUSUAL ASPECTS OF CODON RECOGNITION AS POTENTIAL INDICATORS OF SPECIAL CODON FUNCTIONS

Most codons correspond to amino acids; however, some codons serve in other capacities, such as initiation, termination or regulation of protein synthesis. Although only a few codons have been

assigned special functions thus far, we think it likely that many additional codons eventually may be found to serve special functions. Unusual properties of codon recognition sometimes may indicate special codon functions. For example, the properties of initiator and terminator codons, during codon recognition, are quite distinctive (see below). We find that approximately 20 codons have unusual properties related either to codon position, template activity, specificity, patterns of degeneracy, or stability of codon-ribosome-sRNA complexes. Until more information is available these observations will be considered as *possible* indicators of special codon functions.

Conclusions will be stated first to provide a frame of reference for discussion:

(1) A codon may have alternate meanings. (For example, UUG at or near the 5′-terminus of mRNA may correspond to N-formyl-methionine; whereas, an internal UUG codon may correspond to leucine.)

(2) A codon may serve multiple functions simultaneously. (For example, a codon may specify both initiation and an amino acid, perhaps via AA-sRNA with high affinity for peptidyl-sRNA sites on ribosomes.)

(3) Codon function sometimes is subject to modification.

(4) Degenerate codons for the same amino acid often differ markedly in template properties.

CODON FREQUENCY AND DISTRIBUTION

Often, multiple species of sRNA corresponding to the same amino acid recognize different synonym codons. Degenerate codon usage in mRNA sometimes is nonrandom (Garen, pers. comm.; also von Ehrenstein; Weigert et al., this volume). The possibility that different sets of sRNA may be required for the synthesis of two proteins with the same amino acid composition suggests that protein synthesis sometimes may be regulated by codon frequency and distribution coupled with differential recognition of degenerate codons. Possibly, the rates of synthesis of certain proteins may be regulated simultaneously by alterations which affect the apparatus recognizing one degeneracy but not another (see reviews by Ames and Hartman, 1963; and Stent, 1964).

CODON POSITION

As discussed in an earlier section, the template properties of 5′-terminal-, 3′-terminal-, and internal- codons may differ. Regulatory mechanisms based on such differences have been suggested. Reading of mRNA probably is initiated at or near the 5′-terminal codon and then proceeds toward the 3′-terminus of the RNA chain (Salas, Smith

Stanley, Jr., Wahba, and Ochoa, 1965). It is not known whether mechanisms of 5′-terminal and internal initiation in polycistronic messages are similar. Also, internal- and 3′-terminal mechanisms of termination remain to be defined.

N-formyl-Met-sRNA may serve as an initiator of protein synthesis in *E. coli* (Clark and Marcker, 1966; Adams and Capecchi, 1966; Webster, Englehardt, and Zinder, 1966; Thach, Dewey, Brown, and Doty, 1966). Met-sRNA₁ can be converted enzymatically to N-formyl-Met-sRNA₁ and responds to UUG, CUG, AUG and, to a lesser extent, GUG. Met-sRNA₂ does not accept formyl-moieties and responds primarily to AUG (Clark and Marcker, 1966; Marcker et al., this volume; also Kellogg, Doctor, Loebel, and Nirenberg, 1966). In *E. coli* extracts protein synthesis is initiated in at least two ways: by initiator codons specifying N-formyl-Met-sRNA or, at somewhat higher Mg++ concentrations, by another means, probably not dependent upon N-formyl-Met-sRNA since many synthetic polynucleotides without known initiator codons direct cell-free protein synthesis (Nakamoto and Kolakofsky, 1966). Poly U, for example, directs di- as well as polyphenylalanine synthesis (Arlinghaus, Schaeffer, and Schweet, 1964). Probably codons for N-formyl-Met-sRNA initiate protein synthesis with greater accuracy than codons which serve as initiators only at relatively high Mg++ concentrations.

UAA and UAG may function as terminator codons (Brenner, Stretton, and Kaplan, 1965; Weigert and Garen, 1965). The trinucleotides UAA and UAG do not stimulate binding appreciably of *unfractionated E. coli* AA-sRNA to ribosomes. However, sRNA fraction(s) corresponding to UAA and/or UAG are not ruled out.

Extragenic suppressors may affect the specificity of UAA and/or UAG recognition (see review by Beckwith and Gorini, 1966). The efficiencies of ochre suppressors (UAA) are relatively low compared to that of amber suppressors (UAG). Since amber suppressors do not markedly affect the rate of cell growth, and ochre suppressors with high efficiency have not been found, UAA may specify chain termination in vivo more frequently than UAG. In a study of great interest, Newton, Beckwith, Zipser and Brenner (1965) have shown that the synthesis of protein (probably mRNA also) is regulated by the relative position in the RNA message of codons sensitive to amber suppressors. Therefore, a codon may perform a regulatory function at one position but not at another.

Template Activity

Trinucleotides with little activity for AA-sRNA (in studies thus far) are: UAA, UAG, and UUA,

(perhaps CUA also). In addition, the following trinucleotides are active templates with AA-sRNA from one organism, but not from another: AGG, AGA, CGG, arginine; UUG, (N-formyl-)-methionine; GCG, alanine; AUA, isoleucine; AAG, lysine; UCG, AGU, AGC, serine; and UGA, cysteine (see Universality Section and Table 9). However, some inactive trinucleotides possibly function as active codons at internal positions. For example, the following codon base compositions were estimated with synthetic polynucleotides and a cell-free protein synthesizing system from *E. coli*; AUA, isoleucine; AGA, arginine; and AGC, serine (Nirenberg et al., 1963; Speyer et al., 1963; also see Jones, Nishimura, and Khorana, 1966, for results with AGA). Among the many possible explanations for low template activities of trinucleotides in binding assays are: special codon function; codon position; appropriate species of sRNA absent or in low concentration; competition for codons or for ribosomal sites by additional species of sRNA; high ratio of deacylated to AA-sRNA; cryptic (non-acylatable) sRNA; reaction conditions, e.g., low concentration of Mg++ or other components, time or temperature of incubation.

Codon Specificity

Often synonym trinucleotides differ strikingly in template specificity. Such observations may indicate that template specificities of terminal- and internal-codons differ, or that special function codons or suppressors are present. At 0.010–0.015 M Mg++, trinucleotide template specificity is high, in many cases higher than that of a polynucleotide; for example, poly U, but not UUU, stimulates binding of Ile-sRNA to ribosomes. However, at 0.03 M Mg++ ambiguous recognitions of tri- and polynucleotides are observed more frequently.

Relative template activities of synonym trinucleotides in reactions containing 0.01 or 0.03 M Mg++ are shown in Table 9. In some cases, only one or two trinucleotides in a synonym set are active templates at 0.01 M Mg++; whereas all degeneracies are active at 0.03 M Mg++ (e.g., Glu, Lys, Ala, Thr). In other cases either all synonym trinucleotides are active at 0.01 M Mg++ as well as at 0.03 M Mg++ (e.g., Val), or none are active at the lower Mg++ concentration (e.g., Tyr, His, Asn). Such data suggest that codon-ribosome-AA-sRNA complexes formed with degenerate trinucleotides often differ in stability.

MODIFICATION OF CODON RECOG-NITION DUE TO PHAGE INFECTION

N. and T. Sueoka (1964; also see Sueoka et al., this volume) have shown that infection of *E. coli*

TABLE 9. TEMPLATE ACTIVITY OF TRINUCLEOTIDES IN 0.01 OR 0.03 M Mg^{++}

	U	C	A	G	
U	PHE	SER	TYR	CYS	U
	PHE	SER	TYR	CYS	C
		(SER)			A
	F-MET	SER		(TRP)	G
C		PRO	HIS	ARG	U
		PRO	HIS	ARG	C
		(PRO)	GLN	ARG	A
	LEU	(PRO)	GLN	ARG	G
A	ILE	THR	ASN	SER, CYS	U
	ILE	THR	ASN	SER, CYS	C
		THR	LYS		A
	MET	THR	LYS		G
G	VAL	ALA	ASP	GLY	U
	VAL	ALA	ASP	GLY	C
	VAL	ALA	GLU	(GLY)	A
	VAL	ALA	GLU	(GLY)	G

Legend:

	0.01 M Mg	0.03 M Mg
[box] =	+	+
No Box =	−	+
( ) =	not tested	

Relative template activities of trinucleotides in reactions containing 0.01 or 0.03 M Mg^{++}. A plus (+) sign in the legend means that the trinucleotide stimulates AA-sRNA binding to ribosomes at that magnesium concentration; a minus (−) sign means it is relatively inactive as a template. The results refer to AA-sRNA from E. coli strains B and/or W3100. The data are from Anderson, Nirenberg, Marshall, and Caskey (1966).

by T2 bacteriophage results, within one to three minutes, in the modification of one or more species of Leu-sRNA present in the E. coli host. Concomitantly, E. coli, but not viral protein synthesis is inhibited. Protein synthesis is required, however, for modification of Leu-sRNA.

In collaboration with N. and T. Sueoka, modification of Leu-sRNA has been correlated with codon recognition specificity. sRNA preparations were isolated from E. coli before phage infection and at one and eight min after infection. After acylation, Leu-sRNA preparations were purified by MAK column chromatography and the binding of each pooled Leu-sRNA fraction to ribosomes in response to templates was determined (Fig. 6). The profile of Leu-sRNA (eight min after infection) acylated with yeast, rather than E. coli.

Leu-sRNA synthetase is shown also (Fig. 6D) thus, both anticodon and enzyme recognition sites were monitored. In Fig. 7 the approximate chromatographic mobility on MAK columns of each Leu-sRNA fraction is shown diagrammatically together with the relative response of each fraction to tri- and polynucleotide templates and acylation specificity of E. coli and yeast Leu-sRNA synthetase preparations.

Within one minute after infection, a marked decrease was observed in $Leu\text{-}sRNA_2$, responding to CUG, and a corresponding increase was seen in $Leu\text{-}sRNA_1$, responding to poly UG, but not to the trinucleotides, UUU, UUG, UGU, GUU, UGG, GUG, GGU, CUU, CUC, CUG, UAA, UAG, UGA, or to poly U or poly UC. However, $Leu\text{-}sRNA_1$ was not detected 8 min. after infection.

A marked increase in the response of $Leu\text{-}sRNA_1$ to UUG was observed one minute after infection and an even greater increase was seen eight minutes after infection.

Greater responses of $Leu\text{-}sRNA_3$ and $Leu\text{-}sRNA_{4a,b}$ to poly UC also were observed eight minutes after phage infection. Leu-sRNA fractions 3 and 4 differ in chromatographic mobility and in acylation specificity by yeast and E. coli Leu-sRNA synthetase preparations. Thus, $Leu\text{-}sRNA_3$ and a component in fraction 4 differ, although both fractions 3 and 4 respond to poly UC. The multiple responses of $Leu\text{-}sRNA_{4a,b}$ to poly U, poly UC and the trinucleotides, CUU and CUC, suggest that fraction 4 may contain two or more Leu-sRNA species. Striking increases in response of fraction 4 to poly U were observed one and eight minutes after infection.

Leu-sRNA fractions 1, 2, and 3 are related, for each is recognized by yeast as well as by E. coli Leu-sRNA synthetase preparations. In contrast, $Leu\text{-}sRNA_{4a,b}$ and $Leu\text{-}sRNA_5$ are recognized by E. coli, but not yeast Leu-sRNA synthetase, thus, fraction 4 is related to fraction 5. Two different cistrons of Leu-sRNA are predicted; Leu-sRNA fractions 1, 2, and 3 may be products of one cistron; whereas, fractions 4 and 5 may be products of a different cistron. In this regard Berg, Lagerkvist, and Dieckman (1962) have shown that E. coli Leu-sRNA contains two base sequences at the 4th, 5th, and 6th base positions from the 3'-terminus of the sRNA.

The data suggest the following sRNA precursor product relationships. $Leu\text{-}sRNA_2$ is a product of "cistron A"; the decrease in $Leu\text{-}sRNA_2$ and the simultaneous increase in $Leu\text{-}sRNA_1$ (within one minute after infection) suggests that $Leu\text{-}sRNA_2$ is the precursor of $Leu\text{-}sRNA_1$. The data also suggest that $Leu\text{-}sRNA_2$ is a precursor of $Leu\text{-}sRNA_3$. The following anticodons and mRNA

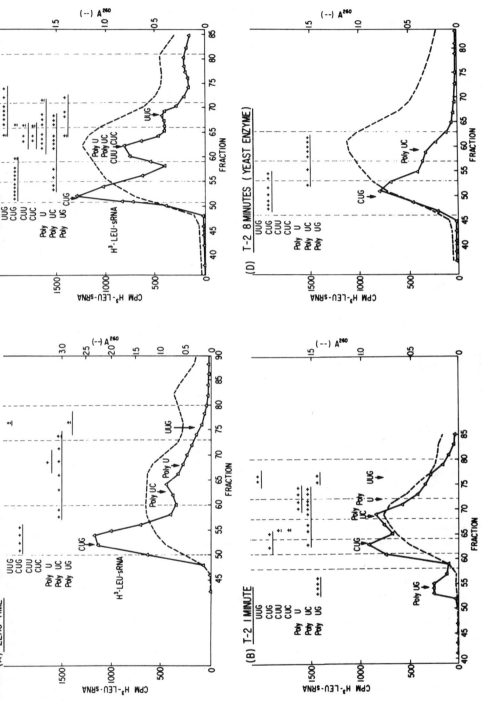

FIGURE 6. The graphs represent MAK column fractions of H³-Leu-sRNA from *E. coli* B before infection (a) and at 1 min (b) and 8 min (c and d) after infection with T2 phage. sRNA was acylated prior to chromatography with H³-leucine using *E. coli* (a, b, c) or yeast (d) synthetase preparations. Column eluates were pooled as indicated by the vertical broken lines; dialyzed against 5 × 10⁻⁴ M potassium cacodylate, pH 5.5, and lyophilized. Then binding of each fraction to ribosomes in response to tri- or polynucleotide templates was determined. At the top of each graph relative responses of Leu-sRNA fractions to templates are shown. Approximate relative responses are indicated as follows: No symbol, no detectable response of Leu-sRNA; ±, possible response; +, slight response; and ++ to ++++, moderate to strong responses. Profiles represented by broken lines indicate A²⁶⁰ units; △–△, represent H³-Leu-sRNA. Data are from Kano-Sueoka, Nirenberg, and Sueoka (unpubl.). Also see Sueoka et al., this volume.

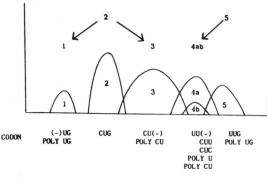

CODON	(−)UG POLY UG	CUG	CU(−) POLY CU	UU(−) CUU CUC POLY U POLY CU	UUG POLY UG
ZERO TIME	±	++++	++	+	+
T-2 1"	++	++	++	+	++
T-2 8"	±	+++	+++	+++	+++
AA−sRNA SYNTHETASE					
YEAST	+	+	+	−	−
E.COLI	+	+	+	+	+

FIGURE 7. Diagrammatic representation of the data shown in Fig. 6. The relative mobilities of multiple species of Leu-sRNA, before and after phage infection, fractionated by MAK column chromatography, are shown at the top. Leu-sRNA peaks are numbered. Arrows represent predicted Leu-sRNA precursor-product relationships (Fractions 2 and 5 possibly are products of different cistrons).

Tri- and polynucleotide codons recognized by each Leu-sRNA peak are shown below. Approximate relative responses of Leu-sRNA$_{1-5}$ to codons are indicated as follows: ±, possible response, + to + + + +, slight to strong responses.

On the bottom are shown the specificities of E. coli (zero time, 1 and 8 min after infection) and yeast (8 min after infection only) Leu-sRNA synthetase preparations for sRNA^{Leu} fractions.

codons are suggested for Leu-sRNA fractions 2, 3, and 1, respectively (note: asterisks represent modifications of a nucleotide base; codon and anticodon sequences are written with 3′,5′-phosphodiester linkages; antiparallel hydrogen bonding between codon and anticodons is assumed): Leu-sRNA$_2$-product of "cistron A", CAG anticodon, [CUG codon]; Leu-sRNA$_3$- derived from fraction 2, C*AG anticodon, [CU(−) codon]; Leu-sRNA$_1$- derived from fraction 2, CAG** anticodon, [(−)UG codon].

Leu-sRNA$_5$ is a product of "cistron B", and differs from Leu-sRNA$_2$ in anticodon and Leu-sRNA synthetase recognition sites. The sequence, CAA, is suggested for the Leu-sRNA$_5$ anticodon, corresponding to a UUG mRNA codon. Leu-sRNA$_{4a,b}$ are derived from fraction 5. Possible anticodons and codons are: C*AA anticodon, [UU(−) codon]; C*IA anticodon, [UU(−), UC(−), UA(−) codons]; C*AI anticodon, [UU(−), CU(−), AU(−) codons].

Since modification of Leu-sRNA after phage infection is dependent upon protein synthesis,

enzyme(s) may be needed to modify bases in Leu-sRNA fractions.

The inhibition of host E. coli, but not viral protein synthesis following viral infection may result from modification of Leu-sRNA fractions. N-formyl-Met-sRNA$_1$ serves as an initiator of protein synthesis in E. coli and responds to two trinucleotides, UUG and CUG, which are also recognized by Leu-sRNA fractions (see previous discussion on special function codons). Possibly, initiation or termination of E. coli, but not viral protein synthesis is affected. Further studies are needed, however, to elucidate the mechanism of viral induced inhibition of host protein synthesis.

ACKNOWLEDGMENTS

It is a pleasure to thank Miss Norma Zabriskie, Mrs. Theresa Caryk, Mr. Taysir M. Jaouni, and Mr. Wayne Kemper for their invaluable assistance. D. Kellogg is a Postdoctoral fellow of the Helen Hay Whitney Foundation. J. Levin is supported by USPHS grant 1-F2-GM-6369-01. F. Rottman is supported by grant PF-244 from the American Cancer Society.

REFERENCES

ADAMS, J. M., and M. R. CAPECCHI. 1966. N-formyl methionyl-sRNA as the initiator of protein synthesis. Proc. Natl. Acad. Sci. 55: 147–155.

AMES, B. N., and P. E. HARTMAN. 1963. The histidine operon. Cold Spring Harbor Symp. Quant. Biol. 28: 349–356.

ANDERSON, W. F., M. W. NIRENBERG, R. E. MARSHALL, and C. T. CASKEY. 1966. RNA codons and protein synthesis: Relative activity of synonym codons. Fed. Proc. 25: 404.

ARLINGHAUS, R., J. SHAEFFER, and R. SCHWEET. 1964. Mechanism of peptide bond formation in polypeptide synthesis. Proc. Natl. Acad. Sci. 51: 1291–1299.

BARGHOORN, E. S., and J. W. SCHOPF. 1966. Micro organisms three billion years old from the precambrian of South Africa. Science 152: 758–763.

BECKWITH, J. R., and L. GORINI. 1966. Suppression. Ann. Rev. Microbiol., in press.

BERG, P., U. LAGERKVIST, and M. DIECKMANN. 1962. The enzymic synthesis of amino acyl derivatives of ribonucleic acid. VI. Nucleotide sequences adjacent to the . . .pCpCpA end groups of isoleucine- and leucine-specific chains. J. Mol. Biol. 5: 159–171.

BERNFIELD, M. 1966. Ribonuclease and oligoribonucleotide synthesis. II. Synthesis of oligonucleotides of specific sequence. J. Biol. Chem. 241: 2014–2023.

BRENNER, S., A. O. W. STRETTON, and S. KAPLAN. 1965. Genetic Code: the 'nonsense' triplets for chain termination and their suppression. Nature 206: 994–998.

BRIMACOMBE, R., J. TRUPIN, M. NIRENBERG, P. LEDER, M. BERNFIELD, and T. JAOUNI. 1965. RNA codewords and protein synthesis. VIII. Nucleotide sequences of synonym codons for arginine, valine, cysteine and alanine. Proc. Natl. Acad. Sci. 54: 954–960.

CERUTTI, P., H. T. MILES, and J. FRAZIER. 1966. Interaction of partially reduced polyuridylic acid with a polyadenylic acid. Biochem. Biophys. Res. Commun. 22: 466–472.

CLARK, B., and K. MARCKER. 1966. The role of N-formyl-methionyl-sRNA in protein biosynthesis. J. Mol. Biol., *17:* 394–406.

CONNELLY, C. M., and B. P. DOCTOR. 1966. Purification of two yeast serine transfer ribonucleic acids by countercurrent distribution. J. Biol. Chem. *241:* 715–719.

CRICK, F. H. C. 1966. Codon-Anticodon Pairing: The wobble hypothesis. J. Mol. Biol., *19:* 548–555.

HEPPEL, L. A., P. R. WHITFIELD, and R. MARKHAM. 1955. Nucleotide exchange reactions catalyzed by ribonuclease and spleen phosphodiesterase. 2. Synthesis of polynucleotides. Biochem. J. *60:* 8–15.

HOLLEY, R. W., J. APGAR, G. A. EVERETT, J. T. MADISON, M. MARQUISEE, S. H. MERRILL, J. R. PENSWICK, and A. ZAMIR. 1965. Structure of a ribonucleic acid. Science *147:* 1462–1465.

INGRAM, V. M., and J. A. SJÖQUIST. 1963. Studies on the structure of purified alanine and valine transfer RNA from yeast. Cold Spring Harbor Symp. Quant. Biol. *28:* 133–138.

JONES, D. S., S. NISHIMURA, and H. G. KHORANA. 1966. Studies on polynucleotides LVI. Further syntheses, *in vitro*, of copolypeptides containing two amino acids in alternating sequence dependent upon DNA-like polymers containing two nucleotides in alternating sequence. J. Mol. Biol. *16:* 454–472.

KELLER, E. B., and M. F. FERGER. 1966. Alanyl-sRNA in the aminoacyl polymerase system of protein synthesis. Fed. Proc. *25:* 215.

KELLOGG, D. A., B. P. DOCTOR, J. E. LOEBEL, and M. W. NIRENBERG. 1966. RNA codons and protein synthesis, IX. Synonym codon recognition by multiple species of valine-, alanine-, and methionine-sRNA. Proc. Natl. Acad. Sci. *55:* 912–919.

LEDER, P., M. F. SINGER, and R. L. C. BRIMACOMBE. 1965. Synthesis of trinucleoside diphosphates with polynucleotide phosphorylase. Biochem. *4:* 1561–1567.

MADISON, J. T., G. A. EVERETT, and H. KUNG. 1966. Nucleotide sequence of a yeast tyrosine transfer RNA. Science *153:* 531–534.

NAKAMOTO, T., and D. KOLAKOFSKY. 1966. A possible mechanism for initiation of protein synthesis. Proc. Natl. Acad. Sci. *55:* 606–613.

NEWTON, W. A., J. R. BECKWITH, D. ZIPSER, and S. BRENNER. 1965. Nonsense mutants and polarity in the *Lac operon of Escherichia coli.* J. Mol. Biol. *14:* 290–296.

NIRENBERG, M. W., O. W. JONES, P. LEDER, B. F. C. CLARK, W. S. SLY, and S. PESTKA. 1963. On the coding of genetic information. Cold Spring Harbor Symp. Quant. Biol. *28:* 549–557.

NIRENBERG, M., and P. LEDER. 1964. RNA codewords and protein synthesis. I. The effect of trinucleotides upon the binding of sRNA to ribosomes. Science *145:* 1399–1407.

NIRENBERG, M., P. LEDER, M. BERNFIELD, R. BRIMACOMBE, J. TRUPIN, F. ROTTMAN, and C. O'NEAL. 1965. RNA codewords and protein synthesis, VII. On the general nature of the RNA code. Proc. Natl. Acad. Sci. *53:* 1161–1168.

ROTTMAN, F., and P. CERUTTI. 1966. Template activity of uridylic acid-dihydrouridylic acid copolymers. Proc. Natl. Acad. Sci. *55:* 960–966.

ROTTMAN, F., and M. NIRENBERG. 1966. Regulatory mechanisms and protein synthesis XI. Template activity of modified RNA codons. J. Mol. Biol., in press.

SALAS, M., M. A. SMITH, W. M. STANLEY, JR., A. J. WAHBA, and S. OCHOA. 1965. Direction of reading of the genetic message. J. Biol. Chem. *240:* 3988–3995.

SÖLL, D., E. OHTSUKA, D. S. JONES, R. LOHRMANN, H. HAYATSU, S. NISHIMURA, and H. G. KHORANA. 1965. Studies on polynucleotides, XLIX. Stimulation of the binding of aminoacyl-sRNA's to ribosomes by ribotrinucleotides and a survey of codon assignments for 20 amino acids. Proc. Natl. Acad. Sci. *54:* 1378–1385.

SONNEBORN, T. M. 1965. Degeneracy of the genetic code: Extent, nature and genetic implications. pp. 377–397. *In:* V. Bryson and H. J. Vogel (ed.) Evolving Genes and Proteins. Academic Press, New York.

SPEYER, J., P. LENGYEL, C. BASILIO, A. WAHBA, R. GARDNER, and S. OCHOA. 1963. Synthetic polynucleotides and the amino acid code. Cold Spring Harbor Symp. Quant. Biol. *28:* 559–567.

STENT, G. S. 1964. The operon: On its third anniversary. Science *144:* 816–820.

SUEOKA, N., and T. KANO-SUEOKA. 1964. A specific modification of Leucyl-sRNA of *Escherichia coli* after phage T2 infection. Proc. Natl. Acad. Sci. *52:* 1535–1540.

THACH, R. E., K. F. DEWEY, J. C. BROWN, and P. DOTY. 1966. Formylmethionine codon AUG as an initiator of polypeptide synthesis. Science *153:* 416–418.

THACH, R. E., and P. DOTY. 1965. Enzymatic synthesis of tri- and tetranucleotides of defined sequence. Science *148:* 632–634.

WEBSTER, R. E., D. L. ENGELHARDT, and N. D. ZINDER. 1966. *In vitro* protein synthesis: Chain initiation. Proc. Natl. Acad. Sci. *55:* 155–161.

WEIGERT, M., and A. GAREN. 1965. Base composition of nonsense codons in E. coli; Evidence from amino-acid substitutions at a tryptophan site in alkaline phosphatase. Nature *206:* 992–994.

ZACHAU, H., D. DÜTTING, and H. FELDMANN. 1966. Nucleotide sequences of two serine-specific transfer ribonucleic acids (1). Angew. Chem. *5:* 422, English Edition.

J. Mol. Biol. (1966) **19**, 548–555

Codon—Anticodon Pairing:

The Wobble Hypothesis

F. H. C. CRICK

Medical Research Council, Laboratory of Molecular Biology

Hills Road, Cambridge, England

(*Received 14 February 1966*)

It is suggested that while the standard base pairs may be used rather strictly in the first two positions of the triplet, there may be some wobble in the pairing of the third base. This hypothesis is explored systematically, and it is shown that such a wobble could explain the general nature of the degeneracy of the genetic code.

Now that most of the genetic code is known and the base-sequences of sRNA molecules are coming out, it seems a proper time to consider the possible base-pairing between codons on mRNA and the presumed anticodons on the sRNA.

The obvious assumption to adopt is that sRNA molecules will have certain common features, and that the ribosome will ensure that all sRNA molecules are presented to the mRNA in the same way. In short, that the pairing between one codon–anticodon matching pair will to a first approximation be "equivalent" to that between any other matching pair.

As far as I know, if this condition has to be obeyed, and if all four bases must be distinguished in any one position in the codon, then the pairing in this position is *highly likely* to be the standard one; that is:†

$$G ==== C$$
$$\text{and} \quad A ==== U$$

or some equivalent ones such as, for example,

$$I ==== C$$
$$\text{and} \quad A ==== T$$

since this is the only type of pairing which allows all four bases to be distinguished in a strictly equivalent way.

We now know enough of the genetic code to say that in the *first two* positions of the codon the four bases are clearly distinguished; certainly in many cases, and probably in all of them. I thus deduce that the pairings in the first two positions are likely to be the standard ones.

---

† Throughout this paper the sign $====$ is used to mean "pairs with". If two bases are equivalent in their coding properties, this is written $\genfrac{}{}{0pt}{}{U}{C}$ or $\left.\genfrac{}{}{0pt}{}{U}{C}\right\}$

However, what we know about the code has already suggested two generalizations about the third place of the codon. These are:

(1) U ⎫ † this already appears true in about a dozen cases out of the possible 16,
    C ⎭ and there are no data to suggest any exceptions.

(2) A ⎫ probably true in about half of the possible 16 cases, but the evidence
    G ⎭ suggests it may perhaps be incorrect in several other cases.

The detailed experimental evidence is rather complicated and will not be discussed here. (For details of the code see, for example, Nirenberg *et al.*, 1965; and Söll *et al.*, 1965.) It suffices that these rules *may* be true, as suggested by Eck (1963) a little time ago. Alternatively, only the first one may be true.

This naturally raises the question: Does *one* sRNA molecule recognize more than one codon, e.g. both UUU *and* UUC. Some evidence for this was first presented by Bernfield & Nirenberg (1965). They showed that *all* the sRNA for phenylalanine can be bound by poly U, although this sRNA also recognizes the triplet UUC, at least in part. More recent evidence along these lines is presented in Söll *et al.* (1966) and Kellogg *et al.* (1966). Again I do not wish to discuss here the evidence in detail, but simply to ask: If one sRNA codes both XYU and XYC, how is this done?

Now if we do not know anything about the geometry of the situation, it might be thought that almost any base pairs might be used, since it is well known that the bases can be paired (i.e. form at least two hydrogen bonds) in many different ways. However, it occurred to me that if the first two bases in the codon paired in the standard way, the pairing in the third position might be *close* to the standard ones.

We therefore ask: How many base pairs are there in which the glycosidic bonds occur in a position close to the standard one? Possible pairs are:

$$G ==== A \tag{1}$$

In my opinion this will not occur, because the NH_2 group of guanine cannot make one of its hydrogen bonds, even to water (see Fig. 1).

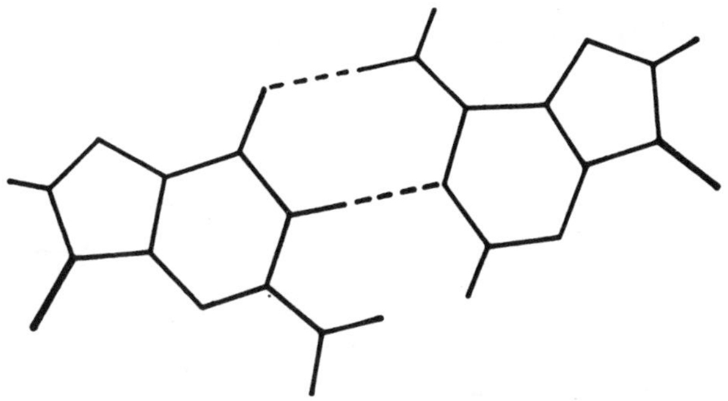

Fig. 1. The unlikely pair guanine-adenine.

$$U ==== C \tag{2}$$

This brings the two keto groups rather close together and also the two glycosidic bonds, but it may be possible (see Fig. 2).

† This symbol implies that both U and C code the same amino acid.

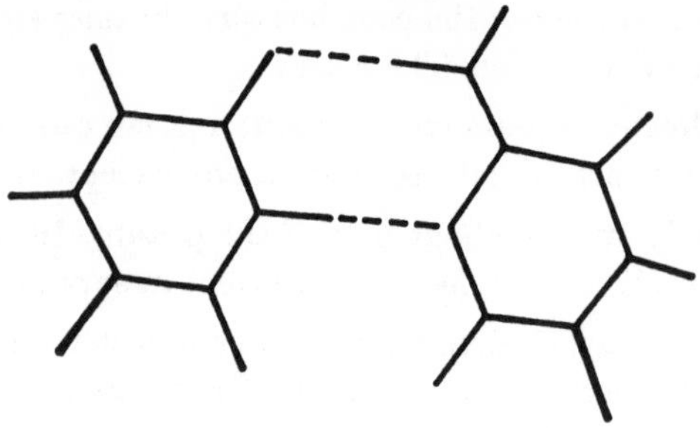

FIG. 2. The close pair uracil–cytosine.

$$U ==== U \tag{3}$$

Again rather close together (see Fig. 3).

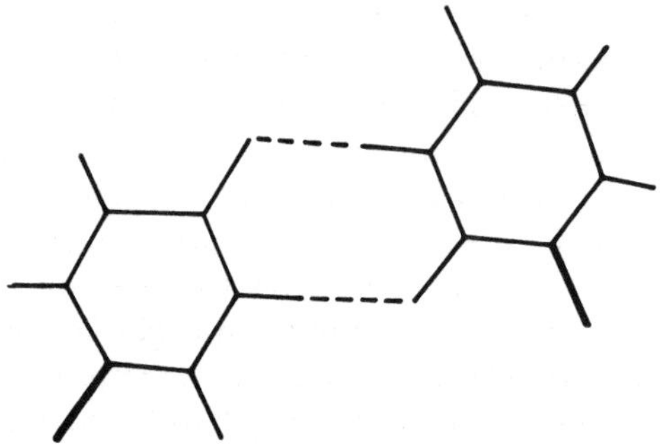

FIG. 3. The close pair uracil–uracil.

$$G ==== U \tag{4}$$
$$\text{or } I ==== U$$

These only require the bond to move about 2·5 Å from the standard position (see Fig. 4).

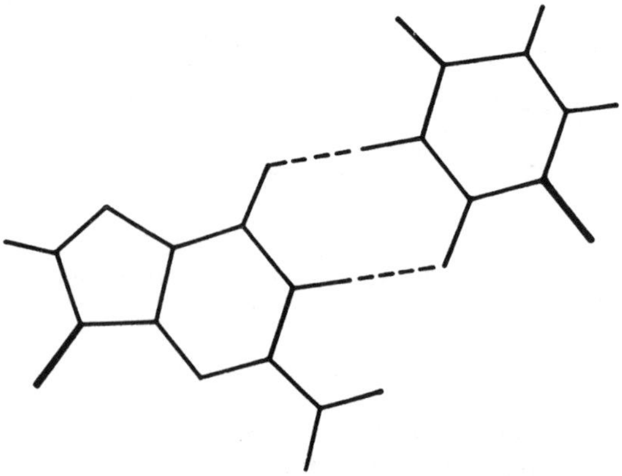

FIG. 4. The pair guanine–uracil (the pair inosine–uracil is similar).

$$I ==== A \tag{5}$$

This is perfectly possible. Poly I and poly A will form a double helix. The distance between the glycosidic bonds is increased (see Fig. 5).

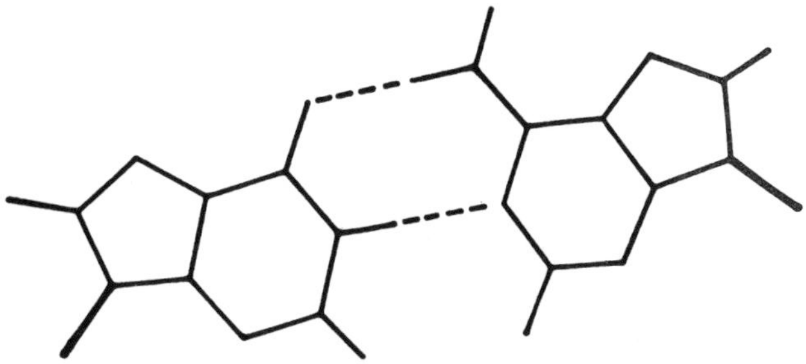

Fig. 5. The pair inosine–adenine.

As far as I know, these are all the possible solutions if it is assumed that the bases are in their usual tautomeric forms.

I now postulate that in the base-pairing of the third base of the codon there is a certain amount of play, or wobble, such that more than one position of pairing is possible.

As can be seen from Fig. 6, there are seven possible positions which might be reached by wobbling. However, it by no means follows that all seven are accessible, since the molecular structure is very likely to impose limits to the wobble. We should therefore strictly consider all possible *combinations of allowed positions*. There are 127 of these, but most of them are trivial. If we adopt the rule that *all four bases* on the codon (in the third position) must be recognized (that is, paired with) we are left with 51 different combinations. This is too many for easy consideration, but fortunately we can eliminate most of them by only accepting combinations which do not violate the broad features of the code. If we assume:

(a) that all four bases must be recognizable;

(b) that the code must *in some cases* distinguish between

$\left.\begin{matrix} U \\ C \end{matrix}\right\}$ and $\left.\begin{matrix} A \\ G \end{matrix}\right\}$ as it appears to do for the pairs

Phe	Tyr	His	Asn	Asp
Leu	C.T.†	Gln	Lys	Glu

(not all of which are likely to be wrong)

then by strictly logical argument it can be shown both that the standard position must be used, and that the three positions on the left of Fig. 6 cannot be used.

This leaves us with only four possible sites to consider one of which—the standard one—must be included. There are therefore only seven possible combinations. I have examined all these, but I shall restrict myself here to the case in which all four positions are used, as this is structurally the most likely and also seems to give the code (called code 4 in the note privately circulated) which best fits the experimental data.

† C.T., Chain termination.

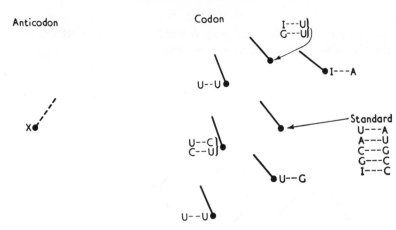

Anticodon   Codon

Fig. 6. The point X represents the position of the C_1' atom of the glycosidic bond (shown dotted) in the anticodon. The other points show where the C_1' atom and the glycosidic bond fall for the various base pairs. (Pairs with inosine in the codon have been omitted for simplicity.) The wobble code suggested uses the four positions to the right of the diagram, but not the three close positions.

The rules for pairing between the third base on the codon and the corresponding base on the anticodon are set out in Table 1. It can be seen that these rules make several strong predictions:

(1) it is not possible to code for either C alone, or for A alone.

For example, at the moment the codon UGA has not been decisively allocated. Wobble theory states that UGA might either:

    (a) code for cysteine, which has UGU and UGC; or

    (b) code for trypotophan, which has UGG; or

    (c) not be recognized.

TABLE 1

Pairing at the third position of the codon

Base on the anticodon	Bases recognized on the codon
U	A G
C	G
A†	U
G	U C
I	U C A

† It seems likely that inosine will be formed enzymically from an adenine in the nascent sRNA. This may mean that A in this position will be rare or absent, depending upon the exact specificity of the enzyme(s) involved.

However it does *not* permit UGA to code for any amino acid other than cysteine or tryptophan. This rule could also explain why no suppressor has yet been found which suppresses only *ochre* mutants (UAA), although suppressors exist which suppress both *ochre* and *amber* mutants (UA^A_G).

(2) If an sRNA has inosine in the place at the relevant position on the anticodon (i.e. enabling it to pair with the third base of the codon), then it must recognize U, C and A in the third place of the codon. Conversely, those amino acids coded only by XY^U_C (such as Phe, Tyr, His, etc.) cannot have inosine in that place on their sRNA.

(3) Wobble theory does not state exactly how many different types of sRNA will actually be found for any amino acid. However if an amino acid is coded for by all four bases in the third position (as are Pro, Thr, Val, etc.), then wobble theory predicts that there will be at least two sRNA's. These can have the recognition pattern:

$$\left.\begin{matrix} U \\ C \end{matrix}\right\} \text{ plus } \left.\begin{matrix} A \\ G \end{matrix}\right\}$$

or

$$\left.\begin{matrix} U \\ C \\ A \end{matrix}\right\} \text{ plus } G$$

Note that the sets actually used for any amino acid may well vary from species to species.

The Anticodons

At this point it is useful to examine the experimental evidence for the anticodon. In the sRNA for alanine from yeast, Holley *et al.* (1965) have the following sequences:

——— pUpUpIp Gp CpMeIpΨp ———

position ——— 36 37 38 ———

Zachau and his colleagues (Dütting, Karan, Melchers & Zachau, 1965) have for one of the serine sRNA's from yeast:

——— pΨpUpIpGpApA$^+$pΨp ———

(A$^+$ stands for a modified A)

For the valine sRNA from yeast, Ingram & Sjöquist (1963) have shown that the only inosine occurs in the sequence:

——— pIpApCp ———

Holley *et al.* (1965) have already pointed out that IGC is a possible anticodon for alanine, and the additional evidence makes it almost certain to my mind that this is correct, and that the anticodons are given in the Table below†:

† *Note added 26 April 1966.* Drs J. T. Madison, G. A. Everett and H. Kung (personal communication) have completed the sequence of the tyrosine sRNA from yeast. The sequence strongly suggests that the anticodon in this case is GΨA, corresponding to the known codons UA^U_C. Since Ψ can form the same base pairs as U, this is in excellent agreement with the previous data.

	Yeast sRNA	
	Anticodon	Codon
Ala	I G C	G C ?
Ser	I G A	U C ?
Val	I A C	G U ?

remembering that the pairing proposed between codon and anticodon is *anti*-parallel. Thus I confidently predict: the anticodon is a triplet at (or very near) positions 36–37–38 on every sRNA, and that the *first two bases* in the codon pair with this (in an anti-parallel manner) *using the standard base pairs.*

However, inosine does not occur in every sRNA. In particular Holley *et al.* (1963) (and personal communication) have reported that the tyrosine sRNA has two peaks, neither of which contains inosine. Moreover, Sanger (personal communication) tells me that there is rather little inosine in the total sRNA from *E. coli.*

Testing the Theory

Two obvious tests present themselves:

(1) To find which triplets are bound by any one type of sRNA. This is being done by Khorana and his colleagues (Söll *et al.*, 1966), and also by Nirenberg's group (Kellogg, Doctor, Loebel & Nirenberg, 1966). The difficulty here is to be sure that the sRNA used is pure, and not a mixture.

(2) To discover unambiguously the position of the anticodon on sRNA, and to find further anticodons. This will certainly happen as our knowledge of the base sequence of sRNA molecules develops. The absence of inosine from any anticodon is obviously of special interest.

In conclusion it seems to me that the preliminary evidence seems rather favourable to the theory. I shall not be surprised if it proves correct.

I thank my colleagues for many useful discussions and the following for sending me material in advance of publication: Dr M. W. Nirenberg, Dr H. G. Khorana, Dr G. Streisinger, Dr W. Holley, Dr J. Fresco, Dr H. G. Zachau, Dr C. Yanofsky, Dr H. G. Wittmann, Dr H. Lehmann and Dr J. D. Watson.

REFERENCES

Bernfield, M. R. & Nirenberg, M. W. (1965). *Science,* **147,** 479.
Dütting, D., Karan, W., Melchers, F. & Zachau, H. G. (1965). *Biochim. biophys. Acta,* **108,** 194.
Eck, R. V. (1963). *Science,* **140,** 477.
Holley, R. W., Apgar, J., Everett, G. A., Madison, J. T., Marquisee, M., Merrill, S. H., Penswick, J. R. & Zamir, A. (1965). *Science,* **147,** 1462.
Holley, R. W., Apgar, J. Everett, G. A., Madison, J. T., Merrill, S. H. & Zamir, A. (1963). *Cold Spr. Harb. Symp. Quant. Biol.* **28,** 117.
Ingram, V. M. & Sjöquist, J. A. (1963). *Cold. Spr. Harb. Symp. Quant. Biol.* **28,** 133.

Kellogg, D. A., Doctor, B. P., Loebel, J. E. & Nirenberg, M. W. (1966). *Proc. Nat. Acad. Sci., Wash.* **55**, 912.

Nirenberg, M., Leder, P., Bernfield, M., Brimacombe, R., Trupin, J., Rottman, F. & O'Neal, C. (1965). *Proc. Nat. Acad. Sci., Wash.* **53**, 1161.

Söll, D., Jones, D. S., Ohtsuka, E., Faulkner, R. D., Lohrmann, R., Hayatsu, H., Khorana, H. G., Cherayil, J. D., Hampel, A. & Bock, R. M. (1966). *J. Mol. Biol.* **19**, 556.

Söll, D., Ohtsuka, E., Jones, D. S., Lohrmann, R., Hayatsu, H., Nishimura, S. & Khorana, H. G. (1965). *Proc. Nat. Acad. Sci., Wash.* **54**, 1378.

DIRECTION OF READING OF THE GENETIC MESSAGE, II*

By Marvin A. Smith,† Margarita Salas,‡ Wendell M. Stanley, Jr.,§
Albert J. Wahba, and Severo Ochoa

DEPARTMENT OF BIOCHEMISTRY, NEW YORK UNIVERSITY SCHOOL OF MEDICINE

Communicated November 24, 1965

It was shown previously[1] that in a cell-free system of protein synthesis consisting of purified *Escherichia coli* ribosomes and *Lactobacillus arabinosus* supernatant, a system of low nuclease activity, oligonucleotides of the type ApApApApApAp... pApApC[2] (AAAAAA...AAC) with an AAC codon at the 3′-end of the chain, directed the synthesis of oligopeptides of the structure Lys-Lys-Lys...Lys-Asn with NH₂-terminal lysine and COOH-terminal asparagine. These results showed (a) that AAC is an asparagine codon (AAA being a known codon for lysine), and (b) that if the biological assembly of the polypeptide chains of proteins proceeds, as currently believed, from the NH₂-terminal through the COOH-terminal amino acid, the genetic code is translated by reading the messenger from the 5′- to the 3′-end of the polynucleotide chain. The latter conclusion would be greatly strengthened if it could be shown that polynucleotides of the type AACAAA...AAA, containing the AAC codon at the 5′- rather than the 3′-end, directed the synthesis of lysine peptides with an asparagine residue at the NH₂-terminal end.

Oligonucleotides of the type ApApCpApApAp...pApApA (A₂CAₙ) were synthesized and tested for lysine (AAA codon), asparagine (AAC codon), and threonine

(ACA codon[3]) incorporation in the *E. coli-L. arabinosus* system. However, these polynucleotides promoted the incorporation of negligible amounts of asparagine and threonine into tungstic acid-insoluble material relative to the amount of lysine incorporated. The low effectiveness of the ApApC triplet at the 5'-end could conceivably be due to the lack of a 5'-phosphate residue. In order to overcome this difficulty, oligonucleotides of the type ApApApApApCpAp...pApApA (A_5-CA_n) and ApApApApCpAp...pApApA (A_4CA_n) were synthesized. The former (A_5CA_n) promoted the incorporation of lysine, asparagine, and small amounts of threonine, whereas the latter (A_4CA_n) promoted the incorporation of lysine, threonine, and traces of asparagine. Carboxypeptidase assays showed that the bulk of the asparagine in the lysine-containing oligopeptides synthesized with A_5CA_n and the bulk of the threonine in those synthesized with A_4CA_n messengers was in NH_2-terminal position. These results provide strong additional support for the conclusion that the genetic message is read in a 5' → 3' direction.

Materials and Methods.—These were as in a previous work[1] except as otherwise noted.

Ribosomes and supernatant with low nuclease activity: *E. coli* ribosomes purified by washing with ammonium chloride followed by chromatography on DEAE cellulose, and *L. arabinosus* supernatant were prepared as previously described.[1] It was important for the present experiments to determine whether these cell fractions had any 5'-exonuclease[4] activity. The virtual absence of endonuclease and 3'-exonuclease had already been ascertained but no specific assays for 5'-exonuclease had been carried out. For this purpose, oligonucleotides of the type A*pCpAp... pApApA (A*CA_n), with the adenine residue at the 5'-end labeled with C^{14}, were prepared. A sample (60 μg, 2500 cpm) of $A^*CA_{\overline{24}}$ was incubated with purified *E. coli* ribosomes and *L. arabinosus* supernatant, under the usual conditions for amino acid incorporation, for 40 min at 37°. After adding 4 vol of cold ethanol, the precipitate was removed by centrifugation and the supernatant concentrated to a small volume under nitrogen. Samples were spotted on Whatman no. 1 paper and developed with 40% ammonium sulfate.[5] Areas corresponding to cyclic AMP, 2'-AMP, 3'-AMP, and adenosine were cut out and their radioactivity was determined. No radioactivity above that of paper blanks of corresponding location or zero time controls was found in any of the areas. From this it may be concluded that more than 99% of the 5'-termini of oligonucleotides of the kind used in this work remain intact during the usual conditions of protein synthesis in the purified *E. coli* ribosomes-*L. arabinosus* supernatant system.

Preparation and characterization of oligonucleotides: The preparation and characterization of the oligonucleotides used in this work will be described in detail elsewhere. The following is an outline of the procedures followed.

Poly A*CA_n and poly $A_2C^*A_n$, with the adenine and cytosine residues, respectively, labeled with C^{14}, were prepared with polynucleotide phosphorylase using ADP as substrate and either A*pC or ApApC* as primer. The polymers were isolated by exclusion chromatography on Sephadex G-100 at 25° in 8.0 M urea, 0.5 M ammonium bicarbonate, pH 8.6, and recovered by evaporation and lyophilization after exhaustive dialysis against distilled water. The primers were prepared by digestion of random poly A*C (1:1) or poly AC* (2:1) with pancreatic ribonuclease, phosphomonoesterase treatment, and size-fractionation by chromatography on DEAE cellulose in ammonium bicarbonate, pH 8.6.[6]

Poly $A_4C^*A_n$ and poly $A_5C^*A_n$, with the cytosine residue labeled with H^3, were prepared by the addition of one single cytidylic acid residue (from H^3-labeled CDP) to ApApApA (A_4) or ApApApApA (A_5) with polynucleotide phosphorylase in the presence of pancreatic ribonuclease, to form ApApApApC*p (A_4C^*p) or ApApApApApC*p (A_5C^*p). This was followed by removal of the 3'-terminal phosphate with phosphomonoesterase. The resulting A_4C^* and A_5C^*, isolated by DEAE-cellulose chromatography in ammonium bicarbonate, were used as primers for the addition of adenylic acid residues from ADP with polynucleotide phosphorylase, and the resulting $A_4C^*A_n$ and $A_5C^*A_n$ polymers isolated as above by Sephadex G-100 chromatography. The A_4 and A_5, used as starting products, were prepared from poly A by hydrolysis in 0.1 M ammonium carbonate, pH 10, at 100° for an appropriate length of time, followed by acid hydrolysis of residual cyclic phosphate ends, removal of the resulting terminal 2'- and 3'-phosphate residues with phosphomonoesterase, and chromatography on DEAE cellulose in ammonium bicarbonate.

A purified preparation of *Micrococcus lysodeikticus* polynucleotide phosphorylase, virtually free of nuclease and with a requirement for primer, was used for the addition of adenylic acid residues to A*C, A_2C^*, A_4C^*, and A_5C^* primers, and for the addition of one (H^3-labeled) cytidylic acid residue to A_4, and A_5, essentially by the procedure of Thach and Doty.[7]

The various polymers were characterized by determining the location of the radioactivity following digestion with pancreatic ribonuclease. In each case all of the radioactivity was recovered in the species expected. A^*CA_n, $A_2C^*A_n$, $A_4C^*A_n$, and $A_5C^*A_n$ yielded A^*Cp, A_2C^*p, A_4C^*p, and A_5C^*p, respectively. The average molecular weight and molecular weight distribution were determined both from the ratio of total nucleotide material (measured by absorbancy) to primer (determined by radioactivity), and from their chromatographic behavior on Sephadex G-100 previously calibrated with poly A, poly C, and poly U of known and uniform degree of polymerization. There was good agreement between the two methods indicating that all polymer chains were of the desired character and were free of poly (oligo) A chains. The chain lengths of the oligonucleotides used are given in Table 1.

TABLE 1

CHAIN LENGTHS OF OLIGONUCLEOTIDES ISOLATED BY CHROMATOGRAPHY ON
SEPHADEX G-100

Series	Polymer	Chain Length	
		Average	Range
A^*CA_n	$A^*CA_{\overline{24}}$	26	15–55
"	$A_2C^*A_{\overline{39}}$	42	30–65
"	$A_2C^*A_{\overline{18}}$	21	15–26
$A_5C^{**}A_n$	$A_5C^{**}A_{\overline{19}}$	25	20–29
"	$A_5C^{**}A_{\overline{10}}$	16	10–20
$A_4C^{**}A_n$	$A_4C^{**}A_{\overline{29}}$	34	27–40
"	$A_4C^{**}A_{\overline{19}}$	24	19–27
"	$A_4C^{**}A_{\overline{11}}$	16	9–19

* C^{14}-label; ** H^3-label.

Amino acid incorporation and isolation of peptides: The incubations, measurement of amino acid incorporation, and isolation of the peptides were as previously described.[1] The specific radioactivity of the C^{14}-lysine was 2 $\mu c/\mu mole$; that of the C^{14}-asparagine, 30 $\mu c/\mu mole$; and that of the C^{14}-threonine, 46 $\mu c/\mu mole$. In the amino acid incorporation assays (Table 1), 5 $\mu moles$ of nonlabeled amino acid (the one that was labeled in each particular incubation mixture) were added to each sample after incubation. Since the oligonucleotide messengers used contained in some cases C^{14}-cytidylic acid residues, the oligonucleotides in experiment 1 were then hydrolyzed, along with aminoacyl (or peptidyl) ~ tRNA linkages, by further incubation for 16 hr at 37° with 0.5 N KOH, thus rendering the nucleotide radioactivity acid-soluble. In experiment 2, in which all of the oligonucleotides used had a H^3-labeled cytidylic acid residue, the samples (0.25 ml) were further incubated, as in previous work,[1] with 0.5 ml of 3% NH_3 for 1 hr at 37°. In all cases samples with labeled oligonucleotide, but without labeled amino acid, were run simultaneously with the experimental samples to correct for any radioactivity that might be contributed by the polymer.

Results.—Amino acid incorporation: The effect of the various oligonucleotides and, as a control, that of random poly AC (15:1) on the incorporation of lysine (AAA codon), asparagine (AAC codon), and threonine (ACA codon) is shown in Table 2. The incorporation of glutamine was not investigated because, as previously noted,[1] the *L. arabinosus* supernatant has low glutaminyl ~ tRNA synthetase activity. All the polymers promoted the incorporation of lysine.

Poly AC promoted, as expected, the incorporation of equal amounts of asparagine and threonine. On the other hand, relative to lysine incorporation, only insignificant amounts of asparagine and threonine were incorporated with A_2CA_n oligonucleotide messengers. As already pointed out, the presence of a terminal

TABLE 2

AMINO ACID INCORPORATION WITH POLY AC AND (Ap)ₙCpAp...pA OLIGONUCLEOTIDES

| | Amino Acid Incorporation | | | | |
| | μμmoles/Sample | | | Per cent of Total | |
Polynucleotide	Lysine	Asparagine	Threonine	Asparagine	Threonine
Expt. 1					
None (blank)*	(115)	(23)	(69)		
$A_2CA_{\overline{39}}$	2032	20	16	1.0	0.8
$A_2CA_{\overline{18}}$	456	5	5	1.1	1.1
$A_5CA_{\overline{19}}$	671	65	18	8.6	2.4
$A_5CA_{\overline{10}}$	302	35	6	10.2	1.7
Expt. 2					
None (blank)†	(61)	(30)	(19)		
Poly AC (15:1)*	8151	912	848	9.2	8.6
$A_5CA_{\overline{19}}$*	954	95	20	8.9	1.9
A_5CA_{10}	445	72	8	13.7	1.5
$A_4CA_{\overline{29}}$	1221	2	42	0.2	3.3
$A_4CA_{\overline{19}}‡$	725	3	36	0.4	4.7
$A_4CA_{\overline{11}}$	298	1	10	0.3	3.2

Conditions as described under *Amino acid incorporation*. Actual incorporation values (blanks without added polynucleotide subtracted from values with polynucleotide) expressed in μμmoles/sample. The cytidine residue in poly A₂CA39 and poly A₂CA18 was labeled with C14, that in A₅CAₙ and A₄CAₙ oligonucleotides was labeled with H³.
* Average of duplicate runs.
† Average of six runs.
‡ Average of triplicate runs.

phosphate residue may be essential for reading of the ApApC triplet at the 5'-end of the chain.

Oligonucleotides of the A_5CA_n series directed the incorporation of asparagine but threonine was incorporated to a much lesser extent. This result, suggesting that the artificial messengers are not read randomly, prompted the preparation and testing of A_4CA_n oligonucleotides. The results were quite conclusive, as these polymers directed the incorporation of threonine but only traces of asparagine.

It may be noted that, relative to the incorporation of lysine, the incorporation of threonine in the experiments with A_4CA_n oligonucleotides was substantially lower than that of asparagine in those with A_5CA_n polymers of similar chain length. No explanation for this discrepancy can be offered at present. As previously reported,[1] the *E. coli-L. arabinosus* system does not cleave C14-labeled heptalysine. However, presence of a threonine aminopeptidase activity would account for the observed results.

Position of asparagine and threonine in peptide chains: Peptides containing C12-lysine and either C14-asparagine or C14-threonine were prepared with $A_5CA_{\overline{19}}$ and $A_4CA_{\overline{29}}$ messengers, respectively, and isolated by carboxymethyl-cellulose chromatography as previously described.[1] As shown in Figure 1, after treatment with carboxypeptidase A the distribution of the peptides containing C14-threonine or C14-asparagine remained essentially unchanged. This result indicates that neither of these amino acids was in COOH-terminal position in the lysine peptides for, as shown previously,[1] COOH-terminal asparagine is rapidly released from lysine peptides by carboxypeptidase A. Carboxypeptidase A is also known to hydrolyze off COOH-terminal threonine.[8] On the other hand, treatment with carboxypeptidase B resulted in the release of about 75 per cent of the radioactivity in each of the two peptides as free C14-threonine or C14-asparagine. Previously,[1] it had been shown that carboxypeptidase B has no effect on the size distribution of lysine peptides with COOH-terminal asparagine, and the same is to be expected of lysine

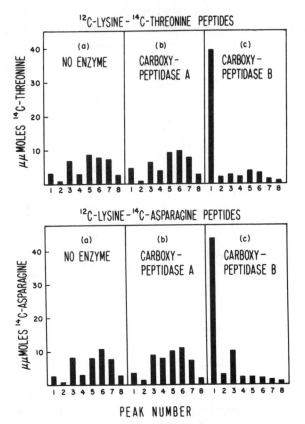

Fig. 1.—Effect of carboxypeptidases A and B on C¹²-lysine-C¹⁴-threonine and C¹²-lysine-C¹⁴-asparagine peptides. Peptides containing 56 μμmoles of C¹⁴-threonine or 60 μμmoles of C¹⁴-asparagine, prepared with $A_4CA_{\overline{29}}$ or $A_5CA_{\overline{19}}$ oligonucleotide messengers, respectively, and isolated as previously described,[1] were fractionated by chromatography on carboxymethylcellulose before (a) or after incubation for 30 min at 37° with either 13 μg of carboxypeptidase A (b) or 1.8 μg of carboxypeptidase B (c). The procedures for carboxypeptidase treatment and chromatography have been described.[1] The effluent was monitored continuously at 220 mμ. Fractions, 0.85 ml, eluted from the column were collected and their radioactivity was measured. Free threonine or asparagine, not retained by the column, are recovered in peak *1*. The succeeding peaks, *2*, *3*, etc., correspond to the dipeptide (1 thr or 1 asn, 1 lys), tripeptide (1 thr or 1 asn, 2 lys), etc., respectively. Free lysine would be recovered in peak *2*.

peptides with COOH-terminal threonine, for carboxypeptidase B requires COOH-terminal basic amino acids for activity.[9] The above results, therefore, indicate that the bulk of the asparagine and threonine in the lysine peptides investigated was in NH₂-terminal position.

Discussion.—The results presented in this paper provide conclusive evidence for the 5′ → 3′ polarity of translation of the genetic message. Recent results of other investigators[10, 11] are in accord with this view. The fact that (a) A_2CA_n polymers promoted but negligible asparagine incorporation, and (b) that most of the asparagine and threonine, incorporated along with lysine in the incubations with A_5CA_n and A_4CA_n oligonucleotides, was in NH₂-terminal position, indicates that reading of the initial triplet at the 5′-end of the chain was frequently missed, possibly for lack of a terminal phosphate. Nirenberg and Leder[12] have noted that the presence of a 5′-phosphate increased the effectiveness of trinucleotides in promoting specific binding of aminoacyl ∼ tRNA to ribosomes. Triplets without terminal phosphate at the 5′-end of synthetic homopolynucleotides have been reported to promote specific binding of aminoacyl ∼ tRNA to E. coli ribosomes.[13] In view of our results, it must be assumed that such binding would not, or would only infrequently, lead to reading of the triplet.

Our results may be interpreted to mean that, irrespective of the occurrence of actual reading leading to amino acid incorporation, translation of the oligonucleotide messengers starts at the 5′-end and that this start sets the reading frame (cf. Table 3). Faulty starts due to "jumping" one or two bases and resulting in shifts of

TABLE 3

READING OF A_2CA_n, A_5CA_n, AND A_4CA_n OLIGONUCLEOTIDES

Oligo-nucleotide		Frame setting	Peptides synthesized
Poly A_2CA_n	(a)	↑ <u>ApApC</u> pApApA pApApA...	Lys-Lys-Lys...Lys; probably traces of Asn-Lys-Lys...Lys
	(b)	A ↑ pApCpA pApApA pApApA...	Probably traces of Thr-Lys-Lys...Lys
Poly A_5CA_n	(a)	↑ <u>ApApA</u> pApApC pApApA...	Asn-Lys-Lys...Lys; probably traces of Lys-Asn-Lys...Lys
	(b)	A ↑ pApApA pApCpA pApApA...	Probably small amounts of Lys-Thr-Lys ...Lys
Poly A_4CA_n	(a)	↑ <u>ApApA</u> pApCpA pApApA...	Thr-Lys-Lys...Lys; probably traces of Lys-Thr-Lys...Lys
	(b)	ApA ↑ pApApC pApApA...	Probably traces of Asn-Lys-Lys...Lys

The vertical arrows mark the initial point of attachment of ribosomes to the messenger. The underlined triplets at the 5′-ends, lacking a terminal phosphate, are rarely read. "Jumping" of one or two bases with ensuing frame shift (as in (b) series of frame settings) appears to occur infrequently.

reading frame (as indicated in the (b) series of frame settings of Table 3) occurred rarely. It should be noted that these shifts must be the result of base "jumping" rather than that of enzymatic removal of 5′-terminal residues from the messengers for, as already pointed out, the cell fractions used in this work were devoid of 5′-exonuclease activity.

Summary.—Synthetic oligonucleotides of the type ApApApApApCpAp... pApApA (A_5CA_n) and ApApApApCpAp...pApApA (A_4CA_n) have an ApApA triplet at the 5′-end, followed by the asparagine codon pApApC in the A_5CA_n series, or by the threonine codon pApCpA in the A_4CA_n series. These are followed in both series by a number of pApApA (lysine) codons. In a system of purified *E. coli* ribosomes and *L. arabinosus* supernatant, of low nuclease content, A_5CA_n oligonucleotides directed mainly the synthesis of lysine oligopeptides with NH_2-terminal asparagine, whereas A_4CA_n polymers directed predominantly the synthesis of lysine oligopeptides with NH_2-terminal threonine. The initial ApApA triplet in these polymers was thus infrequently read. Together with earlier work[1] these results provide conclusive evidence for the 5′ → 3′ polarity of messenger translation. They also show that the above oligonucleotides are not read randomly by the cell-free system.

The authors wish to thank Mr. Horace Lozina for invaluable help with the preparation of tRNA and of ribosomal and supernatant fractions. Their thanks are also due to Miss Maria Pinney for able technical assistance.

* Aided by grants AM-01845, AM-08953, and FR-05399 from the National Institutes of Health, U.S. Public Health Service, and E. I. du Pont de Nemours and Company, Inc.

† Postdoctoral fellow of the National Institutes of Health, U.S. Public Health Service.

‡ International postdoctoral fellow of the National Institutes of Health, U.S. Public Health Service. Permanent address: Instituto Marañón, Centro de Investigationes Biológicas, C.S.I.C., Madrid, Spain.

§ Postdoctoral fellow of the National Institutes of Health, U.S. Public Health Service (to August 31, 1965).

[1] Salas, M., M. A. Smith, W. M. Stanley, Jr., A. J. Wahba, and S. Ochoa, *J. Biol. Chem.*, **240**, 3988 (1965).

[2] Shorthand writing of polynucleotides and abbreviations for nucleotides, amino acid residues in polypeptide chains, etc., are as recommended by *J. Biol. Chem.* and previously used (ref. 1).

[3] See Khorana, H. G., *Federation Proc.*, in press.

[4] Fiers, W., and H. G. Khorana, *J. Biol. Chem.*, **238**, 2789 (1963).

[5] Rushizky, G. W., C. A. Knight, and H. A. Sober, *J. Biol. Chem.*, **236**, 2732 (1961).

[6] Staehelin, M., *Biochim. Biophys. Acta*, **49**, 11 (1961).

[7] Thach, R. E., and P. Doty, *Science*, **147**, 1310 (1965).

[8] Folk, J. E., R. C. Brannberg, and J. A. Gladner, *Biochim. Biophys. Acta*, **47**, 595 (1961).

[9] Folk, J. E., and J. A. Gladner, *J. Biol. Chem.*, **231**, 379 (1958).

[10] Terzaghi, E., Y. Okada, G. Streisinger, A. Tsugita, M. Inouye, and J. Emrich, *Science*, **150**, 387 (1965).

[11] Thach, R. E., M. A. Cecere, T. A. Sundaranjan, and P. Doty, these Proceedings, **54**, 1167 (1965).

[12] Nirenberg, M. W., and P. Leder, *Science*, **145**, 1399 (1964).

[13] Matthaei, J. H., *Naturwissenschaften*, in press.

Reprinted from the Proceedings of the National Academy of Sciences
Vol. 55, No. 1, pp. 155–161. January, 1966.

IN VITRO PROTEIN SYNTHESIS: CHAIN INITIATION*

By Robert E. Webster,† Dean L. Engelhardt, and Norton D. Zinder

THE ROCKEFELLER UNIVERSITY

Communicated by E. L. Tatum, November 22, 1965

Nonsense mutations, when not suppressed, result in the premature termination of growing protein chains.[1]   In a previous publication[2] we described the appearance of a suppressible protein fragment when RNA from a phage mutant was added to protein-synthesizing extracts of *Escherichia coli*.   The fragment was thought to be the amino terminal portion of the phage coat protein.

In this communication, we shall present evidence that this fragment is indeed derived from the amino terminal portion of the coat protein.   In addition, we shall show that, although protein isolated from phage particles has alanine with a free amino group at its amino terminus,[3] both the fragment and the whole coat protein molecules when synthesized *in vitro* have masked amino groups.   The masking group is N-formylmethionine.   A similar finding is reported by Adams and Capecchi.[4]

Materials and Methods.—Bacteria and phage: S26, a nonsuppressing (Su−) strain of *E. coli* K12;[5] f2, wild-type phage; sus4A, a mutant of f2 with a nonsense mutation in the gene specifying the coat protein.[6]

In vitro incorporation: The S-30 system described by Schwartz[7] was employed, but 0.03 M NH_4^+ was used in place of K^+.   When alanine was to be incorporated, 10 mM creatine phosphate and 30 μg/ml of creatine phosphate kinase was added instead of phosphoenolpyruvate and pyruvate kinase.   Uniformly C^{14}- and H^3-labeled L-amino acids were obtained from New England Nuclear. H^3 L-phenylalanine was also obtained from Schwarz BioResearch.   The specific activities used in all calculations were those specified by the suppliers.   The concentration of radioactive label in the reaction mixture was approximately $10^{-5} M$.   The amount of phage RNA added was in the range of 150–300 μg/ml of reaction mixture. Approximately 10–15 lysine-C[14] molecules were incorporated into TCA-insoluble material per molecule of phage RNA added.

Isolation of the "coat fragment": The fragment was isolated from the reaction mixture by gel-filtration.[2] When necessary, it was further purified by electrophoresis on Whatman 3MM paper under cooled varsol at 20 v/cm for 4 hr at pH 1.9.[6] The fragment was located using a Packard model 7200 radiochromatogram scanner and was eluted from the paper with hot water. Further purification of the fragment containing methionine was accomplished, using a Sephadex G10 column at pH 2.5 (8.7 ml of acetic acid and 2.5 ml formic acid/liter of water). Molecular weight determinations were made by gel-filtration through Sephadex G-10 and Biogel P-2 in 0.05 M phosphate buffer at pH 6.8. Size estimates were based on the calibration of the gels which was supplied by the manufacturer.

Electrophoretic identification of the coat fragment: Electrophoresis on cellulose acetate strips (5 × 20 cm Seprapfore III) was performed at pH 1.9 (87 ml of acetic acid and 25 ml formic acid/liter of water), at pH 5.0 (0.03 M potassium acetate), at pH 6.5 (0.05 M potassium phosphate), and at pH 10 (0.03 M glycine). The field strength was 11.5 v/cm. Following electrophoresis for 1 hr, strips were dried by blotting and cut into 0.5-cm segments. Each segment was dissolved in 10 ml of Bray's solution (100 gm naphthalene, 7 gm PPO, and 0.05 gm POPOP/liter of di-ethylene oxide) and counted in a Nuclear-Chicago model 6804 scintillation counter.

Unmasking of N-terminal group: The N-terminal-formyl group of the chymotryptic "tetra-peptide" (D) and the "coat fragment" was removed by treatment at room temperature with 1 N HCl in methanol.[8] After treatment, the mixture was neutralized with a concentrated solution of ammonium bicarbonate and dried by lyophilization.

Enzymic digestion and product analysis: Fingerprinting and radioautography of chymotryptic digests of coat protein and *in vitro* product, as well as counting of carbon and tritium eluted from fingerprint spots, was performed as previously described.[2] Pronase (K. and K. Laboratories) digestion of the "coat fragment" was carried out for 12 hr in 1% ammonium bicarbonate. The products were identified electrophoretically at pH 5.0 (0.03 M potassium acetate). Marker C[14]-labeled N-formylmethionine and H[3]-labeled N-formylalanine were prepared by the method of Waley and Watson[9] and purified by electrophoresis on Whatman 3MM paper at pH 1.9.

Results.—The N-terminal fragment: The sequence of the N-terminal portion of the coat protein of f2 is NH_2ala-ser-aspNH_2-phe-thr-gluNH_2-phe-val....[3] The tetrapeptide ala-ser-aspNH_2-phe and the tripeptide thr-gluNH_2-phe are released from coat protein by chymotryptic digestion (peptides *B* and *A*, respectively, in Fig. 1 of Engelhardt *et al.*[2]). When the nonsense mutation sus4A is suppressed by the bacterial suppressor gene Su-1, a serine residue is substituted for the glut-amine residue in the tripeptide (*A'*). These three chymotryptic peptides can be separated and identified in radioautograms of fingerprints of digests of coat protein from purified phage (*in vivo* protein). There is only one other soluble phenyl-alanine-containing chymotryptic peptide, and it is only slowly released during digestion.

The major product of *in vitro* protein synthesis stimulated by f2 RNA is coat protein.[10] Fingerprints of chymotryptic digests of *in vitro* product would be expected to show peptides homologous with those of *in vivo* protein. However, of the two major spots seen (Fig. 1), one can be identified as the tripeptide (*A*) while the other is a new peptide, *D*, which is uncharged at pH 1.9 and has no *in vivo* homologue. The tetrapeptide, *B*, is not present at its expected position, slightly below the tripeptide. It was surprising to find this peptide missing since, hitherto, a homologue for each peptide derived from *in vivo* protein was found in the digests of *in vitro* product. Peptide *D* was therefore considered likely to be a modified form of the tetrapeptide. Since the tetrapeptide is the N-terminal peptide, its lack of charge at pH 1.9 could be accounted for if its N-terminal amino group were covered.

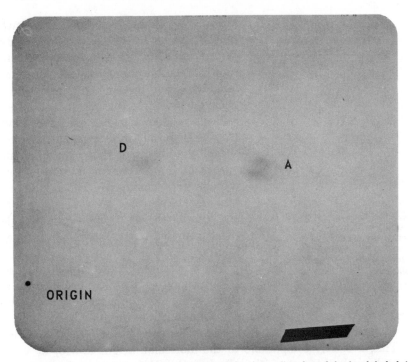

FIG. 1.—Radioautogram of the chymotryptic peptides from C¹⁴-phenylalanine-labeled *in vitro* product stimulated by f2 RNA.   *D* is the "modified tetrapeptide" and *A* is the tripeptide.   First-dimension electrophoresis pH 1.9; second-dimension chromatography in butyl acetate.

In order to study in detail the N-terminal portion of the *in vitro* product, advantage was taken of the fact that the nonsense mutation in phage sus4A is in the codon specifying the sixth amino acid from the amino terminus.   RNA from this mutant in Su- extracts stimulates the formation of a suppressible fragment[2] which should be the N-terminal portion of the coat protein.   The fragment has the same electrophoretic mobility as peptide *D* at pH 1.9, and chymotryptic digestion of the fragment yields material that cochromatographs with peptide *D*.[2]   The fragment should therefore be R-ala-ser-aspNH₂-phe-thr.

The following experiments on the composition and size of the fragment support this hypothesis.   To determine the amino acid content of the fragment, different C¹⁴ amino acids were added one at a time to Su- extracts with RNA from sus4A. To increase the amount of fragment, the extracts were supplemented with 100 μg of Su- sRNA per ml.   A standard for locating and analyzing the fragment was provided by adding simultaneously H³-phenylalanine to each extract.   Figure 2 shows the elution profile of the product made in the presence of C¹⁴-valine and H³-phenylalanine.   The coat fragment, defined by the H³ in the 185th to 193rd ml of effluent appears not to contain valine.   The material in these tubes was pooled and the solvent was evaporated.   An electropherogram at pH 1.9 of the residue is shown in Figure 3*a;* there is less than 0.25 μμmoles of valine for each μμmole of phenylalanine.   It is concluded that the fragment does not contain valine.   An electropherogram (Fig. 3*b*) of fragment prepared in the presence of C¹⁴-threonine and H³-phenylalanine gave a different pattern; phenylalanine and threonine are

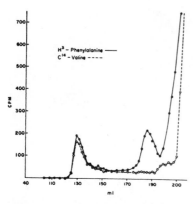

FIG. 2.—Gel-filtration of acetic acid-soluble products of an *in vitro* synthesizing system. Sus4A RNA in Su- extract was used. The radioactive amino acids added were C¹⁴-valine and H³-phenylalanine. The "coat fragment" is in the 185th to 193rd ml of effluent.

present in almost equimolar concentration (phenylalanine/threonine = 0.95). By repeated use of this procedure, the fragment was shown to contain one molecule of alanine, serine, asparagine, and threonine for each molecule of phenylalanine. It was shown not to contain lysine, arginine, histidine, leucine, or valine. [At the time that these experiments were initiated, the details of the composition and sequence of the N-terminal portion of the coat protein were unknown. The results of these experiments provided a valuable clue for placing in order the six chymotryptic peptides derived from the large N-terminal tryptic peptide.]

The size of the fragment was measured by gel-filtration (see *Methods*), using bovine serum albumin and a synthetic tripeptide (phe-ser-thr) as reference markers. Figure 4 shows the elution profile from Sephadex G-10. The results obtained from gel-filtration give a molecular weight of 600–700 for the fragment. This is closely comparable to the molecular weight (>540) of a masked pentapeptide with the composition R-ala-ser-aspNH₂-phe-thr. In a subsequent publication,[11] we will present evidence that the sequence of the fragment is as written above. These results on the size and composition of the fragment together with the fact that production of the peptide is suppressible support the hypothesis that the fragment is indeed the N-terminal portion of the coat protein. Therefore, we conclude that synthesis of the coat protein in Su- extracts with mutant RNA proceeds from the amino terminal end up to the position specified by the nonsense mutation.

Masking group: Characterization of the soluble N-terminal fragment of the coat protein permitted further investigation of the nature of the masking group. The formyl group is one such masking group and is unique among acyl masking groups in that it can be removed by mild acid hydrolysis.[12] Removal of a formyl

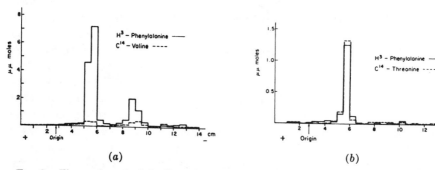

(a)   (b)

FIG. 3.—Electrophoresis of the "coat fragment" on cellulose acetate at pH 1.9. The fragment is at the position marked 5–6 cm. (a) The pattern when C¹⁴-valine, H³-phenylalanine had been added to the extracts; (b) the pattern when C¹⁴-threonine, H³-phenylalanine had been added to the extracts.

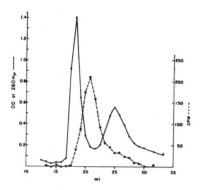

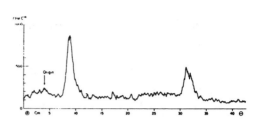

FIG. 4.—Gel-filtration of purified "coat fragment" on Sephadex G-10 for size determination. The fragment is labeled with C[14]-phenylalanine. Bovine serum albumin and a tripeptide (phe-ser-thr) are present as reference markers. The buffer used was 0.05 *M* sodium phosphate pH 6.8.

FIG. 5.—Paper electrophoresis of partially deformylated "coat fragment" at pH 1.9. The fragment was labeled with C[14]-alanine and H[3]-phenylalanine and purified by gel-filtration and paper electrophoresis prior to mild acid hydrolysis. After electrophoresis, the C[14] pattern was obtained using a Packard radiochromatogram scanner. H[3] was counted following elution with hot water.

group from the fragment should be revealed by a more electropositive mobility at pH 1.9. The fragment was labeled with C[14]-alanine and H[3]-phenylalanine, purified by gel-filtration and paper electrophoresis, and treated with 1 *N* HCl in methanol[9] for 1.5 hr at room temperature. After neutralization with NH_4HCO_3, the solvent was evaporated and the residue was dissolved and subjected to paper electrophoresis at pH 1.9. Figure 5 shows that approximately half of the material became positively charged: the amino group had been unmasked. The positive charge did not result from hydrolysis of any of the peptide bonds, since the C[14]/H[3] ratios are the same for the formylated and the deformylated fragments.

Marcker and Sanger[13] have isolated N-formylmethionyl-sRNA from *E. coli* and also found that methionyl sRNA can be formylated in cell-free extracts. Adams and Capecchi[4] present evidence for the incorporation of a formyl group into phage coat protein via this N-formylmethionyl-sRNA. This suggested that the masking group on the coat fragment was N-formylmethionine. Mutant RNA was added to Su- extracts containing C[14]-methionine and H[3]-phenylalanine and the products separated by gel-filtration (Sephadex G-25). At the position characteristic of the fragment, a large amount of positively charged C[14]-labeled material was found. The fragment was separated from this material (assumed to be S-adenosylmethionine) by paper electrophoresis at pH 1.9. Formylmethionine, also known to be synthesized by the extract, has an electrophoretic mobility at pH 1.9, similar to that of the fragment. Therefore, to make certain that the methionine was in the fragment, further analysis was by gel-filtration. It can be seen (Fig. 6) that methionine and phenylalanine are both in the fragment. Had any formylmethionine been present, it would have been at the position of the reference peptide. In addition, when the purified fragment was subjected to electrophoresis on cellulose acetate at pH 1.9, 5.0, and 10.0, methionine and phenylalanine were found in equimolar ratio.

In an attempt to release free formylmethionine, the fragment was labeled with C[14]-methionine and H[3]-alanine, purified and digested with pronase. The digestion

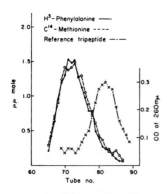

FIG. 6.—Gel-filtration of purified "coat fragment" on Sephadex G-10 at pH 2.5. The fragment is labeled with C^{14}-methionine and H^3-phenylalanine. The tripeptide phe-ser-thr is present as a reference marker.

was subjected to electrophoresis on cellulose acetate at pH 5.0, a pH at which free amino acids, formylalanine, and formylmethionine are all separable. Neither isotopic label was found at the position corresponding to formylalanine, but a small (5–10%) C^{14} (methionine) peak containing no H^3 (alanine) was found at the N-formyl(methionine) position. The majority of the product, however, was composed of free amino acids and incompletely digested fragments that had retained their formyl groups. Further digestion was not profitable because of the deacylase activity of the pronase preparation.

It is probable that the chymotryptic peptide D (Fig. 1) also contains formylmethionine when derived from complete protein chains, as well as from the fragment. Complete protein chains were synthesized using wild-type RNA in the presence of C^{14}-methionine and H^3-phenylalanine, and were isolated by gel-filtration, digested with chymotrypsin, and fingerprinted in the usual manner. Radioautograms revealed a C^{14} (methionine) spot in the position of peptide D, containing C^{14} and H^3 in an equimolar ratio. Treatment of the chymotryptic digest with 1 N HCl in methanol prior to fingerprinting and radioautography yields a new C^{14} and H^3 peptide, D', at a position expected for neutral peptides. The formyl group had been removed, probably releasing the pentapeptide meth-ala-ser-aspNH₂-phe.

Summary and Conclusions.—In extracts of *E. coli*, RNA from the bacteriophage can direct the synthesis of whole phage coat protein molecules. RNA from phage containing a nonsense mutation in the gene specifying the coat protein gives rise instead to a peptide fragment. This fragment has been shown to be the aminoterminal portion of the coat protein, prematurely terminated in its growth at the position specified by the nonsense mutation.

As synthesized in our extracts, both the fragment and the complete protein have the amino group of their N-terminal alanine residue covered by N-formylmethionine. Since this alanine residue has a free amino group when obtained from protein of phage particles, our extracts must be deficient in a way that allows the N-formylmethionine to be retained on protein. Thus, the deficiency of these extracts may have revealed a fundamental principle of protein synthesis—initiation of translation at a unique nucleotide sequence.

Although synthetic polynucleotides of known and random sequence can all stimulate protein synthesis in extracts, it would be advantageous for natural messages such as phage RNA to have a nucleotide sequence that specifies the beginning of protein chains. It would guarantee that the message starts to be read at the right position and thereafter is read in phase.

Several findings, combined with those described above, indicate that there is a unique nucleotide sequence that specifies the amino-terminal portion of all *coli* proteins. (1) Messenger translation proceeds in a $5' \rightarrow 3'$ direction along a polynucleotide chain[14] and most RNA's synthesized using *E. coli* DNA as a template for RNA polymerase have the same $5'$ nucleotide.[15] (2) A particular methionine sRNA, upon which methionine can be formylated, has been isolated from uninfected *E. coli*.[13] (3) Waller[16, 17] has shown that many *E. coli* proteins have either methionine, alanine, or serine as their N-terminal amino acids.   Note that these amino acids are precisely the ones found in the N-terminal peptide of the phage RNA stimulated products.   Perhaps after synthesis *in vivo*, the *coli* proteins are deacylated and amino acids removed by specific amino-peptidases, just as the N-formylmethionine must have been removed from the phage coat protein. During or after deacylation how many, if any, of the amino acids are removed could depend on the proximal amino acids in and/or the tertiary structure of the different proteins.

The start signal, implied by the data in this and the accompanying paper,[4] specifies at a minimum N-formylmethionine and perhaps even N-formyl-methionyl-alanyl-serine.   Its importance lies not only in the fact that there is a unique series of nucleotides meaning "start here," but also in the fact that these nucleotides lead to the incorporation of an amino acid with a blocked amino group. This kind of a start signal has numerous consequences.   It would impose a direction on protein synthesis.   It would preclude the coupling of polypeptides specified by a polycistronic message, regardless of the nature of "stop" codons.   Similarly, it would preclude coupling of polypeptides when nonsense codons, assumed to be homologous to stop codons, are suppressed.   It would explain why such nonsense codons, when not suppressed, lead only to the production of an N-terminal fragment, since peptide synthesis can not restart.   It would predict the existence of another, perhaps suppressible, class of nonsense mutations—mutations to the N-formylmethionine codon in the middle of a gene.   These mutations would probably result in the production of two peptide fragments.   By leading to polypeptide chains that may require trimming prior to being able to function, it would offer a new dimension to the control, in time and space, of protein function.

* Supported in part by a grant from the National Science Foundation.

† National Science Foundation postdoctoral fellow.

[1] Sarabhai, A. S., A. D. Stretton, S. Brenner, and A. Bolle, *Nature*, **201**, 13 (1964).

[2] Engelhardt, D. L., R. E. Webster, R. Wilhelm, and N. D. Zinder, these PROCEEDINGS, **54**, 1791 (1965).

[3] Konigsberg, R., G. Notani, and N. D. Zinder, in preparation.

[4] Adams, J., and M. R. Capecchi, these PROCEEDINGS, **55**, 147 (1966).

[5] Weigert, M. G., and A. Garen, *J. Mol. Biol.*, **12**, 448 (1965).

[6] Notani, G. W., D. L. Engelhardt, W. Konigsberg, and N. D. Zinder, *J. Mol. Biol.*, **12**, 439 (1965).

[7] Schwartz, J. H., these PROCEEDINGS, **53**, 1133 (1965).

[8] Waley, S. G., *Chemistry and Industry*, 107 (1953).

[9] Waley, S. G., and J. Watson, *Biochem. J.*, **57**, 529 (1954).

[10] Nathans, D., G. Notani, J. H. Schwartz, and N. D. Zinder, these PROCEEDINGS, **48**, 1424 (1962).

[11] Engelhardt, D. L., R. E. Webster, and N. D. Zinder, in preparation.

[12] Sheehan, J. C., and Ding-Djung H. Yang, *J. Am. Chem. Soc.*, **80**, 1154 (1958).

[13] Marcker, K., and F. Sanger, *J. Mol. Biol.*, **8**, 835 (1965).

[14] Thach, R. E., M. A. Cecera, T. A. Sundararajan, and P. Doty, these PROCEEDINGS, **54**, 1167 (1965).

[15] Maitra, U., and J. Hurwitz, these PROCEEDINGS, **54**, 815 (1965).

[16] Waller, J. P., *J. Mol. Biol.*, **7**, 483 (1963).

[17] *Ibid.*, **10**, 319 (1964).

TRANSLATION OF THE GENETIC MESSAGE, IV. UAA AS A CHAIN TERMINATION CODON*

By Jerold A. Last,† Wendell M. Stanley, Jr.,‡ Margarita Salas,§ Merrill B. Hille,** Albert J. Wahba, and Severo Ochoa

DEPARTMENT OF BIOCHEMISTRY, NEW YORK UNIVERSITY SCHOOL OF MEDICINE, NEW YORK, NEW YORK

Communicated February 27, 1967

The discovery that certain mutations result in the production of unfinished, amino-terminal peptide fragments of the corresponding wild-type proteins suggested that "nonsense" codons may normally signal termination of polypeptide chain synthesis.[1-3] Moreover, the finding that these "amber" mutations are suppressible, whereby the resulting polypeptide contains serine (codon, UCG) in place of glutamine (CAG) or tryptophan (UGG),[4-6] led to the prediction[2, 3] that UAG is the chain terminator of "amber" mutants. The study of other nonsense ("ochre") mutations suggested further that UAA also functions as a chain termination codon.[3] These suggestions were in accord with the fact that no amino acids are coded by UAG or UAA.[7, 8] There are indications that UAA rather than UAG may be the codon normally concerned with chain termination.[9]

In vitro experiments with synthetic polynucleotides of random base sequence lent some support to the view that UAA is involved in chain termination. The polypeptides synthesized under the direction of U- and A-containing copolymers or natural messengers consist largely of free, i.e., released peptide chains, whereas the peptide chains formed with polynucleotides which do not contain U and A residues are attached to tRNA.[10-12]

In order to determine unambiguously whether UAA is a chain-termination codon, we have studied the *in vitro* translation of a series of oligonucleotides having, along with the chain-initiating formylmethionine codon (AUG) and lysine codons (AAA), leucine (UUA), phenylalanine (UUU), or "ochre" (UAA) codons in specified sequences as follows: (a) AUGAAAAAAAAA...AAA (AUGA$_n$); (b) AUGUAA-AAAAAA...AAA (AUGUA$_n$); (c) AUGUUAAAAAAA...AAA (AUGU$_2$A$_n$); (d) AUGUUUAAAAAA...AAA (AUGU$_3$A$_n$); (e) AUGUUUUAAAAA...AAA (AUGU$_4$A$_n$).

The (a) polymers promoted the incorporation into acid-insoluble products of methionine and lysine; the (c) polymers, that of methionine, leucine, and lysine; and the (d) polymers, that of methionine, phenylalanine, and lysine. On the other hand, the (b) and (e) polymers promoted the incorporation of only small amounts of lysine, with little or no incorporation of methionine or phenylalanine. The inference that the (e) oligonucleotides directed the synthesis and release of *acid-soluble* formylmethionyl-phenylalanine was proved correct by isolation of the dipeptide. This work provides conclusive proof that UAA is a chain-termination codon. It also provides a suitable system for study of the mechanism of chain termination.

Materials and Methods.—These were as in previous work[13, 14] unless otherwise noted.

Amino acid incorporation: The low-nuclease system consisting of purified *Escherichia coli* Q13 ribosomes and *Lactobacillus arabinosus* supernatant,[15] supplemented with initiation factors,[13, 16] was used throughout. In experiment 1 of Table 1 the samples contained the following components in a final volume of 0.125 ml: Tris-HCl buffer, pH 7.8, 60 mM; ammonium chloride, 50 mM;

2-mercaptoethanol, 16 mM; magnesium acetate, 14 mM; ATP, 1.2 mM; GTP, 0.3 mM; phosphocreatine, 18 mM; creatine kinase, 9 μg; *E. coli* W tRNA, 0.60 mg; purified *E. coli* Q13 ribosomes, 7 A_{260} units; *L. arabinosus* supernatant, 0.2 mg of protein; N^{10}-formyltetrahydrofolic acid (FTHF), 8 mM; initiation factors (F_1 and F_2), 6 and 21 μg of protein, respectively; 20 amino acids (one of them with C^{14} label), each 0.2 mM; without or with oligonucleotide messenger, 15–20 μg. The specific radioactivities (μc/μmole) of the labeled amino acids were: lysine, 2; methionine, 20; leucine, 22; and phenylalanine, 40. The composition of the samples in experiment 2 of Table 1 was similar except that only three amino acids, namely, lysine (0.2 mM), methionine (0.02 mM), and phenylalanine (0.02 mM) were present, one of them having C^{14} label. Their specific radioactivities (μc/μmole) were: lysine, 10; methionine, 186; and phenylalanine, 176. After incubation at 37° the reaction was terminated by addition of KOH (final concentration, 0.5 M). The mixtures were kept at 37° for 3 hr, followed by neutralization, and the acid-insoluble radioactivity was determined as previously described.[16]

Polynucleotides: The methods used in this laboratory for the preparation of various kinds of oligonucleotides of specified base sequence have been described.[17] The preparation of the polymers used in the present work is described below.

AUGA$_n$ polynucleotides were prepared[17] with ADP and polynucleotide phosphorylase, using ApUpG[18] (AUG) as primer. For the other polymers, the series of primers ApUpGpU (AUGU), ApUpGpUpU (AUGU$_2$), ApUpGpUpUpU (AUGU$_3$), and ApUpGpUpUpU (AUGU$_4$) was prepared by limited addition of uridylic acid residues from UDP to ApUpG primer with polynucleotide phosphorylase and chromatographic isolation of the individual oligonucleotides. Adenylic acid residues were then added to each of these primers, by incubation with ADP and polynucleotide phosphorylase. For characterization purposes the polymers were prepared with H^3-labeled guanylic acid residues. In the following description this label will be indicated by an asterisk.

ApUpG* was prepared from ApU (lot no. B 3503, Gallard-Schlesinger) as described previously.[17] ApUpG*pU, ApUpG*pUpU, ApUpG*pUpUpU, and ApUpG*pUpUpUpU were synthesized by the addition of uridylic acid residues to ApUpG* under the following conditions. The reaction mixture (pH 8.2) contained the following components (in μmoles/ml unless otherwise indicated) in a final volume of 4.0 ml. ApUpG*, 7.3; UDP (lot no. 1116, Pabst), 40; Tris-HCl, 150; magnesium acetate, 10; EDTA, 1; sodium chloride, 500; polynucleotide phosphorylase, 300 μg of protein/ml. After incubation for 20 min at 30°, the solution was held at 100° for 5 min, cooled, diluted 50-fold, and applied to a column (1.8 $\times$ 39 cm) of DEAE-cellulose (lot no. 1675, 1 mEq/gm, Brown). Oligonucleotides of the form ApUpG* with 1, 2, 3, etc. residues of uridylic acid added to the 3'-end were separated at 25° by gradient elution with ammonium bicarbonate (0.01 M ammonium bicarbonate, pH 8.6, in a 2-liter mixer; 0.5 M ammonium bicarbonate, pH 8.6, in a reservoir) at 1 ml/min. In order to remove water and salt, the oligonucleotides were recovered by flash evaporation and lyophilization. The yields were, in moles of oligonucleotide/mole input ApUpG*: ApUpG*, 0.142; ApUpG*pU, 0.295; ApUpG*pUpU, 0.166; ApUpG*pUpUpU, 0.119; and ApUpG*pUpUpUpU, 0.072. The structure and purity of each oligonucleotide was confirmed by paper chromatography in two solvents (solvent 1, 1.0 M ammonium acetate, pH 7.5/95% ethanol, 6/4, v/v; solvent 2, 40 gm ammonium sulfate plus 100 ml of 0.1 M potassium phosphate, pH 7.0), by degradation with RNase T_1 followed by identification of ApUpG*p plus the expected length of uridylic acid residues (i.e., ApUpG*p plus UpUpU were recovered from ApUpG*pUpUpU), and by the determination of the ratio of uridine to uridylic acid following complete alkaline hydrolysis.

Adenylic acid residues were added to the 3'-ends of each of the purified oligonucleotide primers, and the resulting polymers were fractionated according to chain length and recovered as previously described.[17, 19] The structure was confirmed by the identification of the low-molecular-weight products arising from the degradation of each polymer with RNase T_1 and by pancreatic RNase. For example, ApUpG*pUpU(pA)$_n$ gave rise to ApUpG*p following RNase T_1 digestion, and to ApUp, G*pUp, and Up, in the molar ratio 1/1/1 following digestion with pancreatic RNase.

The polynucleotide phosphorylase was a preparation from *Micrococcus lysodeikticus* with an absolute requirement for primer oligonucleotides. The enzyme catalyzed the polymerization of 6.5 μmoles of ADP/min/mg protein at 37° under the following conditions (reagents in μmoles/ml):

ADP, 40; ApApA, 1; sodium chloride, 500; magnesium acetate, 10; EDTA, 1; and Tris-HCl buffer, pH 8.2, 150.

Isolation and characterization of (H^3)formyl-(C^{14})methionyl-(C^{12})phenylalanine and (H^3)formyl-(C^{12})methionyl-(C^{14})phenylalanine: The incubation mixtures were as described under *Amino Acid Incorporation* (expt. 1 of Table 1) with the following exceptions: H^3-FTFH (formate-labeled, 2000 $\mu c/\mu$mole), 0.022 mM; either C^{14}-methionine (186 $\mu c/\mu$mole) or C^{14}-phenylalanine (352 $\mu c/\mu$mole), 0.02 mM; nonlabeled amino acids, either 19 amino acids, each 0.2 mM, or lysine (0.2 mM) and phenylalanine or methionine (0.02 mM); without or with $AUGU_4A_{\overline{10}}$, 15–20 μg. Pancreatic DNase (electrophoretically purified, Worthington), 25 μg, was also added to the samples to prevent any synthesis of endogenous messenger RNA.

Prior to adding the ribosomes, the samples were incubated for 5 min to allow time for transfer of H^3-formate from H^3-FTFH to met $\sim$ tRNA$_F$.[20] The ribosomes were then added and the incubation was continued for 15 min. The short incubation was chosen to minimize enzymatic removal of labeled formyl residues from the peptides synthesized.[21] After incubation, the samples were chilled in ice and treated with 0.127 ml of 6% perchloric acid. The precipitate was removed by centrifugation and washed three times with 30-μl portions of ice-cold 3% perchloric acid. The combined supernatant and washings were neutralized with 0.168 ml of 1.0 N KOH. The potassium perchlorate precipitate was removed by centrifugation and washed repeatedly with 50-μl portions of cold water until the washings were free of radioactivity. The supernatant and the washings were combined and the pH of the solution was adjusted to 7.8, with Tris-HCl buffer, prior to chromatography on a Dowex-1 (Cl$^-$) column (0.6 $\times$ 5 cm). The column was washed with 10 ml of water, containing 1–2 mg of nonlabeled phenylalanine or methionine, and the formylated amino acids and peptides were then eluted with 8.0 ml of 0.5 N acetic acid adjusted to pH 2.7 with pyridine. This solution was passed through a Dowex-50 (H$^+$) column (0.6 $\times$ 20 cm). The formylated compounds were washed through with 8.0 ml of 0.001 N HCl. For separation of formylmet and formylmet-phe, the eluate was lyophilized, the residue taken up in 0.5 ml of water, and aliquots of the solution were subjected to high-voltage paper electrophoresis, along with markers of formylmet and formylmet-phe, as previously described,[14] except that the electrophoresis was run for 7 hr. For measurement of radioactivity after electrophoresis, the paper was cut into strips (1 cm long, 2.5 cm wide) which were placed in the bottom of scintillation vials. The strips were covered with solvent (4 gm of 2,5-diphenyloxazole (PPO) and 50 mg of p-bis [2-(5-phenyloxazolyl)]-benzene (POPOP) per liter of toluene) and the radioactivity was measured in a Packard Tri-Carb scintillation spectrometer. Under these conditions, the counting efficiency of the two isotopes on Whatman 3MM paper was about 29% for C^{14} and 0.9% for H^3, with 12% of the C^{14} counts appearing in the H^3 channel, and less than 0.1% of the H^3 counts in the C^{14} channel. The total amount of formylmet-phe calculated from the electrophoretic data was corrected for small aliquots of material withdrawn, during the processing of the reaction mixtures, for determination of the acid-soluble radioactivity. This correction was never greater than 6%.

Formylmet-phe was prepared by formylation of L-methionyl-L-phenylalanine.[22] L-methionyl-L-phenylalanine was obtained from the Mann Research Laboratories, Inc., New York.

Results and Discussion.—*Incorporation of amino acids into acid-insoluble products:* As shown in Table 1, oligonucleotides of the series $AUGA_n$, $AUGU_2A_n$, and $AUGU_3$-A_n promote the incorporation of lysine, along with smaller amounts of methionine $(AUGU_{\overline{13}})$, methionine and leucine $(AUGU_2A_{\overline{10}})$, and methionine and phenylalanine $(AUGU_3A_{\overline{10}})$. It may further be noted that the incorporation of methionine and leucine, or methionine and phenylalanine, promoted by poly $AUGU_2A_{\overline{10}}$ or $AUGU_3$-$A_{\overline{10}}$, respectively, is roughly equimolar. Moreover, there is negligible or no incorporation of phenylalanine with poly $AUGU_2A_{\overline{10}}$ and the same is true of leucine in the case of poly $AUGU_3A_{\overline{10}}$. This shows that these polymers are read in phase from the 5'-end.

In contrast to the above results, the incorporation of the various amino acids into acid-insoluble material is markedly diminished when oligonucleotides of the series

TABLE 1
POLYPEPTIDE SYNTHESIS WITH OLIGONUCLEOTIDE MESSENGERS OF SPECIFIED BASE SEQUENCE*

Expt. no.	Incubation time (min)	Messenger	Amino Acid Incorporation†			
			Lysine	Methionine	Leucine	Phenylalanine
1	40	None (blank)	81	43	24	18
		AUGA$_{\overline{13}}$	1261 (1521)	163 (152)	0	0
		AUGUA$_{\overline{11}}$	162 (142)	10 (10)	0	0
		AUGU$_2$A$_{\overline{10}}$	644 (563)	65 (58)	56 (51)	0
		AUGU$_3$A$_{\overline{10}}$	543 (425)	56 (47)	2	62 (50)
		AUGU$_4$A$_{\overline{10}}$	282 (153)	10 (10)	2	4 (9)
2	15	None (blank)	43	3	—	5
		AUGU$_3$A$_{\overline{10}}$	371	29	—	21

* Conditions as described under *Materials and Methods*. In expt. 2 the samples were preincubated for 5 min prior to starting the reaction by addition of the ribosomes.

† Values expressed in $\mu\mu$moles/sample. The first line for each expt. gives the blank values in the absence of added oligonucleotide. All others are net values, the blanks without polymer having been subtracted from the values with polymer. The net values given in parentheses are the combined averages of expt. 1 and three other experiments carried out at different times between August 1966 and February 1967. Duplicate samples were run in each experiment and the results averaged.

AUGU$_4$A$_n$ (AUGU$_4$A$_{\overline{10}}$), having the UAA triplet in the third position from the 5′-terminus, are used as messengers. Although there is some lysine incorporation, that of methionine and phenylalanine is very low. This incorporation is referable to slight contamination of poly AUGU$_4$A$_n$ with AUGU$_3$A$_n$. Table 1 also lists an experiment with poly AUGUA$_{\overline{11}}$, having the UAA triplet in the second position from the 5′-end. Some lysine but little if any methionine is incorporated.

Release of formylmethionyl-phenylalanine upon translation of AUGU$_4$A$_n$ polymers: In order to determine whether acid-soluble formylmet-phe is synthesized and released upon translation of the AUGU$_4$A$_n$ messengers, incubations with and without polymer were conducted with either H^3-FTHF and C^{14}-methionine or H^3-FTHF and C^{14}-phenylalanine. The nonlabeled amino acids were either 19 amino acids (no methionine or no phenylalanine) or lysine with either phenylalanine or methionine. After incubation, any labeled acid-insoluble products, including formylmet $\sim$

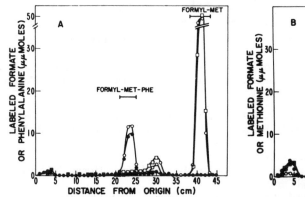
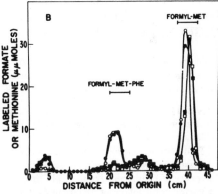

FIG. 1.—Electrophoretic patterns of labeled peptides synthesized with AUGU$_4$A$_{\overline{10}}$ oligonucleotide messenger. Aliquots corresponding to 10% of the sample were used for electrophoresis. The anode is to the right. The position of formylmet-phe and formylmet markers is indicated. (*A*) Incubation with H^3-FTHF and C^{14}-phenylalanine. (*B*) Incubation with H^3-FTHF and C^{14}-methionine. In this experiment the samples contained the remaining 19 C^{14}-amino acids. Two other experiments were carried out with similar results. *Squares*, blank samples (no oligonucleotide added); *circles*, samples with oligonucleotide added. *Open symbols s*(□, O), H^3 label; *solid symbols* (■, ●), C^{14} label.

TABLE 2

H³ AND C¹⁴ RADIOACTIVITY IN THE FORMYLMETHIONYL-PHENYLALANINE AREA OF THE
ELECTROPHEROGRAMS OF FIGURE 1*

Expt.	Radioactive label	Blank sample† (a)	Sample with AUGU₄A₁₀⁻ (b)	Polymer-promoted (b − a)
Fig. 1A	H³ (formate)	3.4	32.1	28.7
	C¹⁴ (phenylalanine)	2.5	26.2	23.7
Fig. 1B	H³ (formate)	4.8	32.6	27.8
	C¹⁴ (methionine)	7.3	34.2	26.9

* Values expressed as μμmoles of formate, phenylalanine, or methionine/sample.
† Sample with no oligonucleotide added.

tRNA$_F$, met $\sim$ tRNA$_M$, and phe $\sim$ tRNA, were removed by precipitation with perchloric acid and the supernatants worked up as described under *Materials and Methods*.

The electrophoretic patterns of the H³- and C¹⁴-labeled products (Fig. 1) show two main peaks. One of them is in the position of formylmet-phe, the other in the position of formylmet. The presence of formylmet would appear to reflect the occurrence of some deacylation of formylmet $\sim$ tRNA$_F$ during the incubation. It may be noted that the blank incubations, with no added oligonucleotide, show roughly the same amount of radioactivity in the position of formylmet but little or no radioactivity in the region of the dipeptide.

The H³ and C¹⁴ radioactivity under the formylmet-phe peak, expressed as μμmoles of product per incubation sample, is given in Table 2. Reference to experiment 2 of Table 1 shows that the formation of formylmet-phe with poly AUGU₄A$_{\overline{10}}$ is of the same order of magnitude as the incorporation of methionine and phenylalanine into acid-insoluble material with AUGU₃A$_{\overline{10}}$ messenger.

The above results indicate that the AUGU₄A$_n$ polymers are translated with the same efficiency as the others except for termination of chain growth and release once formylmet-phe is synthesized. It may be emphasized in this connection that formylmet-phe is not released as peptidyl $\sim$ tRNA (a compound that would be acid-insoluble) but as the free dipeptide. Thus, complete chain termination is achieved. The isolation of formylmet-phe in good yields, upon translation of the 5'-end sextet AUGUUU, also provides further proof for the triplet nature of the genetic code.[23]

We are indebted to Mr. Norton A. Elson for his help in the preparation and characterization of the oligonucleotides used here. Our thanks are also due to Miss Martha Miller and Mr. Horace Lozina for help in various phases of this work.

* Aided by grants AM-01845, AM-08953, and FR-05399 from the National Institutes of Health, U.S. Public Health Service, the Jane Coffin Childs Fund for Medical Research, and E. I. du Pont de Nemours and Company, Inc.

† Postdoctoral fellow of the American Cancer Society.

‡ Present address: Division of Biological Sciences, Department of Molecular and Cell Biology, University of California, Irvine, California.

§ Postdoctoral fellow of the Jane Coffin Childs Fund for Medical Research. Permanent address: Instituto Marañón, Centro de Investigaciones Biológicas, C.S.I.C., Madrid, Spain.

** Postdoctoral fellow of the National Institutes of Health, U.S. Public Health Service.

[1] Sarabhai, A. S., A. O. W. Stretton, S. Brenner, and A. Bolle, *Nature*, **201**, 13 (1964).

[2] Weigert, M. G., and A. Garen, *Nature*, **206**, 992 (1965).

[3] Brenner, S., A. O. W. Stretton, and S. Kaplan, *Nature*, **206**, 994 (1965).

[4] Weigert, M. G., and A. Garen, *J. Mol. Biol.*, **12**, 448 (1965).

[5] Stretton, A. O. W., and S. Brenner, *J. Mol. Biol.*, **12**, 456 (1965).

[6] Webster, R. E., D. L. Engelhardt, and N. D. Zinder, these Proceedings, **55,** 155 (1966).

[7] Nirenberg, M. W., P. Leder, M. Bernfield, R. Brimacombe, J. Trupin, F. Rottman, and C. O'Neal, these Proceedings, **53,** 1161 (1965).

[8] Söll, D., E. Ohtsuka, D. S. Jones, R. Lohrman, H. Hayatsu, S. Nishimura, and H. G. Khorana, these Proceedings, **54,** 1368 (1965).

[9] Garen, A., S. Garen, and R. C. Wilhelmi, *J. Mol. Biol.,* **14,** 167 (1965).

[10] Takanami, M., and Y. Yan, these Proceedings, **54,** 1450 (1965).

[11] Bretscher, M. S., H. M. Goodman, J. R. Menninger, and J. D. Smith, *J. Mol. Biol.,* **14,** 634 (1965).

[12] Ganoza, M. C., and T. Nanamoto, these Proceedings, **55,** 162 (1966).

[13] Salas, M., M. B. Hille, J. A. Last, A. J. Wahba, and S. Ochoa, these Proceedings, **57,** 387 (1967).

[14] Viñuela, E., M. Salas, and S. Ochoa, these Proceedings, **57,** 729 (1967).

[15] Salas, M., M. A. Smith, W. M. Stanley, Jr., A. J. Wahba, and S. Ochoa, *J. Biol. Chem.,* **240,** 3988 (1965).

[16] Stanley, W. M., Jr., M. Salas, A. J. Wahba, and S. Ochoa, these Proceedings, **56,** 290 (1966).

[17] Stanley, W. M., Jr., M. A. Smith, M. B. Hille, and J. A. Last, in *Cold Spring Harbor Symposia on Quantitative Biology,* vol. 31 (1967), in press.

[18] Shorthand writing of polynucleotides and most of the abbreviations used are standard. Other abbreviations are as follows: FTHF, formyltetrahydrofolic acid; tRNA, transfer RNA; met $\sim$ tRNA$_F$, the species of methionyl tRNA whose methionine residue can be formylated; met $\sim$ tRNA$_M$, the nonformylatable species; phe $\sim$ tRNA, phenylalanyl tRNA; formylmet, formylmethionine; formylmet-phe, formylmethionyl-phenylalanine.

[19] Stanley, W. M., Jr., in *Nucleic Acids,* a volume of *Methods in Enzymology,* ed. K. Moldave and L. Grossman (New York: Academic Press, 1967), in press.

[20] Clark, B. F. C., and K. A. Marcker, *Nature,* **211,** 378 (1966).

[21] Capecchi, M. R., these Proceedings, **55,** 1517 (1966).

[22] Sheehan, J. C., and D. M. Yang, *J. Am. Chem. Soc.,* **80,** 1154 (1958).

[23] Jones, D. S., S. Nishimura, and H. G. Khorana, *J. Mol. Biol.,* **16,** 454 (1966).

VII
Proteins Considered as Gene Products

VII

Introduction

The seemingly endless variety of phenotypic effects resulting from gene mutation is beginning to be understood in molecular terms. This understanding is being reached by tracing the effect of a single base-pair alteration in the DNA. Fortunately, there are a number of chemical reagents (discussed in Section IV) that are known to produce single base-pair alterations with a high frequency. Since most permutations of three bases code for some amino acid and a few code for no amino acid, we might predict that the most probable effect of a single base-pair change in the DNA would be the substitution of one amino acid for another in the protein; a single base-pair change might also result in no change in amino acid if the resulting triplet codes for the same amino acid; in the small number of cases where the resulting triplet does not code for any amino acid we might expect premature termination of the protein polypeptide chain. These three kinds of mutation are referred to as missense, sense and nonsense respectively. Yanofsky *et al.* (in collection) in studies of the A subunit of the tryptophan synthetase protein and gene have found a colinear relationship between the position of the missense mutation in the gene and the position of the amino acid alteration in the polypeptide chain. In an equally informative study Sarabhai *et al.*[404] found that the position of a nonsense mutation in the gene for the head protein of T_2 bacteriophage was related in linear fashion to the point of premature termination in the polypeptide chain of the bacteriophage head protein.

In certain cases the effects of missense and nonsense mutations like those observed by Yanofsky *et al.* and Sarabhai *et al.* can be suppressed by producing a second point mutation elsewhere on the chromosome. This brings us to the second subject of this section, suppression. Observations made in Benzer's laboratory were fundamental in bringing clarity to the subject of suppression at the molec-

ular level. Champe and Benzer (in collection, Section IV) observed that certain mutations in the r_{II} cistron of T_4 bacteriophage were ambivalent in the sense that the mutants could grow on one strain of *E. coli* but not on another strain. The growth inhibiting effect on the one *E. coli* strain could be suppressed either by mutation of the bacterium or by adding 5-fluorouracil (5-FU) during virus growth. Since bacterial mutation and 5-FU have parallel effects on the ambivalent viral mutants and since 5-FU is incorporated exclusively into the RNA, it seemed likely that the effect of the suppression was to produce some fault in translation of genetic information. A specific suppressor mutation might be expected to produce a general fault in translation which would tend to reduce to some degree the activity of most enzymes, but it could greatly increase the activity of an inactive enzyme in which the defect is due to a mutation of the appropriate kind. A large number of examples of missense suppression have been found and further analysis has supported the explanation for the phenomenon given here. In particular Carbon, Berg and Yanofsky,[420] and Gupta and Khorana (in collection) have shown that altered tRNAs are involved in different suppressor mutations of tryptophan synthetase. Two kinds of alteration in the tRNA could explain the observed effects. Either the tRNA accepts the wrong amino acid or it tends to pair with the wrong codon after accepting the right amino acid. As indicated in the papers, the former explanation probably applies to the case investigated by Gupta and Khorana (in collection) and the latter explanation probably applies to the case investigated by Carbon, Berg and Yanofsky.[420]

There appear to be three classes of nonsense suppressors depending upon which of the three existing nonsense triplets is being suppressed. Two of these are discussed in the paper by Brenner, Stretton and Kaplan (in collection; this reading should not be attempted until the second and third papers of Section IV have been read). The third is taken up in a more recent paper.[424, 428] The three nonsense triplets are UAG or amber, UAA or ochre, and UGA. Studies by Capecchi and

Gussin,[418] and Engelhardt, Webster, Wilhelm and Zinder[411] have demonstrated that altered tRNAs are the responsible agents in the suppression of the amber-associated nonsense triplet. Presumably one of the nonsense triplets is used for normal termination of the polypeptide chain, but no conclusive evidence has been produced on which triplet is used. Some of the biochemistry of polypeptide chain termination has been considered in Section VI. Nonsense triplets may be required for purposes other than the termination of a polypeptide chain. Special sequences of bases probably signal initiation and termination of transcription and special sequences of bases may also be required to serve as "spacers" on polycistronic messengers.

Translation level suppressors of a different type operate by modifying the reading of messenger RNA on the ribosomes.[429] Streptomycin binds to *E. coli* and other bacterial ribosomes in such a way that it can modify translation and thereby negate the otherwise lethal effects of some mutations. The paper by Davies, Gilbert and Gorini (in collection) considers such a case.

Genetic complementation is a more complex topic than suppression since it depends not only upon the type or position of the mutation but upon the secondary and tertiary structure of the gene-encoded protein. Two chromosomes defective in a given function are said to complement one another if the defect is remedied by putting the two chromosomes in the same cell. Two fundamentally different types of complementation must be distinguished. When the complementing chromosomes have their defects in different functional units or cistrons the complementation process is invariably successful. When the complementing chromosomes have their defects in the same cistrons the complementation process depends upon which mutant pairs are combined, and usually the mutant defects are only partially corrected by the complementation process. Various explanations have been put forth to explain this frequently observed phenomenon of intracistronic complementation. The working hypothesis used by Schlesinger and Levinthal (in collection) and Garen and Garen (in collection) is that intracistronic complementation can be observed for a protein which normally contains two or more identical subunits. When the mutant protein subunits from two defective subunits have defects of the appropriate kind, they can interact to produce a hybrid protein with some activity. Schlesinger and Levinthal (in collection) and Garen and Garen (in collection) provide parallel *in vitro* and *in vivo* observations on alkaline phosphatase mutants which conform to this hypothesis. Crick and Orgel[433] have given further consideration to why subunit interaction should lead to correction of the mutant defects. They speculate that the complementation correctable defects are probably the result of abnormal folding of the polypeptide chain. Effective association between appropriately chosen protein monomers is believed to stabilize the normal folded structure of the protein.

Recent results indicate that there may be additional types of intracistronic complementation. The pertinent complementation studies have been done mostly with mutants of β-galactosidase which normally occurs as a tetramer containing four identical monomers. It has been found that complementation can occur between genes having large complementary deletions.[435] It seems likely that the complementary fragments of complete polypeptide chains interact to form effective subunits that may or may not undergo conversion to multimers. In support of this notion it has been found that the defective enzyme containing a deletion of a certain peptide segment exists as a dimer rather than as the normally occurring tetramer. Complementation with a low molecular weight fragment containing all or a portion of the missing peptide segment produces active enzyme without necessarily producing the transition from dimer to tetramer. Physical-chemical data indicate that one complementing peptide fragment per dimer is sufficient to produce active enzyme.[436] If complementation between polypeptide fragments is common, there might be ways of producing the necessary N- and C-terminal peptide fragments other than by genetic deletions. Zipser and Perrin[431] have shown that complementation can take place on the ribosome between a nascent polypeptide chain and its soluble complement. Sufficiently rapid ribosomal complementation would provide a way of obtaining N-terminal fragments since the growing polypeptide chain could interact with complement when it reached the appropriate length rather than after normal termination. Another way of obtaining N-terminal peptide fragments would be by interjecting nonsense triplets at the appropriate point. C-terminal peptide fragments or virtual fragments might result from poor polypeptide folding. A poorly folded polypeptide might be snipped in two by protease action or merely unfolded enough to permit interaction with a complementing N-terminal fragment. There is no reason why intracistronic complementation involving polypeptide chain fragments should not occur for proteins which normally exist as monomers or multimers. It remains to be seen how common this type of complementation is.

Bibliography

COLINEARITY

404. A. S. Sarabhai, A. O. W. Stretton, S. Brenner and A. Bolle, (1964). Co–Linearity of the Gene with the Polypeptide Chain. Nature 201, 13.

405. T. E. Creighton and C. Yanofsky, (1966). Association of the α and β_2 Subunits of the Tryptophan Synthetase of E. coli. J. Biol. Chem. 241, 980.

406. C. Yanofsky, G. R. Drapeau, J. R. Guest and B. C. Carlton, (1967). Complete AA Amino Acid Sequence of the Tryptophan Synthetase A Protein (α Subunit) and its Colinear Relationship with the Genetic Map of the A Gene. Proc. Natl. Acad. Sci. U.S. 57, 296.

SUPPRESSION

407. C. Yanofsky and P. St. Lawerence, (1960). Gene Action. Ann. Rev. Microbiol. 14, 311.

408. S. Benzer and S. P. Champe, (1961). Ambivalent rII Mutants of Phage T_4. Proc. Natl. Acad. Sci. U.S. 47, 1025.

409. A. Garen and O. Siddiqi, (1962). Suppression of Mutations in the Alkaline Phosphatase Structural Cistron of E. coli. Proc. Natl. Acad. Sci. U.S. 48, 1121.

410. S. Brody and C. Yanofsky, (1964). Independent Action of Allele-Specific Suppressor Mutations. Science 145, 399.

411. D. L. Engelhardt, R. E. Webster, R. C. Wilhelm and N. D. Zinder, (1965). In Vitro Studies on the Mechanism of Suppression of a Nonsense Mutation. Proc. Natl. Acad. Sci. U.S. 54, 1791.

412. G. W. Notani, D. L. Engelhardt, W. Konigsberg and N. D. Zinder, (1965). Suppression of a Coat Protein Mutant of the Bacteriophage f2. J. Mol. Biol. 12, 439.

413. A. O. W. Stretton and S. Brenner, (1965). Molecular Consequences of the Amber Mutation and Its Suppression. J. Mol. Biol. 12, 456.

414. S. Brenner and J. R. Beckwith, (1965). Ochre Mutants, a New Class of Suppressible Nonsense Mutants. J. Mol. Biol. 13, 629.

415. S. Brenner and A. O. W. Stretton, (1965). Phase Shifting of Amber and Ochre Mutants. J. Mol. Biol. 13, 944.

416. E. R. Signer, J. R. Beckwith and S. Brenner, (1965). Mapping of Suppressor Loci in E. coli. J. Mol. Biol. 14, 153.

417. S. Kaplan, A. O. W. Stretton and S. Brenner, (1965). Amber Suppressors: Efficiency of Chain Propagation and Suppressor Specific Amino Acids. J. Mol. Biol. 14, 528.

418. M. R. Capecchi and G. N. Gussin, (1965). Suppression In Vitro: Identification of a Serine-sRNA as a "Nonsense" Suppressor. Science 149, 417.

419. M. G. Weigert, E. Lanka and A. Garen, (1965). Amino Acid Substitutions Resulting from Suppression of Nonsense Mutations II. Glutamine Insertion by the Su-2 Gene. Tyrosine Insertion by the Su-3 Gene. J. Mol. Biol. 14, 522.

420. J. Carbon, P. Berg and C. Yanofsky, (1966). Studies of Missense Suppression of the Tryptophan Synthetase A-Protein Mutant A-36. Proc. Natl. Acad. Sci. U.S. 56, 764.

421. E. Gallucci and A. Garen, (1966). Suppressor Genes for Nonsense Mutations II. The Su-4 and Su-5 Suppressor Genes of E. coli. J. Mol. Biol. 15, 193.

422. P. L. Bergquist and M. R. Capecchi, (1966). Fractionation of a Suppressor sRNA. J. Mol. Biol. 19, 202.

423. D. Apirion, (1966). Altered Ribosomes in a Suppressor Strain of E. coli. J. Mol. Biol. 16, 285.

424. S. Brenner, L. Barnett, E. R. Katz and F. H. C. Crick, (1967). UGA: A Third Nonsense Triplet in the Genetic Code. Nature 213, 449.

425. R. E. Webster, D. L. Engelhardt and N. D. Zinder, (1967). Amber Mutants and Chain Termination in Vivo. J. Mol. Biol. 29, 27.

426. D. L. Engelhardt, R. E. Webster and N. D. Zinder, (1967). Amber Mutants and Polarity in Vitro. J. Mol. Biol. 29, 45.

427. M. R. Capecchi, (1967). Polypeptide Chain Termination in Vitro: Isolation of a Release Factor. Proc. Natl. Acad. Sci. U.S. 58, 1144.

428. D. Zipser, (1967). UGA: A Third Class of Suppressible Polar Mutants. J. Mol. Biol. 29, 441.

429. L. Gorini, R. Rosset and R. A. Zimmerman, (1967). Phenotypic Masking and Streptomycin Dependence. Science **157**, 1314.

COMPLEMENTATION

430. S. Benzer, (1959). On the Topology of the Genetic Fine Structure. Proc. Natl. Acad. Sci. U.S. **45**, 1607.

431. D. Zipser and D. Perrin, (1963). Complementation on Ribosomes. Cold Spring Harbor Symp. Quant. Biol. **28**, 533.

432. (1963). Section on Complementation. Cold Spring Harbor Symp. Quant. Biol. **28**, 517–548.

433. F. H. C. Crick and L. E. Orgel, (1964). The Theory of Inter-allelic Complementation. J. Mol. Biol. **8**, 161.

434. E. Glassman, T. Shinoda, H. M. Moon and J. D. Karam, (1966). *In Vitro* Complementation Between Non-allelic Drosophila Mutants Deficient in Xanthine Dehydrogenase IV. Molecular Weights. J. Mol. Biol. **20**, 419.

435. A. Ullmann, F. Jacob and J. Monod, (1967). Characterization by *In Vitro* Complementation of a Peptide Corresponding to an Operator-proximal Segment of the β-gal Structural Gene of *E. coli*. J. Mol. Biol. **24**, 339.

436. J. K. DeVries and G. Zubay, (1968). To be published.

397

Colinearity of Gene and Polypeptide Chain

ON THE COLINEARITY OF GENE STRUCTURE AND PROTEIN STRUCTURE*

BY C. YANOFSKY, B. C. CARLTON,† J. R. GUEST,‡ D. R. HELINSKI,†
AND U. HENNING†

DEPARTMENT OF BIOLOGICAL SCIENCES, STANFORD UNIVERSITY

Communicated by Victor Twitty, December 18, 1963

The pioneering studies of Beadle and Tatum with *Neurospora crassa*[1] led to the concept that there is a 1:1 relationship between gene and enzyme. Subsequent studies on the structure of proteins[2] and genetic material[3] permitted a restatement of this relationship in molecular terms;[4] the linear sequence of nucleotides in a gene specifies the linear sequence of amino acids in a protein.

Several years ago studies were initiated with the A gene–A protein system of the tryptophan synthetase of *Escherichia coli* with the intention of examining this concept of a colinear relationship between gene structure and protein structure. A large number of mutant strains which produced altered A proteins were isolated, and genetic and protein primary structure studies were performed with these strains to locate the positions of the alterations within the A gene and the A protein.[5–10] It was hoped that with information of this type it would be possible to determine whether a genetic map and the primary structure of the corresponding protein were colinear. Recently, Kaiser[11] has demonstrated the correspondence of the genetic map with the sequence of blocks of nucleotides in DNA. Thus if a colinear relationship could be established between a genetic map and the primary structure of a protein, it would be reasonable to conclude that this relationship extends to the nucleotide sequence corresponding to the genetic map.

In previous reports on studies with the tryptophan synthetase A protein, conclusive evidence was presented for the colinearity of a segment of the A gene and a segment of the A protein.[12, 13] The present communication deals with more extensive data with 16 mutants with mutational alterations in one segment of the A gene and the A protein.

Materials and Methods.—Mutant strains: Of the A-protein mutants examined in detail in this paper, strains A23, A27, A28, A36, A46, A58, A78, A90, A94, A95, A169, A178, and A187 were isolated following ultraviolet irradiation of the K-12 wild-type strain of *E. coli*, and strain A223 was isolated following treatment of the wild-type strain with ethylmethanesulfonate. Mutant A446 (previously designated PR8)[14] and mutant A487 were initially isolated as spontaneous second-site reversions and subsequently were separated from the original A mutants with which they had been associated. Strains $anth_1{}^-$ and $anth_2{}^-$ are blocked prior to anthranilic acid in the tryptophan pathway and respond to anthranilic acid, indole, or tryptophan. $V_1{}^R$ and $V_1{}^R$ $tryp^-$ deletion mutants were isolated by treatment of T1-sensitive populations of the various mutants with phage T1h+. All of the $V_1{}^R$ mutations mentioned are very closely linked to the A gene, and the $V_1{}^R$ $tryp^-$ deletions include the $V_1{}^R$ locus and some segment of the A gene.[15] A stock of unrestricted T1 phage (uT1)[16] was kindly supplied by J. R. Christensen.

Protein studies: The altered A proteins were isolated and examined for primary structure changes as described previously.[6, 7, 9] The ordering of the tryptic peptides mentioned in the paper will be described in detail elsewhere.[17, 18]

Genetic studies: Recombination experiments were performed with the temperate-transducing phage P1kc.[19] Recombination distances between A mutants were obtained by determining the frequency of appearance of *tryp*+ transductants. Transduction from *his*− → *his*+ was scored in each experiment for internal reference, and the ratio of *tryp*+/*his*+ transductants calculated.[20]

Each value was halved to correct for the difference in relative frequency of transduction in the *his* and *tryp* regions.[20] In transduction experiments with leaky mutants (A169, A223, A446, and A487) the plating medium was supplemented with 0.1 μg/ml DL-5-methyltryptophan to suppress growth of the leaky mutants. This supplement has little or no effect on the growth of wild-type recombinants and does not appear to affect the recombination values obtained with nonleaky mutants. In spite of the presence of 5-methyltryptophan, it was frequently difficult to score recombination in experiments with leaky mutants. Anthranilic acid requirement was scored either by picking and streaking or by replication to appropriate test media. Resistance to phage T1 (V₁ᵏ) was scored by picking, streaking, and spot testing with phage uT1. As shown by Drexler and Christensen,[16] P1 lysogeny does not prevent the multiplication of uT1.

Results and Discussion.—*Relative order of mutational alterations in the A gene:* The genetic map based on recombination frequencies, deletion mapping, and three-point crosses is shown in Figure 1.

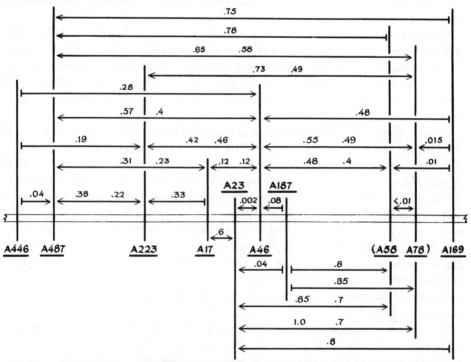

Fig. 1.—The order of mutationally altered sites in the A gene based on recombination frequencies, deletion mapping, and three-point genetic tests. The head of each arrow points to the recipient in each transduction cross. If two values are given, the cross was performed in both directions. In such cases each value is placed near the recipient in the cross.

Recombination frequency data: Recombination frequency data alone establishes close linkage of three groups of mutants: (1) A446 and A487; (2) A46, A23, and A187; and (3) A58, A78, and A169. The recombination values obtained also suggest that the order of these groups is as indicated in the figure, but they do not permit ordering within any of the groups.[21] In most cases recombination experiments were performed in both directions, i.e., each strain served as donor and recipient, and fair agreement was observed between the two values. However, it is evident from the data in Figure 1 that there were some exceptions. The exceptions generally involved leaky mutants, and it is possible that the scoring difficulties encountered with these strains were responsible.

Two of the mutants examined, A23 and A187, gave recombination values considerably higher than those obtained with mutant A46. Other mutants which were independent isolates resembling A23 (A27, A28, A36) and A46 (A95, A178) exhibited the same recombination behavior as the strain they resembled. Extensive mapping experiments with other A mutants and the strains mentioned above indicate that the A23 and A187 recombination values are probably exceptionally high rather than the A46 values exceptionally low. Since the mutational alterations in strains of the A23 and A46 type were probably single nucleotide changes,[22] it would appear that differences of single nucleotide pairs between donor DNA and recipient DNA can influence the frequency of recombinational events. An alternative explanation, that all A23 and A187 double mutants are prototrophic, seems very unlikely on the basis of numerous tests with recombinants from crosses involving A23 and A187.

Recombinants were not obtained in crosses of A23 × A27, A28, or A36; A46 × A95 or A178; or A58 × A90 or A94. On the basis of these tests and the primary structure studies to be described, it was concluded that each of these groups consists of members which arose by repeat identical mutations at the same site. Mutants A58 and A78 are clearly different, but they do not give recombinants at the 0.01 per cent level.

Deletion mapping: Information on the order of the mutational alterations in the relevant mutant strains was obtained in transduction experiments with a series of V_1^R-*tryp*⁻ deletion mutants (Table 1). These latter strains had regions of the A gene deleted, including, in each case, the V_1 locus which is situated at one end of the A gene.[15] Thus all the deletions extended into the A gene from the same side, and are overlapping, but may have different end points in the A gene. The recovery of tryptophan-independent recombinants from a transduction cross between any A mutant and a deletion mutant would indicate that the mutationally altered site in the A mutant was outside the region of the A gene that was missing in the deletion mutant. Recombination values were determined in transduction crosses with some of the deletion mutants to approximate the relative distance from a mutationally altered site in an A mutant to the end point of a deletion.

It is clear from the crosses with T⁻70 and T⁻689 that the altered sites in mutants A23, A46, A187, A58, A78, and A169—but not those in A446, A487, and A223—are within the region of the A gene that is missing in these deletion mutants. The rela-

TABLE 1

RECOMBINATION TESTS WITH VARIOUS TRYP⁻ DELETION MUTANTS

Donor	*his*⁻V_1^R *tryp*⁻ Deletion Mutant Recipient					
	T⁻201	T⁻5	T⁻70	T⁻689	T⁻211	T⁻226
A446	0	0	0.08‡	0.08‡		
A487	0	0	0.19*	0.5		
A223	0	0	0.17	0.06	+	+
A23	0	0	0	0	1.3	+
A46	0	0	0	0	0.86	0.77
A187	0	0	0		1.3	+
A58	0	0	0	0	0.09	0.1
A78	0	0	0		0.1	0.1
A169			0		0.1	0.1
A38	+	+	+	+	+	+

+, 0 = recombinants or no recombinants, respectively, in qualitative transduction experiments.
* = each recombination value represents the uncorrected observed ratio of *tryp*⁺ to *his*⁺ transductants.
‡ A446 gives unusually low recombination values in all experiments.

tive order of the altered sites in mutants A446, A487, and A223 could not be established by quantitative transduction experiments with the same deletion mutants. The quantitative transduction experiments with deletion mutants T$^-$211 and T$^-$226 divide the other mutants into two groups: (A46, A23, and A187) and (A58, A78, and A169). The combined results presented suggest the following order of altered sites: A38......(A446, A487, A223)......(A46, A23, A187)......(A58, A78, A169)......V$_1$.

Three-point genetic tests: Genetic tests employing outside markers were performed to determine relative order within each group of closely linked mutants. These tests are summarized in Table 2. The results obtained support the conclusions concerning group order that were arrived at by the previous methods and indicate relative orders within each closely linked group. Crosses 1–7 establish the order anth......A34......A446......A487......A223......A46, crosses 8 and 9 the order anth ......A46......A78......A169, and crosses 10 and 11 the order anth......(A23, A46) ......A187. The order anth......A23-A46 had tentatively been assigned on the basis of other data.[22] Crosses 12–15 confirm orders established by other methods. The combined genetic analyses with the mutants examined suggest the sequence of mutational alterations shown in Figure 1—A446-A487-A223-A23-A46-A187-(A58, A78)-A169.

TABLE 2

OUTSIDE-MARKER ORDERING OF MUTATIONALLY ALTERED SITES

	Transduction cross		Nonselective markers	Recombinants detected*		$anth^+$ (%)	Order
(1)	34	$\to anth_2^-$-223	$anth_2$	72 $anth^+$;	332 $anth^-$	18	$anth$-34-223
(2)	46	$\to anth_2^-$-223	$anth_2$	180 $anth^+$;	196 $anth^-$	48	$anth$-223-46
(3)	446	$\to anth_2^-$-223	$anth_2$	14 $anth^+$;	112 $anth^-$	11	$anth$-446-223
(4)	487	$\to anth_2^-$-223	$anth_2$	29 $anth^+$;	118 $anth^-$	20	$anth$-487-223
(5)	34	$\to anth_2^-$-487	$anth_2$	86 $anth^+$;	368 $anth^-$	19	$anth$-34-487
(6)	46	$\to anth_2^-$-487	$anth_2$	27 $anth^+$;	28 $anth^-$	49	$anth$-487-46
(7)	446	$\to anth_2^-$-487	$anth_2$	7 $anth^+$;	31 $anth^-$	23	$anth$-446-487
(8)	46	$\to anth_2^-$-78	$anth_2$	52 $anth^+$;	220 $anth^-$	19	$anth$-46-78
(9)	169	$\to anth_2^-$-78	$anth_2$	22 $anth^+$;	24 $anth^-$	48	$anth$-78-169
(10)	187	$\to anth_1^-$-23	$anth_1$	9 $anth^-$;	42 $anth^+$	83	$anth$-23-187
(11)	187	$\to anth_1^-$-46	$anth_1$	14 $anth^-$;	116 $anth^+$	89	$anth$-46-187
(12)	46 $V_1^R\to anth_1^-$-58 V_1^S		$anth_1$; V_1	22 $anth^- V_1^R$;	1 $anth^+ V_1^R$	·4	$anth$-46-58-V_1
(13)	58 $V_1^R\to anth_1^-$-46 V_1^S		$anth_1$; V_1	10 $anth^+ V_1^S$;	1 $anth^+ V_1^R$; 4 $anth^- V_1^{S'}$	73	$anth$-46-58-V_1
(14)	169 $V_1^R\to anth_1^-$-46 V_1^S		$anth_1$; V_1	6 $anth^+ V_1^S$;	1 $anth^+ V_1^S$	90	$anth$-46-169-V_1
(15)	446	$\to anth_1^-$-46	$anth_1$	81 $anth^-$; 20 $anth^-$- 446-46;	22 $anth^+$ 65 $anth^+$ 446$^-$-46	21 76	$anth$-446-46

Order of markers: $anth$-A34 .... (A446, etc.) - - - V_1^R.

* In crosses with the outside marker $anth_2$ the percentage of $anth^+$ recombinants is approximately 20% if the order is $\dfrac{+\quad x}{anth^-\quad y}$ and approximately 50% if the order of x and y is reversed. With the marker $anth_1$ different values are obtained but the order of x and y relative to $anth$ can be clearly established. The explanation for the different values obtained with the two outside markers is not known.

Primary Structure Studies.—Amino acid substitutions have been detected in primary structure studies with each of the 16 A mutants.[6, 7, 14, 17, 18] The substitutions observed and the peptides in which they are present are shown in Figure 2. The conclusions from the genetics studies are also included in the figure (i.e., order of alterations and approximation of recombination distances between alterations). It is apparent that mutants with alterations extremely close to one another in the A gene have amino acid substitutions close to one another in the A protein. Primary structure studies with the A protein[17, 18] have established the linear sequence

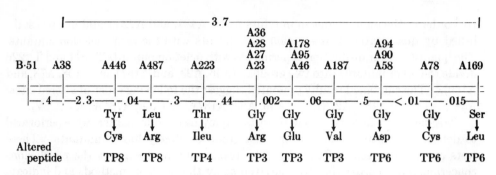

FIG. 2.—Amino acid substitutions in the A proteins of various mutants.[6, 7, 14, 17, 18] The A58, A78, A90, A94, and A169 substitutions will be described in detail elsewhere.[18]

of peptides TP-11, TP-8, TP-4, TP-18, TP-3, and TP-6, constituting a 75-residue segment of the A protein. This sequence and the sequence of the amino acids of most of these peptides are presented in Figure 3. This segment accounts for approximately one fourth of the residues in the A protein and is not at the amino or car-

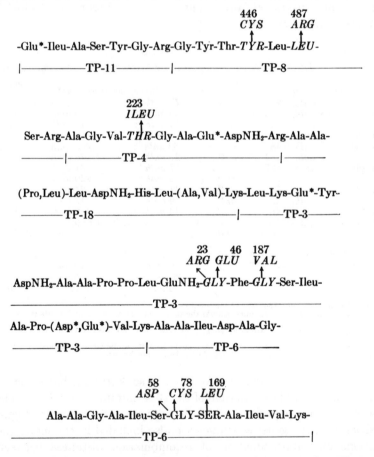

FIG. 3.—Peptide and partial amino acid sequence of a segment of the A protein. The positions of amino acid substitutions in the A proteins of the various mutants are indicated. Based on the studies by Carlton and Yanofsky[17] and Guest and Yanofsky.[18] (* = not known whether present as acid or amide.)

boxyl end of the protein.   The positions of the amino acid replacements in the A proteins of the various mutants are also shown.   It is clear that the positions of the amino acid replacements in the segment of the A protein are in the same relative order as the order of the mutationally altered sites of the corresponding mutants in the A gene.   These findings convincingly demonstrate a colinear relationship between gene structure and protein structure.

The relationship between the map and residue distances observed is also of interest and can be seen most clearly from the representative values summarized in Table 3.   Although the map distance/residue distance ratio varies between 0.01 and 0.05, in most cases this value is approximately 0.02.   It would appear, therefore, that distances on the genetic map are representative of distances between amino acid residues in the corresponding protein.

TABLE 3

RELATIONSHIP BETWEEN MAP DISTANCES AND RESIDUE DISTANCES

Mutant pair	Map distance	Amino acid residue distance	$\dfrac{\text{Map distance}}{\text{Residue distance}}$
A58-A78	<0.01	0	—
A46-A23	0.002	0	—
A58-A169	0.01	1	0.01
A78-A169	0.015	1	0.015
A46-A187	0.08	2	0.04
A23-A187	0.04	2	0.02
A446-A487	0.04	2	0.02
A487-A223	0.3	6	0.05
A446-A223	0.19	8	0.02
A46-A58	0.44	23	0.02
A46-A78	0.52	23	0.02
A23-A58	0.78	23	0.03
A23-A78	0.85	23	0.04
A46-A169	0.48	24	0.02
A23-A169	0.8	24	0.03
A223-A46	0.44	28	0.02
A487-A46	0.48	34	0.01
A446-A46	0.28	36	0 01
A78-A223	0.61	51	0.01
A169-A487	0.75	58	0.01

Summary.—The concept of colinearity of gene structure and protein structure was examined with 16 mutants with alterations in one segment of the A gene and the A protein of tryptophan synthetase.   The results obtained demonstrate a linear correspondence between the two structures and further show that genetic recombination values are representative of the distances between amino acid residues in the corresponding protein.

Note added in proof: Dr. Francis Crick has recently forwarded a manuscript which deals with a study of colinearity in another system (Sarabhai *et al.*, *Nature*, in press).

The authors are indebted to Virginia Horn for performing the genetic analyses described in this paper.   They are also indebted to Deanna Thorpe, Patricia Schroeder, Donald Vinicor, and John Horan for their excellent technical assistance.

* This investigation was supported by grants from the National Science Foundation and the U.S. Public Health Service.
† Present address: B. C. Carlton, Department of Biology, Yale University, New Haven, Connecticut; D. R. Helinski, Department of Biology, Princeton University, Princeton, New Jersey; U. Henning, Max-Planck Institut für Zellchemie, Munich, Germany.

‡ Guinness Research Fellow, on leave from Department of Biochemistry, Oxford, England.

[1] Beadle, G. W., and E. L. Tatum, these PROCEEDINGS, **27**, 499 (1941).

[2] Sanger, F., and H. Tuppy, *Biochem. J.*, **49**, 481 (1951).

[3] Watson, J. D., and F. H. C. Crick, in *Viruses*, Cold Spring Harbor Symposia on Quantitative Biology, vol. 18 (1953), p. 123.

[4] Crick, F. H. C., *Symp. Soc. Exptl. Biol.*, **12**, 138 (1958).

[5] Yanofsky, C., D. R. Helinski, and B. D. Maling, in *Cellular Regulatory Mechanisms*, Cold Spring Harbor Symposia on Quantitative Biology, vol. 26 (1961), p. 11.

[6] Helinski, D. R., and C. Yanofsky, these PROCEEDINGS, **48**, 173 (1962).

[7] Henning, U., and C. Yanofsky, these PROCEEDINGS, **48**, 183 (1962).

[8] *Ibid.*, 1497 (1962).

[9] Helinski, D. R., and C. Yanofsky, *Biochim. Biophys. Acta*, **63**, 10 (1962).

[10] Carlton, B. C., and C. Yanofsky, *J. Biol. Chem.*, **238**, 2390 (1963).

[11] Kaiser, A. D., *J. Mol. Biol.*, **4**, 275 (1962).

[12] Yanofsky, C., in *Synthesis and Structure of Macromolecules*, Cold Spring Harbor Symposia on Quantitative Biology, vol. 28 (1963), in press.

[13] Yanofsky, C., in *The Bacteria*, ed. I. C. Gunsalus and R. Y. Stanier (Academic Press), vol. 5, in press.

[14] Helinski, D. R., and C. Yanofsky, *J. Biol. Chem.*, **238**, 1043 (1963).

[15] Somerville, R., and C. Yanofsky, unpublished observations.

[16] Drexler, H., and J. R. Christensen, *Virology*, **13**, 31 (1961).

[17] Carlton, B. C., and C. Yanofsky, in preparation.

[18] Guest, J., and C. Yanofsky, in preparation.

[19] Lennox, E. S., *Virology*, **1**, 190 (1955).

[20] Yanofsky, C., and E. S. Lennox, *Virology*, **8**, 425 (1959).

[21] On the basis of preliminary two-point mapping data with mutant A2, it earlier had tentatively been concluded that the alterations in mutants A58, A78, A90, and A94 were to the left of the alterations in A17 and A46.[5] The more extensive data presented in Figure 1 and the deletion and three-point data indicate that the correct order is as shown in Figure 1.

[22] Yanofsky, C., in *Synthesis and Structure of Macromolecules*, Cold Spring Harbor Symposia on Quantitative Biology, vol. 28 (1963), in press.

Suppression

SUPPRESSOR GENE ALTERATION OF PROTEIN PRIMARY STRUCTURE*

By Stuart Brody† and Charles Yanofsky

DEPARTMENT OF BIOLOGICAL SCIENCES, STANFORD UNIVERSITY

Communicated by V. C. Twitty, May 22, 1963

Some suppressor genes are known to act by restoring an enzymatic activity that is specifically lacking in a mutant strain. This could be accomplished in many ways, with or without the alteration of the enzyme in question.[1-3] Suppressor mutations have been detected which affect the A protein of the tryptophan synthetase of *Escherichia coli*. Previous studies have shown that alterations in the primary structure of this protein can result from forward mutation,[4,5] reverse mutation,[6] and recombination[6] within the structural gene (the A gene) for this protein. The present paper indicates that a suppressor mutation in a region of the genome distant from the A gene also leads to a change in the primary structure of the A protein.

Pertinent Characteristics of the Tryptophan Synthetase System.—The *Escherichia coli* tryptophan synthetase consists of two separable protein subunits, designated A and B. Together these proteins catalyze the following three reactions:[7] (1) indole + L-serine → L-tryptophan; (2) indoleglycerol phosphate ⇌ indole + 3-phosphoglyceraldehyde; (3) indoleglycerol phosphate + L-serine → L-tryptophan + 3-phosphoglyceraldehyde.[8] Reaction (3) is believed to be the physiologically essential reaction in tryptophan biosynthesis.[7,9] Many A mutant strains produce an altered A protein, designated A-CRM, which reacts with antibody to the normal A protein.[9] All of the A-CRM's detected to date can combine with the normal B protein component, and this complex can catalyze the In → Tryp reaction, but not the other two reactions, i.e., reactions (2) and (3).

Materials and Methods.—The A mutants and suppressed A mutants listed in this paper were produced by ultraviolet irradiation of the K-12 strain of *E. coli*.[9,10] The methods employed for the preparation of transducing lysates of phage Plkc and for transduction with this phage have been described previously.[10] All cultures of suppressed A mutants used for the preparation of extracts were examined for possible changes in the cellular population, such as reversion in the A gene, by appropriate plating and transduction techniques.

Enzymatic assays,[7] and procedures for the heat-treatment and acid-treatment of crude extracts,[11] have been described previously. Procedures used for the isolation of the A protein,[12] as well as the methods for the digestion of the protein with trypsin and chymotrypsin,[13] the isolation of peptides,[13] and the analyses of peptides[4] are described elsewhere.

Results.—Genetic characterization of suppressor mutations: A certain class of tryptophan-independent strains, designated as suppressed A mutants, were isolated in reversion studies performed with various tryptophan synthetase A mutants.[14, 15] These suppressed A mutants were clearly distinguished from revertants which arose by mutation in the A gene. Transduction experiments[15] indicated that the original mutation in the A gene was still present in the suppressed A mutant, and that the site of the suppressor mutation was not linked to the A gene.[16]

Allele specificity tests performed with the suppressor genes in strains A-11 su, A-3 su, and A-36 su indicated that each suppressor gene was allele-specific. Although 50 nonidentical A mutants were examined in tests with each of the suppressor genes, suppression was not detected, i.e., no tryptophan-independent colonies were observed.

Enzymatic characterization of crude extracts of suppressed mutants: Extracts of suppressed mutants differ from extracts of A mutants in that they exhibit low levels of InGP → Tryp activity (Table 1). The level of InGP → Tryp activity restored by a suppressor gene is characteristic of each suppressed mutant. In addition, the ratio of InGP → Tryp activity to In → Tryp activity is quite characteristic for each suppressed mutant, and shows little fluctuation when cultures are grown under similar conditions.

TABLE 1

THE ENZYMATIC ACTIVITIES OF THE A PROTEINS IN EXTRACTS OF VARIOUS MUTANTS AND SUPPRESSED MUTANTS

Strain	A protein-specific activity*		$\frac{\text{InGP} \to \text{Tryp}}{\text{In} \to \text{Tryp}}$ per cent
	In → Tryp	InGP → Tryp	
Wild-type	2.5	1	40
A-36	22	0	...
A-36 su	6	0.25	4.2
A-3	35	0	...
A-3 su	44	0.19	0.44
A-11	31	0	...
A-11 su	55	0.48	0.87

* Units/mg protein.

Physical treatments of crude extracts of suppressed mutants: The low level of InGP → Tryp activity detected in extracts of suppressed mutants could be due to an alteration of the CRM molecules, making them all slightly active in this reaction, or it could be due to the formation of a small amount of a second A protein, which was active in the InGP → Tryp reaction. It would be possible to distinguish between these alternatives, if it could be shown that the physical properties of the A protein that is active in the InGP → Tryp reaction differed from the properties of the CRM protein. The three mutants listed in Table 1 were selected for this study because the A-CRM's in each one could be distinguished from the wild-type A protein by differences in heat- or acid-stability. In comparison to the wild-type A protein, the CRM of A-36 is heat-labile, the CRM of A-3 is heat-stable, while the CRM of A-11 is acid-precipitable.[11]

Figure 1 presents the heat inactivation curves for the two activities found in the crude extracts of two suppressed mutants.   The results obtained demonstrate two important facts about the A proteins in these extracts.   First, the bulk of the In → Tryp activity in suppressed mutant extracts is associated with an A protein with the same heat sensitivity as the CRM in the original mutant (unsuppressed) extract.[11]   Secondly, the A protein active in the InGP → Tryp reaction is clearly different from this CRM in its heat sensitivity, and furthermore resembles the wild-type A protein.   As a control for one of the heat inactivation experiments, crude extracts of the wild-type strain and of strain A-36 were mixed to simulate an extract of A-36 su, and a similar heat inactivation experiment performed.   The inactivation rates of the two activities in this mixture were the same as those observed with A-36 su extracts.

Heat treatment of an A-11 su extract did not differentially inactivate the InGP → Tryp activity or the In → Tryp activity in this extract.   Since the CRM of strain A-11 is as heat-sensitive as the wild-type A protein,[11] no differences would be expected in the two inactivation rates, if the protein bearing the InGP → Tryp activity had the same heat stability as the wild-type A protein.   However, acid treatment of an extract of A-11 su clearly showed (Table 2) that the InGP → Tryp activity was associated with a protein that was more acid-stable than the protein bearing the In → Tryp activity, and was similar in behavior to the A protein of the wild-type strain.   Here again, the bulk of the A protein resembled the A-CRM found in strain A-11.   Similar acid treatment of crude extracts of strains A-36 su and A-3 su led to a loss of activity in both reactions similar to that observed with extracts of the wild-type strain (Table 2).   Since the A-CRM's from strains A-36 and A-3 have the same acid stability as the wild-type A protein,[11] it might not be possible to distinguish these A-CRM's from a second A protein, if that protein had the same stability as the wild-type A protein.

TABLE 2

ACID TREATMENT OF EXTRACTS

Extract	Per cent activity remaining*	
	In → Tryp	InGP → Tryp
Wild-type	58	55
A-11	11	. . .
A-11 su	17, 11	51, 47
A-36	60	. . .
A-36 su	59	57
A-3	58	. . .
A-3 su	61	53

* A protein activity in supernatant solutions following acidification of extracts to pH 4.0.

These findings are consistent with the view that the two types of A protein found in extracts of each suppressed mutant are: an A protein active in the InGP → Tryp reaction (hereafter designated as the su-A protein), which has certain physical properties in common with the wild-type A protein; and an A protein which closely resembles the A-CRM of the parental mutant.

Purification and separation of two A proteins by DEAE column chromatography: These findings, as well as previous observations,[2] suggested the presence of a second type of A protein in extracts of suppressed mutants.   In further studies with extracts of strain A-36 su, it was possible to separate two A proteins by column

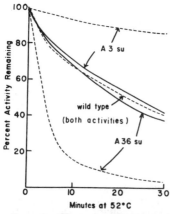

FIG. 1.—Heat inactivation of the A proteins in crude extracts of strains A-36 su, A-3 su, and the wild-type strain. InGP → Tryp activity———, In → Tryp activity - - - -.

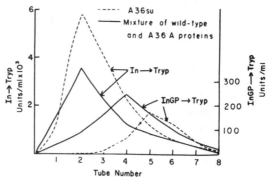

FIG. 2.—Elution pattern from DEAE-cellulose columns of the two A proteins in extracts of strain A-36 su, and of a mixture of the wild-type and A-36 A proteins. A linear phosphate gradient was employed (0.01 M → 0.30 M, pH 7.0), and fractions of 10 ml were collected. Tube #1 refers to the first tube that contains A protein activity.

chromatography (Fig. 2). As can be seen in this figure, the In → Tryp and InGP → Tryp activity peaks are partially separated.

To determine whether the chromatographic properties of the su-A protein were similar to those of the wild-type A protein, purified A proteins from mutant A-36 and from the wild-type strain were mixed to simulate a purified preparation from strain A-36 su. When this mixture was chromatographed employing the conditions used for the first column procedure (as described above), the In → Tryp and InGP → Tryp activity peaks were partially separated (Fig. 2). As shown also in Figure 2, the activity curves were very similar to those obtained by column chromatography of the preparation from strain A-36 su.

The su-A protein was purified further by combining the fractions containing InGP → Tryp activity from several DEAE columns, concentrating by $(NH_4)_2SO_4$ precipitation, and then rechromatographing on a 100 × 1.2 cm DEAE-cellulose column, using a linear gradient of 0.01 M → 0.15 M phosphate (pH 7.0). Since some of the early fractions from the previous column with InGP → Tryp activity contained the trailing portion of the In → Tryp activity peak, two activity peaks were also recovered from the second column. However, under the conditions of rechromatography, the two A proteins were completely separated. The purified su-A protein had an InGP → Tryp:In → Tryp activity ratio of 40 per cent, which is identical to that of the wild-type A protein. Heat inactivation studies showed that both of the enzymatic activities of the purified su-A protein were inactivated at the same rate, a rate identical to that for the heat inactivation of the wild-type A protein. These findings indicate that the su-A protein was completely free of the A-CRM protein. Furthermore, a comparison of the specific activities of the A protein peaks with the specific activity of pure wild-type A protein showed that the su-A protein was 50 per cent pure, while the A-CRM was greater than 90 per cent pure.

Analysis of peptides from the A-CRM and su-A proteins of A-36 su: The two A protein fractions isolated from strain A-36 su were examined in peptide pattern studies. The peptide patterns of a trypsin plus chymotrypsin digest, as well as a chymotrypsin digest of the su-A protein, were found to correspond exactly to the peptide patterns of the wild-type A protein. The peptide pattern of chymotryptic digests of the CRM protein of strain A-36 su showed one difference from a similar wild-type A protein peptide pattern, the position of peptide CP-2, as shown schematically in Figure 3. Although the chymotryptic peptide pattern of the CRM from strain A-36 su differed from the wild-type peptide pattern, it was identical to the peptide pattern of the CRM protein from the original A-36 strain. It had previously been shown that the peptide difference in mutant A-36 was due to the replacement of a particular glycine residue in CP-2 by an arginine residue.[4, 17]

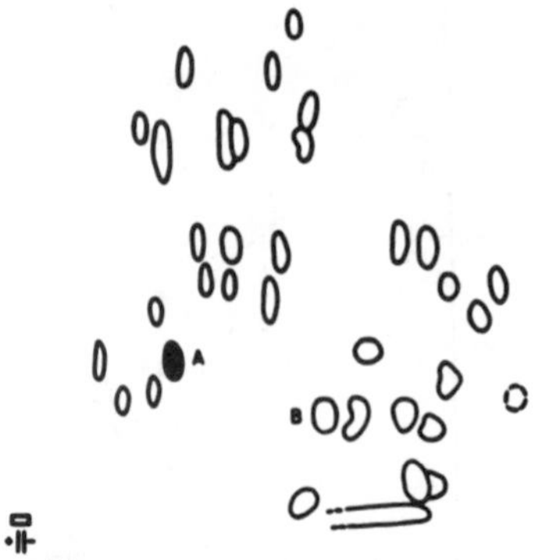

Peptide CP-2 was isolated from the two A proteins from strain A-36 su and its amino acid composition determined. The results of these analyses are compared with the known sequence of amino acids in peptide CP-2 from the wild-type A protein,[17] and with the amino acid composition of CP-2

FIG. 3.—A schematic representation of the position of the major peptides in chymotryptic peptide patterns of both the A-CRM and the su-A protein of strain A-36 su. A = the position of peptide CP-2 from the su-A protein, B = the position of CP-2 from the A-CRM. Peptide CP-2 is in position A in wild-type peptide patterns and in position B in peptide patterns of the A-CRM from mutant A-36. The rectangle in the lower left-hand corner indicates the point of application of the sample.

from A-36 CRM[17] (Table 3). The analyses indicate that peptide CP-2 from the su-A protein has the same composition as the corresponding peptide from the wild-type A protein, while CP-2 from the A-CRM of strain A-36 su has the same composition as CP-2 from the A-CRM of mutant A-36. It is clear from these data that an amino acid replacement occurs in the A protein as a result of the action of the suppressor gene.

TABLE 3

AMINO ACID COMPOSITION OF PEPTIDE CP-2 FROM VARIOUS A PROTEINS

Wild-type	AspNH$_2$-Ala-Ala-Pro-Pro-Leu-GluNH$_2$-*Gly*-Phe
A-36	(Asp*-Ala-Ala-Pro-Pro)-Leu-GluNH$_2$-*Arg*-Phe
A-36 su	
CRM-A	(Asp,* Ala$_2$, Pro$_2$, Leu, *Arg*, Glu*)-Phe
su-A	(Asp,* Ala$_2$, Pro$_2$, Leu, *Gly*, Glu*)-Phe

* Not determined whether present as amide.

Discussion.—Physical and chemical treatments of extracts of three suppressed A mutants indicate that there are two types of A proteins present in each extract. The majority A protein component is indistinguishable from the original CRM protein, whereas the minority component (the su-A protein) has physical and enzymatic properties characteristic of the wild-type A protein. Peptide pattern studies of the two purified A proteins from strain A-36 su also show that the su-A protein resembles the wild-type A protein, while the CRM protein resembles the A-CRM of mutant A-36. Amino acid analysis of the relevant peptides (CP-2) confirmed the fact that there is a difference in amino acid composition of the two peptides. This fact, in itself, is critical since it indicates that the presence of the suppressor gene in strain A-36 su has resulted in a change in the primary structure of the A protein.

The amino acid replacement in the A protein due to the suppressor gene of strain A-36 su is an arginine → glycine change in peptide CP-2. Only small amounts of purified su-A protein were available for study, so it was not possible to perform amino acid sequence analyses on peptide CP-2. However, if one makes the plausible assumption that the glycine residue in this peptide occupies the same position as the arginine residue that it replaces, then the effect of this suppressor gene is to restore an amino acid sequence identical to that of the wild-type A protein.[18] The presence of a glycine residue in this peptide is of particular importance in this case, since it has been shown that A proteins with any one of three other amino acids (alanine, serine, and valine) at this position are functional.[6] Although the amino acid found in the wild-type A protein (glycine) was restored in this case, it should be possible for amino acids other than the wild-type amino acid to be inserted at this position. In this regard, it is conceivable that a suppressor mutation could lead to an amino acid replacement in a protein which would not be possible by a single mutational event in the structural gene for this protein.

It has been found that the mutant phenotype of approximately one third of all the A mutants tested can be reversed by suppressor mutations.[15, 19] One mutant which is not suppressible, strain A-46, is particularly interesting in view of the studies reported in this paper. Although extensive reversion analyses and cross-suppression tests have been performed with this mutant, no suppressors have been found which restore InGP → Tryp activity. The amino acid change in the A-46 protein is a glycine → glutamic acid replacement, and this glycine residue is the same one that is replaced by arginine as a result of the A-36 mutation.[5] It is interesting that in the presence of the A-36 suppressor gene, glycine can replace arginine, but not glutamic acid, at this position in the A protein.

The results of these investigations can be most easily explained by postulating that the consequences of a mutation in a suppressor gene such as the suppressor of strain A-36 su is to produce an alteration in the specificity of incorporation of amino acids into proteins. The amino acid changes which result from this type of alteration could be called "mistakes" in protein synthesis. If the cell containing a mutated suppressor gene is incapable of always translating a certain specific DNA nucleotide sequence into the same amino acid without error, then it is important to determine the extent of this error in translation. The term "mistake level" will be used to indicate how often an amino acid at a particular position in a given protein is replaced at the same position by one or another amino acid. This definition does not include as "mistakes" the replacement of an amino acid by its analogues, or the translation of a nonsense sequence of nucleotides into a known amino acid. The "mistake level" might simply be expressed as follows: amino acid X is found to replace Y at a particular position in a protein in 8 per cent of the molecules. The "mistake level" might also be more complex if many amino acids could replace amino acid Y at this particular position and with different frequencies.[20] In any event, a given "mistake level" can be considered to denote a constant probability of misreading the genetic code independent of what proteins, or types of proteins, are being synthesized.

It is not known to what extent the bacterial cell could tolerate many types of amino acid insertion mistakes. It is probable that very high "mistake levels," single or multiple, if they affected all proteins, would result in lethality. This may explain why all allele-specific suppressors of A mutants examined to date appear to have very low "mistake levels."[21] However, it could be possible to have a fairly high "mistake level" if there were more than one "coding unit" for a particular amino acid (so-called "degenerate coding units"), and if these amino acid coding units were not equally distributed in the DNA. If the suppressor mutation could lead to a translation "mistake" of a minority or infrequently found coding unit, then an amino acid switch found in one protein might not be found in other proteins. In cases where very high levels of an enzyme are restored by the action of a suppressor gene, different interpretations may be applicable.[3]

The finding that some suppressor mutations can reverse the effects of mutations in several genes lends weight to the "mistake in protein synthesis" hypothesis.[22, 23] The fact that a number of different point mutants in the T4r$_{II}$ cistron[22] or in the alkaline phosphatase gene[3] are affected by a single suppressor gene is consistent with this idea and has been interpreted in a similar manner.

There are many ways that the presumed mistake in translation in strain A-36 su might occur. According to our present knowledge of protein synthesis, which

TABLE 4

POSSIBLE SUPPRESSOR "MISTAKES" THAT WOULD LEAD TO THE OCCASIONAL INCORPORATION OF GLYCINE INSTEAD OF ARGININE IN THE A PROTEIN OF STRAIN A-36 su

Mutationally altered component	Effect of alteration	Result
(a) Arginine-activating enzyme	Arginine enzyme activates glycine in addition to arginine	Glycine or arginine coupled to same type of arginine-tRNA
(b) Glycine-activating enzyme	Glycine enzyme pairs with arginine-tRNA in addition to pairing with glycine-tRNA	Glycine coupled to both arginine-tRNA and glycine-tRNA
(c) Arginine-tRNA	Arginine-tRNA pairs with the glycine-activating enzyme in addition to pairing with the arginine-activating enzyme	Glycine or arginine coupled to same type of arginine-tRNA
(d) Glycine-tRNA	Glycine-tRNA pairs incorrectly with messenger RNA, in addition to pairing properly	Glycine-tRNA (charged with glycine), pairs with an arginine-coding unit, in addition to pairing with a glycine coding unit in messenger RNA

tRNA = amino acid transfer RNA.

may be incomplete, the possibilities listed in Table 4 can be considered. It is assumed that all of the alterations mentioned lead only to partial losses in specificity. At the present time, the specificities of these components in strain A-36 su are being investigated to determine whether any one of the components has been altered as a result of the suppressor mutation.

We wish to express our thanks to Deanna Thorpe, Patricia Schroeder, and John Horan for their assistance with various aspects of this work.

The following abbreviations were used: Tryp = Tryptophan; In = Indole; InGP = Indoleglycerol phosphate.

* This investigation was supported by grants from the U.S. Public Health Service and the National Science Foundation.

† Predoctoral trainee of the U.S. Public Health Service.

[1] Suskind, S., and L. Kurek, these PROCEEDINGS, 45, 193 (1959).

[2] Crawford, I., and C. Yanofsky, these PROCEEDINGS, 45, 1280 (1959).

[3] Garen, A., and O. Siddiqi, these PROCEEDINGS, **48,** 1121 (1962).

[4] Helinski, D., and C. Yanofsky, these PROCEEDINGS, **48,** 173 (1962).

[5] Henning, U., and C. Yanofsky, these PROCEEDINGS, **48,** 183 (1962).

[6] *Ibid.*, **48,** 1497 (1962).

[7] Crawford, I., and C. Yanofsky, these PROCEEDINGS, **44,** 1161 (1958).

[8] Crawford, I., *Biochim. Biophys. Acta*, **45,** 405 (1960).

[9] Yanofsky, C., and I. Crawford, these PROCEEDINGS, **45,** 1016 (1959).

[10] Lennox, E. S., *Virology*, **1,** 190 (1955).

[11] Maling, B., and C. Yanofsky, these PROCEEDINGS, **47,** 551 (1961).

[12] Henning, U., D. Helinski, F. Chao, and C. Yanofsky, *J. Biol. Chem.*, **237,** 1523 (1962).

[13] Helinski, D., and C. Yanofsky, *Biochim. Biophys. Acta*, **63,** 10 (1962).

[14] Stadler, J., and C. Yanofsky, *Genetics*, **44,** 105 (1959).

[15] Allen, M., and C. Yanofsky, *Genetics*, in press.

[16] Preliminary transduction studies indicate that the suppressor gene of strain A-36 su is located close to the B_1 locus on the *E. coli* linkage map.

[17] Carlton, B., and C. Yanofsky, *J. Biol. Chem.*, in press.

[18] It cannot be unequivocally stated that the entire amino acid sequence of the su-A protein is identical to that of the wild-type A protein, since amino acid sequence analyses of every peptide from both of these proteins would be required to establish this point.

[19] Yanofsky, C., D. Helinski, and B. Maling, in *Cellular Regulatory Mechanisms*, Cold Spring Harbor Symposia on Quantitative Biology, vol. 26 (1961), p. 11.

[20] It was thought that perhaps a given suppressor gene, known to cause (for example) a histidine → tyrosine switch in the A protein, could be used as a genetic method for identifying tyrosine → histidine mutational changes in other proteins. However, this may not be possible until it is known whether single or multiple amino acid replacements are involved.

[21] "Mistake levels" in suppressed A mutants are estimated from the ratio of the A protein activity in the InGP → Tryp and In → Tryp reactions. If the A protein active in the InGP → Tryp reaction is similar to the wild-type A protein in its enzymatic properties, then this ratio of enzymatic activities can be taken as an indication of the amount of su-A protein relative to the A-CRM protein.

[22] Benzer, S., and S. Champe, these PROCEEDINGS, **47,** 1025 (1961).

[23] Lieb, M., and L. Herzenberg, personal communication.

GENETIC CODE: THE 'NONSENSE' TRIPLETS FOR CHAIN TERMINATION AND THEIR SUPPRESSION

By Dr. S. BRENNER, F.R.S., Dr. A. O. W. STRETTON and Dr. S. KAPLAN

Medical Research Council, Laboratory of Molecular Biology, Cambridge, England

THE nucleotide sequence of messenger RNA is a code determining the amino-acid sequences of proteins. Although the biochemical apparatus which translates the code is elaborate, it is likely that the code itself is simple and consists of non-overlapping nucleotide triplets. In general, each amino-acid has more than one triplet corresponding to it, but it is not known how many of the sixty-four triplets are used to code for the twenty amino-acids. Triplets which do not correspond to amino-acids have been loosely referred to as 'nonsense' triplets, but it is not known whether these triplets have an information content which is strictly null or whether they serve some special function in information transfer.

The evidence that there are nonsense triplets is mainly genetic and will be reviewed later in this article. A remarkable property of nonsense mutants in bacteria and bacteriophages is that they are suppressible; wild-type function can be restored to such mutants by certain strains of bacteria carrying suppressor genes. It was realized early that this implies an ambiguity in the genetic code in the sense that a codon which is nonsense in one strain can be recognized as sense in another. The problem of nonsense triplets has become inextricably connected with the problem of suppression and, in particular, it has proved difficult to construct a theory of suppression without knowing the function of the nonsense triplet.

In this article we report experiments which allow us to deduce the structure of two nonsense codons as UAG and UAA. We suggest that these codons are the normal recognition signals in messenger RNA for chain termination and, on this basis, propose a theory of their suppression.

Nonsense mutants and their suppressors. One class of suppressible nonsense mutants which has been widely examined includes the subset I ambivalent *r*II mutants[1], the suppressible mutants of alkaline phosphatase[2], the *hd* or *sus* mutants of phage λ[3] and many of the *amber* mutants of bacteriophage T4 (ref. 4). These mutants have been isolated in various ways and the permissive (*su*+) and non-permissive (*su*−) strains used have been different. When isogenic bacterial strains, differing only in the *su* locus, are constructed, it can be shown that all these mutants respond to the same set of suppressors. They are therefore of the same class and we propose that all these mutants should be called *amber* mutants.

We may now consider the evidence that these mutants contain nonsense codons. Garen and Siddiqi[2] originally noted that *amber* mutants of the alkaline phosphatase of *E. coli* contained no protein related immunologically to the enzyme. Benzer and Champe[1] also showed that the mutants exert drastic effects and suggested that *amber* mutants of the *r*II gene interrupt the reading of the genetic message. In the *r*II genes, a deletion, *r*1589, joins part of the A cistron to part of the B cistron; complementation tests show that this mutant still possesses B activity although it lacks the A function. It may therefore be used to test the effects of mutants in the A cistron on the activity of the B. Double mutants, composed of an A *amber* mutant together with *r*1589 did not have B activity on the *su*− strain; this effect is suppressed by the *su* strain which restores B activity. This result is explained by our finding that each *amber* mutant of the head protein produces a characteristic fragment of the polypeptide chain in *su*− bacteria[5]. More recently we have shown that the polarity of the fragment is such that it can only be produced by the termination of the growing polypeptide chain at the site of the mutation[6]. In *su*+ strains both the fragment and a completed chain are produced and the efficiency of propagation depends on which of the

Wild Type	Ala . Gly . (Val, Phe) Asp . Phe . Gln . Asp . Pro . Ile . Asp . Ile . Arg . . .
H 36 on	Ala . Gly . Val . Phe . Asp . Phe .
su⁻	
H 36 on	Ala . Gly . Val . Phe . Asp . Phe .
su⁺ I	and
	Ala . Gly . Val . Phe . Asp . Phe . Ser . Asp . Pro . Ile . Asp . Ile . Arg . . .

Fig. 1.   Amino-acid sequences of the relevant region of the head protein in wild-type *T4D* and in the *amber* mutant *H36* on *su⁻* and *su⁺I* strains

suppressors is carried by the strain. In su^+I, the efficiency of propagation is about 65 per cent[7], and the completed chain contains a serine at a position occupied by a glutamine in the wild type[6] as shown in Fig. 1.

In addition to the *amber* mutants, there are other mutants, called *ochre* mutants, which are suppressed by a different set of suppressors[8]. *Ochre* mutants of the A cistron of *r*II abolish the B activity of *r*1589. This effect is not suppressed by *amber* suppressors, which shows that the *ochre* mutants are intrinsically different from the *amber* mutants.

Thus, nonsense mutants may be divided into two types, *amber* and *ochre* mutants, depending on their pattern of suppression. In Table 1, which is abstracted from a larger set of results[8], it can be seen that strains, carrying the *amber* suppressors su^+I, su^+II, su^+III and su^+IV, suppress different but overlapping sets of *amber* mutants, but do not suppress any *ochre* mutants. This is the feature which distinguished the two classes of mutants from each other. Table 1 also shows that *ochre* mutants are suppressed by one or more of the strains carrying the *ochre* suppressors su^+B, su^+C, su^+D and su^+E. These suppressors are also active on various *amber* mutants, and we have not yet been able to isolate suppressors specific for *ochre* mutants. Table 1 also shows that the suppressor strains can be differentiated by the set of mutants they suppress.

Table 1. SUPPRESSION OF *r*II MUTANTS BY *su⁺* STRAINS OF *E. coli Hfr H(λ)*

		Amber suppressors				Ochre suppressors			
		su⁺I	su⁺II	su⁺III	su⁺IV	su⁺B	su⁺C	su⁺D	su⁺E
Amber mutants									
*r*IIA	*HD*120	+	+	+	+	+	0	+	0
	*N*97	+	poor	+	0	poor	poor	+	0
	*S*116	0	0	+	0	0	+	+	0
	*N*19	+	poor	+	0	poor	+	+	0
	*N*34	+	+	+	0	+	+	+	0
*r*IIB	*HE*122	+	+	+	0	poor	+	+	0
	*HB*74	+	+	+	0	+	+	+	+
	*X*237	+	poor	+	0	0	+	+	0
	*HB*232	+	+	+	0	+	0	+	0
	*X*417	+	+	+	+	0	poor	+	0
Ochre mutants									
*r*IIA	*HD*147	0	0	0	0	+	+	+	+
	*N*55	0	0	0	0	+	+	+	0
	*X*20	0	0	0	0	+	0	+	0
	*N*21	0	0	0	0	+	0	0	+
*r*IIB	*UV*375	0	0	0	0	+	+	+	+
	360	0	0	0	0	+	0	+	+
	375	0	0	0	0	+	+	+	+
	*HF*208	0	0	0	0	+	+	0	+
	*N*29	0	0	0	0	0	0	+	0

Unlike some of the *amber* suppressors, all the *ochre* suppressors are weak[7,8]. This has made the isolation of *ochre* mutants of the head protein impossible. We therefore do not know the molecular consequences of *ochre* mutants, but we shall assume that, like the *amber* mutants, they too result in chain termination.

If we accept that both types of nonsense mutants result in termination of the polypeptide chain, we have to ask: at which level of information transfer is this effect exerted ? We have recently shown that it is likely that chain termination occurs as part of protein synthesis, since both types of mutants vanish when the phase of reading of the genetic message is altered[9]. This leads us to conclude that *amber* and *ochre* mutants produce different triplets

which have to be read in the correct phase and which are recognized as signals for chain termination.

Decoding of amber and ochre triplets. We have done two types of experiments which allow us to deduce the structures of the *amber* and *ochre* triplets. First, we studied the production and reversion of *r*II *amber* and *ochre* mutants using chemical mutagens. We show that the two triplets are connected to each other and that we can define their possible nucleotide compositions. Next, we investigated head protein *amber* mutants, to define the amino-acids connected to the *amber* triplet. Comparison of these results with known amino-acid codons allows us to deduce the structures of the *amber* and *ochre* triplets.

The experiments with *r*II mutants depend on the specificity of the mutagenic agent, hydroxylamine. This reacts only with cytosine in DNA, and although the exact structure of the product has not yet been defined, the altered base (called U′) appears to act like T with high efficiency, producing base-pair transitions of the G—C → A—T type[10]. Hence, response of any particular site of the DNA to hydroxylamine is evidence for the existence of a G—C pair at that site. Usually, phage particles are treated with hydroxylamine and, since these contain double-stranded DNA, the alteration of C occurs on only one of the strands. In any given gene, only one of the strands is transcribed into messenger RNA (ref. 11). This is the *sense* strand; it carries the genetic information proper and contains a nucleotide sequence which is the inverse complement of the sequence of the messenger RNA. The other strand, the *antisense* strand, has the same sequence as the messenger. In a phage, treated with hydroxylamine, the altered base, U′, could be on either the sense or the antisense strand of the DNA. Since the *r*II genes express their functions before the onset of DNA replication[12], only sense strand changes will register a phenotypic effect in the first cycle of growth; changes on the antisense strand, while still yielding altered DNA progeny, will go unexpressed (Fig. 2).

We can now examine the reversion properties of *amber* and *ochre* mutants. Champe and Benzer[12] studied reversion of a large number of *r*II mutants using different mutagens. They noted that no *amber* mutant was induced to revert by hydroxylamine. Some of the mutants they studied can now be identified as *ochre* mutants, and their results show that *ochre* mutants are equally insensitive to hydroxylamine. However, in their experiments, the treated mutant phages were plated directly on the bacterial strain which restricts the growth of *r*II mutants. They could therefore detect *sense* strand changes only, and any mutation on the antisense strand would not have been expressed. Strictly speaking, then, their results tell us that neither the *amber* nor the *ochre* triplet contains a C on the sense strand of the DNA, or, if any one does, it is connected by a C → U change to another nonsense codon. To extend this result and to recover all possible mutational changes, we grow the mutagenized phages in *E. coli B*, in which the *r*II functions are unnecessary, and then plated the progeny on strain *K* to measure reversion frequency. Table 2 shows that *amber* and

417

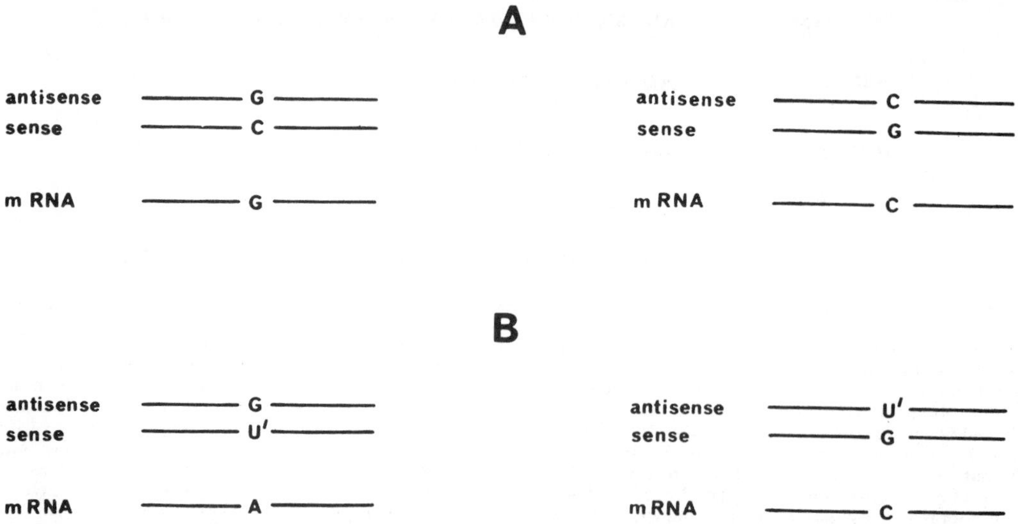

A

B

Fig. 2.   Diagram illustrating the expression of the two types of G–C pairs (*A*) before and (*B*) after treatment with hydroxylamine

Table 2. REVERSION OF AMBER AND OCHRE MUTANTS AFTER ALLOWING DNA REPLICATION

		Reversion index × 10⁻⁷	
		Control	NH₂OH
amber mutants	S116	0·04	0·03
	HD26	0·1	0·2
	S24	0·4	0·9
	S99	0·1	0·1
	N19	0·15	0·13
	HD59	0·0	0·05
	HB232	0·1	0·4
ochre mutants	UV375	0·8	2·0
	360	0·6	0·8
	X27	0·3	0·5
	375	0·8	0·9
	X511	0·2	0·3
	UV256	1·0	230

Phages were incubated in a solution of M NH₂OH in 2 M NaCl and 0·05 M sodium phosphate (*p*H 7·5) for 2 h at 37°. The reaction was terminated by dilution into acetone broth. About 10⁸ phage particles were used to infect a culture of *E. coli* B which was grown to lysis, and the progeny assayed on *E. coli* B and *E. coli* K12(λ). The reversion index is the K/B ratio. The control was treated in the same way except that hydroxylamine was omitted. The mutant UV256, which is not an *ochre* or an *amber* mutant, was used to check the efficacy of the mutagenic treatment.

ochre mutants are not induced to revert by hydroxylamine, and we conclude that in neither mutant, does the triplet in the DNA contain G—C pairs, or, if a G—C pair is present, that triplet is connected by a G—C → A—T transition to another nonsense codon. In other words, subject to the last important reservation, we can conclude that the codons on the messenger RNA contain neither G nor C.

However, we next discovered that *ochre* mutants can be converted into *amber* mutants by mutation. Since *ochre* mutants are not suppressed by *amber* suppressors, plating on strains carrying such suppressors selects for *amber* revertants. Wild-type revertants also grow, but the two can be distinguished by testing revertant plaques on the *su⁻* strain. Twenty-six *r*II *ochre* mutants have been studied and, of these, 25 have been converted into *amber* mutants. A sample of the results is given in Table 3, which shows that the mutation is strongly induced by 2-aminopurine, as strongly as the reversion of the *ochre* mutant to wild type. Other experiments, not reported here, show that the mutations of *ochre* mutants both to the *amber* and to the wild type are also induced by 5-bromouracil, but the induction is weaker than with 2-aminopurine. These results prove that the *amber* and *ochre* triplets differ from each other by only one nucleotide base, and must have the other two bases in common. 2-Aminopurine is a base analogue mutagen inducing the transition A—T ⇌ G—C in both directions[13].

This tells us that one of the triplets has a G—C pair in the DNA. The experiment reported in Table 4 shows that *ochre* mutants cannot be induced to mutate to *amber* mutants with hydroxylamine, even after the treated phages have been grown in *E. coli* B. This shows that it is the *amber* triplet which has the G—C pair and the *ochre* which contains the A—T pair.

Although the insensitivity of the mutants to reversion induction by hydroxylamine might suggest that they contain A—T base pairs only, the conversion of *ochre* mutants to *amber* mutants shows that, in one position, the *amber* mutant contains a G—C pair. The other two bases must be common to both triplets, but we cannot conclude that both are A—T pairs. In fact, both could be G—C pairs and the triplets may be connected to other nonsense triplets by G—C → A—T changes. However, we know that *amber* and *ochre* mutants can be induced by hydroxyl-

Table 3. MUTATION OF *ochre* MUTANTS TO *amber* MUTANTS

	Spontaneous	Reversion index × 10⁻⁷	
		2-Aminopurine	
*r*IIA cistron	(wild type + *ambers*)	wild type	*amber*
N55	0·5	830	280
X20	0·05	100	2,100
X372	0·1	300	2,100
X352	0·06	340	1,500
HD147	0·3	370	50
*r*IIB cistron			
X511	0·2	710	65
N17	0·2	610	80
SD160	0·6	380	390
N29	1·0	3,900	330
AP53	0·7	350	15

Cultures of *E. coli* B in minimal medium with and without 2-aminopurine (600 μg/ml.) were inoculated with about 100 phages and grown to lysis. These were plated on *E. coli* B and on *E. coli* K12(λ) *su⁺*₁. About 50 induced revertants were tested on *E. coli* K12(λ) *su⁻* to measure the relative frequencies of *amber* revertants.

Table 4. INDUCTION OF THE *ochre*→*amber* MUTATION

		Reversion index × 10⁻⁷	
		r⁺	*amber*
360	Control	0·6	0·2
	Hydroxylamine	0·8	0·3
	2AP	200	1,200
UV375	Control	0·8	0·4
	Hydroxylamine	2·0	1·0
	2AP	660	140
X27	Control	0·3	< 0·1
	Hydroxylamine	1·0	0·5
	2AP	7·0	73
375	Control	0·8	0·4
	Hydroxylamine	2·0	1·0
	2AP	1,400	1,700

Hydroxylamine treatment and growth of the mutagenized phages, and 2-aminopurine induction, were carried out as described in Tables 2 and 3.

nine from wild type. This proves that both triplets have at least one common A—T pair.

We now present an experiment which shows that the amber triplet has two A—T base pairs, and which also establishes the orientation of the pairs with respect to the two strands of DNA. Let us suppose that the amber triplet in the messenger RNA contains a U. This corresponds to an A in the sense strand of DNA of the amber mutant, implying that the wild-type DNA contains a T in this strand and a C in the antisense strand. When the wild-type DNA is treated with hydroxylamine to alter this C the change is not effective and normal messenger is still made (Fig. 2, right). On the other hand, if the amber triplet in the messenger contains an A, the mutant will be induced by the action of hydroxylamine on a C in the sense strand of the wild-type phage DNA, and provided that the U' produced acts identically to U in messenger synthesis, mutant messenger will be made. This argument has been tested by the following experiment. Wild-type T4r+ phages were treated with hydroxylamine to induce r mutants to a frequency of 1 per cent. In set B, the phages were then grown on E. coli B, in which the rII functions are not required, to recover all mutants. In set K, the phages were grown through E. coli K12(λ) su⁻, to eliminate from the population all phages with an immediate mutant expression. Amber and ochre mutants were then selected and mapped. Table 5 summarizes the results. About the same number of rI mutants were recorded in each set, and since these mutants show no difference in growth on the two bacterial strains, this shows that the results may be compared directly. It will be seen that amber mutants at the sites, N97, S116, S24, N34, X237 and HB232, recur many times in set B, but are absent or rarely found in set K. At other amber sites, such as HB118, HB129, EM84 and AP164, mutants occur with approximately equal frequency in both sets. The first class fulfils the expectation for a C → U change on the sense strand, while the second class must arise by C → U changes on the antisense strand. This shows that

the amber triplet in the messenger contains both an A and a U. The same should be true of the ochre mutants. However, as shown in Table 5, ochre mutants are not as strongly induced by hydroxylamine as are amber mutants, and we cannot separate the two classes with the same degree of confidence. Nevertheless, since we have already shown that the mutants are connected, it follows that the ochre triplet must also contain an A and a U. We conclude that the amber and ochre triplets are, respectively, either (UAG) and (UAA), or (UAC) and (UAU). If we had a strain which suppressed ochre mutants only, we could specify the third base by studying the induction of the amber → ochre change with hydroxylamine.

Fortunately, we can resolve the ambiguity by determining the amino-acids to which the amber triplet is connected by mutation. In particular, we note that it should be connected to two and only two amino-acid codons by transitions, corresponding, in fact, to the two types of origin of the mutants described here. The third codon to which it is connected by a transition is the ochre triplet. As mentioned earlier, the head amber mutant H36 has arisen from glutamine (Fig. 1). This mutant was induced with hydroxylamine. We have evidence that two other mutants, E161 and B278 induced by 2-aminopurine and 5-bromouracil respectively, have arisen from tryptophan. In a recent study of two amber mutants of the alkaline phosphatase, Garen and Weigert[14] found one mutant to arise from glutamine and the other from tryptophan; and Notani et al.[15] have found an amber mutant to arise from glutamine in the RNA phage f2. In addition, we have examined 2-aminopurine induced revertants of 10 different head amber mutants. Ten to 12 independently induced revertants of each of the mutants have been screened for tryptophan containing peptides by examining the ¹⁴C-tryptophan labelled protein. Among a total of 115 revertants, 62 are to tryptophan. Determination of glutamine involves sequence analysis and takes more time. So far, among the remaining 53 revertants, glutamine has been identified in one revertant of H36. These results suggest that the two amino-acids connected to the amber triplet are glutamine and tryptophan. If the amber triplet is (UAC), then one of these must be (CAC) and the other (UGC); if it is (UAG), then the corresponding codons are (CAG) and (UGG). Nirenberg et al.[16] have shown that poly AC does not code for tryptophan, but does for glutamine. However, they find that the triplet for glutamine clearly has the composition (CAA) and is definitely not (CAC). Since this latter triplet corresponds neither to glutamine nor to tryptophan we can eliminate the first alternative. We note with satisfaction that (UGG) is the composition of a codon assigned to tryptophan[16,17], and this assignment of (UAG) to the amber triplet suggests that glutamine is (CAG).

We can also make a reasonable assignment of the order of the bases in the triplet. Our original argument was based on deductions from a few known triplets and from amino-acid replacement data; it will not be given here. The order of the bases follows directly from a recent demonstration by Nirenberg et al.[18] that the triplet CAG does, in fact, correspond to glutamine. The amber triplet is therefore UAG and the ochre triplet UAA. This assignment is supported by the following additional evidence. We have found a tyrosine replacement in 21 independent spontaneous mutants of the head amber mutant, H36 (ref. 19). This change must be due to a transversion because we have already accounted for all the transitions of the amber triplet. In support of this, we find that the change is not induced by 2-aminopurine. There are six possible transversions of the amber triplet, namely, AAG, GAG, UUG, UCG, UAU and UAC. It has recently been shown that both UAU and UAC correspond to tyrosine[20] which confirms the order. The spontaneous revertants of the amber mutants to leucine, serine and glutamic acid found by Weigert and Garen[21] are further evidence for the assignment. UUG, a transversion of the

Table 5. HYDROXYLAMINE INDUCTION OF amber AND ochre MUTANTS

No. of mutants isolated

	Set B	Set K
rI	2,010	1,823
Leaky or high reverting rII	720	508
non-suppressible rII	1,144	433
amber	319	121
ochre	83	82
Total	4,276	2,967

Recurrences found at different sites

Amber mutants No. found at each site Site	Set B	Set K	Ochre mutants No. found at each site Site	Set B	Set K
cistron			A cistron		
B118	27	15	HD147	2	0
204	1	0	HF220	1	0
97	44	1	HF240	1	0
116	31	2	N55	19	19
11	3	3	X20	9	8
172	9	5	HF219	1	0
24	44	3	HF245	1	0
B129	14	25	N31	3	5
99	12	16	HM127	0	1
19	15	9	N21	2	2
34	8	0			
cistron			B cistron		
E122	1	0	360	11	10
M84	29	21	UV375	2	0
B74	16	5	N24	6	4
237	14	2	375	2	5
P164	28	12	N17	5	3
B232	21	1	HF208	1	2
417	1	0	N7	4	12
D231	1	1	N12	5	7
			X234	0	2
			X191	1	0
			HE267	5	0
			AP53	2	2

T4Br+ was treated with M hydroxylamine (see Table 2) for 2 h at 37° C. Survival was 50 per cent, and the frequency of r and mottled plaques, 1 per cent. 1·2 × 10⁹ phage particles were adsorbed to 10⁹ cells of E. coli B (set B) and to E. coli K12(λ) su⁻ (set K). After 8 min, the infected bacteria were diluted a thousand-fold into 2 litres of broth, incubated for 35′ and lysed with CHCl₃. The burst sizes in both sets were 60. r mutants were isolated from each set using less than 2 ml. to ensure that the mutants selected had mostly arisen from independent events. These were picked and stabbed into B and K, and rI mutants and leaky mutants discarded. The rII mutants were then screened on su⁻III and su⁻B to select for amber and ochre mutants which were then located by genetic mapping.

amber triplet, does in fact code for leucine[22], and reasonable allocations for serine and glutamic acid are UCG and GAG, respectively. Weigert and Garen[21] also find revertants of an *amber* mutant to either lysine or arginine. This may be the final transversion expected since AAG is a codeword for lysine[20].

It should be noted that in the foregoing discussion it has been tacitly assumed that the *amber* and *ochre* signals are triplets. Examination of revertants of *amber* mutants has supported this assumption, since in 41 independent revertants of *H36* the amino-acid replaced is always at the site of mutation, and never in adjacent positions. The 21 revertants that Weigert and Garen[21] isolated reinforce this conclusion.

Function of amber and ochre triplets and the mechanism of suppression. According to present-day ideas of protein synthesis, it is expected that the termination of the growth of the polypeptide chain should involve a special mechanism. Since the terminal carboxyl group of the growing peptide chain is esterified to an *s*RNA (ref. 23), chain termination must involve not only the cessation of growth, but also the cleavage of this bond. Since the *amber* mutants have been shown to result in efficient termination of polypeptide chain synthesis, it is reasonable to suppose that this special mechanism may be provided by the *amber* and *ochre* triplets.

We postulate that the chain-terminating triplets UAA and UAG are recognized by specific *s*RNAs, just like other codons. These *s*RNAs do not carry amino-acids but a special compound which results in termination of the growing polypeptide chain. There are many possible ways of formulating the mechanism in detail, but all are speculative and will not be considered here. The essential feature of this hypothesis is to make the process of chain termination exactly congruent with that of chain extension.

In suppressing strains, a mechanism is provided for competing with chain termination; it is easy to visualize this process as being due to two ways of recognizing the nonsense codon—one by the chain-terminating *s*RNA, and the other by an *s*RNA carrying an amino-acid. Mechanisms of suppression can be classified according to which *s*RNA carries the amino-acid to the nonsense codon.

Alteration in the recognition of the chain-terminating *s*RNA might allow the attachment of an amino-acid to this *s*RNA. This could be brought about either by modifying normal activating enzymes so as to widen their specificity, or by changing the chain terminating *s*RNAs to allow them to be recognized by activating enzymes.

Another possibility is that the region of an amino-acyl *s*RNA used for triplet recognition is modified so that it can recognize the nonsense triplet. Clearly, this alteration must not affect the normal recognition of its own codon by the amino acyl *s*RNA because such a change would be lethal. Either there must be more than one gene for the given *s*RNA, or else the change must produce an ambiguity in the recognition site so that it can read both its own codon and the nonsense codon. Such ambiguity could result not only from mutation in the *s*RNA gene but also by enzymatic modification of one of the bases in the recognition site. The ambiguity, however, must be narrowly restricted to prevent the suppression from affecting codons other than the *amber* and *ochre* triplets. Moreover, the amino-acids which are inserted by the *amber* suppressors must be those the codons of which are connected to UAG. It should be noted that this condition is fulfilled by *su⁺₁* which inserts serine, since serine has been found as a reversion of an *amber* mutant. This theory does not easily explain the *ochre* suppressors. Since these recognize both *amber* and *ochre* mutants the *s*RNA must possess this ambiguity as well.

Another quite different possibility for suppression that has been considered is that the suppressors alter a component of the ribosomes to permit errors to occur in the reading of the messenger RNA (ref. 24). This is probably the explanation of streptomycin suppression[25], but suppression of *amber* and *ochre* mutants cannot be readily explained by this theory. It is scarcely likely that such a mechanism could be specific for only one or two triplets, and for this reason it might be expected to give us suppression of mutants which are not nonsense, but missense, and this has not been found[1,8]. Moreover, the efficiency of *amber* suppression argues strongly against such a mechanism. It is unlikely that a generalized error in reading nucleotides could produce the 60 per cent efficiency of suppression found for *su⁺₁* without seriously affecting the viability of the cell.

It is a consequence of our theory that normal chain termination could also be suppressed in these strains. Since the *amber* suppressors are efficient we have to introduce the *ad hoc* hypothesis that the UAG codon is rarely used for chain termination in *Escherichia coli* and bacteriophage *T4* and that UAA is the common codon. This is supported by the fact that all *ochre* suppressors thus far isolated are weak[7,8]. Another possibility is that neither is the common chain terminating triplet. We cannot exclude the existence of other chain terminating triplets which are not suppressible.

To summarize: we show that the triplets of the *amber* and *ochre* mutants are UAG and UAA, respectively. We suggest that the 'nonsense' codons should be more properly considered to be the codons for chain termination. In essence, this means that the number of elements to be coded for is not 20 but more likely 21. We propose that the recognition of the chain-terminating codons is carried out by two special *s*RNAs.

We thank our colleagues for their advice, and Dr. M Nirenberg for allowing us to quote his unpublished results

[1] Benzer, S., and Champe, S. P., *Proc. U.S. Nat. Acad. Sci.*, **47**, 1025 (1961); **48**, 1114 (1962).

[2] Garen, A., and Siddiqi, O., *Proc. U.S. Nat. Acad. Sci.*, **48**, 1121 (1962).

[3] Campbell, A., *Virology*, **14**, 22 (1961).

[4] Epstein, R. H., Bolle, A., Steinberg, C. M., Kellenberger, E., Boy de la Tour, E., Chevalley, R., Edgar, R. S., Susman, M., Denhardt, G. H., and Lielausis, A., *Cold Spring Harbour Symp. Quant. Biol.*, **28**, 375 (1963).

[5] Sarabhai, A., Stretton, A. O. W., Brenner, S., and Bolle, A., *Nature*, **201**, 13 (1964).

[6] Stretton, A. O. W., and Brenner, S., *J. Mol. Biol.* (in the press).

[7] Kaplan, S., Stretton A. O. W., and Brenner, S. (in preparation).

[8] Brenner, S., and Beckwith, J. R. (in preparation).

[9] Brenner, S., and Stretton, A. O. W. (in preparation).

[10] Brown, D. M., and Schell, P., *J. Mol. Biol.*, **3**, 709 (1961). Freese, E., Bautz-Freese, E., and Bautz, E., *J. Mol. Biol.*, **3**, 133 (1961). Schuster, H., *J. Mol. Biol.*, **3**, 447 (1961). Freese, E., Bautz, E., and Freese, E. B., *Proc. U.S. Nat. Acad. Sci.*, **47**, 845 (1961).

[11] Tocchini-Valentini, G. P., Stodolsky, M., Aurisicchio, A., Sarnat, M., Graziosi, F., Weiss, S. B., and Geiduschek, E. P., *Proc. U.S. Nat. Acad. Sci.*, **50**, 935 (1963). Hayashi, M., Hayashi, M. N., and Spiegelman, S., *Proc. U.S. Nat. Acad. Sci.*, **50**, 664 (1963). Marmur, J., Greenspan, C. M., Palacek, E., Kahan, F. M., Levene, J., and Mandel, M., *Cold Spring Harbor Symp. Quant. Biol.*, **28**, 191 (1963). Bautz, E. K. F., Green, M., Nygaard, A. P., and Boezi, J., *Cold Spring Harbor Symp. Quant. Biol.*, **28**, 201 (1963).

[12] Champe, S. P., and Benzer, S., *Proc. U.S. Nat. Acad. Sci.*, **48**, 532 (1962). Tessman, I., Poddar, R. K., and Kumar, S., *J. Mol. Biol.*, **9**, 352 (1964).

[13] Freese, E., *J. Mol. Biol.*, **1**, 87 (1959). Freese, E., *Proc. U.S. Nat. Acad. Sci.*, **45**, 622 (1959). Howard, B. D., and Tessman, I., *J. Mol. Biol.*, **9**, 372 (1964).

[14] Garen, A., and Weigert, M., *J. Mol. Biol.* (in the press).

[15] Notani, G. W., Engelhardt, D. L., Konigsberg, W., and Zinder, N., *J. Mol. Biol.* (in the press).

[16] Nirenberg, M., Jones, O. W., Leder, P., Clark, B. F. C., Sly, W. S., and Pestka, S., *Cold Spring Harbor Symp. Quant., Biol.*, **28**, 549 (1963).

[17] Speyer, J. F., Lengyel, P., Basilio, C., Wahba, A. J., Gardner, R. S., and Ochoa, S., *Cold Spring Harbor Symp. Quant. Biol.*, **28**, 559 (1963).

[18] Nirenberg, M., Leder, P., Bernfield, M., Brimacombe, R., Trupin, J., and Rottman, F., *Proc. U.S. Nat. Acad. Sci.* (in the press).

[19] Stretton, A. O. W., and Brenner, S. (in preparation).

[20] Trupin, J., Rottman, F., Brimacombe, R., Leder, P., Bernfield, M., and Nirenberg, M., *Proc. U.S. Nat. Acad. Sci.* (in the press). Clark, B. F. C. presented before the French Biochemical Society, February, 1965.

[21] Weigert, M. G., and Garen, A., *Nature* (preceding communication).

[22] Leder, P., and Nirenberg, M. W., *Proc. U.S. Nat. Acad. Sci.*, **52**, 1521 (1964).

[23] Gilbert, W., *J. Mol. Biol.*, **6**, 389 (1963). Bretscher, M. S., *J. Mol. Biol.*, **7**, 446 (1963).

[24] Davies, J., Gilbert, W., and Gorini, L., *Proc. U.S. Nat. Acad. Sci.*, **51**, 883 (1964).

[25] Gorini, L., and Kataja, E., *Proc. U.S. Nat. Acad. Sci.*, **51**, 487 (1964).

MISSENSE SUPPRESSION OF THE TRYPTOPHAN SYNTHETASE A-PROTEIN MUTANT A78*

By Naba K. Gupta and H. Gobind Khorana

INSTITUTE FOR ENZYME RESEARCH OF THE UNIVERSITY OF WISCONSIN, MADISON

Communicated June 23, 1966

Certain suppressor mutations are known which lead to the formation of a functional enzyme in a mutant strain which normally produces an inactive protein.[1] This type of suppression, missense suppression, has been shown to result in the replacement of one amino acid by another in a small fraction of the protein molecules.[2] Thus both the inactive mutant protein and an active enzyme resembling the wild-type protein are produced by the suppressed mutant. For example, mutant A78 of *E. coli* produces an inactive tryptophan synthetase A protein which has a particular glycine residue replaced by cysteine.[3] A suppressed mutant, strain A78-su78, has been isolated in which A-protein activity is restored to the extent of about 2 per cent that of the wild-type A protein.[4] It has been suggested that missense suppression may result from the alteration of one of the cellular components involved in translation, such that the "incorrect" amino acid is occasionally incorporated in response to a given sense codon. Specifically, in the case of strain A78-su78, missense suppression is believed to involve the insertion of glycine in response to a cysteine codon (UGU or UGC).

Synthetic ribopolynucleotides containing two nucleotides in alternating sequence have been shown to direct the *in vitro* formation of specific copolypeptides containing two amino acids in alternating sequence.[5, 6] Thus, for example, poly UG[7] directs the synthesis of a valine-cysteine copolypeptide in a cell-free amino acid incorporating system from *E. coli* B.[6] If suppression resulted in the occasional misreading of one of the codons in these ribopolynucleotides such that an incorrect amino acid were incorporated, it should be demonstrable in the cell-free amino acid-incorporating system, and the nature of the altered component of the translation apparatus could thus be specified. At the suggestion and encouragement of Dr. Charles Yanofsky, we have investigated the nature of the change in the suppressed strain A78-su78. The results, which are reported herein, show that poly UG does, in fact, direct the synthesis of a valine-glycine copolypeptide when the amino acid-incorporating system from the B strain of *E. coli* is supplemented specifically by tRNA from the suppressed mutant A78-su78.

A similar result has been obtained by Carbon, Berg, and Yanofsky[8] with a different suppressed mutant, A36-su36. These authors found that poly AG,[7] which normally directs the synthesis of a glutamic acid-arginine copolypeptide,[6] directs the incorporation of C^{14}-glycine in the presence of glutamic acid when tRNA from the suppressed mutant is added to the amino acid-incorporating system from the nonsuppressed strain. Previously, tRNA has been shown to be responsible for suppression of an amber codon in the genetic material specifying a bacteriophage coat protein.[9, 10]

Materials and Methods.—Poly d(TG:CA)[7] was prepared[11] and generously supplied by Dr. R. D. Wells. Uniformly labeled C^{14}-glycine (66 $\mu c/\mu mole$) and C^{14}-valine (185 $\mu c/\mu mole$) were commercial products. Unlabeled ribonucleoside triphosphates were purchased from Pabst Laboratories. Valylglycine and related di- and tripeptides were obtained from Mann Research Laboratories.

Cultures and culture procedures: Mutant A78 was produced by ultraviolet irradiation of the Ymel stock of the K-12 strain of *E. coli*.[3] Suppressed mutant A78-su78 was isolated as a slow-growing prototroph arising from A78. Genetic tests established that prototrophy was due to suppression. Mutants and suppressed mutants were grown on minimal medium[12] and harvested in late log phase. Cell pastes of mutant A-78 and of suppressed mutant A78-su78 were generously supplied by Dr. Yanofsky.

Preparation of ribosomes and the supernatant fraction from E. coli B: *E. coli* B ribosomes and dialyzed 100,000 *g* supernatant fractions were prepared by a modification of the procedure described by Nishimura *et al.*[13] To the *S*30 supernatant solution was slowly added solid ammonium sulfate (0.14 gm/ml) as described by Wood and Berg.[14] During the addition of solid ammonium sulfate the solution was stirred and the pH of the solution was adjusted to 7.0 by the dropwise addition of 1 *M* ammonium hydroxide. After stirring for 10 min the suspension was centrifuged at 20,000 *g* for 20 min. The supernatant fraction was centrifuged at 100,000 *g* for 2 hr. The ribosomal pellet thus obtained was suspended gently in 2 *M* KCl, 0.03 *M* magnesium acetate, 0.006 *M* β-mercaptoethanol and 0.01 *M* Tris-HCl pH 7.8 overnight at 4°C. The suspension was then gently dispersed and the solution centrifuged at 10,000 *g* for 10 min to remove any insoluble material. The ribosomes were then sedimented at 100,000 *g* for 2 hr and the pellet was suspended in the standard buffer and the suspension stored frozen in liquid nitrogen.

The 100,000 *g* supernatant fraction obtained above after 2 hr centrifugation was again centrifuged at 100,000 *g* for 6 hr. Approximately $^2/_3$ of the supernatant fraction was carefully pipetted off and dialyzed against standard buffer for 20 hr at 2°C with three changes of the buffer. The dialyzed solution was stored in liquid nitrogen.

Preparation of RNA polymerase: The RNA polymerase preparation was fraction 4 in the procedure of Chamberlin and Berg.[15] The preparation incorporated 2750 mμmoles of C^{14} CTP/hr/mg, using calf thymus DNA as the template under the assay conditions of Chamberlin and Berg.[15]

Preparation of tRNA: *E. coli* B tRNA, prepared according to Zubay's method,[16] was kindly supplied by Dr. D. S. Jones. A36-su36 tRNA was a gift from Dr. P. Berg; A78 tRNA and A78-su78 tRNA were prepared by a modification of Zubay's method. The preparation was carried through to the second ethanol precipitation step as described by Zubay.[16] The precipitate was dissolved in 0.3 *M* sodium acetate and *iso*propyl alcohol fractionation was carried out as described. The tRNA fraction was dissolved in 0.1 *M* Tris HCl, pH 9.0, and the solution was incubated at 37° for 1 hr. The solution was further purified by chromatography on a DEAE-cellulose column in 0.02 *M* Tris HCl, pH 7.4.

Paper chromatography: Descending technique with Whatman 3 MM paper was used. The solvent systems used were solvent I, *n*-butanol–water–acetic acid (4:5:1); solvent II, ethanol–water (77:23). The R_f values for glycine and the peptides in solvent I were gly, 0.19; gly-gly, 0.18; val-gly, 0.37; gly-val, 0.40; val-gly-gly, 0.28; gly-gly-val, 0.41.

Assay of polypeptide synthesis: The two-step reaction procedure described by Jones *et al.*[6] was used for cell-free polypeptide synthesis. The components of the reaction mixture in step 1 were the same as described before. The reaction mixture in step 2 contained per ml 42 μmoles Tris-HCl (pH 7.8), 7 μmoles of magnesium acetate, 1.25 μmoles of magnesium chloride, 12 μmoles of β-mercaptoethanol, 0.3 μmole of manganese chloride, 27 μmoles of potassium chloride, 0.2 μmole of GTP, 1.6 μmoles of ATP, 4 μmoles of phosphoenolpyruvate, 6 μg of phosphoenolpyruvate kinase, 22.5 OD$_{260}$ units of ribosomes, 20–30 OD$_{260}$ units of tRNA, 2.5 μc of C^{14} amino acids as specified, 125 mμmoles of C^{12} amino acids where indicated, and poly d(TG:AC), poly UG, excess nucleoside triphosphates, and RNA polymerase as introduced from the first stage of the reaction. The reaction mixture was incubated at 0°C for 10 min and then 320 μg of 100,000 *g* supernatant fraction was added. Incubation was carried out at 37°C and aliquots (50 μl) of the reaction mixture were removed and assayed for C^{14}-incorporation as described by Jones *et al.*[6]

Large-scale preparation of C^{14}-labeled copolypeptide: The first-stage reaction mixture contained in 0.36 ml: 165 mμmoles each of UTP and GTP, 100 mμmoles of poly d(TG:AC), and 0.75 mg of RNA polymerase in addition to the other components as described above. The incubation was carried out at 37° for 1 hr. After the first-stage reaction, 2.5 μc of C^{14}-glycine and 25 OD of either A78 tRNA or A78-su78 tRNA were added in addition to other components described above, in a total volume of 1.25 ml. After incubation for $3^{1}/_{2}$ hr at 37°, the reaction mixtures were chilled in ice and 12 μl of 10 N sodium hydroxide was added. The solution was allowed to stand at room temperature for 1 hr. The total protein fraction was then precipitated by the addition of 60 μl of 100% trichloroacetic acid. The precipitate was washed 3 times with cold 5% trichloroacetic acid, twice with ethyl alcohol–ether (1:1) and twice with ether.

Characterization of polypeptidic product: Acidic hydrolysis and Edman degradation of C^{14}-valyl-glycine dipeptide: The C^{14}-labeled product obtained in the large-scale preparation was dissolved in 0.5 ml of 10 N HCl, and the solution was incubated at 37 or 50°C. Aliquots were spotted on Whatman no. 3 paper along with appropriate markers. After development in solvent I, the chromatograms were cut into $^{1}/_{x}$-in. pieces and the strips counted in a liquid scintillation spectrometer. The radioactive spot at the position corresponding to the valylglycine dipeptide was eluted from the paper and the eluate (700 cpm) evaporated to dryness. The residue was dissolved in 0.1 ml and to it was added 0.2 ml of a 5% solution in pyridine[17] of phenylisothiocyanate, and the resulting solution was kept overnight at room temperature. After addition of 0.2 ml of water, excess phenylisothiocyanate was removed by four extractions with 3 ml of benzene, and a portion (0.1 ml) of the aqueous solution was applied to a paper chromatogram. The remainder of the aqueous solution was evaporated and 0.2 ml of acetic acid saturated with anhydrous hydrogen chloride was added. After 1 hr at room temperature, the acid was removed *in vacuo* and 50 mμ-moles of cold glycine in 1 ml of water was added to the residue. The solution was evaporated to dryness and the residue was dissolved in 0.1 ml water and applied to paper chromatograms alongside a glycine marker. The chromatogram was developed in solvent I.

Results.—Comparison of tRNA from E. coli strains A78 and A78-su78 for poly UG-directed synthesis of valine-cysteine copolypeptide: The results shown in Figure 1 provide, in part, a confirmation of the previous finding of Jones, Nishimura, and Khorana[6] in that the incorporation of C^{14}-valine is dependent on the presence of poly UG and cysteine. The incorporation of C^{14}-valine is seen to be dependent on the addition of tRNA to the amino acid-incorporating system used in the present experiments. The results in Figure 1 also show that equivalent amounts of tRNA's prepared from strains A78 and A78-su78 are indistinguishable in their capacity to stimulate the incorporation of C^{14}-valine.

Comparison of different tRNA preparations for C^{14}-glycine incorporation: Poly UG specifically directs the incorporation of valine and cysteine only.[6] When C^{14}-glycine was tested in the presence of the remaining 19 cold amino acids, no

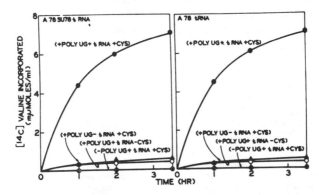

Fig. 1.—Characteristics of the incorporation of C^{14}-valine in the presence of A78-su78 tRNA and A78 tRNA. The reaction mixture at the first stage contained, per ml, 0.62 mg of RNA polymerase, 20 mμmoles of poly d(TG:AC), 0.33 μmole of UTP, and 0.33 μmole of GTP. Incubation was at 37° for 1 hr. These reaction mixtures were taken to the second stage as described in *Materials and Methods.* In the second-stage reaction 13.5 mμmoles of C^{14}-valine (185 μc/μmole), 125 mμmoles cold cysteine, 10 OD tRNA were added where indicated.

incorporation was previously detected. In the present experiments, C^{14}-glycine incorporation was tested in the presence of tRNA preparations from different sources. The results in Figure 2 show that a clear stimulation of C^{14}-glycine incorporation was given by A78-su78 tRNA. This incorporation was dependent on the presence of cold valine and poly UG. Some glycine incorporation was also observed in the absence of cold valine. As discussed below, the nature of this incorporation is not understood. The results summarized in Table 1 show that of the various tRNA preparations tested, only A78-su78 tRNA and A36-su36-su78 tRNA were active in valine-glycine copolypeptide synthesis. The *E. coli* strain A36-su36-su78 has previously been shown to contain two suppressor genes, one specific for mutant A36 and the other specific for mutant A78.[18] Carbon *et al.*[8] have shown that the tRNA preparation from this strain is also active in glutamic acid-glycine copolypeptide synthesis under the direction of poly AG.

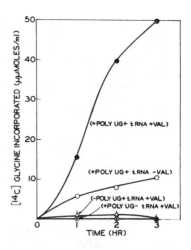

FIG. 2.—Characteristics of the incorporation of C^{14}-glycine in the presence of A78-su78 tRNA preparations. The reaction mixtures at the first stage were the same as described in Fig. 1. In the second-stage reaction 37.5 mμmoles C^{14}-glycine, 125 mμmoles cold valine, 20 OD A78-su78 tRNA were added.

Characterization of the C^{14}-glycine-valine copolypetide: (a) *Acidic hydrolysis:* Acid-insoluble polypeptides containing C^{14}-glycine were prepared as described under *Materials and Methods.* The tRNA used was either from A78-su78 or from A78, and both the incubations were in the presence and absence of cold valine. The radioactive polypeptides obtained were incubated in 10 *N* HCl at 37° and the products were separated and analyzed for radioactivity as described above. Figure 3 shows only the results obtained after acidic hydrolysis for 15 days. The C^{14}-products obtained using tRNA from A78-su78 but no valine (Fig. 3*A*) or using tRNA from A78 with and without valine (Fig. 3*C* and *D*) all released the total of radioactivity in the form of a peak corresponding to glycine. The appearance of this peak was rapid, the maximum being reached within 1 day at 37°. The poly-

TABLE 1

COMPARISON OF DIFFERENT PREPARATIONS FOR
POLY UG-STIMULATED C^{14}-GLYCINE
INCORPORATION IN THE PRESENCE
OF COLD VALINE

tRNA added	μμMoles C^{14}-glycine incorporated/ml incubation mixture
A78-su78	41.4
A36-su36-su78	18.2
A78	2.0
E. coli B	0
A36-su36	0

The reaction conditions were the same as described in Fig. 2. Equivalent amounts of different tRNA preparations were added at the second stage of the reaction in addition to the other components. C^{14}-glycine incorporation in the absence of poly UG was subtracted as background. Incubation time was 2 hr.

TABLE 2

EFFECT OF CYSTEINE ON POLY UG-STIMULATED
C^{14}-GLYCINE INCORPORATION IN THE PRESENCE
OF COLD VALINE

tRNA used	Additions	μμMoles C^{14}-glycine incorporated/ml
A78-su78	None	56
A78-su78	Cysteine	43.8
A78	None	5.8
A78	Cysteine	43.5

The reaction conditions were the same as described in Fig. 2. Where indicated, cold cysteine (125 mμmoles, ml) was added. Incubation time was 3½ hr at 37°.

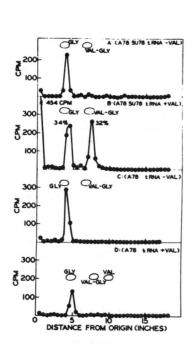

Fig. 3.—Characterization of C14-glycine peptides formed in the presence of A78-su78 tRNA and A78 tRNA. The polypeptide was dissolved in 10 N HCl and incubated at 37° for 15 days. An aliquot was then spotted on Whatman no. 3 paper and developed in solvent I. The chromatograms were cut in $1/2$-in.-wide strips and counted for radioactivity in the scintillation counter.

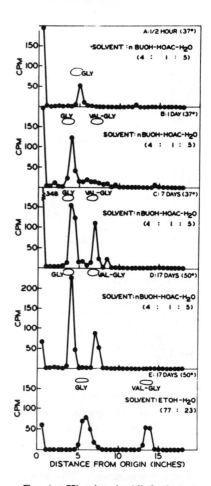

Fig. 4.—Kinetics of acidic hydrolysis of C14-glycine peptide formed in the presence of A78-su78 tRNA and valine. The polypeptide was kept in 10 N HCl and portions were removed and chromatographed in two solvent systems as indicated. Time and temperature of incubation conditions are shown in the figure.

peptidic products obtained in the presence of tRNA from A78-su78 and valine gave the glycine peak, but, in addition, this incubation mixture was *unique* in that the major portion of the radioactivity appeared in the form of a product which slowly hydrolyzed to form a dipeptide with the R_f of markers valylglycine and glycylvaline. Kinetics of acidic hydrolysis of C14-glycine-containing products obtained in the presence of tRNA from A78-su78 and cold valine are further shown in Figure 4. The patterns in Figure 4D and E are those of another sample similarly prepared but incubated at 50° for 17 days. The use of two different solvent systems (Fig. 4D and E) further demonstrates the formation of a product different from glycine and identical in R_f value with the marker dipeptide, valylglycine. It should be added that under the prolonged incubation periods used, the radioactivity in the

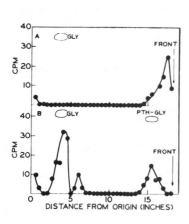

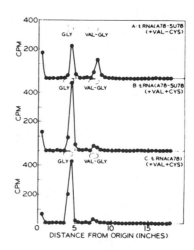

FIG. 5.—Characterization of C14-valyl-glycine dipeptide by Edman degradation. (*A*) Product of reaction of valyl-glycine dipeptide with phenyl*iso*thiocyanate. (*B*) Products released after thiohydantoin step in Edman degradation. Paper chromatography was in solvent I.

FIG. 6.—Effect of cysteine on the nature of C14-glycine peptide formation in the presence of A78 tRNA and A78-su78 tRNA. The polypeptide formed in the presence or absence of cysteine was dissolved in 10 N HCl and incubated at 50° for 5 days. An aliquot was then spotted on Whatman no. 3 paper and developed in solvent I.

C14-glycine peak continued to increase steadily. Under these conditions an authentic sample of valylglycine was found to undergo considerable hydrolysis, and it is therefore likely that the radioactive material at the origin was first converted to valine-glycine dipeptide and/or oligopeptides, which, in turn, hydrolyzed to free amino acids.

(b) *Edman degradation:* The above radioactive product with the R_f of valylglycine was reacted with phenylisothiocyanate and the resulting product was chromatographed in solvent I. The pattern of radioactivity (Fig. 5*A*) showed the expected formation of a compound with an R_f much higher than that of the starting material. This derivative was treated with acid and the product was chromatographed in the same solvent. The results are presented in Figure 5*B*. Approximately 65 per cent of the total radioactivity appeared in the form of free glycine, indicating that at least 65 per cent of the original dipeptide consisted of valyl-C14-glycine.[19] The formation of a second radioactive product traveling near the front was also noted. This presumably was phenylthiohydantoin of C14-glycine and could have originated from C14-glycylvaline.

Inhibition of valine-glycine copolypeptide synthesis by cysteine: Preparations of tRNA from A78-su78 support the synthesis of a valyl-cysteine copolypeptide (in the presence of valine and cysteine) and of a valyl-glycine copolypeptide (in the presence of valine and glycine). It was of interest to examine the effect of cysteine on C14-glycine incorporation in the presence of valine. The results of isotope incorporation experiments (Table 2) using A78-su78 sRNA showed about 20 per cent inhibition of C14-glycine incorporation in the presence of cold cysteine. With A78 tRNA, a severalfold increase of C14-glycine incorporation on addition of cysteine was actually observed. Because of the above-described incorporation of glycine into material other than a valine-glycine copolypeptide, the C^{14}-labeled products (experiments of Table 2) were further analyzed by acidic hydrolysis. The results shown in Figure 6 indicate that the increased incorporation of C^{14}-glycine occurred in a form that rapidly released free glycine. Cysteine markedly inhibited C^{14}-glycine incorporation into the valine-glycine copolypeptide in the presence of A78-su78 tRNA.

Discussion.—The studies in this paper clearly show that the suppressed mutant, A78-su78, but not its parental strain, A78, contains an altered tRNA which brings about the incorporation of glycine in response to a codon for cysteine. Thus when poly UG, which contains alternating cysteine (UGU) and valine (GUG) codons, is used as the messenger in the *in vitro* amino acid-incorporating system, glycine is incorporated in the presence of valine and A78-su78 tRNA. By characterization of the polypeptidic product formed, the above incorporation has been demonstrated to occur in positions adjacent to valine. This substitution of glycine in place of cysteine accounts for the formation of a functional A protein by the suppressed mutant, since the change responsible for the inactivity of the A protein in A78 mutant is from glycine → cysteine. It is also clear from the *in vitro* data obtained in this study that in the presence of poly UG, tRNA preparations from the suppressed mutant incorporate glycine poorly in the presence of valine, compared with cysteine incorporation in the presence of valine. This observation is consistent with *in vivo* data which suggest that only a small fraction of the A-protein molecules produced by the suppressed mutant have glycine at the critical position.

The data obtained in this study show that the addition of cold cysteine inhibited the formation of the valine-glycine copolypeptide. While in these experiments unfractionated tRNA was used, further experiments have been carried out using fractionated tRNA species. Countercurrent distribution of A78-su78 tRNA yields an enriched (at least tenfold) suppressor tRNA preparation, which is well resolved from the bulk of glycine-tRNA and cysteine-tRNA.[20] Addition of cold cysteine and cysteine-tRNA again inhibited the suppressor tRNA activity as measured by poly UG-directed incorporation of C^{14}-glycine in the presence of cold valine and valine-tRNA. From these results, it may tentatively be concluded that the altered A78-su78 tRNA competes with normal cysteine-donating tRNA and that, therefore, the presence of an excess of cysteine competitively inhibits the incorporation of glycine.

In their study of the *in vitro* suppression of the A36 change (glycine→arginine), Carbon *et al.* observed that the addition of arginine had no effect on glutamic acid-glycine copolypeptide synthesis under the direction of poly AG. This result is in contrast with the inhibition herein described of valine-glycine copolypeptide synthesis upon the addition of cysteine. Further studies are clearly necessary to explain the different results obtained in the two systems.

While the involvement of tRNA in missense suppression in A78-su78 and A36-su36[8] is firmly established, the origin of the altered tRNA in the suppressed mutants remains unknown. The most likely possibilities for A78-su78 tRNA are that it is a glycine tRNA with a change in its anticodon, or it is an altered cysteine tRNA which now accepts glycine in place of cysteine. Whatever the nature of the change, it would appear that a very minor species of tRNA is involved since the countercurrent distribution studies referred to above have shown that the suppressor tRNA constitutes a very small fraction of the total glycine acceptor activity present in strain A78-su78.

Summary.—Poly UG, which contains uridylate and guanylate nucleotides in alternating sequence, has previously been shown to direct the synthesis of a valine-cysteine copolypeptide in the cell-free amino acid-incorporating system prepared from *E. coli* B. The same messenger is now shown to direct the synthesis of a copolypeptide of valine and glycine in the presence of valine and glycine when the standard incorporating system from *E. coli* B is supplemented by transfer RNA from the missense suppressed strain A78-su78. Missense suppression in this strain of *E. coli* is thus shown to operate at the level of transfer RNA.

* This is paper LVIII in the series "Studies on Polynucleotides." Paper LVII is by Söll, D., D. S. Jones, E. Ohtsuka, R. D. Faulkner, R. Lohrmann, H. Hayatsu, H. G. Khorana, J. D. Cherayil, A. Hampel, and R. M. Bock, *J. Mol. Biol.*, in press.

[1] Yanofsky, C., D. Helinski, and B. Maling, in *Cold Spring Harbor Symposia on Quantitative Biology*, vol. 26 (1961), p. 11.

[2] Brody, S., and C. Yanofsky, these PROCEEDINGS, 50, 9 (1963).

[3] Guest, J. R., and C. Yanofsky, *J. Biol. Chem.*, 240, 679 (1965).

[4] Guest, J. R., and C. Yanofsky, *J. Mol. Biol.*, 12, 793 (1965).

[5] Nishimura, S., D. S. Jones, and H. G. Khorana, *J. Mol. Biol.*, 13, 302 (1965).

[6] Jones, D. S., S. Nishimura, and H. G. Khorana, *J. Mol. Biol.*, 16, 454 (1966).

[7] Poly UG and poly AG are the abbreviations for ribopolynucleotides containing, respectively, uridylate and guanylate units, and adenylate and guanylate units in alternating sequence. Poly d(TG:CA) is the abbreviation for double-stranded DNA-like polymer, one strand of which contains alternating thymidylate and deoxyguanylate units and the complementary strand of which contains alternating deoxycytidylate and deoxyadenylate units.

[8] Carbon, J., P. Berg, and C. Yanofsky, these PROCEEDINGS, 56, 764 (1966).

[9] Capecchi, M. R., and G. N. Gussin, *Science*, 149, 417 (1965).

[10] Engelhardt, D. L., R. E. Webster, R. C. Wilhelm, and N. D. Zinder, these PROCEEDINGS, 54, 1791 (1965).

[11] Wells, R. D., E. Ohtsuka, and H. G. Khorana, *J. Mol. Biol.*, 14, 221 (1965).

[12] Vogel, H., and D. M. Bonner, *J. Biol. Chem.*, 218, 97 (1956).

[13] Nishimura, S., D. S. Jones, E. Ohtsuka, H. Hayatsu, T. M. Jacob, and H. G. Khorana, *J. Mol. Biol.*, 13, 283 (1965).

[14] Wood, W. B., and P. Berg, these PROCEEDINGS, 48, 94 (1962).

[15] Chamberlin, M., and P. Berg, these PROCEEDINGS, 48, 81 (1962).

[16] Zubay, G., *J. Mol. Biol.*, 4, 317 (1962).

[17] Gray, W. R., and B. S. Hartley, *Biochem. J.*, 89, 379 (1963).

[18] Yanofsky, C., unpublished observations.

[19] This result is in accord with the theoretical expectation that a copolypeptide containing alternating valine and glycine residues would undergo preferential acidic hydrolysis at glycine sites rather than at the sterically hindered valine sites. Thus valylglycine would be the main expected dipeptidic product.

[20] Gupta, N. K., U. L. RajBhandary, and H. G. Khorana, in *Cold Spring Harbor Symposia on Quantitative Biology*, vol. 31 (1966), in press.

STREPTOMYCIN, SUPPRESSION, AND THE CODE*

By Julian Davies, Walter Gilbert, and Luigi Gorini

DEPARTMENT OF BACTERIOLOGY AND IMMUNOLOGY, HARVARD MEDICAL SCHOOL, AND
JEFFERSON LABORATORY OF PHYSICS, HARVARD UNIVERSITY

Communicated by James D. Watson, March 23, 1964

We have found that an external agent, streptomycin, can upset the genetic code, producing specific misreadings during *in vitro* polypeptide synthesis. This interference is at the level of the ribosome-messenger RNA-sRNA complex, for a modification in the ribosome makes the *in vitro* system insensitive to this effect.

Streptomycin[1] is a bacteriocidal agent. It is a basic molecule that can bind strongly to nucleic acids.[2] It interferes with and finally blocks protein synthesis while permitting continued RNA and DNA synthesis.[3] The mechanism of its killing is not known, but the existence of single mutations to high-level resistance suggests a unitary cause, a single, vital point of attack. Spotts and Stanier[4] hypothesized that the ribosomes were the sensitive elements, and work with the *in vitro* system, in which the poly U-directed incorporation of phenylalanine was shown to be inhibited by streptomycin,[5, 6] further implicated the ribosomes as the site of the shift from sensitivity to resistance. The sensitivity to streptomycin has just been shown by Davies[7] and by Cox, White, and Flaks[8] to reside on the 30s subunit of the 70s ribosome. If these 30s subunits are taken from a sensitive strain, the reconstructed *in vitro* system is sensitive, while if they are derived from a resistant strain, the system is resistant.

The Effects of Streptomycin on the Specificity of Amino Acid Incorporation.—Although the incorporation of phenylalanine into hot TCA-insoluble material is blocked (often by 50–75%) by streptomycin, the incorporation of other amino acids, not normally coded for by poly U, is stimulated, Table 1 shows that, using a purified system, the incorporation of isoleucine (UUA, UAA, CAU),[9] and to a much lesser extent serine (UUC, UCC, AGC) and leucine (UUA, UUC, UUG, UCC), is stimulated in the presence of streptomycin. The same is true for crude extracts (Table 2). Tyrosine (UUA) is not noticeably stimulated, nor are the other amino acids. Asparagine (CAA, CUA, UAA) was examined by damping the incorpo-

TABLE 1

C^{14} amino acid	−Poly U	+Poly U	+Sm, poly U
Ala	6	8	8
Arg	8	5	7
Asp	9	8	5
Cys	693	380	396
Glu	24	11	19
Gly	9	8	6
His	30	17	13
Ileu	6	17	340
Leu	17	96	130
Lys	28	21	33
Met	228	102	185
Phe	47	949	452
Pro	10	16	21
Ser	18	11	41
Thr	8	14	7
Try	480	418	482
Tyr	511	396	438
Val	9	13	17

Each amino acid was tested in a 0.050-ml reaction mixture like that for Fig. 2a, containing 0.4 μg of each of the 20 amino acids and 0.1 μC of the labeled amino acid, at 0.19 M NH$_4$+ and 0.0175 M Mg++. 0.3 μg poly U and 1 μg Sm were added as indicated. Results are expressed as cpm/reaction mixture. Significant changes produced by the antibiotic are underlined.

TABLE 2

C^{14} amino acid	−Poly U	Sm	+Poly U	Sm	Km	NeoB	NeoC	DHSm	Om
Phe	80	99	1035	1270	1050	735	690	1210	730
Leu	25	24	400	775	763	545	590	740	275
Ileu	13	13	88	925	985	805	895	860	50
Ser	20	30	36	140	545	515	565	104	23
Tyr	255	240	207	198	286	341	335	212	225

The reaction mixtures contained in 0.5 ml, 0.1 M Tris, pH 7.8; 0.01 M MgAc; 0.075 M NH$_4$Ac; 6 × 10^{-3} M mercaptoethanol; 1 × 10^{-3} M ATP; 5 × 10^{-3} M PEP; 20 μg PK; 3 × 10^{-4} M GTP; 2 × 10^{-4} M of each of 19 L-amino acids minus the C^{14} amino acid; 10^{-5} M C^{14} amino acid (approx. 50,000 cpm per reaction mixture); 20 μg of poly U, and 0.025 ml of dialyzed, preincubated *E. coli* crude extract[7] containing ca. 150–200 μg ribosomes. Antibiotics (5 μg/0.5 ml) were added before the poly U. Mixtures were incubated at 34°C for 30 min. The cpm per reaction mixture are given.

ration of a C^{14}-chlorella hydrolysate with the cold amino acid, with negative results. The experiments with purified ribosomes were done at the optimum ion concentration for phenylalanine incorporation, 17.5 mM Mg++ and 0.19 M NH$_4$+.

The incorporation of isoleucine and phenylalanine as a function of the magnesium concentration is shown in Figure 1. The ammonium concentration was 0.086 M and all twenty amino acids were present. In Figure 1a we see that the incorporation of isoleucine is stimulated by streptomycin by more than a factor of 10 at all magnesium levels, and reaches the same level as the phenylalanine incorporation. The optimum magnesium concentration for this incorporation is very high (about 30 mM at this particular ammonium ion concentration, higher than that for phenylalanine), and at the optimum more isoleucine than phenylalanine is inserted. There is a significant background incorporation of isoleucine in the absence of streptomycin at very high magnesium levels.. Figure 1b compares the streptomycin-stimulated incorporation of sensitive and resistant ribosomes, using a supernatant from a sensitive strain. The streptomycin-resistant ribosomes are essentially resistant to this miscoding.

The stimulation of isoleucine incorporation by magnesium ions alone is akin to the effects observed by Szer and Ochoa,[10] who have shown that the magnesium optimum for the poly U-directed incorporation of leucine was higher than that for

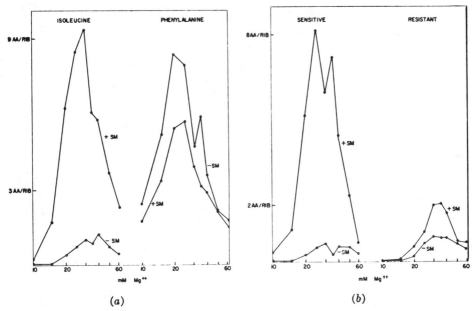

Fig. 1.—Streptomycin effect on the incorporation of isoleucine and phenylalanine at 0.086 M NH_4^+. 0.050-ml reaction mixtures contained 0.010 ml supernatant fraction from *E. coli* B (Sm^s) (the upper two thirds of a 5-hr, 100,000 g centrifugation of a crude extract), 10 μg ribosomes from *E. coli* C600 Sm^s or from a resistant mutant of this strain (the ribosomes were 70s ribosomes isolated on a gradient from an extract preincubated with puromycin (50 μg/ml) and the ATP generating system), 0.1 μg of each of the 20 amino acids and 0.25 μC of the labeled amino acid (0.14 μg of ileu or 0.12 μg of phe), 0.3 μg of poly U, 20 μg ATP, 12 μg GTP, 0.25 μM of PEP, 2 μg PK, 0.10 M Tris pH 7.5, 0.086 M NH$_4$Ac, and MgAc as specified. The mixtures were incubated for 90 min at 30°C. The results are given as moles of amino acid/mole of 70s ribosome; the ribosomes are limiting. Streptomycin (20 μg/ml) was added after messenger. (a) The magnesium dependence of the streptomycin stimulation of isoleucine incorporation and inhibition of phenylalanine incorporation on sensitive ribosomes. (b) Comparison of the stimulation of isoleucine incorporated on streptomycin-sensitive and -resistant ribosomes.

phenylalanine and that there were slight incorporations of isoleucine, serine, and tyrosine in high magnesium, when the amino acids were supplied singly. Our findings differ in that we are following incorporation in the presence of all the amino acids, and we are exploring a still higher (20–60 mM) range of magnesium concentrations.

There is also a monovalent ion effect: if we raise the ammonium ion concentration from 0.086 M to 0.19 M, much more isoleucine is incorporated in high magnesium. Figure 2a shows the streptomycin and magnesium effects in 0.19 M NH$_4^+$ ion. At 30–40 mM Mg^{++}, the code is perturbed sufficiently to put in equal parts of isoleucine and phenylalanine. The additional effect of streptomycin is now only a 2.5-fold stimulation of the isoleucine incorporation near the optimum, but at lower Mg^{++} levels the stimulation is much greater. Again, in Figure 2b, we see that resistant ribosomes do not miscode under the influence of streptomycin.

The Effect of Other Aminoglycoside Antibiotics.—Kanamycin and neomycins B and C are aminoglycoside antibiotics structurally related to streptomycin and appear to have a similar mechanism of action.[1, 11] The streptomycin-resistant strain used in this investigation was highly sensitive, like the streptomycin-sensitive parent, to the effect of these antibiotics *in vivo*. In the poly U system, kanamycin

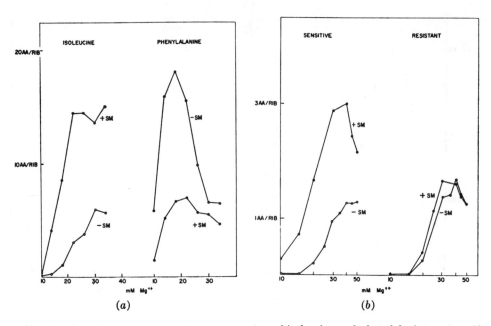

FIG. 2.—Streptomycin effect on the incorporation of isoleucine and phenylalanine at 0.19 M NH$_4$+. The reaction mixtures were as for Fig. 1, but those for (a) contained 0.4 µg of each amino acid plus 0.1 µC of the labeled amino acid, and 10 µg of ribosomes from *E. coli* B. Those for (b) contained 0.1 µg of each amino acid plus 0.1 µC of the labeled amino acid, and 10 µg of ribosomes from *E. coli* C600 Sm$_s$ or Sm^r. Both were at 0.19 M NH$_4$+ and the specified Mg^{++} concentration. (a) The stimulation of isoleucine incorporation and the inhibition of phenylalanine incorporation by streptomycin acting on sensitive ribosomes. (b) Comparison of the stimulation of isoleucine incorporation on streptomycin-sensitive and -resistant ribosomes.

and neomycins B and C all stimulate the incorporation of isoleucine. In addition, they stimulate tyrosine, leucine, and serine as is shown in Table 2. They are indifferent to whether or not the ribosomes are streptomycin-sensitive or -resistant. One such experiment is shown in Figure 3, where the stimulation of serine incorporation by either streptomycin or neomycin C is compared on streptomycin-sensitive and -resistant ribosomes. We observe a small stimulation with streptomycin on sensitive ribosomes, no effect on resistant ribosomes, while with neomycin C there is a marked, identical stimulation on both. This experiment underscores the specificity of the change from sensitive to resistant ribosomes. We expect that the ribosomes from high-level kanamycin- and neomycin-resistant strains may be resistant to the code shifts induced by their respective antibiotics.

These coding alterations have also been observed with a polymer that does not contain U. We tested the effect of the antibiotics on incorporation directed by poly CA (2:1). This polymer would be expected to code well for proline (CAC, CCC, CUC), to a lesser extent for threonine (ACA, CCA, UCA) and histidine (ACC, AUC), and for aspartic acid (GCA, GUA) and glutamic acid (AAC, UAC).[12] Table 3 shows that neomycin and kanamycin stimulated the incorporation of all three amino acids tested—threonine, proline, and histidine. Streptomycin produced a smaller stimulation of histidine and threonine, while causing an inhibition of proline incorporation. It is not possible to identify specific code changes in this system, but it is obvious that such changes do occur, particularly in the presence of neomycin and kanamycin.

Discussion.—The fact that an external agent, acting on the ribosomes, can perturb the code leads to a change in our view of the sources of specificity in protein synthesis. The translation mechanism involves not only the specific hydrogen bonds formed between the sRNA adaptor and the messenger, but also the conformation of the site on the ribosome that holds the sRNA to the messenger: this site must be such as to permit or require only the correct pairing to take place. A modification in this site, for example by the binding of streptomycin, permits a "wrong" sRNA to fit so well against the messenger that a "wrong" amino acid is entered into the polypeptide chain. A further modification, by mutation, changes the structure of the ribosomal site so that the correct sRNA is paired, whether or not streptomycin is present. Still a further modification might make the site require the

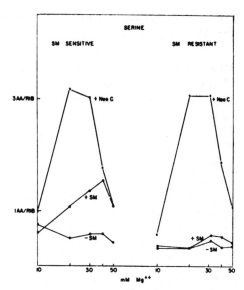

FIG. 3.—Effects of streptomycin and neomycin C on serine incorporation with streptomycin-sensitive or -resistant ribosomes. The reaction mixtures were as for Fig. 1, but contained 0.1 μC of C¹⁴ serine (0.0876 μg) in addition to 0.1 μg of all 20 cold and either 20 μg/ml streptomycin or neomycin C.

presence of a streptomycin molecule in order to function correctly; this would constitute a mechanism for the classical streptomycin dependence.

The streptomycin effect gives us confidence that the point of contact between the sRNA and the messenger is on the 30s subunit, as is suggested by messenger binding experiments,[13] although the growing point of the polypeptide chain is probably on the 50s subunit, along with the site that binds the sRNA.[14]

The large perturbations induced by ion shifts, and the results of Szer and Ochoa,[10] raise questions about the validity of the code determined by the *in vitro* system. One would expect that a valid *in vitro* system would display a code insensitive to small changes in the conditions of assay. The ion effects on the code may be due to a direct influence on the secondary structure of the messenger and the sRNA, as is suggested by Szer and Ochoa.[10] Another possibility is that these higher ionic strengths produce a relaxation in the structure of the ribosomes, making them impose less stringent conditions on the pairing between the messenger and sRNA, in analogy to the streptomycin effect.

The phenomenon of intergenic suppression is thought to involve modifications in the translation process. The suppressor genes produce a restoration of enzymatic activity through inducing either an amino acid replacement[15] or a transition from "nonsense" to sense or from the command to "end the chain" to an amino

TABLE 3

C¹⁴ amino acid	– Poly CA		+ Poly CA			
	—	Sm	—	Sm	Km	NeoB
Thr	351	340	427	450	710	822
Pro	14	18	111	91	215	196
Hist	44	—	71	105	201	177

Reaction conditions as in Table 2, except that 0.05 ml of dialyzed crude extract was used in each incubation. 20 μg of poly CA was used.

acid.[16] The models that have been proposed for such suppressors involve altered sRNA's or activating enzymes.

Recently, however, Gorini and Kataja[17] have demonstrated the existence of a streptomycin-activated suppressor phenotype, which suggests a new mechanism for suppression. This phenotype describes streptomycin-resistant strains that display suppression only when grown in streptomycin. Only in the presence of streptomycin do these cells make a small amount of functional protein. It is evident that the miscoding property of streptomycin offers an explanation for this suppression. We need only imagine that in some cases the mutation, in the structure of the ribosomes, to streptomycin resistance is not complete, that a residual error frequency, a few parts in a thousand in the presence of streptomycin, remains. This error frequency, involving the specific misreading of a subset of code words, would produce the shift of a number of amino acids. The argument is this: we can interpret our finding of a specific shift, phenylalanine to isoleucine, as a forced misreading of U as A in a specific position in a triplet. We might then expect that we could force U to read as A in that position of any triplet (unless there are sequence effects). This converts 16 triplets into other triplets and produces changes in up to 16 amino acids ("up to" because of degeneracy). Since streptomycin upsets the reading of other bases, still a larger number of replacements is possible. Thus, we might expect the streptomycin-activated suppressor to cause a number of different misreadings of the code, resulting in a variety of amino acid replacements or changes in other coded functions.

The involvement of the ribosomes in the accuracy of the reading, and the interpretation we have put upon the streptomycin-activated suppressor suggests that many suppressors may be modifications in the structure of the ribosomes; that is, the product of the suppressor gene is an altered component of the ribosome, whose incorporation in a complete ribosome makes that ribosome alter the code. Such a model would also explain one characteristic of the suppressor genes: since each suppressor would affect a number of different amino acids, different suppressors would have wide and overlapping spectra of repair. If we wished to provide an explanation of very efficient suppression along these lines, we would require the assumption that the triplets that are being misread by this mechanism are uncommon, as has been suggested for other high suppression mechanisms.[16] The assumption that these triplets are associated with rare sRNA's would then permit the suppressed reading to occur faster than the normal reading and would yield large amounts of the suppressed protein.[18]

We conclude by observing that the gross misreading that we find in vitro could be the basic mechanism of streptomycin killing: flooding the cell with nonfunctional proteins would be lethal and would perturb, in an unpredictable way, all other cellular functions. To explain the requirement for growth in the killing phenomenon, we assume that the presence of the messenger prevents the attachment of streptomycin to the ribosomes.[5] During the recycling of ribosomes as the messenger moves through the polyribosome, the ribosomes are free to bind streptomycin. If streptomycin binds irreversibly to the ribosomes when they are exposed, then its action will be irreversible. In order to explain the dominance of sensitivity over resistance[19] we need only observe that an equal mixture of good and bad ribosomes would produce mostly bad proteins because of the multimeric form of many proteins. Such bacteria should not grow in streptomycin but might survive a pulsed exposure, a few good ribosomes enabling the cell to throw off viable daughter cells on subsequent incubation in the absence of the drug. This phenomenon has been shown to occur in Pneumococcus.[20, 21]

Summary.—Streptomycin and related antibiotics cause extensive and specific alterations in the coding properties of synthetic polynucleotides *in vitro.* Streptomycin-resistant ribosomes are resistant only to the shift in the code induced by streptomycin. These findings provide evidence that the ribosomes control the accuracy of the reading and may have a role in suppression.

Experiments by W. Gilbert were carried out in the Biological Laboratories, Harvard University. We wish to thank Mrs. Anne Nevins and Mrs. Susanne Armour for their technical assistance. We thank Dr. J. D. Watson and Dr. B. D. Davis for their interest and support. We are grateful to Dr. M. Lubin for a gift of poly CA, and Dr. W. T. Sokolski for neomycins B and C.

The following abbreviations are used: Sm = streptomycin; Km = kanamycin; Neo = neomycin; CM = chloramphenicol; DHSm = dihydrostreptomycin; poly U = polyuridylic acid; poly CA = cytidylic acid-adenylic acid copolymer; PEP = phosphoenolpyruvate; PK = phosphoenolpyruvate kinase.

* This investigation was supported by grants from the American Cancer Society (E-226-B), National Science Foundation (GB-1307), and U.S. Public Health Service (AI-02011-06; GM-09541-03).

[1] For a general review of streptomycin effects see Davis, B. D., and D. S. Feingold, *The Bacteria,* ed. I. C. Gunsalus and R. Stanier (New York: Academic Press, 1962), vol. 4, p. 343.

[2] Cohen, S. S., *J. Biol. Chem.,* 166, 393 (1946).

[3] Anand, N., and B. D. Davis, *Nature,* 185, 22 (1960).

[4] Spotts, C. R., and R. Y. Stanier, *Nature,* 192, 633 (1961).

[5] Flaks, J. G., E. C. Cox, M. L. Witting, and J. R. White, *Biochem. Biophys. Res. Commun.,* 7, 385 and 390 (1962).

[6] Speyer, J. F., P. Lengyel, and C. Basilio, these PROCEEDINGS, 48, 684 (1962).

[7] Davies, J., these PROCEEDINGS, 51, 659 (1964).

[8] Cox, E. C., J. R. White, and J. G. Flaks, these PROCEEDINGS, 51, 703 (1964).

[9] We give currently suggested codons for reference. See Nirenberg, M. W., O. W. Jones, P. Leder, B. F. C. Clark, W. S. Sly, and S. Pestka, in *Synthesis and Structure of Macromolecules,* Cold Spring Harbor Symposia on Quantitative Biology, vol. 28 (1963), p. 549; and Speyer, J. F., P. Lengyel, C. Basilio, A. J. Wahba, R. S. Gardner, and S. Ochoa, in *Synthesis and Structure of Macromolecules,* Cold Spring Harbor Symposia on Quantitative Biology, vol. 28 (1963), p. 559.

[10] Szer, W., and S. Ochoa, *J. Mol. Biol.,* in press.

[11] Feingold, D. S., and B. D. Davis, *Biochim. Biophys. Acta,* 55, 787 (1962).

[12] Jones, O. W., and M. W. Nirenberg, these PROCEEDINGS, 48, 2115 (1962).

[13] Okamoto, T., and M. Takanami, *Biochim. Biophys. Acta,* 68, 325 (1963).

[14] Gilbert, W., *J. Mol. Biol.,* 6, 389 (1963); Cannon, M., R. Krug, and W. Gilbert, *J. Mol. Biol.,* 7, 360 (1963).

[15] Brody, S., and C. Yanofsky, these PROCEEDINGS, 50, 9 (1963).

[16] Garen, A., and O. Siddiqi, these PROCEEDINGS, 48, 1121 (1962); Benzer, S., and S. Champe, these PROCEEDINGS, 47, 1025 (1961). These suppressible mutations release fragments in the unsuppressed host (Sarabhai, A. S., A. O. W. Stretton, S. Brenner, and A. Bolle, *Nature,* 201, 13 (1964)).

[17] Gorini, L., and E. Kataja, these PROCEEDINGS, 51, 487 (1964); see also Lederberg, E. M., L. Cavalli-Sforza, and J. Lederberg, these PROCEEDINGS, 51, 678 (1964).

[18] This is the modulation hypothesis of Ames, B. N., and P. E. Hartman, in *Synthesis and Structure of Macromolecules,* Cold Spring Harbor Symposia on Quantitative Biology, vol. 28 (1963), p. 349.

[19] Lederberg, J., *J. Bact.,* 61, 549 (1951).

[20] Hotchkiss, R. D., in *Enzymes: Units of Biological Structure and Function* (New York: Academic Press, 1956), p. 119.

[21] Ephrussi-Taylor, H., *Nature,* 196, 748 (1962).

Complementation

J. Mol. Biol. (1963) **7**, 1–12

Hybrid Protein Formation of *E. coli* Alkaline Phosphatase Leading to *in vitro* Complementation

Milton J. Schlesinger and Cyrus Levinthal

Department of Biology
Massachusetts Institute of Technology,
Cambridge, Mass., U.S.A.

(*Received 23 January 1963*)

In vitro complementation has been demonstrated for alkaline phosphatase-negative mutants of *E. coli*. Enzymically active alkaline phosphatase can be formed by mixing monomer subunits derived from inactive purified proteins which are antigenically related to the wild-type enzyme of *E. coli*. Preparations of these proteins purified from four different phosphatase-negative mutants of *E. coli* could be reacted in pairs to yield partially active enzyme. Experimental evidence indicates that the active protein is a hybrid molecule composed of a monomer from each of the mutant proteins used in the reaction. The monomers, which can be prepared from the native protein by mild acid treatment or reduction with thioglycollate in urea, undergo a temperature and metal-dependent bimolecular reaction to yield a product distinct from normal enzyme but with partial enzymic activity.

The normal alkaline phosphatase protein is composed of two identical subunits whose structure is determined by a single functioning genetic unit. These results thus support the theory of hybrid protein formation which has been proposed to account for *intra-cistron* complementation.

1. Introduction

Mutations in a genetic region which determines the structure of a specific enzyme can either prevent the formation of any recognizable protein or can lead to the production of an altered protein with reduced enzymic activity. The altered or missing biological activity in such cases can be restored by genetic recombination, by a second suppressor mutation either within the same gene or elsewhere in the chromosome, by a reverse mutation to the wild-type configuration, or by genetic complementation (cf. review Levinthal & Davison, 1961). This last process can be demonstrated when two chromosomes, each derived from different cells and carrying different mutations in the same genetic region, are introduced into the same cell. The two mutants are said to complement each other if the biochemical function is restored in the heterozygous cell or, in other terms, if the amount of enzymic activity produced in this cell is greater than the sum of the two gene products acting separately. This phenomenon is distinguished from genetic recombination by the fact that this property is not inherited once the two chromosomes have segregated to different daughter cells.

Complementation is not a rare event. Many complementing systems have been described in recent years (Catcheside, 1960; Fincham & Pateman, 1957; Giles, Partridge & Nelson, 1957; Lacy & Bonner, 1961; Gross, 1962; Schwartz, 1962).

However, two fundamentally different types of complementation must be distinguished. If the two mutations are in functionally different regions of the genetic map (different cistrons) then *all* such mutants will complement (Benzer, 1957). This situation can be explained if it is assumed that each cistron determines the structure of a separate polypeptide chain and the cell can function if each polypeptide chain is made in its normal configuration by at least one of the two chromosomes. Complete complementation would then be expected if the different polypeptide chains were part of a single enzyme or determined different enzymes in the same biochemical pathway. In the second type of complementation, the two mutations are in the same cistron and affect the same polypeptide chain. In this case, which we will call *intra-cistron* complementation, recovery of enzymic activity only occurs between *some* pairs of mutants. The amount of active enzyme formed is dependent on the particular pair of mutants used and is generally much lower than in the case of *inter-cistron* complementation described above.

Several mechanisms have been proposed to account for *intra-cistron* complementation. The possibility has been considered that molecular rearrangement or crossing-over at the template RNA or protein level could be responsible for the production of active enzyme. However, the finding that the enzyme made by a complementing cell can have different physical–chemical properties from the wild-type enzyme (Fincham, 1962; Partridge, 1960; Giles *et al.*, 1957) seems to eliminate such mechanisms unless it is also postulated that unequal crossing-over is very common under these circumstances. Another hypothesis, which seems to account in a more satisfactory way for all the known facts, is that protein subunits derived from the same cistron mutated at different points can sometimes combine in a heterozygous cell to produce a hybrid form of the protein with partial enzymic activity (Brenner, 1959; Fincham, 1960). According to this model, *intra-cistron* complementation can only occur in those cases in which the enzymes are composed of two or more identical subunits. The mutant cells would produce altered monomers which could not combine to produce active enzyme, although they might combine to produce a protein antigenically related to the normal enzyme. The complementing cell would produce each of the altered monomers and these could, under some circumstances, combine to produce active enzyme. Only certain pairs of mutants might be expected to complement and the affected protein would be different from that made by the wild-type cell.

Recent experimental results from studies of the alkaline phosphatase of *E. coli* suggested that this system could serve to test the hybrid protein theory of *intra-cistron* complementation. Rothman & Byrne (1963) have shown that this enzyme is a dimer composed of identical subunits and *in vivo* complementation has been reported by Garen & Garen (1963). Levinthal, Signer & Fetherolf (1962) found that the enzyme could be reversibly denatured by treatment with thioglycollate in urea, and studies on the reactivation process indicated that the reduction reaction led to the formation of monomer subunits. Accordingly, proteins (CRM)† antigenically related to alkaline phosphatase were purified from several phosphatase-negative mutants of *E. coli*. Monomer subunits were then prepared and examined for their ability to complement. The results of these studies are presented in this paper. They support the hybrid protein hypothesis of complementation and, in addition, have led to information concerning the structure of the alkaline phosphatase enzyme and on the process by which active enzyme is formed from the monomer.

† Abbreviations used: CRM = cross-reacting material; TCA = trichloroacetic acid.

2. Materials and Methods

Strains. Four phosphatase-negative mutants previously isolated from *E. coli* K10 strain Hfr either by ultraviolet irradiation (U9, U13, U47) or by treatment with ethyl methane sulfonate (S33) were used in these studies. The mutant genes were transferred to a female (F⁻) strain which contained a mutation in the *R2* control region leading to constitutive production of phosphatase activity (Echols, Garen, Garen & Torriani, 1961).

Cell growth and enzyme purification. Cells were grown overnight in batches of 50 l. under the conditions described previously (Levinthal *et al.*, 1962). After harvesting in a Sharples centrifuge, the cells were washed once in 6.7×10^{-2} M-tris buffer, pH 9.0, and resuspended in the same buffer at a concentration of 10^{10} cells/ml. All mutants had a low but detectable amount of enzymic activity and the extraction and purification procedures were identical to those reported for wild-type enzyme (Levinthal *et al.*, 1962). The purified proteins were tested for their antigenic properties by the use of the double diffusion technique of Ouchterlony (1948). In Table 1 the properties of the purified CRM prepared from four

TABLE 1

Properties of purified mutant CRMs

Strain	Specific activity†	% CRM activity	Relative electrophoretic mobility
U47	0·004	100	Fast
U13	0·01	50	Same as wild
U9	2·7	50	Fast
S33	0·35	100	Slow
Wild-type	1200	100‡	—

† Enzyme units/mg protein.   ‡ Wild-type is 100 by definition.

phosphatase-negative mutants are presented. These preparations were estimated to be at least 90% pure from the fact that no protein bands were observed on starch gel electrophoresis, except those usually associated with the alkaline phosphatase, and from the fact that the fractions—which were collected from gradient elution of a DEAE-cellulose column—contained protein and CRM in a constant ratio.

Preparation of monomers. Monomers were prepared by the reduction procedure recently described (Levinthal *et al.*, 1962). As indicated below, they could also be formed by incubating the protein in 5×10^{-2} M-sodium acetate buffer, pH 4.0, at 0°C for 15 min.

Electrophoresis. Starch gel electrophoresis was carried out vertically by a modification of the method of Smithies (1955; Signer, 1962). The techniques for detecting protein and enzymic activity were identical to those already described (Levinthal *et al.*, 1962).

Sedimentation analysis of the monomer and hybrid proteins were performed using the sucrose gradient technique described by Martin & Ames (1961). [¹⁴C]Carboxymethyl alkaline phosphatase, prepared by alkylation of reduced alkaline phosphatase with [¹⁴C]iodoacetate (M. Schlesinger, unpublished experiments), was added to the material layered on the gradient (5 to 20%) as a marker for the sedimentation behavior of the monomers. After centrifugation at 35,000 rev./min in the Spinco SW 39 rotor for 15 hr at 0°C, the centrifuge tube was punctured and fractions of about 0·125 ml. were collected for measurement of TCA-precipitable ¹⁴C and measurement of either direct enzymic activity or of ability to complement and produce active enzyme.

Enzymic activity was measured by the rate of hydrolysis of *p*-nitrophenyl phosphate (Sigma 104, Sigma Chemical Co., St. Louis, Mo.), 0·02% in M-tris, pH 8.0. Samples of the reacting mixtures were added to 2·0 ml. of assay solution at 37°C and, after a short time, 0·5 ml. of K_2HPO_4 (13%) was added to stop the reaction. Absorbancy at 410 mμ was recorded. One unit of enzymic activity is that amount of enzyme which leads to a change of absorbancy of 1·0 units/min. Protein was determined by absorbancy at 280 mμ assuming an absorbancy of 0·770 for a protein concentration of 1 mg/ml. and a light path of 1 cm (Rothman & Byrne, 1963).

Determination of radioactivity was carried out by collecting TCA-precipitated protein on membrane filters (0·45 micron pore size, from Millipore, Inc., Bedford, Mass.). The filters were glued onto planchets with rubber cement, dried and counted in a low background gas-flow Geiger counter.

Antiserum against alkaline phosphatase was prepared by inoculation of rabbits with purified wild-type alkaline phosphatase.

Pronase-P (streptomyces griseus protease), B grade, was obtained from California Corporation for Biochemical Research. Trypsin was obtained from Worthington Biochemical Corporation.

3. Results

Initial attempts to detect enzymic activity by mixing monomers prepared by reduction in urea of CRM under the conditions described as optimal for reactivation of wild-type reduced enzyme (Levinthal *et al.*, 1962) were unsuccessful. It was found, however, that if the reduced CRMs were first acidified to pH 4·0 and the urea removed by dialysis, enzymic activity greater than that observable by the individual CRMs could be obtained after mixing at 37°C in a reactivation buffer. On further investigation it was noted that pre-treatment of the CRM with pH 4·0 sodium acetate buffer alone was sufficient to bring about formation of active enzyme after mixing and incubating the acidified proteins at 37°C. Table 2 compares the enzymic activity

TABLE 2

Complementation of U9–S33 monomers

Protein	Concentration (μg/ml.)	Enzymic activity units/ml.	
		zero time	50 min
U9 mon (R)	320	0·003	0·02
S33 mon (R)	320	0·003	0·003
U9 mon (R)+S33 mon (R)	320	0·003	0·48
U9 mon (A)	320	0·004	0·03
S33 mon (A)	320	0·005	0·3
U9 (A)+S33(A)	320	0·007	5·0
U9 native	200	0·2	0·2
S33 native	200	0·04	0·02
U9 native+S33 native	400	0·2	0·2

The reaction mixtures contained 0·7 ml. of reactivation buffer (10^{-2} M-MgC$_2$H$_3$O$_2$, 6×10^{-2} M-KCl and 6×10^{-3} M-mercaptoethanol), 0·1 ml. of M-tris, pH 7·8, and protein, in a total volume of 1·0 ml. Samples were taken at indicated times after incubation at 37°C for determination of enzymic activity. (R) and (A) refer to preparations of monomers by reduction or acidification, respectively.

observed with the different combination of CRMs and their monomers for the pair of mutants U9 and S33. This pair was chosen as Garen & Garen (1963) had found that it gave relatively high *in vivo* complementation. Only the mixture of monomers led to formation of enzymically active protein and the greatest activity was obtained from those monomers prepared by acid treatment alone.

A detailed study of the conditions for producing enzymically active protein from the U9–S33 inactive CRMs revealed that the reaction proceeded rapidly at 37°C at pH 7·8 and required the presence of a metal ion. As indicated in Table 3, zinc at a

TABLE 3

Effect of metals on U9–S33 complementation

Metal	Concentration	Enzyme units per ml.	
		0 min	60 min
Zn^{2+}	10^{-3}	0·23	5·4
	10^{-4}	0·24	7·2
	10^{-5}	0·21	0·23
Co^{2+}	10^{-3}	0·24	5·4
	10^{-4}	0·22	0·47
Mn^{2+}	10^{-3}	0·31	0·90
	10^{-4}	0·22	0·47
Mg^{2+}	10^{-3}	0·23	0·21
	10^{-4}	0·22	0·22
	10^{-5}	0·20	0·25
K^{+}	10^{-3}	0·18	0·20

Incubation mixtures containing acid-prepared monomers from U9 (80 μg) and S33 (80 μg) and 50 μmoles tris, pH 7·8, in 0·5 ml. were reacted at 37°C.

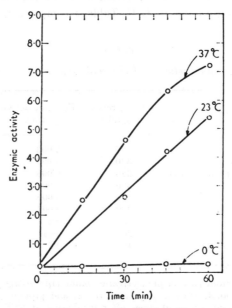

FIG. 1. Formation of enzymically active U9–S33 hybrid as a function of temperature. The reaction mixtures contained 80 μg each of U9 and S33 acid-prepared monomers in 10^{-1} M-tris, pH 7·8, and 10^{-4} M-ZnCl$_2$.

molar ratio of metal ion/protein of about 25:1 was the most active. Of the other cations tested only cobalt showed activity. The pH of the reactivation buffer was not critical between 6·0 and 9·0 but the rate of reaction was temperature dependent and varied with concentration of the monomer proteins. The rate of reactivation v. temperature is indicated in Fig. 1. An activation energy of 6·3 kcal. for complement enzyme formation can be calculated using the rate constants determined at 23 and 37°C. A plot of the initial rate of active enzyme formation v. concentration of protein over a sixteenfold range is noted in Fig. 2. This rate is found to be proportional to the square of the protein concentration as would be expected for a bimolecular reaction.

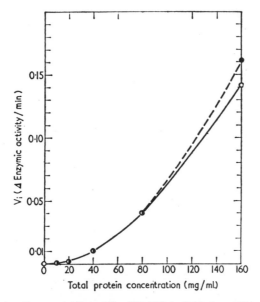

FIG. 2. Initial rate of enzymically active U9–S33 hybrid formation as a function of total protein concentration. The reaction mixtures contained the acid-prepared monomers in 10^{-1} M-tris, pH 7·8, 10^{-4} M-ZnCl$_2$ in a total vol. of 1·0 ml. Assays for enzymic activity were carried out after 0, 5, 10, 20 and 40 min incubation at 37°C. ●– – –● theoretical calculations for bimolecular reaction; ○——○ actual values.

As a further test of the nature of the complementation phenomenon it was important to examine the active protein to determine whether indeed it was a hybrid molecule. Three sets of criteria indicate that this protein is a dimer containing one monomer of each CRM.

(1) *Analysis by starch electrophoresis.* Native alkaline phosphatase prepared from *E. coli* behaves as several electrophoretic species when subjected to starch gel electrophoresis. The reason for this banding is not yet understood but available evidence indicates that it is not due to a technical problem involving extraction or analysis on starch gel (Signer, 1962). Furthermore, the purified enzyme behaves as a single species in analytical ultracentrifugation and a single mutation which changes the charge or enzymic activity of the protein affects all the bands identically (Bach, Signer, Levinthal & Sizer, 1961). When the U9–S33 reaction mixture after formation of active enzyme is subjected to electrophoresis in starch gel, the enzymically active material is also found to have bands and these move to a position intermediate between those of the two parental CRMs (Plate I, no. 4 v. 2 and 3), as revealed by histochemical stain for enzymic activity. Although the most active bands are detectable in this intermediate position, all the bands overlap some of those of the U9 and S33 protein. From these results, the active enzyme appears to be an electrophoretic hybrid of these CRMs.

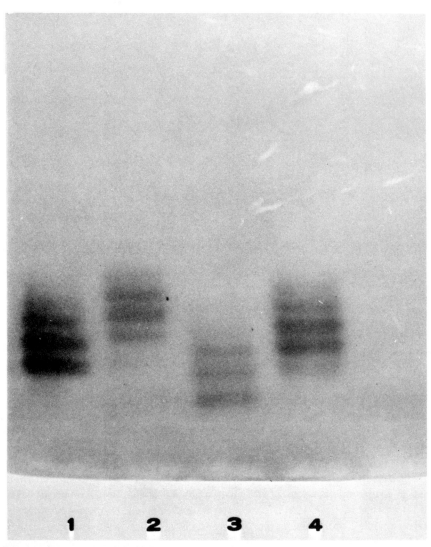

PLATE I. Starch gel electrophoresis. (1) Wild-type enzyme; (2) U9; (3) S33; (4) U9–S33.

All samples, previously acidified to pH 4·0, were incubated 3 hr at 37°C in the presence of 10^{-1} M-tris, pH 7·8, 10^{-4} M-ZnCl$_2$. They were dialysed 16 hr at 4°C against 5×10^{-3} M-NH$_4$HCO$_3$ and lyophilized. The samples were dissolved in 4×10^{-2} M-tris, pH 8·0, and the amounts added to the gel were as follows: wild-type; 12·5 μg, specific activity 732; U9: 370 μg, specific activity 0·8; S33: 320 μg, specific activity 0·43; U9 – S33: 180 μg, specific activity 23.

(2) *Sedimentation studies.* When the acidified S33 CRM is subjected to zone sedimentation in a sucrose gradient, the material which is able to carry out the complementation reaction with U9 sediments at a velocity identical to that of the alkylated monomer. In this experiment (Fig. 3(c)), portions of each fraction collected

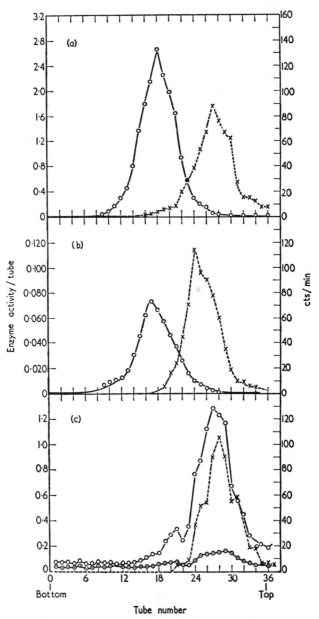

Fig. 3. Sucrose gradient analysis. All samples contained about 3000 cts/min of alkylated wild-type protein ($\times$ $---$ $\times$).
(a) Wild-type enzyme ($\bigcirc\!\!-\!\!-\!\!\bigcirc$) in 10^{-2} M-tris, pH 7·4, 10^{-3} M-MgCl$_2$; (b) U9–S33 hybrid ($\bigcirc\!\!-\!\!-\!\!\bigcirc$) in 10^{-2} M-tris, pH 7·4, 10^{-3} M-MgCl$_2$; (c) S33 acid-prepared monomer in 0·05 M-sodium acetate, pH 4·0 ($\bigcirc$ $---$ $\bigcirc$ assayed at 0 time, $\bigcirc\!\!-\!\!-\!\!\bigcirc$ assayed after 60 min in the presence of U9 monomers).
Details in text.

from the gradient were incubated with 40 μg of U9 monomer in 10^{-1} M-tris, pH 7·8, and 10^{-4} M-ZnCl$_2$ in a total volume of 0·5 ml. Enzymic activity was determined immediately and after 60 minutes' incubation at 37°C. A sedimentation analysis of the enzyme product prepared in the normal complementation reaction mixture of U9–S33 is depicted in Fig. 3(b). By a direct enzyme assay of each fraction it is seen that this material has a sedimentation behavior identical to that of wild-type alkaline phosphatase whose pattern is plotted in Fig. 3(a).

These analyses indicate that the material which participates in the complementation reaction is a monomer having the same sedimentation coefficient as the alkylated material. The molecular weight of alkylated normal enzyme has been shown to be 40,000, half that of the native protein (Rothman & Byrne, 1963).

(3) *Quantitative hybrid formation*. The extent of hybridization as determined enzymically is a function of the relative concentrations of the two monomers. When the ratio of concentration of S33 and U9 is varied from 1:9 to 9:1, the amount of active enzyme produced varies (Table 4). A value of the specific activity of each

TABLE 4

Extent of complementation as a function of relative proportions of monomers

Ratio S33:U9	Enzymic activity units/ml.	Theoretical amount of hybrid protein (μg)	Specific[†] activity units/mg
1:9	2·0	36	55
1:4	2·7	64	42
1:3	4·1	75	55
7:13	3·5	91	39
2:3	5·5	96	57
1:1	5·4	100	54
3:2	5·7	96	59
13:7	4·3	91	47
3:1	3·5	75	47
4:1	3·0	64	47
9:1	1·6	36	45

The total concentration of protein in each reaction tube was 200 μg/ml. Incubations were at 37°C in 10^{-1} M-tris, 10^{-4} M-ZnCl$_2$. See text for details of calculations.

† Enzymic activity/theoretical amount of hybrid protein.

mixture cannot be determined directly since there is no way of measuring the amount of hybrid protein formed. One can, however, determine the theoretical amount of hybrid enzyme in these various mixtures by assuming that the hybrid protein has the same probability of being formed as the separate mutant proteins and that the relative concentration of the various species will depend only on the probability of the different types of collisions. In this case the concentration of the hybrid can be calculated from the binomial expansion formula. When one uses this theoretical amount of hybrid enzyme formed as a basis for expressing specific activity, the values obtained are relatively constant (column 3, Table 4) in spite of the extreme variation in proportions of monomer CRMs used. For the complement enzyme of this pair, the specific activity is 5% that of the wild-type enzyme. These data are thus consistent with the hypothesis that the monomers of these two mutant proteins produce dimers by random collisions.

Complementation of these mutants has provided a convenient assay for the dimerization process, and preliminary information concerning the nature of the alkaline phosphatase monomer has been obtained. In Table 5, data are presented

TABLE 5

Effects of various reagents on complementation

Ratio reagent : protein	Reagent	Enzyme activity units/ml.	% inhibited
	None	3·45	0
2000	0·01 M-IAA†	2·4	30
2000	0·01 M-CMB†	0·78	80
400	0·002 M-CMB†	2·8	20
1/20	Pronase	0·0	100
1/10	Trypsin	0·0	100

The reaction mixtures contained acid-prepared monomers of U9 (50µg) and S33 (50 µg) and reagent in 10^{-1} M-tris, pH 7·8, 10^{-4} M-ZnCl$_2$ in a total vol. of 0·5 ml. Enzymic activity was measured after 80 min at 37°C.

† IAA refers to iodoacetate, CMB refers to *p*-chloromercuribenzoate.

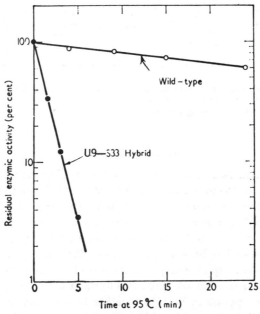

FIG. 4. Heat stability of U9–S33 hybrid enzyme. The reaction mixtures contained 100 µg protein in 10^{-1} M-tris, pH 8·0, 10^{-4} M-ZnCl$_2$ in a total vol. of 0·5 ml.

which show the effect of the proteolytic enzymes pronase and trypsin and of sulfhydryl binding agents on the ability of the monomers to dimerize. The monomers are sensitive to low concentrations of trypsin and pronase. On the other hand, dimerization is relatively insensitive to high concentrations of iodoacetate and *p*-chloromercuribenzoate.

Studies on the nature of the hybrid dimer show that it is distinct from wild-type alkaline phosphatase. The specific activity appears to be greatly reduced and it is considerably more heat labile. Three minutes at 95°C leads to an 88% loss of activity of the hybrid enzyme in contrast to the wild-type enzyme which shows a loss of 12% after 10 minutes at the same temperature (Fig. 4).

Monomers prepared from purified CRMs of two other mutants have been tested for their ability to complement. The results of all possible pairs for the four mutants are presented in Table 6. All reactions were carried out at the same protein concentrations, and the values therefore indicate the relative specific activities of the hybrid molecules, assuming that the probability of hybrid formation is the same between all pairs. All the CRM pairs except S33–U13 show complementation. From preliminary genetic mapping which indicates that U13 and U47 are extremely closely linked (A. Torriani, unpublished experiments) there appears to be no simple correlation between the values noted here and the genetic map distances.

TABLE 6

In vitro *complementation between monomers derived from proteins of p-strains of* Escherichia coli

Strain	U47	U13	S33	U9
U47	0·06	8·4	4·2	5·7
U13		0·01	0·01	2·5
S33			0·05	4·4
U9				0·4

Complementation was examined in reaction mixtures containing 200 μg of total protein, 100 μmoles tris, pH 7·8, and 0·1 μmole $ZnCl_2$ in a total vol. of 1·0 ml. Values are enzyme units/ml. observed after 60 min incubation at 37°C.

4. Discussion

The complementation assay has made it possible to carry out initial studies on the dimerization process for the formation of active enzyme and also to determine certain properties of the monomer subunits. Dimerization of CRM subunits has been found to be a zinc-activated, temperature-dependent bimolecular reaction that proceeds within a broad pH range (6 to 9). Monomers can be formed by treatment of the protein at low pH as well as by reduction in urea. Preliminary results (Fetherolf & Schlesinger, unpublished experiments) indicate that these same properties for monomer formation and dimerization are applicable to the wild-type alkaline phosphatase. The dimer therefore appears to be held together by ionic bonds stabilized by the presence of zinc which is a normal component of the enzyme (Plocke, Levinthal & Vallee, 1962). The disulfide bridges in the enzyme are *intra*-chain since reduction is not necessary to effect monomer formation nor do sulfhydryl binding agents block dimerization. However, the monomer subunits are considerably more labile than the intact protein as they are readily attacked by proteolytic enzymes which do not affect the dimer.

Although only one pair of CRM-forming mutants has been studied in detail, formation of enzymically active hybrid enzymes has been examined among pairs of monomer subunits from four purified CRMs which are synthesized by mutants having different mutation sites within the gene. Of the six possible hybrids, five are partially active enzymes. From these results and preliminary studies of the relative position of these mutants on the gene map, there does not appear to be a simple colinear relation. Two mutants which are very close on the genetic map gave more active hybrids than another pair which map farther apart. *In vitro* complementation can be carried out with crude extracts of mutants and experiments are in progress to determine whether or not any correlation can be found between gene-map position and the ability to complement.

There have been previous reports of *in vitro* complementation for several enzymes (Woodward, 1959; Loper, 1961; Glassman, 1962). In these cases, the mixing of extracts or of chilled cells prior to the extraction of proteins gave partially active enzyme. Results of these experiments suggested cytoplasmic interaction but no definitive conclusion could be made concerning the molecular basis of the phenomenon. The enzyme product could be shown to be different from the normal wild-type enzyme in one of these systems (Partridge, 1960). However, insufficient information was available as to the structure of the enzymes to establish the hybrid protein nature of the product.

Experimental evidence now exists for the alkaline phosphatase of *E. coli*, both with respect to the *in vivo* complementation and the molecular basis of *in vitro* complementation. The structural gene of this enzyme is a single cistron (Garen & Garen, 1963) and the protein, whose structure is determined by this genetic region, is composed of two identical subunits. The experiments reported here indicate that enzymically active proteins can be formed from monomer subunits obtained from inactive alkaline phosphatase proteins (CRM). With the use of highly purified CRMs it has been possible to demonstrate that this active material is a hybrid molecule composed of one monomer from each CRM. Furthermore, the active protein product is distinct from the normal enzyme; it appears to have a much lower specific activity and is considerably more heat labile. The *in vivo* complementation as reported by Garen & Garen (1963) also leads to partially active and heat-sensitive enzyme. These properties are not unexpected since the hybrid protein contains two "lesions" in its structure.

The ability of any particular pair of mutants to hybridize and yield active enzyme would be difficult to predict without detailed knowledge of the tertiary and quaternary structure of the protein and of the requirements for the active site of the enzyme. Furthermore, without such knowledge it is not possible to determine whether the active sites are confined to a single monomer subunit or whether they span across the two monomers. The fact that the dimer formation is necessary for activity could imply either that the active site does bridge the dimer or that the formation of the dimer modifies the tertiary structure of the monomer in such a way as to stabilize the active site in its required three-dimensional configuration. Nevertheless, it is apparent from these studies that the active-site of a "mutated" inactive enzyme composed of multiple subunits can sometimes be restored by the interaction of different mutated subunits which occurs through molecular hybridization.

These experimental results thus support the hypothesis that *intra-cistron* complementation can be accounted for by hybrid protein formation.

This work was supported by grant E-2028 (C5) from the U.S. Public Health Service, and grant G-8816 from the National Science Foundation.

REFERENCES

Bach, M. L., Signer, E. R., Levinthal, C. & Sizer, I. W. (1961). *Fed. Proc.* **20**, 255.

Benzer, S. (1957). In *Symp. on Chemical Basis of Heredity*, ed. by W. D. McElroy & B. Glass, p. 70. Baltimore: The Johns Hopkins Press.

Brenner, S. (1959). In *Symp. on Biochemistry of Human Genetics*, CIBA Found. and Internatl. Union of Biol. Sciences, ed. by G. E. W. Wolstenholme & C. M. O'Connor, p. 304. London: Churchill.

Catcheside, D. G. (1960). In *Microbial Genetics*, Tenth Symp. Soc. for Gen. Microbiol., p. 181. Cambridge: The University Press.

Echols, H., Garen, A., Garen, S. & Torriani, A. (1961). *J. Mol. Biol.* **3**, 425.

Fincham, J. R. S. (1960). In *Advances in Enzymology*, **22**, ed. by F. F. Nord, p. 1. New York: Interscience.

Fincham, J. R. S. (1962), *J. Mol. Biol.* **4**, 257.

Fincham, J. R. S. & Pateman, J. A. (1957). *Nature*, **179**, 741.

Garen, A. & Garen, S. (1963). *J. Mol. Biol.* **7**, 13.

Giles, N. H., Partridge, C. W. H. & Nelson, M. J. (1957). *Proc. Nat. Acad. Sci., Wash.* **43**, 305.

Glassman, E. (1962). *Proc. Nat. Acad. Sci., Wash.* **48**, 1491.

Gross, S. R. (1962). *Proc. Nat. Acad. Sci., Wash.* **48**, 922.

Lacy, A. M. & Bonner, D. M. (1961). *Proc. Nat. Acad. Sci., Wash.* **47**, 72.

Levinthal, C. & Davison, P. F. (1961). *Ann. Rev. Biochem.* **30**, 641.

Levinthal, C., Signer, E. R. & Fetherolf, K. (1962). *Proc. Nat. Acad. Sci., Wash.* **48**, 1230.

Loper, J. C. (1961). *Proc. Nat. Acad. Sci., Wash.* **47**, 1440.

Martin, R. G. & Ames, B. N. (1961). *J. Biol. Chem.* **236**, 1372.

Ouchterlony, C. (1948). *Acta path. microbiol. scand.* **25**, 186.

Partridge, C. W. H. (1960). *Biochem. Biophys. Res. Comm.* **3**, 613.

Plocke, D. J., Levinthal, C. & Vallee, B. L. (1962). *Biochemistry*, **1**, 373.

Rothman, F. & Byrne, R. (1963). *J. Mol. Biol.* **6**, 330.

Schwartz, D. (1962). *Proc. Nat. Acad. Sci., Wash.* **48**, 750.

Signer, E. (1962). Ph.D. dissertation. M.I.T., Cambridge, Mass.

Smithies, O. (1955). *Biochem. J.* **61**, 629.

Woodward, D. O. (1959). *Proc. Nat. Acad. Sci., Wash.* **45**, 846.

J. Mol. Biol. (1963) **7**, 13–22

Complementation *in vivo* between Structural Mutants of Alkaline Phosphatase from *E. coli*

ALAN GAREN AND SUZANNE GAREN

Biology Division, University of Pennsylvania, Philadelphia, U.S.A.

(*Received 20 March 1963*)

In vivo complementation has been observed between alkaline phosphatase structural mutants of *E. coli*. The enzymes produced by complementation are in most cases more heat labile than the standard phosphatase enzyme. This observation, as well as other properties of the complementing strains, suggests that phosphatase complementation results from the formation of hybrid enzyme molecules.

1. Introduction

Complementation concerns the interaction between two genomes that have mutations located in the same functional unit. The question that is posed in a complementation test is whether a function can be performed more effectively by a heterozygous cell that carries both mutated genomes than by homozygous cells that carry either one of the genomes. Complementation is defined as the ability of two mutated genomes to function cooperatively in a heterozygous cell.

It is necessary for a complementation analysis to have an acceptable definition of a genetic unit of function. This is provided by the concept of the cistron which is based on the *cis-trans* test (Benzer, 1957). The purpose of this test is to determine whether different mutations affect the same function. The activity of a heterozygote which carries two different mutations in the *trans* arrangement (i.e. on different genomes) is compared to the activity of a heterozygote in which the mutations are in the *cis* arrangement (i.e. on the same genome). If the *trans* arrangement is less active than the *cis*, the two mutations are classified in the same cistron. By this criterion it is possible to select a group of mutants that can be analysed for intra-cistronic complementation.

Complementation has been observed *in vivo* in various organisms (Case & Giles, 1960; Catcheside, 1960; Fincham & Pateman, 1957; Fincham, 1962; Giles, Partridge & Nelson, 1957; Gross, 1962; Lacy & Bonner, 1961; Partridge, 1960; Yanofsky & St. Lawrence, 1960). The genetic function analysed is usually the specification of a particular enzyme molecule. The evidence indicates that the mechanism of complementation involves interactions between the products of the mutated genomes rather than recombination of the genetic material. A model for complementation has been proposed (Brenner, 1959; Fincham, 1960; Crick & Orgel, personal communication) which postulates that intra-cistronic complementation may occur when the product is a polymeric protein composed of two or more identical chains. In such a case a heterozygous strain could produce a hybrid molecule, containing chains with different mutational alterations, which might be more active than the proteins produced by either of the homozygous parental strains.

Since the enzyme alkaline phosphatase of *E. coli* (Levinthal, 1959; Garen, 1960) is a dimeric protein containing two identical chains (Rothman & Byrne, 1963), it would appear to be suitable for complementation studies. The present report shows that *in vivo* complementation occurs between structural mutants of alkaline phosphatase. The properties of the complementing strains support the protein hybridization model of complementation. In an accompanying paper, Schlesinger & Levinthal (1963) describe *in vitro* complementation with purified phosphatase proteins obtained from structural mutants, thus proving that complementation does involve protein–protein interactions.

2. Materials and Methods

Bacterial strains. The haploid strain is an F^- *E. coli* K12 which has a constitutive mutation in the *R2* regulator gene for alkaline phosphatase (Echols, Garen, Garen & Torriani, 1961). The various phosphatase-negative mutations involved in the present experiments were induced in Hfr *E. coli* K12 (strain K10) and the mutations were transferred by mating into the above F^- strain (Levinthal, 1959; Garen, 1960).

Media. LB broth: Bacto-Tryptone 10 g, yeast extract 5 g, NaCl 5 g, glucose 1 g, 1 N-NaOH 1 ml., H_2O 1 l. *TG medium*: $1 \cdot 2 \times 10^{-1}$ M-tris buffer, pH 7·5; 0·2% glucose; 8×10^{-2} M-NaCl; 2×10^{-2} M-KCl; 2×10^{-2} M-NH_4Cl; 3×10^{-3} M-Na_2SO_4; 1×10^{-3} M-$MgCl_2$; 2×10^{-4} M-$CaCl_2$; 2×10^{-6} M-$FeCl_3$. For high phosphate, $6 \cdot 4 \times 10^{-4}$ M-KH_2PO_4 was added to the TG medium and for low phosphate $6 \cdot 4 \times 10^{-5}$ M-KH_2PO_4 was added.

Preparation of cell extracts. Cultures were grown with aeration to a density of about 4×10^8 cells/ml. in LB medium. The cultures were tested for uniformity with regard to the phosphatase character of the cells by plating on TG agar and spraying the resulting colonies with NPP.† This test was of particular importance with F' heterozygous strains since segregants appeared during growth of the culture. In general, the proportion of F^- segregants was below 5% of the total population. The cultures were centrifuged, washed once and resuspended in a medium containing 0·05 M-tris buffer, pH 7·5, and 0·02 M-$MgSO_4$. The optical density was read at 540 mμ in a 1 cm cell. The cells were broken open in a French pressure cell and the preparation was centrifuged at 5000 rev./min to remove debris. For the experiments involving heat inactivation, the extracts were partially purified by dialysing against a solution of 0·02 M-NaCl in 0·01 M-tris buffer, pH 7·5, and passing the dialysate through a column of DEAE. The phosphatase enzyme attached under these conditions and was eluted with a solution of 0·2 M-NaCl in 0·01 M-tris, pH 7·5.

Enzymic activity assay. A sample of the extract was added to a solution containing 4 mg/ml. NPP in 1 M-tris buffer, pH 8·0. The rate of change of optical density at 410 mμ and 32°C was measured. The values for enzymic activities are normalized to a standard cell density of the original culture. For assays of F' heterozygous strains, the activity values are corrected for the proportion of F^- segregants.

Immunological CRM assay. The technique of Preer & Preer (1959) was used. Rabbit antiserum was prepared by inoculations of purified normal enzyme as antigen. A constant concentration of the serum was assayed in microtubes against serial dilutions of cell extract. The relative amount of CRM in an extract was estimated by the position of the precipitation band in the microtubes as compared with the position of the band formed by a standard solution of the normal enzyme.

Complementation tests

The complementation tests were carried out by means of an F' strain (Jacob & Adelberg, 1959) which carries the phosphatase structural cistron on the episome (Hirota & Sneath, 1961). An F' is capable of transferring its episome to an F^- cell, producing a new F' that contains the episome of the parental F' and the chromosome of the parental F^- If the parental strains have different phosphatase markers, a heterozygote will result which can be tested for complementation.

† Abbreviations used: NPP = *p*-nitrophenylphosphate; CRM = cross reacting materials.

Incorporation of phosphatase-negative mutations into the F′ episome. The *in vivo* complementation tests require various F′ strains, each carrying a particular phosphatase-negative (P^-) mutation on the episome. The first step in the isolation of the mutant F′ strains was to cross the standard F′, which has the standard phosphatase structural cistron (P^+) on both the episome and chromosome (F′ P^+/P^+), with an F⁻ phosphatase-negative mutant (P^-), to produce an F′ P^+/P^- heterozygote. For this cross, cultures were grown overnight at 37°C with aeration in LB broth and then equal volumes were mixed and maintained at 37°C with gentle shaking for 3 hr to allow mating to occur. The mated cultures were spread on TG agar containing 0·1 mg/ml. streptomycin. Streptomycin was used to prevent growth of the streptomycin-sensitive F′ parental strain. The resulting colonies were sprayed with a solution of 4 mg/ml. NPP in 1 M-tris buffer, pH 8·0. The F′ P^+/P^- heterozygotes could be detected by a yellow color reaction.

The next step was to obtain an F′ P^-/P^- homozygote from the F′ P^+/P^- heterozygote. A culture of the heterozygote was exposed to a weak dose of ultraviolet light (approximately 1% cell survivors) and the irradiated culture was plated on TG agar. When the resulting colonies were sprayed with NPP, a mixture of yellow and white colonies was found. The white colonies could represent either F⁻ P^- haploid segregants which had lost the episome, or F′ P^-/P^- cells in which the P^- mutation on the chromosome had been incorporated into the episome. In order to distinguish the F′ from the F⁻ cells, the white colonies were cultured and crossed with an F⁻ strain that had a constitutive mutation in the *R1* regulator gene for alkaline phosphatase. Since the F′ strain used in these experiments carries the *R1*⁺ gene on the episome, the presence of the episome could be detected by testing for the formation of *R1*⁺/*R1*⁻ progeny in the cross (see Echols *et al.*, 1961; Garen & Echols, 1962). Approximately 5% of the colonies tested in this way proved to be F′ P^-/P^-.

The rough complementation test was carried out by mating an F′ strain which had the desired phosphatase marker on the episome with an F⁻ P^- strain and plating the cells on TG agar. The F′ strains used for these crosses required methionine for growth and therefore did not produce colonies on the minimal TG medium; the F⁻ strains were prototrophs. The resulting colonies were sprayed with NPP. If the majority of the colonies showed more intense yellow coloration than either of the parental strains, a positive complementation response was scored.

3. Results

Phosphatase-negative mutations map in a single region of the bacterial chromosome (Levinthal, 1959; Garen, 1960). It is known that this region specifies at least in part the structure of the phosphatase molecule, since some of the mutants produce a structurally altered form of the enzyme (Garen, Levinthal & Rothman, 1961). As a first step in determining whether phosphatase-negative mutations belong to a common structural cistron, a rough *cis-trans* test was performed on 200 independently isolated mutant strains. For this test, phosphatase heterozygotes were formed between the mutant E15 and each of the 200 other mutants. E15 was chosen for these tests because of the possibility that it might have an extended mutational defect in the phosphatase structural region (as indicated by its failure to revert or to produce genetic recombinants in crosses against a number of point mutants) and therefore might not be capable of complementing other mutants from the same cistron. The heterozygotes were streaked on agar plates and the resulting colonies were sprayed with NPP for a qualitative assay of enzymic activity. In all cases, except two, the heterozygotes showed little or no activity. The two exceptional heterozygotes produced about as much enzymic activity as the standard P^+ strain. Further studies on mutations of this type (Garen & Echols, 1962) have shown that they occur exclusively in the *R1* regulator cistron for alkaline phosphatase. Since the *R1* cistron is involved in the control of the rate of phosphatase formation and does not appear to affect the structure of the enzyme, this type of phosphatase-negative mutation has been excluded from the present complementation analyses which are concerned only with structural mutations.

Of the remaining mutants, twenty-two were chosen for additional complementation experiments. All of these contain point (revertible) mutations that map at different genetic sites throughout the phosphatase structural region (Garen, 1960, and unpublished data). The mutants vary markedly in their capacities to produce CRM (material that cross-reacts immunologically with antiserum prepared against the standard

TABLE 1

Properties of phosphatase-negative mutants

Strain	CRM	Enzymic activity
Standard $P+$	100	100
U9	100	8·0
U32	100	3·0
E32b	100	2·7
U40	100	0·1
S33	100	0·1
U57	100	0·1
G41	100	< 0·1
U13	100	< 0·1
U44	25	8·0
U35	25	1·2
S6	15	6·0
U43	5	2·5
E48	5	1·2
E32a	5	0·1
S9	5	< 0·1
U26	5	< 0·1
U18	< 2	0·3
U38	< 2	0·1
G1	< 2	< 0·1
U7	< 2	< 0·1
U3	< 2	< 0·1
U24	< 2	< 0·1
E15	< 2	< 0·1

Extracts of each strain were prepared and tested for CRM and enzymic activity as described in Materials and Methods. The values are normalized to a standard optical density of the culture used in the preparation of the extract. The response of the $P+$ strain is assigned a value of 100.

phosphatase enzyme) and enzymically active phosphatase, as shown in Table 1. It should be noted that the CRM-positive mutants produce a functionally defective form of phosphatase (low specific enzymic activity per unit of CRM).

Although none of the mutants in Table 1 fully complements E15, this criterion alone does not prove that the mutations belong to a single cistron, since the genetic defect in E15 might overlap more than one cistron. The complementation experiments described below, which involve pairs of point mutants, show that all of the mutations can be allocated to a single structural cistron for alkaline phosphatase.

Complementation model

It is convenient to introduce at this point a model for phosphatase complementation in F′ cells (Fig. 1) which can be referred to in discussing the experimental results. It is assumed that each phosphatase structural cistron specifies the synthesis of monomeric protein chains. These subsequently dimerize at random with respect to partner to form phosphatase molecules. In an F′ strain heterozygous for the phosphatase structural cistron, random pairing of monomers can produce three kinds of phosphatase molecules, as shown in Fig. 1. One of the molecules is a hybrid composed of monomers

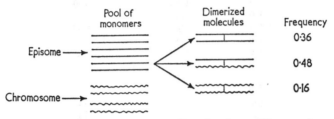

Fig. 1. *Model of* in vivo *complementation for alkaline phosphatase.* The complementing strain is an F′, heterozygous for the phosphatase structural cistron. Each phosphatase cistron specifies monomeric polypeptide chains that dimerize at random with respect to partner to form phosphatase enzyme molecules. The episomal phosphatase cistron is shown to produce on the average 1·5 monomers for every monomer produced by the chromosomal cistron (the evidence for this is given in the text). Complementation is attributed to the formation of hybrid enzyme molecules.

derived from both the episomal and chromosomal cistrons, and it is this molecule that presumably is responsible for complementation. It appears that the episomal phosphatase cistron produces on the average 1·5 monomers for every monomer produced by the chromosomal cistron. The evidence for this (see Tables 2 and 4) is that an F′ strain which carries the standard P^+ cistron in both episomal and chromosomal positions produces about 2·5 times as much enzymic activity as a haploid P^+ strain. Consequently, the three kinds of phosphatase molecules that can be formed by an F′ heterozygote are expected to occur in the relative amounts indicated in Fig. 1.

Complementation between P^- *mutants*

Rough complementation tests were carried out with three mutants (U9, S6 and E15), each of which was tested in pairwise combinations with all of the mutants listed in Table 1. The mutant pairs which showed clear evidence of complementing in these tests were assayed quantitatively. The results are given in Table 2. It can be seen that complementation may involve not only mutants that produce CRM but also mutants that have no detectable CRM (e.g. U18). In the latter case, the fact that complementation can occur presumably indicates that the mutant is capable of producing phosphatase monomers despite the failure to detect CRM. The amount of enzymic activity resulting from complementation varies with different complementing strains. The highest value observed (with strain U9/E32a) is 67% of the activity of the standard F′ P^+/P^+ strain. With the heterozygote strains that do not show complementation it is of course possible that hybrid molecules are formed which have no enzymic activity.

It is noteworthy that one of the mutants (G41) complements with E15 which has a genetic defect that extends over about one-half of the structural cistron. The G41 mutation maps outside of the span of the defect in E15. It is possible that E15 produces a polypeptide chain which can interact with other phosphatase chains.

TABLE 2

Complementation between P⁻ *mutants*

F' complementing strain		Enzymic activity
Episome	Chromosome	
P+	*P*+	240
U9	E32a	161
U9	U26	102
U9	U35	100
U9	U32	60
U9	S33	50
U9	U40	46
U9	S9	42
U9	U57	27
U9	G41a	27
U9	U13	22
S6	U26	116
S6	U57	110
S6	S33	101
S6	U32	88
S6	U40	86
S6	U35	68
S6	U13	68
S6	G41	52
S6	S9	50
S6	U18	19
E15	G41	3

The enzymic activity values are normalized to a standard optical density of the culture used in the preparation of each extract. The activity of the haploid *P*+ strain is assigned a value of 100 (see Table 1).

Heat sensitivity of the enzymes produced by complementing mutants

If phosphatase complementation results from the formation of hybrid molecules (see Fig. 1), these might differ in certain properties from the standard phosphatase

TABLE 3

Heat sensitivity of enzymes produced by complementation between P⁻ *mutants*

F' complementing strain		% of initial enzymic activity remaining after 20 min at 91°C
Episome	Chromosome	
P+	*P*+	100
U9	E32a	100
U9	U32	75
U9	U57	38
U9	S33	3
S6	U57	5
S6	S33	3
E15	G41	1

The procedures are described in the text.

molecule. One of the characteristics of the standard molecule is exceptional resistance to inactivation by heat (Garen & Levinthal, 1960). The heat sensitivity of the enzymes produced by seven complementing heterozygote strains has been compared to that of the standard enzyme (Table 3). Six of the seven enzymes were found to be heat labile under conditions where the standard enzyme is stable.

The rate of heat inactivation of the enzyme from the complementing heterozygous strain U9/S33 is plotted in Fig. 2. The curve appears to contain two distinct slopes, indicating the presence of the two molecular species having different inactivation rates. The lower rate is equal to the inactivation rate of the enzyme from the homozygous mutant strain U9 (Fig. 2). It should be noted that the enzyme produced by the

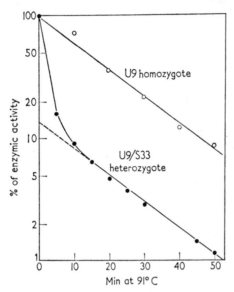

Fig. 2. *Heat inactivation curves of the enzymes produced by the complementing F' heterozygous strain U9/S33 and the homozygous mutant U9 strain (see Tables 1 and 2). The enzymic activity values are calculated as percent of the initial activity of each strain. The experimental procedures are described in the text.*

mutant S33 is inactive (see Table 1) and therefore does not contribute to the inactivation curve of the U9/S33 heterozygote. The results reported in Fig. 2 suggest that the U9/S33 heterozygote produces two enzymically active phosphatases, one a hybrid dimer composed of monomeric units derived from U9 and S33 and the other a pure U9 dimer. The initial slope of the heterozygote inactivation curve can be attributed to a highly labile hybrid enzyme, and the final slope to the more stable U9 enzyme. By extrapolation of the final slope back to zero time, the contribution of the U9 enzyme to the activity in the heterozygote can be estimated as 13% of the total activity. According to the model in Fig. 1, the U9 enzyme would be expected to contribute about 7 units of activity to the heterozygote, or 14% of the total activity.

Enzyme interaction in P^-/P^+ heterozygotes

The occurrence of complementation between P^- mutants has been attributed to the formation of hybrid dimer molecules containing two mutationally altered chains. This mechanism could also lead to an interaction between a P^- mutant and the standard P^+ strain, with the formation of hybrid molecules composed of one normal and one altered chain. In this case the direction of the effect might either be positive or negative, depending on how efficiently the hybrid molecule functioned as an enzyme.

Examples of a positive effect have been found, as shown in Table 4. For these tests, F′ heterozygous strains were used which carried a P^- mutation on the episome and the standard P^+ cistron on the chromosome. The activity produced by strain U9/P^+ was 63% higher, and by strain S6/P^+ 20% higher, than the activity of the haploid P^+ strain. These results may be compared with the predictions of the model in Fig. 1.

TABLE 4

Enzyme interaction in P⁻/P⁺ heterozygotes

Strain		Enzymic activity
Episome	Chromosome	
None	P^+	100
U9	P^+	163
S6	P^+	120

The procedures and calculations are as described for Table 2. The activity of the haploid P^+ strain is assigned a value of 100 (see Table 1).

If a P^-/P^+ heterozygote produced a hybrid molecule which was fully as active as the standard enzyme, the enzymic activity should be 60% higher than in the haploid P^+ strain. Thus it appears that the hybrid produced by strain U9/P^+ is a fully active phosphatase enzyme.

If the effect reported in Table 4 with P^-/P^+ heterozygotes is indeed caused by hybrid enzyme formation, some of the hybrid enzymes might be more heat labile than the standard enzyme. This point was examined with various F′ P^+/P^- heterozygous strains, and the results are given in Table 5. With four of the eight strains

TABLE 5

Heat sensitivity of enzymes produced by P⁺/P⁻ heterozygotes

F′ strain		% of initial enzymic activity after 30 min at 91°C
Episome	Chromosome	
P^+	P^+	100
P^+	U3	100
P^+	U7	100
P^+	U32	100
P^+	E32b	77
P^+	S6	64
P^+	S33	60
P^+	U13	70
P^+	U9	100

The procedures are described in the text.

tested, the enzymes produced by the heterozygotes were inactivated under conditions where the standard enzyme was stable. The rate of inactivation of one of the labile enzymes is plotted in Fig. 3. For these measurements, two reciprocal heterozygous strains were used, one with the P^- mutation on the episome and the other with the same mutation on the chromosome (strains S6/P^+ and P^+/S6 respectively). The inactivation curves for both strains exhibit an initial rapid drop and then remain stable. This is the expected result for a mixture of labile hybrid enzyme and stable standard enzyme. The percent activity remaining after the inactivation curve has levelled off can be used as a measure of the proportion of standard enzyme molecules in the original preparation. The values from Fig. 3 are 14% for the S6/P^+ strain and 61% for the P^+/S6 strain. On the basis of the model in Fig. 1, the P^+/S6 strain should produce 2·25 times as much standard enzyme as the S6/P^+ strain.

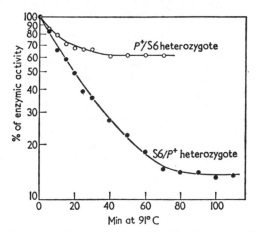

Fig. 3. *Heat inactivation curves of the enzymes produced by the reciprocal F' heterozygote strains* P^+/S6 *and* S6/P^+. Enzymic activity values are calculated as percent of the initial activity of each strain. The experimental procedures are described in the text.

The results in Fig. 3 are in the right direction, although the P^+/S6 strain produces more of the standard enzyme than would be expected (perhaps because the dimerization step occurs more readily for the standard enzyme than for the hybrid enzyme).

4. Discussion

The present experiments have shown that *in vivo* complementation occurs between alkaline phosphatase structural mutants of *E. coli*, and that the properties of the complementing strains are entirely compatible with a model (outlined in Fig. 1) which involves the interaction of polypeptide chains. In an accompanying paper, Schlesinger & Levinthal (1963) report on *in vitro* complementation with purified enzyme proteins obtained from alkaline phosphatase structural mutants, and they present convincing evidence that hybrid molecules are responsible for complementation. The combination of *in vitro* and *in vivo* observations demonstrate the applicability of a protein–protein interaction mechanism to alkaline phosphatase complementation.

REFERENCES

Benzer, S. (1957). In *Symposia on Chemical Basis of Heredity*, ed. by W. D. McElroy & B. Glass, p. 70. Baltimore: The Johns Hopkins Press.

Brenner, S. (1959). In *Symposia on Biochemistry of Human Genetics*, CIBA Found. & Internatl. Union of Biol. Sciences, ed. by G. E. W. Wolstenholme & C. M. O'Connor, p. 304. London: Churchill.

Case, M. G. & Giles, N. H. (1960). *Proc. Nat. Acad. Sci., Wash.* 46, 659.

Catcheside, D. G. (1960). *Microbial Genetics*, 10th Symp. Soc. Gen. Microbiol. Cambridge: The University Press.

Echols, H., Garen, A., Garen, S. & Torriani, A. (1961). *J. Mol. Biol.* **3**, 425.

Fincham, J. R. S. (1960). *Advanc. Enzymol.* **22**, 1.

Fincham, J. R. S. (1962). *J. Mol. Biol.* **4**, 257.

Fincham, J. R. S. & Pateman, J. A. (1957). *Nature*, **179**, 741.

Garen, A. (1960). *Microbial Genetics*, 10th Symp. Soc. Gen. Microbiol. Cambridge: The University Press.

Garen, A. & Echols, H. (1962). *Proc. Nat. Acad. Sci., Wash.* **48**, 1398.

Garen, A. & Levinthal, C. (1960). *Biochim. biophys. Acta*, **38**, 470.

Garen, A., Levinthal, C. & Rothman, F. (1961). *J. Chim. phys.* **58**, 1068.

Giles, N. H., Partridge, C. W. H. & Nelson, M. J. (1957). *Proc. Nat. Acad. Sci., Wash.* **43**, 305.

Gross, S. R. (1962). *Proc. Nat. Acad. Sci., Wash.* **48**, 922.

Hirota, Y. & Sneath, P. H. A. (1961). *Jap. J. Genet.* **36**, 307.

Jacob, F. & Adelberg, E. A. (1959). *C.R. Acad. Sci., Paris*, **249**, 189.

Lacy, A. M. & Bonner, D. M. (1961). *Proc. Nat. Acad. Sci., Wash.* **47**, 72.

Levinthal, C. (1959). *Brookhaven Symp. Biol.* **12**, 76.

Partridge, C. W. H. (1960). *Biochem. Biophys. Res. Comm.* **3**, 613.

Preer, J. R. & Preer, L. B. (1959). *J. Protozool.* **6**, 88.

Rothman, F. & Byrne, R. (1963). *J. Mol. Biol.* **6**, 330.

Schlesinger, M. & Levinthal, C. (1963). *J. Mol. Biol.* **7**, 1.

Yanofsky, C. & St. Lawrence, P. (1960). *Ann. Rev. Microbiol.* **14**, 311.

VIII
Regulation

Introduction

There are four major areas of metabolic regulation that could appropriately be considered in this book: regulation of DNA, of RNA, of protein synthesis and of enzymatic activity. Regulation of DNA and RNA synthesis have been treated to some extent in Sections II and V respectively; they will be briefly discussed here also. Regulation of enzymatic activity will be treated only insofar as it relates to the main topics of this section, which are regulation of RNA and protein synthesis. Current research on this subject has been greatly influenced by the operon hypothesis of Jacob and Monod (1961, in collection). Jacob and Monod suggested that the mechanisms of induction and repression of enzyme synthesis are similar and can be explained in terms of a single model. The genetic elements of the proposed control system consist of a structural gene or genes, a regulator gene, and an operator gene. The structural gene produces a messenger RNA molecule which serves as the template for protein synthesis. The regulator gene produces a repressor RNA molecule that can interact with the operator gene. The operator gene is always adjacent to the structural gene it controls. The operator and associated structural genes are referred to as the operon. Combination of the repressor and the operator gene prevents the structural gene from making messenger RNA. The difference between induction and repression resides in the way metabolites influence the repressor-operator complex: in induction, the inducing metabolite is thought to combine with the repressor to prevent its interaction with the operator gene; in repression, combination of the repressing metabolite and the repressor is believed to strengthen interaction with the operator gene. Since the messenger RNA product of the operon should have the same primary sequence as one of the parent DNA chains, the possibility also exists that the repressor exerts a controlling influence exclusively or partly by interacting with the messenger. The possibility that repressor interacts with a DNA-RNA transient intermediate should also be considered.

Most systems that appear to have operon-like control mechanisms are more complex than the hypothetical model. It is also clear that there are genetic regulatory mechanisms fundamentally different from the operon system which exist both in microorganisms and in higher forms. In spite of this, most of the selected readings deal with the lac operon of *E. coli* which probably conforms most closely to the original operon model. This is the system that is best understood, and a thorough understanding of the regulatory mechanism used by one system will provide a great deal of insight for investigating other systems.

Observations made since the proposal of the operon model necessitate some important alterations in the model. The most serious error in the operon model as presented in the 1961 paper was the prediction that repressor is RNA. This was based largely on an experiment by Pardee and Prestidge[437] which showed that in the presence of 5-methyl tryptophan the synthesis of the lac operon repressor is not inhibited. Evidence was provided that 5-methyl tryptophan inhibited protein synthesis; and it was concluded that since the synthesis of repressor was not inhibited in the presence of 5-methyl tryptophan, repressor could not be protein. More recently Barbour and Pardee[447] and others[448] have found that 5-methyl tryptophan does not inhibit all protein synthesis and that therefore the original conclusion was not valid. In the meantime a great deal of evidence has been obtained on the lac operon and other systems which argues more positively that repressors are proteins: (1) Defective mutants of the repressor gene are partially corrected by suppressor mutations which function at the translation level.[456] (2) Temperature sensitive mutants for repressors have been isolated (Sadler and Novick, in collection). In general, temperature sensitive mutants can only be isolated for genes encoding proteins. (3) For the lac system a protein fraction has been isolated from repressor carrying cells which binds isopropyl-β-D-thiogalacto-pyranoside (IPTG) and other specific inducers of the lac operon.[449] From bacteriophage λ containing cells, a' protein has been isolated which shows many of the characteristics expected of the repressor that keeps the virus in the prophage state (Ptashne, in collection). (4) Inhibitors of protein synthesis inhibit repressor synthesis.[447, 448] (5) A protein has been partially purified which specifically represses the lac operon in a cell-free system. (Zubay, Lederman and DeVries, in collection.)

We now turn to a more detailed description of the regulatory mechanism for the lac operon. The lac operon consists of three structural genes z, y, a, from the operator, β–galactosidase, permease and transacetylase. The operator is adjacent to the z gene. The regulator gene, i, is separated by an appreciable gene distance from the operon. It is known that the operator gene and the first structural gene of the operon, z, are distinct from one another. Between the operator gene and the z gene lies a region called the promoter which is indispensable for gene expression. (Jacob and Monod, 1965, in collection.) The promoter is believed to be the point of initiation of either mRNA or protein synthesis or both.

The operon is transcribed as one continuous polycistronic messenger RNA molecule[442, 445.] In the same directional sense the messenger is translated from the z end (it is not known whether or not the operator region is transcribed), but it seems likely that the RNA is not always fully translated, so that more translations of the z gene are made than of the y gene, and more translations of the y gene are made than of the a gene. This has led to the suggestion that the order of genes in an operon is determined by the relative need for the various gene products. The enzymes most in demand would have their genes stationed nearest to the operator. Certainly the abundance of gene products might be expected to appear in this order.

In a wild type non–induced E. coli cell one to five molecules of β-galactosidase are produced unless inducer is present. Lactose which can serve as an inducer of the lac operon is also a substrate of β-galactosidase. There is good evidence that lactose must undergo par-

tial degradation before it can serve as inducer.[440] The most potent inducers of the lac operon mimic lactose in structure but contain a β-thiol linkage that cannot be hydrolyzed by β-galactosidase. Either natural or synthetic inducers are believed to function by binding to repressor and thereby producing an allosteric transition in the repressor which leads to its displacement from the repressor-operator complex.

Conditions for total induction may be met by 10^{-3} M IPTG or in certain constitutive mutations which have alterations in either the i or o gene so that the repressor-operator complex does not form. Even under these conditions the amount of β-galactosidase synthesized can be influenced appreciably by the so-called glucose effect. The synthesis of many catabolic enzymes is decreased by glucose or related substrates in the growth media. Since the glucose effect operates with considerably less specificity even when specific gene repressor is absent, this second kind of regulation must use different controlling elements. Mutants that do not show the glucose effect have been isolated.

In the original operon hypothesis, it was not resolved if the repressor acts at the gene or messenger RNA level. This may vary from system to system but in the case of the lac operon there is some evidence that the repressor acts at the gene level: (1) it has been shown that repressor binds specifically to DNA containing the lac operator[557] (2) it has been shown that in the repressed state the synthesis of β-gal messenger RNA as well as β-galactosidase is repressed.[558] Point two no longer can be taken as conclusive evidence that repression works at the gene level since recent evidence shows that transcription and translation may be strongly coupled.[465, 467-475] If there is strong coupling, we would expect little production of messenger RNA in the repressed state even if the repressor acted directly on the messenger.

Although the lac operon has the most completely understood regulatory mechanism, we still know little about the structural transition of repressor produced by inducer binding, the structural transition undergone by DNA in binding repressor or the structural nature of the initiation point for RNA synthesis. However, rapid progress is expected on these problems.

A number of other operon-like control systems in bacteria present interesting variations on the lac operon theme. In *E. coli* K eight enzymes are involved in the biosynthesis of arginine.[466] The synthesis of these enzymes is repressed in the presence of arginine. The genes for these enzymes are located in five distinct clusters on the bacterial chromosome; a separate site exists for a regulator gene. It is assumed that arginine, or a compound containing arginine, acts as a corepressor forming a complex with the product of the regulator gene that binds to the operator sites of the five distinct gene clusters. Although a given level of arginine represses the synthesis of all the arginine enzymes, it represses the enzymes in the different clusters to different extents, suggesting that the five operator sites have different affinities for the repressor-corepressor complex.

The synthesis of alkaline phosphatase is repressed by high phosphate and is induced in low phosphate. There are two regulator genes associated with alkaline phosphatase synthesis, both of which are believed to encode proteins. Both regulator genes are required for induction of synthesis. There is no immediate provision for a regulator gene required for induction in the operon hypothesis, so this system appears to present a truly different kind of regulatory phenomena. Garen and Echols[455] have offered an explanation for the presence of two regulator genes.

The operon containing genes required for the biosynthesis of histidine is the largest known operon, encoding about eleven enzymes.[459] As in the synthesis of the arginine enzymes, the synthesis of the histidine enzymes is inhibited by addition of the end-product histidine. However, evidence suggests that it is not the histidine level but rather the histidyl-tRNA level which is effective in repression.[460] It has not been determined yet whether repression works at the gene or messenger RNA level or possibly at both levels.

Some enzymes are involved in the synthesis of more than one amino acid. Freundlich et al.[545] have investigated the enzymes jointly involved in the synthesis of isoleucine, valine and leucine. The synthesis of these enzymes is repressible but only in the presence of all three end-products, isoleucine, valine and leucine.

The operon type of control mechanism is elaborate and it seems likely that bacteria only use specific protein repressors for genes whose products are required in widely varying amounts.[544] There are many enzymes which are required most of the time and it might be more efficient for the cell to produce a fairly constant amount of the corresponding messengers. The amount of messenger formed could be controlled in the simplest manner without a repressor by constructing the gene initiation site (promoter site) so that it has a limited affinity for the attachment of RNA polymerase.

Bacteria such as *E. coli* have short-lived messengers with lifetimes of two to three minutes and control at the gene level would very rapidly affect translation as well as transcription. In spite of their apparent redundancy, control mechanisms that operate at the level of translation may exist for some bacterial messengers. There are other situations where translation level control mechanisms would seem to be indispensable. Some single-stranded RNA viruses function as polycistronic messengers. During the different phases of the viral life cycle after infection, different phage encoded proteins are synthesized in widely varying amounts and there must be a mechanism which selects which regions of the single-stranded RNA are to be translated.[476, 481]

Sueoka and Sueoka[477] have observed an effect after T_2 bacteriophage infection of *E. coli* that may be related to regulation at the level of translation. The phage infection is followed by modification of one of the host cell's leucyl tRNAs as evidenced by a change in the chromatographic elution profile of the tRNA. It is known that host protein synthesis is turned off soon after T_2 bacteriophage infection and it is possible that the mechanism of turning off is related to modification of the

465

host leucyl tRNA. Possibly a tRNA needed for host messenger translation but not needed for phage messenger translation is made unusable. Since there usually is more than one tRNA for each amino acid, this type of control mechanism has wide ranging possibilities and its involvement should be considered wherever translation level control of a number of genes seems likely.

In reticulocytes up to 90 percent of the protein synthesis taking place is directed to the manufacture of hemoglobin. Since hemoglobin contains an equal number of α and β chains and the hemoglobin messenger RNAs are extremely long-lived, it seems likely that there exists a mechanism for control of translation to insure approximately equal numbers α and β chains. Colombo and Baglioni[486] have postulated a mechanism in which the α-polypeptide chains are not released from their polysomes until complemented by β-polypeptide chains.

A Closer Look at Regulation Problems in Higher Forms

The bulk of this volume has been concerned with studies on bacteria and bacteriophage because these microorganisms have provided us with the simplest and most readily available systems for understanding the basic biosynthetic machinery used to make nucleic acids and proteins. Since much of this basic information is now available, molecular biologists are turning more attention to higher organisms to see to what extent the mechanisms of synthesis are similar and to what extent they differ.

The problems of examining higher forms are much greater because of the increased complexity of the organisms and the inability in most cases to produce mutants that are useful for biochemical study. To get some idea of the increased complexity it is only necessary to consider that typical mammalian species contain two to three orders of magnitude more DNA than E. coli. The multicellular organism has subdivided the biochemical work required for survival through differentiation. The way in which each cell type of a multicellular organism develops and maintains its genetic regulatory apparatus is one of the key problems in modern biology and its study represents a natural extension of the investigations discussed in this section.

Cell differentiation, unlike operon control in microorganisms, results in a spectrum of gene activities that is generally hard to alter. Monod and Jacob[543] have suggested that in higher forms this may be explained by interaction between the components of the operons. For example, if one operon produces an inhibitor or corepressor of another operon, once established it might prevent the expression of the other operon altogether. Although interactions between operons of this sort might explain some of the phenomena associated with differentiation, the kind of cell stability and limited gene activity displayed by many differentiated cells suggests the presence of additional genetic regulatory devices basically different from the operon control device.

In conclusion let us consider a regulatory mechanism which might lead to stable differentiated cells without requiring the presence of a wide array of specific repressors to maintain genetic silence for unneeded genes. This model may serve as a working hypothesis for future investigations. In this model, differentiation is explained in terms of a process of gene regulation involving the competition between specific repressors such as are found in operon control systems in bacteria and nonspecific repressors such as histones. This model states that the activity of genes in transcription is inhibited by the binding of repressor at the operator, which is at or overlaps with the initiation point for transcription. There would exist two types of repressors in the cells of higher forms: specific repressors that interact with one or a limited number of operators which have the appropriate specific sequence of nucleotides, and nonspecific repressors or histones which interact with the DNA at any point along its length because of electrostatic attraction. The specific repressors would function by reversible binding in a manner similar to the lac repressor of E. coli. Transcription would occur only when the inducer interacts with the repressor displacing it from the operator. When the inducer concentration drops below a certain level the repressor again combines with the operator and the gene is turned off. The regulatory action of the specific repressor therefore would be completely reversible. Histone similarly would turn the gene off if it became complexed with the operator but would have little effect on transcription if complexed elsewhere. Initiation of RNA synthesis could therefore become sensitive to histone binding but the propagation of RNA synthesis could not. Assuming there are no inducers for histone, there would be only one time during the cell life when a gene whose operator is complexed with histone could become free of histone. This would be during S-phase when both DNA and histone synthesis occur. A newly duplicated operator site has the option of complexing with specific repressor or histone. If a significant quantity of specific repressor is present, it would compete favorably with the histone for the operator site and thereby prevent the binding of histone at the operator site. Following S-phase, inducible operons would have specific repressors rather than histones attached to their operators. The only prerequisite for the conversion of a noninducible to an inducible operon would be that a significant quantity of specific repressor be present during the preceding S-phase. Loss

of inducibility could be similarly explained in terms of loss of specific repressor by inactivation or other means before S-phase. In any particular cell only a limited number of specific repressors would be present so that in most cells most genes would not be in an inducible state. A new gene could only become inducible after S-phase, and then only if there were a build-up of the appropriate specific gene repressor prior to S-phase. The build-up of a new repressor would presumably result from the activation of one of the already inducible operons. This suggests a tight causal relationship between the activation of different groups of operons.

To a great extent it is through a testing of well-defined models like those discussed above that the unique genetic regulatory phenomena of higher forms will become understood. As in microorganism studies the most critical studies will probably rely heavily on the use of cell-free systems in which the crucial macromolecular components can be added or omitted from the biochemical reaction.

The bibliography of this section includes a number of references in selected areas on higher forms, carcinogenesis, antibody formation, embryology and hormones. In most of these areas we are just beginning to gain some understanding of the molecular details of the phenomena in question.

Bibliography

LAC OPERON

437. A. B. Pardee and L. S. Prestidge, (1959). On the Nature of the Repressor of β-galactosidase Synthesis in *Escherichia coli*. Biochem. Biophys. Acta **36**, 545.

438. J. R. Beckwith, (1964). A Deletion Analysis of the Lac Operator in *E. coli*. J. Mol. Biol. **8**, 427.

439. W. A. Newton, J. R. Beckwith, D. Zipser and S. Brenner, (1965). Nonsense Mutants and Polarity in the Lac Operon of *E. coli*. J. Mol. Biol. **14**, 290.

440. C. Burstein, M. Cohn, A. Kepes and J. Monod, (1965). Role of Lactose and its Products in the Induction of Lactose Operon. Biochem. Biophys. Acta **95**, 634.

441. E. Steers, G. R. Craven and C. B. Anfinsen, (1965). Comparison of β-Gal from Normal (i⁻0⁺Z⁺) and Operator Constitutive (i⁻0ᶜZ⁺) Strains of *E. coli*. Proc. Natl. Acad. Sci. U.S. **54**, 1174.

442. D. H. Alpers and G. M. Tomkins, (1965). The Order of Induction and Deinduction of the Enzymes of the Lactose Operon in *E. coli*. Proc. Natl. Acad. Sci. U.S. **53**, 797.

443. F. Jacob, A. Ullmann and J. Monod, (1965). Deletions Fusing the Lactose Operon and the Purine Operon in *E. coli*. J. Mol. Biol. **13**, 704.

444. J. R. Beckwith and E. Signer, (1966). Transposition of the Lac Region of *E. coli* I. Inversion of the Lac Operon and Transduction of Lac by ϕ80. J. Mol. Biol. **19**, 254.

445. D. H. Alpers and G. M. Tomkins, (1966). Sequential Transcription of the Genes of the Lactose Operon and its Regulation by Protein Synthesis. J. Biol. Chem. **241**, 4434.

446. A. Kepes and S. Beguin, (1966). Peptide Chain Initiation and Growth in the Induced Synthesis of β-gal. Biochem. Biophys. Acta **123**, 546.

447. S. D. Barbour and A. B. Pardee, (1966). The Establishment of β-gal Repression in the Mating System of *E. coli* K12. J. Mol. Biol. **20**, 505.

448. T. Horiuchi and Y. Okshima, (1966). Inhibition of Repressor Formation in the Lactose System of *E. coli* by Inhibitors of Protein Synthesis. J. Mol. Biol. **20**, 517.

449. W. Gilbert and B. Muller-Hill, (1966). Isolation of the Lac Repressor. Proc. Natl. Acad. Sci. U.S. **56**, 1891.

450. J. Palmer and V. Moses, (1967). Involvement of the Lac Regulating Genes in Catabolite Repression in *E. coli*. Biochem. J. **103**, 358.

451. W. F. Loomis and B. Magasanik, (1967). The Catabolite Repression Gene of the Lac Operon in *E. coli*. J. Mol. Biol. **23**, 487.

452. C. F. Fox, J. R. Carter and E. P. Kennedy, (1967). Genetic Control of the Membrane Protein Component of the Lactose Transport System of *E. coli*. Proc. Natl. Acad. Sci. U.S. **57**, 698.

453. L. Leive and V. Kollin, (1967). Synthesis, Utilization and Degradation of Lactose Operon mRNA in *E. coli*. J. Mol. Biol. **24**, 247.

454. R. O. R. Kaempfer and B. Magasanik, (1967). Mechanism of β-gal Induction in *E. coli*. J. Mol. Biol. **27**, 475.

ALKALINE PHOSPHATASE OPERON

455. A. Garen and H. Echols, (1962). Genetic Control of Induction of Alkaline Phosphatase Synthesis in *E. coli*. Proc. Natl. Acad. Sci. U.S. **48**, 1398.

456. A. Garen and S. Garen, (1963). Genetic Evidence on the Nature of the Repressor of Alkaline Phosphatase in *E. coli*. J. Mol. Biol. **6**, 433–438.

457. A. Garen and N. Otsuji, (1964). Isolation of a Protein Specified by a Regulator Gene. J. Mol. Biol. **8**, 841.

458. J. Gallant and T. Stoppswood, (1964). Measurement of the Stability of the Repressor of Alkaline Phosphatase Synthesis in *E. coli*. Proc. Natl. Acad. Sci. U.S. **52**, 1591.

HISTIDINE OPERON

459. B. N. Ames and P. E. Hartman, (1963). The Histidine Operon. Cold Spring Harbor Symp. Quant. Biol. **28**, 349.

460. S. Schlesinger and B. Magasanik, (1964). Effect of α-Methyl Histidine on the Control of Histidine Synthesis. J. Mol. Biol. **9**, 670.

461. J. R. Roth, D. N. Anton and P. E. Hartman, (1966). Histidine Regulatory Mutants in *Salmonella typhimurium*. I. Isolation and General Properties. J. Mol. Biol. **22**, 305.

TRYPTOPHAN OPERON

462. F. Imamoto, N. Morikawa, K. Sato, S. Mishima, T. Nishimura and A. Matsushiro, (1965). On the Transcription of the Tryptophan Operon in *E. coli* II. Production of the Specific Messenger RNA. J. Mol. Biol. **13**, 157.

463. T. Okamoto, M. Imai and T. Yura, (1965). The Cell-free Synthesis of Messenger RNA Specific for the Tryptophan Operon in *E. coli*. Biochem. Biophys. Acta **103**, 520.

464. R. H. Bauerle and P. Margolin, (1967). Evidence for 2 Sites for Initiation of Gene Expression in the Tryptophan Operon of *S. typhimurium*. J. Mol. Biol. **26**, 423.

465. F. Imamoto and C. Yanofsky, (1967). Transcription of the Tryptophan Operon in Polarity Mutants of *E. coli*. I. Characterization of the Tryptophan Messenger RNA of Polar Mutants. II. Evidence for Normal Production of tryp-mRNA Molecules for Premature Termination of Transcription. J. Mol. Biol. **28**, 1.

ARGININE OPERON

466. G. A. Jacoby and L. Gorini, (1967). Genetics of Control of the Arginine Pathway in *E. coli* B and K. J. Mol. Biol. **24**, 41.

REGULATION OF RNA SYNTHESIS

467. G. Edlin and O. Maaloe, (1966). Synthesis and Breakdown of Messenger RNA without Protein Synthesis. J. Mol. Biol. **15**, 428.

468. D. W. Morris and J. A. DeMoss, (1966). Polysome Transitions and the Regulation of RNA Synthesis in *E. coli*. Proc. Natl. Acad. Sci. U.S. **56**, 262.

469. W. P. Summers, W. D. Noteboom and G. C. Mueller, (1966). A Regulatory Role of Protein Synthesis on the Activity of RNA Polymerase of HeLa Nuclei. Biochem. Biophys. Res. Comm. **22**, 399.

470. D. H. Shin and K. Moldave, (1966). Effect of Ribosomes on the Biosynthesis of RNA *in Vitro*. J. Mol. Biol. **21**, 231.

471. E. Z. Ron and B. D. Davis, (1966). Specific Stimulation of RNA Synthesis by Methionine in Several Strains of *E. coli*. J. Mol. Biol. **2**, 13.

472. J. D. Friesen, (1966). Control of Messenger RNA Synthesis and Decay in *E. coli*. J. Mol. Biol. **20**, 559.

473. M. Revel and F. Gros, (1967). Stimulation by Ribosomes of a DNA Transcription Requirement for a Translation Factor. Biochem. Biophys. Res. Comm. **27**, 12.

474. G. Edlin and J. Neuhard, (1967). Regulation of Nucleoside Triphosphate Pools in *E. coli*. J. Mol. Biol. **24**, 225.

475. D. Nakada, (1967). Proteins of Ribosomes from Relaxed Particles. J. Mol. Biol. **29**, 473.

REGULATION OF BACTERIOPHAGE NUCLEIC ACID AND PROTEIN SYNTHESIS

476. M. P. Oeschger and D. Nathans, (1966). Differential Synthesis of Bacteriophage-specific Proteins in MS2-infected *E. coli* Treated with Actinomycin. J. Mol. Biol. **22**, 235.

477. T. Sueoka and N. Sueoka, (1966). Modification of Leucyl S-RNA after Bacteriophage Infection. J. Mol. Biol. **20**, 183.

478. G. N. Godson and R. L. Sinsheimer, (1967). Replication of Bacteriophage MS2 VI. Interaction Between Bacteriophage RNA and Cellular Components in MS2-Infected *E. coli*. J. Mol. Biol. **23**, 495.

479. R. A. Weisberg and J. A. Gallant, (1967). A Dual Function of the λ Prophage Repressor. J. Mol. Biol. **25**, 537.

480. J. Tomizawa and T. Ogawa, (1967). Inhibition of Growth of rII Mutants of Bacteriophage T_4 by Immunity Substance of Phage Lambda. J. Mol. Biol. **23**, 281.

481. T. Sugiyama and D. Nakada, (1967). Control of Translation of MS2 Cistrons by MS2 Coat Protein. Proc. Natl. Acad. Sci. U.S. **57**, 1744.

482. M. Ptashne, (1967). Isolation of the λ Phage Repressor. Proc. Natl. Acad. Sci. U.S. **57**, 306.

483. J. R. Kates and B. R. McAuslan, (1967). Messenger RNA Synthesis by a Coated Viral Genome. Proc. Natl. Acad. Sci. U.S. **57**, 314.

484. Y. Imae and T. Fukasawa, (1967). On the Mechanism of Derepression of Host Galactose Operon following Induction of Bacteriophage λ in *E. coli* Strain K12. Biochem. Biophys. Res. Comm. **28**, 38.

TRANSLATIONAL CONTROL

485. D. Karibian and I. M. London, (1965). Control of Heme Synthesis by Feedback Inhibition. Biochem. Biophys. Res. Comm. **18**, 243.

486. B. Colombo and C. Baglioni, (1966). Regulation of Hemoglobin Synthesis at the Polysome Level. J. Mol. Biol. **16**, 51.

487. J. R. Shaeffer, (1967). Evidence for Soluble α Chains as Intermediates in Hemoglobin Synthesis in the Rabbit Reticulocyte. Biochem. Biophys. Comm. **28**, 647.

488. T. W. Borun, M. D. Scharff and E. Robbins, (1967). Rapidly Labeled Polyribosome-Associated RNA Having the Properties of Histone Messenger. Proc. Natl. Acad. Sci. U.S. **58**, 1977.

ALLOSTERY

489. J. Monod, J. P. Changeux and F. Jacob, (1963). Allosteric Proteins and Cellular Control Systems. J. Mol. Biol. **6**, 306.

490. J. C. Gerhart and H. K. Schachman, (1965). Distinct Subunits for the Regulator and Catalytic Activity of Aspartate Transcarbamylase. Biochem. **4**, 1054.

491. J. Monod, J. Wyman and J. P. Changeux, (1965). On the Nature of Allosteric Transitions: A Plausible Model. J. Mol. Biol. **12**, 88.

492. M. M. Rubin and J. P. Changeux, (1966). On the Nature of Allosteric Transitions: Implications of Non-exclusive Ligand Binding. J. Mol. Biol. **21**, 265.

CARCINOGENESIS

493. G. T. Diamondopoulos and J. F. Enders, (1965). Studies on Transformation of Syrian Hamster Cells by Simian Virus 40 (SV 40); Acquisition of Oncogenicity by Virus-Exposed Cells Apparently Unassociated with the Viral Genome. Proc. Natl. Acad. Sci. U.S. **54**, 1092.

494. P. H. Black, A. M. Lewis, N. R. Blacklow, J. B. Austin and W. P. Rowe, (1967). Presence of Adenovirus-Specific Antigens in Hamster Cells Rendered Neoplastic by Adenovirus 1-SV 40 and Adenovirus 2-SV 40 Hybrid Viruses. Proc. Natl. Acad. Sci. U.S. **57**, 1324.

495. M. M. Burger and A. R. Goldberg, (1967). Identification of a Tumor-Specific Determinant on Neoplastic Cell Surfaces. Proc. Natl. Acad. Sci. U.S. **57**, 359.

496. K. Fujinaga and M. Green, (1967). Mechanism of Viral Carcinogenesis by DNA Mammalian Viruses, II. Viral Specific RNA in Tumor Cells Induced by Weakly Oncogenic Human Adenoviruses. Proc. Natl. Acad. Sci. U.S. **57**, 806.

497. R. Axel, B. Weinstein and E. Farber, (1967). Patterns of Transfer RNA in Normal Rat Liver and During Hepatic Carcinogenesis. Proc. Natl. Acad. Sci. U.S. **58**, 1255.

498. L. J. Greenberg and J. W. Uhr, (1967). DNA-RNA Hybridization Studies of Myeloma Tumors in Mice. Proc. Natl. Acad. Sci. U.S. **58**, 1878.

499. R. Wallace, (1967). Viral Transformation of Monkey Kidney Cell Cultures. Nature **213**, 768.

500. M. N. Oxman, W. P. Rowe and P. H. Black, (1967). Studies of Adenovirus-SV 40 Hybrid Viruses, VI. Differential Effects of Interferon on SV 40 and Adenovirus T Antigen Formation in Cells Infected with SV 40 Virus, Adenoviruses, and Adenovirus-SV 40 Hybrid Viruses. Proc. Natl. Acad. Sci. U.S. **57**, 941.

501. B. W. Finch and B. Ephrussi, (1967). Retention of Multiple Developmental Potentialities by Cells of a Mouse Testicular Teratocarcinoma During Prolonged Culture *in vitro* and their Extinction upon Hybridization with Cells of Permanent Lines. Proc. Natl. Acad. Sci. U.S. **57**, 615.

HORMONES

502. A. Korner, (1963). Growth Hormone Control of Messenger RNA Synthesis. Biochem. Biophys. Res. Comm. **13**, 386.

503. U. Clever, (1964). Actinomycin and Puromycin: Effects on Sequential Gene Activation by Ecdysome. Science **146**, 794.

504. C. Kidson and K. S. Kirby, (1964). Selective Alterations of Mammalian Messenger-RNA Synthesis: Evidence for Differential Action of Hormones on Gene Transcription. Nature **203**, 599.

505. H. G. Williams-Ashman, (1965). New Facets of the Biochemistry of Steroid Hormone Action. Cancer Research **25**, 1096.

506. A. S. Meyer, H. A. Schneiderman, and L. I. Gilbert, (1965). A Highly Purified Preparation of Juvenile Hormone from the Silk Moth. Nature **206**, 272.

507. U. Clever and C. G. Romball, (1966). RNA and Protein Synthesis in the Cellular Response to a Hormone Ecdysome. Proc. Natl. Acad. Sci. U.S. **56**, 1470.

508. E. B. Thompson, G. M. Tomkins and J. F. Curran, (1966). Induction of Tyrosine-Ketoglutarate Transaminase by Steroid Hormones in a Newly Established Tissue Culture Cell Line. Proc. Natl. Acad. Sci. U.S. **56**, 296.

509. M. J. Griffin and R. P. Cox, (1966). Studies on the Mechanism of Hormonal Induction of Alkaline Phosphatase in Human Cell Cultures I. Effects of Puromycin and Actinomycin D. J. Cell. Biol. **29**, 1.

510. I. Pastan, J. Roth and V. Macchia, (1966). Binding of Hormone to Tissue: The First Step in Polypeptide Hormone Action. Proc. Natl. Acad. Sci. U.S. **56**, 1802.

511. D. Toft, G. Shyamala and J. Gorski, (1967). A Receptor Molecule for Estrogens: Studies Using a Cell-free System. Proc. Natl. Acad. Sci. U.S. **57**, 1740.

512. C. Kidson, (1967). Cortisol in the Regulation of RNA and Protein Synthesis. Nature **213**, 779.

513. B. Peterkofsky and G. M. Tomkins, (1967). Effect of Inhibitors of Nucleic Acid Synthesis on Steroid-mediated Induction of Tyrosine Aminotransferase in Hepatoma Cell Cultures. J. Mol. Biol. **30**, 49.

ANTIBODIES

514. J. W. Uhr, (1963). Actinomycin D: Its Effect on Antibody Formation *in vivo*. Science **142**, 1476.

515. A. Finkelstein and J. W. Uhr, (1964). Specific Inhibition of Antibody Formation by Passively Administered 19S and 7S Antibody. Science **146**, 67.

516. J. W. Uhr, (1965). Passive Sensitization of Lymphocytes and Macrophages by Antigen-Antibody Complexes. Proc. Natl. Acad. Sci. U.S. **54**, 1599.

517. G. Harris, (1966). RNA Synthesis in Macrophages in Relation to the Secondary Immune Response *in Vitro*. Nature **211**, 154.

518. L. E. Hood, W. R. Gray and W. J. Dreyer, (1966). On the Mechanism of Antibody Synthesis. A Species Comparison of L-Chains. Proc. Natl. Acad. Sci. U.S. **55**, 826.

519. A. L. Shapiro, M. D. Scharff, J. V. Maizel and J. W. Uhr, (1966). Polyribosomal Synthesis and Assembly of the H and L Chains of Gamma Globulin. Proc. Natl. Acad. Sci. U.S. **56**, 216.

520. M. Nakamo and W. Braun, (1966). Fluctuation Tests with Antibody-Forming Spleen Cell Populations. Science **151**, 338.

521. R. M. E. Parkhouse, (1967). Antigen Stimulated DNA and RNA Synthesis in Spleen Cell Suspensions from Immunized Rabbits. Nature **215**, 394.

522. A. A. Gottlieb, V. R. Glisin and P. Doty, (1967). Studies on Macrophage RNA Involved in Antibody Production. Proc. Natl. Acad. Sci. U.S. **57**, 1849.

523. J. Sterzl and M. Jilek, (1967). Number of Antibody-forming Cells in Primary and Secondary Reactions after Administration of Antigen. Nature **216**, 1233.

524. D. E. Mosier, (1967). A Requirement for Two Cell Types for Antibody Formation *in Vitro*. Science **158**, 1573.

EMBRYOLOGY

525. P. R. Gross, L. I. Malkin and W. A. Moyer, (1964). Templates for the First Proteins of Embryonic Development. Proc. Natl. Acad. Sci. U.S. **51**, 407.

526. D. D. Brown and E. Littna, (1964). RNA Synthesis during the Development of *Xenopus laevis*, the South African Clawed Toad. J. Mol. Biol. **8**, 669.

527. D. D. Brown and E. Littna, (1964). Variations in the Synthesis of Stable RNA's during Oogenesis and Development of *Xenopus laevis*. J. Mol. Biol. **8**, 688.

528. P. R. Gross, K. Kraemer and L. I. Malkin, (1965). Base Composition of RNA Synthesized during Cleavage of the Sea Urchin Embryo. Biochem. Biophys. Res. Comm. **18**, 569.

529. P. R. Gross, L. I. Malkin and M. Hubbard, (1965). Synthesis of RNA during Oogenesis in the Sea Urchin. J. Mol. Biol. **13**, 463.

530. J. B. Gurdon and D. D. Brown, (1965). Cytoplasmic Regulation of RNA Synthesis and Nucleolus Formation in Developing Embryos of *Xenopus laevis*. J. Mol. Biol. **12**, 27.

531. G. C. Candelas and R. M. Iverson, (1966). Evidence for Translational Level Control of Protein Synthesis in the Development of Sea Urchin Eggs. Biochem. Biophys. Res. Comm. **24**, 867.

532. D. D. Brown and J. B. Gurdon, (1966). Size Distribution and Stability of DNA-like RNA Synthesized during Development of Anucleolate Embryos of *Xenopus laevis*. J. Mol. Biol. **19**, 399.

533. D. D. Brown and E. Littna, (1966). Synthesis and Accumulation of DNA-like RNA during Embryogenesis of *Xenopus laevis*. J. Mol. Biol. **20**, 81.

534. D. W. Slater and S. Spiegelman, (1966). An Estimation of Genetic Messages in the Unfertilized Echinord. Proc. Natl. Acad. Sci. U.S. **56**, 164.

535. A. H. Whiteley, B. J. McCarthy and H. R. Whiteley, (1966). Changing Populations of Messenger RNA During Sea Urchin Development. Proc. Natl. Acad. Sci. U.S. **55**, 519.

536. H. Denis, (1966). Gene Expression in Amphibian Development I. Validity of the Method Used: Interspecific and Intraspecific Hybridization between Nucleic Acids. Properties of Messenger RNA Synthesized by Developing Embryos II. Release of the Genetic Information in Growing Embryos. J. Mol. Biol. **22**, 269.

537. L. D. Smith, R. E. Ecker and S. Subtelny, (1966). Initiation of Protein Synthesis in Egg of *Rana pipiens*. Proc. Natl. Acad. Sci. U.S. **56**, 1724.

538. R. A. Flickinger, R. Greene, D. M. Kohl and M. Muyagi, (1966). Patterns of Synthesis of DNA-like RNA in Parts of Developing Egg Embryos. Proc. Natl. Acad. Sci. U.S. **56**, 1712.

539. M. Nemer and A. A. Infante, (1967). Ribosomal RNA of the Sea Urchin Egg and its Fate During Embryogenesis. J. Mol. Biol. **27**, 73.

540. J. B. Gurdon, (1967). On the Origin and Persistence of a Cytoplasmic State Inducing Nuclear DNA Synthesis in Frogs' Eggs. Proc. Natl. Acad. Sci. U.S. **58**, 545.

541. M. Crippa, E. H. Davidson and A. E. Mirsky, (1967). Persistence in Early Amphibian Embryos of Informational RNAs of the Lampbrush Chromosome Stage of Oogenesis. Proc. Natl. Acad. Sci. U.S. **57**, 885.

542. D. Epel, (1967). Protein Synthesis in Sea Urchin Eggs: A Late Response to Fertilization. Proc. Natl. Acad. Sci. U.S. **57**, 899.

MISCELLANEOUS

543. J. Monod and F. Jacob, (1961). General Conclusions: Teleonomic Mechanisms in Cellular Metabolism, Growth, and Differentiation. Cold Spring Harbor Symp. Quant. Biol. **26**, 389.

544. A. B. Pardee and J. R. Beckwith, (1963). Control of Constitutive Enzyme Synthesis. p. 255–265 in Informational Macromolecules. Ed. by H. J. Vogel, V. Bryson and J. O. Lampen. Academic Press, New York.

545. M. Freundlich, R. O. Burns and H. E. Umbarger, (1963). Multivalent Repression. p. 287–291 in Informational Macromolecules. Ed. H. J. Vogel, V. Bryson and J. O. Lampen. Academic Press, New York.

546. J. Gorman, P. Taruo, M. LaBerge and H. Halvorson, (1964). Timing of Enzyme Synthesis During Synchronous Division in Yeast. Biochem. Biophys. Res. Comm. **15**, 43.

547. P. C. Hanawalt and R. Wax, (1964). Transcription of a Repressed Gene: Evidence that it Requires DNA Replication. Science **145**, 1061.

548. P. L. Kuempel, M. Masters and A. B. Pardee, (1965). Bursts of Enzyme Synthesis in the Bacterial Duplication Cycle. Biochem. Biophys. Res. Comm. **18**, 858.

549. G. M. Mouren and A. Cozzone, (1966). Inhibition by Actinomycin D of Valine Incorporation into Specific Proteins of Rat Pancreas *in Vivo*. Biochem. **5**, 3684.

550. W. K. Roberts and J. F. E. Newman, (1966). Use of Low Concentrations of Actinomycin D in the study of RNA Synthesis in Ehrlich Ascites Cells. J. Mol. Biol. **20**, 63.

551. A. Gierer, (1966). Model for DNA and Protein Interactions and the Function of the Operator. Nature **212**, 1480.

552. J. Konisky and N. Nomura, (1967). Interaction of Colicins with Bacterial Cells. II. Specific Alterations of *E. coli* Ribosomes Induced by Colicin E3 *in Vivo*. J. Mol. Biol. **26**, 181.

553. A. W. Hsie and H. V. Rickenberg, (1967). Catabolite Repression in *E. coli*: The Role of G-6-Phosphate. Biochem. Biophys. Res. Comm. **29**, 303.

554. E. Yarosh and C. Levinthal, (1967). Exclusion of RNA Bacteriophages and Interference with their RNA Replication by T_4 Phage. J. Mol. Biol. **30**, 329.

555. R. A. Zimmerman and C. Levinthal, (1967). Messenger RNA and RNA Transcription Time. J. Mol. Biol. **30**, 349.

556. L. P. Gage and E. P. Geiduschek, (1967). Repression of Early Messenger Transcription in the Development of a Bacteriophage. J. Mol. Biol. **30**, 435.

557. W. Gilbert and B. Muller-Hills, (1967). The lac Operator is DNA. Proc. Natl. Acad. Sci. U.S. **58**, 2415.

558. G. Attardi, S. Naono, J. Rouviere, F. Jacob and F. Gros, (1963). Production of Messenger RNA and Regulation of Protein Synthesis. Cold Spring Harbor Symp. Quant. Biol. **28**, 363.

559. D. E. Sheppard and E. Englesberg, (1967). Further Evidence for Positive Control of L-Arabinose System by Gene ara C. J. Mol. Biol. **25**, 443.

J. Mol. Biol. (1961) **3**, 318–356

REVIEW ARTICLE

Genetic Regulatory Mechanisms in the Synthesis of Proteins †

FRANÇOIS JACOB AND JACQUES MONOD

Services de Génétique Microbienne et de Biochimie Cellulaire,
Institut Pasteur, Paris

(*Received 28 December 1960*)

The synthesis of enzymes in bacteria follows a double genetic control. The so-called structural genes determine the molecular organization of the proteins. Other, functionally specialized, genetic determinants, called regulator and operator genes, control the rate of protein synthesis through the intermediacy of cytoplasmic components or repressors. The repressors can be either inactivated (induction) or activated (repression) by certain specific metabolites. This system of regulation appears to operate directly at the level of the synthesis by the gene of a short-lived intermediate, or messenger, which becomes associated with the ribosomes where protein synthesis takes place.

1. Introduction

According to its most widely accepted modern connotation, the word "gene" designates a DNA molecule whose specific self-replicating structure can, through mechanisms unknown, become translated into the specific structure of a polypeptide chain.

This concept of the "structural gene" accounts for the multiplicity, specificity and genetic stability of protein structures, and it implies that such structures are not controlled by environmental conditions or agents. It has been known for a long time, however, that the synthesis of individual proteins may be provoked or suppressed within a cell, under the influence of specific external agents, and more generally that the relative rates at which different proteins are synthesized may be profoundly altered, depending on external conditions. Moreover, it is evident from the study of many such effects that their operation is absolutely essential to the survival of the cell.

It has been suggested in the past that these effects might result from, and testify to, complementary contributions of genes on the one hand, and some chemical factors on the other in determining the final structure of proteins. This view, which contradicts at least partially the "structural gene" hypothesis, has found as yet no experimental support, and in the present paper we shall have occasion to consider briefly some of this negative evidence. Taking, at least provisionally, the structural gene hypothesis in its strictest form, let us assume that the DNA message contained within a gene is both necessary and sufficient to define the structure of a protein. The elective effects of agents other than the structural gene itself in promoting or suppressing the synthesis of a protein must then be described as operations which control the rate of transfer of structural information from gene to protein. Since it seems to be established

† This work has been aided by grants from the National Science Foundation, the Jane Coffin Childs Memorial Fund for Medical Research and the Commissariat à l'Energie Atomique.

that proteins are synthesized in the cytoplasm, rather than directly at the genetic level, this transfer of structural information must involve a chemical intermediate synthesized by the genes. This hypothetical intermediate we shall call the structural messenger. The rate of information transfer, i.e. of protein synthesis, may then depend either upon the activity of the gene in synthesizing the messenger, or upon the activity of the messenger in synthesizing the protein. This simple picture helps to state the two problems with which we shall be concerned in the present paper. If a given agent specifically alters, positively or negatively, the rate of synthesis of a protein, we must ask:

(a) Whether the agent acts at the cytoplasmic level, by controlling the activity of the messenger, or at the genetic level, by controlling the synthesis of the messenger.

(b) Whether the specificity of the effect depends upon some feature of the information transferred from structural gene to protein, or upon some specialized controlling element, not represented in the structure of the protein, gene or messenger.

The first question is easy to state, if difficult to answer. The second may not appear so straightforward. It may be stated in a more general way, by asking whether the genome is composed exclusively of structural genes, or whether it also involves determinants which may control the rates of synthesis of proteins according to a given set of conditions, without determining the structure of any individual protein. Again it may not be evident that these two statements are equivalent. We hope to make their meaning clear and to show that they are indeed equivalent, when we consider experimental examples.

The best defined systems wherein the synthesis of a protein is seen to be controlled by specific agents are examples of enzymatic adaptation, this term being taken here to cover both enzyme induction, i.e. the formation of enzyme electively provoked by a substrate, and enzyme repression, i.e. the specific inhibition of enzyme formation brought about by a metabolite. Only a few inducible and repressible systems have been identified both biochemically and genetically to an extent which allows discussion of the questions in which we are interested here. In attempting to generalize, we will have to extrapolate from these few systems. Such generalization is greatly encouraged, however, by the fact that lysogenic systems, where phage protein synthesis might be presumed to obey entirely different rules, turn out to be analysable in closely similar terms. We shall therefore consider in succession certain inducible and repressible enzyme systems and lysogenic systems.

It might be best to state at the outset some of the main conclusions which we shall arrive at. These are:

(a) That the mechanisms of control in all these systems are negative, in the sense that they operate by inhibition rather than activation of protein synthesis.

(b) That in addition to the classical structural genes, these systems involve two other types of genetic determinants (regulator and operator) fulfilling specific functions in the control mechanisms.

(c) That the control mechanisms operate at the genetic level, i.e. by regulating the activity of structural genes.

2. Inducible and Repressible Enzyme Systems

(a) *The phenomenon of enzyme induction. General remarks*

It has been known for over 60 years (Duclaux, 1899; Dienert, 1900; Went, 1901) that certain enzymes of micro-organisms are formed only in the presence of their specific substrate. This effect, later named "enzymatic adaptation" by Karstrom (1938), has been the subject of a great deal of experimentation and speculation. For a long time, "enzymatic adaptation" was not clearly distinguished from the selection of spontaneous variants in growing populations, or it was suggested that enzymatic adaptation and selection represented *alternative* mechanisms for the acquisition of a "new" enzymatic property. Not until 1946 were adaptive enzyme systems shown to be controlled in bacteria by discrete, specific, stable, i.e. genetic, determinants (Monod & Audureau, 1946). A large number of inducible systems has been discovered and studied in bacteria. In fact, enzymes which attack exogeneous substrates are, as a general rule, inducible in these organisms. The phenomenon is far more difficult to study in tissues or cells of higher organisms, but its existence has been established quite clearly in many instances. Very often, if not again as a rule, the presence of a substrate induces the formation not of a single but of several enzymes, sequentially involved in its metabolism (Stanier, 1951).

Most of the fundamental characteristics of the induction effect have been established in the study of the "lactose" system of *Escherichia coli* (Monod & Cohn, 1952; Cohn, 1957; Monod, 1959) and may be summarized in a brief discussion of this system from the biochemical and physiological point of view. We shall return later to the genetic analysis of this system.

(b) *The lactose system of* Escherichia coli

Lactose and other β-galactosides are metabolized in *E. coli* (and certain other enteric bacteria) by the hydrolytic transglucosylase β-galactosidase. This enzyme was isolated from *E. coli* and later crystallized. Its specificity, activation by ions and transglucosylase *vs* hydrolase activity have been studied in great detail (*cf.* Cohn, 1957). We need only mention the properties that are significant for the present discussion. The enzyme is active exclusively on β-galactosides unsubstituted on the galactose ring. Activity and affinity are influenced by the nature of the aglycone moiety both being maximum when this radical is a relatively large, hydrophobic group. Substitution of sulfur for oxygen in the galactosidic linkage of the substrate abolishes hydrolytic activity completely, but the thiogalactosides retain about the same affinity for the enzyme site as the homologous oxygen compounds.

As isolated by present methods, β-galactosidase appears to form various polymers (mostly hexamers) of a fundamental unit with a molecular weight of 135,000. There is one end group (threonine) and also one enzyme site (as determined by equilibrium dialysis against thiogalactosides) per unit. It is uncertain whether the monomer is active as such, or exists *in vivo*. The hexameric molecule has a turnover number of 240,000 mol × min^{-1} at 28°C, pH 7·0 with o-nitrophenyl-β-D-galactoside as substrate and Na$^+$ (0·01 M) as activator.

There seems to exist only a single homogeneous β-galactosidase in *E. coli*, and this organism apparently cannot form any other enzyme capable of metabolizing lactose, as indicated by the fact that mutants that have lost β-galactosidase activity cannot grow on lactose as sole carbon source.

However, the possession of β-galactosidase activity is not sufficient to allow utilization of lactose by *intact E. coli* cells. Another component, distinct from β-galactosidase, is required to allow penetration of the substrate into the cell (Monod, 1956; Rickenberg, Cohen, Buttin & Monod, 1956; Cohen & Monod, 1957; Pardee, 1957; Képès, 1960). The presence and activity of this component is determined by measuring the rate of entry and/or the level of accumulation of radioactive thiogalactosides into intact cells. Analysis of this active permeation process shows that it obeys classical enzyme kinetics allowing determination of K_m and V_{max}. The specificity is high since the system is active only with galactosides (β or α), or thiogalactosides. The spectrum of apparent affinities $(1/K_m)$ is very different from that of β-galactosidase. Since the permeation system, like β-galactosidase, is inducible (see below) its formation can be studied *in vivo*, and shown to be invariably associated with protein synthesis. By these criteria, there appears to be little doubt that this specific permeation system involves a specific protein (or proteins), formed upon induction, which has been called galactoside-permease. That this protein is distinct from and independent of β-galactosidase is shown by the fact that mutants that have lost β-galactosidase retain the capacity to concentrate galactosides, while mutants that have lost this capacity retain the power to synthesize galactosidase. The latter mutants (called cryptic) cannot however use lactose, since the intracellular galactosidase is apparently accessible exclusively *via* the specific permeation system.

Until quite recently, it had not proved possible to identify *in vitro* the inducible protein (or proteins) presumably responsible for galactoside-permease activity. During the past year, a protein characterized by the ability to carry out the reaction:

Ac. Coenzyme A + Thiogalactoside → 6-Acetylthiogalactoside + Coenzyme A

has been identified, and extensively purified from extracts of *E. coli* grown in presence of galactosides (Zabin, Képès & Monod, 1959). The function of this enzyme in the system is far from clear, since formation of a free covalent acetyl-compound is almost certainly not involved in the permeation process *in vivo*. On the other hand:

(a) mutants that have lost β-galactosidase and retained galactoside-permease, retain galactoside-acetylase;

(b) most mutants that have lost permease cannot form acetylase;

(c) permeaseless acetylaseless mutants which revert to the permease-positive condition simultaneously regain the ability to form acetylase.

These correlations strongly suggest that galactoside-acetylase is somehow involved in the permeation process, although its function *in vivo* is obscure, and it seems almost certain that other proteins (specific or not for this system) are involved. In any case, we are interested here not in the mechanisms of permeation, but in the control mechanisms which operate with β-galactosidase, galactoside-permease and galactoside-acetylase. The important point therefore is that, as we shall see, galactoside-acetylase invariably obeys the same controls as galactosidase.†

(c) *Enzyme induction and protein synthesis*

Wild type *E. coli* cells grown in the absence of a galactoside contain about 1 to 10 units of galactosidase per mg dry weight, that is, an average of 0·5 to 5 active molecules

---

† For reasons which will become apparent later it is important to consider whether there is any justification for the assumption that galactosidase and acetylase activities might be associated with the same fundamental protein unit. We should therefore point to the following observations:

(a) There are mutants which form galactosidase and no acetylase, and *vice versa*.

(b) Purified acetylase is devoid of any detectable galactosidase activity.

(c) The specificity of the two enzymes is very different.

(d) The two enzymes are easily and completely separated by fractional precipitation.

(e) Acetylase is highly heat-resistant, under conditions where galactosidase is very labile.

(f) Anti-galactosidase serum does not precipitate acetylase; nor does anti-acetylase serum precipitate galactosidase.

There is therefore no ground for the contention that galactosidase and acetylase activities are associated with the same protein.

per cell or 0·15 to 1·5 molecules per nucleus. Bacteria grown in the presence of a suitable inducer contain an average of 10,000 units per mg dry weight. This is the induction effect.

A primary problem, to which much experimental work has been devoted, is whether this considerable increase in specific activity corresponds to the synthesis of entirely "new" enzyme molecules, or to the activation or conversion of pre-existing protein precursors. It has been established by a combination of immunological and isotopic methods that the enzyme formed upon induction:

(a) is distinct, as an antigen, from all the proteins present in uninduced cells (Cohn & Torriani, 1952);

(b) does not derive any significant fraction of its sulfur (Monod & Cohn, 1953; Hogness, Cohn & Monod, 1955) or carbon (Rotman & Spiegelman, 1954) from pre-existing proteins.

The inducer, therefore, brings about the complete *de novo* synthesis of enzyme molecules which are new by their specific structure as well as by the origin of their elements. The study of several other induced systems has fully confirmed this conclusion, which may by now be considered as part of the *definition* of the effect. We will use the term "induction" here as meaning "activation by inducer of enzyme-protein synthesis."

(d) *Kinetics of induction*

Accepting (still provisionally) the structural gene hypothesis, we may therefore consider that the inducer somehow accelerates the rate of information transfer from gene to protein. This it could do either by provoking the synthesis of the messenger or by activating the messenger. If the messenger were a *stable* structure, functioning as a catalytic template in protein synthesis, one would expect different kinetics of induction, depending on whether the inducer acted at the genetic or at the cytoplasmic level.

The kinetics of galactosidase induction turn out to be remarkably simple when determined under proper experimental conditions (Monod, Pappenheimer & Cohen-Bazire, 1952; Herzenberg, 1959). Upon addition of a suitable inducer to a growing culture, enzyme activity increases at a rate proportional to the increase in total protein within the culture; i.e. a linear relation is obtained (Fig. 1) when total enzyme activity is plotted against mass of the culture. The slope of this line:

$$P = \frac{\Delta z}{\Delta M}$$

is the "differential rate of synthesis," which is taken by definition as the measure of the effect. Extrapolation to the origin indicates that enzyme formation begins about three minutes (at 37°C) after addition of inducer (Pardee & Prestidge, 1961). Removal of the inducer (or addition of a specific anti-inducer, see below) results in cessation of enzyme synthesis within the same short time. The differential rate of synthesis varies with the concentration of inducer reaching a different saturation value for different inducers. The inducer therefore acts in a manner which is (kinetically) similar to that of a dissociable activator in an enzyme system: activation and inactivation follow very rapidly upon addition or removal of the activator.

The conclusion which can be drawn from these kinetics is a negative one: the inducer does not appear to activate the synthesis of a stable intermediate able to accumulate in the cell (Monod, 1956).

Similar kinetics of induction have been observed with most or all other systems which have been adequately studied (Halvorson, 1960) with the exception of penicillinase of *Bacillus cereus*. The well-known work of Pollock has shown that the synthesis of this enzyme continues for a long time, at a decreasing rate, after removal of inducer (penicillin) from the medium. This effect is apparently related to the fact that minute amounts of penicillin are retained irreversibly by the cells after transient exposure to the drug (Pollock, 1950). The unique behavior of this system therefore does not contradict the rule that induced synthesis stops when the inducer is removed from the cells. Using this system, Pollock & Perret (1951) were able to show that the inducer acts catalytically, in the sense that a cell may synthesize many more enzyme molecules than it has retained inducer molecules.

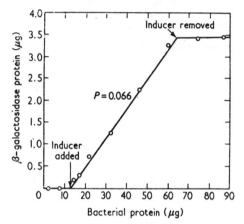

Fig. 1. Kinetics of induced enzyme synthesis. Differential plot expressing accumulation of β-galactosidase as a function of increase of mass of cells in a growing culture of *E. coli*. Since abscissa and ordinates are expressed in the same units (micrograms of protein) the slope of the straight line gives galactosidase as the fraction (*P*) of total protein synthesized in the presence of inducer. (After Cohn, 1957.)

(e) *Specificity of induction*

One of the most conspicuous features of the induction effect is its extreme specificity. As a general rule, only the substrate of an enzyme, or substances very closely allied to the normal substrate, are endowed with inducer activity towards this enzyme. This evidently suggests that a correlation between the molecular structure of the inducer and the structure of the catalytic center on the enzymes is *inherently* involved in the mechanism of induction. Two main types of hypotheses have been proposed to account for this correlation, and thereby for the mechanism of action of the inducer:

(a) The inducer serves as "partial template" in enzyme synthesis, molding as it were the catalytic center.

(b) The inducer acts by combining specifically with preformed enzyme (or "preenzyme"), thereby somehow accelerating the synthesis of further enzyme molecules.

It is not necessary to discuss these "classical" hypotheses in detail, because it seems to be established now that the correlation in question is in fact *not* inherent to the mechanism of induction.

Table 1 lists a number of compounds tested as inducers of galactosidase, and as substrates (or specific inhibitors) of the enzyme. It will be noted that:

(a) no compound that does not possess an intact unsubstituted galactosidic residue induces;

479

TABLE 1

Induction of galactosidase and galactoside-transacetylase by various galactosides

Compound		Concentrations	β-galactosidase			Galactoside-transacetylase	
			Induction value	V	$1/K_m$	Induction value	V/K_m
β-D-thiogalactosides							
	(*iso*propyl)	10^{-4} M	100	0	140	100	80
	(methyl)	10^{-4} M	78	0	7	74	30
	(methyl)	10^{-5} M	7·5	—	—	10	—
	(phenyl)	10^{-3} M	<0·1	0	100	<1	100
	(phenylethyl)	10^{-3} M	5	0	10,000	3	—
β-D-galactosides							
	(lactose)	10^{-3} M	17	30	14	12	35
	(phenyl)	10^{-3} M	15	100	100	11	—
α-D-galactoside							
	(melibiose)	10^{-3} M	35	0	<0·1	37	<1
β-D-glucoside							
	(phenyl)	10^{-3} M	<0·1	0	0	<1	50
	(galactose)	10^{-3} M	<0·1	—	4	<1	<1
Methyl-β-D-thiogalactoside (10^{-4} M) + phenyl-β-D-thiogalactoside (10^{-3} M)			52	—	—	63	—

Columns "induction value" refer to specific activities developed by cultures of wild type *E. coli* K12 grown on glycerol as carbon source with each galactoside added at molar concentration stated. Values are given in percent of values obtained with *iso*propyl-thiogalactoside at 10^{-4} M (for which actual units were about 7,500 units of β-galactosidase and 300 units of galactoside-transacetylase per mg of bacteria). Column V refers to maximal substrate activity of each compound with respect to galactosidase. Values are given in percent of activity obtained with phenylgalactoside. Column $1/K_m$ expresses affinity of each compound with respect to galactosidase. Values are given in percent of that observed with phenylgalactoside. In case of galactoside-transacetylase, only the relative values V/K_m are given since low affinity of this enzyme prevents independent determination of the constants. (Computed from Monod & Cohn, 1952; Monod *et al.*, 1952; Buttin, 1956; Zabin *et al.*, 1959; Képès *et al.*, unpublished results.)

(b) many compounds which are not substrates (such as the thiogalactosides) are excellent inducers (for instance *iso*propyl thiogalactoside);

(c) there is no correlation between affinity for the enzyme and capacity to induce (*cf.* thiophenylgalactoside and melibiose).

The possibility that the enzyme formed in response to different inducers may have somewhat different specific properties should also be considered, and has been rather thoroughly tested, with entirely negative results (Monod & Cohn, 1952).

There is therefore no quantitative correlation whatever between inducing capacity and the substrate activity or affinity parameters of the various galactosides tested. The fact remains, however, that only galactosides will induce galactosidase, whose binding site is complementary for the galactose ring-structure. The possibility that this correlation is a necessary requisite, or consequence, of the induction mechanism was therefore not completely excluded by the former results.

As we shall see later, certain mutants of the galactosidase structural gene (*z*) have been found to synthesize, in place of the normal enzyme, a protein which is identical to it by its immunological properties, while being completely devoid of any enzymatic activity. When tested by equilibrium dialysis, this inactive protein proved to have no measurable affinity for galactosides. In other words, it has lost the specific binding site. In diploids carrying both the normal and the mutated gene, both normal galactosidase and the inactive protein are formed, to a quantitatively similar extent, in the presence of different concentrations of inducer (Perrin, Jacob & Monod, 1960).

This finding, added to the sum of the preceding observations, appears to prove beyond reasonable doubt that the mechanism of induction does not imply any inherent correlation between the molecular structure of the inducer and the structure of the binding site of the enzyme.

On the other hand, there is complete correlation in the induction of galactosidase and acetylase. This is illustrated by Table 1 which shows not only that the same compounds are active or inactive as inducers of either enzyme, but that the relative amounts of galactosidase and acetylase synthesized in the presence of different inducers or at different concentrations of the same inducer are constant, even though the absolute amounts vary greatly. The remarkable qualitative and quantitative correlation in the induction of these two widely different enzyme proteins strongly suggests that the synthesis of both is directly governed by a common controlling element with which the inducer interacts. This interaction must, at some point, involve stereospecific binding of the inducer, since induction is sterically specific, and since certain galactosides which are devoid of any inducing activity act as competitive inhibitors of induction in the presence of active inducers (Monod, 1956; Herzenberg, 1959). This suggests that an enzyme, or some other protein, distinct from either galactosidase or acetylase, acts as "receptor" of the inducer. We shall return later to the difficult problem raised by the identification of this "induction receptor."

(f) *Enzyme repression*

While positive enzymatic adaptation, i.e. induction, has been known for over sixty years, negative adaptation, i.e. specific inhibition of enzyme synthesis, was discovered only in 1953, when it was found that the formation of the enzyme tryptophan-synthetase was inhibited selectively by tryptophan and certain tryptophan analogs (Monod & Cohen-Bazire, 1953). Soon afterwards, other examples of this effect were observed (Cohn, Cohen & Monod, 1953; Adelberg & Umbarger, 1953; Wijesundera &

F. JACOB AND J. MONOD

Woods, 1953), and several systems were studied in detail in subsequent years (Gorini & Maas, 1957; Vogel, 1957a,b; Yates & Pardee, 1957; Magasanik, Magasanik & Neidhardt, 1959). These studies have revealed that the "repression" effect, as it was later named by Vogel (1957a,b), is very closely analogous, albeit symmetrically opposed, to the induction effect.

Enzyme repression, like induction, generally involves not a single but a sequence of enzymes active in successive metabolic steps. While inducibility is the rule for catabolic enzyme sequences responsible for the degradation of exogeneous substances, repressibility is the rule for anabolic enzymes, involved in the synthesis of essential metabolites such as amino acids or nucleotides.† Repression, like induction, is highly specific, but while inducers generally are substrates (or analogs of substrates) of the sequence, the repressing metabolites generally are the product (or analogs of the product) of the sequence.

That the effect involves inhibition of enzyme *synthesis*, and not inhibition (directly or indirectly) of enzyme *activity* was apparent already in the first example studied (Monod & Cohen-Bazire, 1953), and has been proved conclusively by isotope incorporation experiments (Yates & Pardee, 1957). It is important to emphasize this point, because enzyme repression must not be confused with another effect variously called "feedback inhibition" or "retro-inhibition" which is equally frequent, and may occur in the same systems. This last effect, discovered by Novick & Szilard (in Novick, 1955), involves the inhibition of activity of an early enzyme in an anabolic sequence, by the ultimate product of the sequence (Yates & Pardee, 1956; Umbarger, 1956). We shall use "repression" exclusively to designate specific inhibition of enzyme *synthesis*.‡

(g) *Kinetics and specificity of repression*

The kinetics of enzyme synthesis provoked by "de-repression" are identical to the kinetics of induction (see Fig. 2). When wild type *E. coli* is grown in the presence of arginine, only traces of ornithine-carbamyltransferase are formed. As soon as arginine is removed from the growth medium, the differential rate of enzyme synthesis increases about 1,000 times and remains constant, until arginine is added again, when it immediately falls back to the repressed level. The repressing metabolite here acts (kinetically) as would a dissociable inhibitor in an enzyme system.

The specificity of repression poses some particularly significant problems. As a rule, the repressing metabolite of an anabolic sequence is the ultimate product of this sequence. For instance, L-arginine, to the exclusion of any other amino acid, represses the enzymes of the sequence involved in the biosynthesis of arginine. Arginine shows no specific affinity for the early enzymes in the sequence, such as, in particular, ornithine-carbamyltransferase. In this sense, arginine is a "gratuitous" repressing metabolite for this protein, just as galactosides are "gratuitous inducers" for the mutated (inactive) galactosidase. The possibility must be considered however that arginine may be converted back, through the sequence itself, to an intermediate product

† Certain enzymes which attack exogeneous substrates are controlled by repression. Alkaline phosphatase (*E. coli*) is not induced by phosphate esters, but it is repressed by orthophosphate. Urease (*Pseudomonas*) is repressed by ammonia.

‡ We should perhaps recall the well-known fact that glucose and other carbohydrates inhibit the synthesis of many *inducible* enzymes, attacking a variety of substrates (Dienert, 1900; Gale, 1943; Monod, 1942; Cohn & Horibata, 1959). It is probable that this non-specific "glucose effect" bears some relation to the repressive effect of specific metabolites, but the relationship is not clear (Neidhardt & Magasanik, 1956a,b). We shall not discuss the glucose effect in this paper.

or substrate of the enzyme. This has been excluded by Gorini & Maas (1957) who showed that, in mutants lacking one of the enzymes involved in later steps of the sequence, ornithine transcarbamylase is repressed by arginine to the same extent as in the wild type. Moreover, neither ornithine nor any other intermediate of the sequence is endowed with repressing activity in mutants which cannot convert the intermediate into arginine. It is quite clear therefore that the specificity of action of the repressing metabolite does not depend upon the specific configuration of the enzyme site.

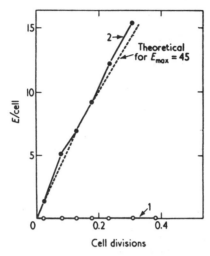

Fig. 2. Repression of ornithine-transcarbamylase by arginine. *E. coli* requiring both histidine and arginine were grown in a chemostat with 1 μg/ml. histidine + 6 μg/ml. arginine (curve 1) or with 10 μg/ml. histidine + 5 μg/ml. arginine (curve 2). Cultures are inoculated with washed cells taken from cultures growing exponentially in excess of arginine. The theoretical curve was calculated from the constant enzyme/cell value reached after 4 cell divisions. (After Gorini & Maas, 1958.)

The same conclusion is applicable to the enzymes of the histidine synthesizing pathway which are repressed in the presence of histidine, both in the wild type and in different mutants lacking one of the enzymes. The work of Ames & Garry (1959) has shown that the rates of synthesis of different enzymes in this sequence vary in *quantitatively* constant ratios under any set of medium conditions, and that the ratios are the same in various mutants lacking one of the enzymes and in the wild type. Here again, as in the case of the lactose system, the synthesis of widely different, albeit functionally related, enzymes appears to be controlled by a single common mechanism, with which the repressing metabolite specifically interacts.

In summary, repression and induction appear as closely similar effects, even if opposed in their results. Both control the rate of synthesis of enzyme proteins. Both are highly specific, but in neither case is the specificity related to the specificity of action (or binding) of the controlled enzyme. The kinetics of induction and repression are the same. Different functionally related enzymes are frequently co-induced or co-repressed, quantitatively to the same extent, by a single substrate or metabolite.

The remarkable similarity of induction and repression suggests that the two effects represent different manifestations of fundamentally similar mechanisms (Cohn & Monod, 1953; Monod, 1955; Vogel, 1957a, b; Pardee, Jacob & Monod, 1959; Szilard,

1960). This would imply either that in inducible systems the inducer acts as an antagonist of an internal repressor or that in repressible systems the repressing metabolite acts as an antagonist of an internal inducer. This is not an esoteric dilemma since it poses a very pertinent question, namely what would happen in an adaptive system of either type, when *both* the inducer and the repressor were eliminated? This, in fact, is the main question which we shall try to answer in the next section.

3. Regulator Genes

Since the specificity of induction or repression is not related to the structural specificity of the controlled enzymes, and since the rate of synthesis of different enzymes appears to be governed by a common element, this element is presumably not controlled or represented by the structural genes themselves. This inference, as we shall now see, is confirmed by the study of certain mutations which convert inducible or repressible systems into constitutive systems.

(a) *Phenotypes and genotypes in the lactose systems*

If this inference is correct, mutations which affect the controlling system should not behave as alleles of the structural genes. In order to test this prediction, the structural genes themselves must be identified. The most thoroughly investigated case is the lactose system of *E. coli*, to which we shall now return. Six phenotypically different classes of mutants have been observed in this system. For the time being, we shall consider only three of them which will be symbolized and defined as follows:

(1) Galactosidase mutations: $z^+ \rightleftharpoons z^-$ expressed as the loss of the capacity to synthesize active galactosidase (with or without induction).

(2) Permease mutations: $y^+ \rightleftharpoons y^-$ expressed as the loss of the capacity to form galactoside-permease. Most, but not all, mutants of this class simultaneously lose the capacity to synthesize active acetylase. We shall confine our discussion to the acetylaseless subclass.

(3) Constitutive mutations: $i^+ \rightleftharpoons i^-$ expressed as the ability to synthesize large amounts of galactosidase *and* acetylase in the absence of inducer (Monod, 1956; Rickenberg *et al.*, 1956; Pardee *et al.*, 1959).

The first two classes are specific for either galactosidase or acetylase: the galactosidaseless mutants form normal amounts of acetylase; conversely the acetylaseless mutants form normal amounts of galactosidase. In contrast, the constitutive mutations, of which over one hundred recurrences have been observed, invariably affect both the galactosidase and the permease (acetylase).† There are eight possible combinations of these phenotypes, and they have all been observed both in *E. coli* ML and K12.

The loci corresponding to a number of recurrences of each of the three mutant types have been mapped by recombination in *E. coli* K12. The map (Fig. 3) also

---

† The significance of this finding could be questioned since, in order to isolate constitutive mutants, one must of course use selective media, and this procedure might be supposed to favour double mutants, where the constitutivity of galactosidase and permease had arisen independently. It is possible, however, to select for $i^+ \rightarrow i^-$ mutants in organisms of type $i^+z^+y^-$, i.e. permeaseless. Fifty such mutants were isolated, giving rise to "constitutive cryptic" types $i^-z^+y^-$ from which, by reversion of y^-, fifty clones of constitutive $i^-z^+y^+$ were obtained. It was verified that in each of these fifty clones the permease was constitutive.

indicates the location of certain other mutations (*o* mutations) which will be discussed later. As may be seen, all these loci are confined to a very small segment of the chromosome, the *Lac* region. The extreme proximity of all these mutations raises the question whether they belong to a single or to several independent functional units. Such functional analysis requires that the biochemical expression of the various genetic structures be studied in heterozygous diploids. Until quite recently, only transient diploids were available in *E. coli*; the recent discovery of a new type of gene transfer in these bacteria (sexduction) has opened the possibility of obtaining stable clones which are diploid (or polyploid) for different small segments of the chromosome.

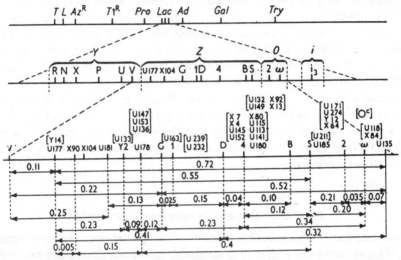

Fig. 3. Diagrammatic map of the lactose region of *E. coli* K12. The upper line represents the position of the *Lac* region with respect to other known markers. The middle line represents an enlargement of the *Lac* region with the four loci *y*, *z*, *o* and *i*. The lower line represents an enlargement of the *z* and *o* loci. Recombination frequencies (given at the bottom) are obtained in two factor crosses of the type $Hfr\ Lac_A^-ad^+S^s \times F^-\ Lac_B^-ad^-S^r$, from the ratios "recombinants $Lac^+ad^+S^r/$ recombinants ad^+S^r." The total length of the *z* gene may be estimated to be 0·7 map units, i.e. about 3,500 nucleotide pairs for about 1,000 amino acids in the monomer of β-galactosidase.

In this process, small fragments of the bacterial chromosome are incorporated into the sex factor, *F*. This new unit of replication is transmissible by conjugation, and is then added to the normal genome of the recipient bacterium which becomes diploid for the small chromosomal fragment. Among the units thus isolated, one carries the whole *Lac* region (Jacob & Adelberg, 1959; Jacob, Perrin, Sanchez & Monod, 1960). To symbolize the genetic structure of these diploids, the chromosomal alleles are written in the usual manner, while the alleles attached to the sex factor are preceded by the letter *F*.

Turning our attention to the behaviour of *z* and *y* mutant types, we may first note that diploids of structure z^+y^-/Fz^-y^+ or z^-y^+/Fz^+y^- are wild type, being able to ferment lactose, and forming normal amounts of both galactosidase and acetylase. This complete complementation between z^- and y^- mutants indicates that they belong to independent cistrons. Conversely, no complementation is observed between different y^- mutants, indicating that they all belong to a single cistron. No complementation is observed between most z^- mutants. Certain diploids of structure $z_a^-z_b^+/Fz_a^+z_b^-$ synthesize galactosidase in reduced amounts, but pairs of mutually non-complementing mutants overlap mutually complementing mutants, suggesting again that a single cistron is involved, as one might expect, since the monomer of galacto-sidase has a single N-terminal group. It should be recalled that intracistronic partial complementation has been observed in several cases (Giles, 1958), and has (tenta-tively) been explained as related to a polymeric state of the protein.

Mutations in the z gene affect the structure of galactosidase. This is shown by the fact that most of the z^- mutants synthesize, in place of active enzyme, a protein which is able to displace authentic (wild type) galactosidase from its combination with specific antibody (Perrin, Bussard & Monod, 1959). Among proteins synthesized by different z^- mutants (symbolized Cz_1, Cz_2, etc.) some give complete cross reactions (i.e. precipitate 100% of the specific antigalactosidase antibodies) with the serum used, while others give incomplete reactions. The different Cz proteins differ therefore, not only from wild type galactosidase, but also one from the other. Finally, as we already mentioned, diploids of constitution z^+/z_1^- synthesize wild type galacto-sidase and the modified protein simultaneously, and at similar rates (Perrin et al., 1960). These observations justify the conclusions that the z region or cistron contains the structural information for β-galactosidase. Proof that mutations in the y region not only suppress but may in some cases modify the structure of acetylase has not been obtained as yet, but the assumption that the y region does represent, in part at least, the structural gene for the acetylase protein appears quite safe in view of the properties of the y mutants.

(b) The i^+ gene and its cytoplasmic product

We now turn our attention to the constitutive (i^-) mutations. The most significant feature of these mutations is that they invariably affect simultaneously two different enzyme-proteins, each independently determined, as we have just seen, by different structural genes. In fact, most i^- mutants synthesize more galactosidase and acetylase than induced wild type cells, but it is quite remarkable that the *ratio* of galactosidase to acetylase is the same in the constitutive cells as in the induced wild type, strongly suggesting that the mechanism controlled by the i gene is the same as that with which the inducer interacts.

The study of double heterozygotes of structures: i^+z^-/Fi^-z^+ or i^-y^+/Fi^+y^- shows (Table 2, lines 4 and 5) that the inducible i^+ allele is dominant over the constitutive and that it is active in the *trans* position, with respect to both y^+ and z^+.

Therefore the i mutations belong to an independent cistron, governing the expres-sion of y and z *via* a cytoplasmic component. The dominance of the inducible over the constitutive allele means that the former corresponds to the active form of the i gene. This is confirmed by the fact that strains carrying a *deletion* of the izy region behave like i^- in diploids (Table 2, line 7). However, two different interpretations of the func-tion of the i^+ gene must be considered.

(a) The i^+ gene determines the synthesis of a repressor, inactive or absent in the i^- alleles.

(b) The i^+ gene determines the synthesis of an enzyme which destroys an inducer, produced by an independent pathway.

The first interpretation is the most straightforward, and it presents the great interest of implying that the fundamental mechanisms of control may be the same in inducible and repressible systems. Several lines of evidence indicate that it is the correct interpretation.

First, we may mention the fact that constitutive synthesis of β-galactosidase by $i^- z^+ y^+$ types is not inhibited by thiophenyl-galactoside which has been shown (Cohn & Monod, 1953) to be a competitive inhibitor of induction by exogenous galactosides (see p. 325).

(see p. 325).

TABLE 2

Synthesis of galactosidase and galactoside-transacetylase by haploids and heterozygous diploids of regulator mutants

Strain No.	Genotype	Galactosidase		Galactoside-transacetylase	
		Non-induced	Induced	Non-induced	Induced
1	$i^+ z^+ y^+$	<0·1	100	<1	100
2	$i_6^- z^+ y^+$	100	100	90	90
3	$i_3^- z^+ y^+$	140	130	130	120
4	$i^+ z_1^- y^+ / F i_3^- z^+ y^+$	<1	240	1	270
5	$i_3^- z_1^- y^+ / F i^+ z^+ y \bar{u}$	<1	280	<1	120
6	$i_3^- z_1^- y^+ / F i^- z^+ y^+$	195	190	200	180
7	$\Delta_{izy} / F i^- z^- y^+$	130	150	150	170
8	$i^s z^+ y^+$	<0·1	<1	<1	<1
9	$i^s z^+ y^+ / F i^+ z^+ y^+$	<0·1	2	<1	3

Bacteria are grown in glycerol as carbon source and induced, when stated, by *iso*propyl-thio-galactoside, 10^{-4} M. Values are given as a percentage of those observed with induced wild type (for absolute values, see legend of Table 1). Δ_{izy} refers to a deletion of the whole *Lac* region. It will be noted that organisms carrying the wild allele of one of the structural genes (z or y) on the F factor form more of the corresponding enzyme than the haploid. This is presumably due to the fact that several copies of the F-*Lac* unit are present per chromosome. In i^+/i^- heterozygotes, values observed with uninduced cells are sometimes higher than in the haploid control. This is due to the presence of a significant fraction of i^-/i^- homozygous recombinants in the population.

A direct and specific argument comes from the study of one particular mutant of the lactose system. This mutant (i^s) has lost the capacity to synthesize *both* galacto-sidase and permease. It is not a deletion because it recombines, giving *Lac*+ types, with all the z^- and y^- mutants. In crosses with $z^- i^-$ organisms the progeny is *exclusively* i^- while in crosses with $z^- i^+$ it is *exclusively* i^+, indicating exceedingly close linkage of this mutation with the i region. Finally, in diploids of constitution i^s/i^+, i^s turns out to be *dominant*: the diploids cannot synthesize either galactosidase or acetylase (see Table 2, lines 8 and 9).

These unique properties appear exceedingly difficult to account for, except by the admittedly very specific hypothesis that mutant i^s is an allele of i where the *structure* of the repressor is such that it cannot be antagonized by the inducer any more. If this hypothesis is correct, one would expect that the i^s mutant could regain the ability to metabolize lactose, not only by reversion to wild type ($i^s \to i^+$) but also, and probably more frequently, by inactivation of the i gene, that is to say by achieving the constitutive condition ($i^8 \rightarrow i^-$). Actually, Lac^+ "revertants" are very frequent in populations of mutant i^8, and 50% of these "revertants" are indeed constitutives of the i^- (recessive) type. (The other revertants are also constitutives, but of the o^c class which we shall mention later.) The properties of this remarkable mutant could evidently not be understood under the assumption that the i gene governs the synthesis of an inducer-destroying enzyme (Willson, Perrin, Jacob & Monod, 1961).

Accepting tentatively the conclusion that the i^+ gene governs the synthesis of an intracellular repressor, we may now consider the question of the presence of this substance in the cytoplasm, and of its chemical nature.

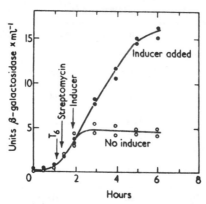

Fig. 4. Synthesis of β-galactosidase by merozygotes formed by conjugation between inducible, galactosidase-positive males and constitutive, galactosidase-negative females. Male ($Hfr\ i^+z^+T6^sS^s$) and female ($F^-\ i^-z^-T6^rS^r$) bacteria grown in a synthetic medium containing glycerol as carbon source are mixed in the same medium (time O) in the absence of inducer. In such a cross, the first zygotes which receive the Lac region from the males are formed from the 20th min. The rate of enzyme synthesis is determined from enzyme activity measurement on the whole population, to which streptomycin and phage T6 are added at times indicated by arrows to block further formation of recombinants and induction of the male parents. It may be seen that in the absence of inducer enzyme synthesis stops about 60 to 80 min after penetration of the first z^+i^+ segment but is resumed by addition of inducer (From Pardee $et\ al$, 1959).

Important indications on this question have been obtained by studying the kinetics and conditions of expression of the i^+ and z^+ genes when they are introduced into the cytoplasm of cells bearing the inactive (z^- and i^-) alleles. The sexual transfer of the Lac segment from male to female cells provides an adequate experimental system for such studies. It should be recalled that conjugation in $E.\ coli$ involves essentially the transfer of a male chromosome (or chromosome segment) to the female cell. This transfer is oriented, always beginning at one extremity of the chromosome, and it is progressive, each chromosome segment entering into the recipient cell at a fairly precise time following inception of conjugation in a given mating pair (Wollman & Jacob, 1959). The conjugation does not appear to involve any significant cytoplasmic mixing, so that the zygotes inherit virtually all their cytoplasm from the female cell, receiving only a chromosome or chromosome segment from the male. In order to study galactosidase synthesis by the zygotes, conditions must be set up such that the unmated parents cannot form the enzymes. This is the case when mating between inducible galactosidase-positive, streptomycin-sensitive males ($\male\ z^+i^+Sm^s$) and constitutive, galactosidase-negative, streptomycin-resistant females ($\female z^-i^-Sm^r$) is performed in presence of streptomycin (Sm), since: (i) the male cells which are sensitive to Sm cannot synthesize enzyme in its presence; (ii) the female cells are genetically incompetent; (iii) the vast majority of the zygotes which receive the z^+ gene, do not become streptomycin sensitive (because the Sm^s gene is transferred only to a small proportion of them, and at a very late time). The results of such an experiment, performed in the absence of inducer, are shown in Fig. 4. It is seen that galactosidase synthesis starts almost immediately following actual entry of the z^+ gene. We shall return later to a more precise analysis of the expression of the z^+ gene. The important point to be stressed here is that during this initial period the zygotes behave like *constitutive* cells, synthesizing enzyme in the *absence* of inducer. Approximately sixty minutes later, however, the rate of galactosidase synthesis falls off to zero. If at that time inducer is added, the maximum rate of enzyme synthesis is resumed. We are, in other words, witnessing the conversion of the originally i^- phenotype of the zygote cell, into an i^+ phenotype. And this experiment clearly shows that the "inducible" state is associated with the presence, at a sufficient level, of a *cytoplasmic* substance synthesized under the control of the i^+ gene. (It may be pointed out that the use of a female strain carrying a *deletion* of the *Lac* region instead of the i^-z^- alleles gives the same results (Pardee *et al.*, 1959).)

If now 5-methyltryptophan is added to the mated cells a few minutes before entry of the z^+ gene, no galactosidase is formed because, as is well known, this compound inhibits tryptophan synthesis by retro-inhibition, and therefore blocks protein synthesis. If the repressor is a protein, or if it is formed by a specific enzyme, the synthesis of which is governed by the i^+ gene, its accumulation should also be blocked. If on the other hand the repressor is not a protein, and if its synthesis does not require the preliminary synthesis of a specific enzyme controlled by the i^+ gene, it may accumulate in presence of 5-methyltryptophan which is known (Gros, unpublished results) *not* to inhibit energy transfer or the synthesis of nucleic acids.

The results of Pardee & Prestidge (1959) show that the repressor *does* accumulate under these conditions, since the addition of tryptophan 60 min after 5-methyltryptophan allows immediate and complete resumption of enzyme synthesis, *but only in the presence of inducer*; in other words, the cytoplasm of the zygote cells has been converted from the constitutive to the inducible state during the time that protein synthesis was blocked. This result has also been obtained using chloramphenicol as the agent for blocking protein synthesis, and it has been repeated using another system of gene transfer (Luria *et al.*, unpublished results).

This experiment leads to the conclusion that the repressor is not a protein, and this again excludes the hypothesis that the i^+ gene controls an inducer-destroying enzyme. We should like to stress the point that this conclusion does not imply that no enzyme is involved in the synthesis of the repressor, but that the enzymes which may be involved are *not* controlled by the i^+ gene. The experiments are negative, as far as the chemical nature of the repressor itself is concerned, since they only eliminate protein as a candidate. They do, however, invite the speculation that the repressor may be the primary product of the i^+ gene, and the further speculation that such a primary product may be a polyribonucleotide.

Before concluding this section, it should be pointed out that constitutive mutations have been found in several inducible systems; in fact wherever they have been searched for by adequate selective techniques (amylomaltase of *E. coli* (Cohen-Bazire & Jolit, 1953), penicillinase of *B. cereus* (Kogut, Pollock & Tridgell, 1956), glucuronidase of *E. coli* (F. Stoeber, unpublished results), galactokinase and galactose-transferase (Buttin, unpublished results)). That *any* inducible system should be potentially capable of giving rise to constitutive mutants, strongly indicates that such mutations occur, or at least can always occur, by a loss of function. In the case of the "galactose" system of *E. coli*, it has been found that the constitutive mutation is pleiotropic, affecting a sequence of three different enzymes (galactokinase, galactose-transferase, UDP-galactose epimerase), and occurs at a locus distinct from that of the corresponding structural genes (Buttin, unpublished results).

The main conclusions from the observations reviewed in this section may be summarized as defining a new type of gene, which we shall call a "regulator gene" (Jacob & Monod, 1959). A regulator gene does not contribute structural information to the proteins which it controls. The specific product of a regulator gene is a cytoplasmic substance, which inhibits information transfer from a structural gene (or genes) to protein. In contrast to the classical structural gene, a regulator gene may control the synthesis of several different proteins: the one-gene one-protein rule does not apply to it.

We have already pointed out the profound similarities between induction and repression which suggest that the two effects represent different manifestations of the same fundamental mechanism. If this is true, and if the above conclusions are valid, one expects to find that the genetic control of repressible systems also involves regulator genes.

(c) *Regulator genes in repressible systems*

The identification of constitutive or "de-repressed" mutants of several repressible systems has fulfilled this expectation. For the selection of such mutants, certain analogs of the normal repressing metabolite may be used as specific selective agents, because they cannot substitute for the metabolite, except as repressing metabolites. For instance, 5-methyltryptophan does not substitute for tryptophan in protein synthesis (Munier, unpublished results), but it represses the enzymes of the tryptophan-synthesizing sequence (Monod & Cohen-Bazire, 1953). Normal wild type *E. coli* does not grow in the presence of 5-methyltryptophan. Fully resistant stable mutants arise, however, a large fraction of which turn out to be constitutive for the tryptophan system.† The properties of these organisms indicate that they arise by mutation of a regulator gene R_T (Cohen & Jacob, 1959). In these mutants tryptophan-synthetase as well as at least two of the enzymes involved in previous steps in the sequence are formed at the same rate irrespective of the presence of tryptophan, while in the wild type all these enzymes are strongly repressed. Actually the mutants form more of the enzymes in the presence of tryptophan, than does the wild type in its absence (just as $i^- z^+$ mutants form more galactosidase in the absence of inducer than the wild type does at saturating concentration of inducer). The capacity of the mutants to concentrate tryptophan from the medium is not impaired, nor is their tryptophanase activity increased. The loss of sensitivity to tryptophan as repressing metabolite cannot therefore be attributed to its destruction by, or exclusion from, the cells, and can only reflect the breakdown of the control system itself. Several recurrences of the R_T mutation have been mapped. They are all located in the same small section of the chromosome, at a large distance from the cluster of genes which was shown by Yanofsky & Lennox (1959) to synthesize the different enzymes of the sequence. One of these genes (comprising two cistrons) has been very clearly identified by the work of Yanofsky (1960) as the structural gene for tryptophan synthetase, and it is a safe assumption that the other genes in this cluster determine the structure of the preceding

† Resistance to 5-methyltryptophan may also arise by other mechanisms in which we are not interested here.

enzymes in the sequence. The R_T gene therefore controls the rate of synthesis of several different proteins without, however, determining their structure. It can only do so *via* a cytoplasmic intermediate, since it is located quite far from the structural genes. To complete its characterization as a regulator gene, it should be verified that the constitutive (R_T^-) allele corresponds to the inactive state of the gene (or gene product), i.e. is recessive. Stable heterozygotes have not been available in this case, but the transient (sexual) heterozygotes of a cross $\male\ R_T^- \times \female R_T^+$ are sensitive to 5-methyltryptophan, indicating that the repressible allele is dominant (Cohen & Jacob, 1959).

In the arginine-synthesizing sequence there are some seven enzymes, simultaneously repressible by arginine (Vogel, 1957a,b; Gorini & Maas, 1958). The specific (i.e. probably structural) genes which control these enzymes are dispersed at various loci on the chromosome. Mutants resistant to canavanine have been obtained, in which several (perhaps all) of these enzymes are simultaneously de-repressed. These mutations occur at a locus (near Sm^r) which is widely separated from the loci corresponding (probably) to the structural genes. The dominance relationships have not been analysed (Gorini, unpublished results; Maas, Lavallé, Wiame & Jacob, unpublished results).

The case of alkaline phosphatase is particularly interesting because the structural gene corresponding to this protein is well identified by the demonstration that various mutations at this locus result in the synthesis of altered phosphatase (Levinthal, 1959). The synthesis of this enzyme is repressed by orthophosphate (Torriani, 1960). Constitutive mutants which synthesize large amounts of enzyme in the presence of orthophosphate have been isolated. They occur at two loci, neither of which is allelic to the structural gene, and the constitutive enzyme is identical, by all tests, to the wild type (repressible) enzyme. The constitutive alleles for both of the two loci have been shown to be recessive with respect to wild type. Conversely, mutations in the structural (P) gene do not affect the regulatory mechanism, since the altered (inactive) enzyme formed by mutants of the P gene is repressed in the presence of orthophosphate to the same extent as the wild type enzyme (Echols, Garen, Garen & Torriani, 1961).

(d) *The interaction of repressors, inducers and co-repressors*

The sum of these observations leaves little doubt that repression, like induction, is controlled by specialized regulator genes, which operate by a basically similar mechanism in both types of systems, namely by governing the synthesis of an intracellular substance which inhibits information transfer from structural genes to protein.

It is evident therefore that the metabolites (such as tryptophan, arginine, orthophosphate) which inhibit enzyme synthesis in repressible systems are not active by themselves, but only by virtue of an interaction with a repressor synthesized under the control of a regulator gene. Their action is best described as an activation of the genetically controlled repression system. In order to avoid confusion of words, we shall speak of repressing metabolites as "co-repressors" reserving the name "repressors" (or apo-repressors) for the cytoplasmic products of the regulator genes.

The nature of the interaction between repressor and co-repressor (in repressible systems) or inducer (in inducible systems) poses a particularly difficult problem. As a purely formal description, one may think of inducers as antagonists, and of co-repressors as activators, of the repressor. A variety of chemical models can be imagined to account for such antagonistic or activating interactions. We shall not go into these speculations since there is at present no evidence to support or eliminate any particular model. But it must be pointed out that, in any model, the structural specificity of inducers or co-repressors must be accounted for, and can be accounted for, only by the assumption that a stereospecific receptor is involved in the interaction. The fact that the repressor is apparently not a protein then raises a serious difficulty since the capacity to form stereospecific complexes with small molecules appears to be a privilege of proteins. If a protein, perhaps an enzyme, is responsible for the specificity, the structure of this protein is presumably determined by a structual gene and muta-tion in this gene would result in loss of the capacity to be induced (or repressed). Such mutants, which would have precisely predictable properties (they would be pleio-tropic, recessive, and they would be complemented by mutants of the other structural genes) have not been encountered in the lactose system, while the possibility that the controlled enzymes themselves (galactosidase or acetylase) play the role of "induction enzyme" is excluded.

It is conceivable that, in the repressible systems which synthesize amino acids, this role is played by enzymes simultaneously responsible for essential functions (e.g. the activating enzymes) whose loss would be lethal, but this seems hardly conceivable in the case of most inducible systems. One possibility which is not excluded by these observations is that the repressor itself synthesizes the "induction protein" and remains thereafter associated with it. Genetic inactivation of the induction enzyme would then be associated with structural alterations of the repressor itself and would generally be expressed as constitutive mutations of the regulator gene.† This possibility is mentioned here only as an illustration of the dilemma which we have briefly analysed, and whose solution will depend upon the chemical identification of the repressor.

(e) *Regulator genes and immunity in temperate phage systems*

One of the most conspicuous examples of the fact that certain genes may be either allowed to express their potentialities, or specifically prohibited from doing so, is the phenomenon of immunity in temperate phage systems (*cf.* Lwoff, 1953; Jacob, 1954; Jacob & Wollman, 1957; Bertani, 1958; Jacob, 1960).

The genetic material of the so-called temperate phages can exist in one of two states within the host cell:

(1) In the *vegetative state*, the phage genome multiplies autonomously. This process, during which all the phage components are synthesized, culminates in the production of infectious phage particles which are released by lysis of the host cell.

(2) In the *prophage state*, the genetic material of the phage is attached to a specific site of the bacterial chromosome in such a way that both genetic elements replicate as a single unit. The host cell is said to be "lysogenic." As long as the phage genome remains in the prophage state, phage particles are not produced. For lysogenic bacteria to produce phage, the genetic material of the phage must undergo a transition from the prophage to the vegetative state. During normal growth of lysogenic bacteria, this event is exceedingly rare. With certain types of prophages, however, the transition can be induced in the whole population by exposure of the culture to u.v. light,

---

† Such a model could account for the properties of the *i*s (dominant) mutant of the regulator gene in the lactose system, by the assumption that in this mutant the repressor remains active, while having lost the capacity to form its associated induction protein.

X-rays or various compounds known to alter DNA metabolism (Lwoff, Siminovitch & Kjeldgaard, 1950; Lwoff, 1953; Jacob, 1954).

The study of "defective" phage genomes, in which a mutation has altered one of the steps required for the production of phage particles, indicates the existence of at least two distinct groups of viral functions, both of which are related to the capacity of synthesizing specific proteins (Jacob, Fuerst & Wollman, 1957). Some "early" functions appear as a pre-requisite for the vegetative multiplication of the phage genome and, at least in virulent phages of the T-even series, it is now known that they correspond to the synthesis of a series of new enzymes (Flaks & Cohen, 1959; Kornberg, Zimmerman, Kornberg & Josse, 1959). A group of "late" functions correspond to the synthesis of the structural proteins which constitute the phage coat. The expression of these different viral functions appears to be in some way co-ordinated by a sequential process, since defective mutations affecting some of the early functions may also result in the loss of the capacity to perform several later steps of phage multiplication (Jacob et al., 1957).

In contrast, the viral functions are not expressed in the prophage state and the protein constituents of the phage coat cannot be detected within lysogenic bacteria. In addition, lysogenic bacteria exhibit the remarkable property of being specifically *immune* to the very type of phage particles whose genome is already present in the cell as prophage. When lysogenic cells are infected with homologous phage particles, these particles absorb onto the cells and inject their genetic material, but the cell survives. The injected genetic material does not express its viral functions: it is unable to initiate the synthesis of the protein components of the coat and to multiply vegetatively. It remains inert and is diluted out in the course of bacterial multiplication (Bertani, 1953; Jacob, 1954).

The inhibition of phage-gene functions in lysogenic bacteria therefore applies not only to the prophage, but also to additional homologous phage genomes. It depends only upon the presence of the prophage (and not upon a permanent alteration, provoked by the prophage, of bacterial genes) since loss of the prophage is both necessary and sufficient to make the bacteria sensitive again.

Two kinds of interpretation may be considered to account for these "immunity" relationships:

(a) The prophage occupies and blocks a *chromosomal* site of the host, specifically required in some way for the vegetative multiplication of the homologous phage.

(b) The prophage produces a *cytoplasmic* inhibitor preventing the completion of some reactions (presumably the synthesis of a particular protein) necessary for the initiation of vegetative multiplication.

A decision between these alternative hypotheses may be reached through the study of persistent diploids, heterozygous for the character lysogeny. A sex factor has been isolated which has incorporated a segment of the bacterial chromosome carrying the genes which control galactose fermentation, *Gal*, and the site of attachment of prophage, λ. Diploid heterozygotes with the structure *Gal*$^-$ λ^-/F *Gal*$^+$ λ^+ or *Gal*$^-$ λ^+/F *Gal*$^+$ λ^- are immune against superinfection with phage λ, a result which shows that "immunity" is dominant over "non-immunity" and has a cytoplasmic expression (Jacob, Schaeffer & Wollman, 1960).

The study of transient zygotes formed during conjugation between lysogenic (λ^+) and non-lysogenic (λ^-) cells leads to the same conclusion. In crosses $\male \lambda^+ \times \female \lambda^-$, the transfer of the prophage carried by the male chromosome into the non-immune recipient results in transition to the vegetative state: multiplication of the phage occurs in the zygotes, which are lysed and release phage particles. This phenomenon is known as "zygotic induction" (Jacob & Wollman, 1956). In the *reverse* cross $\male\lambda^- \times \female\lambda^+$, however, *no zygotic induction occurs*. The transfer of the "non-lysogenic" character carried by the male chromosome into the immune recipient does not bring about the development of the prophage and the zygotes are immune against super-infection with phage λ.

The opposite results obtained in reciprocal crosses of lysogenic by non-lysogenic male and female cells are entirely analogous to the observations made with the lactose system in reciprocal crosses of inducible by non-inducible cells. In both cases, it is evident that the decisive factor is the origin of the *cytoplasm* of the zygote, and the conclusion is inescapable, that the immunity of lysogenic bacteria is due to a cyto-plasmic constituent, in the presence of which the viral genes cannot become expressed (Jacob, 1960).

The same two hypotheses which we have already considered for the interpretation of the product of the regulator gene in the lactose system, apply to the cytoplasmic inhibitor insuring immunity in lysogenic bacteria.

(a) The inhibitor is a specific repressor which prevents the synthesis of some early protein(s) required for the initiation of vegetative multiplication.

(b) The inhibitor is an enzyme which destroys a metabolite, normally synthesized by the non-lysogenic cell and specifically required for the vegetative multiplication of the phage.

Several lines of evidence argue against the second hypothesis (Jacob & Campbell, 1959; Jacob, 1960). First, for a given strain of bacteria, many temperate phages are known, each of which exhibits a different immunity pattern. According to the second hypothesis, each of these phages would specifically require for vegetative multiplica-tion a different metabolite normally produced by the non-lysogenic cells, an assump-tion which appears extremely unlikely. The second argument stems from the fact that, like the repressor of the lactose system, the inhibitor responsible for immunity is synthesized in the presence of chloramphenicol, i.e. in the absence of protein synthesis: when crosses $\male\lambda^+ \times \female\lambda^-$ are performed in the presence of chloramphenicol, no zygotic induction occurs and the prophage is found to segregate normally among recombinants.

In order to explain immunity in lysogenic bacteria, we are led therefore to the same type of interpretation as in the case of adaptive enzyme systems. According to this interpretation, the prophage controls a cytoplasmic repressor, which inhibits specific-ally the synthesis of one (or several) protein(s) necessary for the initiation of vegetative multiplication. In this model, the introduction of the genetic material of the phage into a non-lysogenic cell, whether by infection or by conjugation, results in a "race" between the synthesis of the specific repressor and that of the early proteins required for vegetative multiplication. The fate of the host-cell, survival with lysogenization or lysis as a result of phage multiplication, depends upon whether the synthesis of the repressor or that of the protein is favoured. Changes in the cultural conditions favoring the synthesis of the repressor such as infection at low temperature, or in the presence of chloramphenicol, would favor lysogenization and *vice versa*. The pheno-menon of induction by u.v. light could then be understood, for instance, in the follow-ing way: exposure of inducible lysogenic bacteria to u.v. light or X-rays would transiently disturb the regulation system, for example by preventing further synthesis of the repressor. If the repressor is unstable, its concentration inside the cell would decrease and reach a level low enough to allow the synthesis of the early proteins. Thus the vegetative multiplication would be irreversibly initiated.

The similarity between lysogenic systems and adaptive systems is further strengthened by the genetic analysis of immunity. Schematically, the genome of phage λ appears to involve two parts (see Fig. 5): a small central segment, the C region, contains a few determinants which control various functions involved in lysogenization (Kaiser, 1957); the rest of the linkage group contains determinants which govern the "viral functions," i.e. presumably the structural genes corresponding to the different phage proteins. Certain strains of temperate phages which exhibit different immunity patterns are able nevertheless to undergo genetic recombination. The specific immunity pattern segregates in such crosses, proving to be controlled by a small segment "im" of the C region (Kaiser & Jacob, 1957). In other words, a prophage contains in its C region a small segment "im" which controls the synthesis of a specific repressor, active on the phage genome carrying a homologous "im" segment.

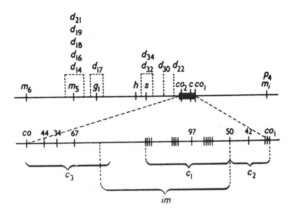

FIG. 5. Diagrammatic representation of the linkage group of the temperate bacteriophage λ. The upper diagram represents the linear arrangement of markers. Symbols refer to various plaque size, plaque type and host-range markers. Symbols d refer to various defective mutations. The C region represented by a thicker line is enlarged in the lower diagram. The figures correspond to various C mutations. The C region can be subdivided into three functional units, C_1, C_2 and C_3; the segment controlling immunity is designated im.

In the "im" region, two types of mutations arise, whose properties are extremely similar to those of the different mutations affecting the regulator genes of adaptive enzyme systems.

(1) Some mutations ($C_I^+ \rightarrow C_I$) result in the complete loss of the capacity for lysogenization in single infection. All the C_I mutations are located in a cluster, in a small part of the "im" segment, and they behave as belonging to a single cistron in complementation tests.

In mixed infections with both C_I and C_I^+ phages, double lysogenic clones carrying both C_I and C_I^+ prophages can be recovered. In such clones, single lysogenic cells segregate, which carry the C^+ type alone but never the C_I type alone. These findings indicate that the wild allele is dominant over the mutant C_I alleles and is cytoplasmically expressed, repressing the mutant genome into the prophage state. The properties of the C_I mutations are therefore similar to those of the recessive constitutive mutations of adaptive systems. The evidence suggests that the C_I locus controls the synthesis of the repressor responsible for immunity, and that the C_I mutations correspond to inactivation of this locus, or of its product.

(2) A mutation ($ind^+ \rightarrow ind^-$) has been found which results in the loss of the inducible property of the prophage, i.e. of its capacity to multiply vegetatively upon exposure of lysogenic bacteria to u.v. light, X-rays or chemical inducers. This mutation is located in the C_I segment. The mutant allele ind^- is dominant over the wild allele ind^+ since double lysogenic $\lambda ind^+/\lambda ind^-$ or diploid heterozygotes of structure $Gal^-\lambda ind^+/F\ Gal^+\lambda ind^-$ or $Gal^-\lambda ind^-/F\ Gal^+\lambda ind^+$ are all non-inducible. In addition, the mutant λind^- exhibits a unique property. If lysogenic bacteria K12 (λ^+) carrying a wild type prophage are exposed to u.v. light, the whole population lyses and releases phage. Infection of such cells with λind^- mutants, either before or immediately after irradiation, completely inhibits phage production and lysis.

The properties of the ind^- mutant appear in every respect similar to those of the previously described mutant i^s of the lactose system. The unique properties of the ind^- mutants can be explained only by the same type of hypothesis, namely that the mutation ind^- affects, quantitatively or qualitatively, the synthesis of the repressor in such a way that more repressor or a more efficient repressor is produced. If this assumption as well as the hypothesis that the C_I mutation results in the loss of the capacity to produce an active repressor, are correct, the double mutants $C_I ind^-$ should have lost the capacity of inhibiting phage multiplication upon infection of wild type lysogenic cells. This is actually what is observed. It is evident that the properties of the ind^- mutant cannot be accounted for by the assumption that the C_I locus controls the synthesis of a metabolite-destroying enzyme (Jacob & Campbell, 1959).

In summary, the analysis of lysogenic systems reveals that the expression of the viral genes in these systems is controlled by a cytoplasmic repressor substance, whose synthesis is governed by one particular "regulator" gene, belonging to the viral genome. The identity of the proteins whose synthesis is thus repressed is not established, but it seems highly probable that they are "early" enzymes which initiate the whole process of vegetative multiplication. With the (important) limitation that they are sensitive to entirely different types of inducing conditions, the phage repression systems appear entirely comparable to the systems involved in enzymatic adaptation.

4. The Operator and the Operon

(a) *The operator as site of action of the repressor*

In the preceding section we have discussed the evidence which shows that the transfer of information from structural genes to protein is controlled by specific repressors synthesized by specialized regulator genes. We must now consider the next problem, which is the site and mode of action of the repressor.

In regard to this problem, the most important property of the repressor is its characteristic pleiotropic specificity of action. In the lactose system of *E. coli*, the repressor is both *highly specific* since mutations of the i gene do not affect any other system, and *pleiotropic* since both galactosidase and acetylase are affected simultaneously and quantitatively to the same extent, by such mutations.

The specificity of operation of the repressor implies that it acts by forming a stereospecific combination with a constituent of the system possessing the proper (complementary) molecular configuration. Furthermore, it must be assumed that the flow of information from gene to protein is interrupted when this element is combined with the repressor. This controlling element we shall call the *"operator"* (Jacob & Monod, 1959). We should perhaps call attention to the fact that, once the existence of a specific repressor is considered as established, the existence of an operator element defined as above follows necessarily. Our problem, therefore, is not whether an operator exists, but where (and how) it intervenes in the system of information transfer.

An important prediction follows immediately from the preceding considerations. Under any hypothesis concerning the nature of the operator, its specific complementary configuration must be genetically determined; therefore it could be affected by mutations which would alter or abolish its specific affinity for the repressor, without necessarily impairing its activity as initiator of information-transfer. Such mutations would result in *constitutive* synthesis of the protein or proteins. These mutations would define an "operator locus" which should be genetically distinct from the regulator gene (i.e. its mutations should not behave as alleles of the regulator); the most distinctive predictable property of such mutants would be that the constitutive allele should be *dominant* over the wild type since, again under virtually any hypothesis, the presence in a diploid cell of repressor-sensitive operators would not prevent the operation of repressor-insensitive operators.

(b) *Constitutive operator mutations*

Constitutive mutants possessing the properties predicted above have so far been found in two repressor-controlled systems, namely the phage λ and *Lac* system of *E. coli*.

In the case of phage λ, these mutants are characterized, and can be easily selected, by the fact that they develop vegetatively in immune bacteria, lysogenic for the wild type. This characteristic property means that these mutants (v) are *insensitive* to the repressor present in lysogenic cells. When, in fact, lysogenic cells are infected with these mutant particles, the development of the wild type prophage is induced, and the resulting phage population is a mixture of v and v^+ particles. This is expected, since presumably the initiation of prophage development depends only on the formation of one or a few "early" enzyme-proteins, which are supplied by the virulent particle (Jacob & Wollman, 1953).

In the *Lac* system, dominant constitutive (o^c) mutants have been isolated by selecting for constitutivity in cells diploid for the *Lac* region, thus virtually eliminating the recessive (i^-) constitutive mutants (Jacob *et al.*, 1960a). By recombination, the o^c mutations can be mapped in the *Lac* region, between the i and the z loci, the order being (*Pro*) *yzoi* (*Ad*) (see Fig. 3). Some of the properties of these mutants are summarized in Table 3. To begin with, let us consider only the effects of this mutation on galactosidase synthesis. It will be noted that in the absence of inducer, these organisms synthesize 10 to 20% of the amount of galactosidase synthesized by i^- mutants, i.e. about 100 to 200 times more than uninduced wild type cells (Table 3, lines 3 and 7). In the presence of inducer, they synthesize maximal amounts of enzyme. They are therefore only partially constitutive (except however under conditions of starvation, when they form maximum amounts of galactosidase in the absence of inducer (Brown, unpublished results)). The essential point however is that the enzyme is synthesized constitutively by diploid cells of constitution o^c/o^+ (see Table 3). The o^c allele therefore is "dominant."

If the constitutivity of the o^c mutant results from a loss of sensitivity of the operator to the repressor, the o^c organisms should also be insensitive to the presence of the altered repressor synthesized by the i^s (dominant) allele of the i^+ gene (see page 331). That this is indeed the case, as shown by the constitutive behavior of diploids with the constitution $i^s o^+/F i^+ o^c$ (see Table 3, line 12), is a very strong confirmation of the interpretation of the effects of *both* mutations (i^s and o^c). In addition, and as one would expect according to this interpretation, o^c mutants frequently arise as lactose positive "revertants" in populations of i^s cells (see p. 332).

(see Table 3, line 12) ... (see p. 332)

TABLE 3

Synthesis of galactosidase, cross-reacting material (CRM), and galactoside-transacetylase by haploid and heterozygous diploid operator mutants

Strain No.	Genotype	Galactosidase		Cross-reacting material	
		Non-induced	Induced	Non-induced	Induced
1	o^+z^+	<0.1	100	—	—
2	$o^+z^+/Fo^+z_1^-$	<0.1	105	<1	310
3	$o^c z^+$	15	90	—	—
4	$o^+z^+/Fo^c z_1$	<0.1	90	30	180
5	$o^+z_1^-/Fo^c z^+$	90	250	<1	85

Strain No.	Genotype	Galactosidase		Galactoside-transacetylase	
		Non-Induced	Induced	Non-induced	Induced
6	$o^+z^+y^+$	<0.1	100	<1	100
7	$o^c z^+y^+$	25	95	15	110
8	$o^+z^+y_U^-/Fo^c z^+y^+$	70	220	50	160
9	$o^+z_1^- y^+/Fo^c z^+y_U^-$	180	440	<1	220
10	$i^+o_{84}^c z^+y^+$	<0.1	<0.1	<1	<1
11	$i^+o_{84}^c z^+y^+/Fi^-o^+z^+y^+$	1	260	2	240
12	$i^s o^+z^+y^+/Fi^+o^c z^+y^+$	190	210	150	200

Bacteria are grown in glycerol as carbon source and induced when stated, with *iso*propyl-thiogalactoside, 10^{-4} M. Values of galactosidase and acetylase are given as a percentage of those observed with induced wild type. Values of CRM are expressed as antigenic equivalents of galactosidase. Note that the proteins corresponding to the alleles carried by the sex factor are often produced in greater amount than that observed with induced haploid wild type. This is presumably due to the existence of several copies of the *F-Lac* factor per chromosome. In o^c mutants, haploid or diploid, the absolute values of enzymes produced, especially in the non-induced cultures varies greatly from day to day depending on the conditions of the cultures.

We therefore conclude that the $o^+ \rightarrow o^c$ mutations correspond to a modification of the specific, repressor-accepting, structure of the operator. This identifies the operator locus, i.e. the genetic segment responsible for the structure of the operator, but not the operator itself.

(c) *The operon*

Turning now to this problem, we note that the o^c mutation (like the i^- mutation) is pleiotropic: it affects simultaneously and quantitatively to the same extent, the synthesis of galactosidase and acetylase (see Table 3, lines 7 and 8). The structure of the operator, or operators, which controls the synthesis of the two proteins, therefore, is controlled by a single determinant.†

Two alternative interpretations of this situation must be considered:

(a) A single operator controls an *integral* property of the z-y genetic segment, or of its cytoplasmic product.

(b) The specific product of the operator locus is able to associate in the cytoplasm, with the products of the z and y cistrons, and thereby governs the expression of both structural genes.

The second interpretation implies that mutations of the operator locus should behave as belonging to a cistron *independent* of both the z and y cistrons. The first interpretation requires, on the contrary, that these mutations behave functionally as if they *belonged to both cistrons simultaneously*. These alternative interpretations can therefore be distinguished without reference to any particular physical model of operator action by testing for the *trans* effect of o alleles, that is to say for the constitutive *vs* inducible expression of the two structural genes in o^+/o^c diploids, heterozygous for one or both of these structural genes.

The results obtained with diploids of various structures are shown in Table 3. We may first note that in diploids of constitution $o^+z^+/Fo^cz_1^-$ or $o^+z_1^-/Fo^cz^+$ (lines 4 and 5), both the normal galactosidase produced by the z^+ allele and the altered protein (CRM) produced by the z_1^- allele are formed in the presence of inducer, while in the *absence* of inducer, *only the protein corresponding to the z allele in position cis to the o^c is produced*. The o^c therefore has no effect on the z allele in position *trans*. Or putting it otherwise: the expression of the z allele attached to an o^+ remains fully repressor-sensitive even in the presence of an o^c in position *trans*. The o locus might be said to behave as belonging to the same cistron as the z markers. But as we know already, the o^c mutation is equally effective towards the acetylase which belongs to a cistron independent of z, and not adjacent to the operator locus. The results shown in Table 3, lines 8 and 9, confirm that the $o \rightarrow y$ relationship is the same as the $o \rightarrow z$ relationship, that is, the effect of the o^c allele extends *exclusively* to the y allele in the *cis* position. For instance, in the diploid $o^+z^-y^+/Fo^cz^+y_U^-$ the galactosidase is constitutive and the acetylase is inducible, while in the diploid $o^+z^+y_U^-/Fo^cz^+y^+$ both enzymes are constitutive.

These observations, predicted by the first interpretation, are incompatible with the second and lead to the conclusion that the operator governs an integral property of the genetic segment *ozy*, or of its cytoplasmic product (Jacob *et al.*, 1960a; Képès, Monod & Jacob, 1961).

This leads to another prediction. Certain mutations of the o segment could modify the operator in such a way as to inactivate the whole *ozy* segment resulting in the loss of the capacity to synthesize *both* galactosidase and permease.

These "o^o" mutants would be *recessive* to o^+ or o^c, and they would *not* be complemented either by $o^+z^+y^-$ or by $o^+z^-y^+$ mutants. Several point-mutants, possessing

---

† Let us recall again that no *non-pleiotropic* constitutive mutants of any type have been isolated in this system, in spite of systematic screening for such mutants.

precisely these properties, have been isolated (Jacob *et al.*, 1960a). They all map very closely to o^c, as expected (see Fig. 3). It is interesting to note that in these mutants the i^+ gene is functional (Table 3, line 11), which shows clearly, not only that the i and o mutants are not alleles, but that the o segment, while governing the expression of the z and y genes, does not affect the expression of the regulator gene.

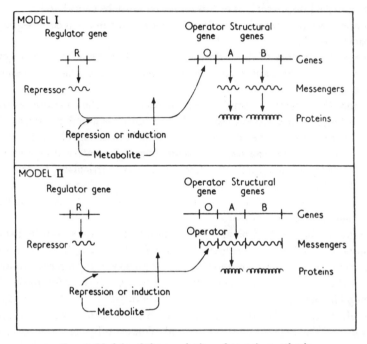

FIG. 6. Models of the regulation of protein synthesis.

In conclusion, the integral or *co-ordinate* expression of the *ozy* genetic segment signifies that the operator, which controls this expression, is and remains attached (see Fig. 6):

(a) either to the genes themselves (Fig. 6, I),

(b) or to the cytoplasmic messenger of the linked z and y genes which must then be assumed to form a single, integral, particle corresponding to the structure of the whole *ozy* segment, and functioning as a whole (Fig. 6, II).

In the former case, *the operator would in fact be identical with the o locus* and it would govern directly the activity of the genes, i.e. the synthesis of the structural messengers.

Both of these models are compatible with the observations which we have discussed so far. We shall return in the next section to the question whether the operator, i.e. the site of specific interaction with the repressor, is genetic or cytoplasmic. In either case, the *ozy* segment, although containing at least two independent structural genes, governing two independent proteins, behaves as a *unit* in the transfer of information. This *genetic unit of co-ordinate expression* we shall call the "*operon*" (Jacob *et al.*, 1960a).

The existence of such a unit of genetic expression is proved so far only in the case of the *Lac* segment. As we have already seen, the v mutants of phage λ, while illustrating the existence of an operator in this system, do not define an operon (because the number and the functions of the structural genes controlled by this operator are unknown). However, many observations hitherto unexplained by or even conflicting with classical genetic theory, are immediately accounted for by the operon theory. It is well known that, in bacteria, the genes governing the synthesis of different enzymes sequentially involved in a metabolic pathway are often found to be extremely closely linked, forming a cluster (Demerec, 1956). Various not very convincing speculations have been advanced to account for this obvious correlation of genetic structure and biochemical function (see Pontecorvo, 1958). Since it is now established that simultaneous induction or repression also generally prevails in such metabolic sequences, it seems very likely that the gene clusters represent units of co-ordinate expression, i.e. operons.

We have already mentioned the fact that two inducible enzymes sequentially involved in the metabolism of galactose by *E. coli*, galactokinase and UDP-galactose-transferase, are simultaneously induced by galactose, or by the gratuitous inducer D-fucose (Buttin, 1961). The genes which control specifically the synthesis of these enzymes, i.e. presumably the structural genes, are closely linked, forming a cluster on the *E. coli* chromosome. (Kalckar, Kurahashi & Jordan, 1959; Lederberg, 1960; Yarmolinsky & Wiesmeyer, 1960; Adler, unpublished results.) Certain point-mutations which occur in this chromosome segment abolish the capacity to synthesize both enzymes. These pleiotropic loss mutations are not complemented by any one of the specific (structural) loss mutations, an observation which is in apparent direct conflict with the one-gene one-enzyme hypothesis. These relationships are explained and the conflict is resolved if it is assumed that the linked structural genes constitute an operon controlled by a single operator and that the pleiotropic mutations are mutations of the operator locus.

We have also already discussed the system of simultaneous repression which controls the synthesis of the enzymes involved in histidine synthesis in *Salmonella*. This system involves eight or nine reaction steps. The enzymes which catalyse five of these reactions have been identified. The genes which individually determine these enzymes form a closely linked cluster on the *Salmonella* chromosome. Mutations in each of these genes result in a loss of capacity to synthesize a single enzyme; however, certain mutations at one end of the cluster abolish the capacity to synthesize all the enzymes simultaneously, and these mutations are not complemented by any one of the specific mutations (Ames, Garry & Herzenberg, 1960; Hartman, Loper & Serman, 1960). It will be recalled that the relative rates of synthesis of different enzymes in this sequence are constant under any set of conditions (see p. 327). All these remarkable findings are explained if it is assumed that this cluster of genes constitutes an operon, controlled by an operator associated with the *g* cistron.

The rule that genes controlling metabolically sequential enzymes constitute genetic clusters does not apply, in general, to organisms other than bacteria (Pontecorvo, 1958). Nor does it apply to all bacterial systems, even where simultaneous repression is known to occur and to be controlled by a single regulator gene, as is apparently the case for the enzymes of arginine biosynthesis. In such cases, it must be supposed that several identical or similar operator loci are responsible for sensitivity to repressor of each of the independent information-transfer systems.

It is clear that when an operator controls the expression of only a single structural cistron, the concept of the operon does not apply, and in fact there are no conceivable genetic-biochemical tests which could identify the operator-controlling genetic segment as distinct from the structural cistron itself.† One may therefore wonder whether it will be possible experimentally to extend this concept to dispersed (as opposed to clustered) genetic systems. It should be remarked at this point that many enzyme proteins are apparently made up of two (or more) different polypeptide chains. It is tempting to predict that such proteins will often be found to be controlled by two (or more) adjacent and co-ordinated structural cistrons, forming an operon.

5. The Kinetics of Expression of Structural Genes, and the Nature of the Structural Message

The problem we want to discuss in this section is whether the repressor-operator system functions at the genetic level by governing the *synthesis* of the structural message or at the cytoplasmic level, by controlling the protein-synthesizing *activity* of the messenger (see Fig. 6). These two conceivable models we shall designate respectively as the "genetic operator model" and the "cytoplasmic operator model."

The existence of units of co-ordinate expression involving several structural genes appears in fact difficult to reconcile with the cytoplasmic operator model, if only because of the size that the cytoplasmic unit would have to attain. If we assume that the message is a polyribonucleotide and take a coding ratio of 3, the "unit message" corresponding to an operon governing the synthesis of three proteins of average (monomeric) molecular weight 60,000 would have a molecular weight about $1{\cdot}8 \times 10^6$; we have seen that operons including up to 8 structural cistrons may in fact exist. On the other hand, RNA fractions of *E. coli* and other cells do not appear to include polyribonucleotide molecules of molecular weight exceeding 10^6.

This difficulty is probably not insuperable; and this type of argument, given the present state of our knowledge, cannot be considered to eliminate the cytoplasmic operator model, even less to establish the validity of the genetic model. However, it seems more profitable tentatively to adopt the genetic model and to see whether some of the more specific predictions which it implies are experimentally verified.

The most immediate and also perhaps the most striking of these implications is that the structural message must be carried by a very short-lived intermediate both rapidly formed and rapidly destroyed during the process of information transfer. This is required by the kinetics of induction. As we have seen, the addition of inducer, or the removal of co-repressor, provokes the synthesis of enzyme at maximum rate within a matter of a few minutes, while the removal of inducer, or the addition of co-repressor interrupts the synthesis within an equally short time. Such kinetics are incompatible with the assumption that the repressor-operator interaction controls the rate of synthesis of *stable* enzyme-forming templates (Monod, 1956, 1958). Therefore, if the genetic operator model is valid, one should expect the kinetics of structural gene expression to be *essentially the same* as the kinetics of induction: injection of a "new" gene into an otherwise competent cell should result in virtually immediate synthesis of the corresponding protein at maximum rate; while removal of the gene should be attended by concomitant cessation of synthesis.

† It should be pointed out that the operational distinction between the operator locus and the structural cistron to which it is directly adjacent rests exclusively on the fact that the operator mutations affect the synthesis of several proteins governed by linked cistrons. This does not exclude the possibility that the operator locus is actually *part* of the structural cistron to which it is "adjacent." If it were so, one might expect certain constitutive operator mutations to involve an alteration of the structure of the protein governed by the "adjacent" cistron. The evidence available at present is insufficient to confirm or eliminate this assumption.

(a) *Kinetics of expression of the galactosidase structural gene*

Additions and removals of genes to and from cells are somewhat more difficult to perform than additions or removals of inducer. However, it can be done. Gene injection without cytoplasmic mixing occurs in the conjugation of *Hfr* male and *F⁻* female *E. coli*. In a mixed male and female population the individual pairs do not all mate at the same time, but the distribution of times of injection of a *given* gene can be rather accurately determined by proper genetic methods. The injection of the z^+ (galactosidase) gene from male cells into galactosidase-negative (z^-) female cells is rapidly followed by enzyme synthesis within zygotes (cf. p. 332). When the rate of enzyme synthesis in the population is expressed as a function of time, taking into

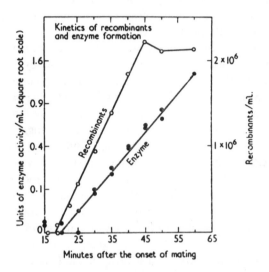

Fɪɢ. 7. Kinetics of enzyme production by merozygotes formed by conjugation between inducible galactosidase-positive males and constitutive galactosidase-negative females. Conditions are such that only the zygotes can form enzyme. Increase in the number of z^+ containing zygotes is determined by counting recombinants on adequate selective medium. Formation of enzyme is followed by enzyme activity measurements on the total population. It is seen that the enzyme increases linearly with the square of time. Since the zygote population increases linearly with time, it is apparent that the rate of enzyme synthesis per zygote is constant from the time of penetration of the z^+ gene. (From Riley *et al.*, 1960.)

account the increase with time of the number of z^+ containing zygotes, it is found (see Fig. 7):

(1) that enzyme synthesis begins within two minutes of the penetration of the z^+ gene;

(2) that the rate per zygote is constant and maximum over at least the first 40 min following penetration (Riley, Pardee, Jacob & Monod, 1960).

These observations indicate that the structural messenger is very rapidly formed by the z^+ gene, and does not accumulate. This could be interpreted in one of two ways:

(a) the structural messenger is a short-lived intermediate;

(b) the structural messenger is stable, but the gene rapidly forms a limited number of messenger molecules, and thereafter stops functioning.

If the second assumption is correct, removal of the gene after the inception of enzyme synthesis should not prevent the synthesis from continuing. This possibility is tested by the "removal" experiment, which is performed by loading the male chromosome with ^{32}P before injection. Following injection (into unlabelled female cells), ample time (25 min) is allowed for expression of the z^+ gene, before the zygotes are frozen to allow ^{32}P decay for various lengths of time. The rate of galactosidase synthesis by the population is determined immediately after thawing. It is found to decrease sharply as a function of the fraction of ^{32}P atoms decayed. If a longer period of time (110 min) is allowed for expression before freezing, no decrease in either enzyme-forming capacity or in viability of the z^+ marker are observed. This is to be expected, since by that time most of the z^+ genes would have replicated, and this observation provides an internal control showing that no indirect effects of ^{32}P disintegrations are involved.

This experiment therefore indicates that even after the z^+ gene has become expressed its integrity is required for enzyme synthesis to continue, as expected if the messenger molecule is a short-lived intermediate (Riley et al., 1960).

The interpretation of both the injection and the removal experiment rests on the assumption that the observed effects are not due to (stable) cytoplasmic messenger molecules introduced with the genetic material, during conjugation. As we have already noted, there is strong evidence that no cytoplasmic transfer, even of small molecules, occurs during conjugation. Furthermore, if the assumption were made that enzyme synthesis in the zygotes is due to pre-formed messenger molecules rather than to the activity of the gene, it would be exceedingly difficult to account for both (a) the very precise coincidence in time between inception of enzyme synthesis and entry of the gene (in the injection experiment) and (b) the parallel behaviour of enzyme-forming capacity and genetic viability of the z^+ gene (in the removal experiment).

These experiments therefore appear to show that the kinetics of expression of a structural gene are entirely similar to the kinetics of induction-repression, as expected if the operator controls the activity of the gene in the synthesis of a short-lived messenger, rather than the activity of a ready-made (stable) messenger molecule in synthesizing protein.

It is interesting at this point to recall the fact that infection of E. coli with virulent (ϕII, T2, T4) phage is attended within 2 to 4 minutes by inhibition of bacterial protein synthesis, including in particular β-galactosidase (Cohen, 1949; Monod & Wollman, 1947; Benzer, 1953). It is known on the other hand that phage-infection results in rapid visible lysis of bacterial nuclei, while no major destruction of pre-formed bacterial RNA appears to occur (Luria & Human, 1950). It seems very probable that the inhibition of specific bacterial protein synthesis by virulent phage is due essentially to the depolymerization of bacterial DNA, and this conclusion also implies that the integrity of bacterial genes is required for continued synthesis of bacterial protein. In confirmation of this interpretation, it may be noted that infection of E. coli by phage λ, which does not result in destruction of bacterial nuclei, allows β-galactosidase synthesis to continue almost to the time of lysis (Siminovitch & Jacob, 1952).

(b) Structural effects of base analogs

An entirely different type of experiment also leads to the conclusion that the structural messenger is a short-lived intermediate and suggests, furthermore, that this intermediate is a ribonucleotide. It is known that certain purine and pyrimidine analogs are incorporated by bacterial cells into ribo- and deoxyribonucleotides, and it has been found that the synthesis of protein, or of some proteins, may be inhibited in the presence of certain of these analogs. One of the mechanisms by which these effects could be explained may be that certain analogs are incorporated into the structural messenger. If so, one might hope to observe that the molecular structure of specific proteins formed in the presence of an analog is modified. It has in fact been found that the molecular properties of β-galactosidase and of alkaline phosphatase synthesized by *E. coli* in the presence of 5-fluorouracil (5FU) are strikingly altered. In the case of β-galactosidase, the ratio of enzyme activity to antigenic valency is decreased by 80%. In the case of alkaline phosphatase, the rate of thermal inactivation (of this normally highly heat-resistant protein) is greatly increased (Naono & Gros, 1960a,b; Bussard, Naono, Gros & Monod, 1960).

It can safely be assumed that such an effect cannot result from the mere presence of 5FU in the cells, and must reflect incorporation of the analog into a constituent involved in some way in the information transfer system. Whatever the identity of this constituent may be, the kinetics of the effect must in turn reflect the kinetics of 5FU incorporation into this constituent. The most remarkable feature of the 5FU effect is that it is almost immediate, in the sense that abnormal enzyme is synthesized almost from the time of addition of the analog, and that the degree of abnormality of the molecular population thereafter synthesized does not increase with time. For instance, in the case of galactosidase abnormal enzyme is synthesized within 5 min of addition of the analog, and the ratio of enzyme activity to antigenic valency remains constant thereafter. In the case of alkaline phosphatase, the thermal inactivation curve of the abnormal protein synthesized in the presence of 5FU is monomolecular, showing the molecular population to be *homogeneously* abnormal rather than made up of a mixture of normal and abnormal molecules. It is clear that if the constituent responsible for this effect were stable, one would expect the population of molecules made in the presence of 5FU to be heterogeneous, and the fraction of abnormal molecules to increase progressively. It follows that the responsible constituent must be formed, and also must decay, very rapidly.

Now it should be noted that, besides the structural gene-synthesized messenger, the information transfer system probably involves other constituents responsible for the correct translation of the message, such as for instance the RNA fractions involved in amino acid transfer. The 5FU effect could be due to incorporation into one of these fractions rather than to incorporation into the messenger itself. However, the convergence of the results of the different experiments discussed above strongly suggests that the 5FU effect does reflect a high rate of turnover of the messenger itself.

(c) *Messenger RNA*

Accepting tentatively these conclusions, let us then consider what properties would be required of a cellular constituent, to allow its identification with the structural messenger. These qualifications based on general assumptions, and on the results discussed above, would be as follows:

(1) The "candidate" should be a polynucleotide.

(2) The fraction would presumably be very heterogeneous with respect to molecular weight. However, assuming a coding ratio of 3, the average molecular weight would not be lower than 5×10^5.

(3) It should have a base composition reflecting the base composition of DNA.

(4) It should, at least temporarily or under certain conditions, be found associated with ribosomes, since there are good reasons to believe that ribosomes are the seat of protein synthesis.

(5) It should have a very high rate of turnover and in particular it should saturate with 5FU within less than about 3 min.

It is immediately evident that none of the more classically recognized cellular RNA fractions meets these very restrictive qualifications. Ribosomal RNA, frequently assumed to represent the "template" in protein synthesis, is remarkably homogeneous in molecular weight. Its base composition is similar in different species, and does not reflect the variations in base ratios found in DNA. Moreover it appears to be entirely stable in growing cells (Davern & Meselson, 1960). It incorporates 5FU only in proportion to net increase.

Transfer RNA, or (sRNA) does not reflect DNA in base composition. Its average molecular weight is much lower than the 5×10^5 required for the messenger. Except perhaps for the terminal adenine and cytidine, its rate of incorporation of bases, including in particular 5FU, is not higher than that of ribosomal RNA.

However, a small fraction of RNA, first observed by Volkin & Astrachan (1957) in phage infected E. coli, and recently found to exist also in normal yeasts (Yčas & Vincent, 1960) and coli (Gros, et al., 1961), does seem to meet all the qualifications listed above.

This fraction (which we shall designate "messenger RNA" or M-RNA) amounts to only about 3% of the total RNA; it can be separated from other RNA fractions by column fractionation or sedimentation (Fig. 8). Its average sedimentation velocity coefficient is 13, corresponding to a minimum molecular weight of 3×10^5, but since the molecules are presumably far from spherical, the molecular weight is probably much higher. The rate of incorporation of ^{32}P, uracil or 5FU into this fraction is extremely rapid: half saturation is observed in less than 30 sec, indicating a rate of synthesis several hundred times faster than any other RNA fraction. Its half life is also very short, as shown by the disappearance of radioactivity from this fraction in pre-labelled cells. At high concentrations of Mg^{2+} (0·005 M) the fraction tends to associate with the 70s ribosomal particles, while at lower Mg^{2+} concentrations it sediments independently of the ribosomal particles (Gros et al., 1961).

The striking fact, discovered by Volkin & Astrachan, that the base-composition of this fraction in T2-infected cells reflects the base composition of *phage* (rather than bacterial) DNA, had led to the suggestion that it served as a precursor of phage DNA. The agreement between the properties of this fraction and the properties of a short-lived structural messenger suggests that, in phage infected cells as well as in normal cells, this fraction served in fact in the transfer of genetic information from phage DNA to the protein synthesizing centers. This assumption implies that the same protein-forming centers which, in uninfected cells, synthesize bacterial protein, also serve in infected cells to synthesize phage protein according to the new structural information provided by phage DNA, *via* M-RNA. This interpretation is strongly supported by recent observations made with T4 infected E. coli. (Brenner, Jacob & Meselson, 1961).

Uninfected cells of E. coli were grown in the presence of ^{15}N. They were then infected and resuspended in ^{14}N medium. Following infection, they were exposed to short pulses of ^{32}P or ^{35}S, and the ribosomes were analysed in density gradients. It was found:

(1) that no detectable amounts of ribosomal RNA were synthesized after infection;

(2) labelled M-RNA formed *after* infection became associated with unlabelled ribosomal particles formed *before* infection;

(3) newly formed (i.e. phage-determined) protein, identified by its ^{35}S content, was found associated with the 70s particles before it appeared in the soluble protein fraction.

These observations strongly suggest that phage protein is synthesized by *bacterial* ribosomes formed before infection and associated with *phage-determined* M-RNA. Since the structural information for phage protein could not reside in the bacterial ribosomes, it must be provided by the M-RNA fraction.

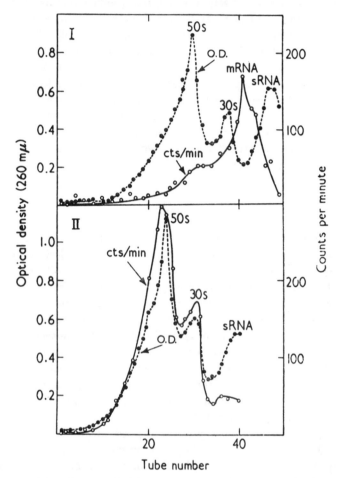

FIG. 8. Incorporation and turnover of uracil in messenger RNA. *E. coli* growing exponentially in broth were incubated for 5 sec with [^{14}C]-uracil. The bacteria were centrifuged, washed and resuspended in the original volume of the same medium containing 100-fold excess of [^{12}C]-uracil. Half the bacteria were then harvested and frozen (I) and the remainder were incubated for 15 min at 37°C (II) prior to harvesting and freezing. The frozen samples were ground with alumina and extracted with tris buffer (2-amino-2 hydroxymethylpropane-1:3-diol) containing 10^{-4}M-Mg, treated with DNase and applied to a sucrose gradient. After 3 hr, sequential samples were taken for determination of radioactivity and absorption at 260 mμ. It may be seen (part I) that after 5 sec, M-RNA is the only labelled fraction, and that subsequently (part II) uracil incorporated into M-RNA is entirely renewed. (From Gros *et al.*, 1961.)

Finally, the recent experiments of Lamfrom (1961) independently repeated by Kruh, Rosa, Dreyfus & Schapira (1961) have shown directly that species specificity in the synthesis of haemoglobin is determined by a "soluble" RNA-containing fraction rather than by the ribosomal fraction. Lamfrom used reconstructed systems, containing ribosomes from one species (rabbit) and soluble fractions from another (sheep) and found that the haemoglobin formed *in vitro* by these systems belonged in part to the type characteristic of the species used to prepare the *soluble* fraction. It is not, of course, positively proved that *inter-specific* differences in haemoglobin structure are gene-determined rather than cytoplasmic, but the assumption seems safe enough. In any case, Lamfrom's experiment proves beyond doubt that the ribosomes cannot be considered to determine entirely (if at all) the specific structure of proteins.

We had stated the problem to be discussed in this section as the choice between the genetic operator model and the cytoplasmic operator model. The adoption of the genetic operator model implies, as we have seen, some very distinctive and specific predictions concerning the behaviour of the intermediate responsible for the transfer of information from gene to protein. These predictions appear to be borne out by a considerable body of evidence which leads actually to a tentative identification of the intermediate in question with one particular RNA fraction. Even if this identification is confirmed by direct experiments, it will remain to be proved, also by direct experiments, that the synthesis of this "M-RNA" fraction is controlled at the genetic level by the repressor-operator interaction.

6. Conclusion

A convenient method of summarizing the conclusions derived in the preceding sections of this paper will be to organize them into a model designed to embody the main elements which we were led to recognize as playing a specific role in the control of protein synthesis; namely, the structural, regulator and operator genes, the operon, and the cytoplasmic repressor. Such a model could be as follows:

The molecular structure of proteins is determined by specific elements, the *structural genes*. These act by forming a cytoplasmic "transcript" of themselves, the structural messenger, which in turn synthesizes the protein. The synthesis of the messenger by the structural gene is a sequential replicative process, which can be initiated only at certain points on the DNA strand, and the cytoplasmic transcription of several, linked, structural genes may depend upon a single initiating point or *operator*. The genes whose activity is thus co-ordinated form an *operon*.

The operator tends to combine (by virtue of possessing a particular base sequence) specifically and reversibly with a certain (RNA) fraction possessing the proper (complementary) sequence. This combination blocks the initiation of cytoplasmic transcription and therefore the formation of the messenger by the structural genes in the whole operon. The specific "repressor" (RNA?), acting with a given operator, is synthesized by a *regulator gene*.

The repressor in certain systems (inducible enzyme systems) tends to combine specifically with certain specific small molecules. The combined repressor has no affinity for the operator, and the combination therefore results in *activation of the operon*.

In other systems (repressible enzyme systems) the repressor by itself is inactive (i.e. it has no affinity for the operator) and is activated only by combining with certain specific small molecules. The combination therefore leads to *inhibition of the operon*.

The structural messenger is an unstable molecule, which is destroyed in the process of information transfer. The rate of messenger synthesis, therefore, in turn controls the rate of protein synthesis.

This model was meant to summarize and express conveniently the properties of the different factors which play a specific role in the control of protein synthesis. In order concretely to represent the functions of these different factors, we have had to introduce some purely speculative assumptions. Let us clearly discriminate the experimentally established conclusions from the speculations:

(1) The most firmly grounded of these conclusions is the existence of *regulator* genes, which control the rate of information-transfer from *structural* genes to proteins, without contributing any information to the proteins themselves. Let us briefly recall the evidence on this point: mutations in the structural gene, which are reflected as alterations of the protein, do not alter the regulatory mechanism. Mutations that alter the regulatory mechanism do not alter the protein and do not map in the structural genes. Structural genes obey the one-gene one-protein principle, while regulator genes may affect the synthesis of several different proteins.

(2) That the regulator gene acts *via* a specific cytoplasmic substance whose effect is to *inhibit* the expression of the structural genes, is equally clearly established by the *trans* effect of the gene, by the different properties exhibited by genetically identical zygotes depending upon the origin of their cytoplasm, and by the fact that absence of the regulator gene, or of its product, results in uncontrolled synthesis of the protein at maximum rates.

(3) That the product of the regulator gene acts directly as a *repressor* (rather than indirectly, as antagonist of an endogenous inducer or other activator) is proved in the case of the *Lac* system (and of the λ lysogenic systems) by the properties of the dominant mutants of the regulator.

(4) The chemical identification of the repressor as an RNA fraction is a logical assumption based only on the *negative* evidence which indicates that it is not a protein.

(5) The existence of an operator, defined as the site of action of the repressor, is deduced from the existence and specificity of action of the repressor. The identification of the operator with the genetic segment which controls sensitivity to the repressor, is strongly suggested by the observation that a *single* operator gene may control the expression of *several adjacent structural genes*, that is to say, by the demonstration of the *operon* as a co-ordinated unit of genetic expression.

The assumption that the operator represents an initiating point for the cytoplasmic transcription of several structural genes is a pure speculation, meant only as an illustration of the fact that the operator controls an integral property of the group of linked genes which form an operon. There is at present no evidence on which to base any assumption on the molecular mechanisms of the operator.

(6) The assumptions made regarding the interaction of the repressor with inducers or co-repressors are among the weakest and vaguest in the model. The idea that specific coupling of inducers to the repressor could result in inactivation of the repressor appears reasonable enough, but it raises a difficulty which we have already pointed out. Since this reaction between repressor and inducer must be stereospecific (for both) it should presumably require a specific enzyme; yet no evidence, genetic or biochemical, has been found for such an enzyme.

(7) The property attributed to the structural messenger of being an unstable intermediate is one of the most specific and novel implications of this scheme; it is required, let us recall, by the kinetics of induction, once the assumption is made that the control systems operate at the genetic level. This leads to a new concept of the mechanism of information transfer, where the protein synthesizing centers (ribosomes) play the role of non-specific constituents which can synthesize different proteins, according to specific instructions which they receive from the genes through M-RNA. The already fairly impressive body of evidence, kinetic and analytical, which supports

this new interpretation of information transfer, is of great interest in itself, even if some of the other assumptions included in the scheme turn out to be incorrect.

These conclusions apply strictly to the bacterial systems from which they were derived; but the fact that adaptive enzyme systems of both types (inducible and repressible) and phage systems appear to obey the same fundamental mechanisms of control, involving the same essential elements, argues strongly for the generality of what may be called "repressive genetic regulation" of protein synthesis.

One is led to wonder whether all or most structural genes (i.e. the synthesis of most proteins) are submitted to repressive regulation. In bacteria, virtually all the enzyme systems which have been adequately studied have proved sensitive to inductive or repressive effects. The old idea that such effects are characteristic only of "non-essential" enzymes is certainly incorrect (although, of course, these effects can be detected only under conditions, natural or artificial, such that the system under study is at least partially non-essential (gratuitous). The results of mutations which abolish the control (such as constitutive mutations) illustrate its physiological importance. Constitutive mutants of the lactose system synthesize 6 to 7% of all their proteins as β-galactosidase. In constitutive mutants of the phosphatase system, 5 to 6% of the total protein is phosphatase. Similar figures have been obtained with other constitutive mutants. It is clear that the cells could not survive the breakdown of more than two or three of the control systems which keep in pace the synthesis of enzyme proteins.

The occurrence of inductive and repressive effects in tissues of higher organisms has been observed in many instances, although it has not proved possible so far to analyse any of these systems in detail (the main difficulty being the creation of controlled conditions of gratuity). It has repeatedly been pointed out that enzymatic adaptation, as studied in micro-organisms, offers a valuable model for the interpretation of biochemical co-ordination within tissues and between organs in higher organisms. The demonstration that adaptive effects in micro-organisms are primarily negative (repressive), that they are controlled by functionally specialized genes and operate at the genetic level, would seem greatly to widen the possibilities of interpretation. The fundamental problem of chemical physiology and of embryology is to understand why tissue cells do not all express, all the time, all the potentialities inherent in their genome. The survival of the organism requires that many, and, in some tissues most, of these potentialities be unexpressed, that is to say *repressed*. Malignancy is adequately described as a breakdown of one or several growth controlling systems, and the genetic origin of this breakdown can hardly be doubted.

According to the strictly structural concept, the genome is considered as a mosaic of independent molecular blue-prints for the building of individual cellular constituents. In the execution of these plans, however, co-ordination is evidently of absolute survival value. The discovery of regulator and operator genes, and of repressive regulation of the activity of structural genes, reveals that the genome contains not only a series of blue-prints, but a co-ordinated program of protein synthesis and the means of controlling its execution.

REFERENCES

Adelberg, E. A. & Umbarger, H. E. (1953). *J. Biol. Chem.* **205**, 475.
Ames, B. N. & Garry, B. (1959). *Proc. Nat. Acad. Sci., Wash.* **45**, 1453.
Ames, B. N., Garry, B. & Herzenberg, L. A. (1960). *J. Gen. Microbiol.* **22**, 369.
Benzer, S. (1953). *Biochim. biophys. Acta,* **11**, 383.
Bertani, G. (1953). *Cold. Spr. Harb. Symp. Quant. Biol.* **18**, 65.

Bertani, G. (1958). *Advanc. Virus Res.* 5, 151.

Brenner, S., Jacob, F. & Meselson, M. (1961). *Nature*, 190, 576.

Bussard, A., Naono, S., Gros, F. & Monod, J. (1960). *C. R. Acad. Sci., Paris*, 250, 4049.

Buttin, G. (1956). Diplôme Et. Sup., Paris.

Buttin, G. (1961). *C. R. Acad. Sci., Paris*, in the press.

Cohen, G. N. & Jacob, F. (1959). *C. R. Acad. Sci., Paris*, 248, 3490.

Cohen, G. N. & Monod, J. (1957). *Bact. Rev.* 21, 169.

Cohen, S. S. (1949). *Bact. Rev.* 13, 1.

Cohen-Bazire, G. & Jolit, M. (1953). *Ann. Inst. Pasteur*, 84, 1.

Cohn, M. (1957). *Bact. Rev.* 21, 140.

Cohn, M., Cohen, G. N. & Monod, J. (1953). *C. R. Acad. Sci., Paris*, 236, 746.

Cohn, M. & Horibata, K. (1959). *J. Bact.* 78, 624.

Cohn, M. & Monod, J. (1953). In *Adaptation in Micro-organisms*, p. 132. Cambridge University Press.

Cohn, M. & Torriani, A. M. (1952). *J. Immunol.* 69, 471.

Davern, C. I. & Meselson, M. (1960). *J. Mol. Biol.* 2, 153.

Demerec, M. (1956). *Cold Spr. Harb. Symp. Quant. Biol.* 21, 113.

Dienert, F. (1900). *Ann. Inst. Pasteur*, 14, 139.

Duclaux, E. (1899). *Traité de Microbiologie*. Paris: Masson et Cie.

Echols, H., Garen, A., Garen, S. & Torriani, A. M. (1961). *J. Mol. Biol.*, in the press.

Flaks, J. G. & Cohen, S. S. (1959). *J. Biol. Chem.* 234, 1501.

Gale, E. F. (1943). *Bact. Rev.* 7, 139.

Giles, N. H. (1958). *Proc. Xth Intern. Cong. Genetics*, Montreal, 1, 261.

Gorini, L. & Maas, W. K. (1957). *Biochim. biophys. Acta*, 25, 208.

Gorini, L. & Maas, W. K. (1958). In *The Chemical Basis of Development*, p. 469. Baltimore: Johns Hopkins Press.

Gros, F., Hiatt, H., Gilbert, W., Kurland, C. G., Risebrough, R. W. & Watson, J. D. (1961). *Nature*, 190, 581.

Halvorson, H. O. (1960). *Advanc. Enzymol.* in the press.

Hartman, P. E., Loper, J. C. & Serman, D. (1960). *J. Gen. Microbiol.* 22, 323.

Herzenberg, L. (1959). *Biochim. biophys. Acta*, 31, 525.

Hogness, D. S., Cohn, M. & Monod, J. (1955). *Biochim. biophys. Acta*, 16, 99.

Jacob, F. (1954). *Les Bactéries Lysogènes et la Notion de Provirus*. Paris: Masson et Cie.

Jacob, F. (1960). *Harvey Lectures*, 1958–1959, series 54, 1.

Jacob, F. & Adelberg, E. A. (1959). *C.R. Acad. Sci., Paris*, 249, 189.

Jacob, F. & Campbell, A. (1959). *C.R. Acad. Sci., Paris*, 248, 3219.

Jacob, F., Fuerst, C. R. & Wollman, E. L. (1957). *Ann. Inst. Pasteur*, 93, 724.

Jacob, F. & Monod, J. (1959). *C.R. Acad. Sci., Paris*, 249, 1282.

Jacob, F., Perrin, D., Sanchez, C. & Monod, J. (1960a). *C.R. Acad. Sci., Paris*, 250, 1727.

Jacob, F., Schaeffer, P. & Wollman, E. L. (1960b). In *Microbial Genetics*, Xth Symposium of the Society for General Microbiology, p. 67.

Jacob, F. & Wollman, E. L. (1953). *Cold Spr. Harb. Symp. Quant. Biol.* 18, 101.

Jacob, F. & Wollman, E. L. (1956). *Ann. Inst. Pasteur*, 91, 486.

Jacob, F. & Wollman, E. L. (1957). In *The Chemical Basis of Heredity*, p. 468. Baltimore: Johns Hopkins Press.

Kaiser, A. D. (1957). *Virology*, 3, 42.

Kaiser, A. D. & Jacob, F. (1957). *Virology*, 4, 509.

Kalckar, H. M., Kurahashi, K. & Jordan, E. (1959). *Proc. Nat. Acad. Sci., Wash.* 45, 1776.

Karstrom, H. (1938). *Ergebn. Enzymforsch.* 7, 350.

Képès, A. (1960). *Biochim. biophys. Acta*, 40, 70.

Képès, A., Monod, J. & Jacob, F. (1961). In preparation.

Kogut, M., Pollock, M. & Tridgell, E. J. (1956). *Biochem. J.* 62, 391.

Kornberg, A., Zimmerman, S. B., Kornberg, S. R. & Josse, J. (1959). *Proc. Nat. Acad. Sci., Wash.* 45, 772.

Kruh, J., Rosa, J., Dreyfus, J.-C. & Schapira, G. (1961). *Biochim. biophys. Acta*, in the press.

Lamfrom, H. (1961). *J. Mol. Biol.* 3, 241.

Lederberg, E. (1960). In *Microbial Genetics*, The Xth Symposium of the Society of General Microbiology, p. 115.

Levinthal, C. (1959). In *Structure and Function of Genetic Elements*, Brookhaven Symposia in Biology, p. 76.

Luria, S. E. & Human, M. L. (1950). *J. Bact.* **59**, 551.

Lwoff, A. (1953). *Bact. Rev.* **17**, 269.

Lwoff, A., Siminovitch, L. & Kjeldgaard, N. (1950). *Ann. Inst. Pasteur*, **79**, 815.

Magasanik, B., Magasanik, A. K. & Neidhardt, F. C. (1959). In *A Ciba Symposium on the Regulation of Cell Metabolism*, p. 334. London: Churchill.

Monod, J. (1942). *Recherches sur la Croissance des Cultures Bactériennes*. Paris: Hermann.

Monod, J. (1955). *Exp. Ann. Biochim. Méd.* série XVII, p. 195. Paris: Masson et Cie.

Monod, J. (1956). In *Units of Biological Structure and Function*, p. 7. New York: Academic Press.

Monod, J. (1958). *Rec. Trav. Chim. des Pays-Bas*, **77**, 569.

Monod, J. (1959). *Angew. Chem.* **71**, 685.

Monod, J. & Audureau, A. (1946). *Ann. Inst. Pasteur*, **72**, 868.

Monod, J. & Cohen-Bazire, G. (1953). *C.R. Acad. Sci., Paris*, **236**, 530.

Monod, J. & Cohn, M. (1952). *Advanc. Enzymol.* **13**, 67.

Monod, J. & Cohn, M. (1953). In *Symposium on Microbial Metabolism*. VIth Intern. Cong. of Microbiol., Rome, p. 42.

Monod, J., Pappenheimer, A. M. & Cohen-Bazire, G. (1952), *Biochim. biophys. Acta*, **9**, 648.

Monod, J. & Wollman, E. L. (1947). *Ann. Inst. Pasteur*, **73**, 937.

Naono, S. & Gros, F. (1960a). *C.R. Acad. Sci., Paris*, **250**, 3527.

Naono, S. & Gros, F. (1960b). *C.R. Acad. Sci., Paris*, **250**, 3889.

Neidhardt, F. C. & Magasanik, B. (1956a). *Nature*, **178**, 801.

Neidhardt, F. C. & Magasanik, B. (1956b). *Biochim. biophys. Acta*, **21**, 324.

Novick, A. & Szilard, L., in Novick, A. (1955). *Ann. Rev. Microbiol.* **9**, 97.

Pardee, A. B. (1957). *J. Bact.* **73**, 376.

Pardee, A. B., Jacob, F. & Monod, J. (1959). *J. Mol. Biol.* **1**, 165.

Pardee, A. B. & Prestidge, L. S. (1959). *Biochim. biophys. Acta*, **36**, 545.

Pardee, A. B. & Prestidge, L. S. (1961). In preparation.

Perrin, D., Bussard, A. & Monod, J. (1959). *C.R. Acad. Sci., Paris*, **249**, 778.

Perrin, D., Jacob, F. & Monod, J. (1960). *C.R. Acad. Sci., Paris*, **250**, 155.

Pollock, M. (1950). *Brit. J. Exp. Pathol.* **4**, 739.

Pollock, M. & Perret, J. C. (1951). *Brit. J. Exp. Pathol.* **5**, 387.

Pontecorvo, G. (1958). *Trends in Genetic Analysis*. New York: Columbia University Press.

Rickenberg, H. V., Cohen, G. N., Buttin, G. & Monod, J. (1956). *Ann. Inst. Pasteur*, **91**, 829.

Riley, M., Pardee, A. B., Jacob, F. & Monod, J. (1960). *J. Mol. Biol.* **2**, 216.

Rotman, B. & Spiegelman, S. (1954). *J. Bact.* **68**, 419.

Siminovitch, L. & Jacob, F. (1952). *Ann. Inst. Pasteur*, **83**, 745.

Stanier, R. Y. (1951). *Ann. Rev. Microbiol.* **5**, 35.

Szilard, L. (1960). *Proc. Nat. Acad. Sci., Wash.* **46**, 277.

Torriani, A. M. (1960). *Biochim. biophys. Acta*, **38**, 460.

Umbarger, H. E. (1956). *Science*, **123**, 848.

Vogel, H. J. (1957a). *Proc. Nat. Acad. Sci., Wash.* **43**, 491.

Vogel, H. J. (1957b). In *The Chemical Basis of Heredity*, p. 276. Baltimore: Johns Hopkins Press.

Volkin, E. & Astrachan, L. (1957). In *The Chemical Basis of Heredity*, p. 686. Baltimore: Johns Hopkins Press.

Went, F. C. (1901). *J. Wiss. Bot.* **36**, 611.

Wijesundera, S. & Woods, D. D. (1953). *Biochem. J.* **55**, viii.

Willson, C., Perrin, D., Jacob, F. & Monod, J. (1961). In preparation.

Wollman, E. L. & Jacob, F. (1959). *La Sexualité des Bactéries*. Paris: Masson et Cie.

Yanofsky, C. (1960). *Bact. Rev.* **24**, 221.

Yanofsky, C. & Lennox, E. S. (1959). *Virology*, **8**, 425.

Yarmolinsky, M. B. & Wiesmeyer, H. (1960). *Proc. Nat. Acad. Sci., Wash.* in the press.

Yates, R. A. & Pardee, A. B. (1956). *J. Biol. Chem.* **221**, 757.

Yates, R. A. & Pardee, A. B. (1957). *J. Biol. Chem.* **227**, 677.

Yčas, M. & Vincent, W. S. (1960). *Proc. Nat. Acad. Sci., Wash.* **46**, 804.

Zabin, I., Képès, A. & Monod, J. (1959). *Biochem. Biophys. Res. Comm.* **1**, 289.

GENETIC MAPPING OF THE ELEMENTS OF THE LACTOSE REGION
IN ESCHERICHIA COLI

François JACOB and Jacques MONOD

Services de Génétique microbienne et Biochimie cellulaire,
Institut Pasteur, Paris

Received January 15, 1965

In $\underline{Escherichia\ coli}$, the ability to ferment lactose depends on two structural genes : $\underline{z}$, which determines the structure of β-galactosidase and $\underline{y}$ which determines that of β-galactoside permease. The two genes are adjacent on the bacterial chromosome and belong to a single operon, the operator ($\underline{o}$) being located on the distal side of $\underline{z}$. This operon also controls the synthesis of β-galactoside-transacetylase, the structural gene of which must be located distal to $\underline{y}$ with respect to $\underline{z}$. The expression of the whole operon is controlled by a regulator gene $\underline{i}$, determining the production of a cytoplasmic repressor susceptible to the action of β-galactosides (Fig. 1). The gene $\underline{i}$ is located outside the operon, but close to $\underline{z}$, conjugation experiments between various mutant strains suggesting the order : $\underline{i}..\underline{o}\ \underline{z}\ \underline{y}$ (Jacob and Monod, 1961 a).

For this order to be determined more accurately, three point test experiments were performed with transduction by phage Pl. By using a donor strain which is $\underline{z}^{+}$ and either $\underline{i}^{+}\underline{o}^{c}$ or $\underline{i}^{-}\underline{o}^{+}$ and a recipient which is $\underline{z}^{-}$ and either $\underline{i}^{-}\underline{o}^{+}$ or $\underline{i}^{+}\underline{o}^{c}$, one can select the recombinants which grow on lactose : they have received the $\underline{z}^{+}$ allele from the donor. One then

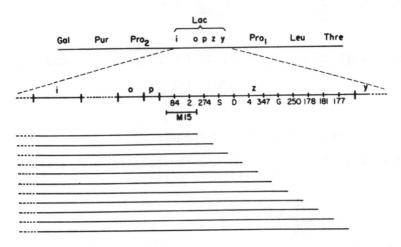

Diagrammatic representation of the Lac segment and of deletions in this region. The upper line represents a segment of the E.coli K12 chromosome around the Lac region. The second line represents an enlargement of the Lac region : i, regulator gene ; o, operator ; p, promotor ; z, structural gene for β-galacto-sidase ; y, structural gene for permease. The figures correspond to single point mutants. The lines below represent the deleted segments in a variety of mutants. M15 was isolated by Beckwith (1964 b). The others by Jacob et al. (1964).

determines the fraction of these z^+ transductants which are also i^+o^+. It is clear, as represented on the top of Table I, that different results will be expected depending on whether i or o is closer to z. The fraction of o^+i^+ among z^+ trans-ductants should be higher in the experiment where the smallest number of cross-over, two instead of four occurs. Reciprocal transduction should therefore provide an unambiguous test of the actual order of the genes.

Several experiments of this type have been performed with different pairs of i^- and o^c alleles in reciprocal combinations. As shown by the results reported in Table I, the sequence can only be $i..o\ z\ y$.

This order can be checked by the use of another marker, Pro_2, involved in proline biosynthesis, which is known to be on the i side of the Lac operon and can be cotransduced with

TABLE I

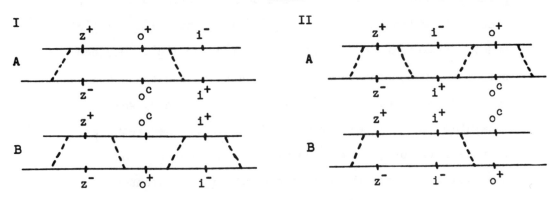

Donor genotype	Recipient genotype	Experiment type	Number of colonies tested	Number of i^+ found	Percent i^+
$z^+o^+i^-_3$	$z^-_1o^+i^-_3$	Control	300	0	< 0.3
$z^+o^c_1i^+$	$z^-_1o^+i^-_3$	B	300	0	< 0.3
$z^+o^c_{15}i^+$	$z^-_1o^+i^-_3$	B	300	1	0.3
$z^+o^c_{307}i^+$	$z^-_1o^+i^-_3$	B	300	1	0.3
$z^+o^c_1i^+$	$z^-o^c_1i^+$	Control	300	0	< 0.3
$z^+o^+i^-_3$	$z^-o^c_1i^+$	A	300	24	8
$z^+o^+i^-_E$	$z^-o^c_1i^+$	A	300	30	10
$z^+o^+i^-_{74}$	$z^-o^c_1i^+$	A	296	34	11.4
$z^+o^+i^-_{313}$	$z^-o^c_1i^+$	A	300	20	6.6

Recipient bacteria were infected with an average multiplicity of about 3 phages grown on donor bacteria. After three successive reisolation on lactose synthetic plates, the recombinants were reisolated twice on glucose synthetic plates. Their inducible vs constitutive character was determined by treatment of the last plate with toluene and ortho-nitro-phenol-galac-toside. In these conditions, i^-o^+ or i^+o^c genotypes give a yellow color whereas i^+o^+ do not.

z mutants (Schwartz, 1963). Interrupted mating experiments

confirmed the order (y) z.....Pro$_2$.....Pur. The order of the

i and o markers could then be deduced from transduction experiments in which the donor is $\underline{Pro}^+ \underline{z}^-$ and either $\underline{i}^- \underline{o}^+$ or $\underline{i}^+ \underline{o}^c$ and the recipient $\underline{Pro}_2^- \ \underline{z}^+$ and either $\underline{i}^+ \underline{o}^c$ or $\underline{i}^- \underline{o}^+$. One can select the recombinants which grow on lactose without proline. They have received the $\underline{Pro}_2^+$ allele from the donor, while retaining the $\underline{z}^+$ allele from the recipient. They require therefore an obligatory crossing-over between $\underline{Pro}_2$ and $\underline{z}$. One then determines the fraction of the $\underline{Pro}^+ \underline{z}^+$ transductants which are also $\underline{i}^+ \underline{o}^+$. It is clear again that different results should be expected depending on whether the order is $\underline{z} \ \underline{o} \ \underline{i} \ \underline{Pro}_2$ or $\underline{z} \ \underline{i} \ \underline{o} \ \underline{Pro}_2$, as represented on top of Table II. The fraction of $\underline{i}^+ \underline{o}^+$ bacteria should be higher when only two cross-overs and not four are required. The results of a reciprocal transduction involving these four markers are reported in Table II. They confirm the results of the experiments reported in Table I and show that the order of markers is $\underline{z} \ \underline{o}..\underline{i}....\underline{Pro}_2$.

The operator being identified by dominant constitutive $\underline{o}^c$ mutations active only in position $\underline{cis}$ is thus defined as controlling the sensitivity to the repressor determined by the $\underline{i}$ gene. Originally, in the same area as $\underline{o}^c$ mutations, other mutations ($\underline{o}^\circ$) were localized, which result in the nonfunctioning of the whole operon. Since these $\underline{o}^\circ$ mutations belong to the structural gene $\underline{z}$, it was thought that $\underline{o}^c$ mutations also belonged to $\underline{z}$. The close proximity of $\underline{o}^\circ$ and $\underline{o}^c$ mutations favored this hypothesis and the terminal part of the $\underline{z}$ structural gene was thus thought to be endowed with three properties : to control the sensitivity to the repressor (as defined by $\underline{o}^c$ mutations), to constitute the obligatory segment in which the synthesis of the $\underline{Lac}$ messenger could be initiated (because of $\underline{o}^\circ$ mutations) as well as to code for β-galactosidase structure.

TABLE II

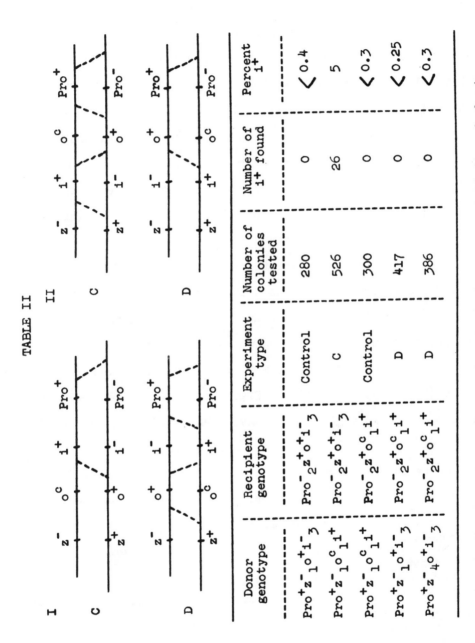

Donor genotype	Recipient genotype	Experiment type	Number of colonies tested	Number of 1^+ found	Percent 1^+
$Pro^+z_1^-o^+1_3^-$	$Pro^-_2z^+o^+1_3^-$	Control	280	0	<0.4
$Pro^+z_1^-o^c1_1^+$	$Pro^-_2z^+o^+1_3^-$	C	526	26	5
$Pro^+z_1^-o^c1_1^+$	$Pro^-_2z^+o^c1_1^+$	Control	300	0	<0.3
$Pro^+z_1^-o^+1_3^-$	$Pro^-_2z^+o^c1_1^+$	D	417	0	<0.25
$Pro^+z_4^-o^+1_3^-$	$Pro^-_2z^+o^c1_1^+$	D	386	0	<0.3

Recipient bacteria were infected with an average multiplicity of about 3 phages grown on donor bacteria. Colonies of recombinants were then reisolated and assayed for genotype as in Table I.

Recent results have led to a partial revision of this interpretation. First, other mutations localized all over the z gene have been found to result not only in the inactivation of β-galactosidase but also in a large decrease (50 to 95 per cent) of the other proteins of the operon (Jacob and Monod, 1961 b ; Franklin and Luria, 1961). The properties of these so-called "polar" mutations are therefore similar to those of $o°$ mutations without being located in the initial segment of the z gene. Furthermore, it has been found by Beckwith (1964 a) that many of the $o°$ mutants are susceptible to the action of external suppressors which are considered to act at the level, not of transcription, but of translation.

Further work with deletions has established that the operator, defined as the locus controlling the sensitivity to the i repressor is not located in the z gene. On the one hand deletions within z, including the known loci ($o°$) in the operator proximal segment, do not alter the regulation of the operon (Beckwith, 1964 b) (see Fig. 1). On the other hand, a large number of $o^c z^+ y^+$ mutants have been isolated all of which appear to result from deletions : such o^c mutations cannot be induced by base analogs ; they are never due to external suppressors ; no o^c — o^+ reversion has been detected as yet ; in a certain fraction (10 to 15 per cent), the mutation affects both o and i. Yet in all cases so far studied, the β-galactosidase produced by such o^c mutants seems indistinguishable from that produced by the wild type, as judged by inactivation kinetics at various temperatures and pH, in the presence or absence of Mg^{++} and substrate (Jacob, Ullman and Monod, 1964). One must therefore conclude that o is distinct from z.

It seems now that polycistronic operons, such as the
Lac operon are transcribed into a single messenger (Ames and
Hartman, 1963 ; Attardi et al., 1963 ; Beckwith, 1964 a ;
Guttman and Novick, 1963 ; Martin, 1963 ; Spiegelman and
Hayashi, 1963). The properties of polar mutants suggest that
the direction of the translation(s) from messenger into peptides is from the operator side. The direction of transcription from DNA into messenger remains however unknown. In
any case there must exist on the operator side, a "punctuation" determining the beginning of the structural segment of
the Lac operon. Deletions of the operator-proximal segment
of z do not alter the promotion of expression, nor the regulation of the operon. Deletions in o decrease or abolish the
susceptibility to the repressor but they do not alter the
expression of the operon. In both cases, the expression of
the intact structural genes is still 100 per cent of that in
the wild type.

However, more than 80 deletions have been isolated
which cover both o and a part of z. On the z side, these
deletions may extend to various sites into z. On the o side,
all deletions extend further than i (see Fig. 1). In nine
cases, out of ten which have been analyzed, the production of
β-galactoside permease and of acetylase was found to be 10
per cent that of the wild type ; in the last case, it was 40
per cent ; but in all cases, this production is the same in
the presence or absence of β-galactosides (Jacob, Ullman and
Monod, 1964).

It seems then that when a deletion covers both o and
the extremity of z, the expression of the operon is possible
only if the deletion extends further than i. This situation
is somewhat similar to that found for the histidine operon of

Salmonella typhimurium (Ames, Hartman and Jacob, 1963). The
class of deletions covering o and the extremity of z, but not
i, must therefore completely abolish the expression of the
operon, except if the deletion extends far enough so that the
intact part of the Lac operon is fused with another operon.
This involves the existence, in between o and z, of an element
necessary for promoting the expression of the operon, or
promotor (p), the order of the Lac region being then
Pro_1....y a p o..i....Pro_2.

Since o^c mutations are not induced by base analogs,
nor by external suppressors, the operator region appears not
to be translated into peptide chain, but it cannot be concluded
from these results whether it is transcribed or not. If
messenger synthesis starts on the o side of the operon, it is
likely to start in the promotor which would then correspond
to a punctuation for the DNA-RNA polymerase. The operator
would then not be transcribed and the repressor would act on
DNA to prevent transcription. If messenger synthesis starts
on the opposite side of the operon, then the operator might
or not be transcribed, and the repressor would act on DNA or
on messenger to prevent the release of messenger. The promotor would then constitute a punctuation for ribosomes. The
first of these models appears a priori more likely in view
of the fact that the expression of the whole operon can be
modified by mutational events on the operator side but not
on the other. A definite answer will be obtained only when
the direction of messenger synthesis will be known.

ACKNOWLEDGEMENTS

The authors want to thank Dr. N.M. Schwartz for a

culture of a Pro_2^- mutant. This work was aided by grants
from the National Science Foundation, the National Institute
of Health, the Commissariat à l'Energie Atomique and the
Délégation Générale a la Recherche Scientifique et Technique.

REFERENCES

Ames, B.N. and Hartman, P. (1963) Cold Spring Harbor Symp.
     Quant.Biol., 28, 349.
Ames, B.N., Hartman, P.E. and Jacob, F. (1963) J.Mol.Biol.,
     7, 23.
Attardi, G., Naono, S., Rouvière, J., Jacob, F. and Gros, F.
     (1963) Cold Spring Harbor Symp.Quant.Biol., 28, 363.
Beckwith, J.R. (1964 a) In "Structure and Function of the
     genetic Material", Abhandlungen der Deutschen Akademie
     der Wissenschaften zu Berlin, 4, 119-124.
Beckwith, J.R. (1964 b) J.Mol.Biol., 8, 427.
Franklin, N.C. and Luria, S.E. (1961) Virology, 15, 299.
Guttman, B. and Novick, A. (1963) Cold Spring Harbor Symp.
     Quant.Biol., 28, 373.
Jacob, F. and Monod, J. (1961 a) J.Mol.Biol., 3, 318.
Jacob, F. and Monod, J. (1961 b) Cold Spring Harbor Symp.
     Quant.Biol., 26, 193.
Jacob, F., Ullman, A. and Monod, J. (1964) C.R.Acad.Sci.,
     258, 3125.
Martin, R.G. (1963) Cold Spring Harbor Symp.Quant.Biol.,
     28, 357.
Schwartz, N.M. (1963) Genetics, 48, 1357.
Spiegelman, S. and Hayashi, M. (1963) Cold Spring Harbor
     Symp.Quant.Biol., 28, 161.

J. Mol. Biol. (1965) **12**, 305–327

The Properties of Repressor and the Kinetics of its Action

John R. Sadler† and Aaron Novick

Institute of Molecular Biology, University of Oregon, Eugene, Oregon, U.S.A.

(*Received 9 December 1964*)

By experiments with mutants having temperature-sensitive repression systems for the *Lac* operon, it has been possible to provide evidence indicating that:

    (a) the *i*-gene product is the repressor, or physically included in it;

    (b) the rate of enzyme synthesis varies inversely with the first power of repressor concentration;

    (c) the repressor is "growth unstable" with a mean life of 1/5 to 1/10 generation;

    (d) inducers cause structural changes in repressor, manifested by altered thermal stability;

    (e) and the repressor is composed of subunits, which have a site for combination with inducers.

1. Introduction

The regulation of the synthesis of specific enzymes is believed to be mediated through the action of specific cytoplasmic substances, termed repressors, which act to damp the flow of information from structural gene to protein (Jacob & Monod, 1961). The repressor hypothesis as proposed by Jacob & Monod has been remarkably successful in accounting for the phenomena of inducible as well as repressible enzyme systems, and it has provided a productive framework for further experimentation. Nevertheless, doubt concerning its validity has originated in part from the paucity of direct experimental evidence concerning the repressor (Stent, 1964) and in part from observations on certain systems that apparently require a more complex explanation (Garen & Echols, 1962; Engelsberg, Irr & Power, 1964).

    In the present work, we have been able to test some of the aspects of the repressor hypothesis and explore some of the properties of repressor through studies on the regulation of the synthesis of β-galactosidase in *Escherichia coli*. Here the evidence indicates that regulation of the "lactose" enzymes is mediated through a single species of macromolecule specified by the *i*-gene (Jacob & Monod, 1961; Willson, Perrin, Cohn, Jacob & Monod, 1964). The induction of β-galactosidase synthesis by certain galactosides, the inducers, shows a specificity only otherwise found in enzymes (Jacob & Monod, 1961; Willson *et al.*, 1964). Further, there is a mutation in the *i*-gene that leads to temperature-sensitive regulation of β-galactosidase synthesis (Horiuchi & Novick, 1961,1965), which is attributable to the presence of a thermo-labile repressor and, therefore, an indication that the repressor is a macromolecule.

† Present address: Department of Biophysics, University of Colorado Medical School, Denver, Col., U.S.A.

It was originally proposed that the repressor acts at the level of transcription of DNA into messenger RNA (Jacob & Monod, 1961). In agreement with this view, it has been found that the level of the *Lac*-specific m-RNA† changes upon induction (Hayashi, Spiegelman, Franklin & Luria, 1963; Attardi, Naono, Rouviere, Jacob & Gros, 1963; Guttman & Novick, 1963). However, the possibility remains that the primary site of action of repressor is elsewhere, the changes in messenger level being secondary consequences of this action.

Likewise, it is unknown whether the *i*-gene product acts *directly* upon some site on the DNA or m-RNA or *indirectly*, for example, through the production of yet another cytoplasmic constituent which in turn is the repressing agent. Also, earlier experiments could not distinguish whether the repressor turns over rapidly or whether it is stable, with the latter possibility requiring that rate of enzyme synthesis vary as a high power of level of repressor (Novick, Lennox & Jacob, 1963; Gallant & Stapleton, 1963).

In the present studies we have attempted to clarify some of these problems by using *i*-gene mutants exhibiting temperature-sensitive control of β-galactosidase synthesis to seek answers to the following questions.

(I) Is the *i*-product the repressor, rather than an enzyme needed for repressor synthesis?

(II) Does the differential rate of β-galactosidase synthesis vary inversely with the first power of level of repressor (R), or is the relationship of some higher order?

(III) Is the repressor a stable molecule?

(IV) Do inducers exert their effect directly upon the repressor, and are there alterations of the structure of repressor produced by inducer, as one might expect?

(V) What additional properties must the repressor have to account for the present results?

In this analysis, we make the assumption that repressor is a substance the effect of which is determined by its concentration in a bacterium. Further, we assume that the number of repressor molecules per cell is not usually so small as to produce significant heterogeneity in the bacterial population, an assumption which has been verified experimentally (Lennox, Novick & Jacob, 1963).

2. Materials and Methods

Nomenclature

The term "temperature-sensitive" is applied to those mutant strains in which the regulation of β-galactosidase synthesis is defective at high growth temperatures but nearly normal at low temperatures. The term "thermolabile", abbreviated TL, is reserved to those strains which produce a heat-sensitive repressor for the *Lac* operon, while the phrase "temperature-sensitive synthesis" (TSS) is applied to those mutants in which synthesis of the specific *Lac* repressor, but not the repressor itself, is heat-sensitive.

Organisms. All experiments described were done with strains of *E. coli* K12 the properties of which are presented in Table 1. The original temperature-sensitive mutants are E103, E303 and E321. The derivation and properties of these are as follow.

(1) For E103: $i^+ \rightarrow i^- \rightarrow i^{TL}$. Isolated as an inducible "revertant" of a full constitutive E106 (Horiuchi & Novick, 1961,1965), this allele is the result of at least two lesions in the *i* region. Its most distinctive property is the fact that repression of β-galactosidase synthesis can be destroyed by heating under conditions where growth is not possible,

† Abbreviations used: m-RNA, messenger RNA; TL, thermolabile; TSS, temperature-sensitive synthesis; IPTG, isopropylthiogalactoside.

TABLE 1

Characteristics and origins of bacterial strains

Strain	Lac	Chromosomal			Episomal			Pro	B_1	Met	Arg	Hist	Sm	Sex	Induced	Uninduced	Origin
		i	z	y	i	z	y										
E103	+	+TL	+	+				+	+	−	+	+	S	Hfr	1·4	0·050	Horiuchi et al., 1962
E103a	−	+TL	+	−				+	+	−	+	+	S	Hfr	1·4	0·050	E103
E322	−	+TL	+	−				+	+	−	+	+	S	F^-	1·3	0·035	E103
E325	−	+TL	+	−	+TL	+	−	+	+	−	+	+	S	F_{lac}	2·7	0·023	E322 and E307
E303	−	s,TSS	+	+				+	−	+	−	−	S	F^-	0·024	0·030	Novick et al., 1963
E304	−	s,TSS	+	−				+	−	+	−	−	R	F^-	0·024	0·030	E303
E310	−	s,TSS	+	−	s,TSS	+	+	+	−	+	−	−	R	F_{lac}	0·003	0·004	E304 and E305
E305	−	+	+	+	s,TSS	+	+	+	−	+	−	−	S	F_{lac}	0·03	0·003	F. Jacob
W14	−	+	+	−				−	−	+	+	+	R	F^-	0·40	0·00047	Tomizawa, 1960
W14D	−	+	+	−	+	+	−	−	−	+	+	+	R	F_{lac}	0·85	0·00048	W14 and E307
E321	−	+TSS	+	−				−	−	+	+	+	R	F^-	0·50	0·020	W14
E323	−	+TSS	+	−	+TSS	+	+	−	−	+	+	+	R	F_{lac}	1·0	0·0015	E321 and E307
W3747	+	+	+	+	+	+	+	+	+	−	+	+	S	F_{lac}	1·8	0·001	S. E. Luria
E307	+	+	+	+	+	+	+	+	−	+	−	−	S	F_{lac}	2·0	0·0005	F. Jacob

The column Lac refers to the ability to grow on lactose as sole carbon source at 37°C. i, z, y refer to the genotypes at these loci on the chromosome, and where present, on the modified sex factor F-Lac. Pro, B_1, Met, Arg and Hist refer to the ability to synthesize proline, thiamin, methionine, arginine or histidine. Sm refers to sensitivity (S) or resistance (R) to streptomycin. Sex indicates mating type. Induced and Uninduced indicate the steady-state specific activity of β-galactosidase during growth at 37°C in the presence or absence of 10^{-3} M-IPTG. Origin notes the source or derivation of each strain.

the degree of de-repression obtained being a function of the time and temperature of heating. Under optimal conditions, de-repression is equivalent to optimal induction with IPTG.

(2) For E303: $i^+ \rightarrow i^s \rightarrow i^{s.TSS}$. Isolated as a *Lac*$^+$ revertant of an i^s strain at 42°C (Willson *et al.*, 1964), this allele is also the result of at least two mutations in the i-gene. It retains the i^s character at all temperatures of growth, in that no augmentation in the rate of β-galactosidase synthesis over that produced by thermal de-repression is produced by the addition of IPTG. This allele differs from that in E103, since heating in the absence of growth has *no effect* on repression of β-galactosidase synthesis. All tests devised to demonstrate thermolability of repressor in this type have been negative. Instead, a number of observations indicate that some precursor of the finished repressor is heat-sensitive.

(3) For E321: $i^+ \rightarrow i^{TSS}$. Its properties are strikingly similar to those of E303, if not indistinguishable (see Figs 1 and 5), with the exception that E321 is inducible by IPTG.

The steady-state differential rates of β-galactosidase synthesis in the presence or absence of 10^{-3} M-IPTG at various growth temperatures are shown for strains E103, E304, and E321 in Fig. 1.

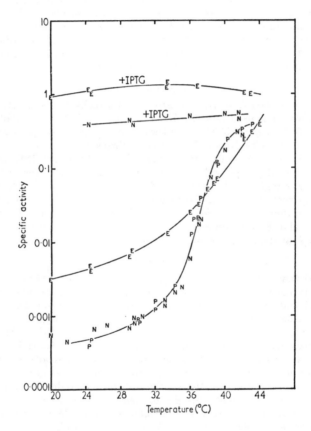

FIG. 1. Steady-state specific activities of β-galactosidase in the presence or absence of 10^{-3} M-IPTG in the strains E103 (i^{TL}), E304 ($i^{s.TSS}$) and E321 (i^{TSS}) during growth at various temperatures.

The letters E, P and N refer to the strains carrying the i-gene alleles i^{TL}, $i^{s.TSS}$ and i^{TSS}, respectively. Each point is the average of duplicate assays. The organisms were grown at the specified temperature for at least 10 doublings prior to sampling for assay. The medium in all cases was F buffer + 0·2% glycerol, supplemented with L-methionine (20 μg/ml.) in the case of E103; L-proline (50 μg/ml.) and thiamin (10 μg/ml.) in the case of E321; and L-histidine (20 μg/ml.), L-arginine (20 μg/ml.) and thiamin (10 μg/ml.) in the case of E304.

Media

Except where noted, all experiments were performed on cells growing in a liquid medium consisting of $M/30$ potassium phosphate buffer (pH 7), $M/50$ ammonium chloride, 10^{-3} $M\text{-}MgSO_4$ plus 0.2% (v/v) glycerol (F buffer plus glycerol) supplemented where necessary with amino acids or vitamins. Matings were performed in Difco Pennassay broth. The phage f_2 was propagated on cells growing in LB broth (Luria, Adams & Ting, 1960). Among the solid media used were Difco triphenyl-tetrazolium chloride–Tryptone broth–sugar (TTC), eosin–methylene blue–broth–sugar agar (EMB), and Davis minimal agar; these have been described earlier (Horiuchi, Tomizawa & Novick, 1962). When bacteria were grown in the chemostat, either nitrogen or carbon was used as the limiting nutrient, and the basic F–glycerol medium was modified accordingly. Thus, the concentration of NH_4Cl in the reservoir was reduced to 15 mg/l. to give a steady-state population of about 7×10^7 cells/ml. in the chemostat growth tube. Similarly, glycerol at 90 mg/l. supported a population of 9×10^7 cells/ml. in the chemostat.

Mutagenesis

The mutagen N-methyl-N^1-nitro-N-nitroso-guanidine (nitroso-guanidine), from the Aldrich Chemical Co., 2639 N. 29th Street, Milwaukee 10, Wisc., was used in the preparation of mutants such as E103a and E321. The parent organism was suspended at a density of 1 to 3×10^9 cells/ml. in sterile 0.1 M-phosphate buffer, pH 6.3, containing freshly dissolved nitrosoguanidine at a final concentration of 5 to 10 $\mu g/ml$. The suspension of cells was incubated at 37°C for 3 to 5 hr, washed, resuspended in sterile diluent and plated. From 10 to 70% of the cells normally survived this treatment.

Selection of E322

The phage f_2 (obtained from N. Groman), which attacks only male strains of *E. coli* K12 (Zinder, 1961), was used to select E322 (F^-) from E103a (Hfr). E103a growing in LB broth at 5×10^8 cells/ml. (37°C) was infected with f_2 previously propagated on E103a at a multiplicity of 20. After lysis and overgrowth of resistant variants (12 hr of incubation subsequent to infection), the culture was streaked out, incubated at 37°C, and 10 resistant clones picked, freed of phage, and tested for their mating type. None of the 10 clones transferred the *Lac* region with measurable frequency to a standard F^- strain ($E64N_3$), but in a mating with a standard *F-Lac* genote (E320) only 2 behaved as normal F^- recipients. One of these was reserved and given the designation E322. Except for mating type, it is identical to E103a with respect to all properties tested (nutritional requirements and the genotype at the loci i, z and y).

Selection of E321

It was noted that the EMB–lactose agar reaction of many $i^+z^+y^-$ strains changes from translucent purple to opaque white when IPTG (10^{-3} M) is included in the medium. It was reasoned that constitutive variants of these z^+y^- strains would give opaque white colonies in the absence of IPTG and could thus be easily distinguished from both the parental type $i^+z^+y^-$ and permease-positive revertants ($i^+z^+y^+$). This method was tested on nitrosoguanidine-treated cultures of Wl4 and E312. Some 12,000 viable cells from each strain were plated on EMB–lactose agar plates (about 300 per plate) and incubated for 18 hr at 42°C. A total of 88 opaque white colonies or sectors were picked, purified, and tested for the constitutive synthesis of β-galactosidase at 30 and 42°C. Of the 88 clones, 26 were found to synthesize β-galactosidase constitutively at 42°C and one of these, termed E321, derived from Wl4, exhibited a 500-fold increase in the rate of synthesis between 30 and 42°C.

The assumption that the mutation in E321 lies in the i-gene is based on the following observations.

(1) There is a close similarity in thermal properties to E303, in which the mutation is believed to lie in the i-gene (Willson *et al.*, 1964).

(2) The i^{TSS} allele is recessive to the i^+ allele, i.e., *F-Lac* heterogenotes carrying i^{TSS} and i^+ are not constitutive at high growth temperatures. Further, i^{TSS}/i^- as well as $i^{s.TSS}/i^-$ diploids show the TSS phenotype; and i^{TSS}/i^{TL} as well as $i^{s.TSS}/i^{TL}$ diploids are de-repressed at high temperatures.

Preparation of F-Lac homogenotes

Cultures of *F-Lac* heterogenotes of genotype z^+y^-/Fz^+y^+ or z^-y^+/Fz^+y^+ normally contain 0·1 to 1·0% *Lac⁻* recombinant segregants. The great majority of these prove to be *F-Lac* homogenotes of genotype z^+y^-/Fz^+y^- and z^-y^+/Fz^-y^+, respectively. The close linkage of the *i* to *z* and *y* suggests that the great majority of such *F-Lac* homogenotes would be homodiploid for the *i*-character from the chromosome alone, and this indeed proved to be the case among *Lac⁻* recombinants isolated from the *F-Lac* heterogenote $i^{s,TSS}z^+y^-/Fi^+z^+y^+$. This finding was used as the basis for the isolation of *F-Lac* homogenotes from the F⁻ strains E322, E304, E321, Wl4 and E312. The resultant *F-Lac* homogenotes were tested for the character of *i*, *z* and *y* by mating with appropriate F⁻ recipients and by examination of the recombinant types obtained, and also by physiological testing to ascertain both the number of *z* genes and the thermal properties of the regulation of β-galactosidase synthesis.

Culture methods

The concentration of bacteria was determined in a spectrophotometer at 350 mμ. Comparison of absorbancy measurements with plate counts and dry-weight determinations established that an absorbancy of 0·100 corresponded to 3×10^7 cells/ml. or to 10 μg dry weight of cells/ml. for bacteria growing in F–glycerol medium. Steady-state levels of β-galactosidase were measured only after the bacteria had grown at the stated temperature ($\pm$ 0·1°C) in F–glycerol medium for at least 10 doublings. In temperature shifts involving batch cultures or chemostats, temperatures reached very nearly their ultimate values within 3 to 4 min.

Transfer of cells to new media

The rapid transfer of cells from a growth medium or buffer to a new growth medium was accomplished through the use of 45-mm membrane filters (0·45 μ pore diameter). The total time required was 2 to 5 min; from 1 to 3×10^9 cells per filter was the optimum number both for rapid filtration and good recovery. Cells were washed on the filter 5 to 7 times by the addition of 100-ml. portions of F–buffer at the appropriate temperature and then resuspended in the new medium previously equilibrated at the proper temperature. To remove suspended material that might interfere with subsequent absorbance measurements, the wash buffer and the new medium were themselves filtered prior to use. To obtain immediate exponential growth of the filtered, resuspended cells, it was found necessary to use a medium preconditioned by growth of the same organism to about 2×10^8 cells/ml. This medium was filtered free of cells, supplemented where necessary with additional amounts of glycerol and amino acids and stored at 4°C until use. Where it was important that all operations be carried out at high temperatures, the procedure was carried out in a warm room at 38 to 40°C with glassware and media equilibrated at that temperature.

Enzyme assays

β-Galactosidase was determined in toluene-treated 1·0-ml. portions of bacterial cultures, as previously described (Horiuchi *et al.*, 1962). Color change was measured in a total volume of 4 ml., using a cuvette of 1-cm light path, and enzyme activities are given in Δo.d.$_{420} \times 1000$/min. Division by the bacterial density, taken as o.d.$_{350} \times 1000$, gives the specific activity; this is a convenient scale, since wild-type strains give fully induced activities near unity.

The galactoside permease was assayed through measurement of the extent of intracellular accumulation of β-methyl-^{14}C-thiogalactoside by non-growing metabolizing cells (Kepes, 1960).

3. Results

I. *Evidence that the* i-*product is the repressor*

The repressor postulated by Jacob & Monod (1961) is a single molecular species with two functional sites, one which interacts with inducer and one which affects the operator, the point in protein synthesis where repression is established. The existence of mutant i-genes having altered specificity toward inducers indicates that the i-product does interact with inducer (Willson *et al.*, 1964). In the present work, evidence has been found indicating that the i-product is also the agent directly responsible for repression; and in this sense it can be concluded that the i-product, having both functions, is the repressor as postulated.

Evidence pointing to the i-product as the repressing substance was obtained by observing the effect on rate of β-galactosidase synthesis of abrupt removal of the i-product. Such removal was achieved by a brief heating of a growing culture of a bacterial strain having an i^{TL} allele. As can be seen in Fig. 2, enzyme synthesis reaches

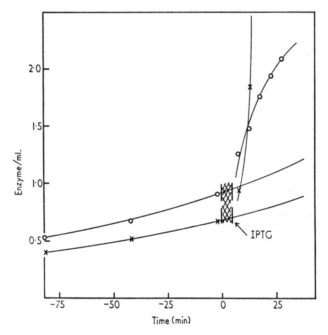

FIG. 2. Demonstration that de-repression is immediate following removal of the i-gene product by thermal inactivation.

Parallel cultures of E103 in minimal medium growing at 25°C were heated at 44°C for 7 min, starting at $t = 0$, indicated by the cross-hatched area, and then returned to 25°C for further growth. To one ($-\times-\times-$), IPTG was added to a final concentration of 5×10^{-4} M at $= 7$ min, while the other received no IPTG ($-\bigcirc-\bigcirc-$).

its maximum rate in a very short time following heating, a time not longer than that observed in a comparison culture de-repressed by the addition of IPTG. The immediate effect of i-product removal must mean that the i-product is the repressing agent (or an essential component). Were the i-product an enzyme involved in repressor formation, one would have to make the additional assumption that the repressor turns over very rapidly, with a lifetime of less than a minute.

II. *Dependence of rate of synthesis of enzyme on concentration of repressor*

Earlier studies sought to determine the relationship between the rate of synthesis of β-galactosidase and the relative level of repressor by observing the rising rate of synthesis that occurs when repressor formation is arrested by the transfer of an

$i^{\mathrm{s,TSS}}$ culture from low to high growth temperature (Novick et al., 1963). Here de-repression occurs relatively rapidly, and it was not possible from such experiments alone to distinguish between two possibilities:

(1) that the repressor is stable and repression varies as a high power of repressor level; or

(2) that the repressor is unstable with a mean life of about 1/10 to 1/5 of a generation, and the dependence of the rate of enzyme synthesis is inverse with the first power of repressor concentration, as originally suggested in the case of similar experiments with alkaline phosphatase mutants (Gallant & Stapleton, 1963).

In order to distinguish between these two possibilities, an independent means for varying the level of repressor was developed here. This method is based on the assumption that a relative increase in number of i-genes in a bacterium gives a corresponding increase in repressor. For example, in an F-genote of type $i^+z^+y^-/Fi^+z^+y^-$, the level of β-galactosidase upon full induction in the F-genote is about 2·5 times that of the haploid i^+z^+. The F-genote is presumably diploid for the Lac genes, and the ratio being larger than two is attributed to the non-synchronous division of the chromosomal and episomal Lac genes (Jacob, personal communication). A similar gene dosage effect should exist for the i-gene, unless its expression is dependent on the level of repressor, this being rendered improbable in another study (Novick, McCoy & Sadler, 1965). Thus the repressor level in the F-genote, i^+/Fi^+, should be 2·5 times that in the haploid, i^+. Likewise it is reasonable to assume a similar ratio for i^{TL} and $i^{\mathrm{TL}}/Fi^{\mathrm{TL}}$, since the fraction of repressor thermally inactivated at any temperature should be independent of the concentration of repressor. It is not clear, however, whether the levels of repressor would be proportional to gene dosage for i^{TSS} and $i^{\mathrm{s,TSS}}$ alleles, where the rate of formation of repressor is temperature-dependent. The most plausible explanation for temperature-sensitive synthesis is the existence of a heat-labile precursor of the repressor in these mutants. Were the precursor a monomer which must be polymerized, it is evident that the level of repressor in the diploid could be much greater than 2·5 times that in the haploid. (It should be noted that the formation of recombinant segregants which prevent such analysis with heterogenotes of type i^+/i^-, for example, is no cause for concern with the homogenotes used here.)

To see the effect of such a change in repressor level, one must make comparisons where the rate of enzyme production, dz/dB, is a function of repressor level (R), e.g. for temperature mutants at intermediate temperatures. The relative rates to be expected are shown in Table 2, where comparisons are made on the alternative hypotheses that the relationship is inverse with the first power of repressor ($n = 1$) or that it is inverse with a high power of repressor. For simplicity, the comparison is made at low rates of synthesis where the indicated approximation can be made. It is assumed as argued above that the concentration of repressor in the "diploid" is 2·5 times that in the haploid.

It should be noted that there is a sharp difference in the expectations of the two hypotheses. For $n = 1$, the ratio of specific activities for haploid/diploid is one, whereas for $n = 5$ it is close to 40.

This test was first applied to strains bearing the i^{TL} allele, and the rates of synthesis of β-galactosidase observed for the haploid i^{TL} and the diploid $i^{\mathrm{TL}}/Fi^{\mathrm{TL}}$ as a function of temperature are shown in Fig. 3. It is evident that the haploid/diploid ratio is at most 1·5, indicating that n cannot be more than 2 (for which the ratio would be 2·5)

TABLE 2

Hypothesis	Expected rate of synthesis		Ratio of rates
	Haploid	Diploid	Haploid/Diploid
$\dfrac{dz}{dB} = \dfrac{K}{K+R} \sim \dfrac{K}{R}$	$\dfrac{K}{R_h}$	$2\cdot5\,\dfrac{K}{2\cdot5R_h}$	1
$\dfrac{dz}{dB} = \dfrac{K}{K+R^n} \sim \dfrac{K}{R^n}$	$\dfrac{K}{R_h^n}$	$2\cdot5\,\dfrac{K}{(2\cdot5R_h)^n}$	$2\cdot5^{n-1}$

$\dfrac{dz}{dB}$ = rate of enzyme synthesis per cell = specific activity in steady state.

R_h = repressor level in haploid.

K = constant.

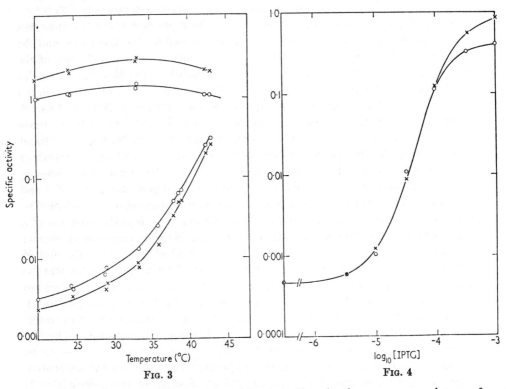

FIG. 3

FIG. 4

FIG. 3. Steady-state specific activities of β-galactosidase in the presence or absence of 10^{-3} M-IPTG at various growth temperatures for the strains E322 and E325.

Parallel cultures of E322 ($i^{TL}z^+y^-$) and E325 ($i^{TL}z^+y^-/Fi^{TL}z^+y^-$) were grown at the specified temperature for at least 10 doublings prior to sampling for assay. The minimal medium used was the same as that specified for E103 in Fig. 1. The upper curves were obtained in the presence of 10^{-3} M-IPTG. Each point for E322 (—O—O—) and E325 (—×—×—) is the average of duplicate assays.

FIG. 4. Steady-state specific activities of β-galactosidase for W14 and W14D growing at 37°C in the presence of various concentrations of IPTG.

W14 ($i^+z^+y^-$) and the derivative F-Lac homogenote W14D ($i^+z^+y^-/Fi^+z^+y^-$) were grown in the specified concentration of IPTG for at least 10 doublings prior to sampling for assay. The medium used was the same as that specified for E321 in Fig. 1. Each point for haploid (—O—O—) and F-Lac homogenote (—×—×—) is the average of duplicate assays on each of three independent cultures.

and is most probably 1. The slight departure from unity in the ratio would result if the relative rates of formation of repressor were even very slightly dependent on gene dose, as was considered above for the i^{TSS} alleles.

A similar result was obtained in a comparison of $i^+z^+y^-$ haploid (Wl4) with an $i^+z^+y^-/Fi^+z^+y^-$ diploid (Wl4D) (see Fig. 4). Here the comparison is made at a series of concentrations of inducer, making the assumption that inducer causes an effective reduction in concentration of repressor, a reduction which is independent of level of repressor. Several other independent pairs of $i^+z^+y^-$ haploids and derivative homogenotes were tested with identical results.

A like comparison (rate of enzyme synthesis *versus* IPTG concentration) was made for $i^{TL}z^+y^-$ *versus* $i^{TL}z^+y^-/Fi^{TL}z^+y^-$ at low growth temperatures (about 20°C), where repression is very nearly normal, with substantially the same results as those shown in Fig. 4.

Further evidence in support of the conclusion that dz/dB varies as $1/R$ comes from experiments (described in section IV of Results) in which it was found that small amounts of repressor produce a sharp reduction in dz/dB in cells initially lacking repressor. Such a reduction would not be expected if there were a high power dependence.

(III) *The "growth-instability" of repressor*

As noted earlier, the first evidence suggesting that repressor is unstable was the unexpected rapid rise in the rate of enzyme synthesis following arrest of repressor formation in i^{TSS} mutants. An illustration of such a rise is given in Fig. 5, where repressor synthesis was stopped in both $i^{s.TSS}$ and i^{TSS} strains by a shift in growth temperature from 30 to 41·5°C. The possibility that there is a thermal inactivation of repressor is discounted by the observation that an i^{TSS} mutant, grown at 30°C and then heated at 42°C for two hours in the absence of growth (no carbon source), showed no appreciable de-repression upon further growth at 30°C. Further demonstration that thermolability plays no significant part in the repressor instability of i^{TSS} mutants is given in Fig. 6. Here are shown the results of temperature shifts (30 to 41·5°C) of an $i^{s.TSS}$ mutant growing glycerol-limited at a number of widely different rates in the chemostat. Were the repressor appreciably thermolabile, de-repression would be relatively much more rapid in cultures growing slowly (15-hour generation time) than in those growing with a generation time of two to four hours. Moreover, the rate of de-repression following the shift to growth at high temperature is independent of the value of the higher temperature (Novick et al., 1963). Evidently the rate of de-repression is related to the amount of growth at the higher temperature.

The finding in the haploid–diploid comparisons that the rate of enzyme synthesis varies inversely with the first power of concentration of repressor forces one to conclude that, in the temperature-shift experiments, repressor does indeed disappear faster than can be accounted for by dilution alone. Thus repressor seems to be "growth-unstable" with a mean life of 1/10 to 1/5 of a generation.

It can be shown that the instability of repressor is a normal phenomenon and not simply a consequence of the temperature shifts. As will be described in section IV, the production of repressor by i^{TSS} and $i^{s.TSS}$ strains is stabilized by the presence of inducer, full repressor levels appearing even at 42°C in i^{TSS} strains growing in the presence of 10^{-3}M-IPTG. Here repressor synthesis can be arrested by removal of inducer with no change in temperature, as shown in Fig. 7. It can be seen that when inducer is suddenly removed from an i^{TSS} culture grown with inducer for many

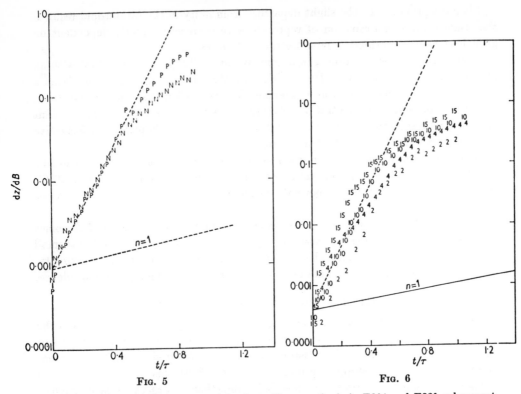

FIG. 5. Kinetics of de-repression of β-galactosidase synthesis in E304 and E321 subsequent to a shift in growth temperature from 30 to 41·5°C.

Cultures of E304 ($i^{s.TSS}z^+y^-$) and E321 ($i^{TSS}z^+y^-$) which had grown for approximately 15 generations glycerol-limited in chemostats (generation times of 5 hr) at 30°C were shifted to 41·5°C at zero time. At zero time and every 10 min thereafter, samples were removed for duplicate β-galactosidase assays and turbidity determinations, taking care not to exceed the over-flow rate.

The rate of synthesis, dz/dB, was calculated as $\Delta z/\Delta B$, the ratio of the increment in β-galacto-sidase to the increment in bacterial density between adjacent measurements. The abscissa t/τ gives bacterial growth in generations subsequent to the temperature shift. The dotted line labeled $n = 1$ gives the expected rise in dz/dB on the assumption of a stable repressor (an e-fold decrease in repressor level for each generation of growth). The letters N and P refer respectively to E321 and E304.

FIG. 6. Kinetics of de-repression of β-galactosidase synthesis in E304 growing at various generation times subsequent to a shift in growth temperature from 30 to 41·5°C.

The numbers given in the Figure, "15", "10", "4" and "2" refer to the generation times (in hr) of the respective cultures. Those cultures with generation times of 15, 10 and 4 hr were growing glycerol-limited in chemostats, whereas that with a generation time of 2 hr was a batch culture. In the chemostat experiments, conditions were the same as those given for Fig. 5. Rate of synthesis, dz/dB, was calculated as in Fig. 5. The abscissa t/τ gives bacterial growth in generations subsequent to the temperature shift. The dotted line labeled $n = 1$ gives the expected rise in dz/dB on the assumption of a stable repressor.

generations at a high temperature, enzyme synthesis stops completely; but upon continued growth at the same temperature, de-repression occurs at a rate identical to that found in a parallel culture subjected to the temperature-shift 30 to 41·5°C. The growth instability of repressor is revealed, therefore, whether de-repression is provoked by a temperature shift or by the removal of inducer.

Moreover, the growth-instability does not seem to be unique to the repressor of i^{TSS} mutants growing at high temperatures. One piece of evidence supporting the

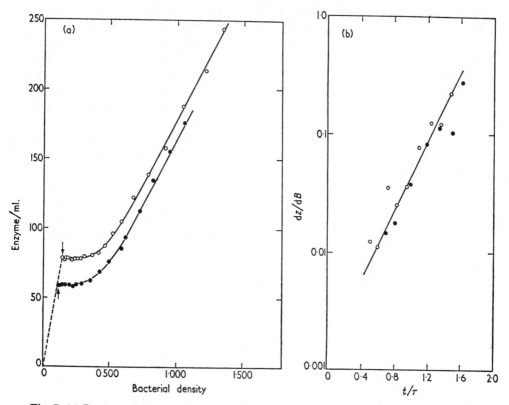

Fig. 7. (a) De-repression of β-galactosidase synthesis in E321 subsequent to removal of IPTG at 41°C or to a shift in growth temperature from 30 to 41°C. Parallel cultures of E321 ($i^{TSS}z^+y^-$), which had grown for 12 doublings at either 30°C (—●—●—) or 41°C (—○—○—) in the presence of 10^{-3} M-IPTG were filtered (at the arrows), washed and resuspended in preconditioned medium lacking IPTG at 41°C (see Materials and Methods).

(b) Kinetics of de-repression in E321 subsequent to removal of IPTG at 41°C or to a shift in growth temperature from 30 to 41°C. As in (a), (—●—●—) refers to the culture growing at 30°C prior to removal of IPTG, and (—○—○—) refers to that growing at 41°C prior to filtration. In this Figure, the results given in (a) are shown in differential form, i.e., the differential rate of β-galactosidase synthesis is plotted on a semi-log scale against generations of growth following the temperature shift. The line through the experimental points gives a value of $n = 3.3$.

hypothesis that this instability is a more general phenomenon is the fact that within the range tested (38 to 43°C) the repressor instability of i^{TSS} mutants is independent of the upper temperature used in shift-up experiments, even though the ultimate rate of enzyme synthesis varies more than tenfold in this temperature range. This suggests that instability of the repressor in i^{TSS} mutants is not reserved solely for high growth temperature, but is present—though undetectable by present means— even at low growth temperatures. A further reason to discount the possibility that instability is peculiar to the particular mutants employed comes from the fact that at lower temperatures the "basal" rate of enzyme synthesis is similar to that in the wild-type strain and not five to ten times higher in the mutant, which would be expected were the repressor unstable only in the mutant.

It should be recalled that there has been reason to believe that repressor is normally a stable molecule. In the original experiments providing evidence for the existence of repressor (Pardee, Jacob & Monod, 1959), it was found that times of the order of a bacterial doubling were required for a newly injected i^+ gene to establish repression in an initially i^- cytoplasm. Similar long delays were found in the re-establishment of repression in an i^{TL} mutant after the inactivation of repressor by pulse heating (Horiuchi & Novick, 1961). In this case the rate of enzyme synthesis falls only by a factor of ten in the generation of growth following heating. These delays could reflect the long time required for the accumulation of substantial amounts of a stable repressor, although they are unaccountably long if dz/dB varies as $1/R$, in which case a very small fraction of the steady-state repressor level would produce a sharp reduction in rate of enzyme synthesis. The discrepancy becomes more severe in the case of an unstable repressor, which should approach its maximum level even more quickly. Many explanations can be imagined for this paradoxical behavior, among them delays in the appearance of repressor (see section V of Results) or delays in sensitivity of the *Lac* operator to repressor. It should be noted, however, that such delays do not always occur. For example, as shown in Fig. 8, when a de-repressed $i^{s.TSS}$ culture growing (generation time of 200 minutes) at 43°C is shifted to 30°C,

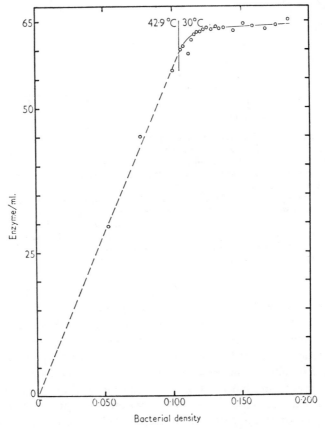

FIG. 8. Onset of repression of β-galactosidase synthesis in E304 following a shift in growth temperature from 42·9 to 30°C.

At the point indicated, a culture of E304 ($i^{s.TSS}z^+y^-$) which had grown at 42·9°C for many generations was shifted to 30°C. The medium was the same as that specified for E304 in Fig. 1. Thermal equilibration of the culture was essentially complete within 3 min following the shift. Each point given in the Figure is the average of four assays.

enzyme synthesis is essentially stopped within 6% of a generation. In a similar shift-down experiment, utilizing the same strain growing carbon-limited in a chemostat with a generation time of 12 hours, no detectable increment of enzyme was synthesized after the temperature shift.

(IV) *Structural changes in repressor caused by inducer*

In the Jacob–Monod model it is proposed that the inducer brings about an allosteric transition ("a discrete reversible alteration of the molecular structure") in the repressor, thereby removing its inhibitory effect on the opérator (Monod, Changeux & Jacob, 1963). That such transitions do actually occur is supported by two independent effects of inducer on the thermal properties of the repressor in the temperature-sensitive mutants.

The first effect is seen in strains having the i^{TL} heat-labile repressor. Here it was earlier found that inducer, added during heating, does not stabilize this repressor against thermal inactivation (Horiuchi & Novick, 1965). It was also observed in these studies that the repressor in i^{TL} strains is not uniformly inactivated; at a given temperature only a certain fraction of repressor can be inactivated, and this fraction increases with temperature. Furthermore, inactivation is irreversible, ruling out some kind of equilibrium as the explanation of the apparent heterogeneity. In the present work it was discovered that in the presence of inducer the heterogeneity is abolished.

The effect of inducer on the stability of i^{TL} repressor is shown in Fig. 9. It can be seen that, after heating an i^{TL} strain at 37°C for 80 minutes in the absence of inducer, the extent of de-repression (measured by the initial slope after return to growth at 25°C) reaches about 20% of maximum (further heating at 37°C gives no additional de-repression). If, however, IPTG is present only during heating, the subsequent de-repression approaches 100%, as can be seen by comparison with a culture fully induced by excess IPTG during growth. The kinetics of repressor inactivation at 37°C in the presence or absence of IPTG (5×10^{-4}M) deduced from data of the type in Fig. 9 is given in Fig. 10.

Since thermal stability of i^{TL} repressor molecules is affected by the inducer, it follows that IPTG produces some kind of structural change in the repressor.

A second demonstration of the interaction of repressor and inducer was found in experiments with i^{TSS} strains. It had been found earlier that the presence of IPTG in the concentration range above 10^{-4}M in cultures of $i^{s,TSS}$ strains at intermediate temperatures *decreases* the rate of production of β-galactosidase (Novick, Lennox & Jacob, unpublished experiments). This effect is shown in Fig. 11. That this effect is due to an increased rate of production of repressor follows from the fact that considerable time is required after addition or removal of inducer to obtain the ultimate rate of synthesis (Fig. 12). Were it the result of an enhancement of repressor effectiveness, the change in rate would be immediate.

To account for this stabilization of repressor formation in the i^{TSS} strains, one must first consider how the synthesis of a specific macromolecule can be temperature-sensitive. As suggested above, a plausible explanation is that some specific precursor is heat-labile whereas the final substance is stable. On this basis, one can suppose in the present case that the precursor has a site for IPTG and is stabilized by it, thus increasing the precursor level and the probability of its conversion to repressor. As will be argued below, it is likely that the precursor is a subunit of a polymeric repressor molecule.

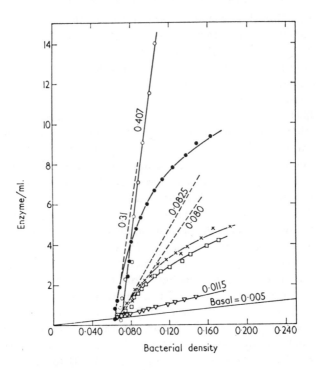

Fig. 9. Effect of IPTG on the thermolability of the i^{TL} repressor.

E103a ($i^{TL}z^+y^-$), which had grown for approximately 10 doublings in F medium supplemented with Casamino acids (200 μg/ml.) and L-tryptophan (10 μg/ml.) at 25°C, was filtered, washed (see Materials and Methods) and resuspended in F buffer containing L-canavanine–H₂SO₄ (100 μg/ml.) and 5-methyltryptophan (100 μg/ml.). To one portion of this suspension IPTG was added to a final concentration of 5×10^{-4} M and it was incubated at 25°C (—▽—▽—). To another the same concentration of IPTG was added, but it was incubated at 37°C (—●—●—). Three other portions were incubated at 37 C without the addition of IPTG. At the end of the incubation period (80 min in all cases), immediately before filtration and washing, one of these (—×—×—) received IPTG to 5×10^{-4} M. All suspensions were then chilled in ice, filtered and washed with iced buffer and resuspended in preconditioned medium containing Casamino acids and tryptophan at 25 C. To one (—○—○—) IPTG was immediately added to a final concentration of 5×10^{-4} M. Growth was immediate in all cases (generation times of 165 to 175 min). All cultures were sampled periodically for 3 hr for turbidity measurements and duplicate β-galactosidase assays. The dotted lines and numbers given in the Figure refer to the initial rates of synthesis (dz/dB) following the heat pulse.

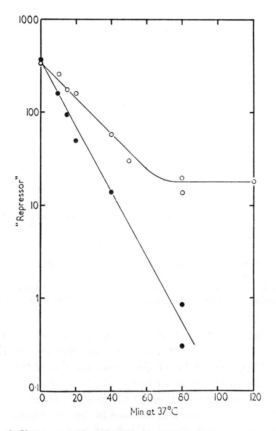

FIG. 10. Kinetics of i^{TL} repressor inactivation at 37°C in the presence or absence of IPTG. Experimental conditions were as described in the legend of Fig. 9. E103a growing at 25°C was removed into buffer containing canavanine and 5-methyltryptophan, and heated for various periods at 37°C in the presence (—●—●—) or absence (—○—○—) of IPTG (5×10^{-4}M). After return to growth at 25°C, each culture was sampled at 10-minute intervals for assay and turbidity determinations. The repressor level was calculated from the initial rate of synthesis following the heat pulse, $(dz/dB)_0$ from the relationship

$$\left(\frac{dz}{dB}\right)_0 = \left(\frac{dz}{dB}\right)_{max} \frac{K}{K + R}$$

where $(dz/dB)_{max}$ was determined on cultures treated identically save for the fact that they received IPTG (5×10^{-4}M) during subsequent growth.

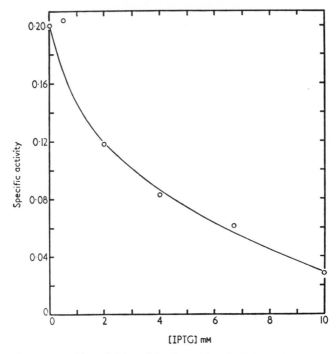

FIG. 11. Steady-state specific activities of β-galactosidase in E304 at 38·5°C in the presence of various concentrations of IPTG.

E304 was grown for a minimum of 10 doublings in IPTG at the specified concentrations at 38·5°C prior to sampling for assay. The medium used was that specified for E304 in Fig. 1.

It might seem surprising to find this apparent interaction of a repressor precursor and IPTG in the case of $i^{s.TSS}$ strains, since the repressor in these strains when present is of the i^s type, i.e. IPTG produces no induction of these strains. However, such strains do begin to be induced by exceedingly large (10^{-1}M) concentrations of IPTG (Cohn, personal communication). If the rate of enzyme synthesis falls as $1/R$, in order to produce the thousandfold increase in rate of enzyme synthesis normally seen upon induction, concentrations of inducer leading to a thousandfold fall in effective concentration of repressor must be employed. To cause a tenfold increase in concentration of repressor, much lower concentrations of inducer should suffice, since such an increase represents a stabilization of only $1/100$ of the total repressor being made.

One would expect to see the same kind of stabilization of production of i^{TSS} repressor by inducer, but the effect should occur at much lower concentrations of IPTG since strains having this repressor are inducible by much lower concentrations of IPTG. That this is the case can be seen in Fig. 13, where the specific activity of cultures grown for many generations at three temperatures at a series of concentrations of IPTG are plotted. It can be seen that at lower concentrations of IPTG there is an inhibitory effect on synthesis of enzyme, attributable to an increased level of repressor. Evidently, at these concentrations of IPTG the increase in repressor exceeds the inducing effect. As expected, at high concentrations of IPTG the bacteria become fully induced, and the expected increase in repressor level is not directly observable.

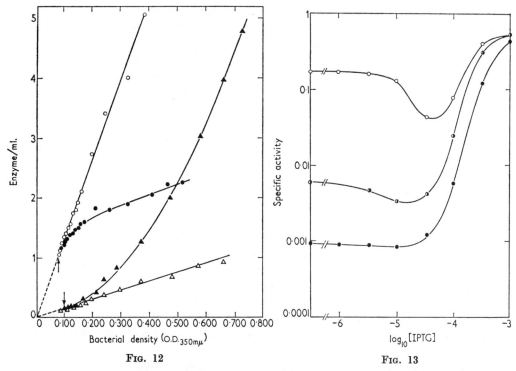

FIG. 12

FIG. 12. Onset of repression or de-repression in E304 at 38°C following the addition or removal of 0·01 M-IPTG.

Parallel cultures of E304 ($i^{s.TSS}z^+y^-$), which had grown in the presence (△, ▲) or absence (○, ●) of 0·01 M-IPTG for at least 10 doublings at 38°C, were at the point indicated (arrows) filtered, washed and resuspended in preconditioned medium. The culture which had previously grown in IPTG was divided into two parts, one part (—△—△—) receiving IPTG at the same concentration, the other (—▲—▲—) none. Likewise the culture which had previously grown in the absence of IPTG was divided into two parts, one receiving IPTG to a final concentration of 0·01 M (—●—●—), the other (—○—○—) none. Samples were removed for assay by turbidity determinations every 15 min initially and thereafter every 30 min. The medium used was that specified for E304 in Fig. 1.

FIG. 13. Effect of various concentrations of IPTG on the steady-state levels of β-galactosidase in E321 growing at three temperatures.

Cultures of E321 ($i^{TSS}z^+y^-$) were grown in the specified concentrations of IPTG for 10 to 15 doublings at the temperatures 29·8°C (—●—●—), 36·2°C (—◑—◑—) and 40°C (—○—○—) prior to sampling for assay. Each point given is the average of two or more assays on each of two parallel cultures.

Another demonstration of the stabilization of repressor formation is seen in Fig. 7(a). Here bacteria grown for many generations at 42°C in the presence of a high concentration of IPTG were removed from IPTG and grown further at 42°C. The presence of repressor is indicated by the immediate cessation of enzyme synthesis following removal of inducer, a synthesis which is resumed as the bacteria become de-repressed upon further growth. The behavior is similar to that of an i^{TSS} culture transferred from 30 to 42°C, and it thus appears that at 42°C in the presence of high concentration of IPTG the bacteria have nearly maximal levels of repressor.

If bacteria growing at 42°C are exposed to IPTG for three minutes, one would expect a production of about 2% of the full repressor level (generation time = 150 minutes). Furthermore, if, as concluded above, dz/dB varies as $K/(K+R)$, where $R_{max} = 1000\,K$, 20 K units of repressor would be formed, leading to a sharp drop in rate of synthesis of β-galactosidase. This expectation has been confirmed in a number of experiments in which three-minute pulses of IPTG (10^{-3}M) produce tenfold decreases in dz/dB in i^{TSS} strains growing at 41 to 42°C.

A more quantitative demonstration of the stabilizing effect of IPTG on repressor formation in i^{TSS} strains is presented in Fig. 14. Here the initial rate of synthesis was observed following removal of IPTG for a series of cultures grown for many generations at various concentrations of IPTG. When the results in Fig. 14 are compared with those in Fig. 11, it can be seen that the apparent K_m for IPTG is about 200 times less in the case of the i^{TSS} repressor than in the case of $i^{\text{s,TSS}}$ repressor. This is about the same ratio as that observed in the concentrations of IPTG required for induction of enzyme formation in the two cases, in agreement with the belief that the same interaction of inducer and repressor is involved in both induction and thermal stabilization.

(V) *The possible polymeric nature of repressor*

A plausible explanation, as noted in section I, for the fact that synthesis of repressor is temperature-sensitive in i^{TSS} strains is that repressor is a polymer, itself thermostable, but assembled from subunits (monomers) which are thermolabile. This interpretation is favored because of the fact that synthesis of repressor is stabilized by inducer, a finding which can be explained by the assumption that the monomer has a site for inducer and that combination with inducer stabilizes it against thermal inactivation.

Another indication that the repressor may be polymeric comes from the fact that in $i^+z^+y^-$ strains the extent of induction rises with the square of inducer concentration (Boezi & Cowie, 1961); this is illustrated in Fig. 15. From the conclusions here that dz/dB varies as $1/R$ and that induction is equivalent to inactivation of repressor, it seems that two molecules of inducer are required to inactivate a repressor molecule, an indication of at least two inducer sites per repressor molecule.

These interpretations of the structure and mechanism of synthesis of repressor lead to the expectation that modest increases in precursor level would cause disproportionately large increases in repressor level in i^{TSS} strains at those temperatures where the precursor is significantly thermolabile. To test this expectation, *F-Lac* homogenotes of E304 ($i^{\text{s,TSS}}z^+y^-$) and E321 ($i^{\text{TSS}}z^+y^-$) were prepared and their steady-state differential rates of β-galactosidase synthesis were compared with those of the respective haploid strains. The results, given in Figs 16 and 17, are in good agreement with this expectation. In the temperature range 36 to 38°C, where the effect is maximal, the *F-Lac* homogenotes of E304 and E321 synthesize β-galactosidase at rates only 1/8 and 1/17 of the respective haploid parents. At low growth temperature the ratio diploid/haploid approaches unity, which is to be expected if the monomeric species is stable and if the rate of synthesis is determined in each case by the level of repressor. At the highest growth temperatures or under conditions of maximal induction, the *F-Lac* homogenotes have rates of synthesis 2·0 to 2·5 times those of the respective haploids, confirming the hypothesis of higher ploidy of the *F*-genotes. In distinction from the marked difference in thermal de-repression between $i^{\text{TSS}}z^+y^-$ and $i^{\text{TSS}}z^+y^-/Fi^{\text{TSS}}z^+y^-$ at a given temperature, under conditions of induced synthesis at low growth temperatures the two strains behave like the corresponding i^+ strains (Fig. 4), indicating that the relationship between rate of synthesis and repressor level is normal in these strains.

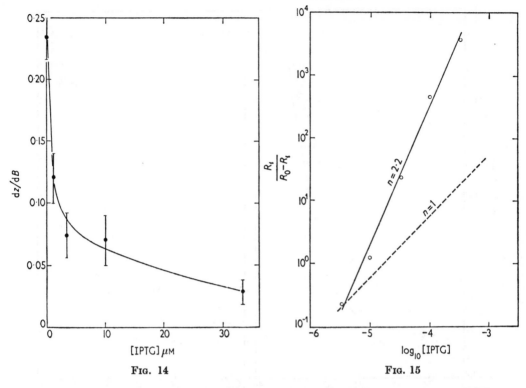

FIG. 14

FIG. 15

FIG. 14. Stabilization of repressor in E321 growing at 41·5°C by various concentrations of IPTG. E321 ($i^{TSS}z^+y^-$) was grown for 10 doublings or more at 41·5°C in the presence of IPTG at the concentrations specified. IPTG was then removed by filtration and washing of the cells, always at 40°C. The cells were then resuspended in preconditioned medium at 41·5°C, and samples for assay in quadruplicate and turbidity determinations were removed at 5-min intervals. Growth was immediate in all cases. The initial differential rates of synthesis (dz/dB) following removal of IPTG shown in the Figure were determined from enzyme/ml. (z) versus turbidity (B) plots in each case. The error bar for each point indicates the uncertainty in the initial rate of synthesis.

FIG. 15. Stoicheiometry of induction with IPTG in strain W14.
Experimental conditions were as given for W14 in Fig. 4. The level of active repressor for each concentration of IPTG was calculated on the basis of the equation $\dfrac{dz}{dB} = \dfrac{K}{K+R}\left(\dfrac{dz}{dB}\right)_{max}$. The total repressor level R_0 was calculated from the same equation using the basal rate of enzyme production (about 0·1% of the fully induced rate). $\left(\dfrac{dz}{dB}\right)_{max}$ was assumed to be equal to the steady-state rate in the presence of 10^{-3} M-IPTG. The ordinate, $R_i/(R_0 - R_i)$, gives the ratio of inactive repressor to active repressor at each concentration of IPTG. The dotted line $n = 1$ gives the expected slope on the assumption that one molecule of IPTG is sufficient to inactivate one molecule of repressor.

Since it is unlikely that the TSS mutations alter the basic mechanism of repression, the lower rate of synthesis in the TSS diploids indicates a disproportionate increase in level of repressor (by a factor of 16 to 34 rather than 2·5) in these diploids. Such disproportionate increases in repressor level in these cases can be explained, as anticipated above, by the assumption that the repressor is a polymer and that in the TSS strains the monomeric precursors are thermolabile. The results are consistent with the hypothesis that the number of such subunits is about four.

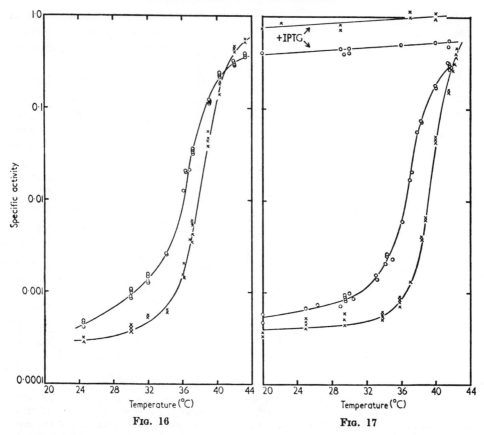

FIG. 16   FIG. 17

FIG. 16. Steady-state levels of β-galactosidase in E304 and E310 at various growth temperatures. E304 ($i^{s.TSS}z^{+}y^{-}$) and E310 ($i^{s.TSS}z^{+}y^{-}/Fi^{s.TSS}z^{+}y^{-}$) were grown at the specified temperature for 10 or more doublings prior to enzyme assay. In all cases both the haploid and the *F-Lac* homogenote were grown in the same shaking water bath to insure identical thermal histories of the two strains. The medium used was that specified for E304 in Fig. 1. Each experimental point for haploid (—○—○—) and *F-Lac* homogenote (—×—×—) is the average of two assays on the same culture at the same time.

FIG. 17. Steady-state levels of β-galactosidase in E321 and E323 growing at various temperatures in the presence or absence of 10^{-3}M-IPTG.
Experimental conditions were the same as those given for Fig. 16. The medium used was that specified for E321 in Fig. 1. In the upper curves IPTG was present in the medium at a final concentration of 10^{-3} M. Each experimental point for the haploid (—○—○—) E321 ($i^{TSS}z^{+}y^{-}$) and the *F-Lac* homogenote (—×—×—) E323 ($i^{TSS}z^{+}y^{-}/Fi^{TSS}z^{+}y^{-}$) is the average of two assays on the same culture at the same time.

4. Discussion

In the present studies, the *i*-gene product is identified more clearly as the postulated repressor of β-galactosidase synthesis. Furthermore, it is shown that the rate of synthesis of β-galactosidase varies reciprocally with the first power of level of repressor, refuting the earlier inference of a high power dependence. A similar dependence has recently been reported for alkaline phosphatase synthesis (Gallant & Spottswood, 1965). The assumption has been made here that the rate of β-galactosidase synthesis is defined uniquely by the level of repressor, other things being equal.

The fact that consistent results are obtained in experiments where repressor is varied by growth temperature in i^{TL} strains and by varying inducer with i^+ and i^{TL} strains supports this assumption and its corollary, that induction is no more than (reversible) inactivation of repressor.

The present results also offer direct evidence for an interaction between inducer and repressor. Such an interaction had been postulated earlier (Monod et al., 1963), and evidence for this first came from the discovery of mutations in the i-gene that lead to an altered specificity toward inducers (Willson et al., 1964). In the present work, from the changes in thermal behavior produced by inducer in the various temperature mutants, it is concluded that the interaction of inducer and repressor leads to a structural alteration in repressor. Such a change in structure in response to the presence of a small molecule like the inducers used here makes it likely that repressor is indeed an allosteric protein, as argued earlier (Monod et al., 1963). The evidence even seems to indicate that repressor is a polymeric protein, as proposed in the allostery model, although there is no evidence in the present studies that the state of polymerization is affected by inducer. It should be emphasized that these considerations require only that repressor be a polymer of units defined in the F-Lac episome, and do not necessarily indicate a homopolymer.

What is unexpected is the conclusion that repressor is unstable under conditions of bacterial growth, although such a finding is not inconsistent with the model of Jacob & Monod. A similar instability can be inferred for λ phage immunity substance from studies of a λ mutant in which prophage induction occurs at higher temperatures but only after growth (Sussman & Jacob, 1962). The fact that disappearance of repressor is closely coupled to growth argues against its being simply an unstable protein. To account for the growth dependence, one could imagine that the repressor is formed through the association of the i-gene product (a protein) with another constituent that is growth-unstable. The most obvious candidate for the latter is m-RNA, although the mean life of repressor is ten to thirty times that usually found for m-RNA (which could result, however, from the association of an m-RNA with a specific protein). Growth instability could also result if the i-gene product were unstable with respect to dilution, as is the case for a polymer in equilibrium with its monomeric elements.

Alternatively, it is possible that the disappearance of repressor is a consequence of the act of repression. For example, if repressor could become attached to the Lac m-RNA, thus blocking ribosome attachment and subsequent translation into enzymes, the kinetics of de-repression observed after shifting to high temperature would correspond to the depletion of the repressor pool through m-RNA synthesis. One would have to imagine that blocking of translation would have the secondary effect of slowing DNA transcription. In objection, there is evidence that repressor does not interfere with translation (Kepes, 1963; Nakada & Magasanik, 1964).

Many points thus remain unsettled. Although the evidence favors the hypothesis that repressor is an allosteric protein, no satisfactory explanation for its growth instability is at hand. Moreover, although it is clear that repressor does interact with inducer, it is not yet settled whether it blocks m-RNA production by a direct action on a DNA operator gene or by an indirect action involving the m-RNA itself.

This work has been supported by grants from the National Institutes of Health of the United States Public Health Service and from the U.S. National Science Foundation. We are indebted to Joan Medved McCoy and Catherine Bates for their technical assistance.

REFERENCES

Attardi, G., Naono, S., Rouviere, J., Jacob, F. & Gros, F. (1963). *Cold Spr. Harb. Symp. Quant. Biol.* **26**, 363.

Boezi, J. A. & Cowie, D. B. (1961). *Biophys. J.* **1**, 639.

Engelsberg, E., Irr, I. & Power, I. (1964). *Bact. Proc.* 19.

Gallant, J. & Spottswood, T. (1965). *Proc. Nat. Acad. Sci., Wash.* in the press.

Gallant, J. & Stapleton, R. (1963). *Proc. Nat. Acad. Sci., Wash.* **50**, 348.

Garen, A. & Echols, H., (1962). *Proc. Nat. Acad. Sci., Wash.* **48**, 1398.

Guttman, B. S. & Novick, A. (1963). *Cold Spr. Harb. Symp. Quant. Biol.* **28**, 373.

Hayashi, M., Spiegelman, S., Franklin, N. C. & Luria, S. E. (1963). *Proc. Nat. Acad. Sci., Wash.* **49**, 729.

Horiuchi, T. & Novick, A. (1961). *Cold Spr. Harb. Symp. Quant. Biol.* **26**, 247.

Horiuchi, T. & Novick, A. (1965). *Biochim. biophys. Acta,* in the press.

Horiuchi, T., Tomizawa, J. & Novick, A. (1962). *Biochim. biophys. Acta,* **55**, 152.

Jacob, F. & Monod, J. (1961). *J. Mol. Biol.* **3**, 318.

Kepes, A. (1960). *Biochim. biophys. Acta,* **40**, 70.

Kepes, A. (1963). *Biochim. biophys. Acta,* **76**, 293.

Lennox, E., Novick, A. & Jacob, F. (1963). *CNRS Symp. on Regulation,* p. 209. Paris: Centre National de la Recherche Scientifique, published 1965.

Luria, S., Adams, I. & Ting, R. (1960). *Virology,* **12**, 348.

Monod, J., Changeux, J. P. & Jacob, F. (1963). *J. Mol. Biol.* **6**, 306.

Nakada, D. & Magasanik, B. (1964). *J. Mol. Biol.* **8**, 105.

Novick, A., Lennox, E. & Jacob, F. (1963). *Cold Spr. Harb. Symp. Quant. Biol.* **28**, 397.

Novick, A., McCoy, J. & Sadler, J. (1965). *J. Mol. Biol.* **12**, 328.

Pardee, A., Jacob, F. & Monod, J. (1959). *J. Mol. Biol.* **1**, 165.

Stent, G. (1964). *Science,* **144**, 816.

Sussman, R. & Jacob, F. (1962). *C.R. Acad. Sci., Paris,* **254**, 1517.

Tomizawa, J. (1960). *Proc. Nat. Acad. Sci., Wash.* **46**, 91.

Willson, C., Perrin, D., Cohn, M., Jacob, F. & Monod, J. (1964). *J. Mol. Biol.* **8**, 582.

Zinder, N. D. (1961). *Science,* **133**, 2069.

(Reprinted from Nature, Vol. 214, No. 5085, pp. 232-234, April 15, 1967)

Specific Binding of the λ Phage Repressor to λ DNA

by
MARK PTASHNE

Department of Biology, Harvard University

Genetic experiments show that a group of genes may be switched off by the product of a regulator gene, called a repressor. An isolated repressor is shown here to bind specifically and with high affinity to DNA, strongly suggesting that, in vivo, repressors block the transcription from DNA to RNA by binding directly to the DNA.

THERE are many examples, in bacteria and their phages, of a group of genes controlled by the product of another gene—a regulator gene. In the classical cases discussed by Jacob and Monod[1], the control is negative and the product of the regulator gene is called a repressor. Repressors act by switching off their target genes; in order to activate these genes the repressor itself must be inactivated. These facts were learned from genetic experiments which do not reveal how repressors work at the molecular level.

The isolation in recent months of two repressors[2,3] makes possible biochemical experiments exploring the mechanism of repression. Many of the models for this mechanism propose different sites for the action of the repressor. According to the simplest model, the repressor binds to a site on the DNA, directly preventing the transcription from DNA to RNA. According to other models the repressor interacts with mRNA or sRNA to block translation of the genetic message from RNA to protein. A prediction of the first model is that an isolated repressor will bind in vitro to DNA containing the receptor site for that particular repressor, but not to DNA lacking this site. The experiments reported here confirm this expectation.

The Genetic System

The protein made by the C_1 gene of phage λ, called the λ phage repressor, is used in these experiments. This repressor blocks the expression of the other phage genes,

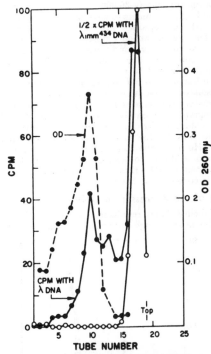

Fig. 2. Specific binding of the λind- repressor to λ DNA. A portion of ^{14}C-labelled λind- repressor, pooled and concentrated from the peak fractions of a DEAE column run, was mixed with 100 μg of λ or λimm[434] DNA. The DNA was preheated at 70° C for 15 min. to minimize aggregation. The solutions were made 0·01 M EDTA, 0·1 M KCl, and 10⁻⁴ M Cleland's reagent, and 5 μg of commercial sRNA was added as an additional inhibitor of possible endonuclease activity. After 5 min. incubation at 37° C, the final volume of 0·7 ml. was layered on a 5–25 per cent sucrose gradient containing 0·05 M KCl, 10⁻⁴ M Cleland's reagent, and 0·5 mg/ml. BSA as carrier. The gradients were spun at 41,000 r.p.m. for 5 h in an SB269 rotor in an IEC centrifuge. Fractions were collected and the DNA peak located by absorbance at 260 mμ. Each fraction was then precipitated on a Millipore filter with TCA and counted in a gas flow counter. The optical density profiles at 260 mμ from the tubes containing λ and λimm[434] DNA are essentially identical. Phages λ and λimm[434] were purified by several bandings in CsCl according to the method of Thomas and Abelson[9], and DNA was then extracted and purified from the two phage preparations using the same phenol and buffer solutions.

keeping the phage chromosome dormant within its host, E. coli. Only a very short segment of the phage genome is involved in this control[4,5], a region including the C_1 gene and the sites which determine the sensitivity of the phage to the repressor. Two phages which differ only in this segment are λ and λimm[434] (see ref. 4). Phage λimm[434], which contains almost all the other known genes of phage λ, makes and is sensitive to the 434 phage repressor only. Therefore, a critical test of specificity is that the isolated λ repressor should bind to λ DNA but not to λimm[434] DNA.

Characterization of the λ Phage Repressor

The isolation of the λ phage repressor was achieved by destroying the host DNA with ultra-violet light, thereby drastically decreasing cellular protein synthesis[3]. These

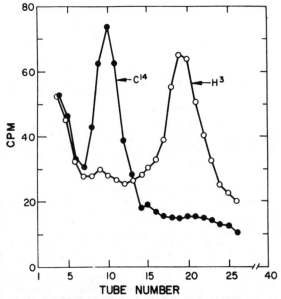

Fig. 1. DEAE-cellulose chromatography of λind- and λ wild type repressors. Extracts of E. coli phage-infected cells containing ^{14}C-labelled λind- repressor in one case and ^{3}H-labelled λ wild type repressor in the other were applied to a DEAE-cellulose column. Fractions from a salt gradient were collected and assayed as described previously[3]. The label used in this and the other experiments reported in this paper was ^{14}C or ^{3}H labelled reconstituted protein hydrolysate.

irradiated cells were infected with many λ phages which, under the conditions of the experiment, synthesized little or no phage protein except repressor. The infected cells were fed radioactive amino-acids, and a single labelled protein was separated from the background label on a DEAE-cellulose column. This protein was identified as the product of the C_1 gene by two criteria: first, it was missing from cells infected with phages bearing amber mutations in the C_1 gene, and second, it was made in modified form by phages which produce temperature sensitive repressors as a result of mutation in the C_1 gene. Electrophoresis and sedimentation of the repressor indicate that it is an acidic protein with a sedimentation coefficient of about $2.8S$, which corresponds to a molecular weight of approximately 30,000.

The binding experiments to be described were performed mainly with the repressor made by the mutant phage λind⁻. The ind⁻ mutation renders the repressor insensitive in vivo to many conditions which inactivate the wild type repressor[6]. For example, a small dose of ultraviolet light delivered to a λ-lysogen will inactivate the wild type but not the ind⁻ repressor. The ind⁻ repressor can be isolated in the same way as the wild type and has approximately the same sedimentation coefficient, but it chromatographs separately from wild type on DEAE-cellulose columns (Fig. 1). The altered chromatographic behaviour may be due to a charge or a conformational change. However, the fact that this mutation in the C_1 gene, from wild type to ind⁻, also changes the behaviour of the protein on DEAE provides further proof that this protein is coded for by the C_1 gene.

Binding of the Repressor to DNA

The labelled λind⁻ repressor was mixed with λ DNA and sedimented through a sucrose gradient. Fig. 2 shows that some of the label sedimented with the DNA, indicating that the λind⁻ repressor binds to DNA. Fig. 2 also shows that this binding is specific: when the repressor was mixed with DNA from phage λimm⁴³⁴, no binding was observed. This experiment has been performed with several different preparations of repressor and phage DNA.

The repressor used in the binding experiments was not isotopically pure. Depending on the fractions pooled from a DEAE column run, as much as 50 per cent of the label might be present in impurities other than the repressor. In order to guarantee that the label sedimenting with the DNA was in the repressor and not in some contaminant, a double label binding experiment was performed. ¹⁴C-labelled λind⁻ repressor was isolated on a DEAE column from a mixture of extracts which included the ³H-labelled products of cells infected with the phage λC_1sus34. This phage bears in its C_1 gene the amber mutation sus34 which blocks production of the repressor[7]. Therefore the ³H will have labelled all the proteins made except the repressor. Fig. 3 shows that about half the ¹⁴C label but none of the ³H label sedimented with the DNA.

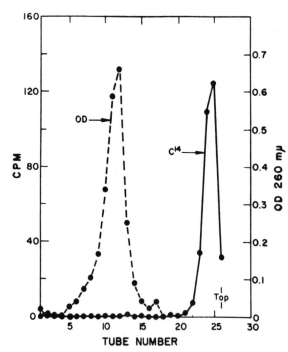

Fig. 4. Binding of λind⁻ repressor to denatured λ DNA. 100 μg of λ DNA was denatured in 0·1 M NaOH and then neutralized with HCl. The salt concentration was adjusted to 0·1 M KCl and a binding experiment was performed using ¹⁴C-labelled λind⁻ repressor as described in Fig. 1. The gradient was spun for only 2·5 h because of the increased sedimentation coefficient of denatured λ DNA in 0·05 M KCl[11].

The repressor does not bind to denatured DNA. Fig. 4 shows that no counts were displaced from the top of the tube when a mixture of denatured DNA and labelled λind⁻ repressor was sedimented through a sucrose gradient. The repressor preparation used in this experiment was found to bind efficiently to native DNA, hence its failure to bind here must have been due to the changed configuration of the DNA.

In several experiments, the wild type repressor was tested for binding to DNA. Some binding was detected, but the results were not as striking as with the λind⁻ repressor. It is possible that the ind⁻ form is less susceptible to inactivation during the isolation procedure or that it binds more tightly to DNA.

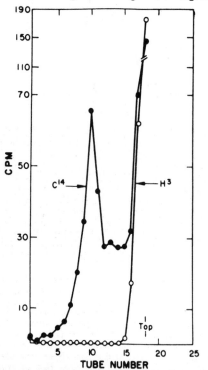

Fig. 3. Selective binding of the λ C_1 product to λ DNA. ¹⁴C-labelled λind⁻ repressor was isolated on a DEAE column from an extract which also contained the ³H-labelled gene products of the phage λC_1sus34. This mixture was then tested for binding to λ DNA as described in Fig. 1. The 260 mμ OD profile of the λ DNA is essentially identical to that shown in Fig. 1. The fractions were precipitated with TCA, dissolved in 1/2 ml. 0·1 M NaOH, and counted in 10 ml. of scintillation fluid containing toluene and Triton X-100 in the ratio 3 : 1 plus 0·4 per cent PPO and 0·005 per cent POPOP[10].

Nature of the Binding

In order for binding to have been detected under the experimental conditions used, the repressor must bind very tightly to DNA. A close examination of Figs. 2 and 3 shows that some of the bound repressor washes off the DNA as it sediments. This suggests that the dissociation constant is of the same order of magnitude as the concentration of DNA binding sites (called operators) in the peak tubes. Assuming a small number of operators per phage genome (there are probably one or two), this value is roughly 10^{-9}–10^{-10} M. A repressor-operator affinity in this range *in vivo* is suggested by the magnitude of derepression observed with the *lac* operon. Since a 1,000-fold increase in β-galactosidase synthesis occurs on induction, the dissociation constant of the repressor-operator complex should be 1,000-fold less than the concentration of free repressor in the cell[8]. The concentration of free *lac* repressor has been estimated at 10^{-7} M (ref. 2), implying that the dissociation constant is of the order of 10^{-10} M.

The finding of the λind^- repressor to λ DNA was noticeably weaker when the complex was sedimented through a sucrose gradient containing 0·1 M KCl instead of the 0·05 M KCl used in the experiments described here. In a gradient containing 0·15 M KCl, no binding was detected. This observation suggests that the binding is partly electrostatic.

The finding that the λ repressor binds specifically and with high affinity to λ DNA strongly suggests that the simplest model for the mechanism of action of the repressor is correct—namely, that the repressor blocks transcription from DNA to RNA by directly binding to DNA. This conclusion is further supported by the recent observation of Dr. W. Gilbert that the *lac* repressor binds specifically to *lac* DNA and is removed by IPTG (W. Gilbert, to be published).

I thank Nancy Hopkins for technical assistance, and also Drs. W. Gilbert, J. D. Watson and S. E. Luria for help. The work was supported by grants from the U.S. National Science Foundation and the U.S. National Institutes of Health.

Received April 9, 1967.

[1] Jacob, F., and Monod, J., *J. Mol. Biol.*, **3**, 318 (1961).
[2] Gilbert, W., and Mueller-Hill, B., *Proc. U.S. Nat. Acad. Sci.*, **56**, 1891 (1966).
[3] Ptashne, M., *Proc. U.S. Nat. Acad. Sci.*, **57**, 306 (1967).
[4] Kaiser, A. D., and Jacob, F., *Virology*, **4**, 509 (1957).
[5] Isaacs, L. N., Echols, H., and Sly, W. S., *J. Mol. Biol.*, **13**, 963 (1965).
[6] Jacob, F., and Campbell, A., *C.R. Acad. Sci., Paris*, **248**, 3219 (1959).
[7] Jacob, F., Sussman, R., and Monod, J., *C.R. Acad. Sci., Paris*, **254**, 4214 (1962).
[8] Sadler, J. R., and Novick, A., *J. Mol. Biol.*, **12**, 305 (1965).
[9] Thomas, jun., C. A., and Abelson, J., *Procedures in Nucleic Acid Research*, edited by Cantoni, G. L., and Davies, D. R., 553 (Harper and Row, New York, 1966).
[10] Modified according to E. Kennedy, pers. comm., from Patterson, M. S., and Greene, R. C., *Ann. Chem.*, **37**, 854 (1965).
[11] Studier, F. W., *J. Mol. Biol.*, **11**, 373 (1965).

Reprinted from the PROCEEDINGS OF THE NATIONAL ACADEMY OF SCIENCES
Vol. 58, No. 4, pp. 1669–1675. October, 1967.

DNA-DIRECTED PEPTIDE SYNTHESIS, III. REPRESSION OF β-GALACTOSIDASE SYNTHESIS AND INHIBITION OF REPRESSOR BY INDUCER IN A CELL-FREE SYSTEM*

BY GEOFFREY ZUBAY, MURIEL LEDERMAN, AND JOANNE K. DEVRIES

DEPARTMENT OF BIOLOGICAL SCIENCES, COLUMBIA UNIVERSITY

Communicated by Erwin Chargaff, August 8, 1967

The operon model for regulation of enzyme synthesis was proposed by Jacob and Monod in 1961.[1,2] The genetic elements of this control system consist of two parts: a locus, i, which directs the synthesis of a repressor, and a locus called the operon which contains the operator gene and associated structural genes. A messenger RNA molecule can be transcribed from the operon, which is believed to contain in one continuous polynucleotide chain the information for making the polypeptides encoded by the different structural genes. It is not known whether the messenger RNA contains a region corresponding to the operator site and, likewise, it is not known whether the repressor stops protein synthesis by interacting with the DNA, the transcribed mRNA, or a hybrid of both. The inhibiting effect of repressor is reversed by inducer which interacts directly with the repressor. Most available genetic and biochemical data favor the idea that repressors are proteins.[2] Confirmation of the repressor-operator model awaits a cell-free biochemical system in which the effect of the repressor on peptide synthesis can be directly demonstrated. In this paper such a system is described for the *lac* operon of *Escherichia coli*.

Materials and Methods.—E. coli strains: r1F': This strain was derived from strain r1, described by Zipser and Newton,[3] by introduction of an episome. r1F' has a deletion of most of the Z gene and carries two i genes, one on the chromosome and one on the episome. This strain was obtained from Dr. D. Zipser.

M107: This strain is F⁻, i⁻, Z⁻, a63su⁺, Smᴿ, and was obtained from Dr. D. Zipser.

Z: This strain is HfrH, B₁⁻, lysogenic for φ80 and φ80lac, and contains a temperature-sensitive repressor for bacteriophage induction. It was obtained from Dr. W. Gilbert.

21F': This strain was derived from strain M15 described by Ullmann, Jacob, and Mohod;[4] it has a deletion of about one third of the α portion of the Z gene. Strain 21F' is i⁻ and carries that portion of the gene for the Z protein present in strain M15 on both chromosome and episome. It was obtained from Mrs. C. Michels.

Preparation of S-30 extract: The cell-free extract of E. coli used in all syntheses is prepared by a modification of the method of Nirenberg[5] described elsewhere.[6]

Preparation of DNA: A partially purified bacteriophage preparation was obtained from strain Z by a modification of the procedure of Kaiser and Hogness[7] as described elsewhere.[8] The DNA is prepared from the bacteriophage preparation by a minor modification of the procedure of Mandell and Hershey.[6,9]

Incubation conditions for synthesis: All materials which require thawing are warmed to 5°C in a water bath. The incubation mixture contains per ml: 40 μmoles tris-acetate, pH 8.0; 4.5 μmoles 2-mercaptoethanol; 14.6 μmoles magnesium acetate; 7.3 μmoles CaCl₂; 0.2 μmole 19 C¹²-amino acids; 2.0 μmoles ATP; 0.5 μmole each of GTP, CTP, UTP; 18 μmoles PEP trisodium salt; 50 μg PEP kinase; 0.1 μmole C¹⁴-L-leucine; 200 μg φ80lac DNA; 50 μmoles potassium acetate; 100 μg tRNA; and 6500 μg protein as S-30 extract. All ingredients except the S-30 extract are mixed together and preincubated for 3 min at 37°C. After adding the S-30 extract, the reaction tubes are incubated at 37°C for 60 min. In experiments where partially purified repressor or IPTG inducer is added, these are mixed with the S-30 extract and the above procedures are followed.

Preparation of α complementation factor: Alpha complementation factor was prepared from strain 21F' by a minor modification of the procedure of Ullmann, Jacob, and Monod.[4]

Assay of incubation mixture after synthesis: Normally, incubation mixtures are assayed for leucine incorporation and β-galactosidase activity. The turbid incubation mixture should be stirred before taking an aliquot for assay.

Assay for C^{14}-leucine incorporation: This assay is described in reference 6.

Assay for β-galactosidase activity: When the source of the S-30 extract is strain M107 or r1F, a 0.1-ml sample of the incubation mixture taken after the synthesis step is mixed with equal volume of α complementation factor. This is allowed to stand for 60 min at room temperature during which time complementation takes place leading to β-galactosidase activity. When the source of the S-30 extract is strain 21F', 0.2-ml samples of the incubation mixture are taken directly after synthesis for the β-galactosidase assay. In either case, 1.5 ml of ONPG solution is added and the β-galactosidase assay carried out as previously described[10] except for a modification suggested by Dr. D. Zipser. At the end of the incubation with the substrate ONPG, 1 drop of glacial acetic acid is added to each tube to precipitate the protein, thus decreasing the background absorption and preventing errors due to turbidity. The tubes are quickly stirred and chilled in ice, then centrifuged in the cold for 15 min at $2000 \times g$. The supernatant is transferred to a clean tube and an equal volume of $1\ M$ Na_2CO_3 is added. The optical density is determined at 420 mμ.

Preparation of partially purified repressor: All steps are carried out at 1° to 4°C. Buffer A is 0.01 M tris-HCl, pH 7.4, 0.01 M $MgCl_2$, $10^{-4}\ M$ EDTA, and 0.006 M 2-mercaptoethanol. Buffer B is buffer A plus 0.2 M KCl. Buffer C is 0.01 M tris-acetate, pH 7.8, 0.014 M magnesium acetate, 0.06 M potassium acetate, and 0.006 M 2-mercaptoethanol. Streptomycin sulfate is obtained from Eli Lilly and Sons. Frozen cells of strain r1F, 170 gm, are thawed and washed once in buffer B. The cells are resuspended in 226 ml of buffer B, chilled to 1°C and lysed in a French pressure cell (Aminco Industries) at 4000–8000 psi. Buffer B, 200 ml, is added to the lysate and the resulting solution is centrifuged at $15,000 \times g$ for 20 min. To the supernatant is added 13.6 ml of 10% w/v streptomycin sulfate. After 15 min of stirring, the precipitate is removed by centrifugation at $15,000 \times g$ for 7 min. This is called fraction I.

The pH of the supernatant is adjusted to 7.0 with 0.5 M NH_4OH, and saturated $(NH_4)_2SO_4$ at pH 7.4 is added to 35% saturation. After 15 min of stirring, the precipitate is collected by centrifugation at $30,000 \times g$ for 10 min, resuspended in 13.6 ml buffer B, and dialyzed overnight against two 1-liter portions of buffer B. This is called fraction II.

Fraction II is then centrifuged for 90 min at 40,000 rpm in a #50 Spinco rotor, and the supernatant is dialyzed overnight against 1 liter of buffer A. This is called fraction III.

Fraction III is mixed with 0.75 vol of hard-packed DEAE cellulose which has been previously rinsed with buffer A. The mixture is gently shaken for 90 min and then poured into a 1.5-cm-diameter column, packed under 3 psi pressure and eluted with buffer B at a flow rate of 1 ml/min. During the elution, a brown band of protein appears on the column. This band is collected and dialyzed for 4 hr against 1 liter of buffer C and rapidly frozen in 0.5- to 1.0-ml aliquots. This is called fraction IV. Fraction IV is used only once after thawing.

The various fractions were assayed for their ability to bind IPTG by the dialysis equilibrium method as described by Gilbert and Müller-Hill.[11] C^{14}-IPTG of specific activity 25 μc/μmole was used at $1.1 \times 10^{-7}\ M$. Protein concentration was measured by the modified Lowry method.[12]

Results and Discussion.—*Description of an assay system for gene activity:* The *lac* operon of *E. coli* consists of an operator gene O, and three structural genes, z for β-galactosidase, y for permease, and a for thiogalactoside transacetylase, adjacent to the operator in that order. Since the β-galactosidase gene is adjacent to the operator and since both transcription and translation are believed to start near the operator, it was thought that evidence for the synthesis of the operator-proximal portion of the β-galactosidase polypeptide chain in the cell-free system would be useful as an assay for gene activity.

The detection of the operator-proximal fragment of β-galactosidase called α has been made possible by the technique of intracistronic complementation developed by Ullmann, Jacob, and Monod.[4] If the α fragment of β-galactosidase is mixed with an extract containing a suitable complementing protein with a deletion in the α region, β-galactosidase activity results. Noncomplemented extracts of either α or the α-complementing protein show no such activity.

In previous studies[10] the α fragment was synthesized in a cell-free system containing a so-called S-30 extract from a *lac⁻* strain of *E. coli* in the presence of $\phi80lac$ DNA and a variety of other components (see *Methods*). The *de novo* synthesis of α was detected after formation by adding an equal volume of suitably prepared extract from another strain containing a complementing protein which combines with the α fragment to produce active β-galactosidase. The amount of enzyme activity was quantitatively estimated by the standard assay procedure of determining the rate of digestion of the substrate ONPG.

In most of the present studies it has been convenient to carry out synthesis and complementation in one step. This is accomplished by using an S-30 extract prepared from strain 21F′ which carries the α-complementing protein. Under these conditions complementation takes place during the synthetic period. As before, the synthesis is completely dependent upon the presence of intact $\phi80lac$ DNA. A typical β-galactosidase assay of the product of this system is shown in Figure 1. The rate of digestion of substrate ONPG is linear for at least 45 hours. In further unpublished observations it has been found that a linear rate continues for over 80 hours, attesting to the stability of the enzyme. If 2 μg/ml of actinomycin D is added or if UTP and CTP are omitted in the synthesis step, no enzyme activity is produced and the peptide synthesis measured by C[14]-leucine incorporation is reduced by more than 90 per cent. Since both of these factors are known to affect transcription rather specifically,[13] this can be taken as strong evidence that $\phi80lac$ DNA is directing the synthesis of α through a messenger RNA intermediate.

It should be emphasized that α has been defined by the genetic complementation test as the operator-proximal segment corresponding to one fifth to one quarter of the entire length of the β-galactosidase polypeptide chain. Since the entire chain is 1173 amino acids in length, this would make the α fragment somewhere between 200 to 300 amino acids in length. It seems likely that there is considerable polydispersity in the β-galactosidase polypeptide fragments synthesized in the cell-free system and that only a fraction of these are in the size range that gives effective complementation. The central concern here is that this fraction can be quantita-

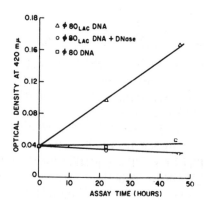

FIG. 1.—Digestion of ONPG substrate by standard incubation mixtures which contained 6500 μg protein/ml of S-30 extract from strain 21F′ and 200 μg /ml of $\phi80lac$ DNA, or of $\phi80$ DNA, or of $\phi80lac$ DNA + 5 μg/ml DNase. Incubation conditions for synthesis and assay are described in *Methods*. The digestion of substrate as measured by the increase in optical density at 420 mμ occurs only when intact $\phi80lac$ DNA is present in the incubation mixture. The enzyme digests substrate at a linear rate for at least 45 hr. With either $\phi80lac$ DNA or $\phi80$ DNA the gross leucine incorporation in this system is 2.4 ± 0.2 mμmoles. Addition of DNase lowers the incorporation by more than 90%.

tively estimated and that its formation requires the presence of the gene for β-galactosidase. Repression of the gene *in vitro* should be detectable by a lowering of the α formed. Before experiments aimed at demonstrating specific repression can be discussed, it is necessary to describe the results on the partial purification of repressor.

Description of partially purified repressor: Gilbert and Müller-Hill[11] were the first to develop a scheme for the purification of the *lac* operon repressor. This scheme is based on the hypothesis that repressor binds inducer. At various stages during purification it should be possible to assay for enrichment in repressor by measuring the binding to inducer. Binding measurements were made by the technique of equilibrium dialysis using C^{14}-IPTG. Gilbert and Müller-Hill were able to achieve some purification of repressor from a crude extract and to show that this IPTG binding substance was a protein. Our goal was to purify the repressor to a sufficient degree so that small amounts of it could be added to a cell-free system to specifically inhibit β-galactosidase synthesis. Partially purified repressor was made from strain r1F by a new procedure described in *Methods*. At various stages in the purification the preparation was characterized according to the method of Gilbert and Müller-Hill (see Table 1). When the same isolation method was used with strain M107 lacking repressor, the yields of protein in the various fractions were found to be about the same but no binding of IPTG was observed in the corresponding fractions II–IV.

TABLE 1

BINDING OF IPTG BY REPRESSOR-CONTAINING FRACTIONS
ISOLATED FROM STRAIN r1F

Fraction	Total yield of protein (mg)	μμMoles IPTG bound/mg protein	Concn. of protein in binding expt., (mg/ml)	Excess bound as % of concn. outside dialysis sac
I	2640	—	—	—
II	880	0.84	22	122
III	210	3.94	7.0	126
IV	55	3.76	11	127

In Figure 2 the ultraviolet absorption spectrum of the purest material, fraction IV, is shown. The maximum is at 278 mμ. There is no indication of substance with an absorption maximum of 260 mμ, so that little if any nucleic acid is present. The absorption spectrum of fraction IV prepared from strains r1F and M107 is similar in this respect.

By combining the information on binding of IPTG obtained here with the estimates of Gilbert and Müller-Hill[11] for the intrinsic association constant for the repressor-inducer complex and the molecular weight of repressor, a rough estimate of the repressor concentration and purity of fraction IV was obtained. The intrinsic association constant, K_{RI}, for the repressor-inducer complex is 0.77×10^6. (Note: this is the reciprocal of the K_m which Gilbert and Müller-Hill refer to incorrectly as the binding constant.) If (R_T) is defined as the molar concentration of inducer binding sites, then $(R_T) = (R) + (RI)$ where (R) is the molar concentration of available binding sites and (RI) is the molar concentration of complexed binding sites. The equation for the intrinsic association constant is $K_{RI} = (RI)/(R)(I)$, where (I) is the molar concentration of free inducer.[14] K_{RI} is given, (I) is known from the concentration of IPTG outside the dialysis sac in the binding study.

(RI) is known from Table 1, and hence (R) and (R_T) can be calculated from the above equations. (R_T) is found to be 47 mμM for a solution of fraction IV containing 1 mg/ml of protein. Gilbert and Müller-Hill have estimated the molecular weight of repressor as 2×10^5 and believe that each repressor molecule contains two IPTG binding sites. Using this information it is calculated that the protein of fraction IV is 0.47 per cent repressor. Fraction IV prepared from strains r1F and M107 was used in subsequent studies.

Experiments designed to test the effect of repressor on synthesis in the cell-free system: The design of these experiments was predicated on the assumption that the inducer, IPTG, which is believed to function by interfering with the repressor-operator complex, should increase α synthesis in the cell-free system when repressor is present but should have no effect on synthesis when repressor is absent.

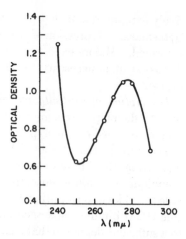

Fig. 2.—Ultraviolet absorption spectrum of the partially purified repressor, fraction IV, prepared from strain r1F in buffer C (see *Methods*).

In these experiments IPTG was used at a final concentration of $10^{-3} M$ since this concentration has been shown to give full derepression *in vivo* in mutants that cannot actively concentrate inducer inside the cell.[15] The synthesis of α was studied in standard incubation mixtures described above in which the S-30 extract contained or lacked repressor. The α formed when the S-30 extract was prepared from strain M107 (lacking repressor) was two to three times higher than when the S-30 extract was prepared from strain r1F (containing repressor). It seemed likely that the lower yield in the latter case was due to the presence of repressor. To test this, $10^{-3} M$ IPTG was added before synthesis and this increased the yield of α in the repressor-containing extract to the higher level. These results suggest that α synthesis is specifically repressible in the cell-free system and that the repression is largely eliminated in the presence of $10^{-3} M$ IPTG as it is *in vivo*.[15]

In the next series of experiments the effect of adding varying amounts of partially purified repressor to an incubation mixture otherwise lacking repressor was studied. In these studies S-30 extract from strain 21F' was used and β-galactosidase activity was measured after the synthesis as already described. These results are presented in Figure 3. The amount of enzyme activity formed in the absence of both repressor and inducer is assigned the value 100. The repressor extract used was the previously characterized fraction IV prepared either from the repressor-carrying strain r1F or the repressor-lacking strain M107. The amount of repressor extract added is expressed as the fraction (fraction IV protein)/(S-30 extract protein). The repressor concentration of fraction IV prepared from strain r1F has already been estimated, and from the amount of fraction IV used it can be estimated that at the three concentrations of fraction IV studied, the repressor concentration is 2.6, 5.2, and 10.8 mμM. The amount of virus DNA added is 200 μg/ml in all the experiments. From the fact that the viral DNA molecular weight is 30×10^6 and that the DNA preparation contains approximately equal amounts of φ80 DNA and φ80lac DNA it can be calculated that the *lac* operator concentration

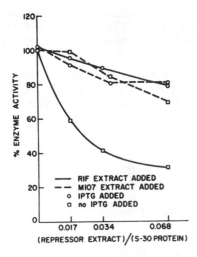

FIG. 3.—Amount of enzyme formed as a function of repressor concentration with or without 10^{-3} *M* IPTG. The enzyme activity is determined from the rate of digestion of ONPG; the amount of enzyme activity found when fraction IV and IPTG are absent is defined as 100%. The amount of fraction IV added is expressed as the ratio of protein from the added fraction IV to the protein in the S-30 extract. Except for the addition of fraction IV and IPTG the conditions for synthesis and assay are the same as those used in Fig. 1. All assays were run for 45 hr.

is 3.7 mμM. This gives a repressor/operator ratio at the three levels of repressor studied of 0.7, 1.4, and 2.8. Because of the number of approximations and assumptions that go into the calculation of the repressor concentration, these ratios should only be regarded as a rough estimate.

In Figure 3 it can be seen that the repressor-containing extract causes a pronounced lowering of enzyme formed to about 30 per cent of normal at the highest repressor concentration studied. The effect of adding repressor appears to be approaching an asymptotic limit. The addition of fraction IV from strain M107 which does not contain repressor causes some lowering of enzyme formed. Addition of 10^{-3} *M* IPTG is without effect on the latter system but it raises the level of enzyme formed in the system containing repressor so that the amount of enzyme formed in the two systems is the same. In all of the experiments reported the gross peptide synthesis was the same as reported in Figure 1. It appears that IPTG is completely reversing the effects of the *lac* operon repressor since the decrease that is not overcome by IPTG is common to fraction IV from both strains r1F and M107. It is concluded that repressor, whether normally present in the S-30 extract or added back to an S-30 extract after partial purification, can inhibit the synthesis of the α fragment of β-galactosidase and this inhibition can be reversed by 10^{-3} *M* IPTG, a specific inducer of the *lac* operon.

Summary.—Previously reported results on the synthesis of the operator-proximal segment of the β-galactosidase molecule in a cell-free system are confirmed and extended. Experiments are discussed that support the notion that the $\phi80lac$ DNA transmits the necessary information through a messenger RNA. That this system is inhibited by specific *i* gene-produced repressor can be demonstrated in two ways: (1) IPTG increases the synthesis two- to threefold in incubation mixtures containing repressor but not at all in incubation mixtures lacking repressor. (2) Partially purified repressor added back to an incubation mixture which does not contain repressor inhibits the synthesis of α. The inhibitory effect does not occur if the repressor is pretreated with 10^{-3} *M* IPTG.

We are most grateful for the technical assistance of Miss Rosemary Marciello and Mr. Tetteh Blankson.

Abbreviations used: IPTG, isopropyl-1-thio-β-D-galactopyranoside; ONPG, o-nitrophenyl-β-D-galactopyranoside; $\phi80lac$, $\phi80$ virus containing the *lac* operon; ATP, CTP, GTP, and UTP, the 5'-triphosphates of adenosine, cytidine, guanosine, and uridine, respectively; PEP, phospho-enolpyruvate.

* This work was supported by a grant from the National Institutes of Health (GM-12768) and a grant from the National Science Foundation (GB 4824). J. K. D. was supported by a National Science Foundation predoctoral fellowship and M. L. was a predoctoral trainee of the National Institutes of Health (5T1 GM570-07).

[1] Jacob, F., and J. Monod, *J. Mol. Biol.*, **3**, 318 (1961).

[2] For a recent review of the subject and references see J. R. Beckwith, *Science*, **156**, 597 (1967).

[3] Zipser, D., and A. Newton, *J. Mol. Biol.*, **25**, 567 (1967).

[4] Ullmann, A., F. Jacob, and J. Monod, *J. Mol. Biol.*, **24**, 339 (1967).

[5] Nirenberg, M. W., in *Methods in Enzymology*, ed. S. P. Colowick and N. O. Kaplan (New York: Academic Press, 1963), vol. VI, p. 17.

[6] Lederman, M. L., and G. Zubay, *Biochim. Biophys. Acta*, in press.

[7] Kaiser, A. D., and D. S. Hogness, *J. Mol. Biol.*, **2**, 392 (1960).

[8] Dixon, K., R. Knecht, and G. Zubay, *Virology*, in press.

[9] Mandell, J. D., and A. D. Hershey, *Anal. Biochem.*, **1**, 66 (1960).

[10] DeVries, J. K., and G. Zubay, these Proceedings, **57**, 1010 (1967).

[11] Gilbert, W., and B. Müller-Hill, these Proceedings, **56**, 1891 (1966).

[12] Oyama, V. I., and H. Eagle, *Proc. Soc. Exptl. Biol. Med.*, **91**, 305 (1956).

[13] McCarthy, B. J., J. J. Holland, and C. A. Buck, in *Cold Spring Harbor Symposia on Quantitative Biology*, vol. 31 (1966), p. 683.

[14] For a derivation of this general equation see Klotz, I. M., in *The Proteins*, ed. H. Neurath and K. Bailey (New York: Academic Press, 1953), vol. I, p. 749.

[15] Herzenberg, L., *Biochim. Biophys. Acta*, **31**, 525 (1959).